BRITISH
CARRIER
AVIATION

BRITISH CARRIER AVIATION

The Evolution of the Ships and their Aircraft

NORMAN FRIEDMAN

CONWAY
MARITIME PRESS

© Norman Friedman 1988

First published in Great Britain in 1988 by
Conway Maritime Press Limited,
24 Bride Lane, Fleet Street, London EC4Y 8DR

ISBN 0 85177 488 1

Typesetting and page make-up by
Witwell Limited, Southport

Printed and bound in Great Britain by
The University Printing House, Oxford

Contents

Acknowledgements

No book of this type can be written without extensive assistance. I am especially grateful to David Lyon and the staff of the National Maritime Museum, particularly the past and present staff of the Draught Room and of the collection at the Brass Foundry; to the staff of the Public Record Office (and particularly to the reproduction department there); to Dr G Mottram and the staff of the Fleet Air Arm Museum, Yeovilton; to Cal Cavalcente, Martha Crowley, Dr Dean Allard and the staff of the US Navy Operational Archives; to Dr Richard van Doernhoff and the staff of the Navy and Army Records Department of the US National Archives; to A D Baker III; to J D Brown; to Roger Chesneau; to Eric J Grove; to Charles Haberlein; to Dr Thomas Hone; to Ian Huntley; to Rear Admiral G F Liardet, CBE, RN; to Lois Lovosello of Grumman; to Dr Richard Osborne; to Alan Raven; to Bruce Vander Mark; and to Christopher C Wright. As in the past, Mr Baker has acted as critic (and technological expert), catching many incipient errors. I remain responsible for those remaining after his comments, and those of other readers of various versions of the manuscript.

All drawings marked ALR in this book are by Alan Raven, and those marked NF are by the author; unacknowledged drawings are taken from Conway Maritime Press publications. Roger Nailer is particularly thanked for those drawings bearing his name.

Photographs marked FAAM were supplied by the Fleet Air Arm Museum, while CPL indicates photographs from the Conway Picture Library. All unacknowledged photographs come from the collections of the US Navy, Roger Chesneau, D K Brown or the author.

I would like to thank my wife, Rhea, for her love and understanding, without which his project could not have been completed.

Introduction

THE ROYAL NAVY INVENTED the aircraft carrier before and during World War I. Between the wars, it introduced the armoured flight deck carrier, which radically changed the capability of the carrier in combat. After World War II the Royal Navy introduced three crucial devices – the steam catapult, the angled flight deck, and the mirror landing aid – which made it possible for carriers to operate high-performance jet aircraft and thus to remain competitive with land-based air forces. The Royal Navy also first demonstrated vertical take-off jet fighters at sea.

There were also great operational innovations. The Royal Navy pioneered ship-launched air reconnaissance and fleet air defence, and invented the torpedo-bomber. It launched the first carrier shore strike, and it was also the first navy to use the carrier-based torpedo-bomber in action, in the raid on Taranto, which prefigured Pearl Harbor.

A cynic might add that Britain also invented the carrier's ultimate enemy, the independent air force, in this case the Royal Air Force. Any history of British naval aviation must take into account the effect of RAF control of British carrier-borne aircraft between 1918 and 1939 and, on a subtler basis, the effect of interservice conflicts of interest after that. The post-World War II role of British carriers, for example, was limited by fear of RAF counters to any RN espousal of a land-attack mission.

This history of the ships and their aircraft is based primarily on the internal papers of the Royal Navy and, where applicable, of the Air Ministry, as they have been preserved in the Public Record Office, Kew, and in the National Maritime Museum, Greenwich. These have been supplemented by a variety of US official reports, currently preserved in the US National Archives and representing the most intimate available foreign point of view. The value of this foreign report is that it often makes explicit matters which are taken for granted by British writers. The US Navy experience also provides a useful contrast, by which, for example, the effect of the separation of the RAF and the RN can be measured.[1]

BRITISH AIRCRAFT CARRIERS and their aircraft developed in response to three major stimuli: evolving strategic and tactical requirements, evolving technology, and the dynamics of the relationship between the RN and the RAF. All were filtered through the Admiralty and the operational fleets.

We may consider first the strategic realities which the British fleet reflected. The basis of British naval thinking was only very rarely codified, because it was extremely well-established and, therefore, well understood within the Service. It is worth making explicit here because it explains much of the thinking which went into the prewar and wartime building programmes.

The key was that, because she was an island, Britain could use her naval power to prevent direct invasion. Staving off defeat also required that she maintain free access to the resources of her Empire, and to such other overseas trade as she might need. Thus no matter whether war were purely European or not, the defence of Britain herself was inextricably linked both to the defence of trade and to the defence of the Empire. The destruction of the Empire would impoverish Britain but, more importantly, it would make her vulnerable to any Continental enemy who might arise.

Britain was never strong enough to control the great powers of the European Continent, but she could hope, by adroit diplomacy or by military intervention, to prevent any one power from combining the resources of the Continent into an overwhelming alliance against her. Military intervention had a special flavour because British seapower, properly applied, guaranteed that Britain herself could not be invaded. Thus the classic British response to a Continental threat was to form an alliance with several land powers. If they won, the problem was solved. If they lost, they had weakened the main enemy, and the effect of the defeat was automatically contained. A new alliance could be formed, and then another, until eventually the main enemy was exhausted and then defeated. This policy was viable as long as Britain had no specially vital Continental partner whose defeat on land was intolerable, that is, as long as hostile control of some particular area on the Continent did not *in itself* threaten the existence of Britain.

Britain, then, always had to deal with threats both by sea (against the world trade which would sustain her in wartime) and by land or sea against the overseas sources of her power, both in the Empire and in friendly trading states.

The British carrier force developed in the context of these realities, at a time of radical change in the underlying strategic environment. Until about 1900, the only powers of consequence to Britain were European. Direct threats to the Empire (apart from the Russian land threat to India through Central

1 See the present author's *Carrier Air Power* (Conway Maritime Press, London, 1981) and *US Aircraft Carriers: An Illustrated Design History* (US Naval Institute, Annapolis, 1983). References in the current work to British interest in American developments have been taken from Admiralty papers; they are not speculation. However, the analogies drawn between British and American experience are generally the author's.

Asia) were few. The main prospective overseas problem was the defence of maritime trade.

However, with the rise of the two great overseas powers, Japan and the United States, Britain faced the possibility that her overseas possessions themselves might be subject to war-time attack on a powerful scale. Given the classic British strategic concepts, the possibility that such an attack would be coupled with a European crisis was particularly frightening. Before 1914, Britain tried to avoid that catastrophe through alliance with Japan, though she was well aware that her Asiatic Empire was a rich prize. The Japanese were restrained as the European war approached by two considerations. First, they were the potential inheritors, as an Allied power, of many of the German Pacific possessions. Second, they had to fear that a very powerful Britain would seize back any Imperial losses after defeating Germany. Neither consideration applied after 1918. It was not so much that Japan had immediate designs on British possessions in and around Asia, as that the Empire was a rich and tempting prize, and that Japan and the United States were by far the most likely future candidates to try to seize parts of it.

The two rising overseas powers presented a particularly difficult problem. Facing a European opponent, Britain enjoyed a geographical advantage: her territory blocks the path from northern Europe to the world ocean. Britain enjoyed no such advantage with respect to Japan and the United States. The British seem to have concluded, about 1920, that war with the United States was unwinnable.[2] They therefore implicitly supported the United States over Japan at the Washington Naval Conference of 1921, abrogating the former Anglo-Japanese Naval Treaty.[3]

Imperial defence required a strong mobile force because it was financially impossible to maintain strong garrisons throughout the Empire. The rise of the British carriers, which helped guarantee the required mobility, coincided with the new requirement that the fleet, the only truly mobile Empire force, be capable of defending the Empire in East Asia. Operations in Asian waters also required a new infrastructure; for the first time, Britain required expensive fleet bases, most notably Singapore, outside her traditional main fleet operating areas, the North Sea and the Mediterranean. Limited postwar budgets had to support the construction both of the new bases and of a new, longer-range fleet, including carriers and their aircraft.

Moreover, Asian imperial defence was only one of the two aspects of British wartime policy; the United Kingdom itself always had to be secured. Given limited British physical resources, there was always a tension between expenditure to ensure the immediate physical security of Britain and that expenditure required to secure Britain against the loss of the overseas resources essential to her wartime survival. Besides shifting the focus of Imperial defence to Asia, World War I also seemed to change the character of the physical threat to Britain herself.

During the war, Germany attacked Britain directly, by the bomber offensive. For the first time, Britain could, it appeared, be defeated from the air. The German World War I raids achieved little in concrete military terms, but they exposed the British population to a threat largely forgotten: direct military attack. The shock of that threat explains the radical steps taken to meet it, including the formation of the independent Royal Air Force.[4]

From 1919 on, then, the British government found itself forced to choose between a traditional strategy based on an invulnerable Britain, and a strategy in which home air defence had to be the paramount consideration. Hence the rise of the RAF, which alone could promise protection against ruinous air

The central problem in carrier design has always been how to adapt a reasonably-sized ship to duplicate, in effect, the facilities of a big airfield ashore. The Royal Navy invented several of the postwar keys to this achievement – the steam catapult, the angled deck and the mirror landing sight, as demonstrated here by the launch of a very high-performance jet fighter, an early Supermarine Scimitar, from HMS Ark Royal, *probably in about 1957. The wire bridle, which will pull the aircraft from the ship, is just visible under its belly.*

attack (either by fighter defence or by the deterrent effect of British bombers) and hence also Britain's apparent willingness to accept a new Continental commitment, intended to keep German bombers out of nearby French bases.

The inherent conflict between what was called the Air Defence of Great Britain (ADGB) and a traditional British global strategy shaped the conflict between the interwar RAF and the Royal Navy, and thus shaped the British carrier force. The author of the Cabinet history of British naval programmes between 1934 and 1941 observed that British forces were always starved until foreign relations became intolerably uncomfortable, at which time the ADGB took clear precedence over the Navy. This must have seemed ironic to naval officers who had been raised to consider the fleet the chief bulwark against any invasion from across the Channel.[5]

2   This conclusion emerges from British internal statements on the logic of the Washington Treaty, and on the extent to which American proposals had of necessity been accepted. The United States was a terrifying prospective opponent because she could not easily be blockaded (and thus could threaten the Empire at will) and because she could support herself entirely on the basis of her internal resources. As early as 1904 a British strategist, Sir Halford MacKinder, warned that the future belonged to the great autarkic land powers, the United States and Russia, because with improvements in transportation (principally railroads) they could compete on equal terms with the great sea powers.

3   Such words may seem bizarre in view of world history since 1921. At the time, however, many Americans believed that ultimately the British would find American world economic power an intolerable rival; it was popularly believed that Britain's main motive for entering World War I had been to quash growing German economic success (much of it at British expense in the Third World). Incidentally, a US attempt to dismantle the European colonial empires (thereby opening them to US trade) was very much a feature of World War II policy.

FROM A NAVAL POINT OF VIEW, this national strategy led inexorably to reliance on the main, or battle, fleet. A main fleet could be defined as an assembly of mutually supporting warships so powerful that only another main fleet could seriously threaten it, just as a capital ship could be defined as an individual ship so powerful that only other capital ships could destroy her.[6] The main fleet was the basis of British sea power for several centuries and is, for that matter, still the basis of current US thinking.

Any prospective maritime enemy would have to choose between concentrating his naval power into a rival main fleet, or allowing the British main fleet complete freedom of action. At the least, such a concentration would necessarily limit an enemy's threat to British seaborne trade, simply by soaking up naval resources.

No prospective maritime rival could simply ignore the British main fleet. Under its cover, large numbers of inexpensive blockaders could shut an enemy off from the world ocean and thus from overseas supplies. Blockade was effective against Germany in World War I and against Japan in World War II. It was, however, limited; it could not defeat a land power which could find all vital resources within either its own or seized territory. On the other hand, the dominance exerted by the main fleet made it possible to attack the periphery of the enemy's territory, for example to land troops along his coast.

Conversely, an enemy seeking to destroy British seaborne trade would have to send out large numbers of raiders. They would necessarily be relatively weak, but then again they would have only to overpower even weaker merchant ships. The presence of the main fleet made it possible for Britain to deploy trade-protection ships in sufficient numbers, since they also could be relatively weak, and thus relatively inexpensive.[7] Thus the main fleet can be understood as the guarantor of sea control.

Carriers and their aircraft offered a valuable contribution to the operation of the main fleet. If an enemy went to sea, aircraft could help find him, bring him to battle, and win the battle. If he refused action, they alone of all naval weapons could destroy him in his defended harbour, in a modern equivalent of the 'cutting-out expeditions' of the age of sail.

Carriers could not, however, supplant the other elements of the prewar integrated main fleet, the purpose of which was to destroy a similar integrated fleet in a decisive battle. It was by no means clear that carrier aircraft could sink modern battleships; every navy of the interwar period believed, with good reason, that only battleship shellfire could be relied upon to disable and sink modern battleships: carrier aircraft could not deliver powerful enough torpedoes, and dive-bombers could not penetrate heavily armoured decks.[8] On the other hand, as doctrine developed between wars, only carrier aircraft could find an enemy fleet, and only they could slow it (or prevent its escape), so that battleship guns could perform their decisive function. Moreover, carrier aircraft were required to control the air over a battle area, so that the battleships could achieve maximum effectiveness through air spotting.

Since the concept of the main fleet survived intact through (and indeed was justified by) World War II, main fleet requirements also shaped the ships designed in wartime, which turned out to be the final generation of large British carriers. After 1945, the Royal Navy justified its attack carriers on a main fleet basis, in this case emphasizing their role in covering convoy escorts and mine countermeasures craft.

Aircraft, which might be carrier-based, were also developed for trade protection. Here the problem was the vast space through which British trade passed, and therefore in which raiders could operate. Now trade protection generally is taken to mean protection against submarine attack, but that was hardly the view during the interwar period. World War I experience seemed to show that enemy submarine operations would be geographically limited and that, moreover, convoying by surface ships was an effective antidote.[9] The air role in ASW was to force submarines down so as to limit their mobility; a submerged submarine enjoyed only a very short range at high speed. If geography limited the U-boats to the area near the British Isles, land-based (RAF) aircraft could perform much or all of this function. However, once the German operational area expanded with the fall of France and Norway, convoy protection was needed over much greater distances, and ideally convoys had to carry their aircraft with them. This consideration led to the escort carrier.

Interwar thinking, then, envisaged trade warfare on a worldwide scale prosecuted by enemy surface ships, either cruisers or converted merchant ships. These had the advantage of very long range and, moreover, a surface raider could locate targets at a great distance, whereas a submarine enjoyed only a very limited spotting range. A single surface raider could expect to destroy shipping more efficiently than could a submarine, as long as she could elude pursuit. Aircraft could extend the range of a searching cruiser; they might even be able to sink the raider by themselves. British policy, then, was to provide all trade protection cruisers with long-range reconnaissance aircraft. Such aircraft were necessarily extremely limited in size, capability and numbers, and by the mid-1930s the ideal solution was clearly a small trade-protection (search and limited strike) carrier. This represented a second thread of British thinking, complementary to the main fleet carrier.

By 1939 there was another threat to shipping: air attack within range of enemy coasts. As the Germans were able to extend such attacks out to sea and (by their possession of the French and Norwegian coasts) along areas inaccessible to British land-based fighters, another type of carrier was added: the trade-protection fighter carrier. Like the other trade-protection carriers, this type existed outside the main fleet, but was shielded from major enemy units by the fleet's power, and thus it was affordable at a reduced level of effectiveness.

See W R Louis, *Imperialism At Bay: The United States and the Decolonization of the British Empire, 1941–1945* (Oxford University Press, Oxford, 1977). Both Britain and the United States maintained plans for war with each other at least until the early 1930s, but they do not appear to have been very serious exercises.

4   It seems likely that airpower made a greater impression on interwar British than on interwar French political leaders precisely because the threat of direct attack on Britain was so much more shocking. As a Continental power, after all, France could be (and often had been) invaded, whereas the Royal Navy had kept British soil largely sacrosanct since 1066.

5   This simplifies a lengthy controversy. Until the advent of steam, prevailing winds made a French invasion of England extremely difficult. As the French adopted steam warships in the mid-nineteenth century, the British began to fear that invasion would indeed be possible, and they fortified the coast facing France. The British Army took responsibility for coast defence, and thus for protection against invasion across the narrow part of the Channel. Ultimately the fear of French assault subsided, and early in the present century the Royal Navy took back this responsibility, basing a mobile coast defence on torpedo craft (submarines and small steam torpedo-boats, the coastal destroyers). The Royal Navy failed to articulate the connection between the defence of Britain and the strength of its concentrated battle fleet.

6   Such definitions were of necessity approximate. Under suitable circumstances (including very favourable geography), submarines could (at least in theory) destroy a battle fleet. Similarly, large numbers of destroyers or torpedo-bombers could sink a battleship. Yet, on the whole, the concept of a fleet which can only be dealt with by the enemy's main fleet remains useful.

7   The one great exception would appear to be the big protected or armoured cruiser, as developed primarily by the French and Russian navies around the turn of the century. The British built large numbers of very expensive large cruisers of their own as a counter. It seems likely in retrospect that both powers found such ships too expensive, as they abandoned such construction within a few years.

8   In theory, level bombers could drop armour-piercing bombs from high enough altitudes for them to develop sufficient speed. However, it was well known that such attacks could easily be frustrated by manoeuvre. Note that the bombers which sank the *Prince of Wales* and *Repulse* off Malaya in December 1941 were large land-based types carrying heavier torpedoes than were issued to Japanese carrier bombers. The ships at Pearl Harbor were sunk by carrier torpedo-bombers, but they were relatively old units with limited underwater protection. The only modern World War II battleships sunk by carrier aircraft were the huge Japanese *Yamato* and *Musashi*, both of which were attacked on a scale inconceivable before the war.

9   Britain, moreover, enjoyed immense geographical advantages; U-boats had to pass far north of Scotland to avoid attack, and this passage in turn drastically limited their patrol endurance. As a result, Britain could expect that convoy would have to be maintained over only a very limited area of the western Atlantic. This limited the demand for convoy escorts. Matters changed drastically with the German seizure of the French and Norwegian coasts, but that could hardly have been expected before the war, when France had the largest (and, most thought, the best) army in Europe.

In theory, a single main fleet would suffice in wartime to dominate the world ocean. This doctrine made sea control affordable for a nation with global interests. It made parity with the United States a rational treaty objective, since, despite very different geographical situations, both nations planned to concentrate the bulk of their naval strength into single main fleets in wartime.[10] Each country assumed that it would fight a single primary maritime enemy.

The single main fleet doctrine broke down in World War II because both countries found themselves fighting not one, but two or three naval wars, all of which were only very loosely connected. Britain recognized this problem, and in the late 1930s began building a Navy sufficient to support several main fleets; the war, however, effectively stopped this programme. The US 'two ocean navy' programme of 1940 had much the same premise, and US industrial capacity did suffice to carry the programme through.

In the British case, peacetime practice distorted the wartime ideal of a single integrated fleet, since global political (and fiscal) considerations demanded that major warships be deployed in many areas. For example, a carrier or carriers had always to be available in Chinese waters, to support the extensive British interests there. However, it was never possible to maintain a very powerful British fleet in the Far East; in the event of war, the main fleet would have to steam out from European waters.

British peacetime dispositions did take account of the variety of possible threats. Thus a large Mediterranean Fleet was maintained partly because of the importance of the Middle East and Suez, but also because a fleet so situated could steam East more quickly than one based in the British Isles, yet could also move into home waters. A second substantial fleet had to be maintained in home waters. The division into Home (or Atlantic) and Mediterranean Fleets was also valued because it made for variety and competition in operational doctrine. By way of contrast, the United States was able to concentrate her main fleet in peacetime in the Pacific.

BRITISH POLICY IN WORLD WAR II exemplifies her classic strategy. Ironically, it was a very successful air defence of Great Britain that made the traditional global and coalition strategy practicable. Britain began the war as part of a coalition, her Continental partner being France. France was knocked out of the war in 1940, but Hitler was unable either to invade or to destroy Britain. Moreover, Britain was able to stay in the war thanks in large part to the strength of her Empire. As in past wars, however, she was not herself sufficiently strong to win, and Germany had acquired sufficient resources to be largely blockade-proof. Britain now sought other partners, and for a time assisted Greece in what turned out to be a failing holding action against the Germans and Italians. When that coalition also collapsed, however, the failure once more of a British army on the Continent did not destroy Britain, because her command of the sea protected and supported her.

Thus Britain was able to hold out until a new coalition was formed, in this case with partners (principally the United States and the Soviet Union) able to remain in the war to the end. As in the Napoleonic Wars, it could not be said that Britain alone defeated her Continental enemy. It could, however, be said that because Hitler failed to defeat Britain he could not end his war on favourable terms before the last coalition defeated him.

Carriers were crucial to sustained British naval operations in European waters, since the German blitzkrieg and the Italian entry into the war greatly reduced the scope of land-based air support. British naval operations, in turn, were essential for British survival, since without them the Axis powers would have seized the vital oil supplies of the Middle East (that is, an

essential Empire resource). Given her survival through the year of fighting more or less alone (June 1940 to June 1941), Britain could await the events which led to the formation of the ultimate, crushing alliance. Thus the carriers exemplified the role of the British mobile main fleet in securing those elements of the Empire without which classical British strategy could not be pursued.

Perhaps the most striking aspect of British operations in the Mediterranean in 1940 was the enormous effect of a very small carrier force, not only at Taranto (where it reversed the local balance of sea power), but also in a series of bombing raids. The Italian air force always grossly outnumbered the British carrier air arm, yet the carriers achieved decisive results. The reason was that the carriers were a mobile, concentrated force. Land-based aircraft were tied to more or less fixed bases, and therefore were difficult, at least at first, to concentrate in overwhelming numbers. It took the Italians and their German allies some considerable time to build up the forces and the organization necessary to attack carrier forces in the Mediterranean, and even then the carriers were still able to protect surface formations (for example as in the Pedestal convoy, 1942). The lesson, that concentrated naval forces can exert disproportionate influence, still seems valid.

It might be also argued that because the main fleet (including carriers) was not available in the Far East during the crisis of December 1941, Britain could not defend the resources of Malaya and Burma, which had helped sustain her European war effort.[11]

Sea control made it possible for the Western Allies to threaten Hitler at many points along the shore of occupied Europe, and so diluted the forces he could actually apply to oppose the decisive D-Day landing. Allied seapower, for example, made it plausible for the Allies to threaten the attack in Norway which Hitler feared, and against which he diverted important resources. Carrier strikes against Norway during 1943–44 may well have contributed to this diversion, although they were also an important way of reducing the German threat to convoys running to northern Russia.

Sea control, and the access to vital overseas resources which it allowed, was ensured by small escort vessels, which in turn were viable only because Germany was unable to deploy powerful surface naval forces. The proof of this connection is that, on the few occasions on which powerful German surface ships did attack convoys, they were able to achieve impressive results.[12] Postwar, this experience was reflected in intense interest in anti-raider weapons, culminating in the earliest British naval tactical nuclear bombs.

The war also demonstrated the limitations of traditional British strategy. Britain could be severely damaged by a direct assault on her overseas sources of strength, in this case both in the Middle East (largely for oil) and in Asia and beyond (for example, India, Australia and New Zealand). Until June 1940, the war was a classical contest with a European power, whose main effect on support for Britain from overseas was through attacks on trade. Britain could, therefore, disperse units earmarked for the Far Eastern main fleet to hunt down raiders, and to provide early ASW cover, pending the mobilization of specialized escorts. However, when Italy entered the war, she automatically threatened the oil supply route through the Mediterranean, and the source of that oil in the Middle East. At the very least, the Italian main fleet had to be dealt with.

Meanwhile, in the Far East, Japan, unengaged in the war, was clearly encouraged by British preoccupation with the European situation. In theory, the British main fleet would have been assembled and sent East to deter the Japanese and, if necessary, to achieve sea control. In fact, the British forces were

10   Parity originally applied only to the main fleets, that is to capital ships. Britain always maintained that she needed larger numbers of cruisers to protect her maritime trade. At London in 1930, however, she agreed to a substantial reduction in cruiser numbers, to hold down naval costs. The cuts in trade protection cruisers made increased cruiser efficiency, through air reconnaissance, more and more important. They also inspired studies of improvised trade-protection carriers, which were a way of making good treaty-enforced deficiencies.

11   British prewar doctrine assumed that the main fleet would not begin the war in place in the East. Rather, it would have to steam out upon the outbreak of war. In theory, Singapore, its base, was designed to hold out until the fleet arrived. In the event, however, despite the size of its garrison, Singapore soon fell. One might ascribe its fall to the secondary role of the garrison within the overall scheme of Imperial defence, and also to the need to concentrate the best commanders and troops to defend the even more vital portions of the Empire already under German and Italian attack in the Mediterranean.

12   Examples would include the attack in which the armed merchant cruiser *Rawalpindi* was sunk, and the case of convoy PQ17 shows how seriously the threat of such units was taken.

Arguably the single most important British interwar naval air decision was a tacit one: not to adopt deck parks. The result was to limit the aircraft capacity of the ships, and thus to force the Royal Navy to plan to operate combat aircraft from its battleships and cruisers. This imposed very severe limits on aircraft design. A Fairey Flycatcher fighter is shown on the revolving take-off platform of the cruiser Enterprise. *The fighter is wheeled, for maximum performance; in combat, it would either land aboard one of the fleet carriers or ditch. Note the exposed petrol stowage (in standard 2-gallon tins) on deck below and abaft the platform. Catapults replaced the take-off platforms, and later aircraft were fitted with floats so that they could train in harbour in peacetime. However, it was always assumed that in wartime the floats would be exchanged for wheels, and British wheeled aircraft of the interwar period were designed to be launched from cruiser and battleship catapults.*

stretched far too thin; because Germany had powerful surface forces, the Home Fleet could not be denuded. The role of the carrier included helping bring the German main forces to action, as the battle against the *Bismarck* demonstrated, and the need to counter the Italian fleet also required carriers. Indeed, it turned out that operations in the Mediterranean required more carriers than had been expected, because air cover (not emphasized in prewar doctrine) was required to deal with heavy land-based air attacks. A carrier force sufficient to support a single main fleet under prewar assumptions could be stretched only so far. Ultimately only two fast capital ships, *Repulse* and *Prince of*

Wales, could be spared for the main fleet role in the East, and there was no spare carrier to accompany them even though established doctrine called for more than one. At the time, there was some hope that such powerfully armed, manoeuvrable ships could beat off air attacks, which was one reason why the new carriers had been designed to operate limited (largely offensive) air groups. Operational experience in the Mediterranean had already shown that this was too optimistic, and the loss of both capital ships off Malaya demonstrated it again.

Early 1942, then, was a time of crisis. The Royal Navy had a carefully-designed fleet building programme, in which aircraft requirements had been balanced with other fleet features. The disaster off Malaya showed that the chosen balance was wrong. Fleet carriers were slow to build, however; if the main fleet needed many more carriers, then some compromise was in order. If, moreover, the Royal Navy would have to operate several reduced main fleets simultaneously, then even more carriers would be needed. The response to this breakdown in naval strategy was the light fleet carrier.

This crisis was not the result of some deficiency in British comprehension of the importance of aircraft, as has often been alleged. Rather, it was an inescapable consequence of the limited size of the British prewar carrier force (due in large part to treaty provisions) and to the character of the prewar British industrial base, which limited the rate at which new ships could be built. Given the belief that battleship firepower would be necessary to destroy an enemy's main fleet, the new battleships had to take precedence.

It is commonplace to compare the Royal Navy unfavourably

with the more air-minded US Navy. Their doctrines for naval air operations were, however, quite similar. The main difference was that the US Navy managed to operate substantially more aircraft per carrier. It therefore managed to take many more aircraft to sea (given a carrier fleet similar in overall size to that of the Royal Navy). For its part, the Royal Navy of the late 1930s desperately sought to increase the number of aircraft at sea, and its carrier building programme in fact considerably exceeded that of the United States. Unfortunately, the war began before much of this programme could be realized, and early war losses were heavy.

Early war experience also clearly demonstrated the value of carrier aircraft, but the British, with their industrial base stretched to the limit, could neither undertake a large new carrier programme nor even produce sufficient naval aircraft. The United States had no such limitation; the carriers which won the Pacific War in 1944–45 were all ordered in 1940. Admiralty papers show that the Royal Navy would have liked to do the same, but that it had no such option. Large numbers of new carriers were ordered later in the war, as the shipbuilding base cleared, but the war ended before many of these ships could be completed or even, in some important cases, begun. The Royal Navy had to rely on the United States to supply the bulk of its naval aircraft, not so much because of the inferiority of new British types, but because most British aircraft production had to go to the RAF. Postwar, British naval policymakers accepted that in a future major war they would again have to rely largely (though by no means entirely) on US supplies. The result was that US carrier aircraft choices had an impact on British carrier design.

In mid-war the Admiralty undertook a thorough analysis of fleet aircraft requirements, leading to a new generation of aircraft (see Chapter 13). These aircraft in turn could be operated only from the new carriers then being ordered; indeed, their characteristics and those of the carriers were developed in parallel. Carrier cancellations at the end of the war were, then, particularly crippling. Moreover, it turned out that design features of existing British carriers made it difficult to modify them to operate new heavy aircraft. As a result, despite the Navy's clear understanding of the potential of naval aircraft, it was forced into drastic postwar operating cuts to finance the completion of the few ships which had survived the cancellations. British attempts to build entirely new postwar carriers failed in 1952 and again in 1965.

After 1945, Britain's Imperial (or Commonwealth) role survived but was directed more towards internal security than towards protection against massive invasion. British government records show a tension between the cost of maintaining security in Europe (that is, maintaining the ability to fight the most likely perceived enemy, now the Soviet Union) and the cost of maintaining security within the Commonwealth. In 1954–57 the decision was taken to deter a possible Soviet attack with the threat of nuclear weapons, while maintaining mobile (that is, largely naval) forces for Commonwealth security. A decade later, with the cost of European security rising, this decision was reversed (in the retreat from 'East of Suez') and the decision was taken largely to eliminate the mobile naval force. Ironically, fifteen years after that decision, the Falklands war showed that Britain still had overseas interests, and still needed strategically mobile naval forces.

THE MAIN FLEET was not only the key to British naval strategy, it was also its most expensive floating element.[13] British resources were badly depleted by the first European war she had fought in something other than her traditional style.[14] There was no question but that the first priority in 1919 was to

Given arrester gear and a crash barrier, a carrier could park her aircraft forward while others landed. She could also accommodate extra aircraft on deck in a permanent deck park. HMS Indomitable *illustrates both possibilities in this 1943 photograph. She is recovering her Albacore torpedo/dive-bombers, parking them forward until all are aboard. This was much quicker than striking each below before landing the next. In this particular case, deck parking also made it easier to accommodate Sea Hurricanes and early Seafires, whose wings did not fold. A Seafire, sitting on an outrigger, is visible just abaft the forward starboard radio mast, which itself is folded down. The Seafire's main wheels are on the flight deck, but the tail wheel is on the outrigger. Note the long round-down at the bow, adopted to improve air flow over the deck, which reduced the effective length of the deck and thus the capacity of the deck park. Deck parking was not really envisaged when this ship was designed.* CPL

recover from the terrible stress of war, making the best possible use of the surviving mass of *matériel* produced in its course. There was, moreover, no possibility of immediate disarmament; the effect of the war had been, if anything, to make the Empire less secure internally, so that additional troops were needed to maintain order.

The combination of new war-developed technology (including carrier airpower) and the need for greater range, to operate in Asian waters, rendered the existing Royal Navy largely obsolete in 1919. It could, moreover, be expected that some technologies, such as aircraft design, would develop quite rapidly in peacetime, so that large forces bought at any one date might well be obsolete within a few years and thus any early modernization could well entail the waste of scarce resources. Yet if modernization were put off too long, the Empire might be lost.

This combination of new and potentially extremely ex-

13 Successive pre-1939 Boards of Admiralty were well aware that convoy operations would figure prominently in any future war. However, small anti-submarine units could be built relatively quickly, or even improvised from the large fleet of fishing craft which Britain then possessed. Main fleet units were a very different proposition; they had to be built in peacetime.

14 That is, Britain had been unwilling to tolerate the defeat of France and so had committed large ground forces. In earlier wars, such as the wars of the French Revolution, Britain had financed her continental partners but had limited her military commitments.

15 Americans will recognize the practice of solving *matériel* problems in the 'out years' of multi-year defence programmes.

pensive defence commitments, and a badly depleted national economy, explains the British interwar armament and arms control policy which in turn shaped the British carrier force. In 1919 the British government faced massive American and Japanese naval building programmes. It ordered new ships for the Royal Navy, but British resources were clearly limited. In 1921 Britain therefore welcomed the Washington Naval Conference as a means of limiting the cost of postwar naval modernisation. Throughout the postwar period, successive British governments hoped to limit the cost of armament through arms control, in the hope that foreign governments could be induced to accept reduced upper limits on their own forces. These proposed limits in turn shaped British building programmes.

Successive British governments hoped, too, that they could look forward to a sufficient interval of peace to ensure economic recovery. After all, they could not maintain military power without a strong economic base (sometimes called the 'Fourth Arm of Defence'). It was particularly attractive to stretch out the timescale of modernization, and that in turn required an estimate of the length of time available before some emergency had to be expected, or provided for. In 1919, therefore, the British Cabinet adopted a secret assumption that no war was to be expected for a decade. This 'Ten Year Rule' was repeated in 1925 and then in 1928; in 1929 it was made self-perpetuating, so that (until the rule was abrogated) a decade of peace was always to be expected. The rule was actually abandoned in

Perhaps the central problem of British interwar naval policy was to reconcile the need to disperse power to enforce British authority throughout a large Empire with the need to concentrate power to match rivals such as Japan. Carriers figured in both types of action. They were the only way to bring air power to distant areas, but they were also badly needed as part of the concentrated fleet. HMS Hermes is shown at Shanghai, 11 December 1930. The weakest of the British carriers, she sufficed for power projection, but can hardly have affected contemporary Japanese calculations. The white hull and darker superstructure were typical of China Fleet practice.

1932, after the Japanese had made their aggressive intentions obvious.

The Admiralty initially saw the Rule as a time limit on the necessary modernization programme. That was also the case with the first renewal (target date 1935). However, in a climate of fiscal difficulty (and occasional crisis), the combination of arms control and the Rule justified heavy cuts in expenditure, on the excuse that deficiencies in equipment or in munitions or in aircraft could all be made up later during the peacetime period. This was particularly the case after the Rule was made self-perpetuating.[15]

From World War I on, naval mobility, at least beyond the North Sea, increasingly meant carriers, because the fleet could not function effectively without air support. Thus, to the degree that British national strategy required large strategically mobile naval forces, it required aircraft carriers. Admiralty documents of the interwar period show clearly that throughout this period the Royal Navy considered naval aircraft essential to success in battle. The question was not whether to support a naval aircraft programme, but rather what the shape of that programme was to be.

The Europe-or-Empire debate current in interwar defence thinking had an important interservice dimension. Although the RAF operated aircraft throughout the British Empire, it was primarily concerned with the defence of Britain, either through fighter interception or through the deterrent threat of its bombers. The RAF therefore considered the European dimension paramount. On the other hand, although the Navy could clearly contribute to the direct defence of the United Kingdom, it had special and unique capability in the defence of the distant parts of the Empire. Thus the RAF was more concerned with the rise of Nazi Germany, the Royal Navy with the rise of an aggressive Japan.

GIVEN BASIC BRITISH NAVAL strategic concepts, World War I experience shaped postwar naval development and, by implication, postwar naval aviation. World War I experience demonstrated both the power and the limitations of the existing main fleet. While the Grand Fleet kept most German surface ships out of the world ocean, and thus protected trade, both directly (from surface raiders) and indirectly (by making small antisubmarine escorts viable), the German 'fleet in being' tied down the Grand Fleet and limited its effect on the land battle. The proposed landings in Flanders, for example, could not be carried out for fear that they would entail naval losses so severe as to eliminate the margin of superiority the Grand Fleet enjoyed. Similarly, the Dardanelles operation, which promised so much for the Russian front, had to be abandoned for fear of excessive capital ship losses. Had the British been able to destroy the German High Seas Fleet in harbour, they would also have been able to risk the major unit losses implicit in coastal landings.

Thus it could be said that wartime experience demonstrated not only the value of the main fleet, but also that a main fleet strategy demanded a decisive engagement. British fleet development of the interwar period, which included the design of the carriers which fought World War II, can best be understood as preparation for a future decisive engagement, either at sea – in which case heavy guns would be required – or against an enemy in harbour, in which case aircraft would be decisive. British theorists studied Jutland because, as the sole example of a recent fleet engagement, it demonstrated the requirements of any future decisive battle.

Jutland itself was less than decisive. Britain did not lose sea control, because the Germans were forced back into harbour, but the RN also failed to achieve a decisive naval victory. Instead, Britain had to maintain her blockading fleet for the rest of the war, constantly risking the loss of ships to minefields (as in the case of the battleship *Audacious*, in 1914), to submarines, or even to accident (as in the loss of HMS *Vanguard*, apparently to unstable powder, in 1917).

Moreover, by imposing a decisive defeat of some kind on an enemy early in a war, it was felt that the Royal Navy could achieve a valuable moral ascendency. British strategists could point to the mutiny and collapse of the German High Seas Fleet in 1918 (and to its failure in action earlier in the same year) as evidence of the effect of such ascendency.[16] Even relatively small forces, aggressively and promptly employed, could have disproportionate effects. This lesson would be quoted after World War II as justification for maintaining an offensive (land or harbour attack) capability in a badly pared-down Fleet Air Arm.

The enemy might, of course, prefer to remain in a defended base. In 1917–18 Admiral Beatty pressed for a mass torpedo-bomber attack on the German fleet in harbour. Between the wars much effort went into special weapons and tactics to solve this problem, culminating in the successful carrier night attack on the Italian battle fleet at Taranto in November 1940. Thus aircraft made it possible for the Royal Navy to seize the initiative early in a war, in a way altogether impossible in World War I.

The Battle of Jutland showed what could go wrong, even when an enemy accepted battle. First, Jellicoe at no stage received sufficient information. He needed effective long-range scouts, as well as aircraft to provide a comprehensive picture of the developing action. Jellicoe had in fact been able to perceive the overall shape of the battle, but it became evident after the war that this had required exceptional insight, not to be expected in future. During the battle itself he lacked accurate information concerning the movements of the German fleet, particularly as the latter slipped from his grasp; he could, therefore, have benefited enormously from action observation. Both scouting and action observation could best be conducted by aircraft organic to the fleet. Conversely, an enemy had to be denied the fruits of his own air reconnaissance. In August 1916 Zeppelin scouts prevented the German High Seas Fleet from falling into a British trap. Afterwards Britain took fighters to sea specifically to drive off such scouts.

Second, the British commander needed some means of slowing down an enemy fleet, which might well initially be faster than his. If an attack could be made at a substantial distance, in conjunction with effective scouting, an enemy fleet could be brought to action, but once action had been joined, a faster enemy fleet might escape unless it was slowed. At Jutland the Germans evaded fatal damage (from the British battle line) by escaping into a smoke screen; air observation could nullify the effect of such a screen, and aerial torpedo attack would make escape impossible. Ideally, sea-based aircraft would also protect the British fleet from enemy torpedo-bombers, and there was some question as to the extent to which torpedo-bombers would require fighter escorts. However, as in the prewar US Navy, British doctrine up to World War II was that the best means of securing air supremacy was to disable or sink the enemy carrier by early air attack, at maximum range.

Third, gunnery was clearly limited by visibility. If indeed the heavy guns were to be the decisive element of a future fleet action, they would require substantial improvement in control. That would come from spotters aloft, in special aircraft. It followed that the enemy had to be denied the opportunity to use similar spotters to control his own fire.

These lessons were applied to the case of the unified main fleet fighting a decisive battle against another main fleet. The reality of World War II was that the Royal Navy had often to operate within easy range of enemy land-based aircraft, far too numerous to neutralize by naval air attack, and without its own aircraft for direct support. Moreover, the issue was often not whether British capital ships could or would survive, but whether much more vulnerable cruisers and destroyers could operate freely near land-based bombers. No one had ever claimed that such ships would be able to survive hits by the most effective anti-ship weapon, the dive-bomber, and wartime experience should not have been as surprising as it was.

In the Far East, where the Navy knew that Japan had large numbers of land-based bombers, the strategy was to force an engagement beyond their range, closer to Singapore than to Japan. *Repulse* and *Prince of Wales* were lost largely because it turned out that the Japanese bombers could indeed operate freely as far south as Malaya. It was not practicable to limit naval operations to areas beyond the range of most land-based bombers, in which limited numbers of fleet aircraft could dominate.

Two other World War I lessons deserve comment here. One was the potential efficacy of surface raiders. It is true that U-boats accounted for the bulk of British shipping losses in World War I, but they were confined for the most part to European waters, and by 1918 it appeared that convoying could defeat them. Individual U-boats also were limited in their ability to detect and to engage relatively fast surface ships. Surface raiders were far more worrying; they enjoyed much longer detection ranges, particularly if they were provided with scout aircraft, they could be well-enough armed to overwhelm anti-sub-marine escorts, and perhaps worst of all, they enjoyed enormous mobility. The British theorists remembered the efforts required to hunt down such lone raiders as the *Emden*, and also the threat of powerful surface squadrons such as Admiral von Spee's.

The surface raider threat in turn explained British naval insistence on maintaining large numbers of cruisers. In order to secure American agreement to the London Treaty of 1930, however, Britain had to accept substantial reductions; thus, particularly after 1930, the RN had to seek some means of magnifying the effectiveness of their remaining ships, and also of improving anti-raider forces in wartime. Aircraft promised to solve both problems. Flying from a cruiser, they could greatly extend her scouting range, and perhaps could even attack a raider on their own. Moreover, it was much easier to improvise a small carrier or seaplane tender than an effective gun-armed cruiser, although in practice the Royal Navy converted merchant hulls for both roles.

Another lesson was more general. Britain benefited enormously from her network of radio direction-finding stations and from her success in code-breaking. Although neither received much publicity outside the service, both the Admiralty and senior operational commanders were well aware of the vulnerability associated with radio transmissions. The Royal Navy therefore adopted a strong policy of what would now be called emission control. This in turn greatly affected carrier operations, since radio navigational beacon operation was discouraged. Early in World War II, it was also reflected in a reluctance to turn on radars at sea, and in the slow development of fighter-control. The absence of navigational beacons partly explained the British preference for two-seat fighters for long-range operation.

Operational experience did not, of course, end in 1918. The Royal Navy found itself involved in the Russian Civil War, in the Near East, and in China. In each case carriers were valued for their ability to bring aircraft to an area far from existing bases. Numbers of aircraft were not nearly as important here as their sheer presence.

16   World War II showed similar examples, such as the relative paralysis of the Italian Fleet after Taranto and Matapan, and the virtual impotence of the German capital ships.

Painfully aware of the need for carriers, yet severely limited both by finances and by the resistance of the Air Ministry, the Admiralty, and particularly Admiral R G H Henderson, devised a number of brilliant subterfuges. HMS Unicorn, *the FAA support ship which could also function as an operational carrier, was perhaps the cleverest. She is shown at Trincomalee in April 1944, with the battlecruiser* Renown *and the fleet carrier* Illustrious. *FAAM*

Nor can the experience of interwar fleet exercises be discounted. The single most important question was how the fleet was to be defended against hostile air attack. As did the contemporary US Navy, the Royal Navy quickly came to the conclusion that carriers would be relatively easy to disable, and therefore that air supremacy at sea could best be achieved by finding and neutralizing the enemy carriers before they had the opportunity to find the British fleet. This in turn imposed stringent requirements for long flying endurance.

As for defending the fleet itself, gunfire was highly rated, whereas before the advent of radar fighter interception seemed less and less likely to succeed as aircraft speeds increased. Warning time was simply not long enough. These two considerations together explain the armoured carrier, capable of sustaining air attack but accommodating only a limited number of strike aircraft.

These were very reasonable views before World War II. Of the three main elements of the air threat, formations of high-altitude level bombers (which could penetrate armoured decks) could be broken up by heavy anti-aircraft fire, and their attacks frustrated by evasive manoeuvres; torpedo-bombers (which had to approach to relatively short ranges at low angles of elevation) could be engaged even by low-angle guns; and dive-

bombers (which could hit manoeuvring ships but could not penetrate thick armoured decks) could be countered by massed heavy machine-guns. These considerations explain why the prewar Fleet Air Arm emphasized torpedo- and dive-bombing, and also why the prewar Royal Navy invested heavily in multiple 2pdr pom-poms.[17]

THE ROYAL NAVY (and, for that matter, the British government as a whole) was continuously faced with a choice between continuing the development of new technology, and putting that technology into production. The penalty for choosing development over production was to be faced by better enemy technology before the next generation of British technology was available. The penalty for choosing production was that, with money spent and facilities allocated, production of better equipment would have to be foregone for some time. British air rearmament, for example, started in earnest in about 1936. At that time the best available engine was probably the Merlin, which could produce about 1000hp. It made for high performance in the Spitfire, but it was not powerful enough for heavier naval aircraft such as the Fulmar and Barracuda. That was irrelevant; the international political situation made rearmament mandatory. During World War II, these same aircraft were often unfavourably compared with US types powered by the 2000hp engines which became available only about 1940 or later; the United States benefited partly because her air rearmament came later. The United States was also fortunate that her economic base was so large that she could afford simultaneous development and mass production.

Timing was not, of course, the only factor. British fleet and carrier operating practice imposed very tight limits on aircraft designers. Overall naval air doctrine determined the number of

17   Unfortunately the Royal Navy chose an ineffective form of anti-aircraft fire control, and did not invest in the necessary remote power control for its heavy anti-aircraft guns. Before World War II, the Royal Navy considered its destroyer guns, which were capable of elevating to only about 40 degrees, effective against level bombers since the bombers would be engaged at a considerable distance from the battle fleet proper. The system broke down in practice because dive-bombers could engage and sink destroyers and cruisers (and carriers), and because they could wreck fire control systems aboard capital ships. Even so, it seems noteworthy that in 1939 the Royal Navy had much more powerful automatic anti-aircraft batteries than, say, the US Navy.

aircraft a main fleet required. The primary roles of the aircraft were to find the enemy and then to slow him, so that he could be brought to battle. Neither was much related to the total size of the fleet; reconnaissance required so many aircraft to cover so many search patterns, and doctrine matched the size of the strike to the number of targets.

Unfortunately, the older British carriers had very limited aircraft capacity. This placed a very heavy burden on the few more capacious ships. During much of the interwar period the total size of the carrier force was limited by treaty, and although the treaty permitted replacement of the earlier ships, finances did not. This situation was well understood, and when the treaty restrictions lapsed the Admiralty began an aggressive carrier construction programme; this was only beginning when World War II began. Moreover, the new carriers (whose numbers were no longer limited by treaty) traded aircraft capacity for protection, on the theory that total aircraft numbers could be achieved by building enough ships. In the event, few could be built, so that it was extremely difficult to make up the loss of three capacious carriers (*Courageous*, *Glorious* and *Ark Royal*) in 1939–41.

Given tight limits on the total number of fleet aircraft, the Royal Navy had to develop multi-role types. Even then the fleet could not accommodate sufficient aircraft aboard its carriers, and British planners expected to catapult numerous wheeled combat aircraft from battleships and cruisers. These schemes might be considered the direct ancestors of later ideas such as the escort cruiser. The requirement that the combat aircraft be launchable by capital ship catapults in turn imposed a limit on overall weight and also on take-off speed (in effect, catapult end speed).

The carrier imposed her own limits: on stall speed (for landing); on folded width, length, and height (for stowage); on maximum wing span (to clear the island when landing or taking off). Aircraft had to be ranged on deck in order to take off for mass strikes; therefore take-off runs had to be short enough for enough strike aircraft to be ranged abaft the first one taking off. This last limitation was eliminated only when all aircraft were launched by catapult.

British air tactics demanded long endurance for maximum striking range. This meant not only extra fuel but, generally, a second or third crewman to navigate. For any aircraft, there is a limit to the spread between high- and low-speed performances. In the case of British carrier aircraft, excellent low-speed performance, both landing and taking off, was required. Given restrictions on total aircraft size and weight, maximum performance inevitably suffered in comparison with apparently similar land-based aircraft. Because other navies, such as the US Navy, worked under less rigorous limits, their aircraft tended to perform better; in the Japanese case, better performance also resulted from much lighter construction, as in the Zero. Only

Because British doctrine was to equate carrier hangar stowage capacity with carrier aircraft operating capacity, British carrier designers adopted double hangars. Eagle's is shown, in 1965. Left to right, the upper hangar shows a Gannet airborne early warning aircraft (with a big radome under its belly), a line of Wessex helicopters, and a Scimitar used for air-to-air refuelling. The lower hangar shows a double line of Buccaneer strike bombers. The foremost on the left has its radome folded back for stowage, and the aircraft on the right has its air brake spread for stowage.

during World War II were the British restrictions eased to a point at which much better aero engines could eliminate the gap between British land- and sea-based aircraft.

There was a reciprocal effect on carrier design. In principle, a carrier could be expected to last about twenty-five years. She therefore had to embody limits (for example on aircraft size and weight) somewhat in advance of those applying to existing aircraft.[18] Until about 1942 those margins were relatively small; they were radically increased at that time, not only to accommodate a new generation of aircraft already in sight, but also because aircraft seemed to be developing at an accelerating rate. British carrier design practice (the closed hangar) and operating practice (all aircraft stowed in the hangar) made these limits particularly important.

Matters were further complicated, late in the 1930s, by the greater priority accorded the RAF fighter force (for ADGB). The Royal Navy's carrier aircraft naturally could not enjoy the same priority for the limited number of very high-powered engines (Merlins) then being produced. Similarly, after World War II RAF and Royal Navy aircraft competed for a limited jet engine production capacity, as well as for other limited resources such as high-powered radars and guided missiles; this kind of competition was inevitable, given limits on total British resources. The Royal Navy suffered further because its production runs were inherently very short, which was itself a consequence of the carrier operating practice drastically limiting the number of aircraft any one carrier could accommodate. Short production runs made naval business unattractive, and often the Royal Navy found itself adapting RAF types designed to meet radically different requirements. Firms specializing in naval aircraft, such as Blackburn and Fairey, naturally were quite small, and thus could not bring aircraft into production as rapidly as could the larger firms enjoying larger RAF orders. This consideration helps to explain the very long gestation of the Skua and Roc.[19]

Weight per horsepower was particularly critical for large multi-purpose, multi-seat aircraft, such as the Swordfish and Barracuda. Limited in overall dimensions, they had also to allow low stall speeds (for short take-offs and limited landing speeds). This required large wings, to provide sufficient lift, which was particularly important with less powerful engines. Large wings in turn limited maximum speed. The Fairey Swordfish was a biplane, not because of some misplaced nostalgia, but because, given the best available engine, it took a great deal of wing area to lift enough fuel plus a heavy torpedo, plus other essential equipment. Swordfish design was also affected by the hope, realized in this case, that three functions (reconnaissance, spotting and torpedo attack) could be united in one aircraft.

Fuel efficiency was important because naval aircraft generally require greater endurance than their land-based counterparts. They must, for example, be able to find their carriers upon returning, even though the carriers may themselves have manoeuvred considerably during the mission. This is one reason why the Spitfire, which did not require very long range, could be so much smaller (and could enjoy so much better performance) than contemporary British naval aircraft. Conversely, when the Spitfire was accepted for naval service, its deficiencies in endurance (and in ruggedness) were quite painful. The generation of aero engines which followed the Merlin and its contemporaries was so powerful that the extra size associated with naval endurance and ruggedness was of much less moment; this is why the Corsair, for example, compared favourably with contemporary land-based fighters. The story of the Blackburn Firebrand shows that even this improvement did not always suffice to offset the penalties associated with earlier British practice.

These considerations explain intense naval interest in exotic means of increasing lift, or reducing landing speed, without paying heavy weight or maximum performance penalties. Examples include a variable-geometry torpedo-bomber tested during World War II and the blown wing of the postwar Buccaneer bomber. The other, and better-known, solution to the inherent problem was to modify the carrier to accept higher take-off and landing speeds. The Royal Navy found itself particularly pressed in this direction after World War II, since it had to operate higher-performance aircraft (to match new land-based types) from carriers designed during World War II. The results included the steam catapult and the angled deck.

Very broadly, then, one might divide naval fighter development into three eras. First, from World War I until about 1930 or even 1935, there was little to distinguish naval fighters from their land-based counterparts. Biplanes had so much lift that they could take off from carrier deck-size runways. Construction was relatively light; the limits imposed by carrier design and operation were not yet onerous.

However, from the late 1920s on, carrier aircraft began to demonstrate effective operation at increasing ranges. Higher speeds made fighter interception less viable, so that the role of the single-seat naval fighter declined. However, existing engines could not confer single-seat performance on such relatively heavy multi-seat naval aircraft as the Skua and the Fulmar.

During and after World War II, naval aircraft performance appeared to improve drastically. Several causes can be cited. First, single-seaters, which always outperformed the multi-seaters, became more important with the appearance of radar. Second, engines improved drastically, particularly after jets were introduced. Third, carrier operating restrictions were relaxed. The general reliance on catapulting, for example, obviated the need for limited take-off runs.

The Royal Navy now finds itself in a fourth era. Severe carrier limitations have once more been imposed, in the form of the abandonment of large-deck carriers. The solution, VSTOL, carries severe performance penalties, just as carrier operation did in the interwar period. And, just as it did during World War II, the Royal Navy can hope to overcome some or all of those penalties through innovative aircraft design. As this is written, for example, there is hope of achieving supersonic performance through plenum chamber burning. The current VSTOLs also echo another earlier approach to the performance gap: superior weaponry aboard the naval aircraft. In the 1930s the Roc was conceived as an interceptor which could manoeuvre its turret to track a target it could not out-fly. In the 1980s advanced air-to-air missiles such as AMRAAM promise the Sea Harrier a longer reach. Unfortunately, the Royal Navy cannot do much to reverse such inherent limitations of its small carriers as their very small aircraft capacity.

THERE IS ALSO the effect of the Royal Air Force and of the associated centralization of aircraft procurement to consider. The World War I Royal Naval Air Service began life as the naval wing of a unified Royal Flying Corps, though it developed quite independently through the war. Problems of national aircraft production led, in 1917, to unified aircraft procurement for both services, a pattern which would persist down to the present. In 1918 the formation of the RAF meant not only that naval aircraft were transferred to another service, but also that the new Air Ministry took responsibility for the procurement and development of all British military aircraft. The Fleet Air Arm was withdrawn from RAF control in 1939, but centralization remained, in the form of the wartime Ministry of

18 The two *Implacable* class armoured double-hangar carriers were a spectacular case in point. They imposed such harsh limitations (at a time of particularly rapid aircraft development) that they could not be used effectively after World War II, and so did not much outlive the aircraft they initally operated.

19 The Admiralty did consider this period (roughly 1933–1939) excessive, and Blackburn was excluded from the design competition which produced the Firefly. However, the firm had its defenders, and the Royal Navy did buy the Blackburn Firebrand.

Aircraft Production (MAP) and the postwar Ministry of Supply. In each case, the Admiralty framed Staff Requirements, but these also had to be passed up through the staff of the relevant procurement Ministry, which sometimes entailed considerable delays.

Although the independent, unified RAF came into existence on 1 April 1918, little changed administratively until after the war. In 1919 the RAF placed all maritime aircraft, including carrier aircraft, under Air Officer Coastal Area (AOCA) who happened to be Air Vice Marshal A V Vyvyan, a former senior naval officer. There was no corresponding senior naval air officer, but the Admiralty did form a small Naval Air Section (NAS) under Cdr Richard Bell Davies. At first the Admiralty dealt directly with AOCA, but the Air Council (the RAF equivalent of the Board of Admiralty) stopped this practice in 1921, apparently fearing that a future government would undo the 1918 unification, as very nearly happened in 1923.[20] Coastal Area was effectively eliminated as the senior carrier air office when the Royal Navy appointed a Rear Admiral, Aircraft (Admiral Henderson) in 1931, a step it announced in May 1930.

Through the 1920s the Admiralty tried to regain control of the Fleet Air Arm; in 1923 it exacted an agreement that all observers and 70 per cent of all pilots would be naval officers. Naval officers who flew had alternative RAF ranks.[21] Perhaps more importantly, the Navy financed most Fleet Air Arm procurement and operation.[22] Within the Admiralty, the Naval Air Section was promoted to Divisional status in 1931, coincident with the establishment of a flag officer to command naval aircraft.

In its fight to maintain control of the Fleet Air Arm, the Air Ministry (RAF) claimed that air power was 'unified', that is, that knowledge of flying and of air tactics was far more important than the specialized knowledge of how to fly from ships. The Ministry repeatedly claimed, for example, that deck-landing was relatively simple and required little special training. These claims culminated, in the 1930s, in a mass demonstration deck-landing by an RAF fighter squadron – the pilots of which had, until very recently, served in the Fleet Air Arm. Note, however, the ease with which Hurricane pilots landed aboard HMS *Glorious* at the end of the Norwegian campaign in 1940.

Operationally, the problem was that many pilots aboard a ship were not formally responsible to the ship's commanding officer, in the sense that they did not belong to the same service. Friction between commanding officers and air commanders naturally survived the end of formal RAF control, the most celebrated case being the problems aboard HMS *Glorious* in 1940.[23]

In May 1937 the government announced that the Fleet Air Arm would be restored to naval control, and this actually occurred on 24 May 1939. The Royal Navy did not, however, regain control of the land-based maritime aircraft it had operated during World War I. During World War II it did have operational control of RAF Coastal Command. One result of this remaining split was that, after the war, partisans of the RAF tried to eliminate much of the Royal Navy by claiming that Coastal Command could do the same job (coastal ASW) less expensively.[24]

Because the Royal Navy financed and, in effect, controlled shipboard but not shore-based maritime aircraft even before 1939, the rivalry between the two predated World War II. For example, the RAF developed large flying-boats as anti-shipping weapons, rather than as a means of augmenting fleet reconnaissance. The US Navy, which operated both flying-boats and carrier aircraft, tended rather to consider the two complementary, and to use its long-range aircraft primarily for reconnaissance.[25]

Numerous historians have observed that, at a stroke in 1918, vast numbers of naval aircraft (and of naval fliers) were torn from the Royal Navy, and the implication is generally that the post-1918 Royal Navy suffered from a fatal lack of air-mindedness. After all, officers rising out of the ranks of the fliers provide air-mindedness, don't they? Certainly the US Navy seems to have derived much of its fascination with carrier warfare from its practice, instituted during the 1920s, of requiring that commanders of carriers and other naval air establishments be qualified pilots. Officers who wanted commands applied for flight training, often at advanced ages, and the US naval air arm prospered.

The reality for the Royal Navy was probably more complex. Many of the most influential early advocates of US naval aviation were not themselves pilots. They learned about aircraft capabilities either at the Naval War College, on the gaming floor, or in fleet exercises. Many non-aviator officers proved extremely adept at using naval aircraft; Admiral Raymond Spruance, a prewar cruiser commander, is perhaps the greatest case in point. In the British case, senior officers certainly saw what naval aircraft could accomplish, because those aircraft were always employed in fleet exercises. Presumably aircraft also figured heavily in war games.[26] On the other hand, the same officers may have been less aware of the inherent limitations of their aircraft.

Some effects of the split were subtle. US and British prewar carrier operating practice differed radically. In US carriers, many aircraft were parked on the flight deck. Aircraft landed into arrester gear and were then wheeled to the bow, where they were parked, protected by a wire crash barrier. This made

British World War I experience in signals intelligence led to an emphasis, later, on radio silence. This extended to air operations. In this 1940 photograph taken aboard HMS Ark Royal, *the panel on the island on the left, with a cross painted on it, was used for visual signalling to aircraft (for instance, to indicate that the deck was free for landings). Similar panels were installed on all earlier British carriers. The folded aircraft on the lift is a Swordfish torpedo-bomber/scout.*

20 The new RAF seems to have been very insistent on its prerogatives, apparently for fear of being submerged by the two older services. Many writers, for example, have remarked on its heavy interwar investments in such apparent luxuries as officers' clubs, the real function of which was to impart a sense of tradition and continuity. Much of the stiffness seems to have come from the creator of the independent RAF, Lord Trenchard.

21 The use of naval officer pilots was officially justified on the ground that they would leave the naval officer corps with some appreciation of flying. It later proved difficult to recruit sufficient numbers of officer pilots, and the Admiralty proposed to use ratings. This the RAF bitterly opposed, on the ground that to do so would violate the logic of the 1923 agreement. It is difficult to avoid the feeling, however, that the RAF wanted to avoid using enlisted pilots of its own. From a carrier design point of view, the controversy was important because officers required better accommodation, which was more difficult to provide in tightly-designed ships. The Air Ministry succeeded in killing the proposal in 1928, but the Amiralty reopened it in 1934, at which time Air Ministry opposition was one of the grounds for the Admiralty attempt to regain control over the Fleet Air Arm.

22 Geoffrey Till, *Airpower and the Royal Navy, 1914–1945* (Jane's, London, 1979) is probably by far the most complete account of the Royal Navy's attempt to regain direct control of the Fleet Air Arm. My own view is that Till somewhat exaggerates the ill effects of RAF control, and the lack of air-mindedness of the Royal Navy. I suggest that comparison with US practice will tend to moderate both views.

23 See J Winton, *Carrier Glorious* (Leo Cooper, London, 1986).

24 Documents released over the past few years at the Public Record Office show that this certainly occurred in about 1954-55. It seems likely that the same logic was applied during the Nott Defence Review of 1980-81, but of course that record has not yet surfaced. For the 1955 case, see my *Postwar Naval Revolution* (Conway Maritime Press, London, 1987).

25 This distinction may not be altogether fair, as the two navies occupied very different strategic situations. The US Navy contemplated a progress across the Pacific in the face of Japanese opposition. Britain had to defend a dispersed Empire against naval attack, and she could not expect the main fleet to gain sea control at the very beginning. Long-range aircraft were the next best thing, a mobile dispersed force which could rapidly be concentrated at the point of attack. Even so, the Royal Navy early recognized the potential assistance the big flying-boats could provide, long before the RAF became interested.

26 Only 'presumably' because British theoretical gaming exercises do not figure prominently in the Admiralty papers preserved at the Public Record Office. Relatively few of the papers of the Royal Naval College, Greenwich, have been released.

27 By this time the reasoning was partly that aircraft permanently deck-parked did not live nearly as long (especially in bad weather) as aircraft protected in hangars. Aircraft were always both scarce and expensive.

28 I am indebted to Dr Thomas Hone for this point. Hone reports that within a short time *Langley* had reduced the average landing interval to 30 seconds, compared to 5 minutes for contemporary British carriers. See his paper, 'Navy Air Leadership: RADM W A Moffett as Chief of the Bureau of Aeronautics,' prepared for the April 1984 meeting of the American Military Institute, Air Force Historical Foundation, and Military Classics Seminar.

29 Not that it was ordered in the first place, but that the order was not and is not considered reprehensible, and that Admiral Mitscher's decision to light searchlights (as beacons) was considered remarkable, rather than the minimum acceptable. The early postwar feature film *Task Force* was a good illustration of the traditions of US naval aviation. It opens with scenes of fatal crashes aboard *Langley*.

30 See, for example, Commander R 'Mike' Crosley, *They Gave Me A Seafire* (Airlife, Shrewsbury, 1986), for reactions to what he (and, by implication, many other British naval pilots) saw as insensitive comments by senior officers in the Pacific in 1945.

31 A wartime British report on deck-landing aerodynamics, preserved in one of the general carrier covers (NMM), described US carriers as hulls with flat decks pasted atop them. British flight decks were carefully rounded down fore and aft, and British carrier islands were often of aerofoil cross-section, for optimum airflow. The Royal Navy also avoided obstructing its flight decks, for example with gun mounts, whereas US *Essex* class fleet

carriers had guns on their flight decks. It is only fair, however, to suggest that the origins of British concern with carrier aerodynamics go back to World War I, before there was any RAF. At that time aircraft were so flimsy that the aerodynamics of the flight deck were crucial, the *Furious* disaster being an important case in point. The US Navy began its experiments with a later (and much more robust) generation of aircraft, and, more importantly, no *Furious*, largely because it benefited from British World War I experience.

32 It was well known at the end of the Pacific War that British naval squadrons had suffered terribly, and much more from deck-landing accidents than from enemy fire. See, for example, Norman Hanson, *Carrier Pilot* (Patrick Stephens Ltd, Cambridge, 1979), for operations off Okinawa. Small carriers also made for smaller air groups, so that, to maintain (say) a given level of combat air patrol, a British carrier might have to operate more intensively, with worse resultant fatigue.

for a short landing interval, since an aircraft could land without waiting for its predecessor to be folded and struck below. Once the aircraft had landed and parked, they could be brought back to the stern in preparation for take-off: the size of the parking area on the flight deck, then, determined how many aircraft a US carrier could operate continuously. This consideration in turn explains why US carriers, such as the *Essex*, were relatively long for their displacement.

This operating practice was well adapted to mass (deck-load strike) attacks, but could not easily support operation by a few aircraft while the mass of the carrier air group remained aboard. This consideration explains such unusual US World War II expedients as hangar-deck catapults and bow arrester gear (to recover aircraft without disturbing the large deck park aft). The problem was not really solved until the invention of the angled deck.

Usable flight deck area was inevitably much greater than hangar area, so the aircraft complement of a carrier which permanently parked her aircraft on deck could greatly exceed that of a carrier limited to hangar stowage. In US carriers total capacity was typically a combination of a permanent deck park and hangar stowage.

The Royal Navy struck aircraft below as they landed. This made for slower operation, since the flight deck had to be clear before an aircraft was allowed to land. A low landing rate in turn could limit carrier capacity (since aircraft had limited endurance). Moreover, if an aircraft had to spend a considerable fraction of its overall endurance waiting to land, this limited its effective range.

This practice also equated maximum aircraft capacity to hangar capacity (aircraft capacity could be smaller, based on a comparison between aircraft endurance and landing rate). Although British naval officers were aware of the advantages of the crash barrier/deck park system, and although the Royal Navy adopted deck parking during World War II, even after the war it generally tended to equate hangar capacity to aircraft capacity.[27]

It is only fair to add here that the Royal Navy found it difficult to accept permanent deck stowage because aircraft on deck tended to deteriorate, particularly in extreme climates such as the Arctic or, before World War II, the tropics. Aircraft could not be purchased in such numbers that they could lightly be discarded. In this sense the small capacity of British carriers forced the Royal Navy into a vicious cycle: production runs were short, therefore prices were high, therefore aircraft could not (many would have said, should not) be thrown away, therefore not so many were needed. In the US case, the nominal capacity of the carriers was much greater, therefore the production runs were much larger, and it was much easier to make up for wastage.

The origins of this distinction are interesting. The US Navy, heavily influenced by British World War I experience, initially followed British practice, so that the US prototype carrier, *Langley*, was initially assigned only about a dozen aircraft. In

1926, however, her commander, then-Captain J M Reeves, insisted that she could carry and operate 3 ½ times as many. He had attended the Naval War College in 1925, and had learned what mass air attacks could do. Reeves' insistence on very quick operations led directly to the institution of the deck park and the crash barrier. He had just qualified as a naval aviation observer, the minimum allowing him to command the carrier, but he was by no means a naval aviator. Indeed, the pilots on the *Langley*, well aware that the innovations were extremely dangerous, opposed them.[28]

Reeves succeeded because the aviators on the *Langley* were directly and unambiguously subordinate to him. As their superior officer, within the same service, he had the right to ask them to take what seemed to him reasonable risks, almost as a matter of course. The British situation was radically different. The captain of a carrier had to accept the views of the RAF contingent on his ship, not because the pilots could complain to the Air Ministry, but because the creation of the separate service implied that they had an expertise he lacked. If the aviators thought five minutes a reasonable landing interval, the captain might complain to higher authority that better equipment for quicker landings was needed, but he could not tell his pilots to do better; he could not overrule their professional judgement.

By all accounts, US pre-1941 naval flying was extremely dangerous. Aircraft did often pitch over the side, and they were badly smashed when landing rapidly into barriers. The survivors of this experience regarded it as normal, and assumed that rising generations of naval aviators would accept it. Because they belonged to the same service, they could demand and expect extremely hazardous operations as a matter of course. The very long-range strike at the end of the Battle of the Philippine Sea, which resulted in the loss of many US aircraft, is a case in point.[29]

Accounts of prewar British naval aviation suggest a much lower casualty rate. It was not that British naval aviators were timid, but rather that there was no – could be no – force driving them to take enormous risks. The senior naval officers, who were using air services, could not guess what they were missing. Indeed, they tended to disbelieve US official figures on carrier capacities. Even after the naval aviators had been reabsorbed by the Royal Navy, many aviators felt a separateness, and a resentment at rough treatment by senior officers.[30]

Similarly, technical issues were resolved by a Navy-RAF committee, which had to give great weight to the airmen's professional views. As a result, British carrier designs showed great attention to landing aerodynamics. American carrier designs did not.[31] The US Navy tended to present potential aircraft suppliers with the unpleasant facts of carrier operation; as a result, they supplied rugged airframes and landing gear. The Air Ministry, by way of contrast, had sufficient bureaucratic power to force the carrier designers to provide environments better adapted to aircraft.

British carrier designers provided relatively short decks because they did not calculate primarily in terms of deck parks. When crash barriers and deck parks were introduced in wartime, these same carriers seem to have suffered from high accident rates compared to contemporary US carriers with much larger flight decks.[32]

It is, of course, impossible to discount the larger political effects of the unitary Royal Air Force. As defence funds became tighter in the 1930s, the RAF clearly considered land-based operations more important than those of the Royal Navy. Attempts at air disarmament paralleled those at naval disarmament. At this time the chief air threat to Britain was the powerful French air force. The RAF was perfectly willing to accept deep cuts in return for reductions in the French bomber force, and it suggested that the Royal Navy shoulder all or most of the necessary costs. The Air Ministry resisted the argument that the Fleet Air Arm was essential to Imperial defence, particularly in the Far East.

Later, as it expanded to meet the threat of World War II, the Air Ministry (which was responsible for overall British aircraft production) inevitably preferred to commit scarce industrial resources to the ADGB rather than to the fleet. This was, however, central government policy, not merely the result of bureaucratic politics, and it is understandable in those terms.

There were also more subtle effects of interservice rivalry. The Royal Navy had to agree, tacitly, not to interfere with an RAF monopoly on air attacks on enemy land targets. Thus one finds Navy proposals to accommodate RAF aircraft aboard carriers for attacks on land targets outside the range of land-based aircraft. For example, a projected RAF Mosquito attack against the Japanese fleet in harbour in 1945 would have been mounted from carriers. The RAF stoutly and fairly success-fully resisted postwar Royal Navy attempts to develop a carrier strike force against land targets.

FINALLY, SOME ACCOUNT of the structure of the Admiralty is in order. Many historians equate the Admiralty (or 'their Lord-ships') with the Royal Navy, but the reality is much more complex. In theory, the Admiralty was responsible for setting basic wartime naval strategic policy and also for supplying the requirements of the deployed naval forces. Traditionally its operational orders had been limited to very general directives, but by 1914 radio communication had greatly expanded its power. Moreover, it was soon discovered that much intelli-gence, particularly signals intelligence, naturally flowed directly into the central Admiralty rather than into the flagships of the deployed fleets. As a result, the Admiralty gained con-siderable operational responsibility.

The Admiralty was headed by the Board of Admiralty (often abbreviated in this book to 'the Board'), consisting of a military branch (four or five Sea Lords, the Vice- and some-times also the Assistant Chiefs of the Naval Staff) and a civilian branch (First Lord, Civil Lord, Parliamentary and Financial Secretary, and Permanent Secretary) corresponding approxi-mately on the one hand to the US Office of the Chief of Naval Operations and on the other to the Office of the Secretary of the Navy. Each Sea Lord was responsible both for the work of the Board as a whole and for his own special area. The First Sea Lord was responsible for overall policy and for operations. He was also Chief of the Naval Staff (CNS), though generally not referred to as such. The Second Sea Lord was responsible for personnel. The Third Sea Lord and Controller was responsible for *matériel*, and the Fourth Sea Lord for stores. At least from 1920 on, the Naval Staff, supervised by the First Sea Lord and VCNS (Vice Chief of the Naval Staff), developed Staff Requirements for new ships and weapons; the Controller was responsible for meeting these. During World War I the position of Fifth Sea Lord, responsible for naval aviation, was estab-lished. It lapsed when aircraft were transferred to the new RAF, and was then re-established when the Royal Navy regained control of the Fleet Air Arm. The Fifth Sea Lord was also Chief of the Naval Air Service and DCNS(Air), assisted by an ACNS(Air). These posts were separate from that of DNAD, the chief of the *staff* air division.

The position of Fifth Sea Lord lapsed in July 1942 and was replaced by Chief of Naval Air Services. It was restored the following year, when the Fifth Sea Lord became Chief of Naval Air Equipment (in effect, Controller for air matters).

Between 1918 and 1939 one member of the Board, generally ACNS or DCNS, was responsible for air matters. The most

Table 1-1: Admiralty Staff And Associated Officers

ACA	Admiral Commanding Aircraft (World War I)
ACNS	Assistant Chief of the Naval Staff, later split into ACNS (A) and ACNS(W) (Aircraft and Weapons); during the World War II there were also ACNS(F), ACNS(H) and ACNS(T), for Foreign, Home and Trade (later anti-U-boat warfare and trade protection)
AOCA	Air Officer (Commanding) Coastal Area (RAF, interwar)
CAOR	Chief Advisor on Operations Research, later DNOR
CNR	Chief Naval Representative (in the World War II Ministry of Aircraft Production). Postwar, CNR was representative to MoS (Ministry of Supply) and this post was held by the Vice Controller (Air)
CNS	Chief of Naval Staff (First Sea Lord)
DACR	Director of Airfield and Carrier Requirements (created 1943)
DAD	Director of Air Division (World War I)
DAE	Director of Air Equipment (created 1943)
DAM	Director of Air Material (created 1938). Split 1943 into Air Equipment (DAE) and Airfield and Carrier Requirements (DACR)
DAOT	Director, Air Organization and Training (successor to DNAO)
DAW	Director of Naval Air Warfare (sometimes Naval Air Warfare and Flying Training Division, DAWT)
DAWT	See DAW
DCNS	Deputy Chief of Naval Staff; combined with Fifth Sea Lord 1957
DCR	Director, Carrier and Airfield Requirements
DEE	Director of Electrical Engineering
DGD	Director of Gunnery Division; became Surface Warfare Division 1964; during World War II, Gunnery and Anti-Aircraft Warfare Division
DMT	Director, Mine and Torpedo (World War I era; later became DTASW)
DNAD	Director, Naval Air Division (eliminated 1943 in favour of DAW and DNAO); this title was revived in 1962 as successor to DAW and DAOT
DNAO	Director, Naval Air Organization Division (created 1943); later DAOT
DNAS	Director, Naval Air Service
DNC	Director of Naval Construction
DND	Director of Navigation and Direction (including fighter direction); became Navigation and Tactical Control 1964
DNE	Director of Naval Equipment
DNI	Director of Naval Intelligence
DNO	Director of Naval Ordnance
DNOR	Director of Naval Operations Research (in World War II, Professor P M S Blackett); later DOR
DOD	Director of Operations Division (split into several divisions in World War II, including DOD(F), DOD(H), in analogy with ACNS)
D of D	Director of Dockyards
D of N	Director of Navigations (later DND)
D of P	Director of Plans
DNOT	Director, Naval Operations and Trade, successor (1962) to DTD and DOD
DNR	Director of Naval Recruiting
DOR	Director of Operational Research
DSR	Director of Scientific Research
DTASW	Director of Mine, Torpedo, and AS Warfare
DTD	Director of Trade Division
DTSD	Director, Tactical and Staff Duties Division (responsible for compiling Staff Requirements)
DTWP	Director Naval Tactics and Weapons Policy Division (successor to DTSD, 1959)
DUSW	Director, Undersea Warfare Division (late 1950s successor to DTASW)
E-in-C	Engineer in Chief, parallel to DNC
NAS	Naval Air Section (interwar, to be distinguished from DNAS)
RAA	Rear Admiral, Aircraft (from 1931); later VAA, Vice Admiral (Aircraft)
SAC	Superintendent of Aircraft Construction (World War I)
SDPC	Ship Design Policy Committee
VCNS	Vice Chief of Naval Staff; after the 1943 reorganization, the Fifth Sea Lord was VCNS (Air)

important of the seven to hold this post were Admiral E C Chatfield (1920–22), Admiral F C Dreyer (1924–27), and Admiral Dudley Pound (1927–29).[33] After 1929 ACNS lost his seat on the Board. After the Navy took back control of the Fleet Air Arm, a new position, ACNS(A) (for air warfare), was instituted, and during World War II there was also an ACNS(W), controlling weapons requirements.

The Admiralty in effect mediated between the deployed fleets and the Departments which provided their ships, aircraft, and weapons. For example, ships were designed by, and built under the supervision of, the Department of Naval Construc-tion, headed by the DNC. Ordnance was provided by the DNO, and ships' machinery by the DNE (and, later, DEE, in charge of electrical engineering). Although all these depart-ments relied to some extent on independent private suppliers, such as the major shipyards, large ships were designed almost completely in-house. That was never true of naval aircraft, whose designs were always the responsibility of the independ-ent manufacturers. In the case of aircraft, the Admiralty (or, later, the Air Ministry) provided requirements but not guidance in design.[34]

As in naval tactics, World War I provided some painful les-

33 Till, p122. As gunnery experts, both Chatfield and Dreyer were intensely interested in air spotting. Chatfield served as ACNS 1920–22, Controller 1925–28, and First Sea Lord 1933–38.

34 Design organizations such as those within the Air Ministry did sometimes estimate gross aircraft char-acteristics as a guide to the feasibility of proposed specifications put out for competitive tender.

sons. *Matériel* had been developed almost exclusively by the Admiralty, with little or no input from the serving commanders, and they sometimes rejected the apparent logic it reflected. The fleets in turn suffered from what they considered insufficient or ineffective staff support, for example in the processing of what would now be termed 'national level' intelligence. Jutland was a notorious example.

The Naval Staff was therefore reorganized in 1920, in the hope of emphasizing the views of the serving commanders. Departments were created to develop specific characteristics for new *matériel*. In theory these were ultimately responsible to senior serving commanders, but in practice the central departments inevitably enjoyed considerable power. Even more inevitably, their power has been exaggerated in the historical record, since most of the documents in the Public Record Office were generated by the staff departments, not by the serving commanders. However, it is also evident that at least one First Sea Lord, Admiral Chatfield, tried hard to curb the departments, reminding them that the views of the serving commanders were to come first, certainly well ahead of any theoretical studies carried out in Whitehall.

Chatfield cannot have been alone in his views. In the case of the Fleet Air Arm, a senior serving position, Rear Admiral Aircraft (RAA), was created in 1931 specifically to provide a unified operational input into naval air policy. It was reasonable to appoint a single RAA because of the main fleet policy: the Royal Navy was built around a single wartime fleet incorporating a single naval air force. As it happened, the first RAA was Admiral Reginald Henderson, who went on to become Third Sea Lord under Chatfield and who was directly responsible for the armoured flight deck carriers.

Early and unfortunate British naval air experience during Word War II made for dissatisfaction with the existing arrangements, and for a conscious effort to adapt the fleet more fully to to air considerations. This effort was reflected in the formation

Admiralty staff studies showed that limited carrier capacity imposed an unacceptable limitation on the total number of aircraft the fleet could operate. The prewar Royal Navy therefore developed aircraft which could operate from capital ships or cruisers, or, for that matter, from harbours, on floats. Carriers had special facilities for handling floatplanes. A float Swordfish hangs from the crane, HMS Ark Royal, *1940.*

of a Future Building Committee, which was responsible for much of the mid- and late-war carrier and aircraft programme. Postwar it became the Ship Characteristics Committee (SCC), an attempt to integrate the views of the different staff and technical departments within the Admiralty.

Again, the reality is distorted by the existence of the record of what would seem to be a powerful and authoritative committee. In fact the SCC often agreed to decisions made privately by the First Sea Lord and the DNC.

In the text which follows, staff officers have often been designated by their positions, as, for example, DNAD, Director of the Naval Air Department. This is partly due to the way the documents are written, but it has a deeper significance as well: DNAD usually represented not so much his own views as those of the Naval Air Department staff. Table 1-1 lists these abbreviations.

IN THIS BOOK, gallons are Imperial gallons, each equal to 1.201 US gallons. I have used the terms lift in preference to elevator, paraffin in preference to kerosene, and petrol in preference to gasoline. After World War II the Royal Navy adopted the US term avgas, and invented a new term, avtur, for jet (turbine) fuel. Note also the use of the terms W/T and R/T (wireless telegraph and radio telephone) for, respectively, morse and voice radio. This was a significant distinction, because a pilot generally could be expected to operate an R/T set but not a W/T set.

2
Beginnings

BRITISH NAVAL AIR EXPERIENCE during World War I included the first combat use of aircraft carriers, and it shaped subsequent development up to, and during, World War II. This experience in turn can best be understood in terms of the way in which British naval strategy changed, under the impact of new technology, in the years immediately preceding the war. Several authors have discussed the origins of British naval air organization in detail, and the account here will necessarily be abbreviated.[1]

From a strategic point of view, perhaps the most important development was underwater weaponry (both torpedoes and mines), which enabled a relatively small craft to attack and damage or destroy a capital ship. Initially, this meant a submarine or a surface torpedo boat or destroyer. However, the torpedo also made the flimsy aircraft into a plausible anti-ship weapon. It seems significant that two of the earliest British naval aviation officers, Captain Murray Sueter and Cdr Oliver Schwann (who would command the carrier *Campania* in World War I), were torpedo specialists from the submarine branch.

In theory, these weapons simplified one classic British naval problem while greatly complicating the other. British naval strategy was built around the main fleet, which could seize and maintain what might now be called maritime supremacy. However, an enemy could always try to destroy the British Empire at its core by invading Britain. The main fleet was not per se an anti-invasion force; it was by no means tied to the British coast. It would, however, certainly threaten the lines of communication supporting any invasion. British national strategy always had to balance the physical security of the British Isles against the need for secure sea lanes (maritime supremacy), which in turn guaranteed that Britain could import the resources to maintain herself. However unlikely, the possibility of invasion always had to be taken seriously.[2]

The traditional British approach to a Continental enemy was close blockade, to keep both his fleet and his commerce raiders from the open ocean. Prevailing winds, moreover, made it very difficult for any sailing fleet based on the Continent to cross the Channel to invade the British Isles. With the advent of steam, this limitation vanished, and substantial investment in fixed coast defences became necessary.[3] No such investment could be altogether satisfactory, because an enemy could descend far from the expensive fixed fortresses. Mobile naval forces could,

in theory, solve this problem, but substantial investment in such forces, tied to specific areas of the British coast, would have precluded the investment in a main fleet required to achieve control of the wider ocean.

Because relatively inexpensive craft could launch torpedoes, and thus could sink or damage large warships and troop-carriers, they promised a practical solution to the British coast defence problem. In about 1904 the Royal Navy took over primary responsibility for British coast defence, and purchased small coastal submarines and coastal torpedo boats (small destroyers). These craft could move along the coast to deal with changing circumstances, and they could be multiplied without impinging seriously on investment in the main or battle fleet.[4]

However, other powers could also buy torpedo craft, preventing the Royal Navy from executing its traditional tactic of close blockade. This change coincided with a British strategic shift, from enmity to entente with France, and towards enmity with Germany. In case of a war with Germany, the main British fleet would have to be based in the north, leaving the North Sea itself to light (hence expendable) covering forces, which could warn of any German fleet sortie. The new strategy, therefore, introduced a new requirement for strategic reconnaissance, to give sufficient warning of a German fleet sortie and then to bring the British fleet into contact. By 1914, moreover, it seemed unlikely that any conventional surface forces, such as cruisers, could survive long in watching positions off the enemy coast. Air reconnaissance seemed the obvious solution.[5]

Aircraft, including airships, also raised new possibilities for tactical scouting. Existing scouts, primarily cruisers, necessarily had to steam relatively close to the fleets they served. Thus, in their own contact with an enemy (or, more probably, with an enemy's cruisers) they revealed the presence of their own fleet. Jutland, for example, began as a meeting of British and German cruisers. An aeroplane or airship, however, need not operate very close to her own fleet, particulary if she had a long-range radio aboard. Thus her presence would not in itself provide an enemy with positive information of the fleet's position. Because the aircraft could fly over any enemy screening force with relative impunity, it could penetrate to observe the movements of the core of his fleet. Finally, because the aircraft could operate far from its own fleet, it could help its fleet evade contact with a

1   See G Till, *Air Power and the Royal Navy, 1914–1945, A Historical Survey* (McDonald and Jane's, London, 1979), A Hezlet, *Aircraft and Sea Power* (Stein & Day, New York, 1970), and S W Roskill, *The Naval Air Service*, Vol 1, 1908–1918 (Navy Records Society, 1969). This chapter is also partly based on L E Pulsipher, *Aircraft and the Royal Navy, 1908–1918*, an unpublished PhD thesis (Duke University, 1981).

2   This was not very different from the later conflict between investment in the Air Defence of Great Britain (ADGB) and in the main fleet, between the two World Wars. Marder decried the 'invasion bogey' in his *From the Dreadnought to Scapa Flow*, on the ground that the Germans could not have afforded the effort. However, the consequence of a successful invasion would have been so terrible that no British government could entirely discount the possibility. One might also see British interest in the threat of a German invasion as an example of the analysis of enemy capabilities rather than enemy intentions, in classic intelligence terms.

3   See T Ropp, *The Development of a Modern Navy* (Naval Institute Press, Annapolis, 1987).

4   The Navy argued that, as long as the main fleet maintained sea control, any landings made would be limited descents. Larger landings would be precluded by the implicit threat to an invader's lines of communication. The British Army argued that an invader might lure away the fleet and descend in force, and therefore that it was essential to maintain a strong mobile reserve inland. This was sometimes held to justify universal national service, the cost of which would have been deducted from resources otherwise available for the main fleet. Ultimately the Committee on Imperial Defence (CID) decided the issue in favour of a combination of the main fleet and a home army large enough to compel an invader to mass enough troops to make him vulnerable to the

The 1912 Beardmore sketch design for a carrier, probably the world's first concrete proposal for such a ship. RINA

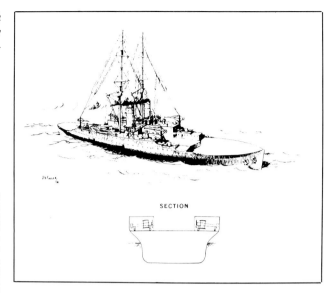

The 1912 Beardmore sketch design for a carrier, probably the world's first concrete proposal for such a ship. RINA

SECTION

British fleet. This led in turn to the formation of the Territorial Army, to make it possible for the British regular Army to be sent overseas in the event of war. Manoeuvres in 1912 and 1913 suggested that under some circumstances, particularly in bad weather, substantial invasion convoys could slip past British naval surveillance, and therefore that scouting was particularly important. See Marder, *From the Dreadnought to Scapa Flow*, Vol I (Oxford University Press, Oxford, 1961), pp 344–358.

5   For example, Admiral Madden, who served as Grand Fleet Chief of Staff 1914–16 (and who was post-war fleet commander), stated just before the war that he considered aircraft the natural replacements for watching cruisers. In fact the Royal Navy was able to rely on code-breaking and other types of signals intelligence, plus picket submarines.

6   The RFC took over responsibility for home defence in February 1916, but the RNAS continued to be responsible for attacks against Zeppelins, both on the ground and in the air, overseas. In effect, then, in parallel with the division of anti-invasion responsibilities, the RNAS was concerned with enemy forces at sea or overseas, the RFC for those forces which had successfully crossed the shore line.

7   There was a Naval Airship Section, organized in May 1909, primarily to build an experimental airship, the *Mayfly*, mainly as a means of gauging the threat of German Zeppelins. It also experimented with aircraft. The airship section was eliminated after the failure of the *Mayfly*, in January 1912. At that time it was headed by Captain Sueter, who argued for a unified naval air service.

8   Pulsipher, p39, quoting Samson's account in his personal papers in the IWM. Samson's access to Wilson was through a personal connection with a Sea Lord.

9   Contemporary Admiralty papers, which Roskill quotes, show that the Admiralty resisted this step, on the grounds that naval aviation had to be thoroughly integrated with ships, rather than constitute what might amount to a separate arm. The Air Council view was in effect that of the Army-oriented RFC, which was much closer to an independent air force. On the other hand, the RNAS was deeply involved in such independent activities as long-range bombing, and several senior naval aviators and associated officers saw matters much as the RFC did.

more powerful enemy. That was certainly the case when the German High Seas Fleet evaded the British Grand Fleet in August 1916.

The new strategy had another consequence. It was entirely conceivable that German units might slip past the watching light forces, and so strike briefly at British soil before British units concentrated in the North could intercept them. Coast defence by light torpedo forces was, therefore, if anything more important. This possibility actually materialized in 1914 and again in 1916, when German battlecruisers shelled Hartlepool, Lowestoft and Great Yarmouth. Thus coast defence had to imply reconnaissance, to detect and track any incoming enemy naval forces.

From 1909 on, aircraft added another factor. Blériot's successful crossing of the Channel implied that, at some point in the near future, Britain herself could no longer feel protected by the sea. This was not in itself an entirely new problem, as the protection of the Channel had been considerably reduced by the advent of steam power, but the threat of aerial bombing was new. In particular, the speed of aircraft made it less than likely that enemy bombers could be intercepted en route. Although early aircraft had only very short endurance and could carry only very small bomb loads, existing airships, such as the German Zeppelins, were not nearly so limited; air attack on Britain was a very real possibility.

Responsibility for British metropolitan air defence was not clearly allocated before 1914, as both the Army and the Navy were responsible for some aspects of coast defence, that is, of defence against threats from overseas. To the extent, however, that the Navy gained primary responsibility, air defence might be seen as a natural extension of the mobile defence against invasion. In practice, the air component associated with the Army, the Royal Flying Corps, went overseas with the Army, leaving the Naval Air Service for the home defence role.[6] This had several consequences. One of the most important was that the Navy had to accept responsibility for the successes of German air raids. It was publicly argued that home air defence had failed, not because of its inherent physical limitations, but because the Admiralty was unwilling to commit sufficient resources. The proposed cure was the unitary Royal Air Force, which would concentrate all its efforts to develop air warfare.

To the extent that RAF control of naval aviation had disastrous effects, then, those effects may be traceable to the association of the Royal Navy with air defence. On the other hand, the metropolitan air defence mission led the Royal Navy to develop a variety of high-powered lightweight fighters, such as

the Sopwith Camel, which in turn proved highly adaptable to primitive shipboard installations. Without these aircraft, there might have been no operational carriers in World War I. Finally, the home air defence mission naturally implied a strategy of striking at the source of potential air attacks, resulting in, among other events, the first carrier strike, the Cuxhaven Raid of December 1914.

BRITISH NAVAL INTEREST in aircraft dates at least from 1 March 1911, when four officers were selected for pilot training; the Admiralty later purchased two Short aircraft. A Naval Flying School was officially established at Eastchurch in December 1911. Its men were on detached duty, and the senior officer, Acting Commander C R Samson, was able to experiment on his own initiative.[7] Samson in turn was able to convince the First Sea Lord, Admiral A K Wilson, of the potential value of aircraft.[8] At a higher level, the new First Lord, Winston Churchill, strongly supported aviation.

Although the naval air arm was formally merged with an embryonic army air arm to form the Royal Flying Corps in May 1912, the Admiralty retained full control of what was now called the Naval Wing. Samson initially commanded the naval pilots, the air stations coming under the Torpedo School. However, effective 25 November 1912 an Admiralty Air Department was formed, under Captain Murray F Sueter, who had been head of the Naval Airship Service in 1911–12 and was thus the senior naval aviation expert. As Director of the Air Department (DAD) he controlled all naval aviation. Samson already commanded the Naval Flying School at Eastchurch.

The Naval Wing was renamed the Royal Naval Air Service (RNAS) on 1 July 1914. It in turn was merged into the unitary Royal Air Force (RAF) on 1 April 1918, not to reappear formally as part of the Royal Navy until 1939.

DAD was responsible to the Second Sea Lord (after December 1913, to the Fourth Sea Lord). As naval aviation expanded during World War I, the Air Division became the Air Service, and thus DAD became DAS, the Director of Air Service, a flag billet. Another post, Superintendant of Aircraft Construction (SAC), had to be created to control procurement; Sueter became SAC. In 1917 DAS became the Fifth Sea Lord, partly to represent the Royal Navy on the Air Council, which had been established in 1916.[9] By this time aircraft were an important element of the Grand Fleet. Its new C-in-C, Admiral Beatty, proposed the institution of an overall air commander, who was appointed in January 1918. Rear Admiral R F Philli-

The first of all British carriers, HMS Hermes, fitted temporarily as a seaplane support ship for the 1913 naval manoeuvres. Note the canvas hangars fore and aft, and the forward flying-off platform. No conclusive photographic evidence exists to show whether she was fitted with a flying-off deck when she recommissioned in 1914. P A Vicary

more became the first Admiral Commanding Aircraft (ACA), Grand Fleet, foreshadowing the later appointment of a Rear Admiral, Aircraft (RAA).[10]

RNAS procurement policy paralleled the policy followed with other new types of craft. The Navy relied on a few private specialist firms for its destroyers and submarines, in most cases seeking competitive designs. Similarly, it bought its aircraft from private manufacturers. The army had had no such experience, so the RFC, with its army roots, preferred the Royal Aircraft Factory. As a consequence, naval aircraft designs tended to be superior, many of them also going into RFC service on land. Competitive procurement became universal when all aircraft procurement was centralized in a new Ministry of Munitions in 1917. The Ministry in turn decided relative priorities for naval and military aircraft production.

The Admiralty tended to turn to particular firms for particular types of aircraft: to Sopwith for light wheeled aircraft (although Sopwith produced several floatplanes), and to Short Brothers and then also to Fairey for heavier floatplanes, such as torpedo floatplanes.[11] Later the RNAS bought de Havilland aircraft, but these were important for shipboard use only postwar. The RNAS was also responsible for the origin of the big Handley-Page bombers, but they had no shipboard role. In addition, the wartime RNAS Experimental Construction Depot at Port Victoria (the Isle of Grain) developed its own designs, numbered in a PV series.

SAMSON REALIZED THAT the key naval question was the extent to which aircraft could be carried aboard, and launched from, ships. He devised a flying-off rig, consisting of two parallel tracks (with the space between filled in for less than half its length), sharply inclined so that the force of gravity would help accelerate the aircraft. Chatham Dockyard installed one on the forecastle of the battleship *Africa*, from which Samson flew a Short S.27 (Admiralty No 38) on 10 January 1912. He was not the first to fly from a warship, but he was the first in the Royal Navy. The take-off run was probably about one hundred feet.

Later a similar but slightly longer platform was installed aboard HMS *Hibernia*, and the S.27 launched on 9 May, at the Weymouth Naval Review, while the ship steamed at 10.5 knots, with the wind blowing from dead ahead at Force 1. When the battleship was shifted to other duties, the rig was transferred to another, HMS *London*, which launched the S.27 on 4 July, while steaming at 12 knots, into a Force 3 wind.[12]

Similar flying-off platforms were used extensively during World War I. They permitted take-offs under most weather conditions, whereas floatplanes hoisted onto the water could take off only in relatively calm conditions. On the other hand, only relatively small, or relatively high-powered, aircraft could fly from a short platform. In 1914 that meant a single-seat floatplane, adapted from a Schneider Cup racer. As aircraft evolved, however, more powerful types could be deck-launched, to the point that in 1917–18 both fighters and two-seat reconnaissance aircraft flew from short platforms built atop capital ship turrets.

Because a carrier had to turn into the wind to launch, each deck launch carried a potential penalty in terms of separation from the main fleet. This penalty, which of course applied to wheeled aircraft as well as to temporarily wheeled floatplanes, was significant for later carrier tactics and consequently for carrier design requirements. On the other hand, a similar penalty attached to launching from the sea, since (at least at first) the carrier had to stop to hoist out her aircraft. Only late in World War I were carriers rigged to hoist out their floatplanes without slowing down substantially.

HMS Riviera *as an improvised seaplane carrier in 1914, still wearing her prewar merchant ship paint scheme.* Engadine *was similar but had different screens and lacked a crow's nest.* FAAM

10   On 19 November 1917 Beatty asked the Board of Admiralty to appoint a Flag Officer to command all the seaplane carriers and aircraft of the Grand Fleet, to be designated Rear Admiral (A), and to fly his flag in HMS *Furious*. His position would be analogous to that of Commodore (F), commanding the destroyer flotillas of the fleet. Rear Admiral R F Phillimore was appointed ACA on 6 January 1918. He had commanded the 1st Battle Cruiser Squadron, 1916–18, and became President of the Postwar Questions Committee, 1918–19.

11   All of these aircraft were described at the time as seaplanes. However, modern usage, which has been followed here, is to distinguish aircraft whose bodies float (seaplanes or flying-boats) from floatplanes. World War I practice was also to describe wheeled aircraft as aeroplanes (in distinction to seaplanes); the usage here is wheeled or deck aircraft.

12   Pulsipher, pp 64–5, quoting Samson's personal papers, credits him with the design of the platform. It was intended for metal construction, and for erection in 5 minutes. However, as actually built it was wooden, and hence semi-permanent. The Short S.27 was a wheeled aircraft with floatation bags, rather than a floatplane, and for the first test it had a 50hp Gnome engine, replaced by a 70hp engine for the second and third flights. Take-off runs while under way were, respectively, about 45 and 25ft (wind at Force 3). Some details were taken from R D Layman, *To Ascend From A Floating Base: Shipboard Aeronautics and Aviation, 1783–1914* (Fairleigh Dickinson University Press, Rutherford, 1979). Many writers date Samson's first flight to December 1911, but Layman convincingly argues for the 1912 date.

13   Early radios were so heavy that until about 1917 even large aircraft carried only transmitters.

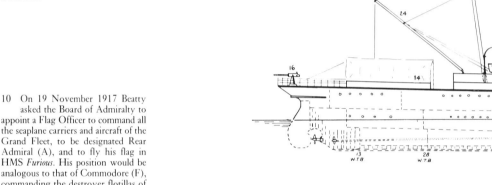

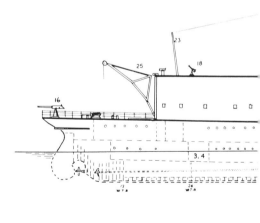

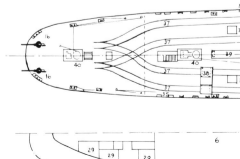

HMS Riviera *general arrangement 1914 and as fitted 1918.* Roger Nailer

Key
1 Bow rudder
2 Petrol store (after 1915)
3 12pdr magazine (after 1915)
4 Bomb store (port), 3pdr magazine (stbd)
5 Wardroom
6 Coal bunker
7 Coal bunker (at side)
8 Boiler room
9 Turbine room
10 Ballast tank
11 Air mechanics' workshop & store
12 Photographic darkroom (after 1915)
13 Forward seaplane shelter (1914)
14 After seaplane shelter (1914)
15 Seaplane hangar (after 1915)
16 12pdr QF gun
17 3pdr HA gun (after 1915)
18 2pdr AA gun (after 1915)
19 Pigeon loft (after 1915)
20 Searchlight (after 1915)

21 Chart room
22 W/T office (after 1915)
23 W/T masts (after 1915)
24 Derrick
25 Jib cranes (after 1915)
26 Capstan
27 Coal hatch
28 Officers' accommodation
29 Cabins
30 L & A to turbines
31 Air compressor and motor
32 Charging board for accumulators
33 Steam heaters
34 Motor generator/air compressor set
35 Bomb racks
36 Hatch to workshop
37 Rails for seaplane trolleys
38 Seaplane trolley (4 carried)
39 Land trolley (2 carried)
40 Steam capstan
41 Funnel casing
42 Turbine casing

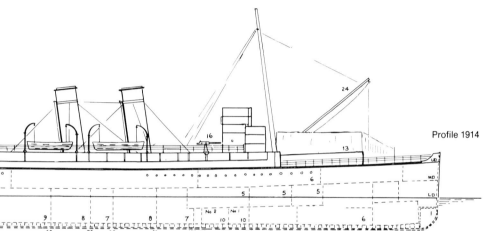

Profile 1914

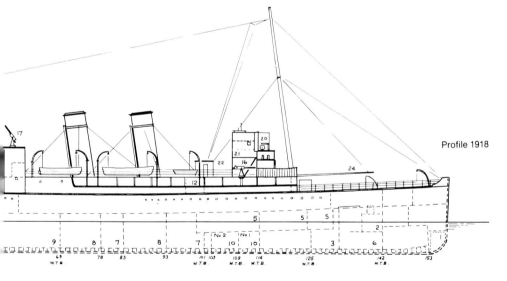

Profile 1918

Upper deck 1918

main deck

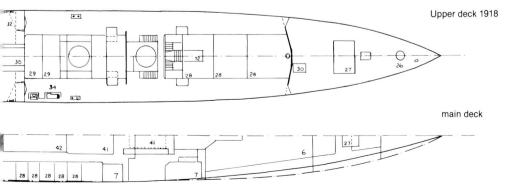

The first two basic aircraft roles were reconnaissance/observation and attack. Both required the attribute of considerable lifting capacity, since reconnaissance and observation depended on airborne radio.[13] By May 1914 practically all British naval aircraft had been fitted with radio transmitters, and a new set with a range of over 90 miles was on order. The Navy was experimenting with radio reception aboard aircraft, but this did not really materialize until after the war.

With his background, Sueter naturally sought to combine the most effective anti-ship offensive weapon, the torpedo, with aircraft. Informal British discussions of torpedo-bombing date from 1910, and on 17 November 1913 Sueter requested two old 14in torpedoes for experiments. He let a contract to Sopwith for a torpedo-carrying floatplane.[14] Finally, late in July 1914, a single-engine Short 74 biplane (with a 160hp Gnome replacing the usual 100hp engine) dropped a 14in (810lb) torpedo for the first time.[15] It was considered sufficient to sink a small cruiser or a merchant ship; the next step was a large seaplane or floatplane capable of carrying the 18in torpedo then standard in submarines and in many destroyers.

The Short biplane participated in the first carrier raid, on Cuxhaven in December 1914. It was just compact enough for ship stowage, but (at RNAS request) in 1913 Short Brothers developed and patented a folding-wing mechanism, allowing much larger aircraft (which could therefore carry useful offensive loads) to be stowed aboard the 2000- to 3000-ton carriers the Royal Navy operated during World War I. Wing folding however meant that the wings not be staggered, and thus resulted in a loss of performance; some later wartime aircraft were designed with detachable wings designed for quick assembly.

Type 74 modified to fold became the Short Folder, which also participated in the Cuxhaven raid. Finally, Type 135 was a Folder with a more powerful engine (135- or 160hp Canton Unne). Developed versions of this first carrier-suitable aircraft served throughout World War I as the Short 166 and 827.[16] These were used aboard a few carriers.[17]

These early Short floatplanes were clearly underpowered. Sueter in turn asked J Samuel White (the destroyer builders, who built aircraft under the company name Wight), Sopwith, and Short Brothers to build specialized torpedo-bombers powered by a new 225hp engine. The Short 184, a standard floatplane throughout the war, resulted. In 1915 Sueter sent Short 184s to Gallipoli specifically to prove that an aircraft could torpedo a ship. At that time he already had offensive operations against the German fleet in mind.

All of these torpedo-bombers were far too large and too

14 Pulsipher, p67, quoting a paper by C L'Estrange-Malone in the Sueter papers. At this time there was also some interest in towing a torpedo from an airship. British interest in torpedo-bombing was not unique; in 1912 an American, Admiral Bradley Fiske, proposed a torpedo-bomber. Fiske was later often credited as the inventor of the torpedo-bomber. The Sopwith Type C required very large wings (given the weight of the torpedo and its limited power), and so was much too large for ship stowage. However, the Short could fold its wings and so was ship-portable.

15 These designations followed the Admiralty serial numbers of the first aircraft of each type, and therefore unfortunately bear only the most limited relationship to design or construction sequence.

16 Admiralty Type designations were based on the serial number of the prototype, and so do not show any particular logic. Thus the prototype Type 135 was Aircraft No 135. The Short S.41, however, was a company designation.

17 By the end of 1915, HMS *Ark Royal* was operating five Short 166 aircraft (including the prototype) at Salonika. The Short 827 was a somewhat smaller aircraft with a different engine, a 135hp Salmson radial. Three participated in the East African campaign in 1916, aboard the armed liner *Laconia*, the armed merchant cruiser *Himalaya* and the balloon ship *Manica*. Others operated from the Mediterranean carriers *Raven II* and *Ben-my-Chree*; the similar Short 830 flew from the carriers *Engadine* and *Ben-my-Chree*.

heavy to lift from the flying-off decks of early British carriers. The Short 184 could be carried in a hold and hoisted over the side, to take off from the water. The much larger bomber required to carry an 18in torpedo could not go aboard a ship, and therefore had to be considered a coast defence weapon. One measure of aero engine progress between 1914 and 1917 was that it was possible, by the latter date, for the wheeled Sopwith Cuckoo to lift an 18in (albeit lightweight) torpedo from a deck.

From 1914 on, another air role also became important: denying the enemy aerial reconnaissance. This was the province of the Sopwith single-engine fighters, initially the Sopwith Schneider (or Sopwith Cup) designed specifically for high performance. It in turn had been derived from the Sopwith Tabloid which, taken over by the RFC and RNAS at the beginning of the war, participated in the earliest overland British bombing raid. Four of these small wheeled aircraft went to Gallipoli aboard the carrier *Ark Royal* in 1915.

Floatplane Schneiders were issued to the early British seaplane carriers as an anti-Zeppelin weapon. Before the advent of synchronized machine-guns they were often armed with special heavy shotguns, firing chain shot. The Schneider in turn was superseded by the Sopwith Baby, a very similar aircraft with a more powerful engine (an open-cowled 110- or 130hp Clerget replacing the 'bull-nose'-cowled 100hp Gnome of the earlier type). They were generally armed with Lewis light machine-guns, either synchronized or firing clear of the propeller disc. Besides Sopwith production, Babys were manufactured by Blackburn and Fairey. They served until 1918, although in 1917 these floatplane fighters were largely replaced by deck-launched wheeled Sopwith Pups, of much higher performance.

Samson, Sueter, and their immediate successors all thought in terms of floatplanes, since there was as yet no way of recovering an aircraft aboard ship. Flying-off decks were used with droppable wheels on the floats. Any wheeled (float-less) aircraft launched from a ship had either to reach a land base or to ditch; during World War I the RNAS paid considerable attention to measures to alleviate the results of ditching.[18]

Floatplane operation in turn had important tactical consequences, as a seaplane carrier had to stop for recovery. For example, standard recovery procedure for the carrier *Campania*, in the North Sea, was for two accompanying destroyers to steam into the wind to make a slick into which the seaplane could land, the pilot trying to come down a quarter mile ahead of the carrier. Hoisting in was itself somewhat delicate, since the aircraft was quite large and could easily be damaged while suspended from the hoisting crane. The entire procedure took at least 4½ minutes, and made the carrier an ideal U-boat target. Moreover, the manoeuvre itself took the carrier out of position in the fleet.[19] All of these disadvantages were well understood, and by 1915 Holmes and Biles (see below) had proposed an alternative means of recovery. It was incorporated into early versions of the design of the carrier *Hermes*, but ultimately abandoned as impractical.[20]

In a larger sense, the complexity of recovery meant that a seaplane (floatplane) carrier could not continuously launch and recover her aircraft; she could not sustain air cover over or near a fleet. She could launch a strike, or she could launch reconnaissance aircraft or spotters to sustain air operations for a limited period. However, even were the sea to be calm enough to make recovery reliable, the carrier would soon fall away from the fleet she accompanied, as she stopped periodically to recover. This was apart from falling out of position to steam into the wind to launch.

As a consequence, sustained reconnaissance depended on long-range aircraft launched from shore, either big seaplanes or rigid airships (which were preferable, given their longer endu-

rance). Unfortunately, the Royal Navy failed to develop effective rigid airships before or during World War I. Until it enjoyed the services of numerous very long-range seaplanes (to maintain nearly continuous air cover of the North Sea), then, it operated at a substantial disadvantage: the German Zeppelins, by contrast, were remarkably successful. Hence the significance of the anti-Zeppelin mission, which could redress the balance of reconnaissance.

The greatest drawback of the floatplane was that it could not take off in rough water. The sheer weight of the floats often limited the load it could carry, particularly if they became partly waterlogged over time. Several early carrier raids, for example, had to be cancelled because floatplanes, once hoisted over the side, could not take off. British torpedo-carrying floatplanes successfully attacked Turkish shipping (in relatively calm waters) in 1915, but the sheer difficulty of taking off carrying a torpedo seems to have precluded later attempts.

It therefore became very important to launch seaplanes from ships' decks, even before on-deck recovery was a possibility. The heavier the load, however, the longer the deck run an aircraft required. Thus the earliest aircraft designed specifically for deck launching, the Fairey Campania (see Chapter 4), was limited to reconnaissance.

Sueter was much more interested in torpedo attack. By October 1916 he had obtained a much longer take-off run in the form of a fully flush deck designed for the new carrier *Argus* (see Chapters 4 and 5). A wheeled (that is, low-drag) torpedo-bomber could take off from such a deck. Sueter hoped that satisfactory arrester gear could be developed, so that it could land back aboard, but this was much less important than flying off. Early in October Sueter invited T O M Sopwith to the Admiralty, and on 9 October he confirmed their conversation in a Most Secret memorandum: he wanted Sopwith to design an aircraft, with 4 hours' endurance, to carry one or two 1000lb torpedoes. It might be catapult-launched (several catapults were then under design). Sopwith's reply was the Cuckoo T.1, the first carrier torpedo-bomber. Although it materialized too late to fight during World War I, the promise of this aircraft caused Admiral Beatty to plan a large-scale torpedo attack on the German High Seas Fleet.[21]

Inherent carrier limitations were reflected in Grand Fleet Battle Orders for their operation. When she joined the fleet in 1915, HMS *Campania* was stationed 5nm astern of fleet centre and 20nm astern of the light cruiser screen. Exercises soon showed that she could not maintain this position, since she was

18 Inflatable air bags, which could keep the aircraft afloat, were the most obvious measure. The problem was that the weight of the engine pulled the nose down, so that a pilot stunned by the impact of landing might well drown before he could be rescued. Many aircraft were therefore fitted with hydrovanes, small auxiliary wings, which could keep the nose up during ditching. Both the vanes and the air bags imposed significant weight, and therefore performance, penalties. Two other correctives were tried: skids could replace wheels, with hydrovanes in front to keep an aircraft from capsizing; or the landing gear could be made detachable, so that the pilot could drop it before ditching, landing directly on the bottom of the fuselage.

19 This account is derived from Pulsipher, pp189–190.

20 It was not, however, altogether unlike the Hein Mat evolved for underway floatplane recovery between the wars, installed in several foreign cruisers, and tested in the 1930s aboard HMS *Ark Royal*.

22 This account of Grand Fleet Battle Orders for carriers is based on A Hezlet, *Aircraft and Sea Power* (Stein & Day, New York, 1970), pp44, 53, 73.

23 This is Roskill's paper No 12.

21 Official interest in torpedo-bombing seems to have been revived by successful dummy attacks, by floatplanes, against the battleships *Dreadnought* and *Hindustan* in the Swin, in October 1916. Unfortunately Sueter's style of operation was very personal, so that progress on the Cuckoo stopped when he went to Italy to command the Otranto torpedo-bombers in January 1917. However, the following month Wing Commander A M Longmore of the Admiralty Air Department saw the Cuckoo fuselage slung from the beams of Sopwith's factory, and at his suggestion it was completed. Longmore presumably acquainted Beatty with the aircraft's potential. The prototype was passed by the Sopwith experimental department on 6 June 1917, and began its official tests at the Isle of Grain on 20 July. In August, Admiral Beatty asked for 200; 100 were ordered in October from Fairfield, with another fifty from Pegler. Unfortunately, the French-built Hispano engine, which powered

the Cuckoo, was badly needed for other aircraft, and the two subcontractors were inexperienced. Their first deliveries were not made until September and October, 1918. In February 1918, fifty more were ordered from an experienced aircraft builder, Blackburn, which began deliveries in May 1918. All of these aircraft were powered by the 200hp Sunbeam Arab engine. The first squadron was formed on 7 October 1918, and it went aboard HMS *Argus* on 19 October 1918. The Cuckoo was well liked for its agility, although its engine was considered unreliable, and was 40lbs heavier than the Hispano. Towards the end of 1917 there was some fear that the 1000lb Mk IX torpedo (170lb warhead) was not powerful enough, and a specification was issued for a new torpedo-bomber to carry the much heavier Mk VIII destroyer weapon (320lb warhead). At the same time the Mk IX was given a new 250lb warhead (total weight 1086lbs). The new bombers were the

Blackburn Blackburd and the Short Shirl; they proved too clumsy for the sort of close-in mass attack British doctrine then favoured, and they never entered British naval service. The Cuckoo itself was unarmed apart from its torpedo, although in 1919 there was some hope that it could be given a forward-firing machine-gun if a more powerful engine (such as the new ABC Dragonfly) were installed. Admiral Beatty had believed that Cuckoos could be so armed, and in fact his proposals included using Cuckoos, once they had dropped their loads, as fighters – a concept realized almost thirty years later in aircraft like the Firebrand, Wyvern, and Skyraider. AIR 1/1316, the official history of British torpedo-planes produced by the Aircraft Armament Torpedo Section, Calshot (revised June 1919), J M Bruce, *British Aeroplanes, 1914–18* (Putnam, London, 1957), and B Robertson, *Sopwith – The Man and His Aircraft* (Harleyford, Bedford, 1970).

HMS Engadine *in 1914.* FAAM

HMS Engadine *as rebuilt in 1915 with a permanent hangar aft.* CPL

not faster than the battle line. Her orders were then changed: upon contact with an enemy by the light cruisers, she would move toward the cruisers at full speed and prepare to hoist out her floatplanes. They would search primarily for U-boats and minelayers; Admiral Jellicoe always feared a hidden underwater trap. Scouting and action observation were the next most important tasks, and if Zeppelins were sighted and *Campania* had fighters on board, they could be launched.[22]

Similar orders applied to HMS *Engadine*, when she became part of the Battlecruiser Fleet. In each case, sustained reconnaissance was impossible.

When the main fleet carrier, *Campania*, was refitted in 1915–16, she was fitted to recover floatplanes while under way, so that in calm seas she could (in theory) fly reconnaissance aircraft continuously. She was also fitted with a kite balloon for action observation, and stationed close to the fleet flagship so that information from it could be passed in combat. Unfortunately she did not sortie with the fleet for the Battle of Jutland (which was fought in a sea so calm that the older carrier *Engadine* was able to hoist out her aircraft), so that the improvements were not tested in combat.

As blimps developed, they became the favoured fleet scouts, because they could maintain station continuously ahead of the fleet. Their activities were limited in bad weather, however, so that they could not entirely replace the usual forward screen of cruisers. By 1917 the alternative, a more or less continuous patrol of the North Sea by large coastal seaplanes, was also a reality.

Grand Fleet aircraft battle orders were again revised in August 1917. Although airships (blimps) were still the primary scouts, there were now enough floatplane scouts for them to be assigned secondary responsibility for continuous reconnaissance. Fleet fighters were assigned to protect British reconnaissance seaplanes and airships, and also to establish air superiority over the battle area.

The orders required a total of five aircraft for concurrent observation of enemy fleet movements at any one time. In 1917 this was increased to ten aircraft for the approach (once the enemy had been detected) and fifteen for the action itself, taking into account the limited endurance of the aircraft.

Spotting was the responsibility of the numerous kite balloons now flown from British warships.

These last revisions in turn showed the value of an aircraft carrier from which wheeled aircraft could be launched and onto which they could land. The advent of the carrier promised something more: torpedo strikes by fleet aircraft, a capability which materialized just after the Armistice in the form of Sopwith Cuckoos flying from the carrier *Argus*.

EARLY IN 1912 Admiral E C T Troubridge, the Chief of Staff at the Admiralty, produced a paper on naval air requirements, both for coast defence and for operation with the fleet. For the latter, he called for four trial ships, preferably large Home Fleet cruisers. Each would carry two small single-engine floatplanes, launched from the ship, using Samson's platform.[23] Troubridge's paper proposed the formation of the Air Department.

In August 1912, preparing to assume direction of the Department, Sueter summarized naval air roles:

(a) Distant reconnaissance support of the fleet
(b) Reconnaissance of the enemy coast, working from cruisers or special aeroplane ships
(c) ASW (both observation and attack)
(d) Mine countermeasures, both by spotting minelayers and by spotting mines
(e) Location of hostile craft in defended areas
(f) Support of submarines by spotting targets
(g) Preventing enemy reconnaissance and observation by attacking enemy aircraft
(h) Protection of surface targets (dockyards, magazines, oil storage tanks, etc.) from air attack

By early 1915, the list had changed considerably, the most important item now being offensive raids. The air offensive had two virtues. First, it could destroy Zeppelins, the primary means both of German reconnaissance and of the German air offensive against Britain. Second, by posing a threat to that air weapon, it could tempt German forces into range of British naval weapons. For example, a carrier raid into German waters could bring Zeppelins over the British fleet and thus within range of British carrier fighters. On a larger scale, it might pull German fleet units out of their safe havens, and into range of the British fleet. This interplay between the direct destruction of enemy forces and their exposure to more general attack was a central theme in many later applications of naval air power.

Sueter anticipated this offensive idea. He was, however, surprised by a new requirement to operate naval aircraft overseas. At Gallipoli, for example, naval aircraft spotted for the battleships, helping them hit targets well beyond their line of sight. In East Africa, naval aircraft located the German cruiser *Königsberg*, hidden up the Rufiji river, and helped monitors destroy her by directing their fire. The associated deployments required special depot ships – that is, aircraft carriers.

In 1912, Sueter proposed a chain of coastal air bases plus fleet aircraft, carried either aboard capital ships or aboard special ships which could also function as aircraft ferries between bases or to the fleet at sea. As a first step, he asked that a merchant ship be attached to the school at Eastchurch to develop aircraft for 'ship [that is, fleet] work.[24] This was approved, but had to be withdrawn due to cuts in the 1913–14 Estimates. Requirements drawn up at this time (about October 1912) were revived about a year later, to form the basis for HMS *Ark Royal*.

The primary requirement was a flush deck, at least 150ft long, forward, from which aircraft could take off. This would be served by a hatch large enough to pass an assembled aircraft (not less than 35 × 18ft, the long dimension being athwartships), and the fore hold, in which aircraft would be stowed, had to include a clear 60 × 40ft space for servicing. If the flush deck were less than 200ft long, the ship would need another deck, at least 70ft long, abaft her superstructure. The specification does not say as much, but it seems likely that this was conceived as a flying-on deck. Derricks would be installed to lift aircraft from the water onto the flight deck forward. Finally, speed would be at least 10 knots, preferably more.

Instead, the cruiser *Hermes* was converted at Chatham during May and June 1913 as a temporary experiment. She was fitted with flying-off rails forward, and her forward 6in gun was landed. Her two after 6in guns were landed to clear her quarterdeck for aircraft stowage. Canvas aircraft shelters were built both on the launching rails forward and on her quarter-deck. Special derricks and three petrol stowage lockers (for 1200, 500, and 300 gallons) were fitted. She was fitted for three aircraft, but carried only two.

Hermes recommissioned on 7 May 1913, taking two unidentified aircraft aboard on 5 July, and making nine flights between then and 14 July. For the manoeuvres she took Nos 48 (a Borel Seaplane, a monoplane) and 81 (the prototype Short S.64 Folder) aboard on 18 July. In the July 1913 manoeuvres, she was attached to the Red fleet (commanded by Vice Admiral Jellicoe, who would later command the Grand Fleet), based at Yarmouth, simulating a reconnaissance Zeppelin with a range of 800 miles. She was not, then, part of the Red fleet proper, and served in effect as an aircraft base ship. The Blue side, defending, had shore air stations at Cromarty and Leven, each with three aircraft.

The manoeuvres revealed that aircraft equipped with radio transmitters could be efficient scouts, and that they could take the strains of being hoisted in and out of a ship. They did suffer some damage in the water, however, and during a gale No 48, sheltered in the flimsy canvas hangar, had her right wing broken off. She had to be replaced by No 55, an 80hp Caudron floatplane, which flew from the ship's flight deck on 28 July 1913 during manoeuvres, steaming at 10 knots into a Force 1 or 2 wind. The deck seems to have been used only twice, the same day, the aircraft landing ashore before the ship entered port.

The manoeuvres also showed that aircraft could be damaged in rough water; the official report called for more ruggedness and for the floats of future naval aircraft to be sprung. For example, when No 81 was forced down by engine trouble on 31 July, she broke several float struts.[25]

Hermes decommissioned into reserve on 30 December, when her aircraft had made about thirty flights between July and October 1913.

Meanwhile, Sueter seems to have convinced a major shipbuilding firm, William Beardmore of Dalmuir, to sketch a combined destroyer/submarine/aircraft depot ship with a flush deck running down its centreline in December 1912, and by early 1913 the Controller was considering it. The depot ship

would carry six aircraft ready for service and four to six in reserve, with 5500 tons of oil, torpedoes, spare parts, six 4in anti-aircraft guns and a powerful wireless outfit, the latter presumably to control her charges. She was probably conceived as a mobile defence base, using her aircraft to direct her torpedo-bearing destroyers and submarines. At 15 knots, she was not nearly fast enough to operate with the fleet, and was probably intended to operate her aircraft from anchor.

The Beardmore design certainly resembled the later carriers, with a flat deck 450ft long running down her centreline. Side superstructures about 220ft long would have housed funnels, ventilators, and the six seaplanes, each in its own hangar with wings spread. The reserve seaplanes would have been stowed in a forward hold.[26]

For the 1914–15 programme, approval was tentatively given to the construction of an 18-knot carrier.[27] It is not clear whether this was intended as a developed version of the Beardmore design of 1912, as no more detailed references have survived. In the autumn of 1913, however, it was clear that the new ship would not be ready until late 1916. To save time, DAD sought and obtained tentative approval to buy a second-hand merchant ship, so that no time would be wasted in gaining experience. The tentative 1912 specifications were, therefore, revived. Ship brokers were canvassed, the choice narrowing to a steamer (No 9727) building at Blyth and an existing ship, the *Konakry*.

The Blyth ship, which became HMS *Ark Royal*, was selected because she was in so early a stage that she could readily be radically modified. Low speed was acceptable because the ship was intended only for experiments. The conversion design was prepared by J H Narbeth, who was responsible for the major World War I carrier designs.

The engines were moved aft to clear a 130 × 44ft flight deck forward, and the hold became a 150 × 45 × 15ft hangar, large enough for ten aircraft. It was served (through a sliding 40 × 30ft hatch) by two cranes. DNC wanted electric cranes, but standard commercial self-powered 3-ton steam units were substituted because they were more readily available. Aircraft would have to fly off the deck into the wind. To make her more seaworthy and to reduce freeboard (so that she could more easily keep her head to wind), *Ark Royal* had special cellular water ballast tanks built around her hangar.[28] She was unique among carriers in also having a small auxiliary sail, aft, to help keep her head to wind. There were also large workshops, on a scale which could not be matched in the later converted seaplane carriers.

Other unusual features were inert-gas petrol stowage, torpedo stowage, and a warming-up shelter for aircraft, under the bridge.

Armament was four 12pdr 12cwt guns (P.III mountings) and two .303in Maxim machine-guns.[29]

Engadine *as rebuilt in 1915, showing a Short 184 (reportedly the machine which spotted at Jutland) on her fantail. Note the two cranes for seaplane handling, folded back against the hangar door.* FAAM

24   This is a reply by Winston Churchill, then First Lord, to Admiral A K Wilson, dated 3 February 1913, and reprinted as Roskill's Paper No 26. The Wilson paper appears neither in Roskill nor in a PRO copy. The 1912 requirements appear in the *Ark Royal* Ship's Cover. Pulsipher reports (p217) that Wilson proposed conversion of an *Eclipse* class cruiser, with a light deck built atop her superstructure and the after funnel hinged so that it could be lowered beneath this deck. Aircraft would land from abaft into a barrier, and would then be transferred by derrick to the forward deck for take-off. The conversion actually carried out, on HMS *Hermes* (very similar to, but slightly faster than, an *Eclipse*), was less elaborate, consisting only of the installation of a short flight deck forward. By 1913 all of these cruisers were obsolete.

25   This account is taken largely from the official report, in AIR 1/626/17/46, supplemented by R D Laymen, *To Ascend . . .*; Layman's account was based on the ship's log.

26   The Beardmore depot ship would have displaced about 15,000 tons (430 × 82ft on the waterline). Although several papers in AIR 1 mention the project and its fate, none gives details; these are from 'Aircraft Carriers,' a paper delivered by the then DNC, Sir Arther W Johns, to the Institution of Naval Architects in 1934. Johns refers, too, to a carrier proposed by Admiral Mark Kerr in 1911 (and described in Kerr's memoirs). It is not mentioned in the AIR 1 carrier papers, and probably, therefore, had little influence on Sueter and his colleagues.

27   *Ark Royal* Ship's Cover, Folio 14. No corresponding design has been found, and a DNC paper in the same Cover implies that the DNC department was unaware of this approval. The reference to the 18-knot carrier is dated 30 December 1913.

28   Some writers have suggested that they were primarily to protect the hangar. The account here is based on the DNC history of British aircraft carrier design, written in 1919 on the basis

HMS Engadine *as fitted, 1915.* Roger Nailer

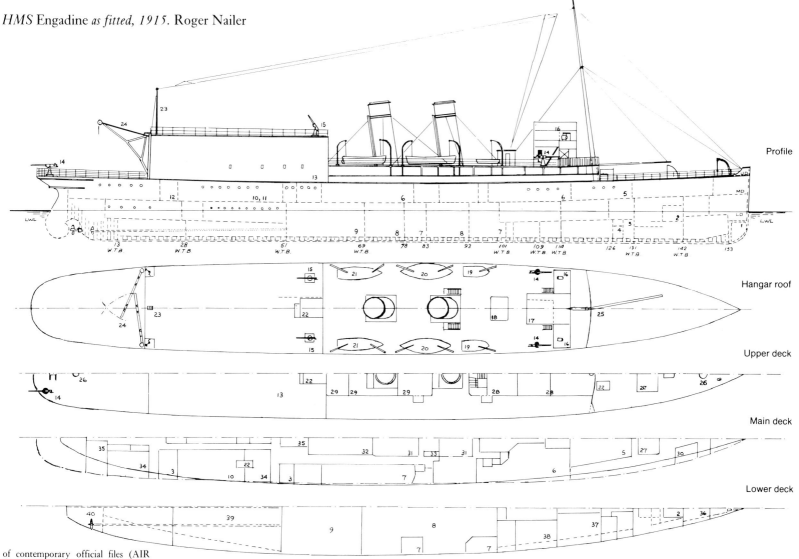

Profile

Hangar roof

Upper deck

Main deck

Lower deck

of contemporary official files (AIR 1/2103/207/31). The protection argument is inherently implausible because the ship was designed as a test platform, rather than as a combatant. The ship did have a bow ballast tank which could be filled to trim her down and thus to add the effect of gravity to the acceleration of an aircraft's engine.

29 Designed weapon load for aircraft (in 1914) was four 18in and two 14in torpedoes, plus one hundred 100lb bombs, five hundred 10lb bombs, and three hundred grenades. At this time aircraft did not yet carry machine-guns. As it turned out, no existing shipboard aircraft could lift an 18in torpedo (the 14in could barely be lifted).

30 This operation had been planned for some time. On 16 November 1914 Sueter recorded that HMS *Empress* might have to go to the Mediterranean at short notice; she would have taken three 100hp Short Folders in packing cases.

31 The ship's commanding officer mentioned four Sopwith Tabloids in a 15 March 1915 report; the figure of two is taken from the British official history. For detailed operational notes on HMS *Ark Royal*, see R D Layman, 'HMS *Ark Royal* – *Pegasus*, 1914–1950' in *Warship International* no 2 of 1976, pp90–108. The account of Williamson's crash is taken from this article, but the conclusion is my own.

Ark Royal was thus the first ship ever to have been designed and built specifically as a carrier, since her radical transformation (while as yet only in frames) made her far more than a conversion.

HMS *Ark Royal* was initially promised for completion in May 1914, but that proved impossible, partly because funds for her construction were not released until the beginning of the 1914–15 financial year in April 1914. Launched on 5 September and commissioned on 9 December 1914, *Ark Royal* was far too slow (10.6 knots on trial) to operate in the North Sea. The British Cabinet decided on the Dardanelles offensive on 13 January 1915, and the next day HMS *Ark Royal* was ordered to the Mediterranean to support the operation, sailing on 1 February.[30]

She carried eight aircraft: one Short Folder (Type 135 with 200hp Salmson engine), two two-seat Wight pusher floatplanes (200hp Canton-Unne engines), three Sopwith Type 807 two-seat floatplanes (100hp Monosoupape engines), and two Sopwith Tabloid landplanes (80hp Gnome engines). Only the single Short, which had participated in the Cuxhaven raid the previous December, was really useful, as the other floatplanes could not take off in choppy weather. None could fly high enough for effective spotting.

The two landplanes never flew from the carrier's deck, and on 7 April they were replaced by Schneider Cup floatplanes.[31] She experienced considerable difficulties operating her over-

Key
1 Bow rudder
2 Petrol store
3 Magazine
4 Bomb store
5 Wardroom
6 Coal bunker
7 Coal bunker (at side)
8 Boiler room
9 Turbine room
10 Air mechanics' mess (stbd)
11 Workship (port)
12 Magazine (stbd)
13 Seaplane hangar
14 12pdr QF gun
15 3pdr HA gun
16 Searchlight
17 Chart room
18 W/T office
19 Dinghy
20 Lifeboat
21 Motor boat
22 L & A to turbines
23 Hinged mast
24 Jib cranes
25 Derrick
26 Capstan
27 Hatch
28 Officers' accommodation
29 Cabins
30 Carpenter's store
31 Funnel casing
32 Engine casing
33 Fan
34 ERAs' mess
35 Galley
36 Chain locker
37 Clothing stores
38 Ship's office
39 Seamen's & firemen's mess
40 Water ballast

loaded aircraft in rough water, and engine failures were frequent. The first casualty was a Sopwith whose propeller broke up while in flight, on 5 March and which therefore crashed, badly injuring the observer, her executive officer, Flight Commander Hugh A Williamson. Williamson was invalided back to England. It seems likely that his experience convinced him that only wheeled aircraft could really be satisfactory, and therefore that arrangements had to be made to land them aboard ship. His 1915 carrier proposal had considerable impact (see Chapter 4).

As an indication of the existing level of technology, one of the large floatplanes carried a 250W transmitter, which had a range of about 50nm and could be received by destroyers. The Sopwiths had a lighter set effective only to about 10nm.

Because *Ark Royal* was not yet ready at the outbreak of war, *Hermes* was re-equipped permanently for air service and recommissioned in October 1914.[32] She was, however, torpedoed by *U27* on 30 October, having just ferried aircraft to the new RNAS shore base at Dunkirk (which had been set up to interdict likely Zeppelin routes to Britain).[33]

During World War I, the Royal Navy produced carriers for three distinct missions. Some, such as the first three 1914 conversions, were intended primarily to strike shore or (more or less) fixed targets. Others, such as HMS *Campania*, were intended to support the fleet at sea, providing friendly reconnaissance and denying the enemy his own aerial reconnaissance. Finally, ships were employed to operate aircraft in distant theatres of war, where the North Sea conditions affecting the first two categories were rare. These distinctions were not, of course, fixed; several ships designed for the first role functioned effectively in the second or third. For convenience, this chapter is concerned with the first, independent strike, role, and very briefly with the third; the next chapter is concerned with carrier development within the Grand Fleet itself.

Throughout most of the war, there was no real hope of building new ships, partly because there was little expectation that the war would last very long, and partly because existing shipbuilding resources were already badly strained coping with the demands of war. Instead, the Admiralty concentrated on conversions, which could be completed much more quickly. However, the pool of available ships was limited by a heavy wartime demand for merchant shipping, even before the German U-boat offensive made the shortage much more acute. Large, fast merchant ships were also needed as armed merchant cruisers, both for trade protection and to enforce the blockade of Germany. Relatively few suitable merchant hulls were therefore available.

By 9 August 1914 Sueter was arranging to obtain two 23-knot steamers as torpedo-seaplane carriers. Two days later he chartered three fast channel steamers (the 22-knot *Engadine* and *Riviera*, and the 18-knot *Empress*), too small and with too little endurance to be useful troop carriers.[34] They were officially described as 'for use with HM Fleet as torpedo-seaplane carriers.'[35] Sueter planned a torpedo strike (by carrier-borne Short 160hp floatplanes) on the German High Seas Fleet lying at anchor.[36] Because the German fleet used several possible bases, the attack had to be preceeded by air reconnaissance, also from the carriers. At this time, too, Sueter seems to have tried to obtain one or more obsolete armoured cruisers (of the 12,000-

HMS Empress, *the third of the initial carrier conversions, as rebuilt in 1915. The aircraft in the hangar is a Sopwith Schneider single-seater, which can be recognized by its 'bull-nose' engine fairing.* FAAM

HMS Ark Royal *as completed, 1915, with floatplanes on her flight deck. It was never used as such.*

ton *Cressy* class) as torpedo-seaplane carriers, but apparently had to settle for the reconverted 5650-ton *Hermes*.

Initially only the fast (22-knot) *Engadine* and *Riviera* were converted into seaplane carriers (at Chatham Dockyard, between 18 August and the end of the month), the slower (18-knot) *Empress* carrying stores and spare aircraft. Later, having been replaced as RNAS transport by a freighter, she too was converted into a primitive carrier (8 September – 10 October).[37] The ships were not extensively modified, but each could

32 Accounts differ, but it appears that the launching track forward, as used in 1913, was fitted at this time. The only good contemporary photograph shows canvas hangars only, one completely covering the forecastle and one aft. The supposition that take-off rails would have been fitted forward is based on Sueter's August 1914 description (AIR 1/185) of the planned conversion of a *Bacchante* class cruiser, a ship similar to (and replaced by) HMS *Hermes*.

33 It seems unlikely that Sueter considered *Hermes* for Grand Fleet service, since in August (see Chapter 3) he was pressing for a large ship for service with the Fleet. *Hermes* was not mentioned in the relevant correspondence.
    In August 1914 *Hermes* was officially listed as a seaplane-carrying ship. The official list of the 'Distribution of War Vessels and Aircraft' (October 1914, current to 30 September 1914) assigned three aircraft to her: Shorts Nos 82, 119 and 905 (Nile type); at the time of her loss, *Hermes* was assigned only Nos 82 and 905. Of these, No 82 was a Short Type 74, No 119 was a Short Folder (three-bay type) and No 905 was a Short S.80 pusher biplane used as a trainer at the Isle of Grain. There was some early interest in adapting the last as a torpedo carrier for the ship; when she was lost, on 31 October 1914, No 905, though assigned, was definitely not aboard.

34 All three were built by Denny for the South Eastern & Chatham Railway Co. *Empress*, launched on 13 April 1907, was a repeat version of SS *Queen* (which had been launched on 4

April 1903). *Riviera* and *Engadine* were improved versions of *Empress*, with some changes and with half a knot more speed. They were launched on, respectively, 1 April and 23 September 1911. Later the Royal Navy came very close to converting others of the same type to seaplane carriers. On trial, at 1835 tons, *Riviera* made 23.034 knots at 11,393shp; *Engadine* was not run at full power. *Empress*, which was always described officially as much slower, made 22.255 knots at 8872shp (at 1805 tons). Dimensions: *Empress*, 310ft (318 over rudder) × 40ft × 13ft 9¼in; *Riviera*, 315ft (323 over rudder) × 41ft × 14ft 2¼in. These data have been taken from D J Lyon, *The Denny List* (National Maritime Museum, Greenwich, 1974). In 1914 Denny was probably the leading British builder of small, fast passenger ships and hence the source of most of the hulls considered for conversion to small seaplane carriers.

35 AIR 1/185.

36 Early in August 1914, Sueter wrote a memorandum for his files, describing the role of the carriers (in AIR 1/185, daily reports of the Air Department). He considered *Engadine* and *Riviera* important primarily for reconnaissance, to a range of at least 200nm, the torpedo role being reserved for later. Bombs might, however, be dropped during early operations, if the opportunity arose. The scheme was to scout Wilhelmshaven and the Kiel Canal so as to find the German fleet, bombing it if possible and then returning for a torpedo strike. For scouting, Sueter proposed to use two Short Folders (Nos 135 and 136), No 800,

and a German-built Albatros (which became No 890), once the latter had been fitted with floats. *Riviera* and *Engadine* would each carry two 160hp Short Folders (with one or two 100lb bombs each) and (in view of the unreliability of their 160hp Gnome motor) one 100hp Short non-folder as a scout (carrying a few light bombs if possible). They would be accompanied by a *Bacchante* class cruiser fitted with a flying-off platform (probably, according to Sueter, the one built for HMS *Hermes*), carrying one 100hp non-folder, one Short pusher with wheels and floats (No 65), and one 100hp Sopwith (No 880), the last of which would have to be hoisted out. The three carriers would be accompanied by thirty to forty submarines and destroyers, and they would get as close as possible to Heligoland during darkness, launching at dawn to (i) attack the Kiel Canal power house, lock gates, etc; (ii) count ships in Wilhelmshaven; (iii) locate any other ships or mines in the Heligoland Bight; and (iv) attack airship sheds. Disabling the Kiel Canal would make it very difficult for the German fleet to use its relatively safe Baltic base at Kiel. Sueter described his plan to the First Lord, Winston Churchill, on 23 August 1914 (AIR 1/2543). At this time he planned to use *Hermes*, *Engadine*, and *Riviera*; *Empress* was still classed as an aircraft transport. Sueter wanted ten bombers for the strike, which would explain the need for at least three carriers and, preferably, some supplementary cruisers.

37 Sueter planned from the first to convert *Empress*, waiting only to see whether the *Engadine* and *Riviera* conversions were successful. AIR 1/185, daily reports of the Air Department, August 1914–February 1915. These reports suggest that he expected to withdraw the ship from her support role as soon as the Expeditionary Force role ended.

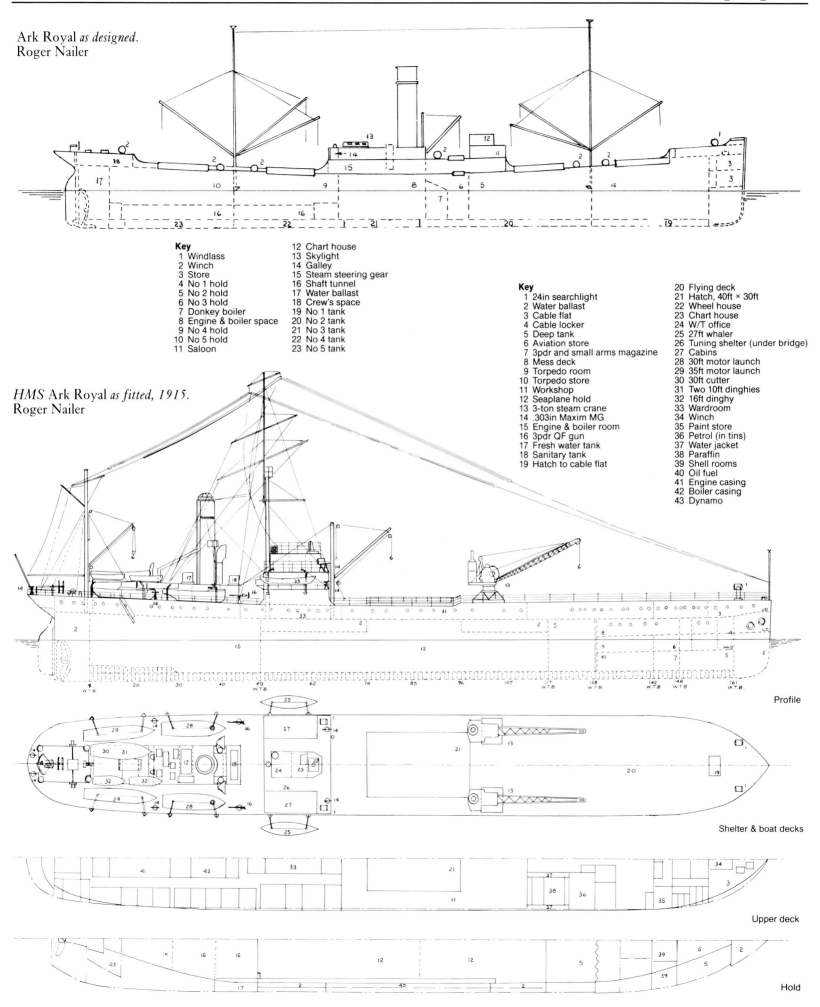

Ark Royal *as designed.*
Roger Nailer

Key
1 Windlass
2 Winch
3 Store
4 No 1 hold
5 No 2 hold
6 No 3 hold
7 Donkey boiler
8 Engine & boiler space
9 No 4 hold
10 No 5 hold
11 Saloon
12 Chart house
13 Skylight
14 Galley
15 Steam steering gear
16 Shaft tunnel
17 Water ballast
18 Crew's space
19 No 1 tank
20 No 2 tank
21 No 3 tank
22 No 4 tank
23 No 5 tank

HMS Ark Royal *as fitted, 1915.*
Roger Nailer

Key
1 24in searchlight
2 Water ballast
3 Cable flat
4 Cable locker
5 Deep tank
6 Aviation store
7 3pdr and small arms magazine
8 Mess deck
9 Torpedo room
10 Torpedo store
11 Workshop
12 Seaplane hold
13 3-ton steam crane
14 .303in Maxim MG
15 Engine & boiler room
16 3pdr QF gun
17 Fresh water tank
18 Sanitary tank
19 Hatch to cable flat
20 Flying deck
21 Hatch, 40ft × 30ft
22 Wheel house
23 Chart house
24 W/T office
25 27ft whaler
26 Tuning shelter (under bridge)
27 Cabins
28 30ft motor launch
29 35ft motor launch
30 30ft cutter
31 Two 10ft dinghies
32 16ft dinghy
33 Wardroom
34 Winch
35 Paint store
36 Petrol (in tins)
37 Water jacket
38 Paraffin
39 Shell rooms
40 Oil fuel
41 Engine casing
42 Boiler casing
43 Dynamo

Profile

Shelter & boat decks

Upper deck

Hold

carry three floatplanes under canvas screens fore and aft (one forward, two aft). As such they mounted the first carrier air raid in history, the attack on the Cuxhaven Zeppelin base on Christmas Day 1914.[38]

Sueter thought of these ships as an independent offensive force. He did not attach the three carriers to the Grand Fleet itself, but instead concentrated them at Harwich, across the North Sea from the Heligoland Bight and Germany.

The attack on Cuxhaven represented the culmination of a series of four bombing raids, the others of which had been mounted from temporary bases in Belgium. In modern terms they might be described as attempts to attack the enemy air threat 'at source'. There was, after all, as yet no anti-Zeppelin fighter to protect the fleet itself from surveillance, although one was being developed. For the first two raids, RNAS aircraft based at Antwerp raided Zeppelin sheds at Düsseldorf and Tondern. Then the Germans seized Antwerp, and British forces had to fall back into France. This put many German bases out of reach of land attack. However, on 21 November the RNAS struck the Zeppelin base at Friedrichshafen from Belfort, in France, near the German frontier, over a distance of about 125 miles. Bases deeper in Germany could be reached only by sea.

On 25 October, following the retreat from Belgium, the British carrier force attempted to strike Cuxhaven, far beyond the reach of land-based aircraft. None of the floatplanes could take off in the somewhat rough weather. This was the first clear indication that reliable operation required deck take-off. The day after the failure, Sueter reported that the new *Ark Royal* would have a flying-off deck. It seems likely, too, that it was at this time that he decided to fit a flying-off deck to the big *Campania* (see Chapter 3), and to acquire a fourth small carrier, the Vickers-built Isle of Man packet *Ben-my-Chree* (launched 23 March 1908), about twice the size of the other three, and thus large enough to accommodate flying-off rails (which, however, were never used successfully). The cause of the 25 October failure must have been well understood; the First Lord of the Admiralty, Winston Churchill, suggested the next day that barges with catapults be used to launch the six bombers.

The new carrier *Ben-my-Chree* was limited in that her hangar was abaft the superstructure, so that only one aircraft could fly off when the ship was under way. However, compared to the *Engadine*s she was more completely equipped, with a testing and repair workshop. She was commissioned on 2 January 1915, and was initially assigned to the Harwich carrier force, with three short Folders and two scouts. She was armed with four 12pdr (18cwt) and two 3pdr anti-aircraft guns (130 and 64rpg, respectively). It seems plausible that *Ben-my-Chree* was obtained specifically to replace the torpedoed *Hermes*; no official record appears to have survived.

It then became possible to rotate the three existing carriers through large refits (by Cunard, Liverpool) without reducing the total strength of the carrier force.[39] The after parts of their boat decks and upper decks were cleared, and a heated weathertight four-aircraft hangar was fitted aft, the foredeck being cleared. Swinging cranes at its after end replaced the earlier merchant-type swinging derricks. These ships were too short to have useful flight decks.[40] Thus, although aircraft were protected while on board, they still could not take off in rough weather. Accommodation for officers and men was much improved, and measures taken to increase the ships' coal capacity to provide 48 hours' endurance at maximum speed. Later the standard requirement would be 600nm or 72 hours at full speed.

It would appear that the three ships were not initially armed. As rebuilt, all three had four 12pdr 12cwt guns (130rpg) and two 3pdr Hotchkiss anti-aircraft guns (64rpg). In 1918, *Riviera* had a single 2pdr anti-aircraft gun added.

The hangar of HMS Ark Royal, *with the hatch open above. The floatplane is a Sopwith Schneider.* CPL

All of this added considerable topweight; *Engadine*, for example, required 45 tons of additional ballast. After refitting, she drew 13ft 10in forward and 13ft 6in aft. Her prewar Plimsoll (maximum draft) marks had been at 13ft, and her side openings had to be plated up for safety. Even then she was at the limit of permissable loading. In August 1917, when she was serving with the Grand Fleet, the addition of a short flying-off deck was suggested; DNC responded that her hull would have to be strengthened, and some coal capacity given up. The deck appears not to have been fitted.

On 25 December 1914 the three seaplane carriers, escorted by the Harwich Force, steamed into the Heligoland Bight and attacked Cuxhaven, near the main German fleet base at Wilhelmshaven. Each carrier hoisted out three floatplanes, and seven of the nine took off successfully. The Germans observed the raiders, and German aircraft attempted to attack the raiding force, though without success. Three of the seven seaplanes managed to return to the force, to be picked up; the other four had to ditch. The raid itself produced little damage. It did demonstrate, however, that carrier-borne aircraft could penetrate deep into Germany, at a time when no land-based aircraft could do nearly as much. Captain Sueter, the advocate of aerial torpedo attack, was particularly gratified to learn that the German battlecruisers in the Schillig Roads formed a perfect torpedo target, lined up fore and aft with almost no gaps between ships. He would later point to this observation as the inspiration for later ideas of mass torpedo attack on the German fleet.

Zeppelins attacked England in January, and again in March, 1915. The Harwich Force tried to repeat the Cuxhaven raid on 29 January, but had to turn back because it seemed likely that the aircraft would be damaged in their flimsy canvas hangars. Then two of the three carriers were withdrawn to be refitted, leaving only the slow *Empress*, with only three aircraft. An attempt to strike the radio station at Norddeich and a nearby Zeppelin base failed because the aircraft could not take off.

By early April, with HMS *Ben-my-Chree* again in service, the Harwich Force was back up to its three-carrier strength. It tried three more strikes (3 May, 6 May and 11 May), but each time was frustrated by the weather. *Ben-my-Chree* tried to launch an aircraft from her rails during the 11 May attack, but its engine backfired and wrecked the starting gear. *Engadine* successfully hoisted out and launched all three of her aircraft, but the fog was so thick that only one could return. The string of failures seemed to prove that the carriers were far too limited to be worthwhile; the carrier force at Harwich was disbanded.

HMS *Riviera* joined the Dover Patrol, whose duties included bombarding the Belgian coast. From 1915 on, she spotted for the monitors, which ultimately carried their own aircraft for this purpose.[41]

38   According to the British Official History, *The War in the Air*, the Admiralty proposed an air raid on Wilhelmshaven and the Kiel Canal as early as 13 August 1914 (Vol I, p368).

39   *Engadine* was rebuilt from 10 February to 24 March 1915, and *Riviera* from 14 February to 7 April 1915. *Empress* was the last to be withdrawn for modernization, beginning her nine-week reconstruction on 20 April 1915. *Ben-my-Chree* did not formally join the Harwich Force until late April 1915. She left for the Mediterranean in May.

40   *Empress*, the smallest of the three, actually was fitted with a short flying-off runway, but it was never used.

41   Experiments began in February 1915, using the old battleship *Revenge* (which was soon renamed *Redoubtable*). At this time two-way radio was too heavy for aircraft; a transmitter was carried aloft and the battleship signalled back by searchlight. This was unsuccessful, and trials began on 7 April 1915 using a two-way radio carried by an aircraft flying either from HMS *Empress* or from the Isle of Grain. After four radio failures, an aircraft from Eastchurch managed to make contact with the battleship, which successfully opened fire at 11,000 yards, this being the first time such a ship had used air spotting. A spotting school was immediately opened at Calshot, and the system was suggested to Admiral Jellicoe. He rejected it because his carrier (see Chapter 3) could not be relied upon to launch an aircraft at sea. However, Jellicoe did fear that the Germans would use air spotters which he could not counter. He was, therefore, greatly relieved when a Schneider floatplane was successfully deck-launched on 6 August 1915. Meanwhile kite balloons (which enjoyed two-way communication by wire) spotted for the ships at Gallipoli. HMS *Riviera* probably spotted for a time during the bombardment of Bruges, 23 August 1915, when she launched three Shorts. They proved unable to spot because at 2500ft they flew above the cloud layer. Success in air spotting did not come until 1916. These data are from *The War in the Air*, Vol II.

HMS Ben-my-Chree *as fitted, 1915*. Roger Nailer

Key
1 Bow rudder
2 Canvas seaplane shelter
3 12pdr QF gun
4 Torpedo warhead room
5 12pdr magazine
6 Bomb room
7 Searchlight
8 Boiler room
9 Engine room
10 Petrol store
11 3pdr HA gun
12 Seaplane hangar
13 Boom
14 Shaft space
15 Aviation workshop
16 Emergency steering position
17 Portable launching platform
18 Seaplane derrick
19 Charthouse
20 18ft cutter
21 25ft motor launch
22 30ft motor launch
23 28ft whaler
24 20ft motor launch
25 Windlass
26 Intelligence office
27 Boiler casing
28 Fan room
29 Engine casing
30 Hatch to workshop
31 Ammunition hoist
32 Sick bay
33 Wardroom
34 Coal
35 Galley
36 Tiller compartment
37 Fresh water
38 Reserve feed water
39 Ballast tank
40 Carpenter's stores

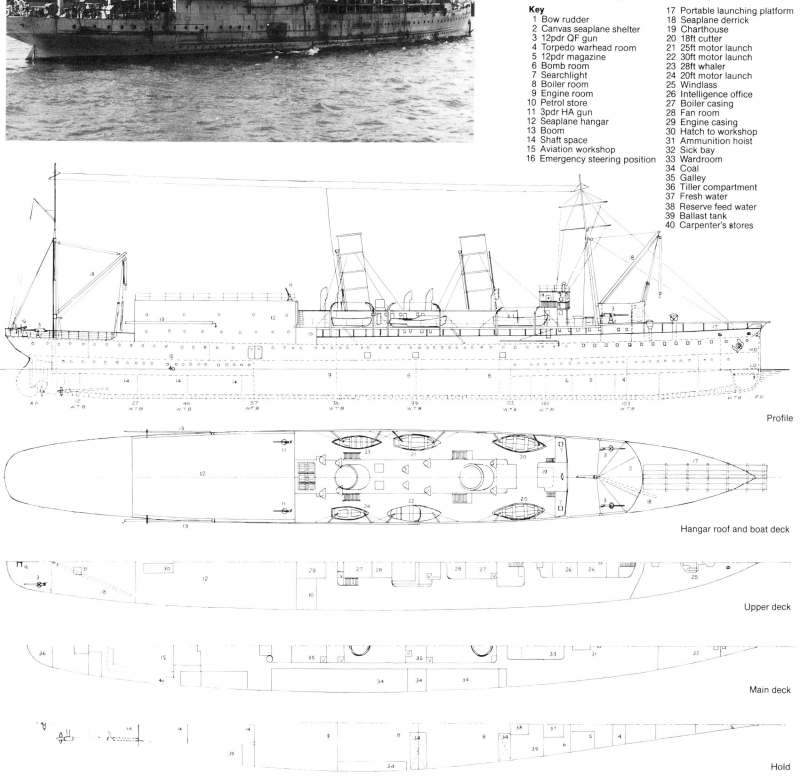

Profile

Hangar roof and boat deck

Upper deck

Main deck

Hold

HMS *Engadine* went to Rosyth in October 1915, as a base ship rather than as an active carrier. She was employed in kite balloon (gunfire spotting) experiments, which in turn led to such an installation aboard HMS *Campania*.[42]

After her large refit, HMS *Empress* went to Queenstown and then to the Mediterranean.

HMS *Ben-my-Chree* also went to the Mediterranean, to support the Gallipoli operation.[43] Sueter hoped that her torpedo-bombers would sink the two key enemy warships, *Goeben* and *Breslau*. In fact this proved impossible, as her aircraft were urgently required for other duties connected with the Gallipoli operation.

They did, however, succeed in torpedoeing three lesser Turkish ships. On 12 August 1915 Flight Commander G H K Edmonds hit a Turkish transport from a range of about 300 yards, dropping his torpedo from an altitude of about 15ft. The ship was already lying on the bottom, but Edmonds had made the first wartime torpedo attack. On 17 August he hit a moving target at Ak Bashi Liman; on the same day Flight Lieutenant G B Dacre, forced down by engine trouble, sank a Turkish tug-boat while he taxied on the water. These three successes in turn motivated the mass torpedo attack proposals of late 1916 and early 1917.

Early in 1915 a new floatplane, the single-seat Sopwith Schneider (Cup), became available. In theory, it could fly high enough (to 10,000ft in 35 minutes) and fast enough (85mph) to destroy a Zeppelin. Since Zeppelins had intercepted the Cuxhaven raid ships, it was clear that they might well be lured out by any other British activity near the German coast – and Schneiders carried by the British force could then destroy them in the air. From May 1915 onwards, then, the Harwich Force tried this tactic. Unfortunately *Ben-my-Chree* failed to launch a Schneider from her short flying-off trackway on 11 May, and the use of this deck had to be abandoned. This left only the unsatisfactory practice of launching from the water, but it was still enough to encourage further attempts.

On 3 July the two fastest carriers (*Engadine* and *Riviera*), operating together, launched a reconnaissance floatplane to fly over the River Ems, in the hope of attracting a Zeppelin attack. Unfortunately, of three Schneiders hoisted out by HMS *Engadine*, two broke up trying to take off and the third was badly damaged. However, the basic tactical idea had been proven.

On 26 March 1915, before the breakup of its carrier force, the Royal Navy had chartered a second Isle of Man passenger steamer, the Armstrong-built *Vindex* (ex *Viking*, launched 7 March 1905). She was commissioned in September, and purchased on 11 October 1915. As converted in ten weeks by Cunard at Liverpool, and fitted with a short (64ft) flying-off deck rather than with launching rails, *Vindex* initially carried four large and one small floatplane aft, and two single-seat aircraft (dismantled) in a small hangar forward. The latter were fitted for quick assembly, and both could be flown off in about 10 minutes. Electric cranes were fitted aft, and derricks forward, for plane handling. Armament consisted of four 12pdr 18cwt guns (130rpg) and one 6pdr Hotchkiss anti-aircraft gun (55rpg); wartime armament summaries always listed two of the 12pdrs as temporarily mounted.

DAS considered *Vindex* a good standard for future seaplane carrier construction, and in later correspondence called for further *Vindex*-type ships. In 1916 he described her flying-off deck as efficient (compared to that of HMS *Ben-my-Chree*) but complained of the limitation imposed by the small hangar.

Her first deck flight was made on 3 November 1915; a Bristol C Scout took off in 46ft, with 27 knots of wind over the deck, the ship steaming at 12 knots. The Scout was faster than the Schneider (93mph) and could fly higher (15,000ft); it was

HMS Vindex *as converted, showing her short flying-off platform.* FAAM

armed with anti-Zeppelin Ranken darts, which the pilot had to drop on the Zeppelin from above. On 29 July 1916 *Vindex* launched the first fighter which actually engaged (albeit unsuccessfully) a Zeppelin.[44]

By early 1916, then, the Royal Navy could expect to operate anti-Zeppelin fighters from a carrier, even in fairly rough weather. On 25 March *Vindex* attacked the Zeppelin base at Tondern. Three Short and two Sopwith Baby floatplanes were hoisted out and actually took off, but did no damage. However, the attack did lure German heavy units out to sea, where the Grand Fleet could engage them. A second raid was therefore mounted on 4 May, *Vindex* and *Engadine* carrying eleven single-seat Sopwith Baby floatplanes armed with 65lb bombs. Unfortunately eight failed to take off, one hit the mast of an escorting destroyer, and one had to return due to engine trouble. The Zeppelins did come out, but the only one to be lost was shot down by a cruiser's 6in gun. Again, the theory that the threat of an air strike could force an enemy out of his otherwise safe haven was proven, but the necessary aircraft did not yet exist.

The final Harwich Force carrier air operation was mounted on 22 October 1916, when *Vindex* hoisted out two reconnaissance floatplanes. They were expected to scout for a planned motor torpedo boat (CMB) raid, but fog largely aborted the mission.

On 7 January 1916 DAS (Rear Admiral C L Vaughan Lee) asked for additional small carriers. He considered 1600 to 1700 gross tons, as in HMS *Empress*, the minimum acceptable, and wanted a minimum trial speed of 20 knots, for 18 in service.[45] The most promising ship was an idle Vickers-built Isle of Man packet, *Manxman*. For the more distant future, DAS was interested in three fast packets under construction: *Nairana* (for service in Australia) and *Lorina* (for the London and South Western Railway) at Denny, and No 431 (*Stockholm*) in the John Brown yards, for the Great Eastern Railway. All of the other fast packets were in service, hence not available.[46]

Lieutenant Holmes sketched a conversion of *Manxman* for DAS, with an 85ft flying-off deck, and hangars for three small floatplanes forward (to use the deck) and four larger ones aft. She would, then, be similar to *Vindex* but with a longer flight deck. The ship's major defect was her limited coal supply (sufficient only for 23 hours at 18 knots, that is, 414nm). DAS

42 Jellicoe would have preferred a dedicated balloon ship, but there were too few merchant ships fast enough to keep up with the Grand Fleet. The Controller (Admiral Tudor) suggested that slow merchant ships be used to inflate and launch balloons, which could then be transferred to light cruisers. This suggestion was only accepted considerably later.

43 In *The Cuxhaven Raid* (Conway Maritime Press, London, 1985), R D Laymen suggests that she replaced the slow *Ark Royal*, which was too vulnerable to the U-boats now operating in the Aegean. *Ark Royal* functioned instead as a more or less static base ship. Sueter himself claimed that he sent *Ben-my-Chree* to the area specifically as a torpedo attack ship.

44 The carrier had been ordered to sea to try to intercept a Zeppelin returning after raiding England. Her wheeled Bristol Scout had to land in the sea (using air bags) after an unsuccessful attack with Ranken Darts.

45 Coal-burning ships were considered good for only 70 per cent of their trial power on a sustained basis, compared to 90 per cent or more for oil-burners.

46 Out of a list of twenty-four existing short-sea ships, only *Leinster*, *Munster*, and *Ulster* (23 knots, 2646 gross tons, 1896–97, on the Holyhead–Dublin run); *Duke of Argyll* and *Duke of Cumberland* (20 knots, 2052 tons, 1909 on the Fleetwood–Belfast run); *Antrim* (20 knots, 1954 tons, 1913, on the Fleetwood–Belfast run); and *Londonderry* (20 knots, 1968 tons, 1904, on the Heysham–Belfast run) were suitable. A list of foreign steamers under British control produced only *Maori* (19 knots, 3399 tons, 1907). The Director of Transport proposed four City of Dublin packets (*Cork*, *Wicklow*, *Carlow*, and *Kerry*) of 1174 to 1230 gross tons, but capable of only about 14 knots. They were rejected as too small and too slow for North Sea operation.

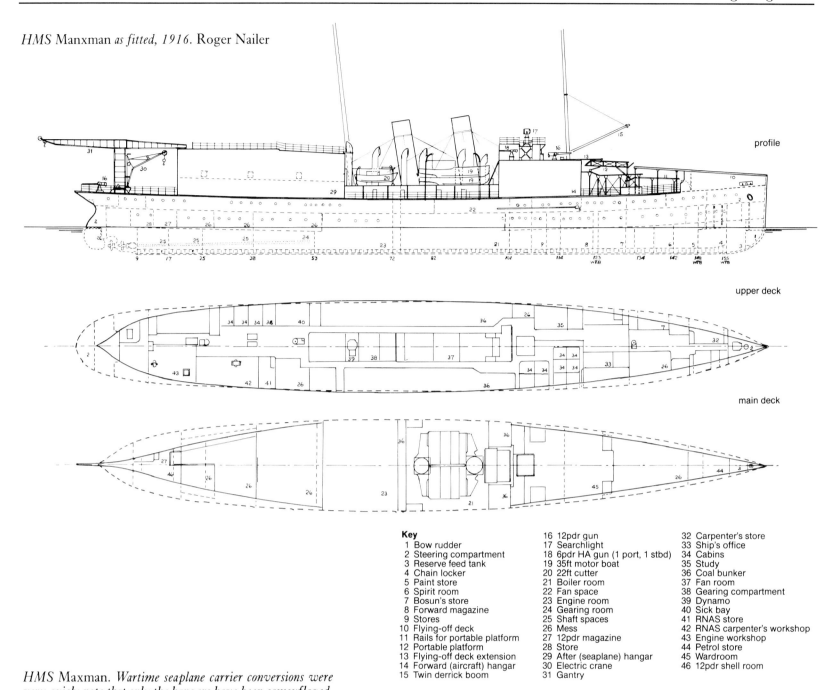

HMS Manxman *as fitted, 1916.* Roger Nailer

profile

upper deck

main deck

Key

1 Bow rudder	16 12pdr gun	32 Carpenter's store
2 Steering compartment	17 Searchlight	33 Ship's office
3 Reserve feed tank	18 6pdr HA gun (1 port, 1 stbd)	34 Cabins
4 Chain locker	19 35ft motor boat	35 Study
5 Paint store	20 22ft cutter	36 Coal bunker
6 Spirit room	21 Boiler room	37 Fan room
7 Bosun's store	22 Fan space	38 Gearing compartment
8 Forward magazine	23 Engine room	39 Dynamo
9 Stores	24 Gearing room	40 Sick bay
10 Flying-off deck	25 Shaft spaces	41 RNAS store
11 Rails for portable platform	26 Mess	42 RNAS carpenter's workshop
12 Portable platform	27 12pdr magazine	43 Engine workshop
13 Flying-off deck extension	28 Store	44 Petrol store
14 Forward (aircraft) hangar	29 After (seaplane) hangar	45 Wardroom
15 Twin derrick boom	30 Electric crane	46 12pdr shell room
	31 Gantry	

HMS Maxman. *Wartime seaplane carrier conversions were very quick; note that only the hangars have been camouflaged.*

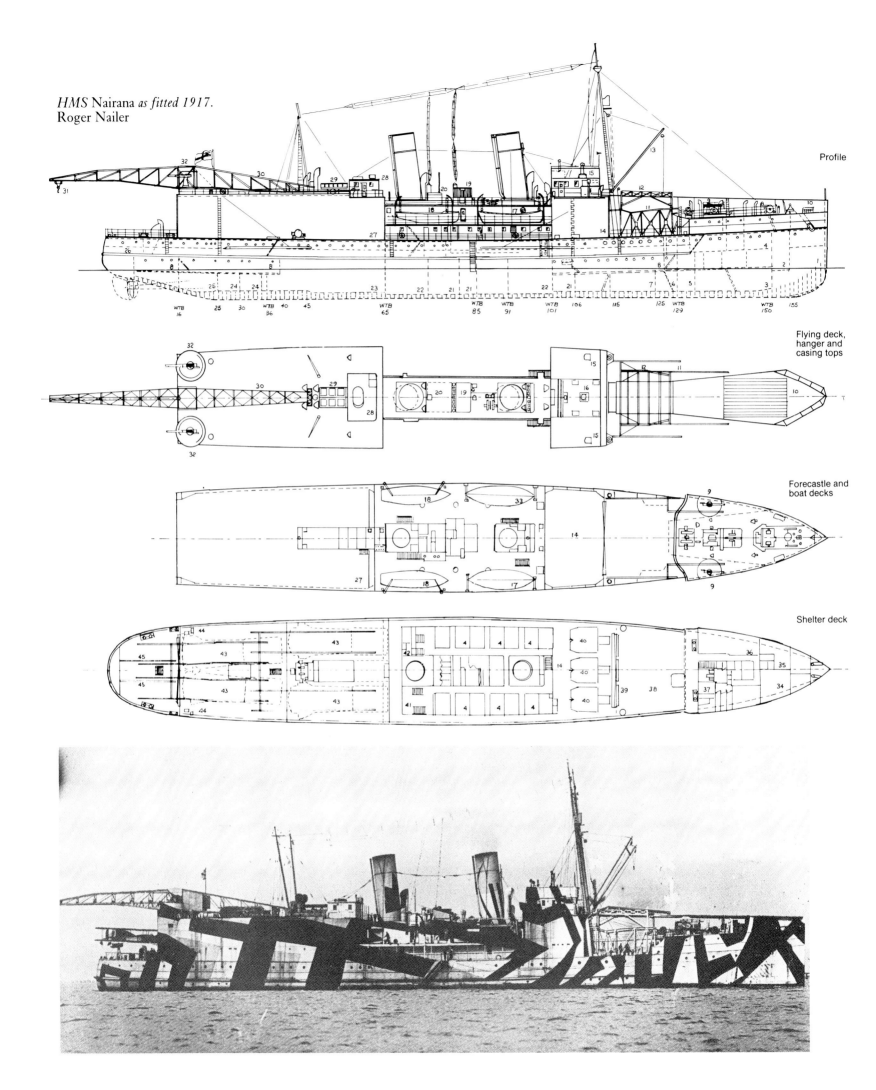

HMS Nairana *as fitted 1917.*
Roger Nailer

Profile

Flying deck,
hanger and
casing tops

Forecastle and
boat decks

Shelter deck

◀ **Key**
1   Fore peak fresh water tank
2   Chain locker
3   Stores
4   Officers' cabin
5   Petrol store
6   Magazine & spirit room
7   Shell & bomb room
8   Mess deck
9   12pdr LA gun
10 Flying-off deck
11 Support rails for portable
    platform
12 Portable platform
13 Twin-boom derrick
14 Forward hangar
15 24in searchlight
16 Wheelhouse
17 28ft lifeboat
18 30ft motor boat
19 Ship's W/T office
20 RNAS W/T office
21 Coal bunker
22 Boiler room
23 Engine room
24 Fresh water tank
25 12pdr magazine
26 Steering gear
27 After hangar
28 Captain's cabin
29 Skylight to engine room
30 Cantilever gantry
31 Traveller (carriage)
32 12pdr HA gun
33 28ft lifeboat & 18ft dinghy
34 RNAS ratings' mess
35 Bosun's store
36 Lube oil store
37 Paint room
38 Forecastle deck handling space
39 Forward hangar shutter
40 Aircraft (wings folded)
41 Dark room
42 Signal office
43 Seaplanes (wings folded)
44 Hoist controller
45 Seaplane trolley rails

Left: *HMS* Nairana. *Note the hatch arrangement in the forward flight deck so that aircraft could be brought from the small hangar under the bridge.*

47   Sueter proposed such an attack in August 1914, and Roskill reprinted a paper dated April 1915 in which the First Lord, Winston Churchill, advocated a torpedo attack by at least ten aircraft on the German Fleet at anchor.

wanted her to be able to steam at maximum speed for 600nm, that is, out into the North Sea and back. This required additional coal stowage, which could be provided on either side of the upper deck amidships, in former passenger spaces, as in earlier carrier conversions. Holmes estimated that she could accommodate 400 tons, with another 50 in bags in her boiler spaces (she had no side bunkers).

The ship already had 225 tons of pig iron on board to counter the list when her thousand passengers moved to one side as she came alongside. As a packet, she drew 10ft 4in forward and 13ft 1in aft, and her Plimsoll line was 3ft above water, with the lowest hull openings about 4ft 3in above her waterline. They would be plated up, as in earlier carriers.

The Admiralty was extremely reluctant to add to the great burden on British shipyards, but DAS persisted. He clearly had offensive operations in mind, writing that he expected good results with a strike force of three or four such ships. He wanted twelve converted, so that he could afford to lose one or two in risky operations (presumably repeat Cuxhaven raids) near the enemy coast. After all, carriers were at particular risk because they had to stop to recover their aircraft. The Admiralty went so far as to draw up a list of remaining short-sea passenger ships, but it shrank from the necessary expenditure of scarce shipyard labour.

A conference met on 30 March 1916 to discuss this proposal, as well as DAS proposals for larger ships to work with the Grand Fleet (see Chapter 3). It was soon clear that Chatham Dockyard could convert her without serious disruption of other work. Its only major project at the time was the cruiser *Hawkins*, which had a very low priority. The Admiralty Board therefore approved the *Manxman* conversion, but extracted the condition that no further conversions be requested until the dire shortage of merchant tonnage had been relieved. This was well before the great shipping crisis brought on by unrestricted U-boat warfare the following year.

As completed, *Manxman* had a forward hangar large enough for four, rather than two, aircraft, plus the usual four-plane hangar aft (which was served by electric jib cranes). A rolling deck was fitted to get aircraft from the forward hangar onto the flight deck. Aft the ship had a centreline cantilever gantry crane, extending far enough aft to hoist up and traverse inboard seaplanes which approached with their engines running, and with the ship under way. This solved a major problem in seaplane carrier operation.

Manxman proved slower than expected, and thus could not generally fly off single-engine floatplanes from her short deck. This inspired experiments with Sopwith Pup wheeled fighters, which proved so successful that landplanes were adopted throughout the British fleet in 1917–18 (see Chapter 3).

Manxman was armed with four 12pdr 12cwt guns and two 6pdr Hotchkiss anti-aircraft guns.

Given the shortage of suitable hulls for conversion, DAS's constructor, Lieutenant Holmes, suggested that the Admiralty design and build an improved channel steamer (similar to the early Denny ships) for further carrier construction. It would be capable of about 22 knots, with an endurance of 600nm at 20 knots, but it would have to be stronger than existing carriers, and a better sea-keeper. Holmes thought it could be built in nine to twelve months, and suggested that a sketch design be developed, as a hedge against possible war losses, as a means of reinforcing the Grand Fleet, and as a reinforcement for the North Sea. For example, it could supplement and then replace the paddle minesweeper anti-Zeppelin patrol line then being planned (see below). Nothing seems to have come of this proposal, and when North Sea carriers were again required (see Chapter 3), they were again improvised from existing ships.

DAS considered *Manxman* superior to anything but the huge *Campania*. She was fitted with an 86ft flying-off deck and a hangar for eight aircraft, with a cantilever gantry to shift them from hangar to forecastle. However, speed was only 18 knots (compared with an expected 21), so that small floatplanes could not be flown off in a calm. *Manxman* was commissioned on 17 April 1916, arriving at Chatham on the 25th. Although the yard had promised to complete her in two months, she was not actually ready until December. This was partly a consequence of the sheer work load on DNC (who was responsible for the conversion design) and on the British shipbuilding industry as a whole (as reflected in subcontracting delays). This delay in turn was sometimes used to exemplify official neglect of the RNAS.

By December, the Harwich Force carrier concept had been discarded, and *Manxman* was assigned instead to the Grand Fleet, going to the Mediterranean in about October 1917. Perhaps her most important achievement was to prove, early in 1917, that a Sopwith Pup fighter could fly off in only 20ft, given sufficient wind over the deck. This led to the development of flying-off platforms for British cruisers and then capital ships (see Chapter 3).

DAS (and Fifth Sea Lord) seems to have maintained interest in North Sea carrier strikes, as distinct from operations in support of the Grand Fleet; he called early in 1917 for conversion of five more seaplane carriers. His programme was later reduced to two, which became HMS *Pegasus* and *Nairana*, and which can most logically be considered direct descendants of *Vindex* and *Manxman*. The two new carriers were, however, attached to the Grand Fleet, and so are described in the next chapter.

BY EARLY 1916 there was intense interest in the use of torpedo-bombers, which had torpedoed three ships at Gallipoli. It seems likely that Captain Sueter considered this demonstration a prelude to a mass attack on an enemy fleet in harbour, either the German fleet at Wilhelmshaven or the Austrians at Pola. Others had much the same idea. In December 1915, for example, Squadron Commander W P de Courcy Ireland, commanding RNAS Great Yarmouth, proposed a torpedo strike by 100 carrier aircraft on Wilhelmshaven, to be executed in the summer of 1916.[47]

The issue was always whether to emphasize shore-based heavy floatplanes, which could carry a weapon (the 18in torpedo) powerful enough to injure large ships, but only to a range of about 200nm, or to emphasize shipboard torpedo-bombers which, although they might not carry so heavy a load, could nevertheless attack the enemy fleets. An Admiralty conference in January 1916 decided that the best approach to a shipboard torpedo-bomber would be a modified Short 184, using a more powerful (Rolls Royce 250hp) engine, and capable of carrying a 1000lb torpedo over a range of 300nm. Meanwhile larger torpedo-floatplanes could be based in East Coast harbours, though they lacked the range to reach the vital target, Wilhelmshaven.

These ideas were dormant for much of 1916, but they were revived at the end of the year. The coast defence role for torpedo-bombers was rejected because, given their limited range, impractically large numbers would have been required to cover the British coast. On the other hand, strikes at the two primary enemy fleet bases were extremely attractive. Given the poor performance of the existing seaplane carriers, and the requirement that their floatplane torpedo-bombers fly from the sea, a strike on Wilhelmshaven seemed out of the question. This left the strike on Pola, which could be mounted from existing bases in Italy. Sueter was offered the command of this operation in January 1917, and he accepted, leaving the Admiralty.[48]

Sueter left behind the Cuckoo wheeled carrier torpedo-bomber project, which became the basis of a series of plans for air offensives against the High Seas Fleet, devised by Admiral Beatty. The German fleet could not be attacked at sea because it refused to leave its protected base at Wilhelmshaven, yet by its existence, it protected the German U-boat bases from mining and other forms of attack. Should the German fleet be neutralized, the U-boats, which were doing such terrible damage, could themselves be destroyed at source.

An aerial torpedo strike was the obvious solution. On 11 September 1917 Beatty proposed quick conversions of eight fast merchant ships or armed merchant cruisers to execute a mass torpedo-bomber strike the following spring. These ships would not be part of the Grand Fleet; instead, they would function as an independent striking force, much like Sueter's 1914–16 carrier flotilla. Each would be fitted with a flying-off deck, arranged to launch five Cuckoo torpedo-bombers in rapid succession. The strike force, then, would be able to launch three 40-bomber waves, as each carrier would accommodate fifteen bombers plus two anti-Zeppelin fighters. Apart from flying-off decks and the necessary hangars, Beatty wanted his improvised carriers bulged and fitted with paravanes to protect them against torpedoes and mines.

The attack would be launched from about an hour's flight distance, after which the carriers would withdraw to a rendezvous in shoal water (so as to make submarine attack difficult) to recover their pilots. The targets, in order of priority, would be the capital ships, the dock gates and floating docks, light cruisers, and torpedo craft. Beatty hoped that the attack would be supplemented by large seaplanes carrying 230lb bombs, which would attack dockyard facilities as well as submarines nested in the dockyard basin. He believed (incorrectly) that a Cuckoo could carry a machine-gun in addition to its torpedo, and thus hoped that, after attacking, the aircraft of the first waves could help protect those of the later ones.

Beatty considered concentration and surprise essential to success. All previous carrier air operations had suffered from delay due to weather, and the Admiral feared that any such delay

would compromise security. He therefore proposed that arrangements be made to convert two more carriers, which would be ready to add their weight to any postponed (and therefore less secret) strike.[49]

The Admiralty was unenthusiastic. Fast merchant ships (the Cuckoo required at least a 20-knot wind over the deck to take off) were in great demand, particularly as a result of the ongoing U-boat campaign. Conversion would not be nearly as quick or as simple as Beatty imagined; British yards were badly congested, not least by repairs to damaged merchant ships and warships. Moreover, the Cuckoo was hardly likely to be a decisive weapon. Although it could lift an 18in torpedo, this torpedo was only a 1000lb type, carrying only 170lbs of explosives, hardly enough to damage a capital ship.

Beatty was unconvinced. He argued that, even if the Cuckoo strike failed actually to immobilize the German fleet, at the least the threat of such a strike would draw the fleet out, into a surface battle the Grand Fleet could expect to win. This was much the same concept which had applied to carrier raids on Zeppelin bases. The Admiralty, however, vetoed the scheme on the grounds that eight fast freighters could not be spared from merchant service. As for Beatty's proposed alternative, conversion of liners, it was felt that as they did not have large enough hatches to take Cuckoos, they would therefore require extensive modification, which in itself would delay the raid past the prime flying (summer) months of 1918.

There was no question but that torpedo-bombers were promising, and 200 Cuckoos were on order. The Admiralty also agreed that air attack was the most promising means of dealing with the High Seas Fleet. However, it also had to admit

The Sopwith Baby was the first purpose-designed British carrier-borne scout or fighter. This Blackburn-built Baby was armed with an upward-firing Lewis gun, above the upper wing; the bomb appears to be a 65lb type. The RNAS probably wanted the upward-firing gun to engage Zeppelins, which would often be encountered above the fighters. The first Baby, an adaptation of the earlier Sopwith Schneider, was delivered in September 1915.

48   Several writers have suggested that Sueter was exiled to Italy because of his disruptive behaviour at the Admiralty. However, the papers on the projected torpedo strike show that he was an enthusiastic supporter of the project, and it would have been natural for its originator (or chief promoter) to have been given the opportunity to earn the credit for a successful anti-ship strike. That no such strike ever occurred does not change the significance of the offer. It seems unlikely that any officer would cheerfully have refused so attractive an operational command. Sueter himself was dismissed later in 1917 after having committed the very serious sin of writing personally to the King to claim partial credit for the invention of the tank. He became bitter, and the usual account of the 'exile' seems to have been based largely on his memoirs. Sueter was also responsible for organizing many of the historical papers on carrier development now in the Public Record Office. They conversely show a noticeable anti-Admiralty flavour, which is equally unlikely to be entirely fair.

49   These details are from Beatty's letter to the Admiralty in ADM 1/8486, quoted by Roskill as his No 189.

As with all other seaplanes, the Baby's performance was limited due to the weight and drag of the floats. It was, therefore, a great advance to fly wheeled aircraft from shipboard. The first wheeled British carrier fighter was the Sopwith Pup, here flying from HMS Manxman. The Pup actually had less power than a Baby, but it enjoyed much superior performance. Pups were also used to test the various arrester gear systems devised at the Isle of Grain in 1917 and 1918. All Pups had been withdrawn from operational service by the end of World War I; the last was No 9944, aboard HMS Vindictive for special experiments. The Pup was specially adapted for carrier operation by Beardmore, as the WB III, with the wings (redesigned to eliminate stagger) folding back along the fuselage. These aircraft also had either folding (for stowage, not for flight) or jettisonable undercarriages. They were not particularly successful in service; presumably the aerodynamic price of carrier adaptation (unstaggered wings for folding) was too high.

that resources, particularly in merchant ships, were stretched very thin, and that direct ASW measures (including repair and replacement of merchant shipping) had to take priority.

On 28 November, however, Beatty proposed that three armed merchant cruisers about to be detached from the 10th Cruiser Squadron (which was blockading Germany) be converted to carriers: *Alsatian*, *Orvieto* and *Teutonic*. In each case he proposed a flying-off deck forward, with a hangar beneath it, and other hangars amidships and aft. It seemed likely that a flying-on deck, using arrester gear then under development (see Chapter 4), could be built above the after hangar. The design concept seems to have evolved within the Grand Fleet, but no detailed plans were ever produced.[50]

At 20 knots, *Alsatian* was the fastest of the three. A 165ft flight deck would be built from the fore end of her superstructure to her bow, forming the roof of a hangar on C deck (and about 17ft above that deck). Removal of the four 6in guns

50 AIR 1/641/122/232 contains a sketch showing where in the ship these hangars and decks were to be placed, and sketches showing possible hangar dimensions, but it seems unlikely that detailed calculations were ever made.

forward would clear a space about 100 × 68ft (max) – 57ft (min) on C deck, or the ship could be built out slightly to provide a 100 × 61ft space (for nine torpedo-bombers or six Fairey III reconnaissance planes). Aircraft would be lifted through a 37 × 19ft hatch at the after end of the hangar, reducing the effective length of the flight deck to about 120ft, which was considered sufficient (if slightly short). Amidships, there was space for a 64ft hangar, wide enough for two bombers or one reconnaissance aircraft. They would be hoisted onto A deck through a hatch, and wheeled along the port side to the flight deck (three boats being removed and the port bridge wing raised). Aft, there was space for a 120 × 68ft (max) – 49ft (min) hangar, sufficient for eight torpedo-bombers or six Faireys. If the arrester gear experiments succeeded, this space could be roofed with a 120ft flying-on deck, and the four 6in guns aft could probably be retained. As in the case of the midships hangar, aircraft stowed aft would be wheeled forward along a ramp on A deck. Stump masts for derricks would have to be fitted: two for the forward hangar, one amidships and one aft.

The large coal supply in the forward holds would no longer be required, so these spaces could be used for ballast. In so large a ship, there would be no difficulty in finding space for shops or petrol.

The other projected conversions would have been analogous. *Orvieto* (17 knots) could have taken a 100ft flight deck (excluding hatch) forward, but no flying-on deck aft, and she could have accommodated twelve torpedo-bombers; *Teutonic* (19 knots) could have taken a 125ft flight deck forward and eight bombers, with a 130ft flying-on deck aft.

A committee, including Commander Holmes (DAS' advisor on naval architecture), as well as representatives of the Director of Plans, DAS, DNC, and the Grand Fleet, visited HMS *Alsatian* in Liverpool on 3 December to evaluate the proposed conversion. Initial estimates were that each ship could be converted in three months.

On 16 December DOD rejected the *Alsatian* conversion, on

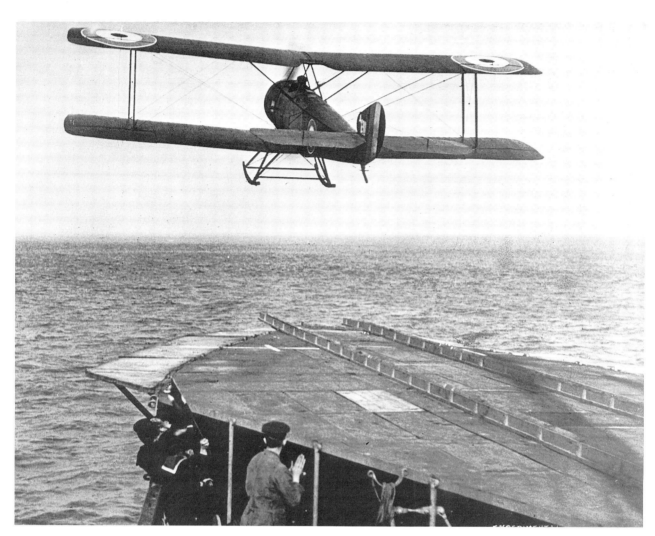

Some early carrier aircraft were fitted with skids rather than with wheels, to make ditching safer. This 1½-Strutter (Ship Strutter) is taking off using the trough laid on the deck of HMS Vindex. *During April 1918, the Marine Experimental Aircraft Depot (Isle of Grain) began modifying 1½-Strutters with detachable wings, skid undercarriages, hydrovanes for safer ditching, air (floatation) bags alongside the engine and 140hp Clerget engines. The machine illustrated here lacks a hydrovane, and was presumably a prototype skid coversion of a standard land-based aircraft.*

The Sopwith 1½-Strutter appeared in 1916, and in 1918 it was the standard fleet spotter and reconnaissance aircraft. this one is flying from a capital ship turret platform. The navalized Ship Strutter had detachable outer wing panels and was fitted with floatation bags. Typically the forward-firing gun of land-based 1½-Strutters was omitted, and the weight saved was allocated to the radio (wireless) set required for effective spotting.

Left: *Throughout World War I, the central goal of British carrier development was the ability to strike at enemy warships, preferably using torpedoes. Admiral Beatty advocated a massed torpedo strike on the German High Seas Fleet in its base as the only way to break the stalemate in the North Sea. This would have released British seapower to influence the war on land more directly. Only in 1918 did something approaching Beatty's requirements, the Sopwith Cuckoo, appear in any numbers. The Cuckoo was the first carrier-based wheeled torpedo-bomber in any navy. It was still somewhat limited, in that it could only drop a lightweight (albeit 18in calibre) torpedo.*

The Short 184 was the main weapon of the seaplane carriers throughout World War I, with about 650 being built for the RNAS. It executed the first airborne torpedo attacks in history, against Turkish ships in the Sea of Marmora. This late production example, built by Shorts, was powered by a 240hp Sunbeam engine. Note the bomb rack slung between its floats, the Scarff ring for the gunner, and the take-off trolley under the main floats. The bombs are probably 112lb types.

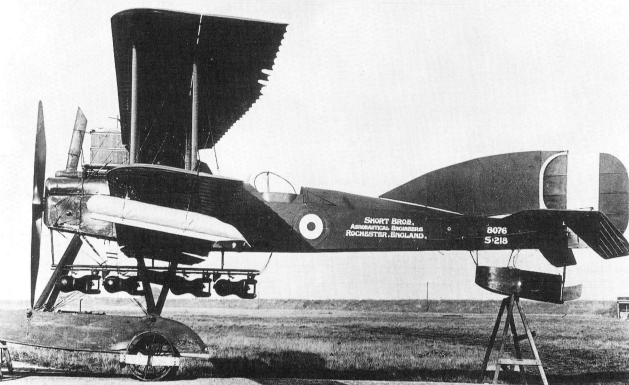

Right: *At the end of World War I, the Camel was the standard British deck- and turret-launched fighter. The navalized 2F.1 (Ship Camel) shown here, had a detachable rear fuselage, steel tubular centre-section struts (instead of the wide wooden struts of the land-based F.1), and air bags for floatation after ditching. Control wires were repositioned outside outside the fuselage so that they would not foul the air bags, and the tail skid was modified to keep the tail up during take-off (to minimize the deck run). Ship Camels could also be distinguished by their armament, consisting of a Lewis gun atop the upper wing and one synchronized Vickers gun (rather than two) in the fuselage.*

the grounds that the ship was too slow for fleet work; she would become another *Campania*. The disbandment of the 10th Cruiser Squadron would not release the three valuable ships. Instead, they would be reassigned to the 2nd Cruiser Squadron, which patrolled west of the Shetlands and Orkneys to intercept raiders or merchant ships, and which also operated in the White Sea and into Murmansk. Moreover, *Alsatian* had been designed, as a liner, to coal by chutes, and so could not effectively coal at any fleet base other than Rosyth. Finally, her complement of nineteen torpedo-bombers seemed far too small to be worthwhile.

Beatty remained dissatisfied, and continued to raise this idea throughout January 1918. The Fifth Sea Lord and the Director of Plans both supported it; they also suggested, as an alternative, the conversion of three County class armoured cruisers (sixteen aircraft each).

Finally, however, the Grand Fleet Maintenance Committee rejected the conversion (21 January 1918). By this time it appeared that conversion would take three to four months if the ships were fitted forward only, and five if aft as well. Both labour and steel (200 to 500 tons of which would have been needed) were in short supply.

By this time, the specially designed carriers *Argus*, *Hermes*, and *Cavendish* were already well advanced. Given what turned out to be over-optimistic expectations for their completion, the Admiralty cannot have seen much point in less satisfactory conversions, which would not have appeared any earlier. The Admiralty argued, too, that too few Cuckoos would be available in time for the 1918 naval flying season.

The first practice Cuckoo attack was actually made the day after the Armistice (12 November 1918), and a hit was scored on a battleship. It turned out that the aircraft often could be heard but not seen (until about 15 seconds before release) in the pervasive North Sea mist.

THE THIRD CARRIER ROLE, operations in distant (and relatively low-threat) areas, deserves some mention here. The first example was probably the series of air operations against the German cruiser *Königsberg*, concealed in the Rufiji river in East Africa. This involved a fair number of floatplanes, but it is not clear whether they had any consistent parent ship. Certainly the auxiliary cruiser *Kinfauns Castle* initially delivered the flying-boat used to find the German cruiser, and in February 1915 she collected two Sopwith floatplanes for this operation at Bombay.

Two German merchant ships seized at Port Said in August 1914 were converted locally and used as carriers: *Anne* (ex *Anne Rickmers*, built in 1911 by Rickmers, Bremerhaven) and *Raven II* (ex *Rabenfels*, built in 1903 by Swan Hunter).[51] They were very crude carriers, hoisting out their aircraft and recovering them from the water. There was, then, little to differentiate them from a British armed merchant cruiser equipped with aircraft during World War I: HMFA *Himalaya* carried a floatplane in 1916–17 for operations off East Africa (and had a temporary hangar aft).

Anne ceased seaplane operations in March 1917, eventually reverting to cargo ship (collier) status. She was replaced by the merchant ship *City of Oxford*, originally used as a dummy battleship and then as a kite balloon ship. She carried four Short 184s.[52]

In January 1915 the new (but slow) *Ark Royal* was despatched to the Mediterranean to support the Gallipoli operation. She was joined in about June by HMS *Ben-my-Chree*, which remained in the Mediterranean until she was sunk (by Turkish shore fire at Kastelorizo) on 11 January 1917.[53]

With the abandonment of Gallipoli, the Allied effort in the

Above and above right. *The former* Ark Royal *during World War II as HMS* Pegasus *(she was renamed in December 1934). The overhead view is dated January 1943; the surface view was taken in June 1942. Note the cross-deck (cruiser or battleship-type) catapult. HMS* Pegasus *served briefly in this guise as a fighter catapult ship. She spent most of the war training capital ship and cruiser catapult pilots, and then became an accommodation/depot ship in 1944. Before the war she was used largely as a catapult trials ship, testing the first carrier accelerator (catapult) in April 1933. She also tested the Hein mat for underway recovery of floatplanes. A prewar proposal to use her as a seaplane tender (to support RAF maritime patrol aircraft) was rejected.*

Mediterranean shifted to Salonika and the Aegean. In addition, operations along the Turkish coast were designed to prevent the Turks from reinforcing other fronts, for example those near the Suez Canal. *Ark Royal* (with five Shorts and two Sopwiths) had been based at Salonika since November 1915, largely to watch the Greek Army and then to support the Allied occupation of the port area. *Ben-my-Chree* was transferred from the Eastern Mediterranean to Port Said (under command of C-in-C East Indies) in January 1916 (carrying two Shorts and two Sopwith Schneider Cup floatplanes) in response to reported Turkish troop movements in Palestine.

This unit operated seaplanes to observe Turkish movements on the sea flank both in Sinai and in Syria, and it employed the two converted German tramp steamers, *Anne* and *Raven II*. *Ben-my-Chree* was transferred here because she could operate higher-performance aircraft. The three ships formed a unit under Squadron Commander C J L'Estrange-Malone (and, after May 1916, Wing Commander C R Samson), operating primarily against Turkish forces in Syria and Sinai.

In one notable operation, *Ben-my-Chree* and *Raven II* were assigned to bomb two critical Turkish railway bridges carrying the single line between Tarsus and Alexandretta, over the Jeihan and Seihan rivers. On 27 December the carriers launched three Shorts and three Sopwiths against the bridge over the Jeihan, dropping a total of seven 65lb bombs (of which two hit) and eight 16lb bombs (of which two hit). They were not heavy enough to destroy the bridge, although sufficient damage was done to delay shipments of heavy guns to the war fronts in Palestine and Mesopotamia.

51   *Anne* displaced 7000 tons (367ft LBP x 47.5ft) and was rated at 10 knots. She served initially as a merchant ship and was commissioned on 4 August 1915, decommissioned on 8 August 1917, later becoming a store carrier and then a collier. *Raven II* was rated at 4678 tons (gross – displacement not known; 390.5ft LBP x 51.5ft) and 10 knots. She was commissioned on 12 June 1915, and renamed *Ravenrock* in 1917, later serving as a store ship, collier, and troop ship. These details are from F J Dittmar and J J Colledge, *British Warships 1914-1919* (Ian Allan, London, 1972). *Anne* was classified as a Fleet Auxiliary; she carried two French Navy Nieuport floatplanes until 1916, after which she was equipped with RNAS aircraft. She operated in the eastern Mediterranean and the Red Sea. *Raven II* also initially carried two French Navy aircraft, being commissioned for the RNAS in 1916. She then carried Short 184s and Sopwith Schneiders. Details of the careers of the two ships are given by K Macpherson, 'Turncoat Carriers', in *Warship International* autumn 1968, pp285-294.

52   4019 gross tons; launched 1882. She was purchased on 28 October 1914, and commissioned on 17 July 1915 as a kite-balloon ship. She was converted in 1917, after the Grand Fleet kite balloons were shifted to combatant ships, and served until 20 November 1918. She was sold in 1920.

PEGASUS (ex-ARK ROYAL)
Gr. Britain - CVS
(June 1942)

The carriers were valuable as the only mobile air force in the area. Thus, early in February HMS *Ben-my-Chree* was sent to the North African coast to reconnoitre Barrani and Sollum in advance of an attack by the Western (Egyptian) Frontier Force from Matruh against Senussi tribesmen. In March, Aden was attacked by a Turkish force which had advanced from Yemen, and which threatened to combine with the local tribes. Because *Ben-my-Chree* was refitting in Port Said, she transferred one Short and five Sopwith Cup floatplanes to *Raven II*. The latter had to stop at Perim Island to assemble her aircraft, which were then stowed on deck, ready to fly. She arrived at Aden on 30 March, and her air attacks helped discourage the tribesmen, without whose aid the Turkish force could not operate. *Ben-my-Chree* later operated off Yemen, and also helped assist the Sherif of Mecca, the ancestor of the current Saudi royal house, in his successful revolt. *Anne* also operated in the Red Sea in support of the Sherif.

From March until May 1917 *Raven II* (chosen because she was slightly faster than *Anne*) searched the Indian Ocean for the German raider *Wolf*, carrying several new Short floatplanes (with 240hp engines) and one Sopwith Baby. Supported by the French cruiser *Pothuau*, she could search over a radius of about 50nm. The carrier also covered a convoy from Bombay to the Red Sea, in company with the cruiser *Brisbane* and the old battleship *Exmouth*, and on the way back to Port Said reconnoitred Turkish positions near Aden. This unsuccessful operation foreshadowed British interwar interest in anti-raider (trade-protection) aircraft.

During 1917–18 the three East Indies carriers helped support General Allenby's successful offensive in Palestine.

Wing Captain F R Scarlett took command of RNAS units in the Eastern Mediterranean in February 1916. With German U-boats active in the area, *Ark Royal* could not operate effectively at sea; she became depot ship at Mudros, her aircraft detached. Scarlett asked that his two kite-balloon ships be replaced by seaplane carriers, one to work on the army's right flank at Salonika, and the other on the coast of Asia Minor (Mersina, Adana, Alexandretta and Beirut). The second role continued, however, to be under the control of Vice Admiral East Indies.

Empress was detached to the Eastern Mediterranean in April 1916. She helped bomb enemy communications in Bulgaria and spotted for several naval bombardments; she also helped pro-

vide a naval presence which ultimately convinced the Greek government to come over to the Allies. After the loss of HMS *Ben-my-Chree*, *Empress* was refitted at Genoa and then transferred to replace her, in April 1917. She was briefly transferred back to the Aegean, arriving on 24 January 1918. The battle-cruiser *Goeben* had sortied on 20 January, had been caught in a minefield, and had then stranded in the Dardanelles. By this time the land-based DH4 pilots at Mudros and Imbros had already made numerous attacks (though with little success), and they were exhausted. The carrier *Manxman* steamed out from Brindisi, carrying two Short 320 torpedo-bombers, which could lift heavy (18in) weapons. They took too long to prepare, and when they were finally ready (26 January) the sea was too rough for them to take off. That day the *Goeben* managed to get away to Constantinople.[54]

Finally, an ASW seaplane carrier was improvised for the southern Aegean. A small land seaplane base was set up at Suda Bay (Crete) in February 1917, and in April the Vice Admiral East Mediterranean reported that with four or five more stations (Syra, Kos, Skyros) he could effectively patrol his area. He needed one or two carriers to support the stations, but none was available. He therefore fitted the sloop HMS *Peony* to carry three seaplanes. She was used to search the Aegean for suspected secret U-boat bases, and then for routine ASW patrol and reconnaissance.

Of the remaining obsolete North Sea carriers, in September 1917, *Engadine* was still attached to the Grand Fleet, *Riviera* was attached to the Dover Force, and *Vindex* was attached to the Harwich Force (5th Light Cruiser Squadron). *Engadine* was briefly attached to the North Coast of Ireland Force, but by March 1918 she was in the Mediterranean, supporting ASW patrols. By May, she had been joined by HMS *Riviera*, and by June 1918 four carriers were assigned to the Mediterranean Fleet at Malta: *Engadine*, *Manxman*, *Riviera*, and *Vindex*. By this time HMS *Empress* was at Gibraltar.

ANOTHER WARTIME CARRIER EXPEDIENT also deserves a brief mention here. In 1915, with Zeppelins raiding Britain, the Senior Naval Officer at Lowestoft asked for a shallow draft carrier, to launch fighters against them from an offshore position. This led to a DAS proposal that each of the new *Ascot* class paddle minesweepers be equipped with two fighter floatplanes. Demountable stub masts and derricks were designed and built, and two Sopwith Babys were carried amidships, just abaft the paddle wheels. Each sweeper was designed to keep the sea for about a week, and the two fighters would have been positioned about 60 miles to seaward. However, the air defence mission conflicted with sweeping operations, and the project was abandoned. None of the twenty-four original *Ascots* seems to have carried aircraft, but each of two of the ex-civilian paddlers on which they were based, HMS *Brocklesby* and HMS *Killingholme*, appear to have carried two or three.

In the summer of 1918 Samson, who was now commander of the seaplane base at Yarmouth, suggested that the Royal Navy convert several lighters, which had originally been designed to launch large seaplanes, to carry Camel fighters. A destroyer could tow the lighter fast enough (about 30 knots) to enable the aircraft to fly off, and it could then be used to attack Zeppelins or German seaplanes. These lighters were used to escort motor torpedo boats, which otherwise would have been quite vulnerable to German air attack. It is not clear how many lighters were converted for this purpose. The first successful take-off was on 31 July 1918, and the first victory (and the last Zeppelin to be shot down during the war) was on 10 August; in both cases Lieutenant S D Culley was the pilot.

53 *Ben-my-Chree* provided a particularly graphic demonstration of the dangers of carrier operation. She had to be abandoned when the fires aboard went out of control, and she continued to burn (until 13 January) even after coming to rest on the bottom, and her bombs continued to explode. She was raised in 1921, re-entering merchant service the following year. The post-loss court martial emphasized the fire danger from apparently (but not entirely) empty tins of petrol, and from wood decks soaked in oil and petrol, and as a result special fire precautions were taken in the *Argus* design. D K Brown, 'The Development of the Aircraft Carrier Prior to World War II,' in *Interdisciplinary Science Reviews*, Vol 8, No 4 (December 1983), p359.

54 At this time there were no other modern torpedo-bombers in the eastern Mediterranean. *Ark Royal* rigged a 14in torpedo to one of her old Shorts, but it could not take off when so loaded. She did succeed in rigging them to carry 300lb depth charges equivalent to 18in torpedo warheads, but the only one used was dropped by a Farman landplane (on 27 January), and then unsuccessfully.

3

The Grand Fleet Carrier Force

THE AIR NEEDS of the Grand Fleet were very different from those of the Harwich Force. The fleet was above all a means of blocking, by surface battle, any German attempt to reach the open seas in force. Its main striking arm, then, was its heavy-calibre gunnery, supplemented by torpedoes aboard destroyers, cruisers, and capital ships. There was not, until 1917–18, any expectation that relatively unwieldy torpedo-bombers could hit high-speed warships at sea. However, it was immediately obvious that enemy aircraft, such as Zeppelins, could detect and track the fleet and thus spoil its chances for successful action. The fleet commander, Admiral Jellicoe, was also painfully aware of the possibility that the inferior German surface fleet might lead him into an underwater trap of U-boats and quickly-laid minefields. Only fleet aircraft had much of a chance of detecting such threats in time for the fleet to veer away.

The threat of enemy reconnaissance was evident almost at the outbreak of war, when the Grand Fleet reported that it had been observed by a Zeppelin and by two aeroplanes. Sueter took this opportunity to suggest that the Grand Fleet be accompanied by an aircraft carrier, which could accommodate eight to twelve seaplanes, which might prevent the enemy from shadowing it. Admiral Jellicoe was enthusiastic. He wanted a ship capable of at least 18 knots, preferably 20 or more. Sueter argued strongly for 20 knots, and asked for a ship with hatches large enough to take a folded aircraft (35 x 15 x 15ftt).

Such ships were quite valuable; most of them had already been earmarked for service as armed merchant cruisers. SCW (who was responsible for wartime conversions) argued that a fast ship would be expensive to convert, and probably would not carry more than six seaplanes. Existing fast liners, moreover, had relatively small hatches, and the depth between decks was quite limited (often 10 to 12ft). Conversion, then, would entail enlarging hatches and quite possibly removing decks, with all the structural problems this would cause. The alternative was to remove the roofs of some of the large saloons, using derricks to lift aircraft from them. This would certainly prove quite expensive.

The War Staff strongly preferred a slower ship (which would, therefore, have been unable to accompany the 18- to 20-knot Grand Fleet). For example, five fast freighters of the *El Paraguayo* class (British Argentine Steam Navigation Co)

could attain 15 knots. They were 440ft long, 8500 gross tons, and had five large hatches (each 27 x 16ft) with sufficiently large holds (50 to 68ft long and 11 to 15ft deep). Sueter would later argue that they, too, would have been expensive to convert, because in their case accommodation for a much-enlarged ships' company would have been needed.

The German ships seized as prizes at the outbreak of war were too slow, as were the ships detained at that time. Two potential candidates, the auxiliary cruisers *Orsova* and *Royal Edward*, were available, but their hatches were too small.[1] This left one excellent candidate, the elderly (1893) but fast (former Blue Ribband holder) Cunard liner *Campania*. Under a 1902 agreement, the Admiralty could buy or lease her as a wartime cruiser, but she had been rejected because of her limited endurance, about 2600nm at 20 knots. She was very nearly worn out, but was run briefly between Liverpool and New York during the autumn of 1914. Under the 1902 agreement, the Admiralty expected to pay £180,000 for her (her 1902 valuation, £356,000, less 6 per cent annual depreciation). However, while the Admiralty secretly deliberated, Cunard decided to dispose of the worn-out liner. Once the decision had been taken to acquire her, she was eventually bought from the breakers, T W Ward, for £32,500, on 27 November 1914.

Sueter's original plan was to cut large hatches in her boat and promenade decks and to remove the upper deck over her First Class Dining Room (except for the side stringers, which might have to be reinforced), to accommodate six to eight floatplanes. In addition, he hoped to accommodate two to three aircraft at each end on the second deck below the weather deck, in enlarged holds. These were very considerable alterations; if the ship were chartered, they would have to be made good at the end of the war. Sueter therefore proposed to buy her. This became much easier after Cunard gave her up for scrap.

The original plan was modified, probably after the failure of the floatplane raid on Cuxhaven on 25 October, to include a 120ft flying-off deck forward, its inboard end dismountable so that aircraft assembled on the foredeck could be hoisted up onto it. Two derricks on either side of the ship (two before the bridge, and two just abaft the first funnel) could hoist seaplanes in and out of the water and in and out of the two seaplane holds, one in the superstructure (for seven large floatplanes) and one forward, under the flight deck (for four small floatplanes, suita-

1   In all, fifteen ships were examined. The five fastest were *Royal Edward* and *Royal George* (20 knots, 11,117 gross tons, their largest hatches 12ft 6in × 14ft); *Calgarian* (armed merchant cruiser, 19 knots, 17,521 gross tons, 18 × 14ft); *Himalaya* (armed merchant cruiser, 18 knots, 6929 gross tons, 13 × 12ft); and *Adriatic* (wheat ship, 18 knots, 24,541 gross tons, 19 × 16ft). The fastest ships in British service, *Aquitania*, *Mauretania*, and *Lusitania*, were all considered much too large and hence much too valuable for carrier conversion. *Aquitania* would be considered again for conversion during World War II.

HMS Campania *emerges from the Cammell Laird yard with her flight deck lengthened and sloped downward, 5 April 1916.* FAAM

ble for deck-launching). The original foremast was removed and one of the midships kingposts replaced it. *Campania* was credited with a capacity for ten or eleven aircraft, including one or two large ones, 50 x 30 (folded) x 16ft. In line with Sueter's interest in torpedo warfare, she was fitted to carry eight 14in torpedoes for her aircraft, as well as her cruiser battery of eight 4.7in QF guns (of an old type) and one 3in AA gun.

Refitted by Cammell Laird, HMS *Campania* commissioned on 17 April 1915. Like the contemporary *Ben-my-Chree*, she was fitted with a flying-off deck, in this case a rather longer 160ft one, inclined very slightly downwards.[2] On 6 August 1915 this deck was used for the first time, a single-seat Sopwith Schneider Cup scout taking off after a 113ft run with 30 knots of wind over the deck (17 from the ship, 13 from the prevailing wind). The scout was the lightest and highest-powered aircraft then in regular naval service; since it required most of the deck, heavier reconnaissance aircraft could clearly not be deck-launched.

Campania was intended both to provide the Grand Fleet with reconnaissance (which required two-seaters) and to deny the Germans reconnaissance by Zeppelin (which required lightly-loaded high-powered single-seaters like the Schneider Cup seaplane). Experience up to October 1915 had shown that the alternative, launching floatplanes from the North Sea, was too unreliable. By this time HMS *Campania* had exercised with the fleet on seven occasions, but had flown her seaplanes only on three; even then she had experienced radio and engine problems. The primary problem was taking off from the open sea. This might be possible using larger seaplanes, but the ship could not carry them. The exercises did demonstrate the problem of recovery; the ship's captain remarked that in combat h would have to keep launching continuously in order to keep enough machines continuously airborne; he would be unable to stop to recover returning seaplanes.

The ship's officers suggested that the launching ramp be lengthened and inclined, so that the acceleration of gravity could be added to that due to the aircraft's engine. However, any longer flying-off deck would block the deck area used to assemble aircraft, so that part of the launch deck would have to be removed each time an aircraft had to be prepared. It was suggested that the fore funnel be split so that a much longer and more steeply inclined (3-degree) flight deck could be fitted. This deck could then communicate directly with hangars atop the liner's superstructure. In addition, a large hangar right aft could house seaplanes, which could be hoisted out onto a clear space between the hangar and the after funnel. The navigating bridge was to be relocated onto a light structure between the two funnels.

As might have been expected, this rather drastic proposal

invited alternatives. At the end of October, Captain Schwann suggested that, if the bridge were moved right back against the fore funnel, a 161ft deck, sloped at 5 degrees, might be fitted. DNC preferred this alternative, because it involved less scarce shipyard labour. However, DAS wanted the longer deck because it was essential that all aircraft, not merely the small fighters, be usable in rough weather. The ship emerged, then, with a 245ft flight deck, and with her two hangars on the upper deck abaft the bridge. The inclined deck included a canvas-shielded area in which aircraft could unfold their wings while protected from the wind. The two forward kingposts were cut down, and later enlarged and shifted aft.

Meanwhile, the success of the kite-balloon experiments aboard HMS *Engadine* (see chapter 2) led, in November 1915, to a decision to fit *Campania* for a balloon as well, the balloon and its fittings replacing the projected large seaplane hangar right aft. Although it did not offer anything like the visual range afforded by an aeroplane, the kite balloon did have the virtue of providing continuous observation. To clear space for the balloons and their associated plant, two of the original eight 4.7in guns (right aft) were landed, and the former mainmast, abaft the second funnel, removed. In its place, the remaining midships kingpost was substantially raised to become a mainmast.

This refit was expensive, and there seems to have been some inclination within the Admiralty for dropping the project altogether. Admiral Jellicoe, however, considered carrier aircraft potentially far too valuable to abandon. He could not afford to rely on land-based aircraft, which had only a limited range and probably could not keep station with his fleet; and the British airship programme was not successful enough to promise any real alternative. Unfortunately, since there was no other available large fast merchant ship, Jellicoe had to operate without a carrier during *Campania's* reconstruction at Cammell Laird, which lasted approximately from November 1915 until early April 1916.

Campania emerged carrying seven large (two-seat) Short 184 floatplanes, and three or four fighters, in hangars rather than in the earlier, inconvenient, holds. She successfully launched a Short (running on a wheeled trolley) from her flying-off deck on 3 June, proving that the problem of rough-sea take-offs had been solved.[3] This success in turn led to an Admiralty order for the first of all specialized aircraft for carrier use, which became the Fairey Campania. The prototype flew on 16 February 1917, and the first joined the ship in the autumn of 1917. Unlike the Short 184, these were pure reconnaissance aircraft, their twin floats connected by struts (hence not suitable for torpedo-carrying). *Campania* continued in service throughout the war, serving in several other small carriers. At the time of her loss in 1918, *Campania* had four on board, together with seven Ship Strutter (navalized Sopwith 1½-Strutter) land planes.

Now that the ship could launch all her aircraft while under way, she could sustain the required number of aircraft aloft without stopping to launch. She still, of course, had to slow or stop to recover them, but she had enough on board to keep launching throughout an engagement.

ON 31 MARCH Jellicoe asked that *Engadine* be attached to the Grand Fleet to supplement *Campania*, primarily to negate enemy aerial reconnaissance by Zeppelins which might otherwise allow the Germans to mine the path of the Grand Fleet. The Admiralty was reluctant, but consented on 10 April, preferring the shorter-range *Engadine* to the longer-range, but slower, *Vindex*, with her short (fighter) flying-off deck.

Jellicoe was not happy with this situation, particularly since

2   This deck is usually described as 120ft long. However, in his report on the successful deck launching, which is reproduced in Roskill, Captain Schwann describes the aircraft as having its wheels 152ft from the bow. It became airborne 39ft from the bow, or 32ft from the point at which the deck became so narrow that its wheels would have gone off the edge. It seems likely that the difference is accounted for by a demountable portion of the deck, over the forward seaplane hatch and assembly area.

3   A contemporary report shows that the shortest run was 66ft, in an 8-knot wind with the ship running at 19.5 knots, and with the aircraft lightly loaded. With the ship at rest (but in a 10-knot wind), a fully-loaded Short 184 became airborne in 150ft.

Bottom: *HMS* Campania *as fitted, April 1916.* Roger Nailer

Key
1 Flying-off deck
2 Fore peak
3 Firemen's mess
4 Trimmer's mess
5 Provisions
6 Cable locker
7 Ammunition working space
8 Air Mechanics' mess
9 Meat locker
10 4.7in Magazine and shell room
11 4.7in Gun
12 Forward seaplane hanger
13 Seamen's mess
14 Reserve coal
15 Coal bunker
16 POs mess (at sides)
17 Firemen and greasers
18 Boiler room
19 Seaplane hangar
20 Seaplane workshop
21 Marines' mess
22 Domestics
23 CPOs
24 Officers
25 Stores
26 Engine room
27 Warrant officers' mess
28 Drinking water
29 Nurse balloon house
30 Silicol engine
31 Kite balloon tent (canvas)
32 Kite balloon hold
33 Wardroom
34 Petrol store
35 Kite balloon store
36 Steering compartment
37 Bomb room
38 Spirit Room
39 3in HA gun
40 Range finder
41 Capstan
42 Wind screen stowage
43 Stump mast
44 Derrick
45 Trunked hatch 40ft = 25ft to hangar
46 26ft lifeboat
47 Whaler
48 Wheel house
49 Light tower
50 Chart house
51 30ft life cutter
52 Funnel
53 Searchlight
54 Seaplane derrick
55 Hatch 45ft = 30ft to hangar
56 16ft dinghy
57 35ft motor launch
58 Fan
59 20ft motor launch
60 30ft derrick
61 Vent to galley
62 30ft lifeboat
63 Two life rafts
64 Carley float
65 Engine room skylight
66 Engine room skylight
67 Searchlight platform
68 Seawater tank
69 Fresh water tank
70 Canteen
71 Brazing shop
72 Refrigerating plant
73 Crew's galley
74 Funnel hatch
75 Silicol store
76 Officers' galley
77 W/T office
78 Kite balloon winch
79 Kite balloon workroom
80 Silicol plant

Above and below: Campania *as originally converted, with a 165ft flight deck.* FAAM, drawing CPL.

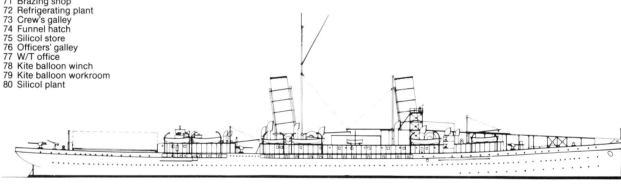

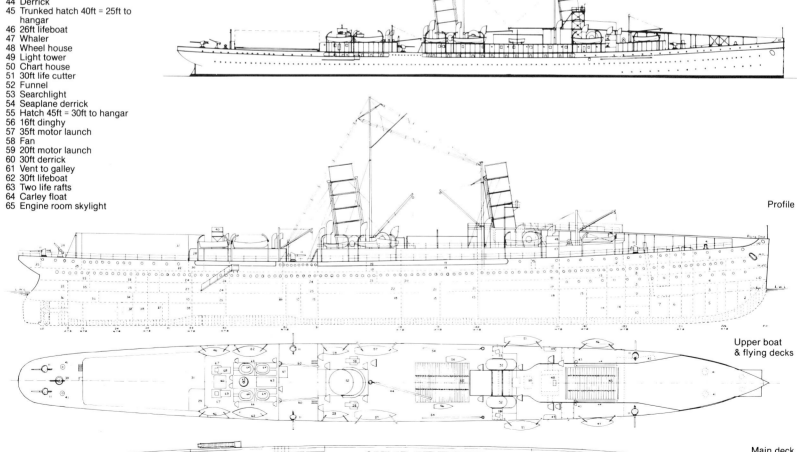

Profile

Upper boat & flying decks

Main deck

Campania in her final World War I configuration. FAAM

Campania was not yet operational. Moreover, given her age and her limited provision of watertight bulkheads, she was potentially extremely vulnerable to submarine attack (though in the end she succumbed to collision during a gale at Scapa Flow, on 5 November 1918). In April 1916, then, Jellicoe and DAS requested another conversion. This time there were three candidates, the fast liner *Wahine*, and the large *Empress of Asia* and *Empress of Russia*.[4] None could be spared. *Wahine* had been earmarked as a minelayer, but was pressed into service in the Mediterranean to carry vital mail and passengers, her high speed protecting her against an increased danger of U-boat attack; she did later serve as a minelayer. The two large *Empress*es had served as armed merchant cruisers in 1914–15, but they were then returned to civilian service, being reconditioned at Admiralty expense. The Admiralty shrank from the expense of reconverting them (twice: once into carriers and then back again into liners after the war) and from the labour which would have to be expended to dismantle much of their upperworks. It was not so much that a reactionary Admiralty disdained to spend valuable labour and money on the weapon of the future, as that there were so many other, quite mundane, drains on a badly stretched British shipbuilding and ship repairing industry. Moreover, by April 1916 aircraft had hardly proven their value at sea.

	Hogging	Sagging
Courageous	6.8/8.6	8.6/8.1
Furious as designed	6.6/9.0	8.0/8.3
Furious as carrier	6.1/8.3	7.1/7.4
Birmingham	4.6/5.65	5.25/5.65
Lion	5.14/7.02	3.42/3.80
M class destroyer	6.25/7.71	5.73/5.47

Jellicoe was certainly a believer; early in May he tried unsuccessfully to revive the Biles-Holmes carrier design (see Chapter 4). It appears, however, that the experience at Jutland (31 May 1916) was decisive. Not only did HMS *Engadine* succeed in launching a Short 184 (which actually observed some of the enemy's dispositions), but conventional surface reconnaissance failed signally to carry out its mission. Even though the carrier failed to transmit her aircraft's message to him, Jellicoe seems to have been deeply impressed. On 22 June, therefore, he asked the Admiralty to provide him with two 20-knot carriers capable of deck-launching all their aircraft, including the heavy Shorts.[5] In July, he asked that HMS *Manxman* be assigned to the Grand Fleet upon completion.

At this time two other proposals were under consideration. Two 'large light cruisers,' HMS *Courageous* and *Glorious*, were nearing completion. They were survivals of Admiral Fisher's early-war Baltic Project, each carrying four 15in guns (in two twin turrets) and having a relatively shallow draft. Neither had any obvious role within the Grand Fleet, and each might therefore be a candidate for some aviation modification carrying a penalty in terms of gun firepower.[6] Their half-sister, HMS *Furious* (two 18in guns) would be completed the following year. From a design point of view, all three were unsatisfactory, their shallow hulls badly stressed by overweight which had accumulated during construction.[7]

On 22 June 1916 the Controller wrote that as the use of seaplanes from battlecruisers had proven practicable, DNC should also investigate installing them aboard large light cruisers as a matter of urgency.[8]

In early July 1916 the proposal was to cut away the existing shelter deck forward, eliminating the CPO and PO reading rooms, and raising the forward 4in guns. Seaplanes would be stowed under the new raised forward shelter deck, behind blast-proof doors, taking off from portable 60 x 12ft platforms on either side of the forecastle deck, abaft the breakwater. These would be raised when required. Stowage would be arranged for 300 gallons of petrol, in the standard 2-gallon tins. DAS proposed an alternative, a single flying-off platform. Both ships would have carried only single-seaters.[9]

Although this represented only a moderate change to the overall design, it entailed an unacceptable delay (estimated as five weeks by DNC, 12 July) to the completion of HMS *Courageous* and *Glorious*. *Furious* was not nearly so far advanced, so she was to be fitted to carry the two floatplanes.

There was also still the Biles-Holmes cruiser (see Chapter 4), one of which Jellicoe had requested before Jutland. DAS had called for the construction of three.

DNC considered it impractical to build new ships from the keel up, particularly since the official view was that the war would not last beyond the end of 1917.[10] Nor would the Controller agree (see above) to cut down any of the few existing fast liners. This left hulls under construction, and particularly two liners which had been building for Italy, but suspended at the outbreak of the war, Beardmore's *Conte Rosso* and Swan Hunter's Hull 967 (which was to have become the *Giulio Cesare*). Swan Hunter's hull was further advanced, but Beardmore's machinery was much more nearly complete. Machinery was, moreover, the controlling bottleneck. Both ships were marginally slower than the Grand Fleet battleships, and both DAS and DNC suggested that boiler power be added, to enable the converted liner to make about 21.75 knots.

On 16 September 1916, therefore, the Admiralty Board approved conversion of the *Conte Rosso*, but rejected conversion of Swan Hunter's 967. Beardmore promised to complete its ship, which became HMS *Argus*, the first true aircraft carrier, by late 1917 (she appeared about a year late). Details of this

4 *Wahine* was built by Denny for the Union Steamship Co of New Zealand (4740 tons, 4436 gross tons, 374 × 52 × 17ft 6in); launched on 21 November 1912, she made 21.23 knots on trial (3804shp at 4128 tons). The two *Empress*es were built by Fairfield for the Canadian Pacific Co (16,810 and 16,909 gross tons; 592 × 68.2ft); launched 28 August 1912 (*Empress of Russia*) and 23 November 1912 (*Empress of Asia*), they made, respectively, 21.2 and 21.4 knots (27,000shp). A DAS conversion proposal for *Wahine* envisaged a continuous fore and aft hangar (four Short 184s and eight Babys) and a 100ft flight deck, with a speed (as converted) of 25 knots. These data were included in a July or August 1916 table of carriers (including Hull 967 – not *Argus* – and the Biles-Holmes project), and it is not clear just how much design work it represented.

5 Jellicoe to Admiralty, 22 June 1916, AIR 1/2583 as quoted by Pulsipher, p229.

6 Four guns made for two-gun salvoes, the control of which would be difficult at best. Fisher seems to have conceived them as fast fire-support ships, to assist in a landing on the German Baltic coast, rather than as conventional combatant ships. In battle they fared poorly against German light cruisers, as their salvoes were not dense enough to hit rapidly-manoeuvring targets.

7 A contemporary table shows stresses in standard 20ft waves. In each case, figures are for keel/upper deck, in tons per square inch:

8 There is, however, no record of any flight from a battlecruiser at this time. The Controller may have been referring to the successful deck take-off from *Campania*.

9 They would have been either Sopwith Babys or the similar experimental P.V.2, a Port Victoria (that is, RNAS) design, which was slower (74 rather than 85 knots at sea level) but could take off at a lower speed (40 rather than 52 knots), and therefore presumably in a shorter distance. The P.V.2 also had a greater endurance, four rather than three hours. The P.V.2 had been designed specifically as a Zeppelin-killer, to carry a 1½ or 2-pdr Davis (non-recoil) gun, but it was decided that such guns would be carried only by airships. It was, therefore, redesigned to carry twin Lewis guns atop the centre section. The P.V.2 had been derived from the P.V.1, a Baby with a new high-lift wing.

10 This proposal did not pass unopposed. A J Balfour, the First Lord, argued that at £750,000 the ship would cost as much as (and hence would displace) four destroyers or two light cruisers. Moreover, given the rapid development of aviation, she would probably be obsolete when completed. He suggested that large shore-based flying-boats would be more effective. DAS countered that only aircraft operating with the fleet could be relied upon to be present when needed, an argument that is still valid, and Balfour withdrew his objection.

The Fairey Campania was the first aircraft designed specifically for carrier operation; its name came from its intended base, HMS Campania. *This F.17 was powered by a 275hp Rolls-Royce Eagle V; the bombs are probably 112lb types.*

conversion, which included a 200ft flying-off deck and space for fourteen Short 184s, are given in the next chapter.[11]

DAS wanted something much more quickly, and Holmes (who was naval construction advisor to DAS; see Chapter 4) proposed, as an interim step, that two 22- to 23-knot County class armoured cruisers due for large refits, HMS *Suffolk* and HMS *Cumberland*, be rebuilt. Flying-off decks 140ft long could be erected on their bows. This was less than the 200ft planned for the *Conte Rosso*, and the ships would not have had flying-on decks, but they would have been available much more quickly. The scheme was rejected; the Admiralty refused to convert existing cruisers. About this time, too, DAS proposed mounting short flying-off platforms aboard existing light cruisers, as a 'gamble.' Early the next year F J Rutland would prove the practicality of this scheme by flying off a very short platform aboard HMS *Manxman*, and DAS's idea would then be implemented.

For the moment, however, the Admiralty tentatively approved a proposal that the large cruiser *Furious*, then under construction, be fitted with a temporary take-off platform forward and a small hangar for two seaplanes. She would retain her forward 18in gun. Before *Furious* could be completed, however, a much more radical modification was approved.

At the end of 1916 Admiral David Beatty, who had commanded the battlecruisers at Jutland, and who was therefore acutely aware of the need for reconnaissance, took over command of the Grand Fleet. Beatty believed that the Germans were pressing the development of their own aircraft, and in February 1917 he credited the High Seas Fleet with six seaplane carriers (it actually had none). Of his three seaplane carriers, only *Campania* was anything like satisfactory. The new *Manxman* was far too slow, and *Engadine* was useless except in the calmest of weather. *Argus* was still expected to be ready in November 1917; she would embark eight reconnaissance aircraft, six anti-Zeppelin fighters and four torpedo-bombers. Most important of all, experiments with arrester gear, which

were still proceeding, promised that the air reconnaissance problem could be solved by deck-launched (and recoverable) aircraft.

On 26 January Beatty convened an Aircraft Committee headed by Rear Admiral Hugh Evan-Thomas, who had commanded the 5th Battle Squadron at Jutland.

The Committee reported early in February 1917. It considered the anti-Zeppelin mission the first priority for shipborne aircraft. The existing Sopwith Baby floatplane was suitable, but its performance was limited. The two ships with flying-off platforms (*Campania* and *Manxman*) could launch the wheeled Sopwith Pup instead, to achieve much higher performance. This had already been done in HMS *Manxman*, on the recommendation of Flight Commander F J Rutland (who had flown the reconnaissance mission at Jutland). He argued that only a Pup could reach a high-flying Zeppelin and, moreover, that by adopting a standard Western Front fighter, the fleet would be able to draw on large existing stocks. This latter argument later justified a policy of adapting standard Western Front (later, RAF) fighters to naval use.

Since the wheeled fighters would often be able to fly when the heavier two-seat floatplanes could not, the Committee recommended that they be fitted with lightweight radio transmitters, with a range of about five miles, so that pilots could pass vital information to the scouting cruisers. These fighters would have to be sacrificed after their flights, as the fleet had no means of recovering them and their range was limited.

The Committee estimated that the fleet required about twenty anti-Zeppelin fighters, based on the assumption that the enemy fleet would be supported by six Zeppelins, each of which would be attacked by two fleet fighters. On the basis of sea experience, Captain Schwann estimated that two of every five flights would fail,[12] hence twelve successful flights would require twenty ready aircraft. Against this requirement, the fleet had only sixteen fighters: six aboard *Campania*, four aboard *Manxman*, two expected aboard *Furious*, and four (which had to be hoisted out) aboard *Engadine*. The Committee suggested that the fighter deficiency be solved by carrying Pups aboard selected light cruisers and other vessels.

The other major fleet aircraft role was close reconnaissance immediately before and during an engagement. The Committee estimated that the fleet required about twelve successful recon-

11 The DNC recommendation may have predated Jutland. DAS argued strongly for the prospective advantages of deck landing, citing experimental work in progress. He favoured the Swan Hunter hull because it was longer and probably better subdivided. At the end of June 1916 a comparison showed:

Hull 967

Dimensions	605 × 76 × 22ft 6in
Displacement	19,000 tons
Power (hp)	22,000 = 20.5 knots
Endurance(nm)	2000/20.5 knots
Fuel	Can be oil
Subdivision	Floats with four compartments flooded
Flight Deck	200ft
Aircraft	12
Deadweight	6530 tons

Conte Rosso

Dimensions	535 × 68 × 26ft
Displacement	18,530 tons
Power (hp)	18,000 = 20.25 knots
Endurance (nm)	6500/15 knots
Fuel	Coal
Subdivision	'More than complies with any Convention requirements'
Flight Deck	?
Aircraft	10 Short 184
Deadweight	5000 tons

12 Based on one radio failure in twelve, one engine failure in the air (during a 4-hour flight) in five flights, and one failure to start in eight flights.

A Fairey Campania, the first aircraft designed specifically to be launched from a carrier deck, runs up its engine between the funnels of HMS Campania. *Note the 4-wheeled trolley under the floats.* FAAM

naissance flights (twenty ready aircraft) for this mission, to maintain two airborne throughout the approach phase, and one throughout the action following (these figures were later considerably increased). Of the four available carriers, only *Campania* could reliably deck-launch heavy reconnaissance aircraft. To help these take off, the Committee recommended that their torpedo fittings be removed, and that the existing 14in torpedoes be removed from the carriers. They were much too small to affect enemy capital ships; for the moment, the aircraft were far more useful for reconnaissance.

Because fleet aircraft could not reliably be recovered, they could provide neither long-range sustained fleet reconnaissance nor screening from enemy reconnaissance forces and U-boats while on passage. For the former, the Committee called for sustained coverage of the North Sea by shore-based flying boats. Blimps, which could keep station with the fleet, were already assigned to the latter duty by Grand Fleet Battle Orders dated 24 January 1917.

The three existing Grand Fleet carriers could provide only twelve two-seat reconnaissance aircraft, of which only those aboard *Campania* could be made available in most weather. Of the other two, *Manxman* was far too slow, good for a sea speed of only 16 knots (and only 14 when cleaning boilers). The Committee therefore considered some alternatives:

(a) Adaptations of County class armoured cruisers
(b) Adaptations of the *Leviathan* class armoured cruisers
(c) Reboilering and otherwise improving *Manxman*
(d) New seaplane carriers, such as, for example, conversion of the Dublin mail packet *Munster*

The two cruiser conversions seemed impractical, and (no matter how fast) *Manxman* could not launch reconnaissance aircraft. The new *Argus* would solve much of the problem, but she would not be ready until at least November (and the Committee probably doubted that date, given past performance in carrier construction).

The large light cruiser *Furious*, almost complete, was availa-

ble for conversion, and the Committee now proposed that her forward single 18in gun be replaced by a 228 x 50ft flying-off deck, and a hangar to accommodate ten reconnaissance aircraft and thus make up most of the deficiency. *Furious* was particularly attractive because of her very high speed, 31 knots, which would permit her to maintain her place in the fleet despite any turn into the wind to launch her aircraft. Beatty agreed reluctantly, arguing against any reduction in Grand Fleet cruiser strength in the face of reports of continued German construction. On the other hand, with only two 18in guns, *Furious* was of limited value as a cruiser, since she could not effectively bracket a target. Beatty seems to have considered her potentially far less valuable than her two half-sisters, *Courageous* and *Glorious*, which could fire four-gun salvoes. Others considered all three worthless, and proposals were later made to convert the two four-gun ships (which were already complete by this time).

Three possible conversions were proposed for *Furious*:

A. Replacement of A turret by a forward hangar (for six reconnaissance aircraft and four fighters) and flight deck. Anti-torpedo nets would be removed. This would actually mean a net reduction in displacement. According to the yard, this scheme would take about fourteen weeks to complete.
B. Construction of hangars fore and aft of A barbette (which would be retained, with its turret), to house three reconnaissance aircraft forward and two fighters aft. This would add 250 tons, largely because the hangars would need heavy bulkheads to withstand the blast of the forward turret (which could fire only on the beam). DNC considered this unsatisfactory, because it drastically reduced metacentric height while making for unacceptable hull stress (due to the added heavy weight at the bow of the long, shallow hull). The yard claimed that this scheme would take about eleven weeks to complete.
C. Beatty himself proposed that the ship have portable hangars on the forecastle, which would be removed when the turret was wanted, or after the aircraft had been launched.

DNC found Scheme A difficult to defend; it seemed a halfway solution. Either the battery was valuable, and worth retaining altogether, or it should be removed altogether. He also considered the forward flight deck clumsy in a fast cruiser. As an alternative, DNC suggested that floatplanes could be carried on the boat deck amidships, and launched from fast lighters which the ship could tow. At this time (mid-February 1917) four such lighters were already being built to be towed by destroyers.

However, the Board approved Scheme A on 19 March 1917, with the proviso that the forward end of the ship between hull and flight deck be plated in, to keep seas from entering between. Even so, the Board wanted the ship's prospective captain informed that she could not be driven at maximum speed in any but fairly fine weather without injuring the flight deck.

The steam-heated (and force-ventilated) hangar below the flight deck was designed to accommodate four reconnaissance two-seaters and four single-seat fighters.[13] Later this figure was increased to six two-seaters and four fighters. A merchant-ship-type hatch in its roof (with coaming) allowed them to be hoisted up by electric winch out onto the flight deck. This winch proved laborious and difficult in bad weather, which in turn inspired the ship's captain to call for installation of a lift. Aircraft were transported by rails and trolleys inside the hangar. The aircraft required eighteen (initially fourteen) more

13 The corresponding bomb was 72 × 100lb, 96 × 65lb, 72 × 16lb, all stowed in the former forward (18in) shellroom. With six two-seaters, the planned bomb load was 100 × 100lb, 50 × 65lb, 78 × 16lb.

officers and eighty (initially seventy) more ratings, but the elimination of A turret eliminated four officers and sixty-three men, for a net increase of only fourteen officers and seventeen men. Stowage was arranged for 8000 gallons of petrol, still in 2-gallon tins.

Minelaying rails, which had been ordered before the decision to convert, were still to be fitted. Moreover, DNO was asked to arrange for quick reinstallation of the forward 18in gun, should this prove necessary. *Furious* was conceived largely as a temporary expedient. Moreover, without one of her two heavy guns, she had little with which to oppose an enemy battlecruiser. The Admiralty approved a Grand Fleet proposal on 7 May to add four triple (fixed) above-water torpedo tubes.

These changes were expected to delay completion of the ship

Table 3-1: *Furious* as Completed, 1917

As inclined (July 1917)

	Deep	Legend	Light	Extra Light
Displacement (tons)	22,890	19,513	18,480	18,105
Draught (ft, in)	25 2	22 1	21 1½	20 9
GM(FS)	5.69	3.80	3.52	3.47

Weights as designed (tons)

	Estimate	Actual	Difference
Hull & Protection	11,814	12,706	892
Armour	698	646	–52
Equipment	870	924	54
Armament	1675	1811	136
Machinery	3030	2945	–85
Oil fuel	3250	3395	145
Coal	100	100	0
RFW & overflow	358	365	17
Total	21,795	22,890	1095

Additions

Flying-off deck, hangar	287.4
Upper deck TT	48.6
Stiffening	130
Added Protection to main deck	115
Flash protection	5
Supernumeraries	15
Paravanes and gear	12.2
SL structures, etc	8
Misc additions	12
Total additions	633.2

Deletions while building

A turret, etc	1117.5
Net defence	126
Total deletions	1243.5

Net Displacement (deep load)	21,794.7

Additions after completion

Flying-on deck with hangar	514
Forecastle deck extended aft	20
Platform between flying decks	60
Extension to flying-off deck fwd	21
Lifts	45
Bulkheads on shelter deck	36
Jib crane and winches	5
Admiral's bridge and shelter	4
Misc	50
Total additions	755

Deletions after completion

Y turret, etc	1335
Mainmast, derrick, etc	70
Y shell room machinery, piping, etc	23
Torpedo control tower	29
One 5.5in mounting, etc	15
One stump mast and derrick fwd	6
Total deletions	1514

Net reduction in displacement	759

Note The ship as completed was 1095 tons heavy, and her metacentric height 0.1ft less than estimated. The difference of 136 tons in armament was largely due to an over-heavy turret. The difference in hull weight was largely due to 441 tons of rivets (which had been undercounted, as a percentage of total hull weight, in the design), to 112 tons incidental to armament, 119 tons incidental to protection, 75 tons incidental to machinery, 67 tons incidental to oil fuel, 53 tons of splinter plating and side protection, 40 tons of framing, bulkheads and protection, 33 tons of structure behind and supports to conning tower and torpedo control tower and 30 tons of bridges. Many items came out light, reducing the difference from 970 to 892 tons.

by about a month, from the end of May to the end of June 1917. *Furious* actually commissioned in July, carrying three Short reconnaissance floatplanes and five Pups. By September, the proportion had been reversed to four two-seaters and three Pups, the two-seaters being recovered from the water alongside the seaplane carriers. The effect of the reconstruction was to save some weight, as shown in Table 3-1.

Meanwhile the national shipbuilding programme was reviewed, on the assumption that the war would last throughout 1918. The new Fifth Sea Lord, Commodore G M Paine, proposed an additional carrier programme, partly to expand his force, and partly to replace the recently lost *Ben-my-Chree*. He wanted one large ship (*Giulio Cesare*) and five small *Vindex* type seaplane carriers. For the small ships, he turned to Denny, which had several fast short-sea craft under construction.[14]

The Board again rejected the *Giulio Cesare*, and changed the DAS programme to two ocean and two North Sea carriers, general characteristics of which would be:

	Ocean Type	North Sea Type
Speed	24–25 knots	24–25 knots
Fuel	oil	oil
Aircraft (single/two-seat)	6/8	4/4
Flying-off	yes	yes
Landing-on	yes	no
Seaplane slip	yes	no
Endurance (days)	5	3

This programme was approved by the War Cabinet, for completion before the end of 1918.

The ocean type was actually the Holmes-Biles/DNC carrier, work on which had been under way for some time (see Chapter 4). Both were initially assigned to Cammell Laird, then split

A Short 184 takes off from HMS Furious, *leaving its 4-wheeled trolley (two wheels for each float) on deck. Note the enormous wingspan this relatively low-powered aircraft required to lift a 14in torpedo, a span which could only be accommodated because the wings could fold. At this time such folding required that the wings be precisely parallel, without any stagger. FAAM*

14 The four Denny ships were *Nairana*, which was actually converted, and *Curraghmore, Lorina,* and *Maid of Orleans,* of which *Lorina* and *Maid of Orleans* were ultimately completed as troopships. All were roughly comparable to HMS *Engadine,* to the point that with *Curraghmore* only slightly advanced the Admiralty asked whether she could be built instead as a repeat *Queen,* ie, much as an *Engadine.* DAS was particularly interested in *Maid of Orleans* because of her high designed speed, 22.75 knots. The ideal was 25 knots, and a length of 320 to 360ft, with an endurance of 72 hours at full speed. The fifth ship was John Brown's *Stockholm,* which had been considered for conversion in 1916.

The first trollies were jettisoned when aircraft took off, but later, like catapult bridles, they were caught and re-used. This example, aboard HMS Furious, *has been caught by two sprung arms extending up out of the flying-off deck; note also that it runs along a guide track set into the deck. This was one of several early schemes to prevent aircraft from swinging while taking off; others included special troughs for tail skids and the double trough aboard HMS* Vindex. *FAAM*

between that firm and Fairfield (14 February 1917). Both were cancelled (due to shipyard congestion) in April, one being ordered instead from Armstrong Whitworth, in July 1917. She became HMS *Hermes*, the first ship in the world to be be laid down as an aircraft carrier.

The Board approved the conversion of a cruiser, HMS *Cavendish*, in June 1917, presumably to replace one of the two ocean-going carriers which had just been cancelled. One of five *Raleighs* (building but with very low priority), she was intended to carry six reconnaissance aircraft. Because she was conceived in connection with the January 1917 programme, *Cavendish* was redesigned to incorporate both flying-off and flying-on decks, the two being separate in her case. The 106ft flying-off deck forward surmounted a small (78 × 49ft, 44ft wide at forward end) hangar, extending beyond it to provide a sufficient take-off run. Aircraft were hoisted by one of two cranes through a hangar roof hatch, as there was no lift. The after (flying-on) deck measured about 193 × 57ft, and on its port side it was connected to the flying-off deck by an 8ft gangway, along which aircraft could be wheeled. The hangar and flying-off deck replaced No 2 7.5in gun, and the flying-on deck replaced Nos 5 and 6, leaving the ship with four such guns. Similarly, the anti-aircraft battery was reduced from six to four.

The upper part of the cruiser's bulge was enlarged to improve her stability, so as to compensate for the considerable topweight added by reconstruction. Reconstruction should have reduced displacement, but the ship came out overweight at about 10,400 tons (legend).

The cruiser design preceded HMS *Furious* in having a short

flying-on deck, but the larger ship was fitted – and tested – first. The failure of HMS *Furious* showed that the cruiser design was impractical, and a modified (island-type) design was submitted to the Board in July 1918. However, by then the cruiser was almost complete, and no one really knew whether the island concept would work. Reconstruction was therefore put off pending the results of tests aboard HMS *Argus* a few months later (see Chapter 4), and it was abandoned entirely after the end of the war. HMS *Eagle* and HMS *Hermes* were ordered completed to new plans, which was practical because they were so much farther from completion.

Cavendish was renamed *Vindictive* in June 1918, to honour the old cruiser scuttled at Zeebrugge. On trials she made 29.12 knots on 63,000shp. When completed she carried about four Griffins (reconnaissance aircraft developed by the Experimental Construction Department at the Isle of Grain, seven of which were built) and a Sopwith Pup. She went to the Baltic carrying Griffins, Camels and 1½-Strutters.

Despite the *Furious* problem, at least one very successful landing was made a few months after she commissioned in October 1918. As a seaplane carrier, she later formed part of the British Baltic naval force, but grounded badly on 6 July 1919. She had to be partly dismantled (2200 tons were removed) to be refloated, and was placed in reserve, used for subsidiary duties in 1920–21, and then rebuilt again in 1923–25 to emerge as a cruiser. The hangar was retained as the only vestige of her carrier design. Because it provided her with substantial protected aircraft capacity, the ship was fitted with one of the earliest British cruiser/battleship catapults.

The North Sea type, too, was initially to have been a fresh design. Conversions of the two most advanced ships considered earlier, *Nairana* and *Stockholm*, were ordered to provide an interim capability. Although they were substantially slower than desired, they did have the requisite endurance, and DNC design capability was badly stretched. Moreover, it was already clear that experiments with arrester gear would soon succeed. Then seaplane carriers incapable of recovering their aircraft would be obsolete. The pure seaplane carrier (North Sea) design was never carried through; only the two interim conversions survived.

Nairana was being built under an Australian government subsidy for a coastal line, Huddart Parker Ltd. In taking her over, the British government had to agree to restore her after the war. She was, moreover, quite far advanced when taken over. The conversion design was therefore limited, to reduce the work which would be required postwar. By way of contrast, the British government bought *Stockholm* outright, renaming her HMS *Pegasus*. Since no postwar reconversion was contemplated, she could be more radically rearranged internally. At her builder's suggestion, she was converted for oil burning.[15]

Armament roughly matched that assigned to HMS *Manxman*, and plans originally called for four 12pdr single-purpose guns and two 6pdr anti-aircraft weapons. The ships were completed with four 12cwt guns, two as single-purpose guns on the forecastle, around the flying-off deck, and two as anti-aircraft guns aft. In *Nairana* the latter were at the after end of the hangar, in *Pegasus* one on the centreline of the upper deck (at the extreme after end) and one on a platform atop the hangar, on the foreside of the main mast. In each case, aircraft weapons included eight 18in torpedoes, plus 100lb, 65lb, and 16lb bombs.[16]

Both the new seaplane carriers had short flying-off decks forward (95ft long in *Nairana*), and both were fitted to recover floatplanes while steaming at 6 knots (they could slip their floatplanes into the water at 19 knots). HMS *Pegasus* carried nine aircraft (five fighters forward and four reconnaissance

15 The John Brown yard pointed out that, even though she might be rated at 9500shp, within 6 or 7 hours her average power would begin to fall, so that over 24 hours average power would be about 8000shp, and over 72 hours, 7000 to 7500. Thus a 21-knot trial speed might equate to no more than 19.5 over a full 72-hour run, even in good weather. On trial on the Skelmorlie mile, *Pegasus* made 20.84 knots (9618shp at 3027 tons).

16 Bomb loads: *Pegasus* (*Nairana* in parentheses) 72 (72) × 100lb, 108 (96) × 65lb, 64 and later 84 (48) × 16lb.

floatplanes aft); *Nairana* was limited to four fighters and four floatplanes.

Both ships had small hangars forward, under the bridge. Aircraft were wheeled out in front of the bridge structure and then raised up to the flight deck overhead by the first lifts in British naval service. The foremast was split to allow the hangar to pass through it. *Nairana* had a centreline gantry crane extending back over her stern, but *Pegasus* had two big swinging cranes at the after end of her hangar.

Nairana was commissioned with four Short 184 and four Beardmore WB III aircraft. In October 1918 she had five Fairey Campanias and two Sopwith Babys (which were replaced by Camel landplanes in time for operations in North Russia in 1919). *Pegasus* was commissioned with four Short 184s and five Beardmore WB IIIs, and in late 1918 had four Ship Camels, one Fairey 184 and three Fairey Campanias.

In January 1918 the Admiralty Operations Committee decided that HMS *Pegasus* should operate only fighters, with *Nairana* to follow suit if this proved successful. By that time both were clearly on the verge of obsolescence.

However, they were also both extremely important. By March 1918 the Grand Fleet could carry forty-three aircraft to sea (aboard nine battlecruisers, the two large light cruisers, and twenty-one light cruisers). As none of these ships could launch and recover floatplanes, none could be used to train pilots or to maintain their proficiency. ACA therefore had to defer any further conversion, arguing that for the present he lacked carriers to replace the reconnaissance capability of the aircraft aboard *Nairana* and *Pegasus*. Both therefore remained in service, in their original configurations, at the end of the war, and both were tentatively included in the postwar British fleet; early in 1919 it was decided that *Nairana* would be purchased outright. However, she was obsolete and money was spent instead on the new full-deck carriers; she was returned to her original owners in 1920. HMS *Pegasus* remained in British service, acting as aircraft (and CMB) mother ship for the 1919 operations in Archangel, northern Russia. She was sold in 1931 and HMS *Ark Royal* was renamed *Pegasus* in 1934 when a new *Ark Royal* (see Chapter 6) was ordered.

Thus, by the autumn of 1917, the Grand Fleet (including HMS *Furious*) had a total of twenty-four deck-launched fighters and nine deck-launched (and thus rough weather) reconnaissance floatplanes. Prospective additions were HMS *Argus* and the converted cruiser *Vindictive*.

Given the Aircraft Committee's recommendations, efforts began to provide the Grand Fleet cruisers with launching platforms for aircraft. A light Deperdussin monoplane had actually been flown from the cruiser *Aurora* (of the Harwich Force) on 5 November 1915, but the take-off run was considered too long to be useful, and the platform used fouled the forward 6in gun.[17] Moreover, the monoplane was of an obsolescent type, so that this experience seemed unlikely to lead to useful results. In January 1917, however, Flight Commander F J Rutland took a Sopwith Pup off HMS *Manxman* in 20ft, proving that existing

---

17   This experiment was part of the anti-Zeppelin campaign described in Chapter 2. The four Harwich ships of the *Arethusa* class, *Arethusa*, *Penelope*, *Aurora*, and *Undaunted*, were all fitted with flying-off ramps in May 1915. *Arethusa* successfully launched a Schneider Cup floatplane at a Zeppelin on 2 June 1915, but the pilot (who of course had no radio) mistook the smoke of the escorting destroyers for the recall signal (a smokescreen), and returned before he could attack. The ramps were removed in August 1915 from all but *Aurora*. For photographs, see A L Raven and J Roberts, *British Cruisers of the Second World War* (Arms & Armour Press, London, 1980), p30. As in contemporary installations, the flying-off ramp consisted of two parallel troughs (for the wheels), with a guide down the middle for the tail skid. Raven and Roberts also show a Sopwith Tabloid (the direct ancestor of the Baby) stowed between *Aurora's* after funnel and searchlight platform. In July 1916 DAS proposed that platforms be fitted to light cruisers 'as a gamble.'

Below: *HMS* Nairana *shows both her flying-off deck and the massive seaplane-recovery gantry aft. Aircraft carried in the hangar below her bridge could be lifted up through a hatch in the flying-off deck.*

Left, below left and right: *HMS* Pegasus *had hangars fore and aft. The postwar view, right, (21 March 1924) clearly shows the hangar doors under her bridge; by this time the forward flying-off deck had been removed, but its plated-up support forward remained. The aerial view clearly shows the seaplane-handling cranes aft. This arrangement matched that of other wartime designs, which were intended to handle both seaplanes (aft) and wheeled aircraft (forward), but which could not recover the latter. FAAM (below left)*

Key
1 Forward trimming tank
2 Chain locker
3 12pdr LA magazine
4 Spirit store
5 Petrol store
6 Provision store
7 Bosun's store
8 Carpenter's store
9 Mess deck
10 Wardroom
11 Cabins
12 12pdr LA gun
13 Flying-off deck
14 Portable platform support rails
15 Portable platform
16 Flying-off deck extension
17 Forward hangar
18 Twin-boom derrick
19 Wheel house
20 Chart house
21 Compass
22 Coding office
23 Aircraft W/T office
24 Range finder
25 Captain's cabin
26 Aerial spray screen
27 Oil fuel
28 Boiler room
29 Fan room
30 Engine room
31 Bomb store
32 12pdr HA magazine & shell room
33 Trimming tanks aft
34 After hangar
35 Engine room skylight
36 12pdr HA gun
37 Engine room exhaust & vent
38 Electric crane
39 RNAS carpenter's workshop
40 RNAS engineer's workshop
41 16ft dinghy
42 25ft whaler
43 25ft motor boat
44 35ft motor boat
45 Sliding shutters
46 Flush hatch to forward hangar
47 Paint store/general store
48 RNAS workshop
49 Sick bay and dispensary
50 Crane hoisting gear
51 RNAS office
52 Issue room

HMS Pegasus *as fitted, 1917.*
Roger Nailer

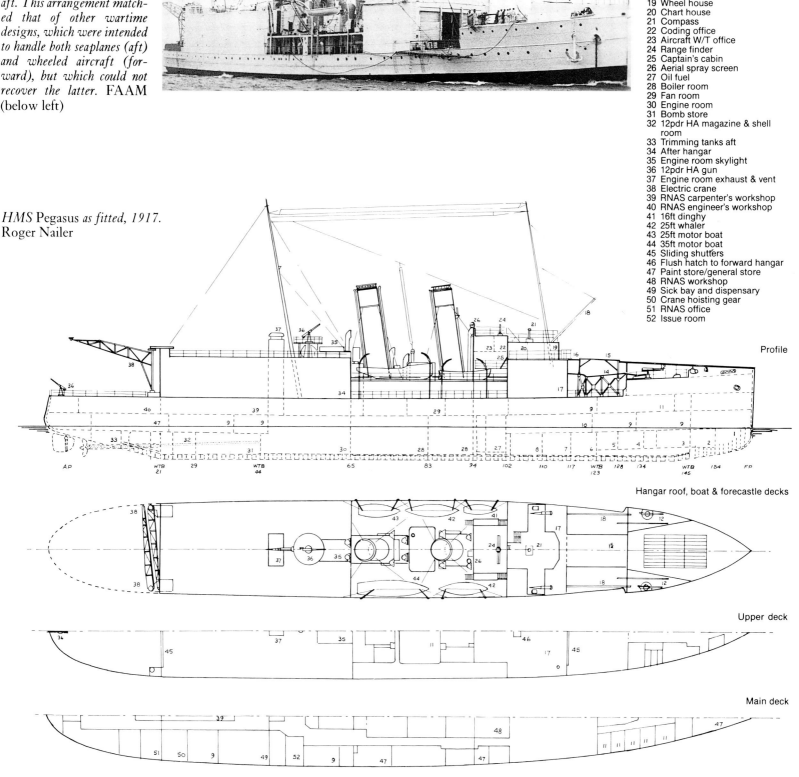

Profile

Hangar roof, boat & forecastle decks

Upper deck

Main deck

high-powered aircraft could indeed fly from platforms short enough not to interfere with other ship functions, or with armament. This in turn led to the experimental installation of a 20ft flying-off platform aboard the light cruiser *Yarmouth* (3rd Light Cruiser Squadron) at Rosyth. Rutland successfully flew a Pup from it in June 1917.

By mid-August 1917, Admiral Beatty was still dissatisfied with the air strength of the Fleet. At a conference aboard the fleet flagship, the Third Sea Lord agreed to fit one ship of each Grand Fleet light cruiser squadron with a lightweight flying-off platform, for one anti-Zeppelin Pup fighter, extending over the forward gun mount: *Caledon*, *Dublin*, *Cordelia*, and *Cassandra*, for the 1st, 2nd, 4th and 6th Light Cruiser Squadrons were selected. In addition, the two large light cruisers which served with the Grand Fleet Light Cruiser Squadrons, *Courageous* and *Glorious*, were to be fitted with similar platforms. Platforms would be fitted to other light cruisers as they became available.

Because these platforms were fixed in train, a cruiser had to leave her position to steam into the wind to launch her Pup. It was for this reason that the captain of HMS *Repulse* had rejected a proposal to fit his ship with a flying-off platform in March 1917.

After a Sopwith Pup launched by HMS *Yarmouth* shot down a Zeppelin over the North Sea (21 August 1917), the captains of most light cruisers wanted to carry their own fighters. On 25 August the Admiralty agreed to fit as many cruisers as possible with flying-off platforms.

The gunnery officer of HMS *Yarmouth*, Lieutenant Commander C H B Gowan, who had been associated with the experiments aboard her, now suggested using a revolving platform, and Rutland soon demonstrated that the aircraft could fly from a platform turned into the wind, even if the ship herself did not steam in that direction. This meant that capital ships could have platforms fitted to their turret tops, and that cruisers could launch their aircraft without losing their place in the formation. On 23 October 1917 the new Admiralty Operations Committee decided that all light cruisers and battlecruisers should have flying-off platforms.

The first flight from a turret trained into the wind was from *Repulse*, on 1 October 1917. Cruiser installations actually trailed those aboard the capital ships; the first flight from a revolving cruiser platform (aboard HMAS *Sydney*) was made on 17 December.

AT THE END OF AUGUST 1917, Wing Captain A V Vyvyan, who was then assistant to DAS (and who was later the RAF officer concerned with naval aviation), reviewed the situation in the Grand Fleet.[18] He considered only HMS *Furious* and the two light cruisers fitted with flying-off decks (*Yarmouth* and *Cassandra*) fully efficient carriers; all the other ships, including the two new ones, were too slow. That Vyvyan listed two cruisers, each carrying only one fighter, as carriers shows how limited existing Grand Fleet air resources really were. However, much more was coming, and Vyvyan could expect full carriers (with landing-on decks) in the near future. He considered it useless to operate floatplanes at sea (due to their limited performance), and inhuman not to provide decks to recover the wheeled aircraft the carriers would have to launch. Grand Fleet air policy without such decks in his view amounted very nearly to the mass suicide of its pilots on each engagement.

Vyvyan considered it unwise to mix the two basic heavy naval aircraft (reconnaissance and torpedo-bomber) aboard any one carrier. He felt that such a policy would hinder the operation of the carrier, because different tactics were associated with each type of aircraft. Reconnaissance aircraft had to be maintained continuously aloft, so a reconnaissance carrier would launch a few at a time, repeating as required. She would, therefore, repeatedly head into the wind and then steam back to regain her place in the fleet. Torpedo aircraft, however, would be launched en masse to make a group attack. They would have to be grouped, ready on deck. By way of contrast, fighters would be launched as required, and splitting them among many ships might actually make more available.

This logic survived the war, and indeed it survives in modern usage; different types of aircraft have different deck cycles, and it still is most efficient to devote a carrier to a single role. In particular, the deck cycles of modern ASW aircraft are so radically different from those of jet fighters and bombers that both the US and the Royal navies have used specialized ASW carriers.[19]

In 1917, reconnaissance aircraft were planned for *Furious*, for the new *Vindictive*, and for the new specially-built carrier, which became HMS *Hermes*. The reconnaissance carriers would steam with the scouting force (the Battle Cruiser Fleet), sending an aerial patrol out 80 to 100nm ahead and abeam. Vyvyan suspected that their most useful mission (prior to action) would be to detect enemy aircraft, including Zeppelins, before they could approach the fleet. Fleet interceptors could be launched to deal with them. After the engagement began, fleet reconnaissance aircraft would have two roles: patrol (primarily to detect enemy submarines) and action observation of the enemy fleet.

Vyvyan suggested that two other *Cavendish* class heavy cruisers be converted to replace possible losses, these ships being faster than HMS *Hermes*, and that another carrier be laid down at once, to take advantage of its greater carrying capacity. Fighters would be carried only aboard cruisers and similar ships, which could accommodate one or two each. Vyvyan argued that to carry them on the larger ships would bleed off vital reconnaissance capability. The newly-converted, but slower, *Nairana* and *Pegasus* could provide a useful fighter reserve.

This left the carrier torpedo-bomber. The Germans were already employing float torpedo-planes, and Vyvyan argued that a dusk attack by twenty-four British torpedo-planes would be extremely difficult to counter. He considered the new *Argus* ideal for them, accommodating twelve or twenty-four and capable of launching either just before an engagement or at its close. In the latter case she might prevent an enemy from escaping, as at Jutland. The ship would have to operate with the battleships, since she was not fast enough to launch repeated reconnaissance flights, since a few turns into the wind would take her far out of position in the fleet. However, far more than HMS *Furious*, she was designed for a quick mass launch – a torpedo strike.

If armed only with torpedo-bombers, *Argus* could recover the fighters (and reconnaissance aircraft) launched by other ships. Without such recovery, the pilots might well be lost.

Vyvyan considered the three early deck-less carriers useful primarily to salvage crashed aircraft (in the wake of the fleet), or to ferry them out to the fleet, using their powerful derricks. He seems to have considered *Campania* too elderly to be worth retaining.

About a month later, Admiral Beatty assembled what he considered his air requirements for the spring of 1918: a minimum of fifteen reconnaissance aircraft, thirty torpedo-bombers (presumably echoing Vyvyan), and fifty fighters. He agreed with Vyvyan that every Grand Fleet cruiser should be equipped with at least one fighter, and battlecruisers (plus *Courageous* and *Glorious*) with more, provided they did not interfere with gunnery. Beatty also agreed that the two new seaplane carriers should be limited to deck-launched fighters. He wanted

18 Vyvyan served prewar as Assistant to the Chief of War Staff; in 1916 he was Assistant to SAC (Sueter), serving as Assistant to DAS 1916–18. He entered the RAF upon its formation, becoming Senior RAF Officer, Mediterranean in 1918, and AOCA (responsible for maritime aviation) 1919–24; he retired in 1925 as an Air Vice Marshal and became a Government Director of Imperial Airways, 1926.

19 Even in the absence of specialized carriers, modern US practice is to split roles as much as possible among the carriers of a force.

20 To be sure, there were some difficulties in landing-on forward. A pilot had to turn in front of the bridge before squaring up to land, at just the time his air speed was so low that his aircraft could not be properly controlled.

HMS Furious *was completed as a strike carrier, retaining her single 18in gun aft. In this form the aerodynamics of her superstructure was largely irrelevant, since any turbulence was manifested mainly in the wake of the ship. However, the mass of superstructure naturally affected any aircraft approaching from astern to land on the ship.* CPL

his two existing large carriers, *Campania* and *Furious*, fitted with flying-on decks (as in *Cavendish/Vindictive*) and hangars aft, with some means of transporting aircraft to the flying-off decks forward.

Beatty did not know whether his two carriers (plus *Argus*, which he believed would soon be completed) could carry this minimum load of reconnaissance and torpedo aircraft, and he feared that *Campania* would soon wear out. He hoped, therefore, that new carriers, with a minimum speed of 22 knots, could be converted.

At this time an Admiralty (probably DAS, that is, Vyvyan) tally showed that, aboard carriers capable of 20 knots or more (including the two new seaplane carriers, *Engadine*, *Furious*, and the light cruisers *Cassandra*, *Dublin* and *Yarmouth*), the Grand Fleet had sixteen reconnaissance aircraft (twelve of which, all but the four aboard *Furious*, had to fly from the water) and fifteen fighters. In the spring of 1918 they would be supplemented by twenty-one reconnaissance aircraft (fifteen in *Argus* and six in *Cavendish*) and fifteen fighters (ten in *Argus*, two each in *Courageous* and *Glorious* and one in *Caledon*).

At this time Grand Fleet Battle Orders required five reconnaissance aircraft aloft at any one time, which meant ten for the approach and fifteen for action – these would just be available, out of deck-launched aircraft, in the spring. The Admiralty view was that the thirty existing fighters barely sufficed, and therefore that as many cruisers as possible should be fitted with flying-off decks.

Experiments in landing-on predated Beatty's formal proposal that HMS *Furious* be fitted with a flying-on deck aft. On 2 August the ship's air commander, Squadron Comander E H Dunning, successfully landed-on in a Pup, having reasoned that, in a strong wind, with the ship running at high speed, his actual speed over the deck would be quite limited. He succeeded again, but on a third try (7 August) his engine stalled and, with the aircraft out of control, he was blown over the side

and killed. On the other hand, pilots flying over the after part of the ship found themselves in very bumpy air. The ship's captain, W C Nicholson, concluded that aircraft should land-on only in what he called 'clean' air, that is, either forward of all eddy-making obstructions, or to one side of the superstructure. He considered that aircraft could land-on forward only if they were provided with some means of judging their position relative to the deck. The existing flying-off deck in HMS *Furious* sufficed only for Pups.[20]

Captain Nicholson opposed Beatty's projected further conversion to HMS *Furious* (12 September), arguing that eddy currents would render landing aft more dangerous than forward, that transferring aircraft between the two flight decks would be difficult and slow, and that removal of the after 18in gun would be an excessive loss of offensive power. Beatty asked Admiralty representatives to confer with him, noting a considerable divergence of opinion among the Grand Fleet pilots.

On the 13th Beatty ordered pilots to fly over the ship, so as to gauge air currents over her stern. Most felt that landing would be impossible due to eddy currents and that only skilled pilots would be able to land on the forward flight deck (and then only in Pups), whereas any moderately-skilled pilot would be able to land any one- or two-seater on a long flush deck, such as that in HMS *Argus*.

On 18 September a conference aboard *Furious* decided that the minimum acceptable modification would be to add the longest possible flush flying-on deck, that is, from the stern right up to the funnel, about 300ft long. This overruled the view of Admiralty officers, who had recently visited the Grand Fleet to inspect the 200ft deck in HMS *Cavendish*; they had hoped that experience would actually reduce even this requirement. The Committee rejected an intermediate solution, a 230ft deck abaft the torpedo control position. Beatty thought that the shorter deck would probably suffice, but was willing to bow to expert opinion; thus he finally accepted the longer deck.

Key
1 Oil fuel
2 Flour and biscuit store
3 Mess deck
4 7.5in BL gun
5 7.5in shell room
6 3in magazine
7 Small arms
8 Provision store
9 Torpedo warhead room
10 Submerged torpedo tube spac
11 Workshop
12 Flying-off deck
13 Forward hangar
14 Derrick
15 Hatch
16 3in QF gun
17 24in searchlight
18 DCT
19 Spotting top
20 Boiler room
21 3in HA gun
22 36in searchlight
23 Control tower
24 Ammunition lobby
25 7.5in magazine
26 Buffer net
27 21in above-water torpedo tube
28 Flying-on deck
29 Engine room
30 HA rangefinder
31 Gun room
32 Coal bunker
33 Engine stripping shop
34 Engineer's store
35 After hangar
36 Gland compartment

Above: *HMS* Furious *as modified in 1918, with a landing-on deck abaft her truncated superstructure. Note the gallows abaft her funnel, from which a crash barrier was suspended. The aircraft on the flying-off deck is probably a folded Short 184.* CPL

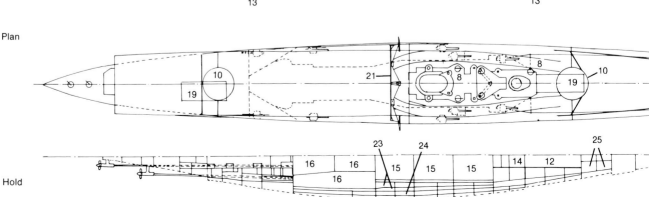

Below: *HMS* Furious *at the end of World War I, armed with ten 5.5in guns, five (rather than the original two) 3in anti-aircraft guns, and two submered and twelve above-water torpedo tubes. This drawing omits the complex arrester gear abaft the safety net.* NF

Key
1 Forward hangar
2 Conning tower
3 Main (18in) director tower (retained although the single 18in gun had been removed)
4 Fire control tower
5 36in searchlight
6 5.5in director
7 24in signalling searchlight
8 3in anti-aircraft gun
9 Safety barrier (net hung from gallows)
10 Former 18in barbette (note that the forward barbette was never used)
11 Submerged torpedo room
12 Bomb stowage
13 5.5in magazine
14 5.5in shell room
15 Boiler room
16 Engine room
17 After hangar
18 Above-water triple 21in torpedo tube
19 Lift opening
20 Anti-aircraft range finder
21 Gallows for safety net
22 Cofferdam
23 Oil fuel
24 Watertight compartment (void)
25 Torpedo drain tank (for submerged torpedo tubes)

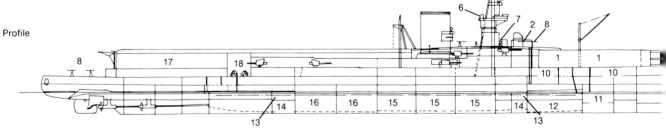

Profile

Plan

Hold

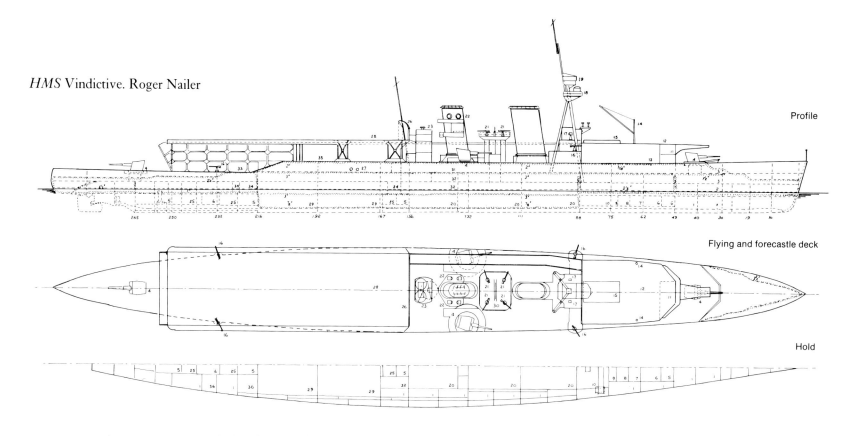

HMS Vindictive. Roger Nailer

Profile

Flying and forecastle deck

Hold

Above *and* right: *HMS* Vindictive *was decked over as a kind of miniature* Furious. *Note the pallisade (wind break) around the flying-off deck forward, and the gallows (for a crash barrier) between the after funnel and the flying-on deck. She saw little service as a carrier, and in 1923–25 her flying-on deck was removed (and two additional 7.5in guns were mounted, for a total of six). The hangar forward remained, and a large experimental cata-pult was fitted above it. In this form the ship tested ship-board aircraft both in support of fleet operations and in defence of trade. These photo-graphs were taken in about 1921. CPL (above)*

Any landing-on deck would eliminate the remaining 18in gun, but the pilots argued that this loss would be more than offset by additional aircraft and by the ability to land (and then to re-launch) other fleet aircraft.

Installation of the long landing-on deck also required that the mainmast and its torpedo control director be removed, entailing major structural work. The pilots hoped, too, that the fore bridge and funnel could be streamlined, and hydraulic lifts installed to serve both the existing forward hangar and an after hangar which might be built under the new landing-on deck.

Some means, probably decking, would be required to transport aircraft between the two decks.

At this time HMS *Furious* was uniquely valuable, as she was the only really fast fleet carrier. The fleet pilots therefore recommended that she should not be rebuilt until another fast carrier, HMS *Vindictive*, joined the fleet in about May 1918. Alternatively, if *Furious* had to be refitted (for other than flying reasons), the opportunity could be taken to remove her after turret and torpedo control tower, and to fit the after (flying-on) deck. Pending this conversion, the forward (flying-off) deck could be filled out and a hydraulic lift fitted, to make it easier to operate two-seaters.

The long flying-on deck planned for *Furious* would be both valuable and unique. One plan, then, was to fit *Glorious* with a flying-off deck, as already existed in *Furious*. This would free *Furious* for the larger conversion, and she would then be able to train pilots for the more difficult conditions to be expected aboard *Cavendish*, with her shorter deck.

These proposals resolved themselves into two alternatives for Admiralty decision. One was to fit a landing-on deck and additional hangar to HMS *Furious*; the other was to convert her near-sisters *Courageous* and *Glorious* to single-ended (flying-off only) carriers. The latter was attractive because it would mult-iply the number of flight decks, and therefore would get more aircraft airborne in a given time. It would also hedge against losses. Further conversion of *Furious* seemed less attractive because she already launched her aircraft quite slowly, and it was by no means clear that she could efficiently operate the larger complement proposed.

In either case, the large light cruisers could accommodate most of the required deck-launched reconnaissance aircraft. This would largely free the new carrier *Argus* for torpedo-bombers. She could carry three or four reconnaissance aircraft on her flight deck, and perhaps twenty torpedo-bombers in her hangar. Because the two types would not be required at the same time, Vyvyan's stricture against mixing types could be ignored. The reconnaissance aircraft would fly off during the approach phase of the battle, before the enemy fleet came within torpedo-bomber range.

Beatty's recommendations for the landing-on deck and extra hangar aboard HMS *Furious* and for the flying-off platforms were approved on 17 October by the Admiralty's new Opera-tions Committee. The alternative, to convert the other two large cruisers, was rejected. Even so, the second reconstruction of HMS *Furious* represented a considerable sacrifice of ship-building capacity, and various simplifications (such as omission of the two lifts) were suggested (and rejected). On 23 October the Operations Committee finally reaffirmed the decision to fit the 300ft deck. HMS *Furious* emerged from Armstrong's yard with her landing-on deck (actually 284 × 70ft) aft, in March 1918. A suggestion that the mainmast be retained and relocated to a position further forward (48ft abaft the funnel) was rejected, to ensure that an aircraft making a bad landing had a better chance of flying off again. Considerable labour was thus saved, and without this tall indicator the ship's course became much more difficult to judge from an enemy submarine.

The flying-on deck was arranged so that air could pass below it on either side, to minimize the turbulence just abaft the ship, and a six-aircraft hangar (with lift) filled the space below the deck in the centre.

Arrester gear and a net, already designed for HMS *Cavendish*, were installed at the forward end of the landing-on deck, the after end of which was rounded-down (again, as in HMS *Cavendish*). The arrester gear, which is described more fully in Chapter 4, was unsuccessful, and throughout 1918 *Furious* served only as a flying-off carrier.

The two lifts were ordered from Waygood-Otis in October, to support a working load of 3 tons at a speed of 40ft per minute. As in all later British carriers, they formed part of the deck when up. It was originally expected that large aircraft would be stowed forward, and smaller aircraft aft, and therefore plans initially showed a larger (48 × 18ft) lift forward and a slightly smaller (46 × 18ft 4in) one aft. However, it was soon decided that the two should be the same (larger) size, for added flexibility.

The forward hangar (120 × 60 × 15ft 6in) was served by a 48 × 18ft hydraulic lift and the after hangar (116 × 33 × 15ft 6in) by a 45 × 18ft electrically-driven lift. The hydraulic lift was preferred. The after hangar also had a stern door (18ft 6in × 14ft) into which aircraft could be swung over the quarter-deck. Aircraft were stowed as closely as possible, the detachable wings of the 1½-Strutters being slung overhead. The Camels had detachable tails, and the torpedo-planes had folding wings. All of these aircraft, then, had to be assembled on deck. To protect them, a wooden pallisade (wind-break) extended completely across the flying-off deck, enclosing about half of it.

Five 5.5in guns, originally on the shelter deck, had to be moved, one of the eleven 5.5s being eliminated altogether. Apparently as partial compensation for the elimination of the remaining 18in gun, the ship was fitted with six sets of triple 21in fixed above-water torpedo tubes. *Furious* was completed with two 3in anti-aircraft guns. After she was bombed by two German seaplanes on 17 June 1918, ACA and Beatty called for additional weapons.[21] Up to that time, Beatty had assumed that the ship's aircraft would suffice to protect her against air attack. *Furious* had been unable, however, to launch her two ready Camel fighters in time to intercept the attackers before they struck; the Camels were launched only in time to shoot down one of the raiders on its way back, and they both had to ditch. The effect of this incident was to reverse Beatty's views on carrier anti-aircraft guns (see Chapter 4). In the case of the *Furious*, one gun was transferred from HMS *Royal Oak*, and two more were fitted, for an ultimate total of five.

Another effect of the raid was to convince the Admiralty of the need to strike at the German naval air bases; until the end of June two special flights of Camels trained for an attack on the Zeppelin sheds at Tondern. Even though *Furious* could launch them from her deck, they were still subject to weather condi-tions, and the raid had to be cancelled once before it was finally launched on 19 July. Seven Camels, each carrying two 50lb bombs, attacked in two flights, one destroying two Zeppelins inside their shed. Another shed, which did not contain a Zep-pelin, was burned, and a third, which was being dismantled, was destroyed. Of the seven Camels, only three were able to return to the fleet to ditch, three landing in Denmark and being interned, and one being lost.

The Tondern raid was the ultimate success of Sueter's strike carrier concept, but it was not repeated, presumably pending the availability of more Grand Fleet carriers, capable of launch-ing and recovering torpedo-bombers, in the autumn of 1918.

After completion to the modified design, *Furious* served as Flagship of the Admiral Commanding Aircraft. In October 1918 she carried six Ship Camels and fourteen Ship Strutters. Early in 1919 she carried nine Ship Strutters and three Cuckoo torpedo-bombers. For Baltic operations (1919) she was equipped with twelve Camels, two 1½-Strutters and four floatplanes.

ON 16 JANUARY 1918 the Operations Committee approved Vyvyan's idea that fleet fighters be largely confined to the cruisers, capital ships, and to the new seaplane carriers, with each of the specialist carriers taking only a few aboard.

The prospect of successful deck-landing made large carriers more attractive than ever, and the Committee now approved a proposal that the Chilean battleship *Almirante Cochrane*, sus-pended at Elswick since the outbreak of war, be completed as a carrier. At the time, she was probably the last remaining large hull suitable for conversion. She became HMS *Eagle*; for details, see the next chapter.

The ageing *Campania* was to be retained for training, the proposal to provide her with a landing-on deck being tabled

21   Two 1½-Strutters were about to be launched for reconnaissance when two German aircraft dropped bombs from 1500ft. Camels were wheeled into place on deck and launched, but they could not catch the Germans, and had to ditch. The light cruiser *Galatea* launched a third Camel, which landed in Denmark. When *Furious* was bombed again, her two Camels managed to force down a German sea-plane. Most accounts mention only one of the two engagements, or seem to merge them. This one is from B Robertson, *Sopwith – The Man and His Aircraft* (Harleyford, 1970).

pending experience with the new carriers. Her deck proved suitable for operating wheeled two-seaters, and in March 1918 approval was granted for her to carry only wheeled aircraft. However, Grand Fleet aircraft resources were somewhat limited, and the fleet's air establishment was not increased to provide for her.

After the successful flight from *Repulse*'s turret on 1 October 1917, similar installations were ordered for the 1st Battle Cruiser Squadron. Other flights followed: 19 November from *Renown*, 6 January from *Tiger* and *Princess Royal*, and 12 January from *Lion*. The 2nd Battle Cruiser Squadron was then fitted. These platforms launched single-seaters; the next step was a longer platform suitable for two-seaters (Sopwith 1½-Strutters). It was developed aboard *Repulse* and *Australia*, at the suggestion of Admiral Leveson in the latter ship. The first attempt, using a flexible rope extension, failed on 5 March 1918, but a 1½-Strutter flew successfully from *Australia* on 4 April. By 1 October 1918, 175 turret platform flights had been made, and ships were being fitted with two platforms, with the longer one for two-seaters forward.[22]

These aircraft were not protected from the weather, and Grand Fleet practice was to maintain them ashore until just before the fleet sortied, when they would be ferried out on lighters. At the end of the war, apart from those aboard carriers, the fleet carried forty-five aircraft, with another thirty-eight aboard cruisers or planned.

LATE IN 1918, a typical Grand Fleet staff view of aircraft needs was that reconnaissance aircraft were most important, followed by fighters and then by torpedo-bombers.[23] Reconnaissance aircraft had to be carried aboard large fast cruisers, speed (at least 30 knots) being essential so that the ship could turn periodically into the wind to fly off her aircraft. The ideal reconnaissance carrier had a long landing deck (also used for flying-off) forward of all superstructure obstructions, and was well-enough armed to take on an enemy light cruiser. Each would carry eight to twelve reconnaissance aircraft. A large fleet would require two or three such ships. It was argued that two, each carrying ten aircraft, were more useful than one carrying twenty, because for a given number of machines they would have to manoeuvre (for landing or flying-off) only half as often and spend less time in regaining position. The existing *Courageous* class seemed particularly suitable for conversion into this type of carrier.

Ideally, these reconnaissance aircraft would create an aerial screen ahead and on the flanks of the fleet. For a large fleet, four to eight aircraft would be required, depending on weather, to observe enemy forces up to 100nm from the cruiser screen (in ideal conditions). Normally North Sea visibility varies from 10 to 40 miles.

Aircraft seemed particularly useful because, unlike cruisers, they could detect the enemy's course at the first sighting, from the direction of his wake. Sopwith 1½-Strutters, with an endurance of three hours, were used, fitted with two-way CW (morse) radios, their transmitters driven by the wind. Tuning was not as sharp as desired, so only fourteen wavelengths could be assigned, five for reconnaissance (from the battlecruisers) and nine for spotting (from the battleships), despite the great demand for aircraft radio work in the fleet.

During 1918 reconnaissance aircraft (1½-Strutters) were often used in Grand Fleet tactical (PZ) exercises, even though weather was unfavourable for long-range flying (as aircraft were less able to spot their carriers in bad weather, hence might be lost). In a tactical exercise late in 1918, the aircraft contacted the enemy 8 minutes before the light cruisers, and they found the enemy main body 23 minutes before it could be sighted by

any battle fleet ship.

In 1918, too, the Grand Fleet began to use its 1½-Strutter reconnaissance aircraft for gunnery spotting. Planes spotted successfully, although they had some difficulty identifying their targets. It was hoped that one aircraft could spot for a full division of four ships. There were some problems. The observer had to function as radio operator; ideally one man would be responsible for each function. Neither observer nor separate radio operator could defend the spotting aircraft, which had therefore to be protected by friendly fighters. After the war, the RAF would argue that spotters should defend themselves, and therefore that they should be four-seaters.

Arrangements for systematic development of aeroplane (as opposed to kite balloon) spotting were developed at a meeting aboard the fleet flagship *Queen Elizabeth* on 5 August 1918. Ideally, each battle squadron would carry its own spotters. In some weather, however, aircraft would be able to fly from carriers but not from turret platforms. HMS *Campania* was therefore assigned to carry six spotters, out of her total of nine aircraft: two for each of the 1st, 2nd and 4th Battle Squadron. Each would carry another four aircraft, plus two in the 5th Battle Squadron, one in HMS *Queen Elizabeth* (fleet flagship), and one in HMS *Canada*, a total of sixteen. Installations in the US 6th Battle Squadron, by comparison, were only beginning at the end of the war. The corresponding assignment of wavelengths was two each for the 1st, 2nd, 4th and 5th Battle Squadrons, and one for *Queen Elizabeth* and *Canada*.

Fighters were valued both to prevent enemy reconnaissance and to protect friendly reconnaissance. After performing these duties, they could turn their machine-guns on the bridges of enemy warships in action, perhaps breaking up enemy destroyer attacks.

Grand Fleet practice in 1918 was to carry one reconnaissance plane and one fighter aboard each battlecruiser, these ships forming the core of the fleet scouting force, but plans called for each ultimately to carry two reconnaissance aircraft only. Each battle squadron was assigned one reconnaissance plane and three fighters for every two ships. Plans were for each battleship division to have adequate aircraft to carry out independent operations, meaning that the division flagship and relief flagship each carried one two-seater for reconnaissance and spotting. All other aircraft in the division were fighters.

Light cruisers carried only fighters, but some were equipped with radios and could transmit when flying, to provide very limited reconnaissance services.

At this time torpedo-bombers were as yet untested; the Grand Fleet officers suggested that, if they proved useful, it might be wise to build a single carrier to accommodate twenty of them.

AT THE END OF THE WAR, Admiral Beatty, C-in-C of the Grand Fleet, wanted six modern carriers for his fleet, with more built to ensure against possible losses. He was not alone in valuing such ships. Beatty's successor, Admiral C F Madden, reported his own list of carrier requirements on 2 December 1919.[24] They were based largely on wartime experience, although Madden was also impressed by the first postwar gunnery spotting trials.

Madden wanted a scouting line of three reconnaissance aircraft maintained during daylight, to be reinforced by six more when contact was made with the enemy fleet. These aircraft would be launched and recovered by special reconnaissance carriers, which Madden called Air Reconnaissance Cruisers (ARC). Madden considered three ships, each carrying eleven reconnaissance aircraft and a few fighters, would be needed. Ideally, the scouting line might be maintained by airships,

22   By 1 October 1918 twenty-two turrets aboard the battlecruisers *Courageous* and *Glorious* had been fitted with flying-off platforms (nine for two-seaters, thirteen for single-seaters). By the spring of 1919, every Grand Fleet battleship was expected to carry two aircraft on turrets, for a total of eighty-seven at sea. This was thirty-three battleships (sixteen two-seaters, fifty single-seaters), four old battlecruisers (four two-, four single-seaters), *Courageous* and *Glorious* and the two *Renown*s (each with one two- and one single-seater), the *Lion*s (each with two single-seaters) and *Tiger* (one single-seater), for a total of twenty-four two-seaters and sixty-three single-seaters. Flying-off was possible because high-powered aircraft needed only very short deck runs. Average take-off runs: with 40-knot wind over deck (WOD), the minimum deck run for a Camel was almost nil. With WOD 30 knots the average Camel take-off run was about 15ft, the average 1½-Strutter run about 35ft (minimum about 23ft). Minimum run for a Camel at 30 knots was about 5ft. At 20 knots, the average Camel run was 22ft, the minimum about 11; the average 1½-Strutter run was about 55ft, the minimum about 45. These figures were based on 160 Camel and fifty 1½-Strutter flights. Data in this footnote are from a report to the US Navy by Lieutenant Chevalier, who was serving with the Grand Fleet, in General Board File 449, 1918.

23   As reported by US officers serving with the Grand Fleet, reporting to the General Board; General Board file 449 for November 1918.

24   ADM1/8576/341. Madden suggested that if the League of Nations imposed arms limitations, large liners suitable for conversion into carriers might be built. This was actually done only by the Japanese, although it was also seriously proposed in the United States by the Maritime Commission.

which would withdraw in the face of enemy fighters, to be replaced by carrier-based aircraft. Madden suggested that the ARC could be provided most economically by converting the three large light cruisers, *Furious*, *Courageous* and *Glorious*.

Each capital ship needed its own artillery observation aircraft (AOA); Madden wanted a carrier assigned to each division of four, carrying eight AOA, though he admitted that one carrier might support two divisions. One fast (at least 28-knot) carrier would be needed to support the battlecruisers.

Madden considered torpedo attack (TA) aircraft an essential element of the future fleet. Their first objective would be to ensure air superiority by striking the enemy carriers; they would also be essential to prevent the escape of a fast enemy fleet (as at Jutland), and to attack an enemy fleet in a fortified harbour. Numbers were clearly needed. Madden suggested twelve TA as the minimum tactical unit, capable of attacking two or three ships, and wanted at least two such units, aboard two carriers. For special operations TA could be accommodated aboard the ARC or the spotting carriers.

The fleet would also need special depth-bomb aircraft, to keep submarines out of its path. Madden suggested that, if the fleet had to remain at sea for a protracted period, it would be easier to maintain such an air patrol than to maintain a substantial destroyer screen. This added a special ASW carrier to his requirements, similar to those used for torpedo attack.

Finally, the fleet needed fighters, both to achieve air superiority and to strafe the exposed parts of enemy warships. Madden proposed a specialized fighter carrier to supplement the fighters aboard the battleships and cruisers.

As Vyvyan had argued, Madden proposed to limit each carrier to a single type of aircraft, except that fighters would be distributed throughout the fleet. They would fly from carriers and from capital ships and cruisers; each capital ship would also carry on reconnaissance aircraft, as during the war.

Madden's requirements added up to a very large carrier force. He suggested that the ARC and at least some of the other carriers should be provided during peacetime, but that others should be converted from suitable merchant ships upon mobilization. Here the logic seems to have been that the ARC had to be special, fast, hulls, hence not conversions. War experience seemed to show that conversions of slower ships were entirely feasible. Madden suggested that the Admiralty build suitable ships, hiring them out for commercial use on terms equivalent to a subsidy, in return for which they would be held in readiness for wartime use.

Total wartime carrier requirements, for an Atlantic fleet of ten battleships and four battlecruisers (four divisions), plus ten light cruisers, came to eleven carriers (three ARC, four for spotters, two for torpedo attack, one for ASW, and one for fighters). Four more spotter carriers would be needed to support battleships and battlecruisers which might be commissioned from reserve, and two more if the two Mediterranean battle divisions joined the Atlantic Fleet. In addition, if the fleet had to operate at a great distance (for example, in the East) it would need supplementary carriers to transport aircraft. Special operations, such as long-range bombing, would also require extra carriers.

These requirements were horrifying, given limited postwar funds. They were reviewed by the Staff in 1920 (see Chapter 5).

Also in 1919, Admiral Phillimore, the former ACA, chaired the Postwar Questions Committee, which conducted a lengthy series of interviews with experienced officers. There was no question but that aircraft would be an essential element of any future fleet, and many of the witnesses considered the torpedo-bomber vital to attack an enemy fleet, particularly if, like the

Table 3-2: Postwar Questions Committee Aircraft, 1920

Carrier	1	2	3	4	5
Reconnaissance	15	20	12	10	12
Fighter	7	7	7	7	7
Torpedo	6	3	9	9*	9

Note *Indicates a bomber for special operations, otherwise a torpedo-bomber. The bomber is assumed to require 1½ times the space occupied by a Panther (two-seat reconnaissance aircraft). Numbers were based on the assumption that HMS *Eagle* could stow thirty Panthers and four torpedo-bombers, the latter equivalent to five Panthers. In 1918 *Furious* carried a mix of all three types.

High Seas Fleet, the enemy took refuge in harbour.[25] Some of the witnesses even suggested that in future the carrier would be the only viable type of warship, and that no warship without aircraft would survive. Captain Goodenough, the cruiser commander who had scouted effectively at Jutland, wanted a carrier for each cruiser squadron. The Staff College considered aircraft so important that fast carriers should be built even at the expense of capital ships.

The Committee recommended that two types of carrier be built, A for the scouting force, and B for the fleet proper.[26] A would normally concentrate on reconnaissance, though it would carry some torpedo-bombers in the event it had to be used to attack the enemy fleet. B would carry the fleet fighters, spotters, and the main force of torpedo-bombers.

Because it would have to operate with fast scouting forces, A would have to be a very fast ship, probably capable of 33 knots; like a battleship, she would be limited in beam to 106ft (to transit the Panama Canal) and in draft to 30ft. She would need greater endurance than a battlecruiser, since she would periodically steam into the wind to launch and recover aircraft; the Committee recommended 1000 miles more at the standard endurance speed of 18 knots (6100nm at 18 knots); this was defined as 85 per cent of the distance the ship could steam on her fuel load. She would be fast enough to escape light cruisers, but would have to be armed with 4.7in guns to beat off destroyer attacks (with a broadside of at least eight), plus at least four 3in anti-aircraft guns. Similarly, she would be protected against destroyer fire (5in HE or less). The ideal was a flush-decked carrier about 800ft long. There would be two lifts, one forward to launch aircraft, and one aft to recover them, both as large as possible.

Type A could operate as a fleet carrier, but the Committee was mindful of its high cost. The Committee wanted any carrier to have a speed advantage of 5 knots over the force with which she operated, so Type B could afford a speed of 26 knots. As in the case of Type A, Type B required endurance beyond that of her consorts, in this case another 600nm at the standard battleship endurance speed of 14 knots (for a total of 6600nm at 14 knots).

In both types, the Committee much preferred petrol stowage in tins to bulk stowage; it was not yet evident that such stowage limited the size and performance of carrier aircraft. The Committee certainly was aware of the limitations imposed by carrier dimensions, however, which was why it wanted the longest possible flight deck and the largest possible lift.

The Committee calculated that the fleet would require five carriers, to support two Battle Fleet units and one Battlecruiser Fleet unit; on this basis, most would be Type B. It listed a typical distribution of aircraft (see Table 3-2). The Committee recommended that HMS *Furious* be rebuilt as a satisfactory carrier, and that the other two large light cruisers, *Courageous* and *Glorious*, be rebuilt as carriers. These recommendations are not dated, but they were probably made during 1920. Thus it is not clear whether they were affected by the June 1920 Naval Staff conference on the carrier force (see Chapter 5), though this seems unlikely.

25 For example, in May 1919, Captain (later Admiral and First Sea Lord) Dudley Pound, who was then D of P(H), argued that successful torpedo-bomber strikes could force an inferior enemy to accept battle, or could redress the balance in favour of a British fleet; it was 'difficult to imagine any form of attack which will be more feared and more difficult to counter than a cloud of fast torpedo-bombers.' It was therefore essential that large numbers be available, but existing and projected carriers could accommodate a total of only eighty (twenty in *Argus*, fourteen in *Furious*, thirty in *Hermes* and twenty-six in *Eagle*, according to Pound). Pound considered this figure grossly inadequate, arguing further that the total number of carriers could not be reduced because that would reduce the strength of the strike which could be launched simultaneously. This led him to argue that *Furious* and *Argus*, both of which were unsatisfactory, had to be retained. He wanted *Vindictive* converted back into a cruiser, because she could carry only reconnaissance aircraft; see ADM 1/8550/28, on the future distribution of carriers. Pound was not a Postwar Questions Committee witness on fleet aviation.

26 These conclusions are taken from Miscellaneous Carrier Cover, No 425; the Postwar Questions Committee notes are in ADM 116/2060.

4

Prototypes

THE STORY OF THE FIRST British full-deck carriers is somewhat tangled. Two designs, one for a cruiser-like ship (which became HMS *Hermes*) and one for a larger liner conversion (HMS *Argus*) were developed almost in parallel. While they were proceeding, HMS *Furious* was fitted with a flying-on deck aft, using the new arrester gear then planned for the flush-deck carriers. Her misfortune led to the decision to eliminate the island structure in HMS *Argus*, and at the same time to reduce it radically in HMS *Hermes* and in the larger *Eagle*, the latter conceived as an enlarged *Hermes*.

By 1915 several officers were convinced that an aircraft carrier had to be able to recover her aircraft while under way. Flight Commander H A Williamson, who had been injured while operating from HMS *Ark Royal*, conceived an island-type carrier and showed Sueter a wooden model in the summer of 1915.[1] He in turn showed it to an experienced senior naval constructor, J H Narbeth. It appears in retrospect that Williamson's model was more a concept for a full (flying-off and landing-on) aircraft carrier than anything approaching a worked-out design. It was perhaps most significant for its approach to the problem of arrester gear. Williamson called for a series of longitudinal wires in an inclined plane, much the system which would be applied to HMS *Argus* three years later, and which the Royal Navy would use throughout the early 1920s. Narbeth was responsible for the British flush-deck and island carriers of 1916–18, but there is no evidence that he was inspired directly by Williamson's ideas.[2]

Sueter was impressed enough to have Williamson's device set up and tested, in the form of a 200 × 60ft grid, at the Marine Experimental Aircraft Depot at the Isle of Grain, which became the World War I arrester gear test site. Trials showed that an aircraft could be brought to rest within 60ft in a slight head wind, and it seemed likely that a fast ship could use a considerably shorter grid. These experiments ceased late in 1915, because no suitable ship was available. They were, however, resumed some time in mid-1916, with a simpler alternative system, three transverse ropes 20ft apart, each with 30lb sandbags at the ends, supported 6in from the ground. An aircraft fitted with a hook could engage one rope after the other, slowing it down gradually. This system was demonstrated in September 1916 with an Avro 504 biplane. Its success seems to have encouraged the decision to complete the liner *Conte Rosso*

as the carrier *Argus*, although the latter actually emerged with a very different system much more like Williamson's original. The 1916 transverse system broadly resembled the modern type.

Arrester-gear work ceased after the September 1916 success, while a 200ft deck (to simulate ship conditions) was built; it could be rotated into the wind. Tests then resumed, using transverse wires, in April 1917. It was soon apparent that an aircraft landing off-centre tended to slew over, even over the side of the deck. Attempts to solve this problem using a sliding cage hung from the undercarriage of the aircraft failed. Then Commander E H Dunning went over the side trying to land aboard HMS *Furious* (see chapter 3) and the longitudinal wires, which (in theory) could also hold an aircraft down to the deck, were revived. This equipment was generally called Busteed Gear, after Squadron Commander H R Busteed, commander of the Isle of Grain station.

HMS *Furious* was completed in March 1918 with parallel-wire arrester gear, consisting of wires strung between two short ramps, on her flying-on deck aft. In theory, an aircraft would land abaft the arrester gear, taxying onto it. Downward-facing hooks hung from its undercarriage would engage the wires, preventing the aircraft from bouncing back into the air (as in Dunning's crash). As the aircraft climbed the second ramp, it would be brought to a stop as the hooks were forced up against the wires. Any aircraft missing the wires would hit a barrier consisting of 2in manila rope, strung from a line between two pole masts.

Sopwith 1½-Strutters with skid undercarriage were used in these tests. They generally missed the wires completely, due to strong 'bumps' created by the remaining centreline superstructure (and the funnel gas). These bumps made aircraft unmanageable at just the moment when control was needed most, when landing. One pilot, for example, tried several times to fly slowly onto the deck, with the ship steaming at 22 knots (total wind over deck 30–35 knots). His speed relative to the ship was very slow, and each time he reached the after end of the deck his aircraft was forced off to port, even though he tried to steer to starboard.

Effective control therefore required a higher landing speed, but in this case the aircraft might well fail to stop in time. With the ship steaming at 16 knots, for example (total wind over

1 Williamson had also suggested a means of landing-on, using wires, in 1912, but it seems unlikely that the 1915 proposal had much in common with the earlier one. Certainly several British officers suggested prewar that carriers should incorporate landing-on decks. It seems unlikely that they were influenced by, or indeed knew of, the successful US landing on the armoured cruiser *Pennsylvania* in 1911.

2 According to the British official history, *The War In The Air*, Vol 4, p37.

deck 30–35 knots) one pilot made a good landing at the centre of the deck but did not engage, and crashed into the barrier at 12 knots. Another failed to hook and crashed at about 30.

The barrier was successful in that crashes usually ruined the wings but left the pilot uninjured. In some cases the fuselage was damaged, but the valuable engine generally was not.

The solution was to combine transverse wires (which could slow down a fast aircraft) with the longitudinal wires (which could keep it from going over the side). Two aircraft landed successfully before the First Lord of the Admiralty on 19 April, wind speeds being 21 and 26 knots (and the ship at 6 and 10 knots, respectively). This success probably bore out earlier observations that funnel gas was a major problem, and hence that bumping would be substantially reduced when the ship steamed at low speed. In another case, the net wind over the deck was only 10 knots, so there was no bumping, and a Pup, landing well forward, stopped in 65ft. It was taken forward, flown off, and landed again, touching well forward and pulling up in 95ft without being damaged.

The combination therefore was successful, but took too long to rig, and the sandbags tended to twist into the longitudinal wires. Thus in 1918 the Royal Navy was still seeking a truly satisfactory arrester gear/carrier combination, which would not require any transverse wires. This was only achieved in HMS *Argus*.[3] Plans to test an alternative Armstrong arrester gear, which seems to have been of transverse type, did not materialize, as air conditions obviously precluded success.

EARLY IN 1916 Captain Schwann, commanding HMS *Campania*, had commented that, had the initial arrester gear tests been only a few months earlier, he would have pressed for a landing-on deck rather than a kite balloon aft aboard his ship.

From the summer of 1915, Lieutenant Gerard Holmes, who had been Assistant Naval Architect for the Cunard Line, and Sir John H Biles, a prominent civilian naval architect, had proposed a more conventional seaplane carrier for the Grand Fleet, which may in some ways have reflected Cunard's experience in the early seaplane carrier conversions. The projected ship had a cruiser-like 4500-ton (450 × 49 × 13ft 6in), 28-knot (38,000shp) hull, the usual centreline uptakes dividing into triple funnels on each side of her hull, surrounded by enclosed passageways. Between them was a hangar extending between an open quarter-deck (to which seaplanes could be brought by crane) and the slightly raised 100ft flying-off deck forward.

The logic of the design was that four small aircraft, which could be launched by means of the flying-off deck, were hangared forward. The five torpedo floatplanes, much too heavy to take off from the deck, were housed amidships. At least in theory, they could be launched and retrieved under way via a slipway aft, down which the floatplanes could ride into the sea nose foward, or up which, having landed and hooked on while taxying aft, they could be drawn. Biles and Holmes seem not to have considered flying-on by wheeled aircraft; presumably the small aircraft would have been floatplanes supported by droppable wheels for take-off, as in other seaplane carriers.

Endurance was five days at 24 knots. Armament consisted of four 4in, one 6in aft, and two anti-aircraft guns.

This proposal was significant as the first attempt to design a Grand Fleet seaplane carrier from the keel up. It served as a feasibility study, to demonstrate that the required capabilities (including fleet speed) could be approached within reasonable dimensions and so, therefore, could costs. However, Holmes and Biles were inexperienced in warship design, and DNC's examination of the design showed that they had been overoptimistic in their weight estimates and that the ship was not sufficiently survivable. It was, for example, not well enough

At least from 1916 on, British carrier designers paid considerable attention to air flow. Models were tested in the wind tunnel of the National Physical Laboratory. To duplicate the air flowing around a real carrier, including flow parallel to the waterline, the laboratory built models including mirror-images of the planned hulls. This is Argus *as planned, with two islands and a bridge connecting them. Note the lattice connecting the flight deck to the hull.*

provided with water-tight bulkheads.

A conference compared the Williamson concept with the Biles-Holmes ship. Holmes suggested that, instead of an island, the flush-deck carrier might better discharge her funnel gases right aft. This idea became the basis for HMS *Argus*.

Sueter seems to have found the Biles-Holmes design very attractive. He ordered it revised with arrester gear aft (having just tested Williamson's idea). In this case, however, the arrester gear consisted of a net slung between two parallel masts. Sueter argued that an aircraft landed at about 60ft per second (about 41mph), but that the ship under way made 46, so that the difference in speed was only 14ft per second, about 10mph. At this speed the collision with the flexible net could do little damage. The great virtue of this system was that it had little impact on the design as a whole, whereas provision for a long landing-on deck would have required substantial redesign. On the other hand, Sueter's arithmetic made no great allowance for advances in aircraft performance.[4] He went so far as to suggest that nets be stretched over the hangar of a seaplane carrier, and a rough wooden model was constructed. However, this proposal to take over *Manxman* for this purpose was rejected, and by early 1917 the arrester gear concept called for a long wire grid (as Williamson had suggested), its length roughly proportional to the difference between aircraft and ship speed, the vertical net acting only as a safety barrier.

Sueter also called for other modifications to the design. By June 1916 the Biles-Holmes seaplane carrier displaced 4700 tons (draft 14ft 2in), and was armed with four 6in guns, four anti-aircraft guns, and a Maxim machine-gun. Construction time was estimated as fifteen to eighteen months. At this time the British government hoped that the war would be over by the end of 1917, a deadline which appears in several contemporary papers.

3   ADM 137/1956, the report of the Advisory Committee on (Naval) Aeronautics. Busteed gear was permanently rigged; officers aboard HMS *Furious* suggested a modified version, called vanishing gear, which could be dropped down onto the deck after an aircraft landed, so that it could taxi out. HMS *Furious* was initially fitted with Le Mesurier gear, consisting of a series of (presumably longitudinal) loops on an endless wire. It received very low priority because HMS *Argus* was scheduled to receive Busteed gear. The latter was intended to work with a skid undercarriage, the horns projecting downward from the crossbrace. There was also some interest in a 'magnetic deck', but it proved impractical.

4   Reviewing the Biles-Holmes design early in 1916, Captain Schwann of the *Campania* commented that, were the net placed right aft, it might even be used to land floatplanes. Although the vertical net never entered service, a very similar device is currently (1987) being used by the US Navy, to recover unmanned aircraft launched by battleships.

Model testing became, if anything, more important after the failure of Furious. *One possibility, illustrated, was to streamline the bridge (reducing it to light cruiser proportions) and the funnel.*

The alternative seemed to be to improve air flow by splitting the ship's superstructure.

The next step was to remove one of the two superstructures. The laboratory happened to remove the starboard-side unit, but the lesson, that a single island was tolerable, had a wider application.

In February 1916 Sueter (and his chief, DAS) proposed that three of these cruiser-carriers be built. He argued that they were needed because the only large fast carrier, HMS *Campania*, was elderly and vulnerable to submarine attack.

The Controller (Rear-Admiral Tudor) very naturally saw the Biles-Holmes project less as a fully worked-out design in its own right, and more as the basis for a proper design, which he assigned DNC to develop. DNC (and, for that matter, the British shipbuilding industry) was badly stretched; although the Grand Fleet needed effective seaplane carriers, it also needed light cruisers, and the carrier would have to occupy a cruiser slip. By this time, too, it was obvious that the short flying-off deck would be inadequate. The Controller therefore suggested that the DNC design incorporate a flush deck (as in Williamson's proposal), as well as bulges (presumably essentially unknown to the two civilian designers), and a 5.5in battery. The DNC design eventually became HMS *Hermes*, the first purpose-built British carrier.

Admiral Tudor hoped, too, that the seaplane carriers would turn out to be a temporary expedient, and that large seaplanes and rigid airships would provide the fleet with the air cover it needed without limiting the production of essential warships of conventional type. This argument, which was raised on several occasions, was generally rejected, first because land-based aircraft could not keep station with the fleet, and second because there was always the possibility that naval operations would develop into open-ocean warfare, far beyond their range.

Biles and Holmes were not to be discouraged. Biles sent the design directly to C-in-C Grand Fleet, Admiral Jellicoe, who was painfully aware of the shortcomings of the *Campania* (which had not as yet returned from dockyard). Even though her captain considered the Biles-Holmes design too small (for example, in that it had so short a flying-off deck), Jellicoe supported the design. Early in May 1916 he asked the Admiralty to build one as soon as possible, or, at the least, to adapt the new large light cruisers of the *Glorious* class to carry some aircraft. The Admiralty did not act on this request, but in September (as noted in Chapter 3) it decided to rebuild the suspended liner *Conte Rosso* as the fleet carrier *Argus*. Meanwhile DNC developed what became *Hermes*, using much the original Biles-Holmes configuration.

Holmes became SAC's naval constructor. As such, he was responsible for the concept of leading uptakes into horizontal ducts, which made it possible to provide a fully flush deck in the first British carrier, HMS *Argus*. It was believed at the time that this configuration could be applied only to a relatively low-powered ship, and that higher power required more conventional uptakes. Hence Narbeth provided an island structure, built around uptakes, in the faster British carriers *Hermes* and *Eagle*.

In the flush-decked *Argus*, the two oval-section uptakes were led through an open space between the hangar roof and the underside of the flight deck. To avoid undue heating of the flight and hangar decks on either side of the uptakes, they were surrounded by outer castings through which electric fans drove cool air. When cruising, smoke was generally vented aft, under the flight deck, to emerge from its after end. However, special arrangements (to avoid back draft) had to be made in a following wind, or when aircraft were landing, or in port. Under those circumstances special dampers directed the smoke through vents on the quarters, where it was expelled by two large electric exhaust fans. These arrangements proved very successful on trial, but they emphasize the complexity of the flush-deck design.

There appears to have been some fear that funnel gases passing aft just under the end of the flight deck would make landing difficult. The open space below the flight deck seems to have been arranged to provide a flow of cool slow air to mix with the high-speed exhaust gases.[5]

The former liner shelter deck became the bottom of the hangar. The hangar roof became the ship's new strength deck, the ship's sides being extended directly upward by deep frames. The hangar was 330 × 68ft (clear width 48ft) × 25ft 6in (clear height 20ft under the deep girders). It was divided into four sections by full-height transverse fireproof roller curtains. The hangar roof in turn supported the separate flight deck 14ft 6in above it. The enclosed spaces alongside the hangar were used to stow spares, wings, propellers, etc, with large workshops immediately forward of the hangar proper, access to which was through large fireproof doors in the forward hangar bulkhead. Otherwise, access between the hangar and the rest of the ship was by air lock. This practice of treating the hangar as a source of considerable danger and structurally isolating it from the rest of the ship characterized British carrier design for another three decades.

Below the shelter deck, the major changes were provision for bomb and petrol sewage, and additional boiler power for somewhat higher speed. The ship was provided with four 200kW steam generators and one 100kW diesel generator (for harbour service).

In 1916–17 'flush deck' had only a limited meaning. Designers such as Holmes were by no means willing to do away with superstructures altogether, thought they were willing to minimize the extent (and particularly the length) of such obstructions on the flight deck. Moreover, designers thought in terms of two separate but connected structures, a flying-on deck aft and a flying-off deck forward. The flying-on deck would support a massive arresting structure, intended to bring an approaching aircraft to a smooth stop, and it was headed by a safety net. The flying-off deck had to be flat. It might be convenient to bring aircraft directly from one to the other, merely fuelling them before re-launching, but it was more realistic to imagine striking aircraft below after they had been arrested, and then moving serviced aircraft up to the flying-off deck.

This type of operation determined what would now be called flight-deck configuration. In HMS *Argus*, a very long space aft was provided for the arrester gear. The minimal superstructure was split into two parallel islands, between which the safety net might be strung.[6] A navigating bridge connected the two islands, leaving about 20ft clear height above the flight deck. The striking-down lift was set just abaft the two islands. It could also be used to bring up large aircraft, which would need longer take-off runs. In the original *Argus* design, the deck narrowed sharply foward, resembling the flying-off platforms of the seaplane carriers. It was fed by a lift just forward of the two islands. The dimensions of the two lifts indicated their functions. Aircraft could be folded before being lowered into the hangar, so the after lift was 60ft long, but only 18ft wide. The extra length allowed for large aircraft, which might have to begin their take-off runs abaft the islands. The forward lift was intended to take aircraft which had already been spread, so that they could be launched in quick succession – an important consideration in a torpedo attack; it measured 30 × 36ft.

However, the forward hatch opening in the flight deck was actually 56ft wide, two 10ft-wide roller platforms closing the gap between it and the lift when the latter was up. When the lift was down, the two platforms could be brought into the centre of the deck to cover the centre of the gap, so that aircraft could roll over it and thus enjoy 30ft more of take-off run.

The hangar was closed aft only by a moveable fire curtain. Seaplanes, then, could be hoisted into it over the stern, by two large cranes. Thus, although *Argus* was designed primarily to operate wheeled aircraft, she was well adapted to the floatplanes

At the end of the war, Furious *was scheduled for reconstruction with an island superstructure, as shown here.*

The ideal was a flush deck, but it seemed very difficult to realize. This was a proposed flush deck design for HMS Eagle, *developed in about April 1918.*

An island configuration was developed for the small carrier Vindictive, *but she was too far advanced to be changed before completion.*

in use when she was designed (which could fly off her flight deck, using the usual droppable wheels or trolleys).

Aircraft arrangements included provision for fuel, which in 1917 was carried in standard commercial 2-gallon tins; *Argus* carried 4000, in a special compartment forward, surrounded by voids. They (and a man) were carried up to the flight deck by lift. As in contemporary magazines, the upward path was interrupted by a fire barrier. Bulk stowage, as in modern carriers, was rejected because existing flexible piping leaked and could not easily be flushed to eliminate explosive petrol fumes.

Armament was four 4in anti-aircraft guns and two 4in low-angle guns (to defend against submarines).

This was much the design concept applied during 1917 to HMS *Hermes* and then to HMS *Eagle*. The *Argus* design was tested in a wind tunnel at the National Physical Laboratory in November 1916. Although the tests showed that her design would make landing-on difficult, no changes were made at the time, and similar twin-island features were incorporated into the 1917 carrier designs. However, in 1918 experience with HMS *Furious* clearly demonstrated the effects of turbulence caused by a massive superstructure, and drastic changes were ordered. *Argus* emerged with a true flush deck, her small chart-house retracting into it.

AS COMPLETED IN MARCH 1918 (see Chapter 3), HMS *Furious* was intermediate between the seaplane carriers and the flat-deck ships. Experience in her operation, particularly with her aero-dynamics, led to modifications to *Argus*, *Hermes* and *Eagle*, which had actually been designed before she became operational.

Following the landing trials, Captain Nicholson decided to use canvas to fair the after part of the ship, so as to try to eliminate the radical variations in wind speed which had caused the bumping. This appears not to have been done. Wind tunnel tests showed that it would have done little good, as the massive superstructure was the main problem.

The landing-on deck was abandoned altogether after nine crashes into the safety barrier. This failure also showed that *Vindictive* would have been unable to recover aircraft. Moreover, it showed that the relatively simple merchant ship conversions Beatty had proposed late in 1917 would have been unable to recover their aircraft, since they, too, would have retained their massive superstructures and centreline funnels.

Much of the ship's unfortunate behaviour had been predicted on the basis of NPL wind tunnel tests. Unfortunately, NPL's assessment of pilot behaviour seems to have been unrealistic. The laboratory assumed that pilots would come in high, but they preferred to fly very close to the deck. In fact they wanted a round-down aft, so that they did not have to fear coming just *below* deck level when the ship pitched.

Furious was, then, entirely unsatisfactory as a carrier, since she could not safely recover her aircraft. Model tests confirmed that the foremast and control top considerably affected air flow over the ship, and there were suggestions that mast and funnel be faired, or that the bridge be replaced by a light cruiser type structure (still set on the centreline) on a flush deck. By June 1918, as in the other fast carriers under construction, DNC was developing a design to convert *Furious* into a single-island (starboard side) ship. Most of the changes were to be concentrated above the forecastle deck, the funnel casing and ventilators being brought out from the centreline and the two foremost 5.5in guns being moved outboard about 5ft. A new superstructure would be built around the funnel to carry anti-aircraft guns, searchlights, and navigating arrangements, and the gangway between the former flying-off and flying-on decks expanded into a new midships deck about 120ft long

(80ft wide). The former conning tower would be eliminated.

Nothing was done immediately, first because it seemed wise to await tests aboard a truly flush-decked carrier, HMS *Argus*, and second because *Furious* was already too valuable to lay up for reconstruction. However, work on the reconstruction design was begun, and continued at least until May 1919, on the understanding that the ship would eventually be rebuilt. This work provided the Admiralty with plans for the reconstruction of all three large light cruisers. The proposed return of *Eagle* to Chile therefore amounted not to the abandonment of carrier aviation, but its postponement pending conversion of one or more of these ships.

ACA proposed early in January 1919 that *Furious* be rebuilt with a completely flush deck. The First Sea Lord, Admiral Beatty, rejected any immediate conversion because it was so important that the ship, still the only really fast British carrier, be available for experimental work during the summer of 1919. She therefore underwent an ordinary refit at Rosyth (4–19 February 1919).

At this time it seemed likely that the ship would be rebuilt beginning in the winter of 1919. There was still some question as to whether she should have an island superstructure, and in principle the decision was put off pending experience with the island carrier *Eagle*. However, by late 1918 money was already clearly tight, as the wartime Vote of Credit was scheduled to expire on 31 March 1919. Numerous cancellations were necessary, not least in order to clear slips for commercial construction to replace war losses. Under these circumstances, it seemed unlikely that the Treasury would sanction completion of HMS *Eagle* as a carrier; instead, the Admiralty was requested to return the ship to Chile.[7] The early reconstruction of HMS *Furious* thus became a moot issue.

ACA strongly supported the flush deck idea, and in January 1919 he asked DNC to report on the possibilities for completion in that form, with either full or reduced power. He was particularly concerned that any further reconstruction be thought through carefully as (in the absence of new carrier construction) HMS *Furious* would probably remain the fastest British carrier for as much as ten or fifteen years. He feared, moreover, that the provision of an island might limit future British carrier aircraft, an idea echoed by many later naval airmen, including those who designed the huge US carrier *United States* in 1946–49.

Armstrong proposed that the funnel be cut off just above the waterline and branched to either side of the ship, emerging through short (2ft) coamings on either side. DNC rejected this idea, as the fold forming the upper side of each transverse uptake would become extremely hot, and therefore would soon collapse. Moreover, with the coamings removed (so that aircraft could fly on), funnel gases would prove highly dangerous to aircraft and to any men on deck. An alternative scheme, in which the uptakes discharged through the ship's sides (as in *Argus*), was also rejected (March 1919).

However, Narbeth would subsequently reconsider the flush-deck approach, and it was eventually applied to HMS *Furious* (see Chapter 5).

THE OTHER LINE OF DEVELOPMENT in British carrier design was represented by *Argus*, with her fully flush deck. She had been designed with two small islands, one of which had actually been mounted (with the other lying on the jetty alongside ready for installation) in April 1918, when the *Furious* trials made it painfully obvious that islands would create problems. At ACA's suggestion, she was fitted with a bridge under her flying deck, to give a clear view forward on either side, supplemented by a temporary (retractable) structure on the flight

5. In his account of early British carrier projects in *Warship* 36 (October 1985), D K Brown states that the air flow under the flight deck was intended to fill in the void left by the ship, and so to smooth out air flow aft. However, it seems noteworthy no such space was provided in the cruiser-carrier *Hermes*, designed by the same group at about the same time. Note, however, that the *Argus* design was complete by late 1916 (and was tested in a wind tunnel at the National Physical Laboratory in November), whereas the *Hermes* design did not emerge until the following April, after wind-tunnel tests would have demonstrated the limited value of the under-deck space. The *Argus* Ship's Cover, which should provide evidence on this score, begins well after the point of such design decisions.

6. In August 1916 the builder, Beardmore, was asked for alternative designs for navigation and ship control, either by structures above the flight deck or, as an alternative, by placing the bridge arrangements right forward and under the flying deck. Both alternatives were considered by a committee of the Naval Air Department in November 1916. It recommended that the bridges be erected on the flight deck, partly because the flush-deck scheme seemed so unworkable from a ship control point of view.

7. It is not altogether clear whether the Admiralty seriously intended to return the ship. Certainly many in the Royal Navy wanted her retained and completed, and certainly, too, the Navy was quick, in 1920, to produce figures showing that she would cost more to return than to complete as a carrier. Admiralty remarks concerning her return have the air of responding almost pro forma to Treasury demands for excessive economies.

HMS Argus *as designed with two islands, from a Beardmore plan dated 3 October 1917, which was brought to the United States by Stanley Goodall. The hangar roof shows the arrangement of the funnel ducts.* NF

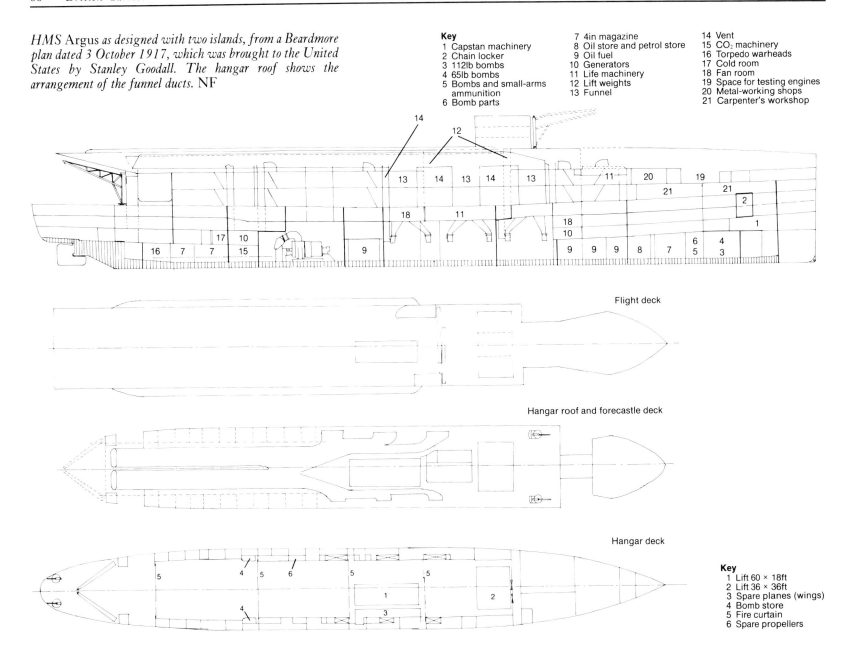

Key
1 Capstan machinery
2 Chain locker
3 112lb bombs
4 65lb bombs
5 Bombs and small-arms ammunition
6 Bomb parts
7 4in magazine
8 Oil store and petrol store
9 Oil fuel
10 Generators
11 Life machinery
12 Lift weights
13 Funnel
14 Vent
15 CO₂ machinery
16 Torpedo warheads
17 Cold room
18 Fan room
19 Space for testing engines
20 Metal-working shops
21 Carpenter's workshop

Flight deck

Hangar roof and forecastle deck

Hangar deck

Key
1 Lift 60 × 18ft
2 Lift 36 × 36ft
3 Spare planes (wings)
4 Bomb store
5 Fire curtain
6 Spare propellers

deck, for use at night, in pilotage waters, and when she was not flying her aircraft. The two large cranes and the anti-aircraft guns planned for mounting on deck were relocated.[8]

Stability was a problem from the first, as liners were designed for very limited metacentric height (for steadiness). Moreover, all of the equipment added to the ship, which was new and therefore could easily gain weight during the design stage, was very high in the ship. At an early design conference before SAC, on 24 November 1916, DNC cautioned that the ship might not be stable enough, but the builder, Beardmore, disagreed, and in March 1917 the firm guaranteed at least 1ft in the light condition, and 2.5ft in load condition (3.3ft in deep condition at the end of 1917). DNC wanted the ship inclined as soon as possible after launch, and on 21 April 1918 an inclining experiment showed 1.6ft in light condition and 3.3ft in load condition (2000 tons of oil fuel; 3.8ft fully loaded). However, as completed the ship needed 600 tons of ballast, 225 in the starboard wings abreast the engine room, 175 in the port wings abreast the engine room, and 200 tons of pig iron in the shaft passages, to maintain the design figures.[9]

At sea, given her high centre of gravity (and the substantial quantities of loose water and oil in her machinery spaces),

Argus had a very low GM and was therefore quite steady; given her high freeboard, she was also very dry. She did tend to heel very noticeably when turning (5 to 10 degrees with 5 degrees of rudder on trial, but at full speed and full helm only 14 to 15 degrees, with a 500 yard turning circle). Her captain reported that she could 'turn like a top' at medium or high speed, but that she manoeuvred poorly at low speed in wind, due to her enormous sail area.

This behaviour raised the question of the proper metacentric height for a carrier. Narbeth favoured limited GM, partly because it made lighter hull scantlings acceptable. DNC found limited GM acceptable because the ship would be on a steady course when launching or recovering her aircraft. The issue then would be her steadiness in a seaway.

Even so, the ship's stability was unsatisfactory. By December 1922, 441 tons had been added since completion (150 tons of ballast, 56 tons of arrester gear, 10 tons to raise the after end of the flight deck, 30 tons for extending funnel ducts, about 75 for painting and 100 miscellaneous). When the ship was inclined in July 1922, her light displacement was 13,503 tons and her metacentric height had fallen by 0.83ft (from 0.49ft at 13,062 tons to -0.34ft). DNC proposed that she be girdled (that is,

8   The removal of the islands seems in retrospect to have been something of a panic reaction. The constructor on the scene, probably W A D Forbes, wrote to DNC that he doubted that removal would make much difference, since the bridges were so much smaller than those in HMS *Furious*. He wanted the ship completed and steamed at speed to test the effect of the islands. They had, after all, vast advantages for other purposes, such as repelling destroyer and submarine attacks, signalling and ship control.

9   Beardmore estimates were based on a light displacement of 11,850 tons, but when inclined officially light displacement came to 12,120 tons, and GM was –0.05ft, the centre of gravity having risen 0.75ft.

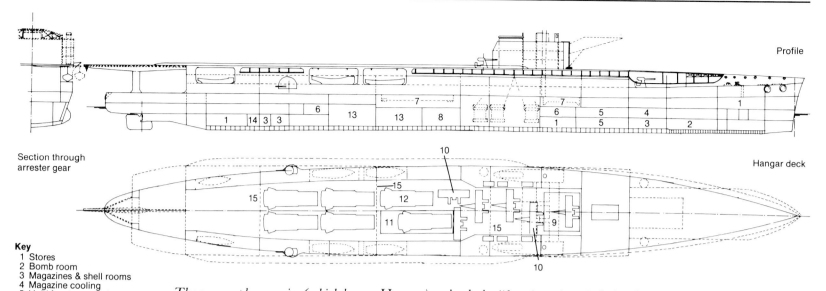

Profile

Section through arrester gear

Hangar deck

Key
1 Stores
2 Bomb room
3 Magazines & shell rooms
4 Magazine cooling
5 Hold for stowage of small aircraft in cases
6 Generators
7 Lift machinery
8 Oil fuel
9 Lift 30 × 30ft
10 Sopwith Baby seaplane
11 Lift 60 × 18ft
12 Short 184 seaplane
13 Engine room
14 Torpedo & bomb room
15 Fire curtain
16 Oil abreast engine and boiler rooms

The new seaplane carrier (which became Hermes) *as sketched in March 1917. The objects in the hangar are Short Seaplanes (184s) and Sopwith Baby seaplanes (the smaller ones); a Sopwith rests on the forward (30 × 30ft) lift. The after lift is 60 × 18ft. The ship shows a gantry aft for seaplane recovery while underway. The raised object on the flight deck is the arrester gear, as yet undefined.* NF

provided with a wooden belt) to restore stability, under the 1923–24 programme. The work was in fact deferred until late 1923, after the two new carriers *Hermes* and *Eagle* had been completed.

However, *Hermes* went to the Mediterranean in August 1924, leaving *Argus* as the only Atlantic carrier. She was needed for training and experimental work, and girdling was deferred until *Furious* could be completed. The formal proposal was submitted to the Board on 12 May 1924. The legend and drawings were approved in March 1925, for completion under the 1925–26 programme.

Girdling provided the occasion for a larger refit, which included new fixed-ammunition 4in guns (as proposed by DNO in November 1923), new radio masts, and bulk petrol stowage. The girdle was 3ft thick and 19ft high, extending over about 70 per cent of the length of the ship amidships (beam over fenders increased to 75ft 9in), deep displacement rising from 16,180 (15,775 as completed) to 16,750 tons. Draft was reduced from 23ft 3in (22ft 9in as completed) to 22ft 10in, and speed reduced by a quarter knot (20.25 to 20.0 knots). The effect of girdling was that it was no longer necessary to carry water ballast in the double bottom and oil fuel compartments, as fuel no longer had to be adjusted to maintain stability.

Sea trials revealed that the horizontal funnels, perhaps the ship's most innovative feature, were entirely successful. *Argus* proved slightly slower than expected (21,500shp = 20.5 knots on a 4-hour trial in 1918; on a contractor's trial in September 1918 she made 21,376shp = 20.506 knots at 15,266 tons). She had twelve cylindrical (Scotch) boilers, six double-ended and six single-ended, and burned about 250 tons of fuel oil per day, so that her 2000 tons were good for eight days at 20 knots, 3840nm. Compared to conventional warship water-tube boilers, the Scotch boilers took longer to raise steam. All had to be used to make full speed, so the ship had to be laid up at regular intervals for boiler cleaning.

Although the *Argus* design always showed space reserved for arrester gear, specific approval to fit it was given only in July 1918. The wires were taken from HMS *Furious*, the system being very similar. In all, fifty-four wires, 9in apart, ran between two ramps set 100ft apart, one just abaft the forward

lift and one just abaft the after lift. Both ramps were 40ft 8in wide and 15in high, the wires being supported between them by a fiddle bridge. The forward ramp was 42ft long, with a 24ft flat section between angled sections at each end; the after ramp was 17ft long, and of triangular section.

The arrester gear was set to port to allow for the erection of a dummy island (see below), which would be used to test the island-starboard arrangement then planned for *Eagle* and *Hermes*. Through this blocked the after lift, it presented no problem since the lift was not yet working.

The first trials, on 30 September, were touch-and-goes, with pilots testing the air flow over the deck. They found no bumps, and on 1 October a Sopwith 1½-Strutter made three successful landings, with wind over deck from 30 down to about 12 knots, in two cases landing well abaft the gear and taxying into it.

In July, the Admiralty decided to defer reconstruction of *Furious* and *Cavendish* (as starboard-island carriers) pending the results of trials aboard *Argus*. DNC observed that no trial aboard a fully flush-deck carrier could fairly represent conditions aboard an island ship, and suggested that Rosyth construct a wood-and-canvas dummy island. Even then, conditions would not be altogether comparable, as the island would not emit funnel gases. The Controller agreed to these trials, and an island similar to that planned for HMS *Eagle* was designed. The structure actually built was simpler, with (in effect) a single broad pseudo-funnel and no tripod mast.

Argus was brought alongside on 4 October, beginning a second set of trials on the 22nd. A smoke box was rigged at the after end of the island, the smoke wake matching NPL experimental data, and covering about two-thirds of the deck edge at the after end of the ship.

As in the first series, the aircraft (this time a Camel and a Pup) first made about forty flights around and over the ship, flying through her wake from all directions. Unfortunately the experienced pilot, in the Camel, suffered engine trouble and crashed. The Pup pilot had not previously flown over the ship, and maintained an unusually high speed (50 to 65mph) to be sure of maintaining control when over the deck. He therefore had to decelerate sharply to land, and frequently missed the wires. On the one occasion when he did touch, going very fast, he fortunately failed to catch the wires, which would have stopped him much too violently.

A Pup landed successfully on 24 October, and by 19 December 1918 thirty-six successful landings had been made, using 1½-Strutters and Pups. *Argus* was then refitted with modified arrester gear (23 December 1918 – 21 March 1919).

The arrester gear did present some problems. If an aircraft's

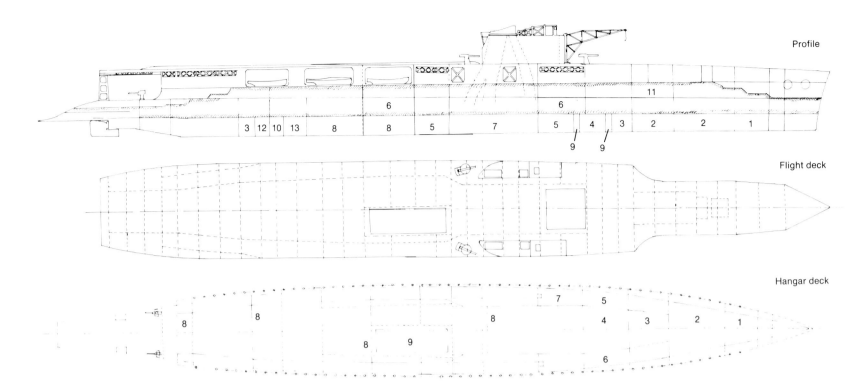

Profile

Flight deck

Hangar deck

The new seaplane carrier as conceived early in 1918. This drawing is adapted from one brought to the United States by Stanley Goodall, who advised the US Navy on carrier design. Flight and hangar decks are shown; note the opening at the after end of the hangar for seaplane recovery up the sloped slipway shown in the elevation. NF

wheels struck the wires they could act as springs, bouncing it over the side; Rutland suggested that gym mats be spread underneath to prevent such bounces. Similarly, an aircraft could swing as it bounced off the after ramp, coming into the wires at an angle. The gear also took a considerable time to rig and unrig, and while it was rigged aircraft could not be ranged over it for take-off.

To solve this last problem, the new gear substituted a depression in the deck (the after lift well) for the above-deck well created by the two ramps. With the lift up, the wires lay flush on deck and aircraft could roll over them as they lined up for take-off. With the lift 15in down, a well suitable for arresting was formed, a 10ft wooden ramp being placed at the forward end of the well. Now there was no longer an after ramp to throw an aircraft back into the air, but the new arrester gear put the after lift out of action, and the sides of the lift opening were a source of danger to an aircraft drifting sideways or slewing. Since the gear was now considerably narrower, it demanded a higher degree of pilot skill.

Both systems were inherently dangerous. If a pilot landed too far aft or too slowly, he might stop abaft the wires and be blown over the side. If he landed too fast, he might have his undercarriage torn off in the wires. He did not necessarily know that any of his hooks had engaged, and so might crack up trying to abort what he took to be a failed landing. There was as yet no Landing Signals Officer; the pilot had to judge his distance and his approach entirely by himself, as at an airfield ashore.

The pilots aboard *Argus* considered the system promising, but wanted a much longer well. The well, however, was objectionable because it projected below the level of the flight deck. In *Argus* this could mean interference with the smoke ducts. In

the spring of 1919 DNC proposed an alternative, to raise the ramps by pneumatic power, and then only after a taxying aircraft rolled over a trigger plate set in the flight deck abaft the arrester gear. The pilots accepted this idea (which was tested in 1920 aboard HMS *Eagle*) with the important caveat that a pilot could not know that he had triggered the ramps, whereas he would feel the bump of falling into a well.

The well was installed aboard *Argus*. DNC initially proposed to use the port side of the after lift (45ft recess), but the pilots wanted (and obtained) the widest space available, 58ft. It turned out that the smoke piping would not be disturbed as long as the recess was 9- rather than 14in deep, and trials with a 1½-Strutter showed that this was acceptable. Experiments began in April 1919, and the landing-on trap was enlarged in October.

This time trials were so successful that the ship was despatched to accompany the Atlantic Fleet on its January 1920 Spring Cruise, carrying eight 1½-Strutters (Clerget engines), four Camel fighters, two Fairey floatplanes (for harbour exercises), and two DH 9As (Liberty engines).[10]

Experience in the Atlantic tended to confirm the earlier view that the primary object of arrester gear was to hold the landed aircraft down on deck, and indeed that pilots should land directly in the trap, so that they were held from the moment of touching. Otherwise ship motion and wind might well still blow the aircraft over the side, as occurred in three cases. Although *Argus* was relatively steady, her deck was very high above water, and this height tended to amplify her motion. When the ship pitched, pilots tended to come in too high for fear of hitting below the flight deck on the down-stroke of the pitch. The ship's captain suggested that the after end of the deck be rounded down to solve this problem.

Following the exercises, a conference was convened aboard *Argus* (13 May 1920) to discuss revised landing arrangements. It decided that the well should be at least 300ft long and 16in deep, with a 60ft run at each end. It later turned out that arrester gear would provide too short a take-off run. The solution was to work the forward ramp by power, so that it could be collapsed and an aircraft run over it while taking off. There was no

10   The exercise programme emphasized air operations, including the first reconnaissance flights from a carrier, as well as action observation during a gunnery and torpedo exercise with HMS *Queen Elizabeth*. In the latter, the aircraft passed enemy report and change of course signals. These exercises showed that stronger aircraft radio transmitters were needed. Signals could be received at 30 to 50nm, but only when little interference was present. More power would also make it easier to take radio direction-finding fixes on aircraft, which were proving valuable as a means of checking aircraft position.

Key
1 Stores
2 Bomb room
3 Magazines and shell rooms
4 Petrol
5 Generators
6 Lift machinery
7 Boiler room
8 Engine room
9 Air space
10 Torpedo warheads
11 RNAS ratings' mess
12 CO₂ machinery
13 Spirit room

Key
1 Capstan room
2 Seamen's & stokers' mess
3 RNAS ratings' mess
4 Mess
5 Intelligence office & ship's office
6 Stoker POs' mess
7 RNAS officers' mess
8 Fire curtain
9 Lift 60 × 18ft

fixed after ramp, the wires being supported aft by an 18in slotted hurdle, which was also power-worked. Between the hurdle and the ramp, 15in hinged flaps were spaced about 50ft apart.

A power-worked pallisade was fitted to keep aircraft which had not been engaged from falling over the side. To balance the increased weight of the arrester gear, 150 tons of permanent ballast were added (total increase was about 240 tons). Pallisades were expected to add another 40 tons high in the ship, requiring another 100 tons of ballast.

The after lift had to be locked in position, and the after end of the deck rounded down to cover the after deck connections for the wires. Foward, the wires fed into a mechanical tensioning device.

This system was installed and tested aboard HMS *Eagle* in the summer and early autumn of 1920, and went to sea aboard *Argus* (which carried ten Panthers and three Fairey IIICs) for the 1921 Spring Cruise.[11] It was quite satisfactory, the only complaint being that the flaps could not house flat. Of forty-five landings, generally in bad weather, thirty-one were made enitrely without damage, and only two involved serious accidents, both attributed to pilot inexperience. This was considered comparable to accident rates ashore. The fleet commander, Admiral Madden, attributed this distinct improvement (over 1920) largely to better arrester gear and easier landings.

Given reliable arrester gear, the fleet could concentrate the tactical implications of carrier operations. The ship had to head directly into the wind to launch or recover her aircraft, thus often in a direction other than the course of the main body.[12] In the worst case, with the wind blowing from astern, the carrier would have to steam opposite, away from the main body, at a relative speed of perhaps 30 to 45 knots. Every minute she spent launching or recovering sent her further away. There might not be sufficient ships to cover a carrier separated from the main body of the fleet, and returning aircraft might not be able to reach her, or even to find her.

Considerable effort therefore went into reducing launch and recovery intervals. During the 1921 Spring Cruise, typical intervals were 30 minutes to launch two aircraft (on a course opposite to that of the fleet), 40 to fly two off and land one, and

25 to land three. One problem was that the rotary-engined reconnaissance aircraft could not be run in place for long periods, and so had to be started up only 1 or 2 minutes before take-off. However, they could take as much as 10 minutes to start.

One question was whether the carrier could operate with the wind slightly off her bow. Tests in 1921 showed that an upward current on the windward side, extending about two-thirds the length of the ship, curled up over the flight deck and eddied across it. For example, when a Panther landed aboard with the ship 5 degrees off the wind, the rising current lifted one wing and the crossing eddies carried the aircraft across the wires. Because the aircraft was tilted, its lee wing was forced under the wires. This slewed it around, causing it to stand on its nose, smashing its propeller. Admittedly, this was in less than ideal weather, with the wind shifting and gusty, so that the ship could not really keep her head to the wind. However, the general lesson seemed to be that aircraft could not land into the existing arrester gear without being damaged, unless the ship remained within 3 degrees of the wind.

One way of reducing the loss of position due to landing was to land aircraft over the bow rather than the stern, when the wind blew the wrong way, so that the carrier would not have to turn out of line. As a test of this idea, the *Furious* model was tested stern to wind in the NPL wind tunnel.[13]

Argus was always very limited as a carrier. She was slow, and her flight deck was so narrow that she was limited to small aircraft (deck landings of Fairey IIIDs were prohibited in June 1928).[14] She had only a single small lift (her after lift had been fixed in place in 1918), and could accommodate no more than eighteen aircraft.[15] Moreover, because she was so small, she was more affected by heavy seas than were the other carriers. She was, therefore, a prime candidate for scrapping to release treaty-limited carrier tonnage for replacements (see Chapter 5). However, she had a strong hull (surveyed in 1927 and found good for another fifteen years), and she survived the interwar period, mainly because the British government was unwilling to pay for a new carrier.

HMS Argus *as completed, 1918, in dazzle camouflage. The masts and charthouse have been raised.* FAAM

11 Tactically, the main lesson of the 1921 Spring Cruise seems to have been the need for continuing improvement in the radio performance of reconnaissance, as transmissions could still be jammed relatively easily. Aircraft could not reliably receive replies to their reports, they could not judge the effect of jamming and hence did not switch to other channels to avoid it.

12 She had steam jets on her stem and on each bow to assist in pointing into the wind.

13 US carriers were later actually fitted with bow arrester gear, specifically to permit aircraft to land over the bow.

14 The small lift (36ft 2in square) could not accommodate Fairey IIID, which was 36ft 9in long when folded. In 1922 DNC suggested that an appendage (25 × 9ft) be added at its after end, but nothing was done.

15 In May 1925 the air complement was only fifteen, consisting of one flight of fighters (three), one of fleet spotters (six), and one of fleet reconnaissance aircraft (six).

HMS Argus as completed, 1918. Note that her large after lift has not yet been fixed in a position slightly below the flight deck, as was later done to form a part of her arrester gear. This drawing has been adapted from drawings included in the DNC history of wartime naval construction. NF

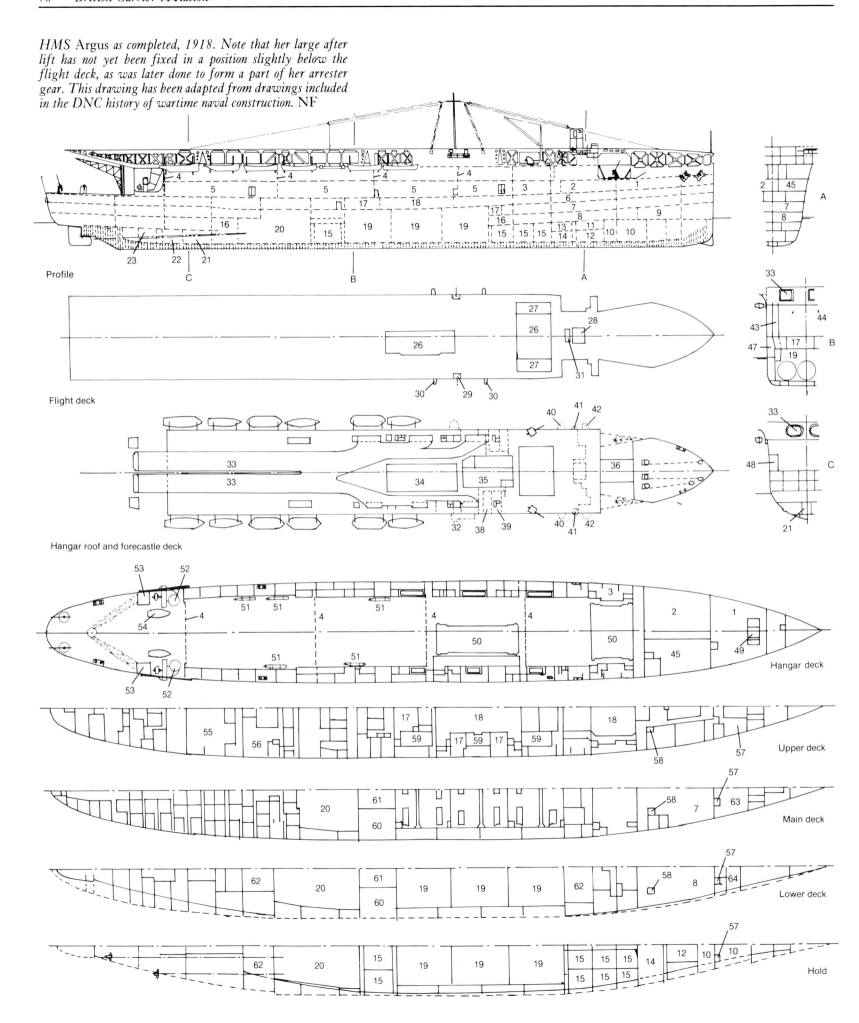

Profile

Flight deck

Hangar roof and forecastle deck

Hangar deck

Upper deck

Main deck

Lower deck

Hold

As money grew tight in the late 1920s, HMS *Argus* was laid up at Plymouth at standard (fourteen-day) notice, and then, in September 1932, reduced to Extended Notice (four months) at Rosyth. She joined the Reserve Fleet at Roysth on 15 December 1932. In January 1936, however, the Royal Navy needed (and the treaties allowed it) additional carriers. In January 1936, DNAD proposed that *Argus* be brought from reserve as a training carrier. Hangar spraying (which had been vetoed in 1929, when she went into reserve), and the new transverse arrester gear would have been installed. Instead, in February 1936, the Controller proposed that she be refitted as a Queen Bee (radio-controlled AA target) tender and training carrier, the former function having been deleted from the planned Trade Protection Carrier (see Chapter 7). The Board approved the conversion on 20 April 1936. Thus Admiral Henderson was able to preserve a potential wartime carrier; design studies showed that the Queen Bee role could have been carried out by a much smaller ship.

This new reconstruction included re-boilering (with destroyer boilers), installation of an accelerator on the centreline, and four-wire arrester gear. Since the new boilers were considerably lighter than the old, and since many of the additions were on the flight deck, reconstruction aggravated the ship's old stability problem. No armament was required, but the space occupied by the six 4in guns was left free. The flight deck was widened by 10ft to make landing easier. This in turn reduced the elevation of guns, should they be required in future; plans for potential re-armament were re-cast to show sponsons for No 1 gun on each side. Completion was originally scheduled for December 1937, but it was delayed to release the accelerator to the new carrier *Ark Royal*. *Ark Royal* was actually completed on 30 July 1938, running her sea trials 10 and 11 August 1938.

Argus was considered an unarmed auxiliary, but there was always the possibility that she might be employed in wartime as an operational carrier, perhaps for trade protection, pending the completion of further carriers. She had not even been included in the naval rearmament programme laid out in 1935, because it had been assumed that she would be scrapped on completion of HMS *Ark Royal* (she was saved by a change in treaty conditions). In 1937 DNO proposed an emergency war armament, to consist of two 4in Mk V guns and one 8-barrel pom-pom, but this was really the wartime battery of an auxiliary. DTSD wanted the most powerful possible battery for trade route operations, using all six existing positions. Since he could not provide a close-range weapon with all-round fire (one on the quarter-deck would have no overhead arc, and would suffer from funnel gas), he sought, therefore, to install two 4-barrel pom-poms, leaving 4in positions. Another alternative was six 4in guns and two 4-barrel pom-poms.

Nothing so elaborate was ever installed. *Argus* began World War II as an unarmed training carrier, in the Mediterranean (which was then at peace). By April 1940, however, she had two 4in guns and three quadruple .5in machine-guns. She was transferred to the Home Fleet during 1940, and then to Force H, temporarily replacing the sunken *Ark Royal*, late in 1941. Her aircraft capacity was very limited, and in January 1942 her captain proposed fitting a safety barrier on her flight deck, so that six aircraft could be parked on deck. It was approved, and DAM suggested similar barriers for the other surviving old carriers. However, a similar barrier proposal (for *Furious*) had already been rejected.

By October 1942 *Argus* was armed with four 4in guns, four small-calibre machine-guns (presumably quadruple .5s), and thirteen Oerlikons, a battery she retained through the war (except that six .303in Hotchkiss were added between October 1943 and April 1944). She served as an operational carrier

during Operation Torch, in November 1942, but reverted to training carrier duty in 1943.

Argus was clearly far too slow and far too tender to function as a first-line carrier during World War II, but from September 1939 on she was valuable as a convoy escort and as an aircraft transport. In May 1941, for example, it was estimated that she could accommodate sixty Hurricanes on her flight deck, in addition to three Fulmars and twenty-nine Hurricanes in her hangar. It is not clear to what extent she actually served as an aircraft transport.

By October 1943 she was listed as 'to be regarded as at six months' notice for operational service,' and on 27 January 1944 the Admiralty ordered her paid off, replaced as deck training ship by an auxiliary carrier. She was too old and her machinery was worn out. However, in March 1944 she was ordered to be taken in hand for refit and conversion to Aircraft Freighter about the end of the year, to carry sixty to seventy aircraft. Instead, she became accommodation ship at Chatham. Scrapping was approved on 6 May 1946, and she was sold that December, scrapping beginning in 1947.

THE DESIGN FOR *Hermes* fell victim, in part, to the radical changes in carrier technology between 1917 and 1918. The 1917 carrier programme called for the two ocean-going ships (one of which became HMS *Hermes*) to be able to operate both land-planes (with flying-off and landing-on decks) and float-planes (with the slipway conceived by Biles and Holmes in 1915 and strongly recommended by Fifth Sea Lord in March 1917). DNC produced a sketch design in April 1917 (sufficient, he claimed, for the builders to proceed) and then a detailed design and legend in January 1918. Details of the April 1917 design are given in Table 4-1. DNC presented the design with two caveats: first, that the bow should be plated up to the flight deck (to protect against seas coming in under the front end of that deck and damaging it), and second, that the ship should be enlarged to provide better accommodation, as the hangar took up much of the internal volume of the hull. Only the first was approved; it in turn required that the two forward anti-aircraft guns be moved onto the flight deck or into the island structures. They thus benefited from improved arcs of fire, and DNC suggested that the two midships anti-aircraft guns might be omitted in favour of four low-angle guns for anti-submarine protection.

In these designs, the air features demanded in February 1917 were supplemented by a bow catapult, which was intended to solve the problem of turning into the wind to launch: a catapult could turn into the wind, no matter what the carrier's course. The Air Department hoped, too, that catapult take-offs would be possible even if the ship rolled and pitched too violently for conventional rolling take-offs. Although ultimately the ship did not receive a catapult, these were important considerations in the much later revival of such devices. At the time, DAS hoped that the catapult could be arranged so as not to obstruct conventional rolling take-offs. In early 1918 five catapults were being built for test; two were complete and one had made successful launches.

The seaplane slip was the other vital design feature. It consisted of a rigid portion attached directly to the ship, a flexibile transitional portion abaft that (to isolate the docking platform from the ship's rolling motion), and then a rigid submerged portion onto which the seaplane would taxi. The submerged portion would carry a trolley, onto which the aircraft would dock and which would be drawn up the stern of the carrier. The entire slipway could then be drawn up on board the ship.

The Air Department saw this slip as a hedge against the possibility that deck-landing aircraft would be unsuccessful,

HMS Argus *in 1918, showing the dummy island fitted for trials. A more elaborate structure, closer to that planned for HMS* Eagle, *was originally planned. Note the big seaplane cranes aft.*

Folded Sopwith Cuckoo torpedo-bombers in the hangar of HMS Argus, *with one on the lift (to the left). The structure between hangar roof and flight deck is clearly visible.* FAAM

and also as a means of supporting large seaplanes flying from shore bases. However, it was clearly experimental. In December, 1917 the Third Sea Lord (Controller) was 'very strongly of the opinion that no such fitting should be put into this ship until practical experiments have been made ... added to which the use of seaplanes in the Fleet appears to be very doubtful in the future.' Even so, when he submitted the fully worked-out design for Board approval in January 1918, DNC listed floatplanes (below) as its aircraft, with wheeled types only as an alternative.

The design was certainly adapted to operating deck-landing aircraft, with a long (500ft) flush deck, 300ft of which was abaft the two islands (each of which carried a single funnel). As in the 1916 Biles-Holmes proposal, a safety net was to be stretched between the islands to stop landing aircraft.

Hermes could be considered a natural development of the Biles-Holmes design, with a flush deck added to cover the midships hangar and the two side passages. The side uptakes extended up into the two islands. Structurally, the flush weather deck became the upper flange of the hull girder, and the side passages became the side walls of the hangar, which was closed forward and on the sides (it was open aft, to admit the floatplanes which would have been drawn up the slipway). This practice survived in later British carriers. It had the virtue of isolating the hazardous hangar area, which was filled with inflammable materials and, perhaps, with explosive petrol vapour. Making the flight deck a strength member also made for a deeper hull girder, and therefore for reduced stresses and lighter scantlings.

The general arrangement of the flight deck, hangars and lifts followed that of HMS *Argus*, the hangar accommodating six Short 184 two-seaters and six single-seat Sopwith Baby floatplanes. This compared with the design requirement to accommodate six single-seaters and eight two-seaters. In addition, a large hold forward of the hangar could take about ten small wheeled fighters. The design showed flying-off and flying-on

16 The catapult would still have been valuable as a means of launching aircraft in rough weather; the US Navy, which had catapults in service, reported that this would indeed be possible. DAS therefore continued to support the proposed catapult installation.

HMS Argus *in 1918, with her after lift lowered to create a pit as part of her arrester gear. This lift was soon fixed in place. Note the openings around the forward lift created by the sliding doors in the deck.*

decks, the bridge and the two funnels occupying two islands, leaving a clear width of 46ft between them. The flush flight deck, then, was over 500ft long, of which 300ft aft (for flying-on) had a clear width of about 70ft. The flight deck forward was well supported so that it could withstand the effects of heavy seas.

Other details generally followed current cruiser practice. Protection was similar to that in the large *Raleigh* class cruisers, but the flight deck (which was the strength deck) had to be fairly thick, adding some additional protection against bombing. Armament, however, was limited to six 4in guns, four of them for anti-aircraft fire and two low-angle (two forward, two amidships, and two aft). DNO requested four more to deal with submarines, but DNC wanted this issue deferred so that building could begin. The Fifth Sea Lord wanted something more (6in guns), but was dissuaded: the ship would always be screened, either by destroyers or by an accompanying cruiser or battle squadron.

The proposed powerplant duplicated that of the current D class light cruiser except for slightly larger boilers (30,000shp for 25 knots, and probably 40,000 for 27 knots if forced, with half the ship's fuel oil aboard). Compared to a cruiser, there was considerably more electrical and evaporating capacity, and two steering engines rather than one.

The ship was deliberately designed so that, were she no longer needed as a carrier, she could easily be converted into a satisfactory cruiser, her fore and aft holds having been designed for use as magazines.

The Legend and drawings for HMS *Hermes* were approved on 17 January 1918. By this time the builders had already ordered about 3000 tons of material, of which about 500 had been delivered. The Admiralty's proposed conversion of the Chilean battleship *Almirante Cochrane* (to become HMS *Eagle*) at the same yard, however, created competition for the same materials and the same labour supply. *Hermes* was laid down on time, on 15 January 1918, but after that progress was slowed because the battleship, which was quite far advanced, could be completed much more quickly.

Just before this, on 8 January, the *Hermes* design had been discussed by Grand Fleet officers, including ACA, aboard HMS *Repulse*. The conference effectively killed the slipway (deck-landing was clearly the wave of the future). It was also sceptical of the catapult, the fear being that it would interfere with natural flying-off; in particular, that any slight mechanical problem with the catapult might disable the flying-off deck altogether. It seemed, first, that a simple rotating flying-off deck, integrated with the flight deck, would be quite satisfactory, since it could be turned into the wind without turning the ship. It would be even simpler to widen the flight deck, so that aircraft could take off athwartships. DNC suggested an 80ft deck; the 100ft called for at the conference would be unsafe in a seaway. By mid-year the Controller had ordered the flight deck widened to 90ft.[16]

The conference objected to the existing hangar design. It wanted the fore and aft passages at the sides dispensed with. This was structurally impossible, and the double hangar walls provided necessary access and ventilation. The hangar arrangement also limited the volume into which petrol vapour could penetrate. The conference also complained that the ship was too slow; 32 knots would have been preferable. DNC countered that such a speed would require a ship the size of HMS *Furious*.

By mid-June, given the failure of the *Furious* trials, the Admiralty was no longer sure what configuration the carriers should have; wind tunnel models were being used to test alternatives. Therefore the builder, Armstrong, was ordered to seek specific Admiralty approval before doing any work above the hangar deck. Somewhat later an island configuration was selected.

The single island presented major problems. First, it introduced a heeling moment. In theory, it could have been balanced by moving the machinery to port, but little could actually be done. The alternative was ballast and fuel. The ship had been designed for 2000 tons of oil fuel, but another 500 could be added for trimming purposes, 1250 tons being stowed to port and 750 to starboard. The heel would reappear when the last 500 tons to port were burned, and then it could be corrected by flooding the port bulge (at a cost in underwater protection).

The other problem was to make up for the ventilators, offices, and uptakes lost when the port island was given up.

DNC also had to answer Admiral Beatty's demand that she be able to meet an enemy light cruiser. He proposed a new armament, eleven 6in guns and one 4in anti-aircraft gun. Ammunition stowage would present some problems (space would suffice only for 180rpg, rather than the usual 200), and some of the aircraft (RAF) ratings would have to pass ammunition and serve the guns. The new gun armament was approved in June 1918, and by December 1918 it had been revived again, to ten 6in and four 4in anti-aircraft. The 6in guns had origianlly been manufactured for the Chilean battleship *Almirante Cochrane*.

The revised design also showed two 44 × 20ft lifts, in place of the initially projected 50 × 18ft 6in and 32 ×'16ft units. The ship was not large enough to accommodate a lift as large as that of HMS *Eagle* (44ft × 33ft).

The net effect of the changes was to increase estimated displacement from 9760 to 10,110 tons, in both cases including 100 tons of permanent ballast.

Construction continued after the end of the war, and Armstrong (Elswick) launched the ship on 11 September 1919. By this time the Elswick yard was scheduled to close, and on 24 October the Admiralty ordered *Hermes* towed to a southern port for completion. She arrived at Devonport in January 1920.

By this time it appeared that HMS *Eagle* would have to be completed for Chile as a battleship, and the only other British ship with the same mounting, her sister-ship HMS *Canada*, would also be sold back to Chile, leaving *Hermes* as the only British ship with that particular type of 6in gun. It appeared, however, that the light cruiser *Birkenhead*, armed with 5.5in guns (as was HMS *Furious*), would also soon be sold; she could exchange guns with *Hermes*. In fact Britain retained *Eagle*, and *Birkenhead* was broken up. *Hermes*, however, was rearmed as proposed in 1920, with ten 5.5in guns.[17]

THE ADMIRALTY HAD BEGUN to seek another large carrier late in 1917. At this time the 28,000 ton Chilean battleship *Almirante Cochrane* lay incomplete on the stocks at Armstrong Whitworth, having been suspended upon the outbreak of war, and her sister ship, *Almirante Latorre*, had been taken over as HMS *Canada*. Given her great size, she was an attractive prospect for conversion. However, when *Canada* had been taken over, the British government had agreed to restore both ships to Chile at the end of hostilities.

At this time the ship's hull was nearly complete, but little of her armour (all of which was in the yard) had been fitted. Her boilers were on board, and the uptakes completed to forecastle deck level, and the machinery was nearly complete. Armstrong was actually manufacturing her boats. However, the guns and mountings planned for the ship had been diverted to monitors,

17 The 5.5 was a new calibre in the Royal Navy, thirty-eight such guns having been taken over from the Greek government at the outbreak of war, together with others aboard two light cruisers then under construction for Greece. This calibre had been chosen to conform with the French 5.5in (130mm) guns then scheduled for the battery of a new Greek battleship under construction in France. They proved very attractive to the Royal Navy, being lighter than the standard 6in, and thus truly hand-worked weapons. In April 1915 DNC therefore proposed to arm HMS *Furious* with them (in place of the triple 4in of her half-sisters). The Controller approved, on the ground that the 6in alternative was too unwieldy (he preferred a 5in gun, firing an 80lb shell rather than the 75lb of the 5.5, but it existed only on paper). The same gun was later used aboard HMS *Hood*.

so she could not be completed as a battleship. Similarly, her electric generators had been diverted to other service.

Because Chilean officers were present at the yard, DNC could not inspect the hull for fear of creating suspicion in their minds. Instead, he had to rely on the Assistant Manager for information on which to base the conversion design. The Board ordered the conversion on 25 January, and the ship was renamed HMS *Eagle* in March 1918.

The outline design for converting *Almirante Cochrane* was submitted to the Admiralty on 8 February 1918. It showed a 640ft flush deck with two 110ft islands, each carrying a tripod and two funnels. They were staggered lengthwise to make it more difficult for a submarine to estimate the ship's course, and were cross-connected with heavy bracing to provide a navigating platform, charthouse, wheelhouse, and the usual bridge equipment. The bracing left a clear height of 20ft over the flight deck, and the islands left a clear 68ft passage between them. This semi-enclosed space (including a portable wind screen forward) would shelter aircraft being assembled (that is, unfolded) for flight. The flight deck itself was 640ft long (220ft forward of the islands, and 310ft aft) and 100ft wide forward, so that (at least in theory) an aircraft could fly off in any direction. The choice of arrester gear was dependent on the outcome of the *Furious* trials.

A flight-deck catapult (as proposed for *Hermes*) was briefly considered, but rejected pending some decision on the smaller ship.

The 400ft hangar was large enough to take any existing naval aircraft; it could accommodate twenty-five Sopwith Cuckoos or a larger number of smaller aircraft. Width varied from 44 to 66ft, depending on the leads of uptakes, fan supplies, access, stowage, and ventilation, and clear headroom was 20ft throughout. The hangar was served by two lifts, one (50 × 20ft) near the bridge structure serving the forward deck, the other (50 × 33ft) at the very after end of the deck, to handle the largest aircraft (such as the twin-engine DH 10, which figured in some calculations), which would need a longer take-off run. Landing aircraft would presumably be pulled backwards out of the arrester gear. One 5-ton (45ft) electric crane was positioned at the after end of each island, to bring aircraft aboard and also to recover seaplanes and crashed aircraft. The starboard crane plumbed the forward lift and could therefore be used to lift aircraft on deck should that lift fail.

Armament was nine 6in (six near the bridges forward, three on the upper – hangar – deck aft), plus four 4in anti-aircraft guns on the navigating platform athwartships. The 6in guns had been ordered for the Chilean battleships, but their elevation was increased from 15 to 20 degrees. The battleship design included four submerged 21in torpedo tubes, but they were omitted in the carrier as they were not of standard service type and as the ship would carry her own torpedo-bombers.

About 15,000 gallons of petrol (in 2-gallon tins) would be stowed on her forecastle deck, protected by plating about an inch thick. The design also included two ready-use bulk stowage tanks (using hydraulic displacement) near the bridges, to fuel aircraft on the flight deck.

DNC hoped to improve her speed (compared to that of the battleship) by reducing weight (largely by reducing armour) and by providing arrangements to burn only oil when high speed was necessary. She was, therefore, rated at 37,000shp burning both coal and oil, but at 55,000 in a special oil-only overload condition, and DNC hoped for 24 knots, and perhaps as much as 25 when burning oil and only lightly loaded. At this time she was expected to carry 3200 tons of coal (arranged as far as possible for protection) and 1750 tons of oil, and to displace 25,900 tons fully loaded, compared to 28,000 for the battleship. As designed, the battleship had four 200kW turbo-generators; DNC proposed to add a 100kW diesel generator (which was later replaced by a 175kW unit, which was available earlier) and, if necessary, additional turbo-generators.

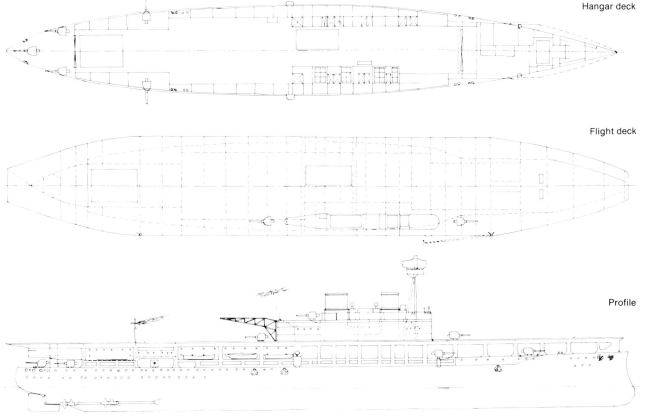

Hangar deck

Flight deck

Profile

HMS Eagle *as redesigned with a single island, July 1918. Note the three triple torpedo tubes on each side.* NF

A Sopwith Ship Strutter aboard HMS Furious, *1918, in her longitudinal-wire arrester gear. Note the hooks on the undercarriage axle and the propeller guards projecting forward of the axle, designed to protect the propeller in case the aircraft nosed over. The wires themselves were suspended over gym mats. Their height can be gauged from the legs of the crew member. The ramp, over which the wires were led, is visible in the foreground.* FAAM

The heavy barbette and main (9in) belt armour of the battleship were, therefore, eliminated. Instead the 4.5in armour intended for the strake between main and upper deck was used in place of the original main belt, with 1in plate worked above that to the upper deck. The side plating was increased to 3in for 3ft below the armour shelf, and above it 40lb protective plating was to be fitted to the side in addition to the 30lb hull plating. The hangar roof was a structural strength deck, and hence it was 40lb plating. The 60lb upper deck formed the floor of the hangar, and there was also a lower protective deck (40lb) 15ft below the upper deck. The two original armour bulkheads (fore and aft), 4in each, were retained.

Estimated complement was 800.

The Board approved outline drawings for the conversion on 14 February 1918, and DNC was asked to consider fitting the ship with above-water torpedo tubes. He offered six triples (as in HMS *Furious*, mounted two on each broadside on the main deck, and one each side on the forecastle, at the cost of 100 tons of coal capacity. DTM objected to the height and exposure of the two forecastle sets, and they were eliminated. The design was already quite tight, with the tubes encroaching on hangar and mess spaces.

Several objections were raised. Unlike *Argus*, *Eagle* used the roof of the hangar as the flight deck, and therefore could not accommodate separate shutters to close off the hangar deck when the lifts were down. DAS objected that this would reduce hangar stowage (since the lifts would generally have to be in the raised position and thus aircraft could not be stowed on them), that the lift openings could not easily be made weather-tight, and that it would be difficult to provide ventilators. Moreover, separation between the flight deck and the hangar deck would greatly simplify the installation and repair of arrester gear. These objections were so serious that DAS was willing to accept a reduction in hangar clear height (to 18ft) to provide his extra deck. However, the extra deck would have added unacceptable weight very high in the ship.

DAS wanted the lifts moved forward, and he wanted neither smaller than 46 × 20, preferably 55 · 22ft (the Aeronautical Technical Department wanted 36 × 55ft),[18] but, again, the larger lift imposed a greater weight penalty. Moreover, DAS wanted to be able to hoist aircraft up onto the quarter-deck and into the after end of the hangar, as in the other carriers.

Finally, DAS objected to any coal burning, since coal dust was extremely destructive to aircraft.

Admiral Beatty, the Grand Fleet commander, feared that the carrier might meet German light cruisers at night. He therefore asked for eight 6in guns and three triple torpedo tubes on each broadside, some of the weight coming from elimination of the 4in anti-aircraft guns (on the ground that fighters would be the ship's best protection against air attack). Beatty reversed his position after HMS *Furious* was bombed later in the year, demonstrating that carriers could be attacked with too little warning to launch their fighters and hence must rely instead on their AA. When the ship was redesigned in April, DNC was able to provide Beatty with his six tubes, but not with the extra 6in guns, and all four 4in were retained.

The major consequence of the *Furious* trials was to bring into question the designs of all the other carriers, all of which were interrelated. In April, the Controller asked DNC to redesign *Eagle* with a flush deck, on an urgent basis. The latter tried a variety of approaches, including funnels discharging through the ship's sides and low funnels on the flying deck itself, hinging or telescoping down to the deck as necessary; no such

18 As actually ordered, the forward lift was 46 × 20ft, the after one 46 × 33ft; they were required to make 35ft per minute over a run of about 25ft. Both were to have been cancelled when the ship was begun again in 1920, but the after lift was retained, its travel increased by about 18in. The standard load was 5 tons and the test dead load 7.5 tons (1921).

approach seemed practicable. Nor did it seem acceptable to narrow the funnels enough to leave a wider free space between them. DNC suggested, therefore, that the funnels be grouped together on the starboard side, leaving the deck to port entirely free. Although a port side location might have seemed more natural for navigation, the senior carrier commander, Captain W S Nicholson, and Wing Captain Clark Hall both pointed out that pilots preferred to come in from port and generally preferred to turn to port, for example when aborting their landings. It has been suggested that existing rotary engines caused aircraft to turn to the left rather than to the right, so that an obstruction to starboard was much less troublesome than one to port. Nicholson later pointed out that a starboard island was consistent with the rule of the road that a ship kept clear of ships on her starboard side.

This scheme was attractive because it was relatively inexpensive, both in time and in labour; it was also applicable to HMS *Hermes*, which suffered from the same problem. New plans were drawn at once, and sketches were shown to Nicholson, to ACA and to Admiral Beatty late in April 1918.

gained about 200 tons fully loaded (26,200 tons, draft 27ft rather than 26ft 10in).

Bombs were stowed in what had been the midships shell-room, on the platform deck between the after boiler and engine rooms, with steam pipes passing immediately overhead. In 1918 the Admiralty decided that bomb rooms would be treated as magazines, but it was by no means certain that bombs were as stable as shells. This issue was revived in 1925 by the ship's captain, the solution being to replace heat-sensitive Amatol-filled bombs with much less sensitive types filled with TNT or with 80/20 Amatol. It seemed unlikely that the bomb room could be efficiently cooled in areas such as the Mediterranean, where the upper decks could reach 90 degrees.

The design was somewhat cramped, this giving rise to an early instance of RAF-Royal Navy friction. The ship could accommodate 900 to 950 officers and men. The RAF initially asked for 246 men, who would be wholly engaged on air work. It was calculated, however, that if they did not serve the guns the ship would have to accommodate 1083, 100 too many. This seemed to leave three disagreeable options: reduce the

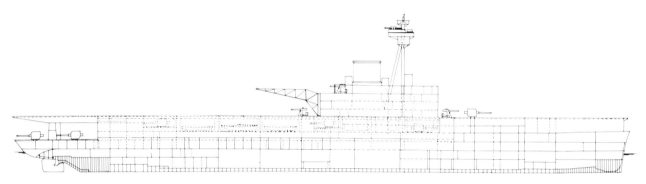

Hermes as redesigned with a single island (March 1920), before the Eagle trials. Note that her flight deck is cut off short of, rather than faired into, the bow. At this stage the main battery consisted of 6in guns and the lighter weapons were 4in anti-aircraft. NF

The new single island (130 × 15ft), as narrow as possible, carried the 4in anti-aircraft guns, searchlights, charthouse, navigating and fighting positions, including the directors needed to engage enemy cruisers with 6in fire. DNC doubted that the tripod mast would make appreciable eddies, and suggested (with Nicholson's agreement) that it would help pilots estimate their heights as they approached. He also imagined (incorrectly) that if the wind was slightly off the port bow the smoke, funnel gases, and all eddies due to funnels and masts would be carried well clear of the ship. An upper navigating position was provided atop the tripod, to give a position free of smoke and gun blast, and in view of congestion on the bridge proper.

Relatively little internal rearrangement was required, although the forward lift had to be moved to the port side, and the clear head room of the forward part of the hangar reduced, probably to about 16ft.

Nicholson was generally enthusiastic, asking only for two more 6in guns (one in the wake of the island and one right abaft the flight deck), so that the ship could match modern light cruisers, with their seven-gun broadsides. Admiral Beatty still wanted 6in rather than 4in guns, and this time he got his wish: by June, when the design was formally approved, *Eagle* had twelve 6in and only one 4in AA gun (the weapon mounted between her funnels). The design also included all three sets of triple above-water tubes.

Compared to the February design, the ship would have

number of stokers (which would cut speed); reduce armament (six 6in guns equalled 100 men); or reduce the number of aircraft. Under pressure, the RAF agreed to cut fifty men without reducing the number of aircraft. The Navy side then found that it could cut twenty-five Engine Room ratings (hydraulic ratings were not needed to operate non-existent gun turrets), twenty unskilled ratings, and five torpedo personnel. This solved *Eagle*'s problem, but not the larger one of whether RAF personnel would do standard miscellaneous shipboard labour, or whether carriers would need larger naval complements, a subtle effect of the split between RAF and Royal Navy.

An analogous single-island design was prepared for *Cavendish* at the same time, but it was not pursued immediately because the ship was so close to completion and so urgently needed. Displacement would have risen from 9750 to 10,200 tons, and mean draft from 17ft 3in to 18ft. This would have cost ¼ knot (29.5 rather than 29.75 knots). Main armament (four 7.5in) would not have changed, but the four 3in QF guns of the existing design would have been eliminated and the four 3in reduced to two. The two submerged torpedo tubes would have been eliminated, but four fixed single above-water tubes would have been retained. These changes would have bought a much larger hangar, accommodating twelve rather than six two-seaters, and a continuous flight deck, 330 × 65ft (50ft wide amidships) in place of the previous 70 × 40ft flying-off deck forward and 192 × 57ft landing-on deck aft.

WITH THE END of hostilities, completion of the two new carriers was no longer urgent. Indeed, in mid-1919 it seemed quite possible that, given its own fiscal problems and its 1914 agreement to sell the ship back to Chile if desired, the British government would have to complete HMS *Eagle* as a battle-

19   DNC comments to Admiral Phillimore, 9 March 1920, in connection with the Postwar Questions Committee, in the *Hermes* Ship's Cover.

ship, and thus that the Royal Navy would lose its most advanced carrier. This would leave HMS *Hermes*.

She was clearly a compromise, and she attracted some criticism. In November 1918, Rutland, who had now joined the RAF, complained to DNE that she was too small and too slow. High speed was essential for the ship to keep station within the fleet (allowing for turns into the wind for take-offs and landings), and to provide sufficient wind over deck. Sheer size would minimize pitching and rolling, and landing would be easier on a wide deck. For the future, Rutland thought that minimum acceptable carrier dimensions would be 700 × 68ft (for a 90ft wide landing deck).

Rutland considered 28 knots the minimum acceptable ship speed; some heavy aircraft, such as the DH 9A, might require as much as 36 to 40 knots of wind over the deck to take off. He argued, too, that because aircraft had limited speed and limited range, they would have to be launched from the van of a formation. To remain there, a carrier would need high speed.

Given these considerations, only two carriers, *Furious* and *Vindictive*, were fast enough, but neither could successfully recover her aircraft. The two ships under construction, *Hermes* and *Eagle*, were too slow, although Rutland thought *Eagle* large enough to be a useful training carrier.

Beyond all of these considerations lay the issue of flush deck versus island configuration. The *Argus* trials were proceeding, and Rutland suspected they would show that future carriers should be flush-decked. He recognized that smoke disposal was a problem in a high-powered ship, but suspected that, given sufficient time, it could be solved.

These were deadly arguments, and Rutland asked whether HMS *Hermes* should be built at all. An attached but unsigned reply (probably by the carrier specialist in DNC, J H Narbeth) in the *Hermes* Ship's Cover argued that, whatever Rutland's views of aeronautical reality, *Hermes* had been designed quite specifically to Air Department requirements. In fact she would

be rather faster (at 26–27 knots) than required (24–25 knots) in 1917. Her flying deck was larger than that requested by the Air Service (a 300 × 70ft landing deck and a 200 × 70ft flying-off deck). The Board decision to acquire HMS *Eagle* (24 knots) was advanced as further proof that *Hermes* was quite fast enough.

The DNC memo went further. Rutland wanted a margin of speed over the mass of the fleet, but the fleet would want similar speed in its own non-aviation ships. Moreover, Rutland's minimum requirements would probably entail a ship so large and hence so expensive that it would not be affordable, particularly given the postwar requirement for retrenchment.

On the other hand, the writer did enclose a drawing showing how HMS *Furious* could be fitted with horizontal funnels and therefore with a flush deck. This was probably the origin of the design actually presented in 1920. The DNC memo certainly dates from late 1918. A detailed sketch, produced in 1919, showed that horizontal uptakes would consume practically the entire hangar. Presumably this led to the double-hangar arrangement actually adopted.[19]

AT THE ARMISTICE, HMS *Eagle* was about nine months from completion. On 13 February 1919 the Controller asked that she be accelerated, if possible, to complete for flying trials in the summer of 1919. This was urgent, as *Eagle* then represented one of the two alternative carrier types, and the one proposed for HMS *Furious* and for HMS *Hermes*. However, the decision had already been taken to avoid further expenditure on new construction, and all British warship building in private yards was proceeding very slowly. Clearly HMS *Eagle*

HMS Eagle *was completed to the minimum possible extent for her 1920 trials, with only one funnel and a simple brige. However, the original design envisaged a cut-off forward end to her flight deck, which caused airflow problems.* CPL

Left: *A Blackburn Dart torpedo-bomber lands in the longitudinal-wire arrester gear of HMS* Eagle, *about 1923. The wires were intended not to stop the aircraft (as in modern arrester gear), but rather to keep it from being blown over the side of the ship. They were disliked because a pilot could not be sure that he had been caught, and therefore he might try to bolt, and thus to damage his aircraft if, in fact, it had been caught. Any drift across deck was also dangerous.* FAAM

Left: *A Flycatcher fighter, taking off from the lower flight deck, clearly shows the downward-facing hooks on the undercarriage axle, intended to engage the longitudinal-wire arrester gear. Aircraft designed to use such gear had to have their axles far enough down to keep the propeller from hitting the deck (or the wires) as the aircraft engaged, and thus could not be simple adaptations of land-based aircraft.*

20   The contractual situation was different. The British government had to pay specifically for all work done by Armstrong. On the other hand, since it had to maintain the staff of a dockyard, most of the cost of work there would be borne in any case. Once the possibility of return to Chile had been raised, further expenditure (to take the ship further from her battleship configuration) at Armstrong was not justifiable.

21   The formal Admiralty decision was taken early in September 1920; at this time the sale of other ships to Chile was still under negotiation, and the Treasury was informed of the Admiralty decision in that context.

could not be completed very soon as an operational carrier. Instead, work at the builder, Armstrong, was stopped on 21 October 1919, and the following 20 April she left for Portsmouth Dockyard, arriving on 26 April 1920.[20] The ship's resale to Chile was advanced as a possible economy.

The ship was decked over, but only two of her boilers were operable, since only one of her two funnels had been erected. The lifts had not been delivered (they were cancelled after failing to meet requirements) and she could not handle aircraft on her hangar deck. However, she was suitable for flying trials (to test the island configuration), but only at low speed, about 15 knots.[21] In November 1919 the Board of Admiralty approved her use for such trials.

Late in 1919 Admiral Madden, the Fleet C-in-C, proposed that the remainder of the plant be completed, so that she could participate in fleet tactical exercises to determine future fleet air needs. This would involve fitting the second funnel, and completion of remaining boiler room ventilation, and means of handling aircraft on board. This work would not have delayed her eventual completion for Chile, since the manufacture of new 14in mounts was the controlling factor there. *Eagle* was more attractive than *Argus* because she was faster; air officers felt that a carrier should be 5 knots faster than the fleet she accompanied, so as to launch and recover her aircraft without undue loss of station. The 18-knot *Argus* would limit the fleet to 13 knots. With all boilers on line *Eagle* could probably do 23, which would make a great difference.

The Board vetoed Madden's idea, because by early 1920 there was no money for anything so extensive. It is possible, too, that the Board feared that additional work on the machinery would actually reduce the apparent cost of restoring the ship to the Chileans, and so would make resale more attractive to the Treasury. The Admiralty's argument against resale was always economic, that it would cost a very great deal more to restore the ship to her original design (as the Chileans required) than could be realized by the sale, and that it would cost much less to complete HMS *Eagle* as a very efficient carrier than to build a new one from the keel up.

The flying trials tested two main features: the island configuration and the arrester gear already largely developed for HMS *Argus*. The ship was commanded by Captain W S Nicholson, who had commanded HMS *Furious* in 1918, and who represented the Naval Staff. The senior Air Service representative was Samson, the former senior Navy aviator, and now Chief of Staff to AOCA. Samson's view throughout was that the island was an unacceptable hazard. He (and the Air Ministry) maintained that the island represented an excessive limitation on the future development of naval aircraft (because it limited their wing span), and that it was a serious hazard in rough weather. It was true that pilots familiar with HMS *Argus* preferred HMS *Eagle* despite her island, but the official view was that this preference could be traced more to the better round-down of the larger carrier's deck, and that the *Argus* problem had been cured by a simple modification.

Nicholson considered the island a tolerable hazard, perhaps even an occasional benefit to the pilots, since it provided a visual indication of their height. They soon became accustomed to its presence. Flush decks were clearly attractive for the future, but only if sufficient navigating facilities could be provided. Otherwise it would be essential to provide a small island, as far forward as possible. This was particularly important because the carrier would have to manoeuvre often, and radically, to launch and recover her aircraft, with numerous large ships nearby. The alternative, to discharge funnel gases right aft, entailed its own hazards, as pilots were discovering aboard HMS *Argus*. DNC pointed out that the island was already the

bare minimum required to accommodate ship control, funnels, radio and guns.

Both wind tunnel tests and the trials themselves showed that the island was a relatively minor problem. As in the case of HMS *Argus*, a carrier with or without an island was extremely dangerous as soon as she turned slightly out of the wind, the rush of air off the weather side of the hull creating overwhelming air currents. An aircraft flying in low over the stern with the wind about 10 degrees on the port bow, for example, was thrown clear to starboard, against its controls. The main effect of changes in the island was to reduce its wake with the wind dead ahead. The island could be made insensitive to wind direction by streamlining, but this required a considerable reduction in length (otherwise it would have been too wide, to maintain the proper length-to-breadth ratio). Even then, the ship could not be made safe for wind more than 5 degrees from the centreline.

Elaborate experiments at NPL showed no great advantage in reducing the height of the island as long as the funnels were retained. Test shapes included a short rectangular island (88 × 15ft), an island reduced to funnels and a pole mast, a streamlined form, an island of reduced height or reduced area, and an island with a streamlined tail added.

The conclusion, at the end of the trials, was that the island did not spoil the carrier – that HMS *Eagle* was still the best available ship – but that flush decks would be better in future. By this time the reconstruction design of HMS *Furious* (as a flush-decker) was well advanced.

Other, minor, aerodynamic features of the design were also tested. Flights over the ship established that camber, which had been applied to the after end of the flight deck, materially reduced the air bump felt as compared with the level deck in *Furious* and *Argus*. The squared-off forward end of the flight deck produced an air bump which aircraft had to fly over when taking off. When the ship was completed for service, therefore, the deck was continued forward to the bow and the space between it and the hull plated in.

As in *Argus*, the trials began with flights over and around the ship to test air currents (and to compare with wind tunnel results), followed by touch-and-goes (Camels, Panthers, Cuckoos), then by actual landings with ship's head to wind, landings with ship's head not to wind, landings with motion on ship, then with heavier aircraft (Bristol Fighters, DH 9s). Finally, arrester gear, fitted aft, was tested to find out whether it would be possible to reduce the length of flying-on deck in future carriers.

The arrester gear tests turned out to be the most important of the series. Although it was understood that the *Argus* trials showed that maximum length was important (so that aircraft would land in the wires instead of abaft them), the gear initially installed was about 170ft long. It was also too far forward, allowing pilots to land 100 to 200ft abaft and taxi into it. Moreover, the gear as initially fitted allowed for too short a take-off run. It was therefore shifted aft by the ship's company, to a position 110ft from the stern.

Landings began on 1 June, and by 16 June fifty-nine successful landings had been made, mostly without using the arrester gear at all; it became clear that the gear was too short. It was lengthened to 320ft, extending from an after ramp (78ft aft, that is, directly forward of the fore side of the after lift) to a new forward ramp forward of the movable (Admiralty-type) forward ramp originally installed. The movable ramp was kept raised for landings, to help keep the long wires clear of the deck. The wires were also supported by vertical grooved planks, 10ft × 12in × 1in, at 90 and 190ft from after ramp, which fell when struck by a landing aircraft. The wires were therefore 9 to 12in

off the deck. Work was completed by about 1 July.

Aircraft now actually landed in the wires (as the *Argus* conference had proposed), and they could alight even in bumpy air. It was, however, clear that the wires would have to be very long to be effective in rough weather, since a pilot approaching a pitching ship would find it difficult to choose his landing position very accurately. Pilots would probably tend to land amidships; one contemporary estimate was that 60 or 70 per cent would touch within 100ft abaft amidships, and that the rest would land between 100ft abaft and the stern. The implication was that the wires should extend between a point about 100ft forward of amidships (to cater to aircraft landing slightly abaft amidships) back to about 50 to 70ft forward of the stern. Unfortunately such wires would cover the after lift, posing the question how quickly they could be unrigged to clear it.

The next step was to replace the boards with collapsible flaps. Unfortunately, when the undercarriage knocked down one flap, only the wires over that flap went down; wires on either side were still high enough to engage the hydrovane or one wing. The solution was to connect the flaps, so that when one went down, so did the others in line with it across the deck. Ideally, when an aircraft was hooked, the remaining flaps would be collapsed and the mechanically operated ramps lowered, bringing the complete system flush with the deck.

By mid-July, seventy-three landings had been made, only one of which was unsuccessful (the aircraft flipped over on its back); the accident was attributed to the makeshift character of the arrester gear. By this time the ship had successfully recovered aircraft while rolling 5 degrees, and while pitching 2 or 3 degrees.

Trials were resumed on 3 August 1920, with the arrester gear moved forward so that the after end of the ramp just cleared the after lift. The value of the long gear, as suggested by experience with *Argus*, had been proven, and the gear now functioned correctly even when an aircraft drifted sideways across it.

Having decided (see below) to complete HMS *Eagle* as a British carrier (and therefore being under no pressure to return her to a yard for completion for Chile), the Admiralty now decided to continue trials until a satisfactory type of arrester gear had been developed. Early in August it was decided to modify further the flaps holding up the wires. Further improvements (fully revised power-operated gear) had to await completion of the ship.

By 10 August, 107 landings had been made; the efficiency of the gear was fully proven. Some slight accidents were attributed to the location of the after ramp too far forward; several aircraft just touched the ramp and were thrown back up into the air. More generally, it was noted that pilots tended to land too far aft, to avoid the ramp. They disliked it, and its removal later had what was described as 'a certain moral effect.'

The flaps were revised late in August, and further rough weather trials began in September. This time the wires seemed too high, with 17in flaps, and landing aircraft were badly jolted. In one case an aircraft put a wheel on a wire and tipped over so badly that one wing went under a wire. However, the wires sagged between the flaps, and the sag would be greater after any one flap had been knocked down. If the wires were too low, they would not be caught at all. After the first series of trials, the flaps were cut to 15in and inclined to lower the wires further. This proved satisfactory.

Even with 15in wires, any tendency to tip would cause damage. One Panther, for example, hit the after ramp, rode forward, and a wire slipped over the hydrovane and smashed the propeller. To avoid this trouble the after ramp was removed altogether, and the after end of the wires was covered with a small fairing and a collision mat; the wires were supported by a 12in board 30ft from the end.

Above and above left:
HMS Eagle *as completed,
1923. When anti-aircraft
armament was reviewed in
1927, it was suggested that
the flight deck be cut back aft
and the aftermost 6in gun be
replaced by a high-angle
weapon. This was not done,
however, and the ship was
little modified before her loss
in 1942.*

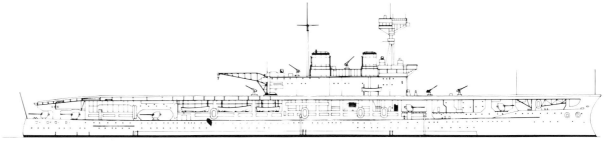

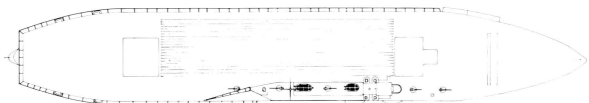

HMS Eagle, *1924, profile
and plan.* ALR

Rough water trials off the Orkneys in October emphasized some limitations of the arrester gear: aircraft rarely landed horizontal relative to the ship's deck, since they could not bank back and forth to follow the ship's roll. The period for a double roll was about 12 seconds, and for a double pitch about 8½ seconds, so that each pilot saw several of each as he approached. Largest recorded roll angle was 5½ degrees each way, largest pitch 2½ degrees total. A Panther two-seater, for example, landing when the port side of the ship was up, touched its left wheel first, causing it to tilt over to the right, and probably also drift to the right. The starboard wing tip went under the wires, four wires came up over the hydrovane and smashed the propeller. The starboard hydrovane was pulled out of its fastening, the wing tip was broken, and one spar of the starboard wing cracked. The Panther had been pulled 8ft across the deck to starboard.

There were some obvious correctives. Small extensions to the hydrovanes could keep the wires from coming up over them. Wings could be provided with skids at their tips, again to keep aircraft from tipping over through the wires. Alternatively, the undercarriage could be made wider (to catch more wires), and higher so that the propeller could not come into contact with the wires. By this time it was obvious that the easiest way to stop an aircraft moving down the deck was to increase its air resistance by bringing its tail down; the hooks could be placed to achieve that end. Another lesson was that hooks could easily strike the deck itself in a bumpy landing. To avoid damage to the undercarriage axle, they were best mounted on a false axle fixed beneath it. More generally, the effects of bumpy landings showed the prospective advantages of shock-absorbing (oleo) undercarriages, which were then under development.

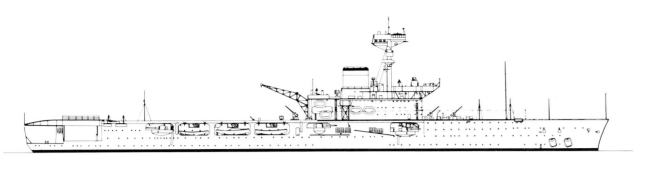

HMS Hermes, *as built profile and plan.* ALR

In general, the rough water trials showed the value of sheer size in a carrier, for steadiness, and the need for aircraft specially designed for carrier operations, for example with special undercarriages. The *Eagle* trials, then, were the origin of British aircraft designed specifically for deck-landing, as opposed to land-planes modified for carrier work. In particular, problems with the DH 9 bomber led the Air Ministry to lay out carrier landing requirements in some detail.

Well before the tests had been completed, on 14 July 1920, Nicholson recommended that the ship be retained for British service. He considered her the most successful carrier to date, large enough to accommodate sufficient spotters (that is, aircraft about the size of a DH 9) for the entire Atlantic Fleet. This was a key consideration, given the value then being placed on air spotting. Admiral Madden, the Fleet commander, strongly supported Nicholson, commenting that *Argus* could handle reconnaissance aircraft but not the heavier spotters.

Nicholson recommended that the ship be completed to burn oil fuel only, as coaling would be slow and laborious owing to cramped deck space, and as coal smoke would interfere with landing and coal dust (when coaling) would damage her aircraft. He also recommended that her 6in guns and torpedo tubes be eliminated in favour of an all-anti-aircraft battery (or, if 6in were required, that only the three after weapons be retained). Elimination of the 6in guns would also eliminate the big tripod mast carrying their controls and thus would reduce the size of the island.

The trials had already shown that arrester gear should be at least 300ft long, and that it should be clear of the lifts. Nichol-

son suggested, therefore, that the forward lift be moved to the extreme forward end of the hangar, set athwartships (and at least 32ft long). Wires could extend between the two lifts. At this stage Nicholson still wanted Admiralty-type power ramps, one just forward of the after lift and one about 250ft further forward, with flaps at intervals of 60ft. Both lifts could be used for flying-off, either forward or aft. Normally aircraft landing-on would be struck down aft, pulled backwards out of the arrester gear. He also wanted an efficient mechanical means of moving aircraft through the hangar. DNC noted that the plans already showed overhead rails and hooks. Finally, he wanted a gryo-stabilizer, if possible (it was not).

Given Nicholson's emphatic support, the Board decided to retain the ship and complete her as a carrier, to a slightly modified design.[22] At about the same time the Naval Staff wanted *Furious* rebuilt, followed by either *Courageous* or *Glorious* (see Chapter 5), and all three carriers were included in the Draft Statement to the Cabinet on Naval Construction. For a time it appeared that *Eagle* could be completed as early as the end of 1921 or early 1922. However, she could not be taken in hand (at Portsmouth) before February 1921. At this time the draft 1921–22 Estimates showed nineteen ships under construction (including *Hermes*) plus a new construction programme consisting of two carriers (*Eagle* and reconstruction of *Furious*), six battleships, two battlecruisers and a minelayer, plus a floating drydock for 1922–23.

Eagle was completed to a slightly modified design. As proposed in 1918, the three 4in anti-aircraft guns were restored, and two more added, for a total of six. Nicholson failed to

22 In his 1983 article, 'The Development of the Aircraft Carrier Prior to World War II,' D K Brown considered HMS *Argus* the earliest example of the fire precautions and attention to petrol hazards which characterized British designs. He attributed to this concern the very small number of British avgas fires but also the limited petrol capacity of British carriers. For some examples, see Chapters 10, 12, 14 and 16.

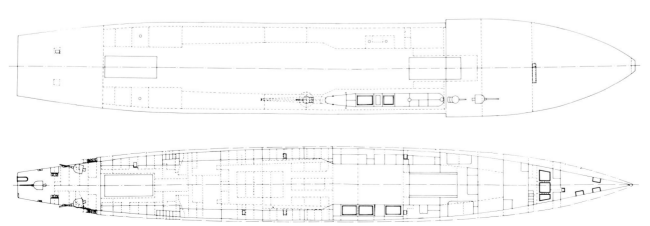

HMS Hermes, *flight and hangar decks.* NF

eliminate the nine 6in, and the tripod therefore remained. The torpedo tubes were dispensed with.

The ship was completed to burn oil fuel only, initially with a capacity of 3000 tons. This was increased to 3750 when she was bulged, 500 of which was ballast to balance the island. As actually inclined after completion, her deep displacement was 26,880 tons; load displacement was 23,930 tons.

After this work had begun, it was decided to bulge her; the 6ft deep bulge structure was based on that of HMS *Royal Sovereign*. It was kept entirely below the waterline so as not to further increase the already substantial metacentric height of the ship, and to make construction easier. It cost about half a knot in speed.

In August 1921 Narbeth suggested that bulk petrol stowage replace the former 2-gallon tins; it was almost essential with the large aircraft coming into service. Total capacity was 8100 gallons, which turned out not to be very much. In one average day, 1 May 1924, the ship consumed 1524 gallons, and C-in-C Mediterranean was calling for a minimum of 18,000 gallons, or 1000 per aircraft.

Another air arrangement matched those proposed by Nicholson: 328ft of arrester gear between two lifts. The proposal for completion showed a 50 × 33ft lift aft and a 47 × 36ft lift forward, but the 46 × 33ft after unit originally ordered was used. Nominal capacity was twenty-five large or thirty small aircraft.

Trials were very successful, showing no vibration and little motion in a seaway. She was as sensitive to her helm as *Hermes*, with a tactical diameter (at full speed and full helm) of about 800 yards. She handled well despite her large sail area.

On trial on 9 and 10 September 1923 *Eagle* made 24.37 knots on 52,100shp at 24,550 tons, and 23.29 knots on 45,600shp at 24,900 tons. The former figure was a practical limit, since the alteration made to enable her to make 50 to 55,000shp required that steam pressure in the first stages of the HP turbines be limited to 100lbs. Beyond this point there was grave risk of damage to the turbine joints. At 52,100shp

Table 4-1: *Hermes* Legend

	29 March 1917	1919	1921
LBP (ff)	540		548
LWL (ft)			578 5
LOA (hull) (ft)	578		
LOA (ft)	596[1]		594[2]
Beam, moulded (ft)			69 10½
Beam, extreme (ft)	70		70 3
Load draught (ft) fwd	16		19
aft	17 6		20 6
Displacement (tons)	9000		11,850
Freeboard (ft) fwd	28 0		
amids	27 0		
aft	12 0		
Deep draught (ft)	18 9		21 2
SHP	40,000		40,000
Speed (knots)	27		
Fuel (tons)	1000/2000		
Complement	330		
Armament			
6in	—	11	—
5.5in	—	—	7
4in HA	6 (250rpg)	1	4
Protection			
Side armour	3in		
Deck armour	1in (over steering gear)		
Weights (tons)[3]			
Hull	5620	6906	7100
Protection	410	420	721
General equipment	465	521	573
Aircraft equipment and armament	100	123	330
Armament	100	432	444
Machinery	1135	1143	1232
Oil fuel	1200	1455	1000
Margin	120	—	100
Displacement	9450	11,300	11,500
GM	5.5	3.2	4.5[4]

1 To after end of gantry.
2 Pencilled in: 615ft 3in (presumably as built)
3 Weights for 1917 refer to legend of 19 December, which differs somewhat from that of March. Data of 1919 are from the Calculation Book, dated 5 April, which reflects the shift to a single island. The 1919 figure for oil fuel includes 55 tons of culinary coal and 50 tons of reserve feed water.
4 It is not clear why DNC used a much lower figure in 1921.

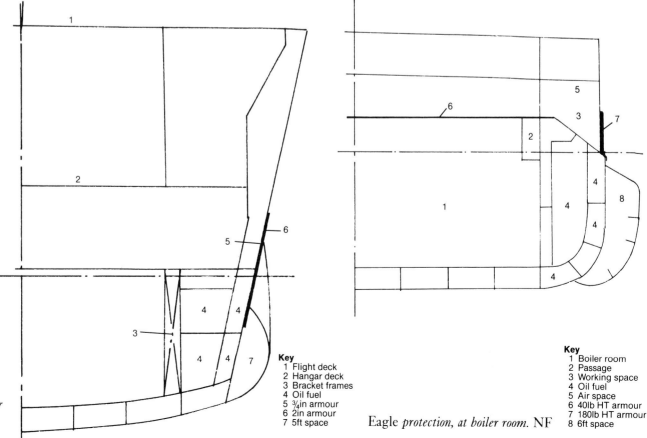

Hermes *protection, at boiler room.* NF

Key
1 Flight deck
2 Hangar deck
3 Bracket frames
4 Oil fuel
5 ¾in armour
6 2in armour
7 5ft space

Eagle *protection, at boiler room.* NF

Key
1 Boiler room
2 Passage
3 Working space
4 Oil fuel
5 Air space
6 40lb HT armour
7 180lb HT armour
8 6ft space

these joints showed slight leakage, so C-in-C suggested limiting her to 50,000shp, at the cost of about ¾ knot.

FURTHER CHANGES TO *Hermes* were ordered in May 1921, to reflect the lessons of the *Eagle* trials. Although not extensive in themselves, they made a considerable difference in so tight a design:

(a) Lifts were moved apart to allow a longer arresting gear (307 instead of 240ft). The flying-off deck forward was lengthened from 168 to 172ft, the overall length of the flight deck increasing from 594 to 598ft.

(b) Lifts were enlarged so that wings could be spread in the hangar (to 36ft × 36ft 7in rather than the earlier 50 × 20ft).

(c) The 5.5in battery was reduced from ten to seven (the 4in battery remained at four guns, but provision was made to add four multiple pom-poms). Pending experience with aircraft, the after 5.5in gun would not be mounted, so that the ship might commission with only six. There was also some interest in adding a fifth 4in anti-aircraft gun.

(d) A bullet-proof shelter was provided for the bridge officers.

(e) An anti-aircraft control top was added.

(f) A braced tripod mast was provided to support the anti-aircraft and surface fire controls. The mast had to be free of vibration, and fore and aft stays were rejected because setting them up would alter the parallelism between the directors and the guns.

(g) Arrangements were made to handle seaplanes aft

(though not in the form of a slipway). They would be hoisted over the quarter-deck (which is why the seventh 5.5in gun was deleted; DGD wanted this gun retained, as it was the only one bearing within 20 degrees of right aft. He suggested that seaplanes be handled instead either by the flight deck crane abaft the island, or by cranes on either side aft so that seaplanes could be hoisted in on either quarter).

(h) A form of general messing was provided, and oil replaced coal in the galleys.

These were the last of a considerable series of additions to a relatively small ship. In November 1921 DNC pointed out that the GM in legend condition was only 2.4ft (1.2ft in light condition) compared with 5.5ft (not counting free surface) as designed. The principal changes detrimental to GM to date had been:

Main battery	300 tons
Multiple pom-poms	100 tons
Structure for guns	150 tons
Magazine fittings, additional structure	50 tons
Arrester gear, pallisades	60 tons
Aircraft	30 tons
Complement (approximately doubled)	150 tons
Masts and control towers	30 tons

These totalled 870 tons, almost 10 per cent of the original displacement of 9450 tons. Displacement had grown to 11,430 tons, and draft from 16ft 9in to 19ft 10in. GM had fallen, correspondingly, to 2.9ft (not counting free surface).

HMS Argus *near the end of her first career, with a wooden girdle visible at her waterline.* CPL

Above and right: *HMS Eagle in the late 1930s, with 8-barrel pom-poms forward of and atop her island, and with arrester gear aft (two wires are clearly visible). The windbreaks are folded down for flying, and the crane is trained outboard.* FAAM

DNC argued that experience with *Argus* (which had a small GM) and with *Eagle* (which had a large one) showed that carriers should have substantial metacentric heights. In this case, to increase GM to an acceptable 4.5ft, the ship would need at least 3ft 6in more beam (or, better, 4ft, to allow for future additions). DNC proposed that this work be carried out as part of the 1922–23 programme. This seems not to have been done, however.

On trial, *Hermes* made 26,178 knots on 41,318shp at 12,250 tons in 25 fathoms of water. She showed very little vibration. Experience in the Far East, in typhoon and monsoon weather, showed that she behaved well in heavy seas. However, she had

considerable sail area; as a result, with a strong wind on or near the beam she required as much as 25 to 30 degrees of weather helm at low speed, which could make it difficult to alter course suddenly to leeward.

She did show one serious peculiarity. Due to her island design, her boiler room air intakes, which could not be made water-tight, came underwater at a heel angle of about 30 degrees. The other carriers suffered from much the same problem; it was not at all clear that the usual calculation of their range of stability was valid; *Hermes*, for example, was credited with a range of 66 degrees. *Furious* immersed her intakes at 34 degrees, yet was credited with a range of over 89 degrees. *Eagle*

immersed her uptakes at 40 degrees. One possible solution was to carry the intakes between the deep girders of the flight deck, letting them into the sides of the island. In that case the angle of immersion would increase, for *Hermes*, to 58 degrees.

THERE WERE FEW MODIFICATIONS to *Hermes* and *Eagle* between the wars. *Eagle* was refitted in 1926, her longitudinal arrester gear being removed in favour of a flat deck and pallisades. The ship had been completed with two twin Lewis guns on her control top. Petrol stowage was increased to 14,190 gallons, and a 600-gallon ready use tank was fitted on the port side of *Eagle*'s gallery deck. In 1927, *Eagle* was armed with nine 6in guns, five 4in anti-aircraft guns, four .303in Maxim machine-guns, and ten Lewis guns.

In 1929, in common with other British carriers, *Eagle* was fitted with salt water sprays to fight hangar fires, which would have been confined by her hangar fire curtains. At about this time two single 2pdr pom-poms were added, both forward of the two 4in guns forward of her island.

In 1921 a special Committee on Anti-Aircraft Gunnery proposed a new standard of carrier armament, including a new multiple pom-pom gun. By 1927 the new Mark M pom-pom was sufficiently well advanced for the Admiralty to develop plans for mounting it (when it appeared) aboard existing carriers. Unfortunately very little space was available aboard the two oldest fleet carriers. The conference recommended that 4.7in anti-aircraft guns replace *Eagle*'s 4in guns, and that two multiple pom-poms replace two of her 6in single-purpose guns, although they would have very limited sky arcs. At this time the ship had already asked for fifteen additional Lewis guns, the Admiralty suggesting single pom-poms instead. A conference on carrier anti-aircraft armament, convened in 1927, ruled in favour of the Lewis guns, and in 1928 the total Lewis battery was twenty-six guns, all in twin mountings.

Eagle was refitted in 1931–32. No 4.7in guns were added, but the 4in anti-aircraft gun between her two funnels was replaced by an 8-barrel pom-pom.[23] At this time a High Angle Control System (HACS) for the remaining 4in guns was

mounted at the after end of the control top. Finally, an early quadruple .5in machine-gun was mounted aft, on the starboard side of the flight deck. It was shifted to the port side and a second .5in mounting installed forward of the single barrel pom-pom in April 1934. During a second refit in 1936 two more .5in guns were added, sponsored out to both sides of the flight deck forward, together with the second pom-pom, forward of the island, and bomb magazine capacity was increased. *Eagle* was also fitted with arrester gear at this time.

A more elaborate anti-aircraft rearmament was proposed but rejected at this time. It was decided to fit two pom-pom directors and to shift the 4in HACS from the after to the forward part of the fire control top.

When war broke out in 1939, *Eagle* was refitting at Singapore. She was to have been fitted with a Type 72 aircraft homing beacon at this time, but this appears not to have been done. She was not otherwise modified, and her only damage until her loss appears to have been two hangar fires. The first followed explosion of a 250lb bomb as it was being returned to her bomb room, on 14 March 1940. The flash of the explosion went up the bomb lift trunk into her hangar, and one Swordfish was set afire. The hangar sprays were effective, but they severely damaged all but four of the aircraft in the hangar. The main fire, in the bomb room and 4in magazine, was extinguished within an hour. The second hangar fire, apparently more serious, occurred on 20 September 1941, and the ship had to be refitted.

In June 1941 planned modifications for HMS *Eagle* included installation of two pom-pom directors (Mk IV) with Type 282 radars, plus Type 285 on a modernized HACS, and an air search radar (Type 279 or equivalent). Some of these changes had been authorized in February. The ship was refitted by Cammell Laird from 30 October 1941 to 9 January 1942. Her .5in guns were replaced by twelve Oerlikons, and the 4in director was moved to the forward end of her control tower. It was fitted with Type 285 fire control radar. At this time the ship was fitted with her Type 72 aircraft homing beacon, and a Type 290 search radar fitted, with its aerial at the head of the

23   The 4in gun and its pedestal were removed, but the base for its mounting remained; the pom-pom was to starboard of the base. The second M Mk V pom-pom would have been placed forward of the forward 4in gun.

24   Details of the 1941–42 refit are taken from J D Brown, 'HMS *Eagle*' (Warship Profile No 35).

25   She was considered proof against 750lb underwater hits against her magazines, or 440lb (aerial torpedo) hits against her boiler rooms and wing engine rooms, making her better protected than *Furious* or *Courageous*. Notes by Sir Stanley V Goodall, 12 October 1938, in Miscellaneous Carrier Cover (425B).

mainmast. Splinter protection (gun tubs or 'zarebas') was erected around the guns on the flight deck.[24]

The ship could not be re-boilered, and after refitting she was considered good for no more than 20 knots. Fuel stowage was reduced to 2990 tons (2780nm at 17.5 knots), to provide space for 3000 more gallons of aviation petrol.

Eagle was hit by four torpedoes (fired by *U73*) on 11 August 1942, during Operation Pedestal, fleet escort of a Malta convoy. They were spaced about 40ft apart abeam the port wing engine room, and the ship soon listed to 30 degrees. She sank 4 minutes after the first hit, 789 officers and ratings being saved, with 160 lost. The damage was so massive that loss was inevitable, and no detailed official analysis was made.[25]

Hermes was smaller and more difficult to rearm. Throughout

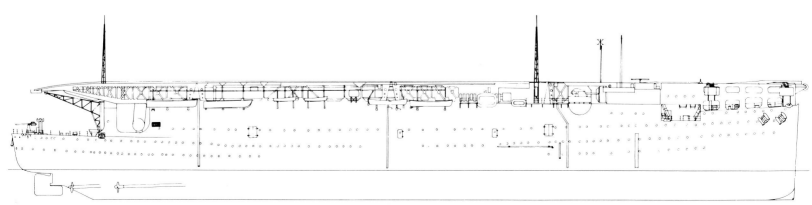

HMS Argus, *January 1943. Note the black paint applied aft, in the region affected by funnel gases. The small air search radar antenna has been obscured, probably by the wartime censor.*

most of her career, she was assigned seven 5.5in guns but mounted only six (see above). By 1927 one of her four 4in guns, abaft the superstructure, had already been removed because it obstructed flying-on, and it could not be remounted on the island because of insufficient stability. To compensate for this reduction in anti-aircraft firepower, the Admiralty had already approved mounting two single pom-poms (2pdr machine cannon), one on the island and one in a well abaft the island, but as of March 1927 this had not yet been done. Replacement of existing 5.5in guns by multiple pom-poms was ruled out in view of the ship's very limited broadside. In 1927 she also carried four .303in Maxim machine-guns, and after 1928 sixteen Lewis guns, in twin mounts. The two single pom-poms were removed in 1932, replaced by quadruple .5in machine-guns.

Hermes was fitted with arrester gear prewar, but it is not entirely clear when this was done; the gear had not yet been approved at the time of her big refit (1933–34).

In 1937 carrier anti-aircraft batteries were reviewed, and it was decided that *Hermes* would be rearmed, her three 4in guns removed and replaced by two twin 4in (fore and aft of her island), and two 8-barrel pom-poms (one on the flight deck forward on the starboard side, and one on C deck). She would have been fitted with one HACS. Outline drawings were passed to Devonport in December 1937 but the yard's work load was such that detailed planning could not begin until June 1938. The work would actually have been done between September and December 1939, but the war intervened and the ship was never radically rearmed.

She was fitted with two quadruple .5in machine-guns and Oerlikons, but never with radar. It is not clear whether the Type 72 aircraft homing beacon was ever fitted.

She was lost on 9 April 1942, when more than fifty Japanese dive-bombers hit her with more than forty 250kg (550lb) SAP bombs. As in the case of HMS *Eagle*, the sheer scale of attack made her loss inevitable, and no official damage analysis was conducted.

Below and opposite: *HMS* Argus *as a trade protection and training carrier during World War II. The object on the flight deck aft (to port) is a funnel hatch; a funnel duct emerged from the starboard side, as shown in the profile.* ALR

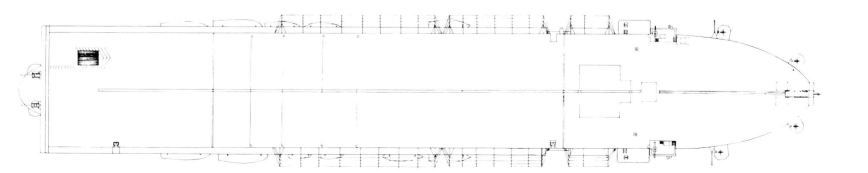

5

The Postwar Carriers

BY THE END of 1918, naval aircraft had clearly proven their value. The question, for the postwar British naval establishment, was how many were needed and how they were to be accommodated. Although the new RAF now owned the aircraft, it was understood, at least at first, that they would be provided in the numbers the Admiralty needed. The senior RAF officers concerned were naval veterans; Air Vice Marshal Vyvyan had been Assistant DAS, and his Chief of Staff, Group Captain Samson, had been one of the first naval aviators.

In early 1919 plans called for *Furious, Argus, Vindictive, Nairana, Pegasus, Vindex* and *Ark Royal* to be retained for fleet service, and *Eagle* and *Hermes* to be completed. Four seaplane carriers were still on charter, serving abroad: *Engadine, Empress, Riveria* and *Manxman*. This rather expansive plan was soon scaled down. In May, DCNS proposed that *Vindictive*, which had been damaged by grounding, be converted back into a cruiser. She had never been particularly satisfactory, and would have needed extensive reconstruction as a carrier. DAD proposed that she and *Furious* be laid up pending a decision as to whether to convert them into carriers with proper landing-on decks, pending experiments aboard HMS *Eagle*. DCNS agreed in the case of *Furious*, but *Vindictive* was reduced to care and maintenance status pending her reconversion to a cruiser.

Work continued on both *Hermes* and *Eagle*, and the surviving seaplane carriers were employed abroad, pending the appearance of true carriers. *Ark Royal* went to China and *Pegasus* to the Mediterranean. Of the other wartime conversions, only *Nairana* was left on the fleet list by September 1919, and she was for disposal.

Naval aircraft performed four vital functions: reconaissance, which entailed a more or less fixed number scouting out to some distance; spotting, with numbers proportional to the size of the fleet; fighting (to protect the first two functions and then the fleet itself); and torpedo attack. It was by no means clear what an individual carrier could do; hence Admiral Madden's interest in the 1920 exercises. There was some question as to which types of aircraft would be aboard the carriers. For example, in August 1919 the Board understood that the only carrier in commission, *Argus*, would be limited to torpedo-bombers. However, spotters needed at least three seats and hence could not fly from turret tops; they, too, would have to go aboard future carriers.

The battlefleet proper could not be maintained at its 1918 peak, but in 1918–19 most naval officers expected a return to prewar practice, in which a substantial modern reserve fleet backed a large active fleet. The war fleet, the basis for all planning, would be the sum of the two. Sufficient carriers, for example, both active and reserve, had to be provided to support not merely the active deployed fleet or fleets, but rather the larger war fleet. In 1919, the projected fleet included twenty-three active battleships, ten reserve battleships, and six active and two reserve battlecruisers, a total of forty-one capital ships (plus *Courageous* and *Glorious*, in reserve).[1] In fact the 1919–20 budget was sharply cut, with much of the projected reserve fleet going on the sale list, but the sheer size of the fleet, equivalent to perhaps ten wartime battle divisions (including battlecruisers), affected early fleet air planning.

Thus in July 1920 Admiral Madden revived his December 1919 paper (see Chapter 3) to propose a war establishment of:

(a) three reconnaissance carriers, each with eleven reconnaissance aircraft and five fighters
(b) one carrier for each of four Atlantic Fleet divisions, each with eight spotters and four fighters
(c) two carriers each with twelve torpedo-planes and six fighters
(d) one carrier with twenty-five fighters
(e) one carrier with twelve depth-bomb aircraft (bombers) and six fighters

Madden's total, then, was eleven carriers, with thirty-three reconnaissance, thirty-two spotters, thirty-six torpedo-planes (including depth-bomb planes), and seventy-four fighters, plus fourteen reconnaissance aircraft on capital ship turrets and twenty-four fighters on capital ship turrets and in light cruisers.

At the same time Admiral Chatfield (ACNS) laid out what he considered *minimum* requirements for the Postwar Navy of thirty-six capital ships (nine Divisions); see Table 5-1. Both estimates entailed expensive carrier conversion or new construction (the cost of Madden's carriers was estimated at £30 million). They were discussed in the light of the ongoing *Eagle* trials, at a Naval Staff meeting on 23 July 1920. Admiral Chatfield, then ACNS and later instrumental (as First Sea Lord) in British carrier development, was chairman, and the attendees included Captain Nicholson (of HMS *Eagle*), Captain F C

1 The earliest postwar fleet list included all the surviving dreadnoughts. It showed two battle squadrons and a fleet flagship (eleven ships: the ten 15in battleships and HMS *Canada*), plus a battlecruiser squadron (five ships) in the Atlantic Fleet, a battle squadron (six 13.5in battleships) in the Home Fleet, and another battle squadron (six 13.5in battleships) in the Mediterranean. The reserve fleet included ten battleships, three of them for gunnery training, and the two oldest battlecruisers. The battlecruiser *New Zealand* was assigned to the China Station. In September 1919 Admiral Madden, C-in-C Atlantic and Home Fleets, wanted a fully-manned fleet in European waters powerful enough to maintain British supremacy in the Atlantic: sixteen battleships, three battlecruisers, and the two carriers *Argus* and *Eagle*, plus lesser warships.

2   It could be argued that because reconnaissance and torpedo aircraft would not be launched during the gun engagement, the spotter carriers could accommodate these types as well. The figure of three became enshrined, even after the battlefleet had suffered drastic reduction. Its origins were forgotten; in 1926 Admiral Dreyer wrote of a 1920 study which showed that the fleet required three carriers for reconnaissance.

Dreyer (DGD, and thus deeply interested in provisions for spotting aircraft), DNC (d'Eyncourt), DNC's carrier expert (Narbeth), Vyvyan, and Air Commodore J M Steel (Director of Operations and Intelligence of the Air Ministry).

On the basis of the *Eagle* trials, it was estimated that a carrier could launch six aircraft in a single operation, and another six about half an hour later. This seems to have established six aircraft as the Fleet Air Arm tactical unit (the flight). It also meant that, if the fleet required eighteen spotters airborne more or less simultaneously, they would have to come from three carriers. Moreover, if the spotters were distributed among only two carriers, one might be unavailable in emergency. Thus three was the ideal figure. Vyvyan did argue, successfully, that it was unnecessary to provide sixty spotters to maintain eighteen continuously aloft; forty-five would suffice. Chatfield's other figures (twenty-two reconnaissance and twelve torpedo, plus as many fighters as possible) were accepted.

Of three spotter carriers, one would have to be fast enough to work with the battlecruisers. Of the existing ships, only *Furious* met this requirement. She would carry ten spotters for the two battlecruiser divisions, plus the reconnaissance aircraft. *Hermes* was too small for spotters (she would carry only fighters). The big *Eagle* could carry twenty-five (five battleship divisions) plus other aircraft, and *Argus* ten (two battleship divisions) plus fighters. The conference ultimately decided to provide the battlecruisers with two fast carriers, one for the spotters (plus fighters and torpedo-bombers) and one for reconnaissance only. These would be conversions rather than new construction, that is, *Furious* plus either *Courageous* or *Glorious*. HMS *Eagle* would have to be completed as a carrier.

Given the requirement to launch a flight of six aircraft very rapidly, future naval aircraft would have to be suitable for rapid preparation for flight. Detachable wings and fuselages, features of existing types, were unacceptable in future designs.

Since finances would limit the total number of carriers, it was important to increase the number of aircraft per ship. DNC was developing the *Furious* reconstruction design, and he provided her with a double (two-level) hangar. A proposal to rebuild *Eagle* on similar lines was rejected, partly because the resulting ship would have very great freeboard, which in turn would tend to magnify the effects of her motion. *Furious* was acceptable because of her lower freeboard.

Similarly, it was desirable for naval aircraft to be multi-purpose. Vyvyan pointed out that the fighter and reconnaissance roles could be combined, as they had been in wartime in the two-seat Bristol Fighter, which was, coincidentally, the largest aircraft which seemed suitable for naval use. Single-seat fighters could thus be eliminated. Although this idea did not immediately bear fruit, in 1924 the Air Ministry did issue the fighter-reconnaissance Specification which ultimately produced the Hawker Osprey. Spotters were also a problem. It was clear that they would have to be three- or even four-seaters; the only available three-seater, the DH 9, was too large for carriers and had other undesirable characteristics. It was clear that only a large carrier could accommodate a future spotter.

Table 5-1: Air Requirements Of The Postwar Fleet, 1920

Reconnaissance

In the air	6
Relief aircraft	12
Spare aircraft	4
Total	**22**

Spotters

The wartime requirement was 2 per division, or 18 planes up at a time:

In the air	18
Relief aircraft	36
Spare aircraft	6
Total	**60**

Torpedo-planes or bombers

1 flight	12
Spare aircraft	nil
Total	**12**

Fighters

No separate fighter carrier; fighters would have to be accommodated aboard the other carriers and in capital ships and cruisers.

Total

Except for fighters, Chatfield's total was 94 aircraft.

Future carrier armament policy was also addressed. Steel suggested that carriers rely entirely on their speed to escape surface forces; Vyvyan preferred sufficient guns to beat off minimum attacks (for example by two destroyers). DNC pointed out that a carrier could not be armoured against bombing, and therefore that she would have to depend upon her guns.

The July conference had two important consequences. First, it ensured both the completion of HMS *Eagle* and the conversion of at least two of the large light cruisers. Second, it established a tacit main fleet requirement for at least five carriers. The three spotter carriers were an absolute minimum.[2] Later it was often argued that two more were required to meet distant commitments (for example, to maintain a carrier in Chinese waters) and to allow for refits. This was sometimes described as a requirement for three carriers with the main fleet in the Far East, and two more for Home waters and the Mediterranean. In either case, the two excess ships were not a very large cushion against emergencies; post-1945 US planning, for example, has generally provided a total of three carriers for each required deployment. The required total of five motivated British tonnage demands at the Washington Conference.

More subtly, the arguments leading up to the conference typified a method of analysis; the numerical estimate of the air needs of the fleet *as a whole* persisted through the interwar period. Numbers developed in this way had to be compared with the capacity of existing and planned carriers. They would generally have led directly to carrier construction, had it not been for treaty limits on the total size of the British carrier fleet.

DESIGN WORK ON the *Furious* reconstruction began in response to a verbal request from the Controller on 5 July 1920, before

Inboard profile of Glorious.

Key
1 Hangar
2 Boiler room
3 Engine room
4 Bomb magazine
5 Aviation fuel stowage
6 Magazine
7 Aircraft lift
8 Oil fuel stowage
9 Aircraft and ship small-arms magazine
10 Aircraft repair and maintenance facilities
11 Torpedo magazine

the Admiralty Staff Conference. It was clearly attractive: as she was, *Furious* was of little value, but reconstruction, at an estimated cost of £1.3 million, would be only about a third of the cost of building a new carrier of similar size.

By this time it was generally accepted that the ideal carrier would be flush-decked, like HMS *Argus*. However, *Furious* produced six times the volume of funnel gas produced by *Argus*, and during 1919 E-in-C testified before the Postwar Questions Committee that it was impossible to vent this much gas without using a conventional uptake. Now Narbeth suggested that the uptake be trunked under the flight deck, and its disadvantages under some conditions (such as smoke in the living spaces, and air bumps aft) should be accepted. It might even be impossible to develop full power, but the speed-power curve was so steep at its upper end that little speed would be lost.

Funnel trunking down the sides would take up much of the space used for the hangar of earlier carriers, just under the flight deck. To make up for this intrusion, Narbeth provided another, shallower, hangar under the first. In theory, one lift could serve the upper hangar, bringing up heavy aircraft aft; the forward lift would serve the lower hangar. Narbeth estimated that the double hangar could accommodate fifteen large (reconnaissance or torpedo) and thirty small (fighter) aircraft, or thirty large aircraft, or forty small ones. In theory, larger aircraft would be carried in the upper hangar, flying off the long flight deck, and small ones in the lower, flying off the short lower flight deck.

Reconstruction was approved in principle on 26 July 1920, to be carried out under the 1921–22 Programme, and to take about two years. The Narbeth scheme was applicable, at least in theory, to the other two large light cruisers, *Courageous* and *Glorious*, although it turned out that they were different enough to require fresh drawings.

The double hangar naturally made for greater freeboard, and hence for a livelier flight deck. Narbeth argued that, given the Staff Requirement for ten spotters plus torpedo-planes and fighters, the double hangar was inevitable. A single-hangar *Furious* could probably carry only four spread and six folded spotters (based on DH9A dimensions) and about two torpedo-planes or four fighters. With a double hangar, she could carry ten spotters, five torpedo-planes and twenty fighters, something much closer to a useful load.

Narbeth hoped to limit freeboard by limiting clear hangar height to about 13ft. A survey of existing aircraft showed that wheeled aircraft generally did not exceed a height of 13ft, but that projected floatplanes might be as much as 15ft high. Existing fighters were 8ft 6in (Camel) to 10ft 3in (Nighthawk) high, although a floatplane or amphibious version of the new fighter (which became the Flycatcher) might be up to 13ft high. It seemed wise to allow at least 2ft clearance for aircraft in each hangar, thus, 13ft for fighters and 17ft for reconnaissance or torpedo aircraft. In this case a small (13ft) hangar could take all fighters, two-seat reconnaissance, and three-seat spotters. A large (17ft) hangar could take torpedo aircraft, amphibians, and Fairey III floatplanes. An increase to 18ft would allow for future developments.

Many aircraft under development could not be accommodated in the 13ft hangar, so that in future it would be probably be limited to fighters. However, given overall limitations on carrier stowage, policy called for most fighters to be carried aboard capital ships and cruisers. Thus it seemed wise to make the shallower hangar 15ft, despite the increase in freeboard this entailed. It would then accommodate all fighters and all reconnaissance types.

In the end, the choice was to provide both hangars with 15ft clear height. The flight deck ended well aft of the bow, and

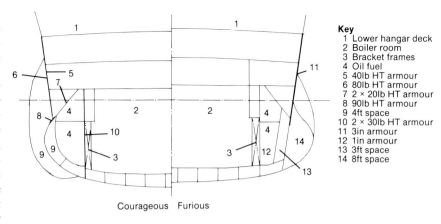

Key
1 Lower hangar deck
2 Boiler room
3 Bracket frames
4 Oil fuel
5 40lb HT armour
6 80lb HT armour
7 2 × 20lb HT armour
8 90lb HT armour
9 4ft space
10 2 × 30lb HT armour
11 3in armour
12 1in armour
13 3ft space
14 8ft space

Comparative cross-sections of Courageous *(left) and* Furious *(right) to show protection.* NF

In explaining the Courageous *design, DNC called it a 'funnel' type to distinguish it from large-island ships like HMS* Eagle. *Even so, unlike the carriers sketched in 1923, the ships did have usable islands. Note the bridge, shown here on the side of the funnel, which could be swung out over the flight deck for air control. This photograph was probably taken shortly after the ship was completed; as refitted in the late 1930s,* Courageous *(but not* Glorious) *had a raised charthouse just forward of her funnel. The objects at the after end of the island are probably connected to the movable panels used to signal aircraft not fitted with radios.*

below it the upper hangar opened (through two large doors forward) onto a short lower flight deck. Both of the lifts of the earlier plan (now serving both hangars) were retained, so that in theory aircraft could take off from three positions, two on the upper and one on the lower flight deck. Freeboard was only about 3ft higher than in *Argus*. DNC tried to reduce the effect of this freeboard by making the ship steadier, perhaps by fitting a gyro-stabilizer (which did not materialize in the end).

After wind-tunnel experiments at NPL, the fore end of the upper flight deck was rounded off. In theory, this made for steadier air conditions over the flight deck when the ship was

3   In July 1921 it was estimated that the hogging stress (deck/keel) would be 8.8/3.9 tons per square inch at 21,250 tons, compared to 9.0/6.6 in the original two-gun design (18,350 tons) and 8.3/6.1 as the ship was completed with one gun (18,300 tons). The corresponding sagging stresses were 8.0/4.2 tons at 23,000 tons, compared to 8.3/8.0 (20,000 tons, two turrets) and 7.4/7.1 (20,030 tons, one turret).

4   As inclined in August 1925, light displacement was 21,896 tons, compared to a calculated figure of 21,120 tons, GM being only 3.04ft compared to the calculated 5.0ft. Of the lost GM, 0.84ft was due to the 756-ton increase in displacement.

5   Even so, *Furious* had the 4in guns removed temporarily to test the take-off of a large aircraft, as a test for *Courageous* and *Glorious*. NAS suggested a guide rail to fly large aircraft from their lower flight decks.

not pointed directly into the wind.

The upper flight deck functioned as a strength deck for the rebuilt ship, considerably reducing hull stresses.[3]

DNC submitted his sketch design to the Board on 23 March 1921. It must have been a revelation; *Furious* could accommodate as many aircraft as *Hermes* and *Eagle* combined. They were suddenly obsolescent, even though neither had yet been completed. *Furious* was laid up at Rosyth, and on 11 April DNC asked for permission to begin cutting her down to the upper deck even before complete drawings were available. Rosyth had to begin work in May to provide work for men then finishing *Hood*, *Thunderer* and some battle practice targets.

The final design was submitted to the Board in October 1921. The Admiralty decided in February 1922 to transfer the ship to a southern yard (Devonport) for completion. She had been cut down at Rosyth, and there was some question as to her strength; for safety she was put into steaming condition, with one boiler room (six boilers, 30,000shp = 20 knots) in working order, temporary uptakes and funnel, and a temporary bridge.

Furious was bulged, her legend displacement initially estimated at 21,000 (with 80ft bulges) and then at 23,130 tons.[4]

The upper flight deck was 576 × 92ft, and the lower was

Both ships had their flight decks extended slightly aft soon after completion. This is HMS Courageous. *She retained her low quarter-deck throughout the rest of her operational life.* CPL

about 200ft long. The upper deck was long enough to accommodate 340ft of arrester gear. Pallisades were not indicated in the plans, but they could be (and were) fitted when a suitable type emerged. Admiral Phillimore, the wartime carrier commander, complained in May 1924 that the two 4in guns on each side of the lower flight deck blocked it so that heavy aircraft could not be launched. He feared that the flat forward portion of the upper deck was too short for them. The reply was that with 25 knots WOD, they could take off in 130ft, and because the deck was so wide three and probably four could be ranged forward of the ramp, and six could be flown off in quick succession. Moreover, heavy aircraft could not be started up in the hangar before flying off the lower flight deck, as this entailed an unacceptable fire risk in the enclosed space.[5]

As a result of wind tunnel tests at NPL, the forward end of the flight deck was made elliptical both in profile and in section, the depth from the beam at the middle to the beam at one end

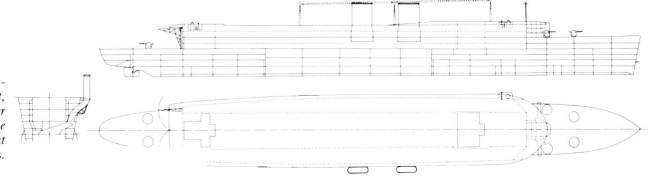

The 16,500-ton aircraft carrier of 1923. Note that, although she has funnels, her controls are still under the forward end of the flight deck, as in HMS Furious.
NF

Right and below right: *HMS Furious shortly after completion; the photograph from stern is dated 23 November 1925. Note the prominent seaplane cranes and the after opening into the lower hangar. The abaft photograph also shows the large smoke opening at the stern. In the forward view, note the raised (but retractable) charthouse.*

being 7ft. This section was carried aft to just abaft the forward lift, where the beam at middle sloped down 4ft 6in to form a fixed forward ramp for the arrester gear; in addition, cabins and offices were accommodated under the raised section forward. *Courageous* and *Glorious* were similar, but the depth forward was increased to 7ft 3in because the transverse girders under the flight deck were 3in deeper. Because the curvature and the ramp were aerodynamic rather than arrester-gear features (although the ramp was well adapted to fitting the latter, and its slope did help slow aircraft), the flight deck was not levelled off when arrester gear was eliminated in 1927.

The lower hangar, about 550ft long, varied in width from 35 to 50ft. It contained store rooms, shops, offices, etc. The upper hangar was 530 × 50ft, much of the difference between its width and the beam going into two smoke ducts. Floor areas were, respectively, 26,000 and 27,000sq ft. Both were subdivided by steel roller curtains to contain any fires. The lower hangar was open aft, with two cranes to lift amphibians and floatplanes into it.

The RAF complement (325 men) was based on twelve spotters, twelve aircraft, six reconnaissance aircraft, and six fighters.[6] Several alternative aircraft complements were developed. For example, the upper hangar could carry eight spread and sixteen folded torpedo-planes, with another twenty-eight (folded) in the lower hangar, a total of fifty-two aircraft. Alternatively, the upper hangar could carry eighteen folded Panthers and fifteen folded torpedo-planes, for a total of sixty-one aircraft. Yet another alternative for the upper hangar was four spread and ten folded Panthers, plus ten folded torpedo-planes, for a total of fifty-two aircraft. The aircraft complement set by NAS in March 1934 was two flights of spotters, two torpedo flights, one reconnaissance flight and one fighter flight, a total of thirty-six aircraft.

The design provided bulk stowage for 24,000 gallons of petrol, and 4000 of lubricating oil, all piped both to the hangars and to the flight deck by steam pumps. However, petrol piping was a problem; there was always the fear of leakage and of the accumulation of explosive vapour. In November 1923, therefore, the design was changed to show two 600-gallon ready-use tanks on the upper deck, from which aircraft and the ship's boats could be fuelled. The main tanks could be pumped less often, and the risk of explosion correspondingly reduced. The ready-use tanks could be emptied when in the presence of the enemy, or even jettisoned overboard. Main bulk stowage was, therefore, reduced to 20,000 gallons; in 1939 the ship carried a total of 20,800 gallons of petrol.

The lifts were designed to bring a torpedo-bomber (maximum dimensions: 46ft span and 46ft length) up to deck after it had been spread below. Ideally, each lift would have been square, but that was not practical, and the lifts were cruciform instead. The Air Ministry asked that the long portion of the cross be wide enough (36ft) to bring up two spotters together, but this proved impossible. The Air Ministry still wanted the largest possible lifts, both to accommodate future developments and to permit special operations by large aircraft, for instance torpedo-bombers normally based ashore, which could carry 21in torpedoes.

The two lifts were initially to have been 44 ×39ft. In the final version, they catered for aircraft with a spread span of 47ft (25ft

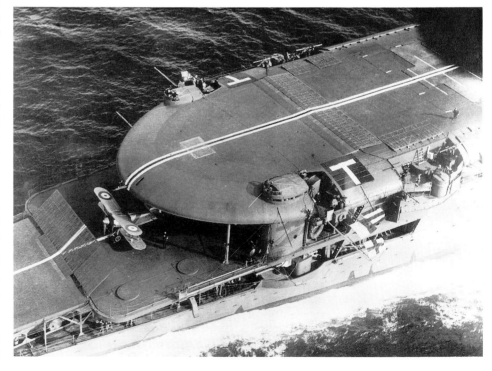

6 It would have been 251 for twenty-four aircraft. The Royal Navy complement was 893.

7 Originally twenty-four torpedoes, two per aircraft, were provided. DAS complained in June 1921 that the ship might have to operate for many months without being rearmed, and the figure was revised to three weapons per aircraft. In November 1922 the planned bomb load was 100 × 1800lb, 150 × 112lb and 600 × 20lb. Later (January 1923) the RAF substituted 520-for 1800lb bombs, and it was decided that two 520lb would be provided in lieu of each 1800lb. However, the Air Ministry rejected a proposal to eliminate the heavy bomb lift, since it was developing a 1000lb bomb, and wanted room for future growth.

8 The port position was used for flying control, the starboard for ship control. Unofficially they were known, respectively, as 'Pip' and 'Squeak', the retractable navigation bridge being 'Wilfred.'

9 The very similar *Courageous* and *Glorious* were later increased to 4000 tons of oil to match, and were considered good for 80 hours at 90,000shp, or about 2400nm. In 1939 they carried 3570 tons of fuel oil, and were rated at 5030nm at 16 knots.

10 This is deduced from Admiral Madden's memorandum on fleet policy, February 1919. Roskill dates the Ten Year Rule from a Cabinet memorandum written the following August.

Left: *HMS* Furious *had two parallel control positions, one to starboard for navigation, and one to port for air control. The letter* T *was part of a visual signal for aircraft. The wind breaks are flat on the upper flight deck, although the wind break protecting the lower flight deck (with a fighter warming up) is up. Note the empty gun positions on the lower flight deck; the mounts had been removed for experiments in launching large aircraft in connection with the completion of the* Courageous *class. This photograph was taken in about 1927.*

folded) and a length of 46ft. They were required to lift a 10-ton weight at 30ft per minute, or a 5-ton weight at 50ft per minute. Later this changed to 5 tons at 35ft per minute. Travel was 39ft 6in for the forward lift and 36ft 6in aft. When the ship was completed the forward lift could bring an aircraft up from the lower hangar in 49 seconds, from the upper in 30. The forward lift could bring an aircraft up from the lower hangar in 41 seconds, to the upper hangar in 30. Corresponding figures for the after lift were 40 and 30 seconds.

Narbeth had assumed that, as reconstructed, *Furious* would have to sacrifice much of her former battery. This proved unnecessary; she gave up her torpedo tubes, but retained all ten 5.5in guns, and gained six 4in anti-aircraft guns (two forward on the lower flight deck, and four aft). Space was provided for four multiple pom-poms (two forward and two aft). There were two independent (port and starboard) fire control systems, each with a clear view fore and aft, and with separate directors for main and anti-aircraft batteries. Two anti-aircraft computers were adjacent to their directors, but the main armament calculator (the Dreyer Table) was located on the lower deck.

Aircraft were served by three bomb rooms, one forward for large bombs and two aft for small ones; she could also accommodate thirty-six torpedoes.[7]

The ship was navigated from duplicate positions on each side, connected by a gangway under the flight deck, off which were the charthouse, signal office, radio direction-finder and intelligence office. Both were connected by voice tubes with the conning tower, on the lower deck, from which the ship was actually steered. Like *Argus*, she had a retractable charthouse on her flight deck, in this case at its forward end.[8]

Design endurance was initially 4300nm at 16 knots, but in 1921 the design was revised, the 500 tons of ballast in the original re-design being eliminated in favour of 600 more tons of oil fuel. Beam was increased instead (by 2ft in half-beam), so the total increase was 700 tons. Total fuel was then 4035 tons, for 5300nm at 16 knots (but E-in-C later estimated she was good for 6000/16). In 1939, *Furious* carried 3950 tons of oil fuel and was rated at 5610nm at 16 knots.[9]

Design speed was 30.5 knots. On trial, 3 April 1925, the ship made 30.03 knots at 90,895shp. She encountered no rough weather, but she seemed very steady and reasonably free of vibration.

However, the horizontal funnels were less than successful; the spaces surrounding them because notably hot, a maximum temperature of 146 degrees F being registered. The hot steel near the funnels tended to bend, the upper hangar bulkhead deflecting about 2⅛in. Smoke hung low around the after end of the ship, particularly when the expeller fans were in use. This portion of the ship was sometimes uninhabitable, and always uncomfortable. These results were later used to justify the decision (which had already been taken) to use more conventional uptakes in the next two conversions, *Courageous* and *Glorious*.

Perhaps the most important post-completion modification was the total elimination of the arrester gear so carefully developed in 1918-20. Pilots did not like it; they could never be sure that their aircraft had engaged successfully, and attempts to bolt after what they considered bad landings could easily result in crashes. Landings even slightly off centre could also be dangerous. Moreover, as aircraft became heavier, they were easier to control on deck. An alternative system, in which deck-edge pallisades were used to keep aircraft from blowing over the side in rough weather, was tested very successfully aboard HMS *Furious* in 1926, and arrester gear was ordered removed from all British carriers, the following year. Arrester gear was not installed, initially, aboard the new carriers *Courageous* and *Glorious*.

The elimination of the gear had valuable additional benefits. British carriers had floatplanes aboard for training when in port, since they could not launch and recover wheeled aircraft without some wind over the deck. This practice explains why so many British carrier aircraft of the interwar period were designed with interchangeable wheels and floats. Floatplanes could land on a flat metal deck, but only if it was clear of the arrester gear wires. The floats were for peacetime use only, and it was always understood that they imposed an excessive sacrifice of performance for wartime missions.

The other benefit was that, without the arrester gear, naval aircraft did not need elaborate high undercarriages (to keep propellers clear of the wires), with their associated drag. They could, therefore, be more or less identical to land-based types, and would be less expensive. From an RAF point of view, in the absence of arrester gear, carriers could operate land-based aircraft and, in theory, squadrons could shift between land and naval work.

Like the other early British carriers, *Furious* took much longer than expected to complete. All were given very high priority, and delays irritated the Admiralty because it was then pressuring the Air Ministry to provide naval aircraft. Delay was therefore embarrassing at best; at worst it could be used as an excuse to deny the Navy the aircraft it needed.

DNC pointed out that his limited staff was very hard pressed, that the new carriers had many novel design features, that they needed extensive changes of armament (especially in *Hermes*, which in turn entailed considerable increase in complement), that lifts were difficult to design, and finally that construction was slowed by the shifts from one yard to another, presumably adopted in the first place to maintain a steady work load. Although in 1922 DNC hoped that *Furious* would be the last of the bad delays, much the same criticism applied to *Courageous* and *Glorious*.

AS A RESULT of the July 1920 Staff Conference, it was decided that either *Courageous* or *Glorious* would be rebuilt as a carrier. In July 1921 both were being used as Turret Drill Ships, *Courageous* at Portsmouth (where both her 15in turrets were needed) and *Glorious* at Devonport (where only one turret was needed). The latter was, therefore, the best candidate for reconstruction, since she could be replaced by the monitor *Marshal Soult*, which was then intended for disposal. On 27 July 1921 the Board formally chose her for conversion. Originally she would have duplicated the *Furious* reconstruction, but the Washington Treaty radically changed that (see below).

THE TEN YEAR RULE was a second major factor in naval air development. By February 1919 official policy envisaged no war within ten years.[10] To the Admiralty, this translated into a requirement to formulate a ten-year modernization programme, much as the post-1945 Admiralty would do in 1947. To the British Cabinet, however, the Rule was a formula for drastic cuts in defence spending, such as a proposed reduction of almost a third in the 1920-21 budget. The Ten Year Rule was extended on 6 May 1925, with the Cabinet specifically ruling out aggressive action by Japan before 1935. This in turn pushed back the date for naval modernization. The Ten Year Rule was made self-perpetuating in 1928 (extended automatically each year), finally dying in 1932 in the face of Japanese action in the Far East. It was symptomatic of a larger government policy of retrenchment in defence, and of the British attempt to seek security through arms limitation treaties rather than through unilateral strength.

The Board's first approach to postwar fleet policy (1918-19) was to maintain a capital ship fleet equal to that of the United

Above, top and right: *HMS* Courageous *is shown shortly after her completion, on 27 February 1928. Note the flight deck pallisades just abaft her island, intended to prevent aircraft (landing without benefit of arrester gear) from falling over the side. Ironically, the flight deck itself was humped abreast the island precisely to allow installation of the longitudinal-wire arrester gear abandoned before the ship was completed. As completed, the ship was armed almost entirely with 4.7in anti-aircraft guns, although after 1927 provision was made for later installation of 8-barrel pom-poms. The view from aft, which must also date from soon after the ship's completion, shows the flight deck ending almost at the after end of the hangar. It was later extended in both ships. Note the door and cranes at the after end of the hangar, to handle floatplanes. Aircraft handling cranes are also visible at the forward end of the hangar.*

11 The argument was that the only possible near-term competitors were the United States and Japan, of which the United States had a declared policy of achieving and maintaining parity with the greatest naval power, that is, Britain. Japan was discounted as a serious naval rival, but her distance from the centre of British power increased her relative effectiveness. Given the Anglo-Japanese treaty, Japan would probably take the British side in a dispute with the United States and so reduce any American inclination to bluff Britain. The Fleet commander, Admiral Madden, wanted to use the battlecruisers to force the United States to split her fleet between Atlantic and Pacific.

12 ACNS memorandum for the Board, 12 May 1920, in ADM 167/62. The proposed programme was to begin four capital ships early in the next programme year (1921–22), begin one minelayer (HMS *Adventure*), convert *Eagle* and *Furious*, complete small ships under construction and lay down four more capital ships under the 1922–23 programme.

13 The 25,000-ton figure appears in the relevant Admiralty telegram to the delegation in Washington, but the design study justifying it has not come to light. No reference appears in the context of the 1923 25,000-ton study.

14 DNC (d'Eyncourt) pointed out that including *Ark Royal* and *Pegasus*, the Royal Navy already had 80,500 tons of carriers, and thus could not carry out the planned *Glorious* conversion. He suggested that, since all but *Hermes* were conversions, they were much less efficient (on a tonnage basis) than new ships. For example, a specially-built carrier equivalent to *Eagle* would probably displace about 15,000 tons, and one equivalent to *Furious*, 16,000. On this basis he equated *Argus* to 12,000 tons, *Pegasus* to 3,000 tons and *Ark Royal* to 4,000, giving a total equivalent tonnage of 63,000. New conversions were particularly important because the existing carriers were so slow and so inefficient. On the basis of equivalent tonnage, the sacrifice of *Eagle* and either *Hermes* or *Argus* would buy conversion of the more useful (and much more capacious) *Courageous* and *Glorious*. It is not clear whether DNC's equivalence proposal was actually tabled at Washington.

15 ADM 1/8702/151, Programme of Construction and Reconstruction, 1923–26.

States.[11] Since war was per se unlikely, the reserve (war fleet) ships could exert only very limited influence. Numbers of active ships would determine the relative balance of naval power in peacetime disputes.

Most ships under construction were cancelled, and ships in commission reduced accordingly. In particular, three battlecruisers, which would have duplicated HMS *Hood*, were cancelled. This was not an aviation decision, but it had important implications for British carrier development. These ships were rough equivalents of the US *Lexington* class, construction of which had been interrupted by the war. Had their construction continued, they would have fallen victim to the Washington Treaty and, like the *Lexingtons*, they might well have been converted into large carriers.

The British government expected the United States to cancel its big wartime building programme after the Armistice. When this did not occur, the Admiralty pointed to the need to maintain parity, and the Cabinet agreed to a programme of new construction, including large new battlecruisers.[12] These had hardly advanced when the Washington Treaty cancelled them, and so there was no possibility of converting them. Instead, the interwar Royal Navy relied primarily on three much smaller ships, the converted large light cruisers *Courageous*, *Furious* and *Glorious*. They had considerable aircraft capacity, but their origins showed in limited size and protection.

The treaties limited any further British carrier construction. The Royal Navy came to Washington in 1921 with the requirement for five carriers in hand. DNC estimated that a successful ship could be built on 25,000 tons, so the British proposal was for a total of 125,000 tons.[13] The initial US proposal was for 80,000 which seems to have been intended to allow for the reconstruction of two battlecruisers as 40,000-ton carriers (which figure the United States put forward as a suitable upper limit on carrier tonnage).[14]

At this time the United States was proposing a 35,000-ton limit on battleship tonnage, and the British delegation pointed out that 40,000-ton carriers were inconsistent with such a figure. They counter-proposed 45,000-ton capital ships (which would have permitted completion of a super-*Hood* class battlecruiser). In the end, the US delegation compromised. Future carriers would be limited to 27,000 tons (for a total of 135,000, keeping the British five-carrier figure in mind). However, each signatory was permitted two 33,000-ton ships, which might be converted from capital ships scheduled for scrapping. Both the United States and Japan used this clause to convert two unfin-

ished ships into large carriers. Britain had no capital ships far enough advanced to convert, and she was not scrapping any recent battlecruisers which might have been fast enough to be worthwhile. Instead, she converted all three of the large light cruisers which, because they were not even mentioned in the Washington Treaty, she could have retained. This left 20,100 tons for new construction, allowing for two new large light cruiser conversions.

The treaty also allowed Britain to scrap the three inefficient carriers existing in 1921 (*Argus*, *Hermes*, and *Eagle*) at any time in exchange for new ships. However, existing modern (post-treaty) carriers could not be scrapped until their service lives (twenty-five years) had been expended. It was further argued that *Furious*, already a semi-carrier at the time of the Conference, could be included in the experimental category, hence could be scrapped whenever the British government chose to do so.

THE ADMIRALTY TRIED two post-treaty approaches: design of new carriers within the available tonnage, and the conversion of the two remaining large light cruisers. In June 1923 D of P reviewed the British carrier situation. *Argus*, *Eagle*, *Furious* and *Hermes* could, it was thought, accommodate the aircraft required to support the projected twenty-capital-ship fleet, but the first three ships were too slow, and this fleet allowed neither for deck training nor for wartime expansion. He therefore proposed that *Glorious* be converted as soon as *Furious* was completed, and then *Courageous* after *Glorious*, unless experiments with *Furious* showed that new construction was necessary. At this time the Washington Treaty allowed new capital ship construction beginning in 1931. Given limited resources, Britain would be unable to build both new battleships and new carriers after that date. However, the expected date of completion of the reconstructions clearly allowed at least one new carrier to be laid down well before 1931. D of P's schedule showed either the third large light cruiser conversion or the first new carrier in the 1925–6 programme, and the second (or the first new carrier) in 1927–28.

At this time fleet air requirements were not yet fully developed; the fleet was understood to need twenty-four spotters, twenty-four reconnaissance aircraft, twenty-four fighters and twelve torpedo-bombers, the total of eighty-four having been derived from existing capacity rather than from some more abstract study.[15]

More elaborate arguments were marshalled to support a pro-

Furious *as rebuilt, showing smoke exhausting both from her flight-deck vents and from the side vents aft.* FAAM

jected ten-year modernization programme (27 March 1924).[16] The decision had been made definitely to rebuild both large light cruisers, and Britain had by far the most numerous carrier force, built and building, in the world, with 20,500 tons left in her treaty allowance. She also had several obsolete carriers which could be scrapped at any time. If she discarded HMS *Argus*, she would be free to build one of the two 33,000-ton ships allowed by the treaty. Discarding the inefficient *Eagle* and *Hermes* would add enough tonnage to build both. Experience seemed to show that anything short of 30 knots was insufficient for a fleet carrier, which condemned the three slow carriers to subsidiary service, quite apart from any difficulty due to their very limited capacities.

The three fast carriers could accommodate a total of 136 aircraft, and the only firm requirements were twenty-four reconnaissance planes and twenty-four spotters. Although only eighteen torpedo-bombers were in service, at least thirty-six were needed (and the total requirement would probably be much greater). Similarly, there was no firm upper limit on fighter requirements. The three large carriers could, in theory, accommodate eighty-four large aircraft plus fifty-two fighters, with additional fighters aboard the capital ships and cruisers. However, if one was refitting, the fleet might be limited to only eighty-six aircraft (the required eighty-four large types and only two fighters). The only solution was another 30-knot carrier, able in theory to accommodate at least fifty aircraft; this seemed possible (given the studies described below) on about 19,000 tons. Alternatively, small ships (below 10,000 tons), not limited by the treaty, could be built.

There was an inherent conflict between building a small number of carriers capable of launching heavy aircraft and the need for numbers of decks to launch large numbers of aircraft very rapidly, since the launch rate per deck was limited. The suggested programme, then, was to lay down 17,000-ton 30-knot carriers in 1926, 1930 (replacing *Argus*), 1933 (replacing *Furious*) and 1936 (replacing *Hermes*). This proved impossible, as the Treasury observed all too clearly that Britain already possessed a formidable carrier fleet. As noted below, the Admiralty did come very close to achieving this programme in 1923, and could hope to do as well during the late 1920s. After 1929, however, finances worsened drastically, and very little could be done.

The 1924 study noted that at any stage of a European war, or during the latter stages of a Far Eastern war, operations might well take place near an enemy's coast, in which case all the carriers would be required to accompany the main fleet. However, studies of trade protection already showed that carriers would be needed to protect merchant ships from enemy air attack in areas such as the chops of the English Channel, the Mediterranean, and the Formosa Straits. The only option open to the Royal Navy would be to build unregulated carriers, of less than 10,000 tons. This option was rejected for the present because the Royal Navy could barely afford fleet carriers, and because it feared the fiscal consequences of an unrestrained arms race in small carriers. However, designs were put in hand for contingency construction.

In 1923 the Controller assigned DNC to explore two alternatives. One, which became Scheme A (and was sometimes

16   ADM 1/8672/230.

Glorious as refitted in 1935; her quarter-deck was raised to lower deck level and her flight deck extended aft.

Courageous shows her new accelerators and her large charthouse, about 1935, before installation of a Type 72 homing beacon. By this time 8-barrel pom-poms had been mounted forward. CPL

referred to as Light Cruiser A), would displace less than 10,000 tons, and therefore was entirely unregulated by treaty. It had the highest priority (Table 5-1). The alternative was to build within the treaty limit, the maximum being 33,000 tons. The Controller asked for alternative 33,000- and 16,500-ton designs, to explore the effect of different tonnages. However, Britain had only 20,000 tons available, and even when she scrapped *Argus* she would have only about 35,000. DNC had already claimed that 25,000 would suffice.

The two studies, then, were 16,500- and 25,000-ton carriers, Schemes B and C. They were submitted in November 1923 (see Table 5-2). The 16,500-ton displacement nearly filled the remaining British tonnage allowance. If the least satisfactory existing carrier, HMS *Argus*, was discarded, two such ships could be built. It followed that, unless the 25,000-ton ship was clearly vastly superior, the 16,500-ton ship (or some variation thereof) would actually be built.

Work on Scheme A began late in May 1923, based loosely on the existing cruiser-sized carrier, HMS *Hermes*, but with roughly the aircraft capacity of HMS *Argus* (which was more than 50 per cent larger but which, like all carriers converted from merchant ships, was relatively inefficient). Narbeth was

still senior carrier designer. His first approach was a hybrid island-less carrier. The flight deck would be used only to fly on, the usual launching area forward replaced by a retractable catapult. This would give clear vision forward from a bridge below flight deck level (as in HMS *Argus*), and it would revolve to launch aircraft into the wind, without any need for the carrier herself to turn. This idea was revived later for proposed merchant ship conversions. The hangar aft would be 16ft high and 50ft wide, and aircraft would usually be shipped through a door at the stern. The lifts would have to be large enough to take any aircraft which could fit the hangar.

Given the nature of the Washington Treaty, it was crucial that standard (fuel-less) displacement be held below 9000 tons. Narbeth therefore instructed Payne, the constructor in charge of the preliminary design, to err (if necessary) on the low side of that figure, using new high-strength steel to hold down the hull weight, and simplifying and reducing the fittings. He suggested that the design begin with the characteristics given in Table 5-1, with protection similar to that in HMS *Hawkins*, fuel as in *Hermes*, and power scaled down from *Hermes* to give a speed of 24 knots loaded, or 25 light. Armament would be limited to anti-destroyer guns and small anti-aircraft guns:

Table 5-2: Cruiser A compared to *Hermes*

Data in square brackets refer to revised design.

	Design A	Hermes	First Estimate
LBP (ft)	530	548	575
LWL (ft)	560	578 5	
LOA (ft)	581	598	
Flight deck length (ft)	76	90	75
Hangar (ft)	350 × 48	328 × 48	
Lifts (ft)	35 × 38	37 4 × 36	
Beam, WL (ft)			62–65
Beam, outside bulges (ft)	69	70 1½	65–70
Draught (no fuel) fwd/aft (ft)			16/19
Load draught fwd (ft)	16 [15 16]	18 9	
aft (ft)	19 [18 6]	19 11	
Displacement (tons)	9800 [9750]	11,500	
Freeboard (ft) fwd	28		
amids	21		42
aft	12		
SHP	40,000	40,000	30,000
(originally 32,000 for 25 knots)			
Speed, legend (knots)	27 [26.5]	26	24
Fuel at legend (tons)		1000	
Oil fuel capacity (tons)	2000	2000	
Complement	700 [720]	724	

Armament

5.5in	5 (200rpg) [—]	6 (100rpg)	
4.7in HA	[7 (240rpg)]	—	
4in HA	3 (144rpg)	4 (144rpg)	
Pom-poms	[8 (800rpg)]		

Protection

Armour		100lb over machinery spaces [80lb magazines and bomb rooms, 60lb steering gear]	

Aircraft

Max Stowage

	Design A	Hermes	
Fighters (spread)	27	21	
Reconnaissance aircraft (Panther, spread)	22	17	
Spotters and torpedo-planes (folded)	18	16	
Amphibians (Seagull, folded)	18	17	

Working Stowage

Fighters (spread)	25	18	
Reconnaissance aircraft (Panther, spread)	18	12	
Spotters and torpedo-planes (folded)	16	13	
Amphibians (Seagull, folded)	16	14	

Weights (tons)

	Design A	Hermes	First Estimate
General equipment	750 [855]	900	650 (ship 500, RAF 150)
Armament	400 [275]	444	450
Machinery	1350 [1060]	1230	1300
(Horizontal funnel)	200 [—]		
Fuel	1000	100	200
Armour	650 [460]	720	850
Hull	6300 [7000]	7100	6350
Margin	100	100	
Displacement	9800 [9750]	11,500	9000

17   In *Furious* they were only about 34ft above water. Although they were provided with water-tight covers, the covers had to be removed in very rough weather.

18   Early in November a seventh 4.7in gun was added, but the arrangement was considered too congested, the forward gun being too close to the port and starboard guns just for-ward of the bridge. Because the ship was very fine forward, it was difficult to work satisfactory anchor and cable arrangements with it. An alternative battery, two twin 6in, was tried, but it was too expensive because the guns had to be moved far from the ends. As a result, the flight deck would have been 75ft shorter and the hangar 20ft shorter.

Narbeth's rough sketch showed eight 4in anti-aircraft guns in recesses covered by flaps, and seven 5.5in anti-destroyer guns beneath the flight deck, four forward and three aft.

Payne's design (June 1923) is described in Table 5-1. By clearing the foward 96ft of the hull, he could provide sufficient clear vision to dispense with the retractable charthouses of *Argus* and *Furious*. Inside, by placing the boilers aft, he could avoid the long horizontal smoke ducts of HMS *Furious*. The machinery would duplicate half the set used in the cruiser *Emerald*. Payne could not quite provide Narbeth's full gun battery, but he did show two 5.5in and one 4in forward, and three 5.5in and two 4in anti-aircraft aft. This was a somewhat cramped arrangement; the after 5.5 was so far aft that it would be swamped in anything but calm weather, and it would also be shaken up at high speed. Two guns could be mounted amidships, but their ammunition arrangements would be unsatisfactory.

The 9000-ton ship could accommodate all existing naval aircraft, but at a tight fit, leaving no margin for future growth. The catapult as the sole means of launching also severely limited her. The design showed, too, that the maximum unlimited carrier, at 10,000 tons, could accommodate as many aircraft as the slightly larger *Hermes* (which did come within the treaty limit) at 30 knots. This idea was not pursued further in 1923, although it was briefly revived in 1930. At that time the US Navy was considering building flight-deck cruisers, which were essentially unregulated carriers with substantial gun batteries. Scheme A provided the potential basis for a British equivalent. In February 1930, for example, it was presented to DNAD with the notation that it could accommodate twenty-five Flycatcher fighters, or sixteen S/R or torpedo-bombers of current type.

Payne was also responsible for the two larger ships. Both designs emphasized maximum speed (to escape possible surface attackers) and maximum aircraft capacity. It turned out that on 16,500 tons a carrier could combine high speed (34.5 knots at standard displacement, 33 knots deeply loaded) with a large hangar space (nearly as large as that of the much larger *Furious*), partly by replacing internal horizontal uptakes with external fixed funnels outside the flight deck, that is, by restoring a small island, a proposal parallel to that then being made for *Courageous* and *Glorious*. Payne estimated that to revert to horizontal funnels, the smaller ship would have to be 1000 to 2000 tons larger. As an additional benefit, the boiler and engine room intakes could be raised.[17]

The chief sacrifice due to a reduction of almost 6000 tons was in armament. Sufficient displacement remained to provide substantial protection.

In both the 16,500-ton and the 25,000-ton designs, the combination of high speed and a large hangar required great length. The larger ship (alternative C in Table 5-3) had both a heavier armament (including six 8in guns in twin turrets) and heavier, though very limited, protection (deeper on the sides, with a 1in deck over the machinery as well as a deck over the magazines). However, the 8in guns crowded out hangar space, so that the gain in aircraft was very limited. Given the limited available tonnage, the 16,500-ton ship was clearly preferable. On 20 November 1923 the Board authorized DNC to proceed with it. The legend and preliminary drawings were approved on 28 November, with an all-anti-aircraft armament (six 4.7in guns).[18]

None of the modern carriers had as yet been completed: *Furious* was expected in March 1925 and (over-optimistically) *Courageous* and *Glorious* at the end of 1926–27. Only *Hermes* and *Eagle* were close to completion.

Even so, the new carrier was a very serious project. The

19   The remainder of the programme was eight 10,000-ton cruisers, three patrol submarines, one submarine depot ship, one destroyer depot ship, one minelayer, two destroyers, a yacht to replace HMS *Triad* at Hong Kong, and two Yangtze Gunboats. The carrier was officially justified on the basis of a need to build up the treaty limit, and to keep up with developments in naval aviation (justification for items in the emergency programme, by D of P, 22 December 1923).

Table 5-3: 1923 Carrier Designs (12 November 1923)

	Hermes	Furious	B	C
LBP (ft)	548	735	735	780
LOA (ft)	598	786	765	820
Beam, extreme (ft)	70	89 6	80	92
Draught, std displacement, fwd	18 9	23 6	19	23 6
aft	19 11	24 6	21	25 6
	(legend)	(legend)		
Std displacement (tons)		22,000	16,500	25,000
			20,300	29,500
Freeboard (ft) fwd	28	27 3	35	35
amids	21	20 4	25	30
aft	12	14 3	16	16
SHP	40,000	90,000	120,000	180,000
Speed (knots) light	26	31	34.5	34.5
deep			33	33
Fuel capacity (tons)	2000	4000	3500	4000
Endurance (nm)			6000	6000
Complement			1050	1200
Armament				
4.7in HA			6 (240rpg)	6 (240rpg)
5.5in QF	6 (200rpg)	10 (200rpg)		
4in HA	4 (144 + 50rpg)	6 (144rpg)		
8in				6 (130rpg)
Protection				
Side armour			1½in over magazines and steering gear 2in side plating 6ft deep 14ft deep over machinery 1in deck over machinery	
Aircraft				
Spotters or torpedo-planes (Darts or Bisons)	13	36	32	36
Fighters (Flycatchers)			35	50
Reconnaissance aircraft (Panthers)			32	42
Amphibians (Seagulls)			32	42
Weights (tons)				
General equipment & aircraft equipment	900	1460	1400	1700
Armament	440	630	350	1100
Machinery	1230	3200	3300	5100
Fuel	1000	1000	—	—
Armour, protection	720	3930	600	1600
Hull	7110	12,130	10,860	15,500
Margin	100	100	—	—
Displacement	11,500	22,450	16,500	25,000

Blackburn Baffin torpedo-bombers over HMS Furious, *in the mid-1930s. This photograph has been retouched, but it clearly shows the raised quarter-deck (1931–32 refit) and the two quadruple pom-poms forward on the lower flying deck (with two 4in guns less visible abaft them).*

Admiralty reaction to the Ten Year Rule, a ten-year modernization programme, included tentative plans for up to four such carriers, the necessary tonnage to be realized by scrapping the three least satisfactory existing ships, *Argus*, *Eagle* and *Hermes*. This seems to have been more a maximum programme than a serious plan, and it was fiscally impossible; these last two had not yet even entered service, although the success of the *Furious* design clearly showed that they were obsolete.

For the immediate future, the general run down of British naval shipbuilding had caused a depression in the industry, and the Board hoped that the Conservative government then in office would seek a loan for new construction for what amounted to relief during the winter of 1923–24. The tentative programme (which would be begun earlier than usual, for relief purposes) was approved by the Board on 21 November, a memorandum already having been presented to the Prime Minister. It included one new 16,500-ton carrier.[19] In the event, the Conservative government fell, to be replaced in mid-January by the first British Labour government. The latter abandoned the new programme, although this did not end Admiralty interest in a new carrier.

Design work proceeded, though slowly (due to congestion in the DNC design department) until the end of 1923. By December DNC knew that the design could not be ready for 1 March, the beginning of the 1924–25 financial year. By this time the Naval Staff had come to favour more anti-destroyer firepower (5.5in guns). DNC himself decided that the ship had to be somewhat larger (by 700 tons, with 6in more beam and 3in more draught) because she had insufficient GM (at most 4ft in the light condition, compared to 5ft for *Furious* and 4ft to 4ft 6in for the new cruisers), due to her extreme fineness and shallow depth; her form cost about 1ft of GM compared to a *Furious* form of similar displacement. The required shp was also greater than had been anticipated (66,000ehp at 16,500 tons for 34.5 knots, according to model tests). If the hull form were slightly changed, hull depth could be slightly increased to make the new carrier roomier below the waterline.

By early 1924, then, the new carrier design showed a standard displacement of 17,200 tons, and DNC estimated that she would take three years to build. This last figure was used for all later British pre-World War II carrier planning. The new carrier was initially scheduled for the 1925–26 Programme, but after the renewal of the Ten Year Rule in 1925 it was deferred to 1929. By that time the financial situation was much worse, and the carrier was deferred again, to 1932. It was eventually ordered in 1934 as HMS *Ark Royal* (see Chapter 6). These delays were justifiable in that, with three carriers in commission and three large carriers either newly completed or under construction, the Royal Navy was well ahead of its rivals in carrier strength, though not in number of aircraft afloat (due to its method of operating aircraft from carriers).

By October 1924 the 17,200-ton design seemed obsolescent in view of new estimates of the future size of aircraft. Ideally, future hangars would need a clear height of 16ft or more (compared to 15ft in the design), and a clear width of at least 50ft (the design showed 48, with reductions in the wake of the boiler room vents). The 17,200-ton carrier would probably carry about as many aircraft as *Furious*, hence many fewer than *Courageous* or *Glorious*. She lacked the upper hangar flying-off deck incorporated in the three big conversions, and considered quite valuable at the time. Her most important advantage would be her speed, 33 to 34 knots compared to 30 to 31 for *Furious*.

On this basis, it seemed that a satisfactory 33- to 34-knot carrier, accommodating forty aircraft (as in HMS *Furious*), with a large flying-off deck, would displace about 19,000 to 20,000 tons. Even then armament would have to be limited (probably to six 4.7in guns), and the ship would probably have to be navigated from a small island.

THE BOARD APPROVED conversion of both the remaining large light cruisers, *Courageous* and *Glorious*, in 1922. Initially they were to have duplicated *Furious*, with flush decks and 5.5in guns, but DGD proposed that the armament issue be reopened.[20] The treaty permitted the Royal Navy so few carriers that any loss (for example, to a cruiser) would be very serious. The maximum carrier gun calibre was 8in, and no carrier could be armed with more than ten guns above 6in calibre.

It had to be assumed that carriers would become separated from the main fleet as they manoeuvred to launch and recover aircraft, and therefore that they might be engaged by enemy cruisers. They would also have to rely largely on their own weapons for anti-aircraft defence. Heavy guns (8in) would be useful for both roles, to drive off the new 8in cruisers and to break up enemy air formations at long range. The lighter high-angle guns would be fully engaged by aircraft almost directly overhead. Atlantic Fleet exercises E J 1, 2, 3 and 4 (February – March 1922) showed that in three cases out of four, a carrier (presumably armed with 5.5 or 6in guns) engaging a cruiser would have been sunk, although in two cases the light cruiser would also have been damaged or sunk by the torpedo-planes.

Thus the carrier of the future needed either high speed (to escape) or an adequate escort (which would weaken the main fleet), but ideally also 8in guns suited to high-angle fire. The

Right: *HMS* Glorious *steams in company with the destroyer* Wisheart *during the Spanish Civil War 1938. Note the national (neutrality) marking on her flight deck, and the two accelerators at the fore end of her main flight deck. By this time 8-barrel pom-poms had been mounted on the lower flight deck (as planned in 1927), and a quadruple .5in mount is visible abaft the pom-pom director just abaft the break of the upper flight deck. A similar mount is visible aft. By this time the ship had been fitted with arrester gear, but in this photograph it does not seem to have been rigged. The aircraft on deck is probably a Swordfish.*

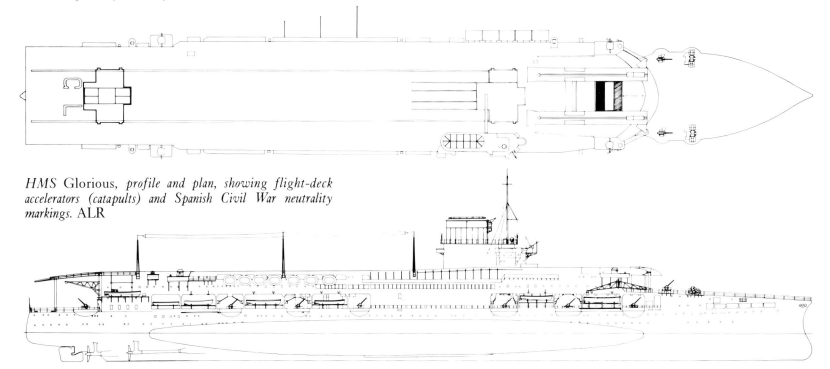

HMS Glorious, *profile and plan, showing flight-deck accelerators (catapults) and Spanish Civil War neutrality markings.* ALR

Left: Seen here in the late 1930s, Glorious shows her pom-poms and the air control bridge which swung out from alongside her funnel.

alternatives, in order of preference, were 6in guns capable of more than 30 degree elevation (new mounting); existing 6in (maximum elevation 30 degrees); 5.5in capable of 30 degrees (17,300 yard range); 5.5in capable of 25 degrees (16,000 yard range); 6in capable of 20 degrees (15,600 yards).

DNC was asked to investigate the 8in gun. Anti-aircraft guns were already a serious problem due to blast interference, and in a flush-decker the 8in turrets would have to be on fore-castle and quarter-deck, precluding blast-free anti-aircraft guns there. DNC rejected mounting an 8in turret forward because this would eliminate the lower flying-off deck. Single guns could be mounted at the hangar corners, but this too was unattractive. DGD was unwilling to back off; the Americans were mounting 8in guns aboard *Lexington* and *Saratoga*. DNC did admit that *Furious* could mount one 8in in lieu of each forward 5.5, but at the cost of heavy structural alterations.

There was one other factor. In 1921 the Naval Anti-Aircraft Gunnery Committee recommended specially strong anti-aircraft batteries for carriers, since they could be disabled by a few deck hits. The ideal was seven 4.7in guns, three on the island, two before it and two abaft it, with a director at the masthead. In addition, the committee recommended that each carrier be armed with multiple 2pdr pom-poms, two on each side below the flight deck, two forward and two aft, plus light machine-guns to deal with point-blank bombing.

There was as yet no *Courageous* design, so much more could be done. In fact the study of possible 8in positions determined her ultimate configuration, although in the end no such guns were mounted. DNC's first approach was to mount five, replacing Nos 1 and 3 5.5in guns, plus one on the quarter-deck. This would cost hangar space, but it encouraged a request for a further feasibility study (4.10.23).

The 8in guns required direct vertical ammunition supplies, so the guns had to be relatively far from the ends of the ship. They therefore had to encroach on the hangar and flight deck, hangar space already being limited by the big horizontal funnels. Narbeth soon realized that he could restore hangar capacity by replacing the horizontal ducts with a conventional vertical uptake. To avoid the problems of the island carriers, he drastically limited the structure around the uptake, and described the ship as a 'funnel' carrier, hence not a reversion to the island configuration.

Alternatives reported in December 1923 were:

(a) Twin 8in on CL fore and aft, island. This restricted the volume of the magazines and required that torpedo protection be extended fore and aft. Capacity: thirty-five large aircraft or fifty-six Flycatchers. The anti-aircraft battery was only four 4in.

(b) Twin 8in aft, two single sided forward, island. The forward flight deck was preserved, but the two forward mounts had to be served by broken hoists. This version included eight 4in anti-aircraft guns (four forward and four aft), which could not be lincuded in (a) Capacity: thirty-five large aircraft or fifty-six Flycatchers.

(c) Island type with eight 6in (broadside), six 4in; fifty-one large aircraft or sixty-seven Flycatchers. This demonstrated the volume advantage of the island type. It had no fire astern.

(d) Flush deck type with eight 6in and six 4in; thirty-seven large aircraft or sixty-three Flycatchers (*Furious*: thirty-six large aircraft or 52 Flycatchers).

DNC (W J Berry) found (a) and (b) unattractive, since it seemed unwise to rely on only two or three main battery mounts. There seemed little to choose from between (c) and

(d), though (c) was attractive, and would be more so if she could be armed with the twin 6in gun then being planned for the *Nelson* class battleships. DGD argued, however, that as the carrier would have to stand up against modern cruisers she would need 8in guns, and it seemed best to superimpose two 8in turrets aft, with two 6in on either side forward.

In a new design, (e), the two twin 8in were mounted aft, the anti-aircraft battery being reduced to four 4in. Capacity was forty-one large aircraft or fifty-four Flycatchers.

There were two further possibilities:

(f) Ten 6in, eight of them in four twin turrets, the other single, firing ahead. Capacity: forty-two large aircraft or fifty-six Flycatchers.

(g) (f) modified with one turret replaced by two 4in, with slightly greater hangar capacity. Capacity: forty-seven large aircraft, sixty Flycatchers.

DNC liked design (c) best, because it maximized the number of aircraft – which, after all, were the main battery. He considered (e) the best 8in alternative. In February 1924 ACNS introduced a third alternative, an all-anti-aircraft battery (4.7in guns), which was already being planned for the new carrier. ACNS considered cruisers, rather than destroyers, the main potential enemy, so that 8in guns seemed essential. However, design (e) would be expensive, and the new mounts (with their poor ammunition supply) would take nearly a year longer to manufacture. The Sea Lords met, and in February 1924 the Controller was asked to consider the all-4.7in design.

DNC developed two more designs, both modified versions of (c):

(h) The four 6in guns aft were retained, the six 4in anti-aircraft guns being replaced by 4.7in, and four 4.7s were mounted on the lower hangar deck, two on each side, with lesser elevation. Because the ammunition supply to the latter guns could not be direct, ready-use supplies had to be placed in the hangar, reducing its capacity. The 4.7in guns had to be closely spaced, and would suffer some blast problems. Capacity was fifty-one large aircraft or sixty-three Flycatchers.

(j) The all-4.7in ship, with eighteen guns: four on the upper hangar deck forward, twelve on the lower hangar deck, and two on the upper deck aft. No ready-use ammunition supplies would be needed. Capacity: fifty-two large aircraft or sixty-five Flycatchers, very nearly as in (c).

(j) was selected in March 1924. Advantages included a uniform battery of guns using cased ammunition (a great advantage in an unarmoured ship), and a four-cornered fire control system, so that four air targets could be engaged simultaneously. Hopes of being able to engage cruisers seem to have been abandoned.

In line with the requirement that each carrier be armed with four 2pdr pom-poms, appropriate positions had to be earmarked (the mounts would not be ready for about a decade). DNC proposed the positions with the best overhead arcs: two on the upper hangar deck forward, replacing the forward pair of 4.7in guns, and two replacing 4.7in guns on the upper deck aft. DNO preferred four lower-deck 4.7s (Nos 1 and 6 on each side), arguing that the pom-poms would find it extremely difficult to hit any target above 60-degree elevation due to its very high angular velocity. The decision was to mount 4.7in guns in the indicated positions until pom-poms were available.

DNC had proposed, and the Naval Staff had now accepted, the idea of the island. It would be kept very short (the goal was initially a length of only 60ft), and very far forward, so that it would not interfere with landing-on.[21] Because expeller fans

20 The 6in cruiser mount was an alternative, but DAS wanted the carriers to standardize on the 5.5in gun. Given the likely rise of the new 8in cruisers permitted by the treaty, ACNS did ask in November 1922 whether the two ships would be more valuable unconverted, as commerce protectors. The question was moot at the time because no money for conversion was as yet available.

21 The island had to be lengthened aft for a longer funnel, and forward for a standard compass, so in August 1924 it was 73ft 6in long. Fire controls and radio were deliberately kept off the island, to hold down its size.

Left, opposite top and opposite bottom: *The last photographs of HMS* Glorious, *taken on 7 June 1940, the day before she was sunk, with Hurricanes on board. These photographs were taken by Mr Frank Clements of the Naval Canteen Service, HMS* Highlander. FAAM

were no longer needed, the width of the lower hangar could be maintained all the way to its after end, so that aircraft could be passed by the cranes in and out of the hangar from aft while spread. The idea was debated and accepted at the JTC, although the Air Council (equivalent to the Board of Admiralty) objected. There was also some hesitation within the Naval Staff, since the Washington Treaty debarred the Royal Navy from rebuilding the two carriers after completion. If the island was a mistake, it would haunt the navy for another twenty years. DNC retorted that the *Eagle* trials showed that a much worse island (twice the size) was satisfactory, and that the Air Ministry objections were little more than surmise. By late summer the conversion design was very far along, and any new design would entail a delay of more than another year.

In 1926 C-in-C Mediterranean called for reversion to a flush-deck design; E-in-C's reply showed the savings associated with the island. In *Furious*, the funnels, uptakes, and expeller fans (but not the casings fitted in the wake of the funnels after trials) weighed 410 tons, compared to 215 tons in *Courageous*. The 180,000sq ft used for funnel ducts in *Furious* went largely for accommodation in the later carriers. The heavy ducts, high in the ship, even cost stability.

Given the island design, the new conversions would carry more aircraft than HMS *Furious* (thirty rather than twenty-four heavy aircraft – torpedo, spotter and reconnaissance), although the provisional torpedo-bomber complement was the same. Much depended on the bomb load of the new spotter-reconnaissance (S/R) which had just been proposed to the Air Ministry. In May 1924 a figure of 50 per cent more bombs was therefore proposed. This was possible in the after bomb room (325×112lb and 900×20lb bombs), but the forward bomb room would be congested with 230 520lb bombs. There was no alternative which was both floodable and served by the bomb lift. NAS was willing to accept this reduction because all three carriers had the same number of torpedo-bombers, which were the only aircraft capable of lifting the 520lb bomb.

The issue of hangar height was raised in the JTC in February 1924, the committee deciding on 16ft from deck to underside of girder in both hangars, to allow for future developments. Hangar runways were eliminated but eyebolts were provided in convenient positions to lift engines or aircraft parts.

The Board approved the sketch design in April 1924. By July, Devonport had stripped *Courageous* down to her forecastle deck. *Glorious*, at Rosyth, was in similar condition at the beginning of August. The completed design was submitted to the Board on 6 January 1925, and approved by the Sea Lords on 22 January; the formal minute of approval was dated 12 February 1925. The plan was to strip *Glorious* at Rosyth, keeping her there nearly to the end of the 1925–26 year, then transfer her to Devonport. Work on *Courageous* at Devonport was dependent on completion of *Furious*, after which she could be accelerated.

Flight-deck configuration generally matched that of HMS *Furious*, except for the short island. The lifts were of similar size

Furious was modernized just before the outbreak of war; her 5.5in armament was replaced by twin 4in anti-aircraft guns, and a small island (for fire control and a Type 72) was erected. The island did not, however, replace the original pair of ship- and air-control positions flush with her flight deck. She is shown on 7 November 1942.

and shape, travel being 40ft 9in for the forward unit and 38ft 6in for the after one (specified times from flight deck down were 64 and 61 seconds, from the lower hangar deck up, 60 and 57 seconds). The initial specified aircraft complement was three fleet spotter or reconnaissance flights, two torpedo flights and four fleet fighter flights. One of the fighter flights had four (rather than six) aircraft, for a total of fifty-two. These choices reflected the physical layout of the hangars, since ideally the aircraft of each flight were grouped together between fireproof curtains hanging from above. Thus it was no simple matter to reorganize the air complement with, say, longer aircraft, since the latter might not fit properly between the fixed curtains.

Conversion plans initially showed 30,000 gallons of petrol and 3750 of lubricating oil. However, in May 1925 *Eagle* reported that she had consumed 1524 gallons in one day, and suggested that the standard should be 1000 gallons per aircraft. It seemed quite possible, moreover, that future aircraft would burn fuel faster, as was indeed to be the case. Capacity could be increased by fitting tanks of a special shape in the existing tank compartments, as the existing stowage in cylindrical tanks was quite wasteful, or (to 40,000 gallons) by using a lower deck compartment (which could not, however, be well protected). The only counter argument was that a larger carrier might fly a smaller proportion of her aircraft on a daily basis, that is, that her nominal capacity might rather exceed her operational capacity. In 1939 both ships had a capacity of 34,500 gallons.

The only really controversial question was whether to fit catapults, an issue first raised in 1926. As in 1917–18, they seemed attractive because a carrier might use them to launch her aircraft without losing her position in the fleet. A new argument was that they might also be used to launch ASW and reconnaissance aircraft to cover a fleet sortie just before the fleet left harbour and thus before any carrier had wind over her flight deck. It was also argued that they could be used to launch seaplanes in harbour, when the water was too rough for conventional take-offs.

The only available units were the air-powered or cordite-fired types going aboard cruisers and capital ships. Their main defect was that they fired very slowly; by one estimate it would take an hour to launch a flight (six aircraft), whereas the same aircraft could fly off a deck in under 8 minutes.[22] Carriers lost position primarily because of delays in landing-on, not launching.

In 1926, moreover, HMS *Furious* reported that she could launch aircraft in any flyable weather and on most occasions while at anchor (particularly those in which the sea was too rough for floatplanes). She had also successfully launched aircraft with the wind 6 degrees off the bow, as well as downwind. All of this made catapults much less attractive, and ultimately, in 1929, killed the idea, but only after considerable detailed planning had been done. The planning seems significant because it clearly led to the idea of installing catapults in the flight decks of later British carriers (and then aboard *Courageous* and *Glorious* as well). The later catapults (which were termed accelerators) differed radically from those proposed in 1926, in that they could fire repeatedly with very short intervals between shots.

The catapults in cruiser service in 1926 fired their aircraft at 45 knots, and required some wind to function. Launching in still air required that a 7000lb aircraft be accelerated to 55 knots, and this in turn required a cordite rather than an air catapult. Even then an aircraft would sink below the level of the catapult before gaining enough speed to rise. The chief candidate was a Vickers model, 73ft 9in long, intended for HMS *Hood*.

The catapult could be mounted either on the upper hangar

Table 5-4: *Courageous* and *Furious* (Legends, 6 January 1925)

	Courageous	*Furious*
LBP (ft)	735	735
LOA (ft)	786	786 6
Beam, extreme (ft) (over bulge)	90	89 6
above water	110	90 9
Legend draught (ft) fwd	24	23
aft	25	24
Legend displacement (tons)	23,250	22,450
Freeboard to top of forecastle deck at side, forward (ft)	27	30 1
Freeboard to top of forecastle deck at side, amids (ft)	57	
Freeboard to upper deck, aft (ft)	14	17 1
Freeboard to forecastle deck, aft	22	23 2
Deep load draught, mean (ft)	27 6	27 2
SHP	90,000	90,000
Speed (knots) legend	30.5	31
deep	29.5	
Oil fuel (tons) legend	1000	750
	4000	4025
Complement as private ship		1213
Flight deck length (ft)	538 6	
Clear width (ft)	100	
Forward flight deck	156	
Armament		
5.5in	—	10 (200rpg)
4.7in AA	18 (250–300rpg)[2]	—
4in QF AA	—	6 (150rpg)
3pdr Hotchkiss QF	—	4
2pdr Mk M pom-pom	4 (14,400rpg)[1]	4
Maxim guns[3]	—	4
Lewis guns	—	14
Protection		
Side armour upper edge above legend line (ft)	20	
Side armour lower edge below legend line (ft)	6	
Thickness amidships	3in	
Thickness forward	2in	
Protective deck	¾in and 1in	
Flight deck	⅝in D quality	
Weights (tons)		
General equipment	870	850
Armament	760	630
Machinery	3130	3200
Fuel	1000	1000
Aircraft & equipment	710	610
Hull & Protection	16,680	16,360
Board margin	100	100
Displacement	23,250	22,280

1 To replace four 4.7in guns.
2 250 for each 4.7in capable of elevating to 90 degrees and 300 for the 4.7s on the lower deck. This was modified in April 1926 to a total of 4920 (4020 in the main magazine and 900 in the old torpedo body room), or 240 per 90 degree gun, and 390 per 60 degree gun, plus 300 star shell and 378 practice. *DNO*
3 It was approved on 1 May 1920 that the machine-gun armament of carriers would be four Maxim guns (.303in) and ten Lewis guns in double mountings.

deck (at side or centreline) or on the flight deck, forward of the island. No position was ideal. A catapult on the side of the upper hangar deck (or lower flight deck) would interfere with the anti-aircraft battery (and cost two 4.7in guns) and would increase the overhang of the ship, complicating docking. A catapult on the centreline, while attractive from a ship-handling point of view, would be difficult to install and might interfere with take-offs from the lower flight deck.

This left the position forward of the island, on the starboard side. Installation would require that some of the round-down on the side of the deck (provided to suppress cliff eddies) be surrendered. Aircraft would have to be raised onto the catapult by inclined plane or special trolley, since there was no space for a crane forward of the small island. Worse, the catapult would have to fire athwartships, since its recoil had to be taken up by

22 In February 1929 C-in-C Mediterranean Fleet estimated that a carrier could fly off twelve torpedo-bombers and 12 fighters in 10 to 12 minutes, but would require 36 to 40 minutes to recover them.

23 The key seems to have been a letter written by Admiral Henderson, former captain of HMS *Furious*, in
November 1928. It had been argued
that a carrier might sometimes have to
launch a single reconnaissance aircraft,
and that she ought not to have to turn
into the wind to do so. Henderson
argued that they rarely worked singly,
so that if one relief was needed, half a
dozen would be. The carrier could fly
them off in under 8 minutes. Worse,
only the obsolete Flycatcher and Fairey IIID were stressed for catapulting.

its roller path. Even so, the flight deck position was the most attractive, partly because it was the only one really protected from spray. In February 1927 the Controller ordered one installed aboard *Glorious* under the 1928 Estimates. Devonport was ordered to prepare detailed drawngs, and flight deck plating was specially strengthened.

This was not the end of the catapult story, as both the Air Ministry and the two senior C-in-Cs afloat (Mediterranean and Atlantic fleets) objected strongly.[23] As a result, the catapult was finally rejected in February 1929. The ship was later fitted with a pair of flush-deck catapults (accelerators); see Chapter 6.

THROUGHOUT THE 1920s the British government tried to reduce the prospective cost of defence by further limiting warship size by treaty. In the spring of 1926, for example, it considered proposing a new limit of 23,000 tons at the forthcoming 1927 Geneva Conference. The Naval Air Section of the Naval Staff needed confirmation that a new carrier, arranged as *Courageous*, could accommodate about fifty aircraft and achieve at least 30 knots on this displacement. The then DNC, Berry, suggested that more modern machinery could actually add about 1.5 knots (120,000 vs 90,000shp), but that the new ship would be relatively unprotected. Her underwater protection would not equal that on a new contemporary submarine depot ship, and her decks would be penetrated by relatively small bombs. Berry wanted to add about a thousand tons of protection, and considered 24,000 tons a better limit, with 25,000 tons really satisfactory to take into account new developments.

In June 1927 the Assistant Chief of the Naval Staff (ACNS) reviewed required numbers in hopes of further cuts. He suggested that a single carrier only in the Home and Mediterranean fleets would be acceptable from a tactical point of view, so that the wartime modern total could be reduced to four ships. On 22,500 tons, approximately the tonnage of *Courageous*, a ship could accommodate about as many aircraft (fifty-two), about the same flying facilities, and could achieve 30 knots (deep load) with about the endurance of HMS *Nelson*. From a treaty

point of view this was very attractive, as four carriers would cost much less than five. They would accommodate fewer aircraft in total, which would cost less to buy and to man. This logic will be familiar to any student of recent attempts at arms limitation. The problem was that carriers were something more than a simple drain on the national purse: they were required for operational duties. For example, if the life of a carrier were taken as twenty-four years, two of those years would be taken up in refits. Thus, although the Navy List might show four carriers, during eight years at least one would be away at all times, for an effective force of three. It was also argued that three carriers were inadequate from a tactical point of view. One compromise was to retain five ships but keep only four in commission, rotating the others through refits.

A reduction to 22,500 tons was also attractive from this point of view, as the Washington Treaty total of 135,000 tons would accommodate six such ships, compared to five 27,000-ton ships. If in fact there was little to choose in aircraft capacity or sea-keeping between 22,500 and 27,000 tons, the greater number of ships was quite attractive from a tactical point of view.

At this time it seemed likely that Japan would press for a reduction to 90,000 tons of carriers, in which case Britain could retain four of 22,500 tons each. In the event that five were required, then the global limit might usefully be set at 115,000 tons. That would leave Britain and the United States without much excess tonnage. Japan would probably object, since she would be left with 15,500 tons (on a 5:5:3 basis), not quite enough to build an efficient ship. The Admiralty planners reached the conclusion that a satisfactory carrier could be built on 22,500 or 23,000 tons, but that it would be extremely difficult to convince the Japanese to accept the appropriate change in overall limits.

The 1927 Geneva Conference failed, and in London in 1929–30 the Admiralty pressed for a 25,000-ton, rather than a 23,000-ton, limit. The Cabinet did, however, extract an admission that not all ships would be built to the limit, and global

Furious is shown, probably under repair, at the Philadelphia Navy Yard in 1942. Radar antennas above the high-angle director atop her island are barely visible. This refit was completed on 21 March 1942.

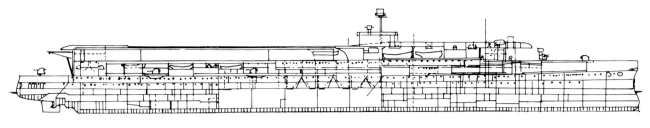

Internal profile

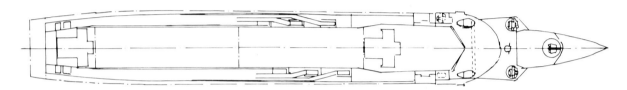

Flight deck

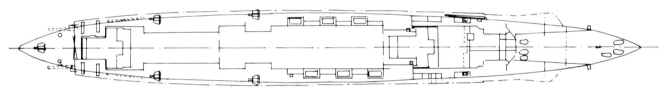

Upper hangar

Lower hangar

HMS Furious *as modern-ized, in about 1942. Note the volume taken up by the smoke ducts extending aft along both sides of her upper hangar, as shown in the deck views. Note also that she still has the two streamlined control positions alongside the fore end of the flight deck.* NF

figures as low as 100,000 tons were discussed. A memorandum on the negotiating position in London shows that the Admiralty considered it in the British interest to hold down the number of carriers, particularly if the fleet as a whole had to be cut.

DNC was ordered in 1931 to develop a new carrier design which would be used to guide the British delegates to the abortive 1932 Geneva Conference. His success with a 22,000-ton design led directly to a British offer to reduce total carrier tonnage to 110,000 tons. Although this new limit was not adopted, at the London Conference (1935) the British delegation did succeed in reducing the unit limit to 23,000 tons. However, the London Conference also eliminated the earlier limits on total ('global') carrier tonnage.

The 1934 ship therefore occupied a peculiar position. She was built to a tonnage limit proposed, but never adopted, and was therefore somewhat smaller than she might otherwise have been. At the same time, the then British government assumed that global limits would continue. Since tactics were based on a total number of fleet aircraft, it followed that each of the limited number of allowed carriers would have to accommodate as many as possible. This explains both the double-hangar design and also the effort to fit *Ark Royal* with a deck barrier, so that she could operate her large air group. Once the global limit had been removed at the next conference, there was no longer much point in accommodating the maximum number of aircraft per carrier, as the Fleet's aircraft could be distributed among a larger number of ships. Thus *Ark Royal* was never duplicated.

THE THREE BIG CARRIERS were little modified between the wars. Like *Eagle* and *Hermes*, they had their anti-aircraft batteries reviewed in 1927. *Furious* might have had her existing mixed battery of 5.5in single-purpose guns and 4in anti-aircraft guns replaced by a uniform battery of 4.7s, but this would have required considerable alteration, and it was not done. The only suitable multiple pom-pom positions were currently occupied by 5.5 and 4in guns. As the ship had only five 5.5in on her broadside, only one could be replaced, for a total of two such mounts. It would be possible to mount four single pom-poms (2pdr) on sponsons built out from the ship's side below the flight-deck level, and the ship had already requested fourteen more Lewis guns (1926).

For *Courageous* and *Glorious*, the plan called for Nos 3 and 8 (foremost and aftermost broadside positions) or Nos 4 and 8 4.7in guns on each side to be replaced by multiple pom-poms; the latter had better sky arcs. There was also a proposal to mount three single pom-poms on platforms built out from the ship's sides below the flight-deck level, and adjacent to the searchlight platforms, with another on a similar position just abaft or abreast the island.

The single pom-poms themselves would ultimately be replaced by quadruple .5in machine-guns, which were still in the design stage.

Furious completed in 1925 with six single 4in anti-aircraft guns, two right aft on the quarter-deck and four forward, on the lower flight deck. The four forward guns were temporarily removed (1926–27) for trials of the lower flight deck (in connection with *Courageous* and *Glorious*), and only two were remounted. Aft, the quarter-deck was raised during a large refit in 1930–31, and the two single 4in replaced by a single weapon. In 1927 the ship also had on board four single pom-poms (newly mounted), four Maxims, and ten Lewis guns. After 1928, however, she carried forty-two Lewis guns.

In 1931 *Furious* had a single 8-barrel pom-pom aboard, and by 1933 she had two, replacing two of her flight-deck 4in guns.

Two quadruple .5in guns were added in 1935. By 1938 *Furious* was the only carrier still mounting single 2pdrs; she then had two.

The mixed main battery was clearly obsolete by this time, and *Furious* was rearmed under the programme already described for *Eagle* and *Hermes*. The plan was to remove all her 5.5 and 4in guns as well as the two surviving single pom-poms; the two 8-barrel pom-poms on the lower flight deck and the two quadruple .5in guns on the flight deck would remain. Six twin 4in and two more 8-barrel pom-poms would be mounted, the pom-poms on the flight deck itself, one twin 4in on the former lower flight-deck (which would no longer be usable), one on the quarter-deck, and the other four on the broadside, aft, for a broadside of eight 4in guns. A small island was built to accommodate the gun directors, air defence positions, ready-use magazines, and the Type 72AX homing beacon. It did not incorporate any navigation features, so the ship still had to be directed either from flight-deck level or from the retractable navigating position. The lower flight deck was raised, and two sets of HACS installed, one at the lower flight deck and one on the island.

Some of the work was done during normal short refits between 1936 and 1938, and then it was completed at Devonport during the winter of 1938–39, the ship recommissioning in May 1939. Wartime modifications were quite limited; Oerlikons (ultimately twenty-two) were added around her flight deck and radar (Type 285 for gunnery and Type 290 for air search) was fitted. The guns received splinter protection ('zarebas').

In this form HMS *Furious* remained active until 1944, her last major operation being the strikes against the German battleship *Tirpitz* in April 1944. Her flight deck was relatively short, and a ramp, in effect a ski-jump, was built at its forward end to help the heavily laden Barracuda dive-bombers get off. On 31 August 1944 DNC reported that she was completely worn out, and on 15 September the Controller ordered her laid up. Her last employment was as a target in the postwar Ship Target Trials, and she was sold for breaking up in 1948.

Courageous and *Glorious* were completed with sixteen 4.7in guns rather than the planned eighteen, leaving space for two multiple pom-poms. They were initially assigned four single pom-poms, four Vickers machine-guns (other carriers had Maxims), and the usual ten Lewis guns (increased to forty-two in 1928). As in HMS *Furious*, their quarter-decks were raised to lower hangar deck level during large refits in the 1930s; each also had a pair of accelerators fitted at the forward end of the upper flight deck. *Courageous* was test ship for the British transverse arrester gear. *Glorious* had her flight deck lengthened aft in 1935 (total length increased to 570ft), with a more pronounced round-down. She could be distinguished by the pair of prominent vee-struts supporting the extended after part of the flight deck. This modification was not applied to her sister ship, although it was considered.

In 1934, each had two 8-barrel pom-poms (on the lower flight deck, forward of the 4.7in guns there), and *Glorious* was scheduled to be fitted with a third, abaft her island (which had been done by early 1935). Each also had two .5in machine-guns added the following year. By 1938, *Courageous* also had the third 8-barrel pom-pom. As test ship for the prototype Type 72 homing beacon, *Courageous* was fitted with a tripod mast (as well as a special house on her island).

HMS *Courageous* was hit by two torpedoes fired by *U20* and sunk on 17 September 1939. Her sister ship, *Glorious*, survived to fight in the Norwegian campaign the following spring. She was sunk by shellfire from the German battleships *Scharnhorst* and *Gneisenau*, 18 June 1940.

Left: Furious *in her final configuration, late 1943 or early 1944. Her air search radar mast is barely visible forward of the mast carrying her aircraft homing beacon. Note the raised charthouse on her flight deck, and the dark area aft, where she still exhausted her funnel gases.*

6

The New Carrier

FROM ABOUT 1930 on, British carrier design ideas began to change. Like his colleagues, DNC was well aware of the apparently intractable problem of insufficient aircraft stowage. Although many Admiralty documents continued to dismiss the much greater capacities of American carriers, he began to think in terms of the deck parks that made that capacity possible and, by extension, in terms of the transverse arrester gear which kept landing aircraft from crashing into those parks. Ironically, the basic idea for such arrester gear had been evolved by W A D Forbes of the DNC Department during World War I, and had been passed to the United States after the war. It had not been adopted by the Royal Navy, but when Forbes reviewed wartime test reports and films, he was surprised at their crudity. They had demonstrated little, if anything. DNC therefore pressed for the revival of arrester gear.

This was a delicate subject. Carrier capacity had been negotiated with the RAF, which was loath to admit that the Navy might suddenly need many more aircraft. The new arrester gear was, therefore, invariably justified externally as a means of raising the allowable landing speed, and thus of making higher-performance aircraft carrier-compatible. It was sometimes also justified on the ground that a carrier using it did not have to steam into the wind at full speed while recovering aircraft, and therefore might conserve fuel or reduce engine wear, both important issues.[1]

However, DNC documents generally emphasized the value of a deck park as a means of increasing the effective aircraft complement. The Board agreed, and an experimental set of wires, Mark I, was installed aboard HMS *Courageous*. It employed automobile-type friction brake drums to absorb the energy of landing, one problem being to bring the aircraft to a gradual halt without any sudden jerk, which would damage it.[2] Forbes considered Mark I primarily a means of measuring the forces a future standard arrester gear would experience.

The first trials, on 20–22 January 1931 aboard HMS *Courageous*, employed a single wire. A Fairey IIIF made seven runs. The wire proved to be situated too far aft, and the pilot tended to land further forward. Trials had to be conducted with at least 18 knots of wind down the deck, since otherwise the aircraft would be unable to take off again if it failed to engage the wire. Two more wires had to be installed, and the mechanism moved aft. Further trials that September were successful, and procurement of two more prototypes was approved in December, to be

installed in HMS *Courageous* during a November-December 1932 refit. Mark II was an abortive friction-brake production model; the hydraulic Mark III was adopted instead.[3]

The effect of arrester gear was to make the forward end of the flight deck valuable both for permanent parking and to park aircraft as they landed. Tactically, parking aircraft rather than striking them below one by one would make for much quicker recovery. From a design point of view, it made the recent split-deck carriers much less attractive, since it divided a single deck into a landing zone aft and a launch zone forward.

Deck parking required something more, a safety barrier between the wires and the deck park proper. Barrier development seems to have been difficult, and it appears that the first

---

1   As a measure of success, in 1934 DNC (Sir A W Johns) delivered a paper on aircraft carrier design before the Institution of Naval Architects. Narbeth commented that it was unfortunate that arrester gear was being installed, and that he hoped that instead it would be carried individually by aircraft, in the form of brakes. He seems to have been altogether unaware of its consequences for carrier capacity, yet at the same time (as noted in the text) Johns was using the capacity argument. The basic Admiralty paper, MF 0946/32, which is preserved in the Ship's Cover for HMS *Hermes*, gives both arguments. Arrester gear is advocated as a means of allowing landing-on in adverse wind conditions, and (by reducing the need for wind over deck) perhaps as a means of reducing a carrier's loss of position within a fleet. Carrier machinery would suffer less wear and tear (a particularly important consideration for the flimsy ex-light cruisers) and fuel consumption would be reduced. Then the paper goes on to mention the added aircraft capacity.

2   In Mk 1, the arrester gear was essentially a wire led to two winches, the energy of landing being taken up by friction brakes on the winches. In practice it was very difficult to equalize forces on the two winches, so that the wire pulled further from one than the other and aircraft tended to be slewed about, sometimes violently, when landing. The other problem was

that, if the tension in the wire was constant during landing, the arresting force built up as the wire paid out. Because the hook was well below the thrust line of the aircraft, and because the wire did not dip towards the deck (particularly as it tightened), the aircraft tended to come to rest in a tail-up position. When the tension was released for unhooking, then, the aircraft would be jerked violently back and into the deck. The hydraulic system of Mk III and subsequent arrester gear was designed, then, to allow for a smooth build-up of the arresting force, and steady reduction in tension as the aircraft was brought to rest (so that the retarding force was made a function of aircraft speed). Another problem of arrester gear design was that the wire had to be supported sufficiently far above the deck, typically at a height of about 4in. In the *Courageous* and *Ark Royal* designs this was accomplished by means of folding stanchions across the deck, which normally lay forward at a 60-degree angle. They were spring loaded, so that they could be pushed down by aircraft wheels hitting them. Unfortunately aircraft with retractable landing gear, beginning with the Skua, had much smaller wheels, so much so that if the aircraft landed near a stanchion (and thus, well off-centre) they could go under the wire. In the *Illustrious* and later carriers the stanchions were replaced by 'deck springs,' pieces of round steel bar bent into bow-shape and secured at one end. These sup-

ported the wire without offering any resistance to a wheel passing over. The single deck spring in *Illustrious* was often hit by arrester hooks, so it was replaced by two or three springs in later designs.

3   Mk 1 was designed to arrest a 6000lb aircraft landing at 60 knots in 200ft, that is, with a maximum deceleration of 1 g. Mk 3, of 1933, had similar performance for an 8000lb aircraft landing at 60 knots, but in 140ft, and Mk 3*, in *Ark Royal*, was generally similar (but with a maximum deceleration of 1.5 g). The maximum had to be increased to 2 g in Mk 4 (*Illustrious* class), which could deal with aircraft weights of up to 20,000lbs with a 150ft pull-out. Mk 5 was not used, Mk 6 (of similar performance to Mk 5) going into the *Implacable* class. By 1950 it had been modified to accept entry speeds as high as 81 knots, and a deceleration as high as 3.4 g. Mks 7 and 8 were used in the *Majestic* class (7000 to 15,000lbs, 60 knots, 1.75 to 2 g, 150ft, later modified for higher performance). Mk 10 was used in HMS *Eagle*, the first truly postwar carrier (12,500 to 30,000lbs, 75–88 knots entry speed, 2.3–3.7 g in 160ft) and Mk 11 was similar (*Hermes* class). Mk 12 and Mk 13 were the jet arrester gear introduced in the early to mid-1950s. These data are from J H B Chapman, 'The Development of the Aircraft Carrier,' a paper presented before the Institution of Naval Architects in 1960.

4   It has not been possible to establish with certainty the date at which DLCOs were introduced. In his history of British carriers, a book based largely on interviews (and hence possibly inexact with regard to dates), Paul Beaver gives the date as 1937. Certainly *Ark Royal* had a DLCO when she used her barrier and arrester gear in 1939. In 1936, just before the introduction of the barrier and DLCO, American observers of HMS *Hermes* were much struck by what they saw as the sloppiness of pilots' approaches, the actual approach being entirely up to the pilot. These pilots said that they would never tolerate detailed landing control by an officer, who might be junior to them. The effect of a deck landing control system, as was then in force in the US Navy, was to standardize approach techniques quite rigorously.

unit was fitted only in 1939, aboard HMS *Ark Royal*. From a pilot's point of view, the wires were perhaps an annoyance, but nothing more. A pilot could judge his approach, and bolt if he thought he had missed. However, bolting into a barrier was much more dangerous, and pilots meeting the barrier for the first time disliked it heartily: it was clearly a pilot-killer.

The solution was to take away the pilot's independence. In about 1937 the Royal Navy introduced Deck Landing Control Officers (DLCO), pilots specially trained to ensure that pilots approached at optimum speed, attitude and angle of descent.[4]

Unfortunately, DNC's ideas about deck parking seem not to have had much operational impact before World War II, probably for three reasons. First, the Fleet Air Arm was badly under strength, so there was no real pressure to accommodate more aircraft aboard each ship. Matters would probably have been rather different had the war not begun until, say, 1941. Second, there was obviously no pressure on the Admiralty to admit to the outside world that it could accommodate the requisite total number of aircraft (for the fleet as a whole) aboard fewer ships; the Admiralty knew that its stated requirements almost certainly fell well short of reality, and it badly wanted more carriers. The stated requirement for the number of carriers, for example, did not take war losses into account. Third, the ships built immediately after the *Ark Royal*, the armoured carriers, were ill-suited to permanent deck parking, since their design tacitly assumed that any aircraft left on deck during an air attack would be destroyed. DNC did mention a deck park in the design description he submitted to the Board, but it could

have little significance. Notional deck parking (for use in published statistics) was proposed as a means of hiding the advent of the armoured hangar (see Chapter 7), but this was never intended to correspond to any operational reality.

During World War II the need for more aircraft per carrier soon became evident, and the Royal Navy found itself using the deck parks for which its ships had been designed. However, because the deck park had not been taken very seriously by the Naval Staff, the men to fly and service the additional aircraft could not easily be accommodated, and British carriers proved badly crowded in wartime.

Certainly the DNC Department was quite explicit in its calculations. In 1931 the Board decided to install arrester gear, and that November the Department calculated the effect of a twelve-plane deck park on the stability of HMS *Eagle*. She was particularly important, not only because of the spectacular increase in capacity (from eighteen to thirty), but also because the Admiralty wanted to gain experience in deck stowage before approving the new carrier design then under way. *Eagle* was appropriate because she had a large enough flight deck for deck stowage to be worthwhile, as well as a hangar small enough to be embarrassing. The Board seems to have expected to stow flight deck aircraft with their wings spread, but it hoped that denser stowage, with wings folded, would be practical. Physically, the deck park required that arrester wires and a safety barrier be fitted, and also that some arrangements be made to secure deck aircraft in rough weather.

Actual installation had to await the trials of the two improved

Design A, the double-deck carrier design of 1931. NF

Design B, the full-length flight deck carrier design of 1931, which led to Ark Royal. NF

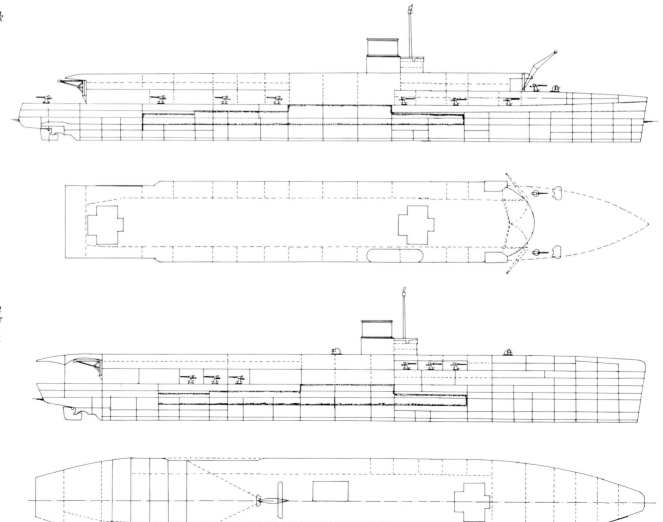

Table 6-1: The 1931 Carrier

	Courageous	A	B	C	Legend
Decks	double	double	double	single	single
LBP (ft)	735	770	750	735	735
Length on deep line (ft)	774	810	790	775	775
LOA (ft)	786	815	805	790	790
Beam (ft)	90	92	92	93 0½	93 6
Draught (ft) std	23 10	23	22 9	22 0⁷/₁₂	22 9
deep	27 6	26 6	26 6	26 3	
Freeboard (ft) to flight deck amids	60 8	62 5	62 8	60 8	61 3
forecastle deck aft	13 4	22 3	22 6	22 5	63 3
deck fwd	27 5	28 3	28 6	43 2	
Displacement, std (tons)	22,500	23,500	22,250	22,430	22,750
Flight deck length (ft)	(1) 590	606	606	766	766
	(2) 152	157	147	—	
breadth (ft)	100	100	84 6	84 6	100
SHP	90,000	120,000	90,000	90,000	90,000
Boilers	18	12	10	10	
Speed (knots) std	30.5	32.5	30.75	30.5	30.5
deep	29.75	32	30	29.75	29.75
Endurance at 16 knots (nm)	5680	6650	7600	7600	
Oil fuel (tons)	3900	3000	4100	4200	4200
Emergency fuel (tons)		5100	5200	5300	5300

Armament

	Courageous	A	B	C	Legend
	16 4.7in	16 5.1in	16 5.1in	12 5.1in	14 5.1in
	(12 290rpg,	(12 290rpg,	(12 290rpg,	(290rpg)	(10 290rpg,
	4 240rpg)	4 240rpg)	4 240rpg)		4 240rpg)
	4 2pdr	2 Mk MM	2 Mk MM	2 Mk MM	2 Mk M
		(1500rpb) ————————————————————————————			(1500rpb)
		8.5in mg (quad) ————————————————————————			8 .5in (quad)
		(2500rpb) ————————————————————————————			(2500rpb)

Protection

	Courageous	A	B	C	Legend
Belt (machinery)	3in HT total	3in NC on 1½in D	3in NC on 1½in D	3in NC on 1½in D	3in on ½in[3]
(magazines)	3in HT total	2in NC on ½in D	2in NC on ½in D	2in NC on ½in D	2in on ½in (fore and aft of machinery)
Side armour: upper edge above legend line (ft)	20 8	22	22 3	22 11	21 9
lower edge below legend line (ft)	3 10	3	2 9	2 4	3 3
Deck over machinery	1in HT	1½in NC			1¼in
Magazines					
roof	2in to ¾in HT		2in NC on ⅜in		2in[4]
sides	1in HT	all: 3in on 1½in D aft, 2½in on 1½in fwd			2½in on 2 × ¾in (fwd)
bulkheads	1in HT	all: 2½in on ⅜in fwd & aft			3in on 2 × ¾in (aft)
	320lbs	450lbs ————————————————			450lbs
Aircraft	52	60	60	60	60[2]

Weights (tons)

	Courageous	A	B	C	Legend
General equipment	1020	1110	1000	1080	1090
Armament	665	930	930	490	850
Machinery (no RFW)	3040	3440	2820	2820	2840
Aircraft equipment	740	1010	1010	940	1060
Protection & hull	17,035	16,910	16,400	16,800	16,860
Margin	—	—	—	—	—
Displacement	22,500	23,400	22,250	22,430	22,750

1 Aircraft in new designs: 24 Handley Page T/B or 21 Vickers T/B; 18 Fairey IIIF S/R; 6 Osprey fighters; 12 single-seat Nimrod fighters.
2 Hangars: upper 526ft × 61ft × 16ft 3in; lower 405 × 50ft × 16ft 3in. Length of upper hangar is measured between bulkhead forward of No 1 lift and fire proof curtain on fore side of No 3 lift; lower between end fire curtains. *Courageous* hangars, by way of comparison, were: upper, 475ft × 58ft × 16ft 3in; lower, 332ft × 50ft × 16ft 3in.
3 1½in bulkheads at ends of machinery spaces and 1¼in deck over machinery.
4 Shell room sides 2 × ¾in, shell room ends 1in; steering gear 1¼in roof, 1½in sides.

prototypes aboard HMS *Courageous*, in 1932. *Eagle* did not receive arrester gear during her big refit (at Devonport, completed in March 1933), but she was fitted out with increased bomb stowage appropriate to her enlarged air group, twelve T/B, twelve F/R and six S/R, which required deck stowage. By January 1934, then, only *Courageous* and *Glorious* had arrester gear, though all carriers were scheduled for installation. *Eagle* herself was fitted only during her large 1936–37 refit.

In January 1934 DNC worked out the number of F/R aircraft (Ospreys) which each carrier could accommodate on deck. The two full-deck carriers, *Eagle* and *Hermes*, could each take twenty, or about as many aircraft as in their hangars. The two-deck carriers were much more cramped: fourteen in *Furious* and eighteen each for *Courageous* and *Glorious*. These figures were never used to calculate the full capacity of the British fleet.

AT THIS TIME, too, a catapult (accelerator) appeared which could be installed flush with the deck. In effect, this could replace the lower flying-off deck of *Furious* and *Courageous*. Like the new arrester gear, it was conceived by W A D Forbes.

In March 1931 Forbes suggested that a means of accelerating aircraft along the flight deck would make a valuable complement to arrester gear. Aircraft could take off with less wind over the deck, and, given arrester gear, the carrier itself could be made slower. He conceived an accelerator which would not have to give the full take-off speed required of a battleship or cruiser catapult, and which therefore could be relatively compact. For example, an average acceleration of only 1 g could provide a speed of 30mph in only 30ft. Possible sources of power included flywheel, air, cordite – or the ship's hydraulic system. The latter was attractive because it did not require a ready-use locker or an additional air compressor. Forbes suggested that an air-loaded fluid accumulator with sufficient reeving could, in effect, replace the cordite unit of a standard catapult.[5]

Forbes' accelerator could be built flush with the deck, thus overcoming the great objection to the catapult which had been proposed for HMS *Glorious* a few years earlier (see Chapter 5). Moreover, because it was powered by the ship's hydraulic system rather than by cordite charges, it could fire frequently and

5 The proof of Forbes' priority as inventor is that his 3 March 1931 memorandum suggests that the accelerator idea is worth patenting. A copy is preserved in the Miscellaneous Carrier Cover (No 425A). Forbes commented that the accelerator could be useful in a cruiser-carrier then under consideration. It seems likely that US carrier catapults were an independent parallel development. Certainly the US Navy led in battleship/cruiser catapults, but (after an early start in *Lexington* and *Saratoga*) it lagged both in introducing and in using carrier catapults; it even seems likely that US observations of British carrier catapult practice in the Mediterranean in 1940–41 had considerable impact on catapult installation in the *Essex* class.

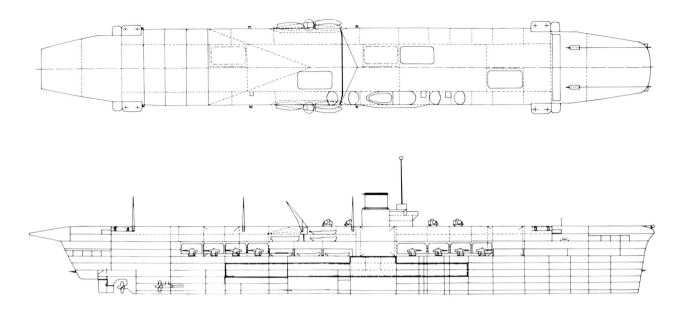

The original 1934 carrier design, with single 4.7in anti-aircraft guns. The dot-and-dash lines on the flight deck indicate the originally proposed lift positions; the final positions are shown by the solid lines. The side belt is indicated in the side view. The crosses in the deck view are quadruple .5in machine-guns. NF

6   British designations were inter-leaved with US ones, to avoid confusion with US catapults supplied aboard Lend-Lease carriers. Standard US World War II types were H.II and H.IV; the 'B' meant British and in both cases the 'H' meant hydraulic. Similarly, British steam catapults were designated in a BS series.

over a long period, and thus could become an important means of launching carrier aircraft. Although Forbes did not say as much in his memorandum, a carrier could use her accelerator to launch aircraft without turning into the wind. Early in World War II, for example, US Navy observers were impressed by the way in which British carriers could catapult-launch their fighters without turning out of the protective screen of cruisers and destroyers.

As these devices improved, by 1944–45 they became the primary means of launching carrier aircraft. Without some artificial means of acceleration, a carrier aircraft had to start far enough back up the deck to achieve take-off speed. The heavier its load, and the higher its maximum performance, the higher its take-off speed, and thus the further back it had to start. However, the carrier's striking power was largely determined by how many aircraft she could range on deck, ready to take off. Thus, even if wartime aircraft could take off on their own, powerful accelerators greatly enhanced their effectiveness. Of course, very slow carriers, such as escort carriers, could not generate very much wind over deck, and accelerators made it possible for them to launch modern high-performance aircraft, just as Forbes' arrester gear made it possible for them to recover such aircraft.

Postwar, jet aircraft could not make rolling take-offs; they would have needed decks of prohibitive length. Accelerators,

Table 6-2: Comparison of 1931 and 1933 Requirements

	1931	1933–1934
Aircraft	60	72 (and larger than 1931)
Armament	16 or 12 5.1in	16 4.7in
	2 Mk M pom-pom	4 Mk M pom-pom
Protection above water:		
belt	3in	4.5in
deck	2in	3.5in
	(magazines only)	(magazines, shell-rooms, machinery)
Protection underwater	450lbs	750lbs
Endurance	7000nm at 16 knots	same
		Increased complement
		Increased petrol stowage

by then called catapults, made jet operation possible; in effect they made a few hundred feet of deck equivalent to thousands of feet of concrete ashore. By 1948 the Naval Staff had decided explicitly that in future the catapult would be the primary means of launching carrier aircraft.

In all of these devices, a trolley or towing hook was towed along the track by a wire rope led around sheaves to a cylinder and piston unit below, the force on the piston being multiplied by an arrangement of sheaves and pulleys (typically with an 8:1 ratio; Forbes initially imagined a 6:1 ratio). The piston was driven by compressed air, acting as a spring, and transmitting a force applied by the ship's hydraulic system.

Forbes' original idea, of accelerating aircraft to less than flying speed, did not survive. Thus the original device installed aboard HMS *Courageous* and *Glorious* could accelerate a 7000lb aircraft to 56 knots. It was also installed aboard HMS *Ark Royal*. The next British system, B.H.III, was designed for 11,000lbs and 66 knots.[6] It was later improved to launch 14,000lb aircraft at the same end speed, and after World War II units in the *Colossus* class were modified to launch 20,000lb aircraft at 66 knots. The following British design, B.H.V (aboard the wartime *Ark Royal* and *Hermes* classes), was initially designed for 20,000lbs and 75 knots, and then redesigned for 30,000lbs to reflect a wartime decision that this would be the maximum carrier aircraft weight. End speed was 75 knots. In each case, mean acceleration (that is, mean stress on aircraft and pilot) was determined by end speed and track length. Track length in turn was limited by flight deck dimensions. Both B.H.V and the most powerful version of B.H. III were 151ft long, which required B.H.V to achieve a mean acceleration of 2.6 g. This in turn imposed structural requirements on the aircraft it would launch.

The Royal Navy initially distinguished between catapults,

Newly completed, and not yet armed, Ark Royal *lies at the Cammell Laird dock in 1938.*

which were the mechanisms aboard battleships and cruisers, and accelerators, aboard carriers. The distinction was not always clear, but it usually hinged on the method of moving the aircraft. Catapults employed trolleys which supported the full weight of the aircraft, since often they launched floatplanes. Because many aircraft had to be able to operate from carriers and from capital ships and cruisers, they were fitted with spools to which these trolleys could be attached.[7] The spools in turn became the natural strong points to which accelerating forces could be applied, aboard carriers as well as aboard the other ships. They were arranged to suit a tail-up attitude.

The earliest British accelerators towed aircraft by means of their front spools. However, because of their position, such attachment imposed excessive loads on the tail wheel; legs had to be provided to keep the accelerated aircraft tail-up. The wire towing bridles were also unsatisfactory (they tended to strike the deck, and could foul the tail wheel), and they, too, were replaced by legs; the aircraft was thus pulled on a four-legged trolley, with its weight still supported by its wheels.

Unfortunately, the trolley took time to rig, and this in turn defeated part of the purpose of the accelerator.[8] Moreover, during World War II the requirement to be able to launch standard carrier aircraft types from battleship and cruiser catapults was abandoned. Once this decision had been made, aircraft could be built with attachment points adapted to tail-down launch, and the cumbersome trolleys could be abandoned. This had already been done in the US Navy, which did not operate fighters and carrier attack aircraft from its capital ships and cruisers.

The distinction between accelerator and catapult was gradually abandoned, and in this book the two terms will hereafter be used interchangeably.

THE LONG-TERM MODERNIZATION PLAN, developed in 1923–24, always envisaged construction of one or more new carriers, first about 1926, then in 1929, and then in 1931. The 1929 date was put back well before it came due, but early in 1931 it still

seemed possible that a ship would be ordered late that year or early the next. In fact it was delayed until 1934.

The basic requirements were decided in a meeting on 15 April 1931 in the Controller's office; those present included three former carrier commanders, Rear Admirals R G H Henderson (who would soon become RAA) and H J S Brownrigg, and Captain D F Moir. The two principal issues were speed and aircraft capacity.

It was generally agreed that a carrier required high speed in order to be able to operate independently of cruiser protection, that is, to be able to evade enemy cruisers and battlecruisers. She needed at least 27 knots (30 was preferable) to operate aircraft, but 32 for evasion. DNC noted that this speed in itself ruled out the 16,500-ton ship studied in 1923. The conference decided that DNC should develop alternative designs for 30- and 32-knot ships, the latter in greater detail.

Endurance would match that of HMS *Nelson*, 10,000nm at 16 knots. It was later argued that a carrier steaming with a battle fleet would have to steam out of line to launch and recover aircraft, and that therefore she needed a substantially greater endurance than that of the battlefleet.

As for aircraft capacity, the issue was how many a ship could operate efficiently. Experience in *Courageous* and *Glorious* suggested a limit of about forty-two, but Henderson argued that with good organization and with greater use of the flight deck (for ranging up a strike, not for parking) as many as sixty might usefully be accommodated. Henderson carried this point, with the caveat that sixty was a wartime limit; ships would operate fewer in peacetime. At this time the US Navy was claiming a capacity of seventy-four aircraft for each of its two ex-battle-cruisers, *Lexington* and *Saratoga*, but the Royal Navy seemed to have assumed that such figures included large numbers of spare aircraft. Petrol (avgas) stowage was to exceed that of the existing carriers.

All present agreed that the new ship should have an island superstructure, since experience showed it preferable for ship

7   This requirement is traceable to the disparity between the number of combat aircraft the fleet required, and the number of spots aboard its carriers. See Chapter 8 for typical interwar calculations.

8   The legs typically folded down onto the trolley track. A single track trolley was fitted in the *Illustrious* class, *Indomitable* and *Unicorn*. It proved unstable and vulnerable to damage, and in the *Implacables* it was replaced by a more stable twin-track trolley, which was more stable but could still accept some errors in aircraft positioning. It was also easier to stow when not in use. The twin track was also installed in the *Colossus* class, the *Majestics* being the first to do away with trolleys altogether.

Table 6-3: *Ark Royal* Design, 3 May 1984

	New Design Overall FD 30 knots	C Design Overall FD 30 knots	Courageous (1931)	Final Design
LBP (ft)	685	735	735	685
LOA (ft)	800	790	786 3	800
LWL (deep) (ft)	725	775	779	725
BEXT (ft)	94	93 6	90	94
Draught (legend) (ft) fwd	23 3	21 10½	23 1½	22 1
aft		23 9	24 7¼	23 10
Std displacement (tons)	22,800	22,430	22,500	22,000
Freeboard (ft) hanger deck, fwd	40 9	43 3	27 6	
Flight deck, amids	59 6	60 9	60 9	
Lower hanger deck, aft	22	22 6	13 8 (upper deck)	
Draught deep, mean, (ft)	27 9	26 6	27 6	27 4
Height of 4.7in above WL, (ft) fwd	30	49 6 (5.1in)	27 10½	
aft	30	30 6 (5.1in)	28	
SHP	96,000	90,000	90,000	102,000
Speed (knots) legend	30.75	30.75	30.5	
deep	30	30	29.75	30
Avgas (tons)	345	140	120	
Oil fuel, total (tons)	4400	4200	3900	4370
Complement, private	1500	—	1330	1600
Endurance at 16 knots (nm)	10,500	7600	5680	11,200
Armament				
4.7in HA/LA	16 (300rpg)	—	16	16
5.1in HA/LA	—	12	—	—
Mk M pom-pom (8-barrel)	4 (1600rpb)	2 (1500rpb)	2 (4-barrel)	4 (1800rpb)
.5in machine-guns	8 (2500rpb)	8 (2500rpb)	6 (10,000 rounds per mounting)	8 (10,000 rounds per mounting)
Protection				
Upper edge of belt above LWL (ft)	22	23	20 9	9
Lower edge of belt below LWL (ft)	2 9	2 6	3 4½	7⁵
Lower edge of belt below ext deep LWL (ft)	7 6	7	7 6	
Belt	4½in on ½in	3in on ½in	2in on 1in	4½in
Bulkheads fwd	2½in on ⅜in	1½in (ends of machinery spaces)		
Bulkheads aft	2½in on ⅜in			2½in
Magazine roof	3½in on ⅜in			
Magazine side fwd	1½in	2½in on 2 × ¾in	1in	
Magazine side aft	1½in	3in on 2 × ¾in	1in	
Magazine end	2½in on ⅜in	2½in	1in	
Machinery spaces	3½in on ⅜in	1¼in prot plate	1in	
Steering gear roof	1½in	1¼in 2 × ½in or 2 × ¾in		3½in
Steering gear side	1½in	1½½in 2 × 1in	1½in	
Torpedo protection	750lbs	450lbs	320lbs	750lbs
Aircraft				
Torpedo-bombers	48	24	27	48
Spotter/reconnaissance aircraft (Fairey IIIF)		18	10	
Fighter/reconnaissance aircraft (Osprey)	24¹	6	6	24¹
Single-seat fighter (Nimrod)		12	9	
Total aircraft	72	60	52	72³
Weights (tons)				
General equipment	1090	1080	1020	1105
Aircraft equipment	1100	940	740	1115
Armament	910	790	665	835
Machinery	2570	2890	3040	2440
Armour, hull	17,130	16,800	17,035	16,505²
Board margins	—	—	—	—
Std displacement (legend)	22,800	22,430	22,500	22,000

1 Osprey replacement (dive-bombers).
2 Armour and protection, 2850 tons; hull, 13,655 tons.
3 Bombs: 360 500lb, 300 250lb, 576 100lb, 800 20lb; stowage for seventy-two torpedoes at forward end of lower end of lower hangar (but sufficient stowage for ninety-six warheads, to allow for increased torpedo stowage; torpedoes would have to be stowed in the hangar). The first sketch design showed ninety-six 250lb bombs, and the ratio of the three heavy bombs was set at 30:8:48. Stowage for B bombs was not set at this stage; if carried, they would displace other types.
4 At 14 knots; endurance 14,300nm at 10 knots.
5 Below deep waterline. Belt 24ft 6in deep (total) over boiler rooms; extends over entire length of magazines and machinery.
6 Protective deck over entire length of belt.

operation and no great impediment to flying. It was true that the island presented an obstacle to aircraft flying on, but it seemed likely that arrester gear then under development would stop aircraft before they reached the island. Moreover, a flush arrangement (as in *Furious*) entailed running uptakes through the hangar space, limiting its capacity, as well as costing weight.[9] The uptakes would heat the hangar, and their smoke could make landing-on difficult. On the other hand, the asymmetric weights in an island had to be balanced by liquid loads, so that an island carrier of equal displacement would suffer some endurance penalty.[10]

Similarly, all agreed on two hangars and two flight decks, as in *Courageous*, rather than one, as in the contemporary USS *Lexington*. The double hangar in the converted cruisers had

9   The estimated weight penalty in *Furious*, as compared to *Courageous*, was 500 tons.

10   Alternatively, the ship could have an asymmetric hull, a solution adopted in the later US carrier *Wasp* (CV 7). DNC does not seem to have considered such a solution at this time.

made for very considerable aircraft capacity on limited displacements. It did make for a higher profile, but this brought the flight deck higher above water and thus made it drier in rough weather.

The chief argument for the second flight deck was that it permitted the carrier to fly off aircraft while recovering others on the principal flight deck. The conference observed that the deck was limited to smaller aircraft, whereas in theory a carrier with efficient arrester gear could recover aircraft while others took off forward (as in contemporary US practice).

Other characteristics generally followed those of the existing large carriers. The ship would have two main lifts large enough to take aircraft with their wings spread, as well as one or two small service (bomb) lifts. However, the wide lifts then in use

Like all previous British carriers, Ark Royal was designed to achieve optimum air flow over the flight deck, particularly in the landing area. Here the ship is being towed from the yard of her builders, Cammell Laird, as yet unarmed. The fairing under her long overhang is clearly visible. The top of the overhang was rounded down, and thus could not be used to park aircraft. The later armoured hangar carriers were completed with similar long round-downs, but the limitation they placed on deck parking was not acceptable in wartime, and their decks were gradually flattened out.

(47 × 46ft in *Courageous*) occupied valuable centreline space, and could not be used while aircraft were landing or taking off. If instead they could be limited to the width required for aircraft with their wings folded, then in theory they could be moved over to the side of the ship, and used while aircraft were flying on. If possible, space would be provided for six to eight dismantled aircraft as spares.

Considerable study was then being devoted to anti-aircraft weapons, as a result of which the conference called for four groups of four dual-purpose guns. Larger weapons (which were permitted by treaty) were ruled out, on the ground that a carrier would never duel with a cruiser; she would use her superior speed to escape.[11] Thus her only likely surface opponents would be destroyers, and 4.7in guns would suffice. The proposed 1931 Staff Requirements also included four pom-poms and eight multiple (.5in) machine-guns.

Speed was clearly the main protection, but some armour was needed to ensure against lucky hits. At this time British carrier-borne bombers could deliver 500lb bombs in level attacks, and British carrier fighters were expected to drop their 20lb bombs directly on enemy flight decks. The most powerful British torpedoes had 750lb warheads. The proposed standard of magazine protection, then, was the 500lb SAP bomb and the 6in (cruiser) shell. The heavy warhead was expected to determine

the required degree of underwater protection and the flight deck would be armoured against 20lb bombs.

By October, the Controller, Admiral R B Backhouse, felt that advances in arrester gear and in catapults made it unlikely that any future carrier would need two flight decks. DNC was already working on sketch designs of both flush and double-deck types, and his 32-knot double-deck design (which came closest to meeting the requirements set earlier in the year) was clearly overweight. This design was worked out in considerable detail, and DNC also submitted single- and double-deck 30-knot designs on 9 December 1931 (see Table 6-1).

All were double-hangar island designs, stowing sixty aircraft. They had lifts large enough to take spread aircraft (as in earlier ships), cranes for seaplanes (four fore and aft in A and B, two aft in C), an armament of 5.1in dual-purpose guns (a calibre then being considered, but ultimately abandoned) plus two multiple pom-poms (Mk MM) and machine-guns. Magazines were indeed protected against 6in fire, but there was not enough weight to provide comparable protection for the waterline belt (over the machinery). DNC suspected that welding, which was being introduced, would save enough on the total weight of the hull to make good this deficiency. He was able to provide a lightly armoured flight deck (against 20lb bombs) and substantial underwater protection (bulges and subdivision). All three sketch designs showed minimum turning circles, and power boats of good carrying capacity (to service seaplanes in harbour). Petrol capacity exceeded that of earlier carriers. As

11   At this time it seemed unlikely that any navy would be able to build very large fast capital ships capable of bringing 30-knot carriers to bay. The collapse of global limitations changed the rules drastically, with the result that ships such as the German *Scharnhorsts* emerged – and the *Glorious* was not fast enough to escape off Norway in June 1940. This action encouraged contemporary US officers to press for an 8in battery in the next carrier, as well as protection against heavy cruiser (8in) shellfire. The protection, though not the guns, survived in what became the *Midway* design.

Table 6-4: *Ark Royal* Inclining Experiment Data

Condition	Deep	1/2 Oil	Standard (all ammunition)
Displacement (tons)	28,481	26,142	22,870
Draught	27ft 9.6in	26ft 0.2in	23ft 5.5in
GM	6.65	5.63	3.33
GZ	4.09	3.65	2.80
Angle	34.5	33.5	31
Range	>90	>90	48

Newly completed, Ark Royal *displays neutrality markings on her forward port twin 4.5in gun mount. Note the two empty port side pom-pom platforms; she had not yet been fitted with a satisfactory crash barrier, and without it pilots were apt to bolt to port, away from the island. Twin accelerator tracks are visible forward.* FAAM

noted, endurance was very important; allowing for 5 per cent unusable oil, Scheme B was expected to make 9100nm at 16 knots, or 11,600nm with oil fuel in her buoyancy tanks. At this time HMS *Nelson* was rated at 9200nm, and it was estimated that the carrier would fall short in fleet operations by 1600 to 2600nm, unless emergency oil stowage was used.[12]

The 32-knot double-deck design, Scheme A, displaced 23,000 tons, and so exceeded the new tonnage limit the British government wished to adopt. DNC commented that substantial savings could be achieved by deck stowage of aircraft, as in the US Navy. About half the aircraft could be stowed permanently on the flight deck, which would save about 1500 tons and reduce the 32-knot carrier to about 22,000 tons (and the 30-knot type to about 21,000). In this case, as in the US Navy, overall flight deck length would be a determining factor, and it could not be reduced much below 750ft (as in Scheme C), with beam, draught or both adjusted to suit the reduced displacement.

Displacement (hence cost) could also be reduced by cutting speed; DNC estimated that 2 knots cost about 1200 tons, so that a 29-knot carrier might displace about 21,500 tons. He

argued that, from a flying point of view, the main value of speed was in reducing the landing run. Thus, with the advent of arrester gear, carriers might not need so much speed, and carrier speed might perhaps be equated to that of the battle line. As matters stood, a carrier which would have to turn out of line periodically to launch and to recover aircraft would require some margin of speed over that of the battleships. For example, the US Navy, with a 21-knot battle line, was building a 29.5-knot carrier, USS *Ranger* (CV 4). By analogy, one might imagine that the 23-knot British battle line would have to be accompanied by 31- or 32-knot carriers.

DNC continued work on the full-length (single flight deck) design. If the second flight deck were to be eliminated, then it would be desirable to fit a third lift, to take full advantage of arrester gear by making it easier to clear the deck. This third lift would serve only the upper hangar at the fore end, and its additional weight could be limited by making it large enough only to take folded aircraft. Even so, the upper hangar would have to be lengthened 36ft to balance the loss of usable length it entailed. On the other hand, the additional volume bought by bringing the upper hangar to full length would make it possible to reduce the overall length of the ship, compared to earlier 30-knot designs. DNC estimated that the 30-knot ship would grow 445 tons – 535 for the additional flight deck, hangar walls and flats forward, less 90 tons saved by shortening the hull. Another 55 tons might be saved by using lighter fittings and incidentals, compared to the earlier *Courageous*.

The proposed design showed a somewhat beamier (93ft 6in beam) asymmetric hull to balance the weight and moment of her island structure. This ship was about the same length as the existing *Courageous*, and she would have a metacentric height (GM) of about 3.75ft in the light condition, trimming about 1ft by the stern in the deep condition. Normal deep displacement (buoyancy chambers empty) would be 27,600 tons, and full speed at this load was estimated as 29.75 knots.[13]

12 *Nelson* endurance as given in the official return of British warship characteristics, CB.1815, of April 1931. However, official conferences sometimes used a figure of 10,000nm at 16 knots. The existing carriers were deficient: in 1927 *Courageous* was expected to achieve only 6000nm at 16 knots (when *Nelson* was being credited with 7000nm at this speed).

13 Based on tank tests showing 47,300ehp and an estimated propulsive coefficient of 0.53. Trials of *Courageous*, which had a somewhat similar hull form, showed that an addition of 600 tons cost 0.11 knots.

Extra beam did carry a cost. Design C could have been dry-docked in most major British docks, but the slightly beamier version could not dock in Devonport Nos 9 and 10, Malta No 4, and Gibraltar No 1. The larger ship could, however, dock in Locks C and D at Portsmouth, and in the floating docks at Devonport, Rosyth, Malta, and Singapore. Similar issues would figure in wartime designs for very large carriers.

At this stage E-in-C demanded greater machinery weight, 62.2 rather than the previously quoted 60lbs per shp, even though the machinery would run faster (260 rather than 230rpm) to save weight.

Compared to earlier versions of the design, there were fourteen rather than sixteen heavy dual-purpose (5.1in) guns, because the shorter hull provided less space. This omission saved 80 tons, and could be justified on the grounds that, when aircraft were being operated in *Courageous*, all the guns could not be served. On the other hand, the forward three guns on each side were about 20ft higher than in the earlier designs. Similarly, the two pom-poms were on the forward side of the island, 25ft higher than in previous designs, in which they were on the flight deck.

Forward seaplane cranes, which had been included in earlier two-deck designs, had to be omitted, as there was no break in the deck line near the bow; this in turn balanced some of the weight added by the third lift.

This final flush-deck version of the design is described in the final column of Table 6-1.

The conclusion, then, was that the British government could reasonably support a substantial reduction in the upper limit to carrier displacement. At the least, it could afford 24,000 tons, and success in arrester gear development would allow for a 22,000-ton limit. Admiral Backhouse went further. Even the 22,000-ton design was much larger than USS *Ranger*. Why should that be? Backhouse agreed with DNC that aircraft should be stowed on deck, commenting that this 'may not sound attractive, but it is easy to fit wind screens or baffles to the parking area.' He definitely wanted a belt thick enough to resist 6in fire, that is, 4in armour.

Even though the existing large carriers were beginning to provide relevant operational experience, the new one would have enough new features to require further trials. Backhouse therefore proposed that the first carrier be completed before the next was begun; he suggested that one be included in the 1933 programme for completion by March 1937. Tonnage for the new carrier would be provided by laying up or scrapping both *Argus* and *Hermes*. The new carrier alone would have carried many more aircraft – at least sixty – than the two she replaced, on far less tonnage. This decision would make it possible to avoid spending money on a large refit planned for *Argus* in 1933.

The new design depended on the success of the new arrester gear, trials of which were planned for early 1933. These in turn would determine whether the Royal Navy could abandon its double flight-deck designs. Because the decision on flight-deck configuration really would decide the overall design of the ship, the new carrier design could only be confirmed in about April 1933. She could then be ordered with the other 1933 ships, and laid down in 1934. In fact there was some delay and the *Ark Royal* was ordered under the 1934 programme. However, in September 1932 the Controller suggested that the first new carrier be included in the 1933 programme (for completion in 1936), followed by another in 1936 for completion in 1939, another in 1939 for completion in 1942, and then one in 1945 for 1948 and one in 1947 for 1950. Both the number of ships and the timing were dictated by the allowable replacement dates of the big ex-cruisers *Glorious* and *Courageous*; the

Table 6-5: Carrier Alternatives, December 1934

	A	B	C	D	E	F
Speed (knots)	30	30	27	30	—	—
Side armour	as *Ark Royal* (VS 6in)	as A, but VS 4.7in	as B	VS 4.7in on magazines only (none on ER & BR)	as B	as D (no deck over ER & BR)
Results						
Length (ft)	650	700	740	775		
Beam (ft)	93	90	87	87		
Depth (ft)	83 6	80 6	75 6	75 6		
Speed (knots)	29	29	29	32		
SHP	99,000	75,000[1]	73,000[2]	116,000[3]		
RPM	230	170	170	260		
Aircraft	60	72	72	72		
Protection						
side	4½in	4½in	4½in	magazines only		
deck	3½in	3½in	3½in			
bulkhead	2½in	2½in	2½in			

1 Or 80,000 at 200rpm
2 Or 78,000 at 200rpm
3 Or 120,000 at 280rpm (this was the only 4-shaft design)

replacement of *Furious* involved some ambiguities.[14]

It was clear in 1931–32, then, that under existing treaty conditions the new carrier was badly needed, and that her construction would entail some scrapping of existing ships. The Admiralty, however, advised strongly against any scrapping prior to completion of the new ship, unless some great reduction in tonnage had already been agreed. For example, to break up the obsolete *Argus* would reduce total British tonnage to only 122,750 tons, 12,250 tons below the Washington limit, and well within the 125,000-ton limit the British government advocated. Any further scrapping would place Britain in an undesirable bargaining position.[15] Moreover, there was reason to imagine that Britain would require at least some small carriers for detached missions, that is, for the protection of British interests in what would now be called the Third World. In February 1932, therefore, the Controller, Admiral Backhouse, suggested that *Hermes* be refitted in 1933 for eight or nine years' more service.[16]

Thus the 1931 design had to be considered more than a test of admissable treaty terms. However, no carrier was included in the 1933 programme, and the 1931 carrier design formed the basis of a further design study, which in turn became the *Ark Royal* of 1934.

Work on Staff Requirements for the new carrier therefore resumed in the summer of 1933, based on the conclusions reached in 1931 and on the existing large-carrier design. Although the 1932 arms limitation conference had failed, the British government still hoped to impose the 22,000-ton limit.[17] However, the pressure to operate more aircraft had, if anything, intensified, so that the new complement was seventy-two larger aircraft.

The first draft requirement called for a 900ft flight deck, of about the same width as that in *Courageous*. It was soon reduced to 800ft in the interests of docking in existing facilities and of handiness. There was some question as to the effects of wind on the enormous sail area represented by a ship with a full 800ft flight deck; after all, some difficulty had been experienced with *Courageous* and her sisters. At an Admiralty conference in November 1933, the captains of those ships argued that increasing sail area by about 20 per cent without any corresponding increase in draught would increase risks in confined anchorages, but the RAA and Vice Admiral Henderson, the former RAA, both of whom had commanded carriers, considered this risk acceptable. DNC was ordered to conduct model tests at Haslar to decide the point.[18]

14 At Washington *Furious* had been included in the list of experimental ships which could be replaced at will. However, she had been rebuilt afterwards, and there was some question as to whether this reconstruction had removed her experimental status. The Controller's schedule implied that the British government would scrap *Furious* when convenient, not when her nominal lifetime expired.

15 The Admiralty hoped that the British government would extract some modification in existing rules allowing the scrapping of the older carriers in return for any further reduction in overall tonnage, to permit new construction. It seems to have been reluctant to scrap HMS *Eagle*, despite that ship's inefficiency in terms of aircraft per ton (eighteen aircraft total).

16 At this time the US Navy was considering construction of a 'flight deck cruiser,' in effect a small carrier of less than 10,000 tons and therefore not included in the global carrier tonnage limit. Backhouse suggested that *Hermes* should not be scrapped until the idea had been tested. At about the same time the US Navy came to the conclusion as a result of wargaming that the idea was fatally flawed. For the full story, see this author's *US Cruisers: An Illustrated Design History* (US Naval Institute Press, Annapolis, 1984).

17 The memorandum of November 1933 on Staff Requirements for the new carrier (prepared by the Director of the Tactical Division) contains the comment that future treaty restrictions were uncertain, but that the 22,000-ton limit was important both to reduce the cost of the new ship and to ensure that she could fit into existing dry and graving docks.

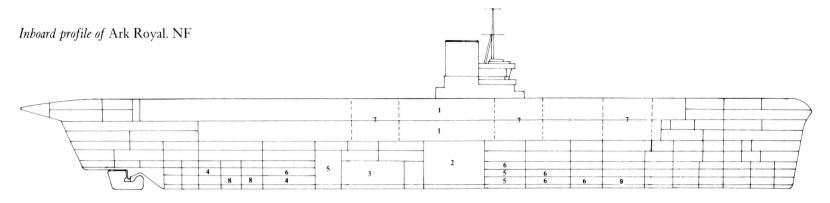

Inboard profile of Ark Royal. NF

Key
1 Hangar
2 Boiler room
3 Engine room
4 Bomb magazine
5 Aviation fuel stowage
6 Magazine
7 Aircraft lift
8 Oil fuel stowage
9 Torpedo magazine

The tentative Staff Requirement called for three lifts, two capable of taking the largest Fleet Air Arm aircraft with wings folded, and the third with wings spread. Because future aircraft were all to fold, the requirement was changed in November 1933; all three were to take folded torpedo-bombers (TSRs), and all were to be offset from the centreline, the two forward lifts en echelon. The smaller the lifts, the greater the hangar capacity, but in approving this change DNAD cautioned that the new ship would be unable to accommodate obsolescent non-folding types in peacetime. In wartime, she would be unable to accommodate RAF aircraft for combined operations, either for special operations beyond the range of land-based RAF aircraft, or for the emergency reinforcement of such distant areas as Hong Kong. These were not trivial points; wartime experience would include both cases. When she commissioned, HMS *Ark Royal* could not accommodate the only available naval fighter, the non-folding Nimrod. Nor could she strike below the highest-performance interceptors available to the Royal Navy for the first years of World War II, the hooked Hurricane and the Seafire. As forecast in the mid-1930s, the Royal Navy sometimes, therefore, had to adopt an American-style deck park.

Lift dimensions were 45 × 22ft, chosen on the basis of torpedo-bomber dimensions (37 × 18ft).

Although surviving documents do not explain the 900ft requirement, it seems likely that it was associated with the evident success of both arrester gear and accelerator, and with a hope of using, at least temporarily, a deck park.[19] Certainly the final Staff Requirements issued in 1934 did envisage a combination of four arrester wires and a crash barrier, and 'while it is not proposed normally to keep aircraft permanently on deck, a large parking space is nevertheless required ahead of the crash barrier to enable aircraft to be kept ranged up if required, and ready for use at short notice.' The crash barrier would fold down so that aircraft could taxi into the parking space upon landing.

The success of both arrester gear and accelerator made it possible to accept a maximum speed of 30 rather than 32 knots, on the ground that aircraft could now fly off and land back on without so much wind over the deck. Both RAA and C-in-C Home Fleet disagreed; they pressed for the higher speed, or at least for no relaxation of earlier proposed allowances for heavy engine construction to accept substantial sustained high-speed operation. RAA, for example, argued that it would still be desirable for aircraft to make rolling take-offs, since a catapult would take at least three times as long, and thus would greatly impede concentration of a strike in the air. Similarly, the arrester gear and the crash barrier required a considerable wind speed over the deck.

DNC studies soon showed that unless other proposed characteristics were drastically modified, the new carrier could not be expected to make more than 30 knots at deep load (corresponding to 30.75 at standard load), or 1.25 knots less than an M class (Town class) cruiser.

Armament was another major change: the new carrier would have sixteen 4.7in dual-purpose guns in four groups, supplemented by four Mk M pom-poms and by eight multiple .5in machine-guns. Low-angle fire, to deal with possible attacks by destroyers, was an important consideration, and had led to earlier interest in a 5.1in gun. This same consideration favoured a broadside of at least six guns. However, for high-angle fire at least eight were required, based on recent studies, and elevation had to be at least 70 degrees. Effective fire control required a dual-purpose director for each group of four guns. Finally, single mounts were favoured over twins on the ground that they enjoyed a higher rate of fire.

It was argued that guns should be mounted well below the flight deck, to avoid blast damage to aircraft. Guns immediately below the flight deck might be able to engage aircraft on the opposite beam, but it was argued that their command would be extremely limited and that, because they could not be expected to fire at elevations below about 45 degrees, their value would be extremely limited.[20]

The 5 or 5.1in gun was rejected because its rate of fire would be insufficient: a man could not easily handle the 108lb fixed round comprising its shell and cartridge case. Moreover, it seemed likely that the existing 4.7in gun could match expected 5.1in performance by using a heavier shell with a better shape.[21]

Existing studies showed that pom-poms were the only useful counter to dive-bombers, with at least two multiple mounts (plus smaller calibre machine-guns) bearing on any one target. Thus the carrier required four to produce adequate ahead and astern fire, arranged so that two could fire from beam to beam right ahead and right astern. The .5in guns and Lewis guns (not specified, but required) were intended to deal with strafers and

18 Tests at Haslar showed that the new carrier would actually be handier than HMS *Courageous*, partly because her sail area was more evenly distributed fore and aft. Haslar tested models in artificial wind, and also towed models of the *above water* portions of the ships submerged, at a slight angle to the direction of motion. The new ship was expected to benefit from the placement of her slightly larger rudder directly in the wake of the centreline propeller; *Courageous* had four screws, so she could not exploit this effect.

19 If, upon landing, aircraft could be held temporarily in a deck park before being struck below, then recovery could be substantially quicker than in earlier carriers, in which a recovered aircraft had to ride the lift down before another could land. This type of operation would not equate to a US style permanent deck park, in which a large fraction of the total air complement of the carrier would always reside on deck, with the hangar reserved largely for maintenance.

20 Maximum elevation was expected to be 70 degrees. Against a relatively slow (120-knot) target at 8000ft a gun firing only at elevations between 70 and 45 degrees could fire for only about 33 seconds. The 70-degree maximum was chosen because it was the expected angle to a level bomber at the moment of bomb release. That is, the guns would fire until an aircraft actually dropped its bomb, then switch to another target, as the bomber would be able to take violent evasive action. Pom-poms were designed for higher-

angle fire (80 degrees) because they were expected to engage dive-bombers.

21 Note, however, that in discussions of new destroyer weapons the Treasury had objected to a 5 or 5.1in weapon on the ground that it would lead to a new arms race. It seems at least plausible that the choice of 4.7 over 5.1in was based in part on a desire to avoid paying the heavy initial and logistical price of introducing a totally new calibre. As for the argument about the weight of a round, the US Navy found separate shells and cartridge cases quite satisfactory in its 5in/38 and 5in/54. The 5.1in gun was tested in the destroyer *Kempenfelt*; its failure led to the decision to replace the existing 50lb 4.7in shell with a new 62pdr. This in turn led to the decision to build a new anti-aircraft gun, the 4.5in, to fire a new 55lb shell. A proposal to develop a new twin 4.7in BD mounting for the *Nelsons* was, therefore, rejected. See *Progress in Gunnery*, an official Admiralty publication, for 1935.

low-level bombers (most likely fighters) attacking the flight deck itself.

The requirement to protect shellrooms and machinery against 6in fire was reaffirmed, and the staff sought corresponding protection against dive-bomb attack using 1000lb armour-piercing weapons, which were said to be in US service. This required 3½in NC armour. Note that within a few years this thickness would be equated with the 500lb SAP bomb; the difference was in likely terminal velocity. The new underwater protection requirement (750lbs of TNT) corresponded to that required for contemporary British battleships.

The largest bomb then in British naval service was the 500lb, which set the standard for bomb hoists in the new carrier. However, the hoists were to be designed for easy conversion to take 1000 or 1500lb bombs.

This time considerable attention was paid to the question of carrier endurance compared to that of the fleet, which in turn would determine the oil fuel load. The overall design of the ship was based, not on performance at the required standard displacement, but on performance with full or partially full fuel tanks. Thus the designer had to begin with an estimate of full load displacement.

Endurance was usually stated as a fixed mileage at a fixed cruising speed, but calculations were actually considerably more complex; the requirement was 'not less than that of the battlefleet, allowing for flying operations.' In 1933 new capital ships were being designed (for construction after 1936, when the 'building holiday' enforced by the treaties would end), and they were to be capable of:

> 200 hours at 16 knots with steam for 18 (3200nm);
> plus 8 hours at full speed;
> plus 16 hours at 18 knots with steam for full speed (288nm);
> plus 12 hours at 16 knots with steam for full speed (192nm);
> all with a foul bottom (6 months out of dock).

The fuel figure thus attained was to be increased by 35 per cent (a figure chosen by the E-in-C) to allow for abnormal consumption due to weather, damage and oil left in tanks. To whatever figure resulted would be added sufficient additional fuel to give 14,000nm/10 on trial, that is, with a clean bottom. In fact it was not expected that a ship whose tonnage was limited by treaty could meet the last condition.

These figures had a direct tactical and strategic significance. Tactically, the 200-hour run might be construed as the run towards and away from the battle area. The 28 hours at 16 or 18 knots with steam for full speed were runs within a possible battle zone, for example, while the fleet was under the threat of air attack, and the 8 hours at full speed could be equated to the decisive battle itself. The longer trial endurance figure could be associated with the steaming run towards the battle area. The British expected to fight a decisive battle somewhere north of Singapore; it is about 2600nm from Singapore to the Japanese port of Kobe. A fleet steaming to the East could generally move in steps of about 2000nm: less than a thousand miles from any British base to Gibraltar; about 2000 across the Mediterranean to Alexandria, then through the Canal and down to Aden; then about 2100nm to Trincomalee in Ceylon, and then about 1600nm to Singapore. By way of contrast, contemporary US naval plans envisaged operations extending over more than twice these distances. The result was that when Singapore was overrun, the British fleet in the Far East faced much greater distances than those for which it had been designed. For example, the run from Sydney to Kobe is almost 4400nm.

A carrier had to be able to operate her aircraft during all phases of the approach to battle. She had, for example, to fly off scouts and an anti-submarine screen throughout the approach to the battle zone. Thus in 1933 the Admiralty Staff proposed that the 200 hours of steaming into the battle zone (above) translate into 150 hours at 16 knots with steam for 30 (2400nm) plus 50 hours at 25 knots with steam for 30 (that is, flying); the 28 hours at cruising speed with steam for full speed equated to another 30 hours at 25 knots with steam for 30. Finally, like the battleship, the carrier would steam at full speed during the allowed 8 hours of actual combat.[22]

RAA was sceptical; he saw no basis of experience, except that in unfavourable winds a carrier might have to steam a considerable distance at high speed in order to rejoin the fleet. Carriers might also have to make high-speed runs to bring an

22 The extra 2 hours at 25 knots with steam for 30 might be equated to additional time flying off and recovering the long-range air strike force. Surviving documents do not make this point explicitly.

advance guard of RAF aircraft into action in peacetime crises, as in the case of HMS *Courageous*, sent to Palestine in 1929. In this case it might be well to make her endurance speed substantially higher than that of other fleet units; RAA (Admiral Henderson) suggested 5000nm at 24 knots, based on the run from Port Said to Singapore. As for the relationship between fleet endurance and carrier endurance, he suggested that the carrier might have to steam as much as 25 or 33 per cent of the time at higher speed to fly and to regain station. The figures above represent one of RAA's examples: 25 per cent of the time at 25 knots when accompanying a 16-knot fleet. RAA estimated that high speed for a 20-knot fleet would be 30 knots, and for a 10-knot fleet, 20 knots.

Endurance figures in turn determined the required petrol capacity. In August 1933 DNAD proposed sufficient fuel for ten days of operation by an average of twenty aircraft in daylight and six at night, on the basis of about 27 gallons per hour per aircraft. This came to 80,000 gallons. RAA and C-in-C Home Fleet considered this far too conservative, as aircraft fuel consumption was rising rapidly. A Nimrod fighter, for example, cruised at 29.8 gallons per hour, and at maximum speed burned 60. They therefore proposed a total of 100,000 gallons of petrol, plus a proportionate amount of lubricating oil (whose consumption came to about $\frac{1}{27}$ that of petrol, about 4000 gallons). Petrol stowage in turn had to be protected and dispersed; the Staff Requirement called for no more than 25,000 gallons in any one position.[23]

In contrast to previous practice, the new carrier would not have seaplane cranes right aft, so that her stern could be built up to the level of the flight deck. She would have two cranes amidships, folding down when not in use, and capable of hoisting seaplanes up to the flight deck.

Table 6-2 shows differences between the 1931 and 1933 Staff Requirements.

The preliminary sketch design and the legend were submitted on 3 May 1934 (see Table 6-3). Standard displacement was 22,800 tons, 800 over the limit set in the staff requirements, and 300 more than in *Courageous*. Thus the Board approved the design on 21 June in the expectation that 800 tons would be saved.[24]

Otherwise the design met or exceeded requirements. DNC reduced its waterline length to 725ft (compared to 779 in *Courageous*) to fit the new carrier into as many graving and dry docks as possible. On the other hand, beam was increased compared to that of the earlier carrier, to balance much greater length (including a 40ft overhang aft) and its arrester gear and accelerator, but the machinery deep in the hull was 470 tons heavier. Mean draught was about that of the earlier carrier.

The flight deck was slightly lower and narrower than in *Courageous*, and accommodated two accelerators forward, with four arrester wires (increased to eight in the final design) aft and a crash barrier. It was pierced by three lifts of an unusual new two-level type, which travelled only half as far as the single-level lifts of the *Courageous*. On each upward trip the upper level of the lift would bring an aircraft from the upper hangar to the flight deck, while the lower level brought another from the lower to the upper hangar. A short (one deck) lift run made for a quick cycle, 20 seconds. Alternatively, an aircraft could be permanently stowed on the lower level of the lift.

A hydraulic ram could drive this type of short-travel lift directly, instead of the numerous wires and balance weights of earlier types. Moreover, only one hole in the three decks (flight and two hangar) would be open at any one time, compared with two as in the past, and the narrow lifts left gangways to pass aircraft along the flight and hangar decks. Narrower lifts made it easier to provide sufficient hull strength (since they

represented smaller breaks in the hull girder), and, because they ate up less internal space, they made for smaller hangars and hence for more space for other purposes, such as accommodation; the total floor area of the three lifts was equivalent to the space required to accommodate 300 ratings.

Each of the two hangars was 60ft wide and had 16ft of clear headroom; lengths were 564ft for the upper and 452ft for the lower hangar. Hangar deck space was 60,960sq ft, compared to 53,170 for *Courageous*. In the final approved design the upper hangar was lengthened by 4ft, and the two after lifts moved forward.

Gun armament consisted of sixteen single 4.7in dual-purpose guns in groups of two, sponsored slightly outboard of the lower hangar deck, two 8-barrel (Mk M) pom-poms fore and abaft the island, and eight quadruple .5in machine-guns. The initial design showed 300 rounds per 4.7in gun (plus a total of 300 star shells for the ship); in the final approved design this increased to 400 per gun. Three bomb rooms were forward, three aft.

The 96,000shp was provided by three sets of geared turbines, each fed by two boilers in a boiler room. The three engine rooms were abreast, as were the three boiler rooms, and the triplets were separated lengthwise by 16ft of smaller compartments containing evaporators and other auxiliaries. This arrangement was favoured because it limited the total length of the armoured citadel and because it provided good protection against underwater attack, for example by 'B' bombs. Uptakes from the three boiler rooms were grouped into a single compact uptake in the island structure. Power was increased to 102,000shp in the final design, submitted in November 1934.

Total generating capacity in the final design was 1600kW (up from 1350 in the sketch design), comprising three 350kW steam turbines and two 275kW diesel sets (150kW in the sketch design). Two of the steam generators were in the wing engine rooms, the other steam generator and the two diesels in an auxiliary engine room group on the port side abeam the island, under protection between the main and lower hangar decks. In the final version of the design they were moved down, to a position abeam the boiler rooms. This dispersion provided a degree of protection. The ship was actually completed with six 400kW turbo generators (one in each boiler room, and three behind armour on the main deck, to port), and entirely without diesel generators. As a result, disruption of the boilers eliminated electric power.

For strength, the main longitudinal machinery bulkheads were made continuous.

Side protection consisted of a 4.5in belt 16ft 6in wide (16ft in the final version of the design), 312ft long, covering magazines and machinery, with its upper edge at the upper deck level. It rose to the lower hangar deck level abreast the island, protecting the uptakes and the auxiliary machinery. The belt was covered by a 3.5in deck.[25] This armour was considered immune to 6in shellfire, and the 3.5in deck was considered proof against 500lb SAP bombs dropped from 9500ft, or against 1000lb AP bombs dropped from 5500ft. As in *Courageous*, the flight deck was protected against 20lb bombs. Bullet-proof plating would be spread over the bridges, a modification recently approved for HMS *Courageous*.

The final version of the design had very similar protection, but showed somewhat thicker armour over the steering gear, and 1in plating over the roof of the small arms and pyrotechnics magazine. In addition, the armour over the after petrol stowage was raised from the lower to the upper deck level, and extended outboard to the side armour, to protect the lubricating oil and the petrol control compartment.

Underwater protection, sufficient to defeat a 750lb charge,

23 Petrol was carried in two 25,000-gallon tanks, as well as sixteen of 3125 gallons each, all under armour. The tanks were arranged in three groups: two forward in the hold next to the boilers, carrying 50,000 gallons, and, in the original design, six others, three in the hold and three on the platform deck abaft the engine rooms.

24 This was somewhat deceptive. Although *Courageous* was completed at 22,500 tons, by 1934 additions made or contemplated (arrester gear, accelerators, pom-poms) were equated to at least 300 tons more. When her quarter-deck was raised and the after end of her flight deck altered for better air flow, *Courageous* would displace about 23,000 tons standard. The cut-back to 22,000 was vital because the carrier was to be laid down after what became the 1935 London Conference, and because the British government intended to call for a 22,000-ton limit there. In fact the resulting treaty incorporated a 23,000-ton limit.

25 The deck extended over the full beam of the ship at the lower hangar deck, but the section a deck level down, over the magazines, extended only to the inner torpedo-protection bulkhead on each side.

Right and opposite: Although her hull and flight deck were carefully streamlined, unlike later British fleet carriers, Ark Royal *did not have a streamlined island, as these two 1940 views show. She also had the original form of the Type 72 homing beacon, which could not be mounted in combination with any other (for instance, radar) antenna. Thus, although she was an extremely valuable fleet unit, she could never be fitted with air search radar.*

contained 2400 tons of oil fuel, which in wartime would have to be replaced by water as it was burned.

In addition to the usual transmitting and receiving aerials, the new carrier design showed an aircraft homing beacon, which by the autumn of 1934 had been designated Transmitter Type 72X. It in turn had to be carried at the head of a tripod mast, trials at Southsea Castle having shown that any obstruction (such as a topmast) would ruin its performance. Such a beacon might seem inimical to British notions of radio silence; in 1934 it was explained as perhaps impractical in war but still a valuable safety aid in peacetime.

The sketch design and legend were approved by the Board on 21 June, with the proviso that the 22,800-ton displacement be reduced to 22,000. This was achieved by including only three-quarters of the bombs and of the planned 4.7in and Mk M pom-pom ammunition in the standard displacement, a tactic the DNC also used in some contemporary and slightly later treaty ships. This was only a paper reduction, as space was provided for the full war load. In fact in the final design DNC was able to increase capacity substantially, with 400 rather than the required 300 rounds per 4.7in gun, and with 300 rather than ninety-six 250lb bombs.

There were also minor improvements, such as an enlarged bridge (to provide a satisfactory plotting room). Estimated complement increased from 1500 to 1600.

THUS DESIGNED, *Ark Royal* herself set the standard for future British naval aircraft. For example, there was some question as to whether the Navy could adopt monoplane torpedo-bombers (TSR), because the Naval Staff was by no means certain that their wings could be folded to the requisite dimensions. There was some argument in 1935–36 that biplanes were inherently more suitable because they could be folded into smaller packages. On the other hand, the Air Ministry estimated that a biplane paid a 15 per cent speed penalty (10 per cent if its undercarriage retracted).

The Air Staff (RAF) considered it ludicrous to limit a ship which might serve twenty years to obsolete types of aircraft, or, for that matter, to a weight limit of 8000lbs (the lifts could actually take 11,200lbs). In January 1935 it argued that all future aircraft would be fast monoplanes with retractable undercarriages, using variable-pitch propellers and flaps to reduce their landing speeds. Night bombers would reach 235mph and fighters 300mph; the Fleet Air Arm would have to switch to monoplanes to meet the threat of attack by land-based (and probably future ship-borne) aircraft. Some within the Naval Staff had rejected this view, arguing the need for substantial numbers of aircraft within limited ship dimensions. The Air Staff saw the choice as substantial numbers of useless slow aircraft, or smaller numbers of adequate modern ones, flying from a modified *Ark Royal*.

In February 1935, therefore, it called for the largest possible lifts and for substantially larger hangars, with 20ft clear height (a dimension which also considerably limited naval aircraft). DNC estimated that such an increase in the overall depth of a ship (8ft) would cost substantially more beam, and would not really be practicable. An increase in hangar height to 18ft

would have been feasible, but at a cost of 200 tons. The direct cost would have been £22,000 to £25,000.[26] DNC also considered a lesser change, to 17ft 6in clear height, but in the end the original dimensions were not changed.

The issue was resolved in mid-1935, with the realization that monoplanes were actually smaller than biplanes for the same load, and that they could indeed be folded successfully. Both the Osprey replacement (which became the Skua) and a 230mph torpedo-bomber then under consideration were smaller than existing types. Henderson, by now Controller, tried to defer a decision on hangar headroom to December 1935. Headroom was not changed.

In fact the new aircraft were larger than their predecessors (the Skua was 2ft 7in longer than planned), and the projected stowage of seventy-two aircraft was impossible. Maximum stowage, in 1938, was estimated as forty-two Albacore torpedo-bombers and eighteen Skua fighters or, at the outside, forty-four Albacores and twenty-two Skuas. The sixty-aircraft complement was considered the maximum for sustained opera-

26   The limit was set by the deep beams under the hangar decks, which accommodated fire curtains. The 4ft increase in hull depth would reduce metacentric height to 6ft 9in in deep condition, but it would also increase hull strength, so that the forward lift could be enlarged to 46 × 25ft. The increase in hull weight could be balanced by cutting nominal ammunition stowage to half of capacity (195 tons).

The ship had to be completed without her crash barrier, as its development had been delayed. She was, therefore, completed without the two extra pom-poms (see below) planned for positions on the port side abeam her island, on the theory that a pilot landing at night, without a barrier, would tend to keep to port, away from the island. He might well tend, therefore, to crash into the pom-poms. The two mountings ordered for the ship were diverted to other services, a welcome step in view of their scarcity. The shortage was so severe that it was proposed that the 1938 carriers have four rather than six such mountings.

There was also considerable interest in a revised gun arrangement. Alternatives were (a) to keep the original arrangement, with all guns on the lower hangar deck; (b) to move them all to the upper hangar deck, open-spaced; (c) to group them in fours, with three on the lower and one on the upper hangar deck; (d) two on each hangar deck in each group of four; (e) four groups of three on the lower hangar deck and two twins on the flight deck, one before and one abaft the island; (f) five twins on the flight deck, three before and two abaft the island, with the two after groups of three each at the upper gallery deck level, open-spaced.

The argument for moving the guns up was that space on the lower hangar deck was limited. The counter-argument, which had already been articulated during the early design phase, was that the additional topweight and potential blast were not worth the very limited cross-deck arcs. Moreover, the hangar deck space liberated could not be used to stow aircraft, since the fore-aft gangway was still needed for access. Scheme (d) in particular was rejected because it broke up the available space and exposed the crews of the upper guns to the blast of the lower ones. In scheme (f), the island would have to be moved forward and the parking space reduced.

In the event, no modern 4.7in dual-purpose gun was produced, the last single mountings appearing in the Australian seaplane carrier *Albatross*. For high-angle use the 4.7 was superseded by the 4.5in, a twin upper deck mount (Mk III) being introduced. Later carriers and capital ships used a twin between-decks mount, in which much of the structure of the mount penetrated below decks. Although the record is not clear, it appears that the decision to abandon the single 4.7/4.5 led immediately to the presentation of two more schemes, the second of which (eight pairs of 4.5in guns on the upper gallery deck level) was adopted by the Controller in March 1935. It cost 150 tons, and avoided blast interference by spacing the mounts 64ft apart. At the same time two more pom-poms (for a total of six) were added on the port side. Presumably it was impossible to place twin mounts on the lower hangar deck.

WHILE THE DESIGN for *Ark Royal* was being completed, negotiations for the next naval treaty (which would become the London Treaty of 1936) were in progress. The Japanese announced in April 1934 that they intended to renounce the Washington Treaty, but they were still waiting to consider a new treaty. Among their proposals was a reduction in carrier tonnage to 20,000; the United States made a similar proposal. In December 1934 the D of P asked DNC whether Britain could tolerate this new limit. The results show just how tight the *Ark Royal* design was.[28]

DNC tried six alternatives. It was hoped that it would be possible to maintain the horizontal and underwater protection worked into the *Ark Royal* (though in alternative F there was 3½in over the magazines only), as well as the necessary endurance. Light anti-aircraft weapons were not to be reduced, but it was permissible to cut the main battery from sixteen to twelve 4.5in guns. Other possible weight savers were a reduction in deck protection from 3½in (500lb bomb dropped from

tions and maintenance. Even these cases required undesirable permanent stowage on a lower lift platform. DNAD considered forty Albacores and twelve Skuas a more realistic complement. Given the overall limits on carrier capacity, this decline, from seventy-two to fifty-two aircraft, was taken very seriously. Worse still, fifty-two aircraft amounted to 4⅓ squadrons, so that tactically the natural complement was only forty-eight aircraft.[27] One possibility was to place aircraft in an area forward of the fore lift, substituting six Skuas for four Albacores to stow a total of forty-two Albacores and eighteen Skuas. Adaptation to the larger new aircraft required that hangar fire screens be moved, so that the originally planned complement of seventy-two could no longer be accommodated in any case.

This problem was not confined to *Ark Royal*; the newer *Illustrious* also suffered (see Chapter 7), and reduced air complements were one reason for the lower hangar (accommodating twelve aircraft) in the 1938 carrier. Worse was to come: in February 1935 Henderson predicted that, within a few years, the forty-eight aircraft would be cut to forty.

27 Squadrons could operate nine or twelve aircraft.

28 These studies are in the Miscellaneous Carrier Cover (No 481).

HMS Ark Royal, *profile and plan.* ALR

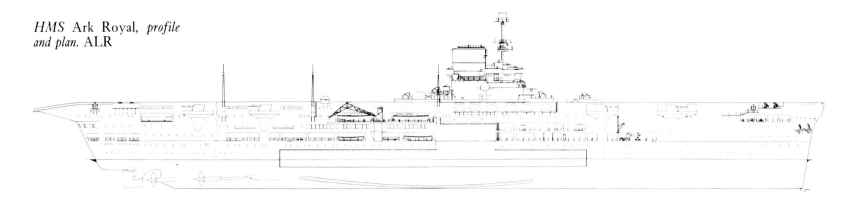

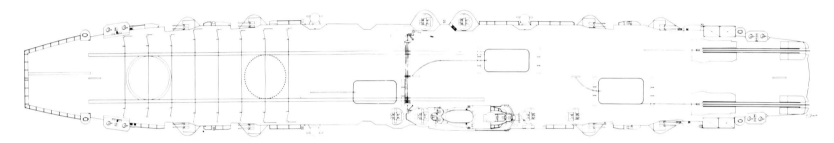

10,000ft) to 3in (7000ft), and to rearrange the long-range anti-aircraft battery as in the US carrier *Ranger*, on sponsons just below flight deck level (but using twin 4.7in guns instead of single 5in). This latter choice, which was actually incorporated into the *Ark Royal* design proper, may have originated in the 20,000-ton studies. Another possibility was reduced underwater protection, which would save beam.

Table 6-5 shows DNC's alternatives. Version A was cramped but satisfactory, with speed and aircraft capacity reduced. Given the problems of the *Ark Royal* herself, the aircraft capacity was probably somewhat overstated.

In the alternative B, hull depth was reduced by 3ft by working the upper deck between the hangars rather than below them, saving the depth of the deep girder under one hangar deck. Because length was reduced only 25ft, hangar length (hence capacity) could be maintained. However, double platform lifts could not have been fitted, and the flight deck (hence strike capacity) would have been reduced. The twin-shaft machinery would have been accommodated in wing compartments, the centreline machinery space of the *Ark Royal* being (in effect) empty. DNC suggested that this design might prove very cramped.

Alternatively, one deck could be omitted altogether, as in version C. In this case the ship would actually be longer than the *Ark Royal*; she could have double-platform lifts and she could accommodate all seventy-two aircraft.

In both B and C, reduced hull depth would make it difficult to fit air pre-heaters around the uptakes. Pre-heating saved about 5 per cent in fuel consumption. Much more importantly, it reduced funnel gas temperature from 850 or 1000 degrees F down to 650. Hotter funnel gas would make for bumpier air astern of the ship. E-in-C was reluctant to give up pre-heating. In these designs very low rpm had to be accepted, and DNC suspected that it might be too low for the required power per shaft. Of the two versions, C was clearly better than B.

The Controller wanted greater speed, so DNC tried a fourth alternative, D, in which protection was reduced to boxes (3½in roof, 2½in side, 2in ends) around the magazines, sufficient to resist 500lb bombs and 4.7in shellfire. In this design one deck was omitted, as in Scheme C.

These estimates were submitted on 21 January. In May Forbes worked out another alternative, in which sixteen 4.5in guns were mounted in pairs, with six rather than four 8-barrel pom-poms, but no .5in guns. This, too, could be built on 20,000 tons, but the design suffered a considerable loss in accommodation when the guns were moved to the upper gallery deck level.

Finally, a limited armoured carrier was sketched. Early in October 1935 a meeting chaired by ACNS asked for a ship to carry thirty-six TSR, with 3in and 1in flight deck armour (over an assumed length of 520ft out of a total of 800), with a 2in waterline belt, and protection against bombs and torpedoes on the scale of that in *Ark Royal*. Armament would be eight 4.7in single-purpose guns and six Mk M (8-barrel) pom-poms, and speed 28 to 30 knots; displacement would be 19,000 to 21,500 tons. This seems to have been the earliest British approach to the armoured carrier described in the next chapter.[29]

IN THE SPRING of 1936, with *Ark Royal* complete to her main deck, British carrier design practice shifted radically, to single armoured hangars (see Chapter 7). The Naval Staff naturally asked whether *Ark Royal* could be reconstructed as a 36-aircraft armoured-deck carrier. DNC answered that displacement would increase to 24,000 tons if the existing 3.5in armoured deck (over magazines and machinery) were retained. Some of it was already in place by early May. Displacement could be reduced to 23,500 tons if some were scrapped, and thickness reduced to 2in. In this case, however, the ship would be 500 tons over the new treaty limit, and she would still need about 18in more beam. This was not to mention serious delays, and the need for wholly new lift designs, which were expected to be very time-consuming. The scheme was dropped.

However, interest in better protection remained. The flight deck, designed to resist 20lb bombs, was ¾in D plating amidships and ⅝in D plating at its ends. Stability limited it to ⅞in, which would provide no material improvement against SAP bombs, but might be desirable against light-case (general purpose) weapons. At this time there was little information about the effect of GP bombs, and any decision had to be deferred.

29 Miscellaneous Carrier Cover (No 481). No record of any sketch designs has been found. The DNC notes in the Cover say that the meeting was in ACNS room, 5 October 1935; they make no mention of the Controller (Admiral Henderson), but presumably he was present.

The alternative, to replace the D plating with NC armour, was rejected because of the delay which this entailed.[30] An increase to ⅞in D plating would cost 150 tons, or half a foot of metacentric height. An inch of NC (700 tons) would cost, net, 240 tons (¾ft of GM); but more importantly, it would cost six months.

Erection of the flight deck was scheduled for December 1936. At the end of August, the Controller, Henderson – the man responsible for the armoured carriers – decided that the deck would not be changed, although new GP-bomb trials would go ahead.

ON TRIALS IN MAY 1938 HMS *Ark Royal* made 31.733 knots at 103,055shp at 22,381 tons (compared to a design figure of 30.75 at 22,000 on 102,000shp) and a month later she made 31.214 knots at deep load (27,525 tons) on 103,012shp compared to a design figure of 30.0 knots on 102,000shp at 27,720 tons. The principal post-trials modifications were a higher funnel (8ft) to keep smoke from the upper pom-pom directors abaft it, and some stiffening aft to counteract vibration.

Standard displacement as completed was 22,585 tons, with the ship reported (under treaty rules) as 22,500. More significantly, weights as inclined differed substantially from weights as calculated. Inclining experiment data are presented in Table 6-4.

The ship was little modified through the first months of World War II.

The issue of non-folding aircraft, however, was revived in July 1940 at the request of the ship's captain, supported by VAA; it seemed the only way to place high-performance fighters at sea in the short term. The ship proposed that No 1 lift be widened 8ft, which would have sufficed to stow the Spitfire, Hurricane, or Grumman Wildcat. VAA found that to widen the lift to 33ft would require fairly complete reconstruction, since loads were taken at the sides of the structure; the lift well would have to be widened and the spaces surrounding it rearranged. Similarly, the fire curtains in the hangars would have to

Shown in 1940, Ark Royal *displays her heavy deck-edge battery and her new degaussing cable. Note also the pulleys of her two bow accelerators. The prominent openings in her hull, which are typical of virtually all British carriers, were required to work the ship in harbour, or when going alongside, since the flight deck could not be cluttered with the necessary cleats and cables. Openings amidships accommodated the ship's boats. There was no open deck extending across the hull, as in contemporary US practice; instead the hangar was closed off by double walls. The gallery near the bow, just below the flight deck, was for quadruple .5in machine-guns, with a 44in searchlight just abaft it.*

be rearranged. Such reconstruction would take several months, and the ship could not be spared for six months. DNC commented that this change probably could not be carried out during a planned three-month refit in the United States. VAA felt, then, that it would be better to wait for the folding Spitfire (which became the Seafire) then under development. Meanwhile, RAF fighters, which could not fold their wings, could be carried on the flight deck.

The ship was worked very hard, and consequently was refitted only twice in wartime: at Liverpool (10–29 October 1940) and at Gibraltar (11–13 June 1941). Her bridge was extended during the latter period, and reportedly two multiple pom-poms were added. The only other major wartime alteration was the addition of a degaussing cable. Radar could not be fitted because there was only a single mast, supporting the Type 72 homing beacon.

Nothing more could be done before the ship was lost on 14 November 1941. In fact she was considered far too useful to spare for an extended dockyard period, so that at the time of her loss the ship had not been extensively refitted for three years, and numerous approved improvements and alterations had not been carried out. She had been somewhat strained by sustained high-speed steaming, much of it in rough weather.

As the first (and, in the event, only) case of a modern British

30   NC of 1in thickness had about twice the resistance of ¾in D plating. Trials in 1929 showed that a 50lb GP bomb dropped from 2000ft would penetrate 25lb (⅝in) D plating. However, the bombs involved had streamlined steel nose caps in lieu of fuses. In 1930–31, 120lb GP bombs rebounded from 40lb (1in) D plating and broke up; it was concluded that GP bombs were not suitable to attack carrier decks. As a result, the Royal Navy limited itself to 250lb and heavier bombs, reserving 20lb bombs for mass use.

Pilots could land into arrester gear without external control, but the barrier changed the situation entirely. It was no longer possible to leave bolting to the pilot's discretion. This Avenger has just engaged, and two barriers are visible abeam the carrier's island. The pilot has followed the instructions of the DLCO in the foreground.

fleet carrier being lost during World War II, the loss of HMS *Ark Royal* naturally was examined for future lessons. *U81* hit her on her starboard side abreast the island while the ship was steaming at 22 knots, at 1541 in the afternoon. There was no visual warning, at least not from the starboard side, although the sea was calm.[31]

Some of the blast vented up the bomb trunk forward of the island, and the ship whipped violently, aircraft with torpedoes bouncing off her flight deck. Internally, however, she showed very little shock damage. Her radio masts, for example, seemed practically undamaged. The centre of the explosion seems to have been between the keel and the starboard side of the ship, and analysis suggested that the hole was 130ft long and 30ft wide. This was much larger than expected for a single contact torpedo hit; on the other hand, it took some time for the ship to stop, and her forward speed may have helped open up the hole. There was some speculation that the torpedo had a non-contact (below the keel) warhead, but its internal effect was much less than would have been expected for such an attack.[32]

After the ship had been hit, her starboard boiler room, air spaces, and oil tanks began to flood, as did the main switchboard room and the lower steering position. At this time the boilers were connected as partial units. The port and centreline boilers continued to steam, although the centreline rooms began to flood from underneath. The engine rooms continued to run, but communications to them failed after a short time (which was why the ship took too long to stop).

The initial list was 10 degrees, increasing to 17 to 18 within 20 minutes. At this point the captain decided to evacuate his ship, the auxiliaries (generators) in the port and centreline boiler rooms being left on. Then, 49 minutes after the explosion, parties still on board were ordered below to try to save the ship. Unfortunately, several key men had already been taken off.

The obvious damage control measure was counter-flooding, and the list was soon reduced to 14 degrees. Unfortunately, several manhole covers and armoured doors had been left open, and the ship continued to flood from below.[33] Moreover, as the ship listed, water came up through the uptakes of the starboard boiler room to flood over into the centreline boiler room (and, later, into the port boiler room). Steam failed at about 1700, 1 hour 19 minutes after the hit, but it was restored in P.1 boiler room by 2115. By that time the list had gradually increased back to 18 degrees. As water came up over the elbow of the port boiler room, it reduced the area available for the funnel gas to escape, and the uptake casing became so hot that fires broke out. Steam was lost again, 10 hours 34 minutes after the hit. The loss of steam power was particularly crippling because the ship had only steam generators.

The list had been reduced to 16 degrees but by now it was back at 17 and increasing rapidly; it was 20 degrees at 0245 (11 hours 4 minutes after the hit), then 27 at 0400. The captain ordered the remaining men on board to abandon ship, and all were off by 0430, 12 hours 19 minutes after the hit (when the list was 35 degrees). HMS *Ark Royal* capsized and sank at 0613 (12 hours 49 minutes after the initial hit), hanging for a time at a 45 degree list. She had been under tow, for Gibraltar, since 2035 the previous night, at a speed of 2 knots.

The key vulnerability was the lead of the boiler uptakes beneath the lower hangar deck, the port boiler room flooding at a list of 19 degrees. Uptakes could not have been led through the lower hangar itself as this would have reduced aircraft capacity, and the uptakes would not then have been protected by the hangar deck armour, so more armour (hence more – unacceptable – weight) would have been required. In this sense the ship was lost due to the interaction of the treaty tonnage

31 This account is based largely on the report of the Board of Inquiry, ADM 234/508.

32 Non-contact (which at that time meant magnetic) warheads were of considerable interest to the British, German, and US navies of the time, because they promised enormous lethal effect per explosion. They became fully reliable only after World War II, and are now in general use. The Board of Inquiry convened after the loss of the ship believed she had been hit by a non-contact torpedo, but the later Admiralty commission thought otherwise. Because there had been no visible torpedo track, it seemed likely that the ship had been hit by an electric torpedo, and DTM thought it unlikely that such a torpedo could be fitted with a workable magnetic detonator. Moreover, there had been no reports of non-contact hits over the previous twelve months. The two alternatives were a non-contact hit fired from port and a contact hit (at the turn of the bilge) by a torpedo fired from starboard. The weapon was almost certainly a G7e electric torpedo; contrary to DTM it had been designed with a combination impact and magnetic detonator. However, the magnetic detonator had proven unreliable, and it was withdrawn in 1940, to be reintroduced in improved form in 1943. Data from the 1950 Admiralty publication, *German Torpedoes and Development of German Torpedo Control*, B.R. 1972 (ADM 234/466).

33 Several US cruisers in the Pacific later suffered badly from the same problem, water flooding up through escape scuttles which had been left open.

Seen here sinking in November 1941, Ark Royal *shows little visible difference from her original configuration. The most prominent war modification was a degaussing cable around her hull. Her loss was partly due to her lack of emergency diesel generators, and partly due to a crucial design weakness, the uptake crossing under her lower hangar. However, it turned out that the most important problem was unfamiliarity with stability and counter-flooding. HMS* Indomitable *survived torpedo damage in 1943 primarily because the Admiralty drew this latter lesson, and caused the vital knowledge to be much more widely disseminated.* CPL

limit (actually the British proposal for a limit, which was below the figure actually adopted) and British carrier operating practice (which dictated the use of a double hangar for maximum aircraft capacity).

The ship also flooded across her boiler room fan flat, which spread across the ship. Thus the flooding of the starboard boiler room soon made it desirable to shut down the centreline boilers and then ultimately the port ones. *Indomitable* and *Victorious* were fitted with partial 8ft-high longitudinal water-tight bulkheads to break up this space, and similar bulkheads were later fitted to *Illustrious* and *Formidable*. Plans were also made to raise the uptakes of existing carriers, although this entailed major shipyard work.

Because the torpedo tore up so much of the ship's bottom, she took an initial list well beyond that envisaged in the ship's damage control books. The Board of Inquiry noted that counter-flooding intstructions were provided only for lists up to 8 degrees. Analysis showed that, had the port engine and boiler rooms been flooded after steam finally failed, *Ark Royal* would have come to something like an even keel, retaining enough buoyancy to reach harbour. By this time, however, the

situation was clearly extremely difficult.[34]

Damage control was complicated because the main control switchboard room and telephone exchange, both wholly below the waterline towards the damaged side, were flooded rapidly. The situation would have been better in later ships; in *Illustrious* these were on the main deck (above the waterline), though still off the centreline, and in *Implacable* they were on the centreline on the main deck. In *Unicorn* they were on the lower deck, just below the waterline, and one lesson of the loss of *Ark Royal* was that they should be brought higher in the ship.

The ship initially lost electical power because ring main switches opened due to damage to the main itself, to its control wiring, to the flooding of the main switchboard, and to shock. In later ships some circuit breakers were locally controlled, to avoid the consequences of loss of the central control room.

Emergency diesel generators were approved for installation in existing and future carriers, and long-term policy was to use large diesels in place of some steam generators. Unfortunately existing diesels could not function at lists greater than 20 degrees.

Lessons included the need to carry uptakes and fan intakes higher in the ship, so that they would be less floodable; to make the main switchboard and phone exchange less floodable; to review the control of the ring (electrical) main to avoid premature shut-down; to install diesel generators in all ships; to counter-flood if lists after damage exceeded 6 degrees; to establish flooding boundaries (by closing manholes, etc) as soon as possible after a hit; and to avoid interference with the damage control organization when evacuating a ship. Above all, it was essential that detailed understanding of stability be widely promulgated.

The new carrier then under design, which became the next *Ark Royal*, was the principal beneficiary of these lessons (see Chapter 12).

34 For years after the war, the loss of the *Ark Royal*, illustrated by a large floodable model, was a standard lecture at the Royal Navy damage control establishment, HMS *Phoenix*. The main lesson was that prompt and audacious counter-flooding could have saved the ship; the Board of Inquiry's conclusion was that the ship's company was not sufficiently conversant with the realities of her stability, and that damage control theory and application should be much more widely understood.

7

The Armoured Carrier

BRITAIN WAS UNIQUE among the carrier-operating powers to build ships whose hangars were armoured against serious air attack.[1] They responded to a well-understood problem: of all classes of major warships, only an aircraft carrier could not protect her offensive power against the striking power of an equivalent warship. The problem became more acute as aircraft gained in performance, particularly in speed. That is, in about 1930 one might reasonably imagine that fighters aboard a carrier could be scrambled to meet attackers detected visually by outlying destroyers. As bomber speed increased, the available warning time shrank drastically, and the efficacy of the single visually-directed interceptor declined. Seagoing officers, who witnessed successful torpedo and bomber strikes in exercise after exercise, were particularly inclined to expect the enemy's bombers to penetrate.

For Britain, the limited aircraft capacity of existing carriers was a second important point. The Fleet Air Arm had vital reconnaissance and offensive tasks to perform. Given limited capacity, then, fighters might well be squeezed out. After all, defensive fighters were only one way of dealing with enemy aircraft. Exercises using the new radio-controlled targets strongly suggested that fleet anti-aircraft guns could also deal effectively with incoming attackers. Major ships would have to survive some damage, however; there was little hope of shooting down all the aircraft in an enemy strike.

This is not very different from the logic represented by the current generation of VSTOL carriers, the *Invincibles*. Now the heavy fleet anti-aircraft guns have been replaced by missiles, and the primary role of the carriers is a combination of strike and anti-submarine search/attack. In this case, it was expected that the role of the long-range fighter would be taken over almost entirely by surface-fired weapons. Some might suggest that the experience of the Falklands showed that this shift was not altogether practicable, just as the Royal Navy found, particularly in the Mediterranean in World War II, that there was no substitute for defensive fighters. In this case the presence of radar, which made for effective early warning and for fighter control, drastically changed the relationship between fighters and surface anti-aircraft guns.

The ships described in this chapter are often described as armoured carriers. In fact, they were carriers with protected hangars; the expanse of flight deck outside the hangar was essentially unarmoured. In this they responded to the view of many carrier commanders that the large target represented by the hangar, with its many aircraft and its vast amount of explosive and inflammable material, was just too easy to hit and thus too great a danger not merely to the effectiveness but to the very survival of their ships. This was, after all, proved explicitly by the fate of the four Japanese carriers at Midway. It might be argued that without armouring the entire expanse of flight deck a designer could not guarantee that the carrier would remain in action after, say, a dive-bombing attack. The appropriate response is that so much armour just could not be accommodated so high in the ship, particularly if, as in the British case, the ships had to be designed within treaty limits.

Even hangar protection carried significant penalties. On about the same displacement, HMS *Illustrious* was designed to carry just half the air group projected for HMS *Ark Royal*. In effect, the armoured carrier exchanged one of the hangars of the earlier ship for overall hangar protection. She was also substantially shorter. As a result, when deck parks were introduced in wartime, she still suffered a substantial penalty.

Britain completed six protected-hangar ships, divided into three closely related classes, during World War II, followed by two more, her last fleet carriers, during the decade which followed. Opinion as to the efficacy of these ships shifted radically, both during and after World War II. During the war, they were criticized for their relatively small air groups for their tonnage, to the point that the final British wartime design, the *Malta*, was nearly unarmoured. In 1945, however, armoured carriers such as HMS *Formidable* were able to shrug off Kamikaze attacks which disabled their US contemporaries. It is often suggested that the subsequent US decision to armour the flight decks of the postwar super-carriers reflected this success.

This is not quite true. In US wartime and prewar carriers, the flight deck was designed as a superstructure. In British carriers, from the *Ark Royal* onwards, the flight deck was integral with the hull, serving as its upper strength member. Because US ships had shallower hull girders, they suffered from higher stresses, and this problem was aggravated as ships became longer and longer. Thus the shift to a British-style hull (with integral flight deck) in the postwar ships was almost inevitable. Given that shift, the flight deck had to be strong enough to keep the ship from breaking up, and this in turn implied some considerable thickness. Resistance to bombs was a distinctly secondary consideration.[2]

1. USS *Midway* had an armoured flight deck but no armour covering the hangar sides. The Japanese *Taiho* and *Shinano* both had armoured flight decks but lacked any substantial protection to the hangar sides. A diagram of the armour of the carrier *Taiho*, for example, prepared for the US Naval Technical Mission to Japan immediately after the end of the war, shows 25mm of DS and 5mm of CNC armour steel on the flight deck (a total of almost 4in), but only 25mm DS splinter protection (less than 1in) on the hangar sides, with 16mm DS and 37mm CNC on the floor of the lower hangar (a total of about 2in). The drawing, based on Japanese data, was Enclosure 65, ND-50-1002.7. Original plans of the ship seem not to have survived. Similarly, accounts of the giant *Shinano* indicate little or no hangar side protection.

2. See this author's *U.S. Aircraft Carriers: An Illustrated Design History* (Naval Institute Press, Annapolis, 1983) for details. Armouring was a consideration in the abortive *United States* (CVA 58), but it was among the weights reduced when the smaller *Forrestal*, the basis of subsequent US carriers, was designed. The only wartime US carriers to have armoured flight decks were the *Midways* and the sheer weight of their decks presented serious structural problems. Moreover, the topweight represented by these decks had to be kept relatively low, the result being far too little freeboard.

Design F, 22 February 1936. NF

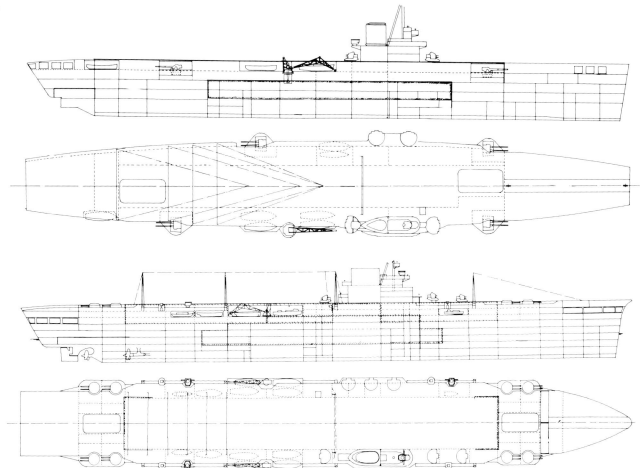

Design WB. NF

As for the surviving wartime ships, the tightly integrated armoured design proved a distinct drawback postwar, when the Royal Navy sought to reconstruct its carriers.

IT WAS CLEAR from the beginning that flight deck armour would have to be paid for out of hangar (that is, aircraft) capacity. As long as the Royal Navy was limited in the number of carriers it could build, therefore, such armour was distinctly unattractive. Conversely, flight deck protection became viable as soon as the treaty limit on the total carrier fleet collapsed. Thus the decision to build the armoured carriers was closely tied to the outcome of the second London Naval Conference of 1935–36, which produced the 1936 London Treaty.[3]

The British government approached the treaty conference with two opposed aims. On the one hand, it hoped to use continued naval arms control to avoid an expensive competition in naval armaments. On the other, having abandoned the Ten Year Rule in 1932 (due to Japanese aggression in the Far East), it had to take the possibility of war into account, and it had therefore to shape its forces to strategic requirements. Moreover, with the rise of Nazi Germany came the very real possibility that Britain would have to deal with two enemies.

Of the two other principal treaty powers, the United States, although she feared Japanese expansionism, was still primarily interested in restraining new construction. American public opinion prohibited any approach to naval co-operation with Britain in Asia, which might have made it possible for each country to reduce naval spending.[4] Japan sought parity (which was particularly unacceptable if Britain had to maintain powerful forces both in European and in Asiatic waters) and actually withdrew from the treaty in 1934. Thus Britain and the United States faced an additional requirement to shape programmes

and limitations to deter the Japanese from unrestrained construction. Matters were complicated by Japanese secrecy concerning new construction.

In March 1934 the First Sea Lord, Admiral Chatfield, drew up a strategic analysis of the British position, calling for a fleet powerful enough to protect the Empire in Asia while securing Britain against the strongest European power. This was barely consistent with the existing treaty system: the ordained ratio of British to combined Japanese and, say, Italian strength was 5:4.75. Chatfield hoped that fleet modernization could be made affordable by cutting the tonnage of individual capital ships, to 25,000 (or at most 28,000) tons for battleships (rather than the 35,000 previously permitted) and to 22,000 tons for carriers. On the other hand, to place the fleet on a strategic rather than on an affordable basis required Chatfield to reaffirm the classic British requirement for seventy cruisers (partly for trade route protection), where Britain had accepted a limit of fifty at London in 1930, in happier strategic circumstances. Chatfield hoped, too, to eliminate the oceanic submarine either by abolition or by limiting them to 250 tons. This might have been considered an attainable goal, since all of the treaty powers expected to depend on sea control rather than on sea denial in wartime. It became utterly impractical once Germany had rejected the Versailles Treaty and begun her naval (including submarine) rearmament. Abolition of submarines would have limited Chatfield's need for convoy escorts and would greatly have simplified his problems.

Chatfield hoped that a new treaty could extend to 1945, leaving the Royal Navy sufficient breathing space for modernization, given the favourable (5:5:3) treaty ratio affirmed both in Washington in 1921 and then in London in 1930. Straitened British finances made any more ambitious expansion to match

3   This account of the British position at London is based largely on Stephen Roskill's *Naval Policy Between the Wars* (Collins, London, 1976). The interpretation is the author's own.

4   In theory, the 5:5:3 Treaty ratio would have equated to 10:3 for an Anglo-American alliance facing Japan. However, in the absence of such an alliance, neither side could feel altogether comfortable with no more than a 40 per cent edge over its most important prospective naval enemy, Japan, particularly as its fleet would have to operate so far from home. Moreover, the actual, as opposed to the permissable, ratio of naval strength was much less than 5:3, because Japan had spent heavily on modernization and new construction, whereas the two Western powers had not.

Table 7-1: Small Trade Protection Carriers, 1935

	F	G	J
Armoured flight deck	yes	no	yes
LFD (ft)	600	600	600
BWL (ft)	80 6	75	84
Std draught (ft)	21 4	21 8	22
Std displacement (tons)	14,600	13,500	17,000
			(17,600)
Deep displacement (tons)	16,900	15,800	20,000
SHP	53,000 (4 boilers, 1 engine room, 4 turbo-generators)		66,000
Shafts	2	2	3
Speed, deep (knots)	27	27.25	28
Speed, deep, half power (knots)	23 clean		23.25
	21 6 months out of dock		21.5
Oil fuel, deep (tons)	2000		2500
Endurance, at 12 knots (nm)			
clean			10,000
6 months out of dock	7500		8250
Cost	£2.8m	£2.7m	£3m

Armament

5.25in	2 twin (400rpg) ———————————
8-barrel pom-pom	4 (1800 rpb) ———————————

F and *G* have a 600 × 81ft flight deck and a single 290 × 40 × 16ft hangar (15 TSR), lifts at each end (45 × 22ft). *J* has a 660ft flight deck and a single 436 × 60 ×16ft hangar (24 TSR). *F* and *G* stow 20,000 gallons of petrol; bombs: ninety 500lb; seventy-five 250lb; 144 100lb; 200 20lb; 1600 8½lb. No stowage space for torpedoes – none in *Hermes*. *J*: 40,000 gallon of petrol; 180 500lb bombs, 150 250lb, 40020lb, 3000 8½lb.

In *F* and *J*, the flight deck was 2½in NC on 25-40lb D steel (against 500lb SAP dive-bomb or 500lb bomb dropped from 5000ft) extending nearly the full width of the flight deck, and in *F* it extended from the forward end of the hangar to about 67ft from the after end of the landing deck and parking area. In *J* the armoured deck length was 480ft, including both lifts, 2in NC bulkhead at forward end. In the case of *J*, the displacement in parentheses corresponds to a 3in flight deck. *G* is protected against 20lb bombs, as in earlier carriers (25-40lb D flight deck).

Side belt 4½in C as in *Ark Royal*, over magazines and machinery spaces and from HD to about 3ft 6in below standard waterline. Reduction to 3in NC would save 220 tons and £45,000.

2in NC at hangar deck level protects magazines, bomb rooms, petrol from 6in fire, with 2in NC bulkhead at forward end of forward magazine group and at after end of after magazine group. 50lb D on hangar deck to cover machinery against splinters. *G* is protected as in *Ark Royal*, with 3½in NC over magazines and machinery, and 2½in bulkheads. In *G*, deck protection of magazines and machinery against cruiser fire is of a higher order than in *F*, making use of the weight which otherwise would go into a heavier flight deck. Reduction of the belt to 3in NC and of the deck over it to 2½in NC would save 550 tons (£81,000).

As in *Ark Royal*, 3½in NC over sloping roof of steering gear compartment, with 2½in NC on bulkheads at ends of this compartment.

unrestrained foreign building extremely unattractive. Unfortunately, the Japanese government had already announced that it considered its ratio (60 per cent of British or American tonnage) unacceptable; it wanted parity. The one bright spot here was Chatfield's belief that Japan's naval expansion (at least in cruisers) would be limited by her building facilities. After all, Britain needed her seventy cruisers at least partly to deal with prospective Japanese cruiser attacks against trade routes. The 70-cruiser situation was further complicated by the US policy of maintaining parity with Britain in this as in other categories, despite the differences between the strategic situation of the two countries. In a time of US fiscal austerity, US delegates could be expected to press for a lower limit on cruiser numbers, to reduce the cost of their policy.

As expected, the US position, as articulated in the late autumn of 1934, was to call for further reductions, not rearmament. The British stressed their need for strength both in Europe and in Asia. Since they could not rely on US assistance, they themselves needed a sufficient margin of naval power. US delegates did secretly agree with the British that neither country would agree to any increase in relative Japanese naval strength. They also agreed to avoid any naval race between them.

Meanwhile the French were concerned with the beginnings of German naval rearmament; they were also loath to abandon submarines. Just as Britain required sufficient strength to face both a European power (most probably Italy, but now perhaps Germany) and Japan, France had to face both Italy and a resurgent Germany. These strategic realities had to fit into a political situation in which, both in 1921 and in 1930, Italy had been granted parity with France. Moreover, the British government, facing so severe a threat in the Far East, had to be disposed to accede to some measure of German rearmament.[5]

All of these entanglements made it most unlikely that the Conference would continue global limitation in any category. The United States rejected British proposals on the qualitative limitation of battleships, although the British delegates were able to hold down the unit sizes of carriers (though to 23,000 rather than 22,000 tons) and cruisers (to 8000 tons rather than the 7600 proposed).

The failure of the battleship proposals is significant here because it raised the price of new British battleships above what it might otherwise have been, and thus absorbed money which might otherwise have gone into carriers. Much more significant was the elimination of global limitation: after the Washington Treaty lapsed on 31 December 1936, none of the signatory powers was obliged to limit her total naval forces. The only restraining feature was a requirement that new naval programmes be published in advance. In theory this requirement would have acted as a deterrent, since naval rivals would be able to begin their own programmes in response, preventing any one power from achieving any great advantage. However, Japan never signed the treaty, and since she was the major naval threat faced by the two largest signatories, and since her secrecy was extremely effective, the effect of the treaty was largely negated.[6]

When *Ark Royal* (Chapter 6) was laid down in 1934, the goal was a five-carrier force of maximum aircraft capacity, all units of which would accompany the main fleet(s). Washington and

5   According to Roskill (p292), in June 1934 the British and French agreed to allow Germany five capital ships (including the three 'pocket battleships'), one carrier, seven light cruisers, twenty-five destroyers, and 5000 tons of submarines. The Anglo-German Naval Agreement, signed the following year, allowed substantially higher figures. It was accepted on the ground that it provided some useful restraint, and also that it helped avoid the two-front disaster the British government feared.

6   Japan was not the only destabilizing factor. Even had she not greatly expanded her fleet, the British and the French would still have had to deal with a rearming Germany. By 1936 the Soviet Union was also rearming, and no one knew just what that would ultimately mean.

Design M, 1937, for a small carrier. NF

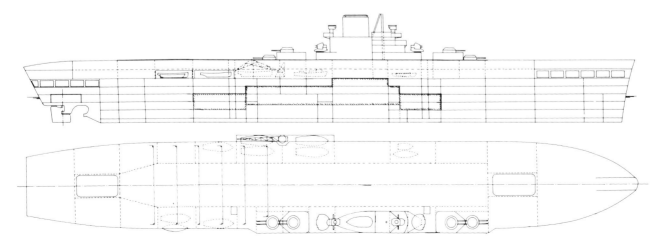

Design D, 2 February 1938.
NF

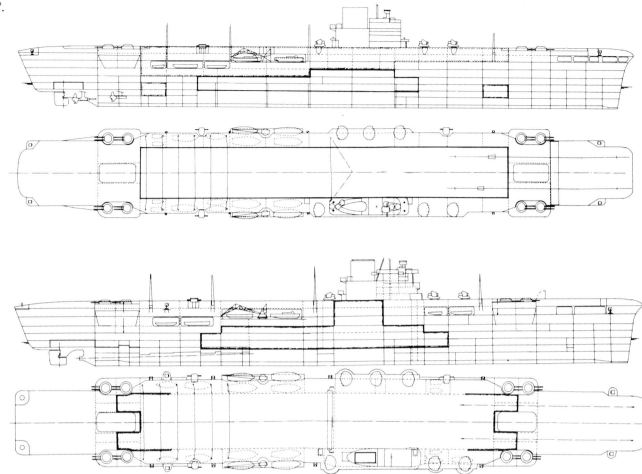

Table 7-2: Fleet Carrier Alternatives, 1936

Design	Ark Royal	X	Y	Z	ZA
Armoured flight deck	no	yes	no	yes	yes
Displacement (tons)	22,000	23,000	19,600	22,000	23,000
LWL (ft)	725	670	670	725	725
Flight deck length (ft)	800	720	720	760	760
Beam (ft)	94	100	91	92	94
Std draught (ft)	23	24	23	23 3	23 6
SHP	102,000	80,000	72,000	72,000	90,000
Speed (knots)	30	28	28.25	28.25	29
Speed, half boilers (knots)	23.5	23	23	24	
Oil fuel (tons)	4370	4500	4000———		
Endurance at 14 knots (nm)	12,000	11,000	11,500	11,000	11,000
SHP	102,000	80,000	72,000	72,000	90,000
Catapults	2	2	2	1	1
Lifts		3	2 45 × 22ft ———		
Wires			6———————		
Fwd of crash barrier		350ft		385ft	
Abaft crash barrier		370ft		375ft	
Petrol (gallons)	100,000	80,000	80,000	60,000	
Cost	£3.85m	£3.9m	£3.5m	£3.8m	£4.05m
Armament[1]	16 4.5in	16 5.25in (400rpg)———————			
	6 pom-poms	6 pom-poms (1800rp)———————			
	8 .5in mg				
Bombs					
500lb	360	405	270		
250lb	300	340	225		
100lb	576	650	432		
20lb	800	900	600		
8.5lb	6000	6000	4500		
Torpedoes	72	81	54		
Bomb lifts		2 pairs———————			
Protection					
Flight deck	—	3in	—	3in	3in
Magazines/machinery	3½in	2in	3in	2in	2in
Steering gear	3½in	3in	3in	3in	3in
Belt	4½in C	750lb———————			
Aircraft	48 TSR 24 DB	54 TSR	54 TSR	36 TSR	36 TSR

1 Length of flight deck armour is 500ft for *X*, 620ft for *Z* and *ZA*, and includes the lifts. Side belt is 4.5in NC, deck over magazine and machinery spaces is 2in NC, except for *Y* where it is 3in. 2.5in NC bulkheads, 3in NC over steering.

The modified Illustrious *design* (Indomitable). *Note the extended flight deck armour and the two accelerators forward.* (3 March 1938). NF

London (1930) Treaty restrictions on carrier replacement, moreover, dictated that a second unit could not be laid down until 1937. Then Italy invaded Ethiopia, and on 1 July 1935 the Royal Navy began to mobilize against the possibility of war with Italy, to be ready to support a League of Nations sanction against the aggressor. The chief effect of mobilization was to reveal deficiencies in the existing naval organization.

The British war plan involved operation from a forward base, either Malta (which was insufficiently protected) or, probably, Navarino Bay in Greece. It was immediately clear that the Royal Navy would have to provide aircraft for local defence and reconnaissance; there could be no sufficient peace-time provision of land-based aircraft. Similarly, it was clear that British resources for trade protection (primarily against surface raiders) would be badly stretched. In this case, too, the solution would be aircraft operating from an improvised base, most likely a sheltered bay or inlet.

There was, then, an urgent requirement for some kind of aircraft depot ship or trade-protection carrier, to support a combination of reconnaissance and fighter cover. Negotiations between the Admiralty and the Air Ministry led to approval of a programme of four such ships, one of which would be included in the 1936 programme, that is, before the next fleet carrier. In October 1935 the Admiralty envisaged two alternative types of trade-protection carrier, a medium ship carrying thirty amphibians and a small type carrying fifteen. At this time it was estimated that the smallest protected carrier would displace 14,500 tons, and would carry fifteen aircraft.

HMS Illustrious, *newly completed in 1940, displays the long bow and stern round-downs intended to improve air flow over her flight deck. She introduced the Type 72DM aircraft homing beacon, designed so that other electronics (originally high-frequency radio direction-finding loops) could be mounted above it, on the same mast. This made it possible to mount one of the two antennas of a Type 79 air warning radar on the tripod mast and the other on a shorter mast abaft the island. Only later could Type 79 (and similar long-wavelength British air warning radars) operate with only a single antenna. In this form* Illustrious *mounted the air attack on the Italian fleet at Taranto, the culmination of almost two decades of British study of means of dealing with an enemy fleet-in-being. The Mediterranean Fleet Air Battle Orders written in the 1930s, for example, included specific instructions for torpedo settings for use in shallow anchorages.* CPL

Early drafts of the 1936 programme also included a Mobile Naval Base depot ship, for much the same reason, and also in response to the lessons of the Ethiopian War.[7]

In October 1935, then, the Admiralty formally replaced its earlier target of five large carriers with three large ones and four trade-protection carriers. The latter could be used separately, for example to support cruisers on trade routes, but (if properly designed) they could also be employed within the main fleet. This shift was practicable because the Admiralty doubted that the treaty then being negotiated would continue to impose limits on total British carrier tonnage.[8]

If the fleet was to enjoy the services of more than five carriers, then it might no longer be necessary to cram the maximum number of aircraft into each. By the end of 1935 it no longer seemed practicable to operate as many as seventy-two aircraft from the *Ark Royal*. It also seemed important, for tactical reasons, to operate whole numbers of squadrons (of twelve aircraft each): thus twenty-four, or thirty-six, or forty-eight aircraft per carrier. Opinion differed as to whether twenty-four or thirty-six was best, balancing flexibility and the number of decks against total cost. At this time, too, the advent of the TSR (the Swordfish), which combined the T/B and S/R functions in one airframe, made it possible to reduce the required

number of fleet aircraft to 360.

The D of P considered eight carriers a desirable tactical minimum.[9] Counting the *Ark Royal* as seventy-two aircraft, the fleet required another 288, which could be accommodated in eight 36-aircraft carriers, or in six 48-aircraft ships. If the *Ark Royal* were more realistically considered a 48-aircraft ship, then the fleet required another 312 aircraft, which could be accommodated aboard seven more 48-aircraft ships, or nine 36-aircraft ships. As a consequence, the 'new standard' of naval strength, drafted late in 1935, called for eight fleet carriers, to be supplemented by five trade-protection carriers and one training carrier, for a total of fourteen ships. This draft policy supplemented the initial requirement already quoted.

Late in 1935, then, the Royal Navy suddenly had to produce a new carrier design (for the trade-protection ship), to meet the requirements of the following year's programme. Up to this point, Staff Requirements and design work had all been designed to support the full-size fleet carriers, and the assumption had been that the 1937 ship would be a repeat *Ark Royal*. There was no time to develop conventional Staff Requirements, because there was no small-carrier design experience on which they

7   The Mobile Naval Base Defence Organization (MNBDO) had been developed since World War I. The base ship would serve as headquarters for the Senior Naval Officer, depot ship for controlled mining (for base defence), and would provide a measure of anti-aircraft defence before shore defences had been set up. She would also be primary radio ship for the base. The idea was not new; the dreadnought *Agincourt* had been earmarked for conversion (and stopped by the Washington Conference in 1922). Later, the Admiralty had assumed that merchant ships would suffice. Experience of the mobilization for the Ethiopian War showed that something more specialized, with a powerful anti-aircraft armament, a heavy ship's radio outfit and underwater protection was needed. Roskill identifies the origin of the MNBDO with the need to strengthen existing but insufficiently fortified bases, Malta

and Alexandria in particular, against air attack. In theory the MNBDO would establish short anti-aircraft defences within 48 hours of the fleet's arrival, and within a week the port would be safe against submarine penetration. By 1935 the MNBDO mission had been expanded to deal with entirely unprepared places such as Navarino Bay.

8   The draft 1936 programme also included a Queen Bee (radio-controlled target) tender, which would be essential to maintain fleet anti-aircraft readiness. She was to be able to carry eight such aircraft, and of launching four in quick succession. This in turn would have made her a carrier under treaty provisions. In late 1935, however, this seemed irrelevant since it was so unlikely that quantitative (global) limitation would survive the 1935 Conference. The Board eliminated the Queen Bee tender from the

programme in January 1936. Stores and fittings (catapults, for example), for conversion of a merchant ship to a Queen Bee tender would be procured in peacetime, and at least two suitable ships earmarked. After considering and rejecting the trade-protection carrier early in 1936, the Controller reconsidered the Queen Bee tender. He suggested as an alternative that *Argus* undergo a 'large repair' and be fitted as a Queen Bee tender; she would have at least a decade more life in her. First Sea Lord approved in April 1936, and the necessary funds (£248,000) were included in a supplement to the 1934 budget.

9   This figure was based on an agreed minimum of five carriers for a wartime Eastern Fleet and three for a wartime Western Fleet, to meet demands for continuous long-range reconnaissance, a powerful striking force, spotting, action observation fighters.

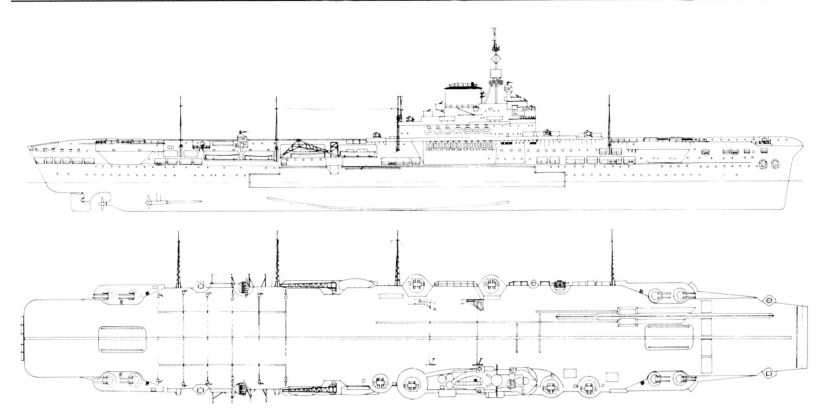

10 Several writers have remarked on the speed with which Henderson pushed through the armoured carrier. Given the circumstances, it would seem that speed was needed if the Navy was to exploit the opportunity provided by the 1936 Trade Protection Carrier. Forbes later commented that he was surprised that the armoured flight deck carrier aroused so little comment; the reason was that the Admiralty worked hard to keep it secret. For Forbes' account, see D K Brown, *A Century of Naval Construction* (Conway Maritime Press, London, 1983), pp. 143–145. Forbes owed his continued direct contact with Henderson to the absence of the then DNC, Sir A W Johns.

could be based. This in turn meant that the new ships could embody radically different thinking.

The Controller, Admiral Henderson, allowed the responsible constructor, W A D Forbes (who had designed *Ark Royal*), a free hand, requiring only that the new ships be armoured against 500lb bombs (that is, against the weapon their dive-bombers would deliver) and against cruiser shellfire.[10] His practice of personal and restrained control over the evolution of the design is reflected in the phrase prefacing many of the relevant sketch design submissions, 'on the verbal instructions of Controller.' In fact, however, the new design reflected existing practice, so that the omission of formal Staff Requirements really meant that no new decisions would be taken on issues such as steaming endurance and underwater protection. Moreover, there was a close personal relationship between Henderson and Forbes, the two often coming to London together on the train. Henderson was therefore well aware of the design alternatives, and of the consequences of his desire for flight deck armour.[11]

Henderson issued his orders some time early in January 1936. He began with an armoured-hangar trade-protection carrier, taking an unarmoured version as a check of relative costs, but soon afterwards he formally asked for alternative protected and unprotected versions of a fleet carrier.

As the most experienced British carrier commander and the first RAA, Henderson was clearly aware of the vulnerability of existing ships. As Controller he knew that, with treaty restrictions on total carrier tonnage swept away, he could afford to trade aircraft for armour. Moreover, both as a carrier operator and as Controller, he was probably well aware that the earlier attempt to stuff the maximum number of aircraft into one ship would probably fail, so that trade-off might well seem worse on paper than in reality. Finally, at the end of 1935 the Admiralty was painfully aware of the air threat, in the war Britain had just avoided. Experiments with Queen Bee drones seemed to demonstrate the efficacy of gun defences, and experiments with fighter interception seemed to show that at least some enemy bombers would generally fight their way through. The armoured hangar was the physical expression of this perception.

It has been suggested, too, that Henderson was influenced by

Illustrious as completed, 1940. Note the mainmast (for the second Type 79 antenna). Hangar side armour does not show because it was inboard, on the hangar wall itself. In the plan view, note the streamlining applied to her island and funnel. ALR

his First Sea Lord, Sir Ernle Chatfield, a former gunnery expert who was determined that the new generation of warships would not suffer magazine damage like that which had destroyed the battlecruisers at Jutland. Certainly Chatfield demanded and got better-protected battleships and cruisers; in the case of the battleships gun power was actually sacrificed for protection. The armoured-hangar carrier might be construed as a parallel sacrifice of aircraft capacity for protection.

Henderson's ships were all to be armed with 5.25in guns like those of the new battleships. The trade-protection carriers, designated Schemes F and G, were submitted on 25 February 1936, and are described in Table 7-1.[12] Each 14,600-ton ship could accommodate fifteen torpedo-bombers (TSR), at a cost

11 This relationship was particularly close because DNC (at that time Sir Arthur Johns), who would normally have intervened between the Controller and the chief carrier designer, was absent because he was extremely ill. His successor, Sir Stanley Goodall, reportedly considered the close relationship destructive, and exiled Forbes to Malta Dockyard, although as late as 1940–41 he considered Forbes his obvious successor. For his part, Forbes reportedly resented the fact that it was Goodall who delivered the paper describing his masterpiece, HMS *Ark Royal*, at the Institution of Naval Architects in 1939, although it was then standard practice for the DNC to deliver his subordinates' papers in this way. Forbes later returned as AD Materials in the Admiralty, but never held another design post. Forbes himself had been on ACA's staff in 1918, and for many years after World War I he was the first

Secretary of the Joint Technical Committee and also a liaison officer with the RAF. He became Head of the Carrier Design section in 1931, and thus was responsible for the run-up to the *Ark Royal*. In about 1966 Forbes recalled that he had made seven or eight design studies before Henderson was sufficiently satisfied to have him produce a formal sketch design for submission to the Board.

12 Existing references do not account for Designs A to D. The trade-protection carrier was associated with a Queen Bee tender, for which design studies A, B, and C had been conducted. The Board approved incorporation of Queen Bee features in the trade-protection carrier when the former was deleted from the 1936 programme, in January 1936. The decision to make *Argus* the Queen Bee tender saved the trade-protection carrier from this dual role.

of £2.8 million. The approved programme included only £1.5 million, and the Controller rejected the trade-protection carrier as too expensive. He concluded that a second (upper) hangar would add little to the cost of the ship but would double her aircraft capacity. This observation justified the *Illustrious* class. It resulted in a further sketch design, J.[13]

The fleet carrier was less urgent; DNC submitted Designs X, Y, Z, and ZA on 2 April 1936, to carry forty-eight and thirty-six TSR in double and single hangars respectively (see Table 7-2). It turned out that ships sized for sufficient speed could accommodate fifty-four TSR, and the designs were worked out on that basis. ZA was a modified version of the 36-aircraft design with more powerful machinery (triple vice twin screws).

From the constructor's point of view, the provision of thick armour at the flight deck level, at whatever cost in hangar capacity, was a most impressive achievement. For example, the contemporary US Navy (which did not consider hangar capacity particularly important), considered about 1in the maximum which could be supported, on the basis of topweight. The British solution was to minimize the structural weight (beyond the weight of the armour itself) associated with the deck, to minimize its topweight penalty. The flight deck armour itself was used for strength, without any backing, and the supporting structure beneath it was particularly finely calculated.[14] In contrast to contemporary US practice, British carriers already used their flight decks as structural members, and a number of cruiser designers had incorporated side armour directly into the skins of their ships (as structural members). Even so, Forbes' concept was extremely bold. US wartime experience in attempts to design US-style carriers with a similar degree of deck protection (and without hangar side protection) demonstrates his success; the results were extremely massive, leading ultimately to the *Midways*.

Henderson's immediate reaction was that flight deck armour exacted a considerable cost in speed, nearly 2 knots. Carrier speed would become even more important if, as seemed inevitable, the accompanying battle line were composed of much faster ships.

There was an obvious conflict between the trade and fleet carrier construction, and DCNS and the Controller considered the latter much more urgent. On 28 April 1936 ACNS held a meeting to discuss carrier characteristics, as well as the overall issue of the distinction between fleet and trade-protection ships. Deliberations were based on the carrier characteristics developed under Henderson's guidance (Tables 7-1 and 7-2).

Perhaps the most important decision was to abandon the distinction between the two categories. Trade-protection carriers built in peacetime would have to be able to work with the fleet. Instead, the terms 'large' and 'small' carrier were substituted; large carriers would be able to accommodate forty-eight TSR (although under normal conditions they would not operate more than thirty-six). The conference recommended that the small carrier have half this capacity (twenty-four TSR).

Table 7-3: *Illustrious* Compared to *Ark Royal* and *Courageous*

	Sketch	Final	Ark Royal	Courageous
LBP (ft)	670	673	685	735
LWL (ft)	710	710	725	669
LOA (ft)	745	753 3	800	786 3
BEXT (ft)	94	95	94	90
STD displacement (tons)	23,000	23,000	22,000	22,500
Draught, ME (ft)	24 1½	23 10	22 11	23 10½
Draught, deep (ft)	28 1½	28	27 4	27 6
Flight deck freeboard (ft)	43 4½	43 2	60 7	60 9
Length (ft)	758	753	800	
Hangar size (ft)	458 × 60	458 × 62		
SHP (max)	111,000	111,000	102,000	90,000
SHP (normal)	92,500	92,500		
SSTG		6 × 400kW		
Speed, deep (knots)	30/29	30/29	30	29.75
Speed, ½ power (knots)	25	25		
Oil fuel (tons)	4400	4640	4400	3900
Endurance at 14 knots, d & d (nm)	12,000	12,500	12,000	6900
Complement		1286	1600	1360
Petrol (gallons)	50,000	50,000	100,000	36,000
Armament				
4.5in twin BD	8 (400rpb)	8	—	—
4.5in twin UD	—	—	8 (400rpb)	—
4.7in HA/LA	—	—	—	16 (270rpg)
Mk M pom-pom	6 (1800rpg)	6	6 (1800rpg)	3 (1600rpg)
.5in mg			8 (2500rpg)	2 (2500rpg)
Torpedoes	54	45	72	54
Bombs				
500lb	270	250	360	120
250lb	216	650[3]	300	72
100lb	432	100	576	144
20lb	576	600	800	422
8½lb	400	—	6000	—
Aircraft	30 TSR	30 TSR	48 TSR	52 TSR[1]
	6 DB	6 DB	24 DB	
Weights (tons)				
General equipment	1000	1030	1105	1020
Aircraft equipment	860	1050	1115	740
Machinery	2450	2385	2440	3040
Armament	1125	1025	835	665
Armour, protection[4]	5050	5090	2850	} 17,035
Hull	12,515	12,420	13,655	
No margins listed				
Std displacement	23,000	23,000	22,000	22,500

1 27 Torpedo-bombers, 10 Fairey IIIF (S/F), 6 Osprey (F/R), 9 Nimrod (SSF)
2 Fleet fighters.
3 400 conventional bombs and 250 B bombs.
4 Protection figures included only half the weight of the flight deck, on the ground that it was at least partly a structural weight.

By this time the basic concept of flight deck protection had already been accepted; the conference affirmed that any carrier had to be protected against air, surface, and underwater attack.

The conference reviewed three alternative levels of protection. A 3.5in deck could keep out 500lb (semi-armour-penetrating) SAP dive-bombs, as well as 1000lb AP bombs dropped from 5500ft. A 3in deck could also resist 500lb dive-bombs, as well as similar bombs dropped from 7000ft (9500ft for a 3.5in deck). Finally, a 2.5in deck would resist 500lb bombs dropped either from 5000ft or by a dive-bomber. The conference chose a 3in deck for Scheme J.

As for protection against shellfire, a 4.5in C belt and 2in NC deck would be altogether immune to destroyer (4.7in) fire. The same combination would protect against 6in fire between 7000 and 19,000 yards; a 2.5in deck would extend protection out to 22,000 yards. A 4.5in NC belt would protect against destroyer fire beyond 3000 yards. The conference decided to protect against short-range destroyer and long-range cruiser fire, by means of a 4.5in cemented (C) belt and a 2in NC deck. The idea was that, even though a cruiser might be able to destroy the aircraft, the carrier herself would survive.[15]

The standard of underwater protection was that of the *Ark Royal*, a 750lb charge. An alternative, 1000lbs, was rejected.

In common with the new battleships, all these carriers would be armed with the new 5.25in twin dual-purpose gun: sixteen in large carriers, eight in small. Large carriers would have six, small carriers four, 8-barrel pom-poms. The conference rejected

13 Given Forbes' account of his extremely close and informal relationship with Henderson, it is entirely possible that the Controller knew from the beginning that the armoured trade-protection carrier was a non-starter, and that he intended almost from the beginning to use it to pry increased numbers of ships from an unwilling Air Ministry. He was certainly dedicated to the carrier cause, and he was certainly ingenious (as in the cases of HMS *Argus* and HMS *Unicorn*; see Chapter 8) in using existing non-carrier requirements to provide the Navy with flight decks usable in an emergency. The entire depot ship/ trade-protection carrier/fleet carrier story can be read as an example of this tactic. In this case the formal requirements surviving on paper tell only a fraction of the full story.

14 D K Brown (op cit, p145) reports that, long after the ships had been built, the supporting under-deck structure was studied by a leading structural engineer, who admitted that he would have used about twice as much material.

15 There was some hope that newer armour would be so much more effective that thickness could be reduced and weight saved. For example, a new 2.5in plate would be nearly as good as the existing 3in.

two small (14,500-ton) carrier designs, F and G, as insufficiently seaworthy, and recommended that the small 1936 carrier be built to a 17,600-ton design, J (see Table 7-1), modified for higher speed (29 knots emergency speed with all boilers lit, 28 with one off line). J was also to be more heavily armoured, with a 3in flight deck (adding 350 tons) and 2in deck armour over machinery, rather than the 1¼in D steel originally proposed (to deal with plunging cruiser fire). This was expected to add another 250 tons (the original expectation was 140). As for the fleet carrier planned for 1937, design X, modified to take forty-eight aircraft, was recommended.

The conference confirmed Henderson's initiative: all subsequent carriers would have armoured flight decks, a feature so important that it was well worth keeping secret. This presented a problem; under the treaties, the British government was obliged to circulate outline details, including air complements, of new ships before they were laid down. The leap from seventy-two aircraft aboard a 22,000-ton *Ark Royal* to thirty-six aboard a 23,000-ton *Illustrious* would surely have suggested some dramatic leap in protection. Extended discussion within the Admiralty produced a solution: the new armoured carriers were officially listed with the number of aircraft they *could* carry, American-style, including a deck park.

Overall, carriers were clearly needed so badly that the conference called for not fewer than two per year from 1936 on. Even at that rate, it would be some years before the eight modern fleet carriers could materialize.

Henderson disagreed with the idea of two alternative types

Formidable as completed in 1940. The two radar antennas and the DF loop on the foremast are clearly shown. Note the streamlining applied under the bow overhang. CPL

of carrier. The notional twenty-four TSR of a small carrier would not suffice for trade route operation, since large numbers of aircraft would be needed to hunt down a raider. Nor could such a ship afford anything less than maximum speed. Moreover, it was not yet really certain that global limits were dead. If they were reimposed, the Navy might find that it had consumed its allowance without providing sufficient numbers of sea-based aircraft. Finally, trade route operation demanded a larger, rather than a smaller, carrier to operate in rough weather, including, for example, monsoons.

The Controller also pointed out that, because no 5.25in upper deck (UD) mount was being designed, new carriers would probably have to be armed with 4.5in UD guns as in *Ark Royal*.

At this time, however, the position was still that the 1936 ship would be the small carrier. Thus, on 4 May Henderson asked DNC to redesign J in line with the conference recommendations, and to consider carrying belt (4.5in NC) armour up to the flight deck, thus eliminating internal horizontal armour over the area bounded by the belt, giving two-thirds of the hangar protection against all shellfire, plunging or direct.

DNC produced four alternatives. In JA, flight deck armour was increased to 3in, machinery deck protection to 2in. A 3in deck was expected to keep out a 500lb SAP bomb dropped

Key
1 Hangar
2 Boiler room
3 Engine room
4 Bomb magazine
5 Aviation fuel stowage
6 Magazine
7 Aircraft lift
8 Oil fuel stowage
9 Aircraft and ship small-arms magazine
10 Torpedo magazine

Inboard profile of Formidable.

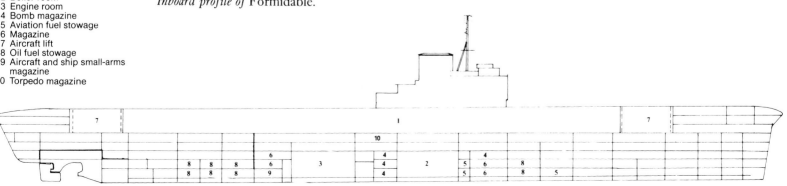

Victorious steams out of Hvalfjord, Iceland, in October 1941, in much her original configuration. Note that one of her radio masts is tilted over (aft). These masts were not themselves antennas; they supported long wire (HF) antennas strung between them. Such antennas could be very efficient, and the Royal Navy was always much concerned with reliable long-range radio communications. Postwar, it preferred not to follow the US Navy in adopting whips, which were more convenient for ship arrangement and for flying operations, but which were much less efficient as antennas.

from 7000ft; the 2in deck would resist the same bomb dropped from 3500ft. These additions cost 800 tons of displacement (17,800 tons) and £130,000. Speed was listed as 28.75 knots (emergency, with boilers forced) or 27.75 knots (normal), a reduction of a quarter knot.

JB was more austere, with 3in flight deck armour extending only over the width of the hangar and 1in NC on the hangar sides, and the 4.5in C belt carried all the way up to the hangar deck over the full length of the magazines and machinery spaces. On the hangar deck, 3in NC was worked at the sides and 1.75in NC inside the hangar in way of the magazine and machinery spaces. The reduction from 2in NC inside the hangar was possible because the 1in hangar sides provided substantial protection against plunging shellfire which missed the flight deck. Displacement fell to 17,560 tons, and the added cost (compared to J) was estimated as £110,000.

In JC, the belt was worked on the sides of the hangar abreast magazines and machinery spaces, as the Controller had suggested, with 1in NC on the sides of the hangar outside these spaces. The flight deck armour extended the full width of the flight deck, and 3in NC was worked on the hangar deck abreast the magazine and machinery spaces outside the hangar at the sides (but not inside the hangar). This combination gave complete protection to the magazines and machinery and to about half the hangar against bombs and 6in shells arriving beam-on, but incomplete protection against attacks before and abaft the beam. The considerable topweight had to be compensated by about 2ft more beam, and displacement rose to 17,890 tons (cost £170,000).

The next step, JD, was to extend 4.5in C armour over the whole length of the hangar, and over the ends of the hangar and lifts. The 3in NC flight deck armour covered the hangar and

lifts only, so that the length of protected flight deck was reduced from the 480ft of the JA to JC designs to 436ft. Now the entire hangar (as well as magazines and machinery) was protected against both bombs and 6in fire from all angles of attack.

Displacement rose to 18,370 tons, and power had to be increased to 80,000shp; even so, speed fell another quarter-knot. Compared to J, the additional cost would have been £250,000.

This was very expensive for a small carrier. As a comparison, Henderson asked DNC to design an unarmoured (hangar) carrier for twenty-four TSR; it became scheme L (July 1936). Magazine and machinery received cruiser-grade (*Leander*) protection,[16] and speed was held to 27.75 knots (deep; 53,000shp). The result would have displaced 12,700 tons (standard) with a flight deck 645ft × 80ft. As Henderson had suggested, the armament was four twin 4.5in rather than 5.25in guns, with four pom-poms. Estimated cost was £2.25 million.

By July, however, Henderson had carried his point. The First Sea Lord, DCNS and ACNS concurred: the 1936 carrier would be a full fleet ship, of 23,000 tons. Design L was never submitted to the Board. However (see below) the small carrier was considered again the following year.

BY 1936 THERE WAS substantial interest in accelerating the naval building programme. In June 1936 the Committee on Imperial Defence sub-committee on Defence Policy and Requirements (DPR) asked for proposals. The First Lord suggested that the 1936 programme be expanded from one carrier to two; by this time the 1935 three large/four small carrier programme had been abandoned. Indeed, in July 1936, in answers prepared for Questions in Parliament, the Admiralty stated that it had no final figure on its carrier requirements, but knew that it needed more quickly. It therefore proposed two carriers in each of the next three programmes (1936, 1937 and 1938), after which the situation could be reviewed. Any faster rate of production would have to be at the expense of battleships and cruisers, 'and as it is particularly undesirable to start a race in carrier building, it is thought best to stick to the annual figure of two.' However, an internal memorandum of this period, describing the Admiralty's desired 'new standard' of naval strength, lays out a programme of eight fleet and five trade-protection carriers.

16 Box protection to magazines: 2in NC roof, 3.5in NC sides, 2.5in NC ends; machinery: 1.25in D roof, 3in NC sides, 1.5in D ends.

Table 7-4: Small Carrier Designs, 1937

	M	N
LBP (ft)	600	650
LWL (ft)	625	675
LOA (ft)	650	700
BEXT (ft)	88	83 (outside armour)
Std displacement (tons)	17,440	16,500
Draught (ft)	22 9	19 6
Draught, deep (ft)	26 9	23 6
Flight deck freeboard (ft)	41 8	43 6
SHP	102,000	100,000
Shafts	3	4
Speed (knots) std	29¾	30½
deep	29 ½	30
Oil fuel (tons)	4000	3500
Endurance at 14 knots (nm)	12,000	10,000
		(6 months out of dock)
Complement	1000	1000 (private ship)
Petrol (gallons)	25,000	28,000
Armament		
4.5in	8 (400rpg)	8 (400rpg)
2pdr pom-pom	2 (1800rpb)	4 (1800rpb)
Torpedoes	27	30
Bombs		
500lb	50	60 (200)
250lb	300	360 (400)
250lb B	100	120 (250)
100lb	200	240 (200)
20lb	200	200 (240)
Protection		
Side	4½in C	3½in NC
Bulkhead	2½in NC	1½in NC
Hangar bulkhead	1in D	
Deck	3in NC	2in NC
Machinery	1¼in	1½in or ¾in
Flight deck	3in NC	2½in NC
Steering gear	2½in NC	2½in NC
Underwater	750lb	
Aircraft		
TSR	18	20 (old type)
Weights (tons)		
General equipment	900	800
Aircraft equipment	625	780
Machinery	2470[1]	2005
Armament	700	580
Armour, protection	2845	2010
Hull	9900	10,325
Margin	—	—
Std displacement	17,440	16,550

1 In M, includes tropical allowance; similarly in *Illustrious*, where it is 2385 tons

HENDERSON'S DEMAND that the new carrier be fast made it unlikely that the large (48/54-aircraft) ship would be adopted. He ordered a fresh set of studies, Schemes W, WA and WB (which have not survived), which added protection and substituted 4.5in BD guns for the much heavier 5.25s of the earlier studies. The hull was shortened to save weight, and its added resistance overcome by using more powerful machinery. Scheme WB was developed into a full sketch design, which DNC submitted late in June 1936.

Details of the developed design are given in Table 7-3. The hangar was fully protected by 3in NC on the flight deck and by 4.5in C sides and ends; the magazines and machinery (citadel) were protected by a 4.5in C side belt covered by 3in C decks and enclosed by 2.5in NC bulkheads. The belt was carried up to hangar deck level, and the hangar deck itself was 3in thick outside the hangar walls (1in thick outside the citadel, as splinter protection). To further protect the waterline, the 4.5in C belt was extended 30ft at each end of the citadel, closed by 2.5in NC bulkheads.

In the final version of the design, approved by the Board late in the year, the belt extended 9ft below and the deep waterline extensions were 28ft forward and 24ft aft.

Unfortunately, the lifts could not be armoured. Instead, 4.5in C vertical armoured shutters were placed at the hangar ends, the lift lobbies being outside them. In theory, as it was understood prewar, since the ship would not be operating her aircraft during battle, the armour doors leading to the two lifts could be closed and the hangar completely protected. However, in practice during World War II carriers had to launch and recover their fighters during combat; carrier radar made fighter interception a practical proposition. As a result, the shutters sometimes could not be closed, and blast from outside the protected part of the flight deck could and did enter the hangar.

Hangar-roof armour covered 62 per cent of the total flight deck length. Fire curtains divided the hangar into thirds, to

An Albacore landing on HMS Victorious, *probably in 1941. Note the carrier's extensive round-down aft, and the Fulmar fighters parked forward, protected by the crash barrier.*

HMS Indomitable *was a modified* Illustrious *with a second hangar abaft her intakes, and also with an enlarged forward lift. She also differed from her three predecessors in having a somewhat longer island, with the high-angle director tower further from its forward edge. Note the three Sea Hurricanes on starboard side outriggers, with a fourth on deck aft, and the wind break folded down forward for air operations. Her tilting radio masts are also down. This photograph was probably taken in 1941 or 1942. FAAM*

Below: Victorious, *in late 1942, with an Albacore overhead, shows an outrigger carrying a Sea Hurricane, with two more Sea Hurricanes parked forward. Note the arrester wire just abaft the second Sea Hurricane. For a time, about 1942–44, British aircraft carriers were equipped with a few bow wires, so that they could recover aircraft while steaming astern. It is not clear whether any British fleet carrier actually did so, but at least one MAC-ship had to steam astern to reduce the wind speed over deck for landing in a gale. Note that the radio masts have been tilted over for flying operations.*

Table 7-5: The 1938 Carrier

	A	D	1938 Design	Indomitable (Redesign)
LBP (ft)	690	690	690	673
LWL (ft)	730	730	730	710
LOA (ft)	758	758	760	740
BEXT (ft)	93	95	95 8½	95
Flight deck length (ft)			760	
Hangar size			456 × 62 × 14ft	
			208 × 62 × 16ft	
STD displacement (tons)	23,500	23,313	23,000	23,000
Draught, ME	23 6	22 9	22 4	23 10
deep	27 9		26 9	27 11
Flight deck freeboard (ft)	42 3		49 10	48 11
SHP	140,000		140,000	111,000
SHP, forced	152,000		152,000	
Speed, (knots) std	32.5-33		32.5-33	30.5
deep	32-32.5		32-32.5	30.0
Oil fuel (tons)	4750	4750	4850	4517
Endurance at 14 knots, d & d (nm)	11,000	11,000	11,000	11,500
Complement	1300	1390	1470 (flag)	1400
Petrol (gallons)	50,000	70,000	81,000[1]	70,000
Armament				
4.5in twin UD	8	8	8 (400rpb)	8 (385rpb)
2pdr pom-pom	6	6	6 (1800rpb)	6 (1800rpb)
.5in mg			—	—[3]
Torpedoes		54	54[2]	54
Bombs				
500lb	90	120	120	120
250lb	530	650	650	650
250lb B	170	240	240	240
100lb	350	500	500	500
20lb	470	600	600	600
11.5lb	2640	3000	3000	3000
Protection				
Flight deck			3in NC	
Hangar side			1½in NC	
Belt			4½in C	
Deck			2½in NC	
Bulkheads			1½in, 2in C	
Magazine sides			2in, 1½in NC	
Magazine roofs			3in, 2in NC	
Magazine ends			2in, 1½in NC	
Steering gear ends			2in NC	
Roof			3in NC	
Aircraft				
TSR	27	48	48	45
FDB	6	—	—	—
Weights (tons)				
General equipment	1010	1075	1080	1200
Aircraft equipment	910	1110	1110	1090
Machinery	3140	3140	3140	2440
Armament	985	1010	1010	1010
Armour, protection	4660	3730	3760	4090
Hull	12,795	13,250	13,350	13,170
Margins	—	—	—	—
Std displacement	23,500	23,315	23,450	23,000

1 Changed to 94,500 in 1939
2 Changed to 63, 1939
3 2 .66in machine-guns (2500rpb)

support the planned three squadrons, thirty-six aircraft. At this stage these consisted of thirty bombers and six fighters (dive-bombers); there is also some indication that a pure bomber (TSR) air group was planned. The torpedo stowage was predicated on the all-TSR group, and the Naval Staff suggested that it might be reduced to forty-five to match the mixed group. Table 7-6 shows how bomb stowage was calculated.

The 4.5in guns high above the waterline presented some problems in ammunition supply. Magazines adjacent to the guns would have added too much topweight; instead, ammunition was supplied by hoist to the upper deck, then by horizontal conveyor to the guns.

Aircraft arrangements broadly matched those of *Ark Royal*. Although the two lifts were of the same size as those in *Ark Royal* (46 × 22ft), they were of a very different design, carrying a heavier load (6 tons: 13,440lbs) and faster (30-second cycle).

As completed, the ships had one rather than two accelerators.

The design initially called for two accelerators, but in 1937 the Joint (Admiralty-Air Ministry) Technical Committee objected, on the grounds that there was no hope of independently loading two aircraft side by side. In that case, a single accelerator (catapult) on the port side would be just as good as two crammed together. The only argument in favour of two was to allow for one breaking down, and to increase the speed with which the first two aircraft could be launched.

In the course of design, the standard catapult load was increased to 11,000lbs (launched at 66 knots) with an overload of 14,000lbs (at reduced speed). Requirements for a two-catapult installation, agreed in April 1938, called for a 95ft stroke and a 40-second launching interval in each catapult, with both in action.

Machinery layout broadly matched that in *Ark Royal* but the engine and boiler rooms were more widely spaced (36ft apart), and all the auxiliary machinery was outside the main machinery compartments. In the final version of the design, of six 400kW turbo generators, two were in the wing engine rooms and four on the main deck within the armoured citadel. Four 60kW diesel generators were later fitted.

Designed endurance matched that of *Ark Royal*.

The hull was symmetrical, the moment of the island being balanced by making the wing oil fuel tanks abreast the torpedo protection on the port side 15in wider than the corresponding tanks on the starboard side. In addition, 400 tons of ballast was carried in the port side protection system.

Estimated cost was £4.05 million, compared to about £3.75 million for *Ark Royal*.

Henderson circulated the design 'for your *very* earliest remarks, please' on 25 June 1936, finding the Naval Staff enthusiastic; it called only for minor changes in the location of the flight deck pom-poms and for the addition of four quadruple .5in machine-guns. Thus amended, the design was brought before the Board by Henderson on 8 July, and it was approved on the 21st.

Two ships of this type were included in the 1936 programme, HMS *Illustrious* and HMS *Victorious*. Their final design was brought before the Board on 30 November 1936, and approved 14 December 1936.

Few changes were made at this stage, but all were potentially painful, since the ship had been designed without margins, and since it was just within the tonnage limit incorporated in the new treaty. Final Staff Requirements called for 100 tons more armour, for example, and the only compensation DNC could offer was a reduction in ammunition included in the standard displacement condition. Matters became so desperate that on 28 July 1936 he asked that a Board memo be passed to all departments emphasizing the 23,000-ton limit. Weight saving was actually quite successful, the lead ship coming out underweight. By the end of the war, however, HMS *Illustrious* displaced 2980 tons more than at completion. Inclining experiment results are summarized in Table 7-7.

DNC knew that, even as designed, the ship would be extremely cramped. Worse, complements tended to grow during service. In the case of the new carrier, this tendency would be aggravated in wartime by drastic increases in air complements (using deck parking), by the installation of radar and associated electronics, and by greatly expanded light anti-aircraft batteries. In 1936, DNC considered the situation so drastic that he suggested that the number of officers be reduced by using some rating (enlisted) pilots and observers. In October 1943, after refitting in the United States, *Victorious* accommodated about 1750 men, supporting thirty-six fighters (Grumman Wildcats) and eighteen torpedo-bombers (Avengers). At that time she had forty-three single Oerlikons aboard.

The hangar was widened 2ft (to 62ft; approved by the Board 11 December 1936) at Air Ministry request, even though the Admiralty resisted an attempt to increase the maximum folded aircraft width from 18ft to 18ft 6in. At this time the Air Ministry wanted to go to 19ft, in hopes of placing twin-engine aircraft at sea, and DNC offered to increase hangar width to as much as 64ft in the 1937 ships. These figures reflected required clearances of at least 15in between hangar sides and aircraft, and 24in between aircraft, which would stow three abreast. In these ships the hangar walls were actually 62ft 6in apart, as horizontal stiffeners 3in deep were worked into them; the extra 3in made passage around the aircraft much easier. Should 19ft aircraft be adopted, clearance at the sides would nominally be only 12in, but the extra 3in would help enormously.

Aircraft were changing very rapidly, and it was ludicrous to associate the hangar of a ship, which would probably last twenty years, with the aircraft designed (or actually in service) when it was completed. DNAD concluded that there was little point in anything but the largest possible hangar, which would exact the least possible penalty on the aircraft designers. The larger the hangar, the easier access to the aircraft stowed in it. Moreover, a wider hangar would better be able to take advantage of advances in aircraft design which might, perhaps, drastically *reduce* folded width. For example, a 64ft hangar could accommodate four 13ft aircraft abreast with 2ft 6in gangways.

This was a fundamental problem in British carrier design, since the structure surrounding the enclosed hangar constituted the vertical web of the ship's strength girder. It could be sacrificed – compressed to add hangar width – only to a limited extent. By way of contrast, US-style open hangars were inherently much wider, albeit at a substantial structural penalty.

In the case of *Illustrious*, the wider hangar cost 50 tons (in additional structure), and the Controller required that it be compensated for in order to keep the ships within treaty limits. DNC could not extend the hangar any further without redesign, but within roughly the same dimensions he could change the ships' form to gain another 2ft, at a cost of about 60 tons. At this point the machinery tenders (proposals) were already 75 tons heavier than allowed for in the design. To make matters worse, ACNS wanted more armour.

The planned .5in machine-guns at the ends of the flight deck were eliminated. The forward ones spoiled the lines of the bow to the point that they could be expected to draw water up; moreover, the eddies they created might cause problems to aircraft coming off the accelerator. Henderson felt that it would be difficult to keep the two at the after end manned during flight deck operations; it had been his experience in *Courageous* that people stayed away from the quarter-deck when aircraft flew on. The magazines intended to feed these weapons were retained against the possibility that the new .661in machine-gun or an Army twin 2pdr proved so much better than the .5in as to require their use.

The new design was aerodynamically superior to HMS *Ark Royal*, with an aerofoil-section funnel and island and a very long round-down aft. In addition, the form of the hull forward reflected wind tunnel tests. In practice, the very long round-down aft limited effective aircraft capacity, and it had to be drastically reduced during World War II.

The two 1937 ships were ordered as repeat *Illustrious* types (confirmed by the Controller on 6 November 1936) although the second of them, *Indomitable*, was redesigned (see below). *Formidable* essentially duplicated the first two ships.

The ships were designed with electronics limited to the Type 72 aircraft beacon atop a tripod mast, the usual radios (with their aerials hung from tilting masts alongside the flight deck), and provision for asdic (sonar) which was not, in the event,

Effective flight deck length determined the carrier's striking power, since piston-engined aircraft had to be warmed up before they could fly. They could not be run up inside an enclosed hangar. The simplest way to increase striking power, then, was to eliminate the after round-down, accepting worse air flow over the flight deck. HMS Victorious *shows Albacore torpedo-bombers ranged on deck to take off in 1943. She must already have lost most of her round-down aft, since one of the bombers is shown well aft on the flight deck.*

fitted. They were completed with Type 79 air-search radars, which required two antennas, one above the Type 72 beacon, and the other on a mainmast abaft the island. Later, when Type 79 was modified so that a single antenna sufficed, it was possible to add a second air-search set, Type 281, operating on a different wavelength, to provide fuller air cover.

THE SMALL CARRIER could not be dismissed altogether, and early in 1937 Henderson again asked for sketch designs in connection with the 1938 programme. Schemes M and N were submitted on 20 March 1937 (see Table 7-4). M matched *Illustrious* in overall characteristics, except that it had half the battery (two rather than six pom-poms) and half the air complement, less hangar protection, and was ¾ knot slower. Design N showed the effect of trading off an additional 2 knots, two pom-poms and two aircraft against protection.

It appears from the context that these studies were intended to deal with suggestions that the Fleet might be better off with smaller ships. Henderson forwarded them to ACNS with an accompanying minute showing how poor a bargain they were. Basing his arguments, presumably, on the Scheme L exercise of the previous year (which had not been circulated), he observed that at one end of the spectrum 11,000 tons would buy 28 knots, eight 4.5in guns, a flight deck protected against GP bombs (without side protection), and twelve aircraft, at a cost of not less than £2.5 million. This was absurd; the twelve aircraft might find an enemy but certainly they would not suffice to attack him. N could be expected to cost £2.86 million, and the somewhat larger M, £2.995 million — but for only a third more (about £4.05 million in total) a really satisfactory carrier,

HMS Victorious *at Pearl Harbor on 4 March 1943. Note that, unlike* Illustrious, *she has her Type 272 surface-search radar atop her bridge structure. The two objects further forward are Type 282 pom-pom control radars, controlling the two pom-poms forward of the island. By this time the British Type 72 homing beacon had been replaced by a US-supplied YE. Note, however, that the ship still had only a single air-search radar (79 or 279), with two antennas (the antennas are the same size, hence the same frequency).*

HMS Indomitable *in the Clyde, 1943, after her return from the United States and after a shorter British refit (largely concerned with her electronics). The chain at the stem is for a pair of paravanes, a standard self-protection measure in both World Wars. When they were streamed, the clamp was drawn down to the forefoot, and cables drawn out by a paravane on either side. This device was effective only against moored mines, and thus was largely forgotten with the advent of modern bottom (influence) weapons. However, as recent events in the Persian Gulf show, moored mines are still a problem, and paravanes remain a very cheap countermeasure. This particular paravane gear was designed specifically for the new armoured carriers.*

E-in-C stated that the maximum available would be 126,000 to 135,000shp, but he considered these figures excessive for three shafts, as they would entail low propulsive efficiency. The designers were therefore forced to a four-shaft arrangement, for 140,000 to 152,000shp.

This in turn made for a longer machinery compartment, so the belt had to be 304ft rather than 292ft long. As the 23,000-ton treaty restriction still stood, some reductions were necessary. Hangar deck armour was reduced from the 120lbs (3in) of *Illustrious* to 100lbs (2.5in), which was considered sufficient to resist gunfire. DNC argued, moreover, that any bomb would have to penetrate both the flight deck and another (gallery) deck before striking the hangar deck, and therefore that this lesser thickness should be accepted. Similarly, bulkheads at the ends of the hangar were reduced from 4.5in to 2in on the ground that they would not be exposed to normal (head-on) attack. Plating in the underwater protection was also reduced.

These reductions were welcome because the Royal Navy was finding armour supply difficult; Henderson wanted them extended to carriers already under construction.

DNC simultaneously developed a design for a ship trading protection for more aircraft, a development encouraged by the obvious failure of *Ark Royal* (see Chapter 4). Preliminary Staff Requirements for a ship to operate forty-eight Albacores were received on 23 December 1937, and Sketch Designs D and D1

an *Illustrious*, could be purchased.

Thus the 1938 carrier (Table 7-5) began as a slightly improved version of the existing armoured design. DNC submitted Sketch Design A on 18 January 1938. The initial instructions were to repeat *Illustrious* but with higher power for higher speed, to be achieved by forcing the machinery. The

(D with 5.25in guns) were submitted on 9 February 1938 (see Table 7-5).

Hangar width was reduced from the 64ft of Design A to the 62ft of the *Illustrious*, and the 4.5in magazines were moved directly under the guns. Speed and machinery matched those of Design A, with four engine rooms and four boiler rooms, two boilers per room. The ships were completed with seven 400kW turbo generators, each in a separate water-tight compartment.

The key issue was hangar height within a hull of broadly fixed dimensions. The new TSR, the Albacore, had a height of only 12ft 3in when folded, and 13ft when spread; it could, therefore, fit within a 13ft 3in hangar; earlier carriers had a 16ft clear height. If 13ft 6in was considered acceptable, then the carrier would displace 23,135 tons (23,585 with 5.25in guns). On the other hand, the full 16ft deck height was required to accommodate amphibians. The sketch designs therefore showed a 13ft 6in upper hangar and a 16ft lower hangar (23,315 and 23,790 tons, respectively). DNC concluded that 5.25in guns could be obtained only at the sacrifice of hangar deck height – that is, of seaplanes, amphibians, and possible new types of wheeled aircraft. The upper hangar would accommodate thirty-three aircraft, the lower one, fifteen.

A further change of policy in 1939 made a 14ft lower hangar height acceptable; as built, both ships had these hangars.

As in Design A, armour had to be sacrificed. In this case the hangar sides were reduced from the 4.5in of earlier designs to 1.5in; and the deck over the belt (the hangar deck) would be 80 rather than 100lbs, increased to 100lbs outside the hangars. The belt could not be extended to cover the magazines, which were therefore given box protection (4.5in sides, 2in deck and bulkheads).

Estimated costs were £4.7 million for A, £4,675 million for D and £4.95 million for D1.

Sketch Design D became the basis for a design submitted to the Board on 2 August and approved on 17 November 1938; it is described in Table 7-5. Two ships of the 1938 design, HMS *Implacable* and HMS *Indefatigable*, were built. However, only *Implacable* was included in the 1938 programme as finally implemented, *Indefatigable* being held over to 1939. This cut in the 1938 and 1939 programmes was due to a government decision to ration available funds among the services, and to reject Admiralty demands. It might, then, be seen as a consequence of increased British fear that war might come with Germany rather than with Japan.[17] Another carrier would have been included in the 1940 programme, but it was crowded out by emergency programmes, and carriers did not reappear in British naval programmes until 1942.

The legend actually exceeded the treaty limit, and DNC had to promise to save 450 tons during construction. Even in the final sketch design, armour had to be reduced below that promised in Design D; the deck covering the belt was 1.5in (60lb) NC between the hangar walls, and 2.5in (100lb) NC outside. However, where this deck was entirely outside the hangar, it was 2.5in NC at the sides and 2in on the centreline, on the theory that bombs or shells striking the centreline would have travelled through more decks and side plating. Contemporary US battleship designers saved deck weight by similar reasoning.

Box magazine deck protection was 3in where the magazines were not covered by the flight deck, and 2in otherwise, with 2in and 1.5in NC bulkheads.

In April 1939 it was proposed that the hangar side armour of both ships be increased from 1.5in NC to 2in NC, to protect against low level attacks with 500lb SAP bombs. This was the same threat against which the 1.5in plating had been installed, but it appeared that newer aircraft would release their weapons

Table 7-6: Bomb Stowage Aboard HMS *Illustrious*, 1936

Type	Aircraft	Per Aircraft	Loads	Total	Rounded
500lb SAP	30 TSR	3	1	90	100[1]
	6 FDB	1	1	6	
B	30 TSR	6	1	180	200[1]
	6 FDB	1	1	60	
250lb SAP	30 TSR	6	3	540	550
	6 FDB	2		36	
100lb A/S	30 TSR	6	2	360	400
	6 FDB	2		24	
20lb	30 TSR	12	1	360	600
	6 FDB	8	5	240	
Practice	30 TSR	8	10	2400	3000[2]
	6 FDB	8		380	

Revised Bomb Stowage, late 1936

This was based on substitution of fleet fighters (Fulmars) for the Skua fighter/dive-bombers; the Fulmars could not carry 500lb, B or 250lb bombs.

Type	Aircraft	Per Aircraft	Loads	Total	Rounded
500lb	30 TSR	3	2	180	200
250lb	30 TSR	6	2	360	400
100lb	6 FF	6	5	180	200
20lb	30 TSR	12	1	360	600
	6 FF	8	5	240	
8.5lb	36 a/c	8	20	5760	6000
B	20 TSR	6	2	240	250

1 The stowage of the two types should be interchangeable. Lifts should be large enough to take the B bomb, which is of greater diameter than the SAP.
2 Cases only. Can be stowed anywhere convenient.

HMS Illustrious *in March 1943. The wartime censor has not completely obliterated the Type 281 radar on the pole mast abaft the island, and the aerofoil shape of the funnel is visible. Note the board visible above the superfiring pom-pom; it was a visual indicator to signal to aircraft, the type used aboard British carriers throughout the interwar period. By this time it cannot have been much used. The aircraft on deck are Grumman Martlet IIs.*

at higher velocities. The resulting increase in weight would clearly have exceeded the treaty limit; it was balanced by reducing the lower hangar to the same limited height (14ft) as the upper. This in turn meant that the ships could no longer house floatplanes in their hangars, although they did have a space at the forward end of the upper hangar where the clear height under the beams was 15ft 9in. Unfortunately, it was soon evident that amphibians entering service would exceed the allowable height; the new Sea Otter was expected to be 16ft 3in high,

17 See, for example, the official history, M M Postan, *British War Production* (HMSO, London, 1952), p6.

At Trincomalee on 14 May 1944, HMS Illustrious *shows the lantern of a Type 272 surface and low level air-search radar on the fore side of her island. By this time, too, her type 79 had been converted into one-antenna Type 79B, using the original antenna atop the island; the stub mainmast carried a Type 281B, which had a different wavelength. Because the lobe (fading) patterns of the two radars differed, together they gave both excellent overall coverage and an indication of target height (since a target would fade from one radar while the other could still pick it up). Even so, by this time a specialized pencil-beam height-finder was badly needed, and each fleet carrier was scheduled to receive the new Type 227.* FAAM

perhaps even 17ft 6in. On this basis any possibility of carrying amphibians in the new carrier was rejected.

Ironically, it appears that the ships were actually built with 1.5in NC hangar sides.

While under construction, the design was considerably modified: the flight deck was raised aft, the forward lift was enlarged to take non-folding aircraft such as Sea Hurricanes and the early Seafires (to 45 × 33ft), the flight deck was extended abreast the forward lift, splinter protection was added, the bow was modified, and diesel generators were fitted. All of this added about 540 tons in deep condition.

Although the armament of the 1938–39 carriers matched that of their predecessors, the pom-pom battery was rearranged, one being moved from the after end of the island to the port side. This balanced the battery, and so made it less necessary for any gun to fire across deck.

WHILE THE 1938 CARRIER was being debated, the fourth ship of the earlier type, HMS *Indomitable*, was modified. She was subject to an estimated eight-month delay due to late delivery of some of her armour (from Czechoslovakia), and early in 1938 it was proposed that she could be altered to reflect many of the features of the 1938 ships, without incurring any major delay in completion. DNC quickly developed the legend given in Table 7-5, which was approved by the Board on 31 March 1938.

She was not altered from keel to upper deck, but by adding 6ft to the total hull depth (73ft 9in rather than 67ft 9in as in *Illustrious*) the constructors were able to provide two hangars. The added topweight was balanced to some extent by reduced hangar side armour (1.5in NC rather than 4.5in C). The forward lift was moved aft 16ft, and the after lift moved forward 24ft, the arrester wires being spaced 20 rather than 24ft apart to maintain the distance between the forward wire and the crash barrier. An extra gallery deck accommodated the necessary increased FAA personnel, boats, and aircraft equipment. As in the *Implacables* the upper hangar had reduced clear headroom (14ft), although the lower (short) hangar had the full 16ft.

It also proved possible to enlarge the forward lift, which served only the upper hangar, to 45 × 33ft, to take non-folding

Table 7-7: Inclining Data, HMS *Illustrious*

Condition	Average Action (Condition A)	Deep (Condition B)	Half Oil	Standard	Light (Condition C)	Extreme Light
Displacement (tons)	27,122	28,210 [28,619]	25,796 [26,192]	26,760 [23,207]	22,260	20.978
Mean draught BP (ft)	26 10.75	27 8.36 [28 1.25]	25 10.15 [26 3.13]	25 5.3 [23 10.75]	23 0.17	21 11.38
Trim BP by stern (ft)	1 8.25	2 2.58 [1 4.5]	2 0.89 [1 1.75]	2 7 [1 7.5]	3 1.3	3 10.01
GM virtual	7	7.75 at 0 degrees; 7.99 at 5 degrees [8.26]	6.52 [6.8]	4.94 [5.35]	5.02	5
GM solid	7.58	8.3 [8.57]	7.15 [7.42]	4.97 [5.35]	5.02	5
Angle of heel	5.5 degrees S	4.5 degrees S	7 degrees S	11.5 degrees S	11.5 degrees S	10.5 degrees S
Max GZ	4.11	4.32 [4.99]	4.05 [4.15]	3.40 [3.55]	3.45	3.35
Angle for max GZ (degrees)	31.5	32.5 [31.5]	32 [33.5]	32 [31.75]	32	32
Range (hangars intact)	88	>90 [same]	82.5 [85]	59.5 [65]	58	53
Range (hangars free flooding)	56.5	59	55	50.5	50.25	49.25
Angle at which BR vents submerge (degrees P)	38.25 [37.5]	37	39.5 [42.75]	42.75	45.25	44.25

Note Data above were taken with 21 Swordfish and 12 Skuas aboard, and with a complement of 1322. Calculated data (in square parentheses) was based on an air complement of 30 Swordfish and 6 Skuas, and a complement of 1276.

Definitions
Deep Condition: ship fully equipped with all OF tanks 95 per cent full (240 gallons per ton), and with all RF tanks full.
Average Action Condition: ship fully equipped with wing OF tanks 95 per cent full and double bottom and remaining OF tanks 47.5 per cent full and with petrol tank compartments flooded with salt water and RF tanks full.
Half Oil Condition: ship fully equipped with all OF tanks 47 per cent full and with RF tanks full.
Std Condition: as Deep Condition less oil fuel, reserve lubricating oil, reserve feed water, petrol, FAA lubricating oil, paraffin, coal and coke, ⅓ bread, provisions and spirits (that is, provisions based reduced to 2 months wartime basis), fresh water in excess of 3 gallons per man per day for 8 days, and 2pdr sub-calibre guns and ammunition.
Light Condition: ship with machinery in working condition with naval stores consumed, but no oil fuel, water (including reserve feed), provisions, canteen or officers stores on board.
Extreme Light Condition: Light Condition, less all ammunition (including FAA) small arms, aircraft and petrol.

Implacable *external profile and plan.*

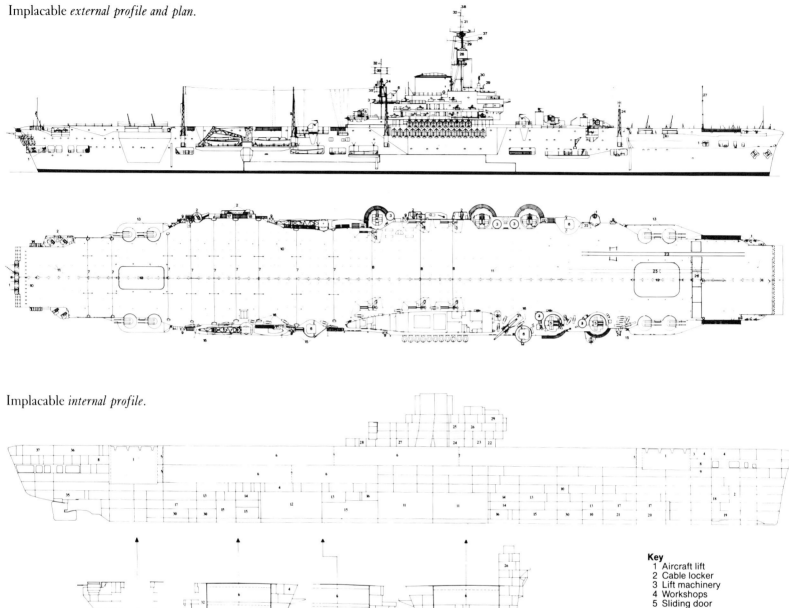

Implacable *internal profile.*

Key
1 Aircraft lift
2 Cable locker
3 Lift machinery
4 Workshops
5 Sliding door
6 Hangar
7 Fire curtain
8 Torpedo body room
9 Torpedo parting space
10 Catapult gear compartment
11 Boiler room
12 Engine room
13 Auxiliary machinery
14 Bomb room
15 Aviation fuel
16 Pom-pom magazine
17 4.5in magazine
18 Asdic office
19 Asdic compartment
20 Practice bomb store
21 Torpedo warhead room
22 Fighter ready room
23 Flight control room
24 Briefing room
25 Operations room
26 Aircraft direction room
27 TBR ready-room
28 Aircraft handling party
   ready-room
29 Compass platform
30 Oil fuel
31 Fan room
32 Bomb lifts
33 Bomb transfer lobby
34 Small-arms magazine
35 Steering gear
36 Main plane store
37 Spare parts store

aircraft, particularly high-performance fighters. The after lift, which matched earlier ones in floor size (45 × 22ft), served both hangars. The lifts were initially designed for 14,000lb loads, but were ultimately balanced to take 20,000lbs each.

In wartime the ship carried forty-five aircraft in her hangars, and could also accommodate twenty parked on deck.

Like the *Illustrious* class, *Indomitable* had one accelerator on her flight deck.

AN ADDITIONAL FLEET CARRIER was tentatively included in the 1940 Supplementary Programme, continuing the rate of one per year. Because it was to have been ordered in the spring of 1941, it had to be a minimally modified *Implacable*; there was no time (or manpower) to develop a wholly new ship. This design was, in effect, the end of the story begun in 1936, of armoured-hangar carriers built within treaty limits.

The principal desired changes were:

(a) flight deck protection against a 500lb SAP (semi

armour-piercing) bomb dropped by a dive-bomber from 3000ft instead of a 500lb bomb; improved deck protection over magazines

(b) increased air complement (fifty-four aircraft) of aircraft with narrower folded width (13ft 6in rather than 18ft), with corresponding increase in the number of flying personnel

(c) correspondingly increased petrol stowage

(d) revised bomb stowage

(e) forward lift enlarged to 45 × 33ft, to take non-folding aircraft

(f) flight deck 10ft wider

(g) clear height of hangars increased by at least 6in

All of this was to be accomplished with minimum changes to the basic *Implacable* design, and without reducing the GM (in standard condition) below 4.6ft.

This made it impossible to add flight deck armour (that is, topweight). DNC was able to stow fifty-two of the narrower

Type 277, the pencil-beam height-finder, displaced the high-angle director tower from the top of the island to the deck forward of the island. It replaced one of the six 8-barrel pom-poms, which is why the late-war armament of the Illustrious class includes only five such weapons. Ships so modified had their mainmasts braced by tripod legs, and a Type 293 (short-range air search for gunnery) radar mounted on it, together with the Type 281B. In addition, the British Type 72 aircraft homing beacon was replaced by a US-supplied YE, as shown here. The lattice mast just forward of the island carried a VHF radio direction-finding antenna. Two of the ships could be distinguished by the legs on their stub mainmasts: Formidable's were abaft the mast, while those of HMS Victorious were forward of the mast. Formidable also had diagonal cross-bracing. By 1945 only Illustrious lacked these modifications; she still had her Type 272 radar and her director tower was still atop the island (although one of her pom-poms had been removed; it had been replaced by Bofors guns). She did, however, have the YE homing beacon in place of the original Type 72. IIMS Victorious is shown, late in the war, with a Corsair on the outrigger forward of the island.

aircraft, stowing them four abreast, and accommodating the increased personnel by shortening the lower hangar from 208 to 150ft. The upper hangar would be 456ft long. Strength sufficed for the new 20,000lb aircraft, and the addition of 6in hangar depth was relatively easy to accomplish, as the beams could be cut back. The flight deck would be widened by extending it on the port side. At this stage the ship was expected to displace 23,200 tons.

At a Contoller's meeting on 10 February 1941, it was decided that the ship would follow the existing *Implacable* as closely as possible, except for five vital changes:

- the high-angle directors would be concentrated in the island structure
- port side extension of the flight deck
- enlargement of the forward lift to 45 × 33ft
- magazine crown armour increased from 3 to 4in
- increased hangar clear height; lower hangar reduced to 150ft length

DNC was then asked to investigate fitting a wider lift aft, which was adopted.

Revision of *Implacable* drawings began on 12 March 1941, and approval to place an order was sought. It was denied, and the design continued to evolve under the pressure of war experience. Greater diesel power, which would be available even if the boilers were put out of action, was to be provided by replacing one turbo generator with two diesels. The machinery and boiler spaces were to be more minutely subdivided. DNC decided to increase the beam to improve stability. The Naval Staff wanted both lifts to serve both hangars, and there was still intense interest in thicker flight deck armour.

By this time the design was less and less a repeat *Implacable*. In August 1941 the Controller verbally instructed DNC to examine these issues, the result being three proposals:

(a) *Implacable* with a thicker (4in) flight deck and increased (100ft; 5ft increase) beam, 25,300 tons, 31.5 knots

(b) a carrier with a thicker flight deck and complete (equal length) double hangars; beam increased to 104ft 6in, displacement to 27,000 tons, and speed 30.5 knots; overall depth increased from 71ft to 80ft

(c) a carrier with a 3in flight deck (as *Implacable*), but full double hangars; beam increased to 100ft, displacement 25,000 tons, speed 31.5 knots deep

Increased beam was to maintain the 4.85ft GM of the original *Implacable*.

These proposals were discussed at a Naval Staff meeting in September 1941, and carrier Staff Requirements revised accordingly. By this time it was obvious that flight deck protection designed to deal with 500lb bombs had been outclassed. A much thinner flight deck could serve effectively as a burster, a thick deck over the citadel protecting the vitals from any resulting splinters. DNC was asked to produce an alternative of this type; on 26,500 tons alternative (d) had a 1.5in flight deck and a 6in deck over her citadel. Beam would have been 100ft, and speed 30.5 knots deep.

On 27 September 1941 DTSD chose (b) as the basis for fresh Staff Requirements, and a new carrier design was begun on 9 October. Construction of the 1940 'repeat *Implacable*' was approved on 28 November 1941, but this became an entirely new design, the *Ark Royal* of the 1942 programme, which is treated in a later chapter.

It seems fairest to consider this 1940–41 effort as a reflection of both the strengths and the inherent weaknesses of the 23,000-ton designs. Their strength was that they could be adapted relatively easily to take much larger air groups consisting of much heavier aircraft. Their weakness was that, because they had been designed so tightly (to fit within treaty-ordained limits), they could not easily be modified to meet such wartime requirements as much-increased generating capacity or subdivision. Once major redesign was required, it was easier to begin afresh.

As for comparisons with foreign construction, the US *Essex* class comes to mind. It is only rarely appreciated that the *Essexes* were much larger ships. First and most important, although they were loosely based on treaty-limited ships, they were designed and built outside the treaty regime, and their original design tonnage was 27,500. Second, because they were not nearly so heavily armoured, they were much larger for their tonnage. To the extent that aircraft capacity is a function of volume or of flight deck area, that difference was decisive; an *Essex* could support about twice as many aircraft as an *Illustrious*. Postwar, the looser structural connection between the

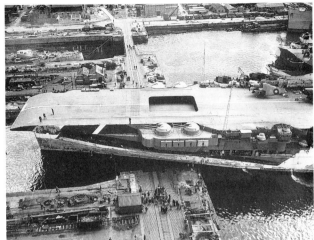

Left, far left, below left, below far left, bottom: Indomitable *as refitted at Norfolk, USA, 7 April 1944, with a US-type SM-1 pencil-beam height-finding (and low-level air search) radar atop her bridge, and a US-type YE beacon in place of her Type 72. The overall view from aft clearly shows her three barriers and her arrester gear, as well as the stern gallery for 20mm cannon. Note the new sponsons added for additional anti-aircraft weapons: one just abaft (and well below) the two after starboard side pompoms, for a quadruple Bofors, with another opposite on the port side (just visible in the right-hand corner of the photograph taken from abaft the island, and to port), and two more, just forward of the after 4.5in guns on either side of the flight deck, for new twin Bofors guns. All the aircraft on deck are Avengers.*

Essex hull and flight deck made modernization or reconstruction cheaper and simpler, with vast consequences for the future of US and British naval aviation.

In wartime, however, the US Navy found the armoured carriers fascinating. After having examined HMS *Formidable* in 1940, the US naval attaché commented that, were he crossing the Pacific, he would prefer her to a *Yorktown*, the closest US equivalent, on the basis that she might carry fewer aircraft, but she would be much more likely to get there.

THE FIRST FOUR armoured flight deck carriers led extremely active wartime lives, and HMS *Illustrious* suffered and survived – particularly severe damage. *Illustrious* is famous for having launched the Taranto strike in November 1940, crippling the Italian fleet. *Victorious*, newly commissioned, joined the *Bismarck* chase and one of her aircraft made a crucial hit. *Formidable* fought at Matapan. All operated in the Pacific in 1945, impressing US observers with their ability to shrug off Kamikaze hits.

Illustrious survived probably the worst bomb damage done to a carrier during World War II. Off Crete on 10 January 1941 she was hit by eight bombs: (i) a 500lb landed directly on S.2 pom-pom; (ii) a 1000lb bomb passed through the port forward end of her flight deck, bursting 10ft above water outside the ship; (iii) a 1000lb bomb passed through her after lift and exploded 10 to 20ft below the lift platform; (iv) a 1000lb bomb passed through the armoured flight deck on the centreline, bursting 10ft above the hangar deck, destroying the spray in the after hangar, scattering the fire curtains, and causing a severe fire in the after hangar; (v) a 500lb bomb hit the edge of the after lift, bursting high in the well, and increasing the damage due to hit (iii); (vi) a 1000lb bomb passed through P.1 pom-pom, hit the top of the armour belt, but did not explode (it caused a fire, possibly due to the pom-pom ammunition); (vii) a 1000lb bomb near-missed the starboard side aft; (viii) during a second attack, a 500lb bomb passed down the after lift well, completing the destruction of the lift structure.

Illustrious was taken into Malta harbour for emergency repairs; there, she was attacked again. On 16 January there were several near misses and then in a second attack that same day, a 1000lb bomb passed through the flight deck aft to explode 13ft below in the captain's day cabin. In a fifth attack, the ship suffered several near-misses, and in a sixth a 1000lb bomb (the tenth hit) near-missed her on the port side, smashing in enough of her plating to cause an immediate 5 degree list to port. Shock effects of the hit cracked the port turbine feet and caused other machinery damage.

The ship was temporarily repaired at Alexandria between 25 January and 10 March 1941, and then departed via Suez for permanent repairs in the United States. En route she docked at Durban so that her underwater damage could be examined. She arrived at Norfolk Navy Yard on 12 May 1941, leaving on 28 November. Norfolk was relatively close to Washington; HMS *Illustrious* made a considerable impression on the US Navy and probably was an important factor in the genesis of the *Midway* design.

Repairs included installation of a new lift. The long round-down aft, which severely limited usable deck space, was partially flattened out, adding 50ft to usable flight deck length. As designed, out of a total length of 745ft (the ship as completed was actually 743ft 6⅜in long), only 620 had been usable, the long round-downs, particularly aft, being provided to improve the aerodynamics of the deck.[18] The short usable flight deck length proved a distinct drawback, for example limiting the number of Swordfish the ship could fly off to attack Taranto. At this time, too, the ship's catapult was modified to permit

US-style tail-down launching, although British aircraft (and US aircraft built to British orders) still had to be launched by trolley. These changes were typical of the class. As part of the US refit, ten US-made 20mm Oerlikon cannon were installed.

The centreline propeller shaft was repaired, but it was never really satisfactory, and it later caused severe vibration when the ship ran at high speed. The gland packing of the centre shaft deteriorated so badly that the centre propeller was actually removed before the Okinawa (Sakishima Gunto) operation, reducing speed to 24 knots (with severe vibration above 19).[19] This damage, combined with the effects of underwater shock in 1945, ultimately put the ship out of action (see below).

Upon the ship's return to Britain (23 December 1941) her radar was modernized, Type 281 replacing her original Type 79 and Type 285 being fitted to one of her four 4.5in directors (all were ultimately fitted). This modification again was typical of the class.

Illustrious was refitted by Cammell Laird between 4 March and 8 June 1943. At this time she received VHF fighter control radio, a Type 272 surface search radar in a lantern-type radome on her forebridge, and pom-pom control radars (282, ranging only). The two aerials of Type 281 were replaced by a pair of air-search radars, to give complementary coverage, 79M and 281M. Twin Oerlikons (Mk V) replaced the existing single mounts, and an attempt was made to fit more single and twin mounts. In May 1943 she had sixteen twin and two single Oerlikons. Another two twin Oerlikons were added between then and April 1944. During the 1943 refit, too, depth charge stowage was doubled, to 144.[20]

Two more arrester wires, abaft the after lift, were added during the 1943 refit, increasing the effective landing length of the deck aft by 45ft. Ultimately all ships of the class had three wires added to their original six, and all but *Illustrious* had two more added forward.[21]

It was probably also at this time that the ship was fitted with outriggers (beams which could support the tail of an aircraft, while its main wheels remained on the flight deck) on the starboard side foward of the island, so that she could keep her new complement of ten non-folding Seafire IICs permanently on deck; they were too large to go down her lifts. These modifications also were typical of the class as a whole. Further modifications were made by Cammell Laird (24 October – 26 November 1943): usable flight deck length was extended once more, another pair of twin power-operated Oerlikons was added, and the catapult was strengthened to launch fully-loaded Barracudas.

Illustrious was refitted again, en route from the Eastern Fleet to the Pacific, at Durban (14 August – 10 October 1944). The

18 *Illustrious* had a particularly long round-down, and therefore gained 120ft of usable deck length through refits. The other ships gained proportionately less. The quoted lengths are subject to some uncertainty. The official publication, 'Particulars of H.M. Ships' (CB 1815), listed *Illustrious* and *Formidable* as 740ft long, *Victorious* being 745ft long. The figure given her was taken from the report of trials by HMS *Illustrious*, and presumably it is more accurate. Similar uncertainties apply to final lengths as rebuilt.

19 *Illustrious* was notorious for vibration postwar, and in 1945–46 the centre shaft was fitted with a five-bladed propeller in hopes of curing it. The problem was temporarily solved, but it returned in 1947, reportedly due to wear on the wing shafts.

20 In May 1943 the ideal close-range anti-aircraft battery was set at six 8-barrel pom-poms and fifty-four Oerlikons.

21 US observers of the early British arrester gear installations (about 1935) doubted that they were intended to permit deck parking, because they were so far forward. It seems more likely that the designers sought to place the wires at a position of minimum deck motion. In wartime, once deck parking had been accepted, the landing area had to be extended aft. The forward wires permitted landings over the bow (as in the US Navy), but were given up late in the war. *Indomitable* was completed with eight wires aft, three barriers, and two bow wires forward.

Implacable, *14 June 1944, with the after lower pom-pom removed.*

8-barrel pom-pom on the flight deck abaft the island was removed, but this loss of firepower was compensated by the addition of a pair of 40mm guns, and another two twin Oerlikons were added. A new US YE aircraft homing beacon was fitted at Durban, but it was not possible to fit two planned radars, 293 for target indication (short range air search) and 277 height finding and surface search, replacing 272). The boilers were retubed, and arrangements installed to fuel destroyers at sea.

In October 1945 *Illustrious* had six 8-barrel pom-poms, plus three single 40mm guns, nineteen twin 20mm, and fourteen single 20mm.

Illustrious suffered Kamikaze damage on 6 April 1945, a bomb-carrying Judy (D4Y3) skidding past her superstructure into the water. The only immediately apparent damage was a large hole in the 272 radome forward of her bridge. However, the Kamikaze's bomb exploded underwater near the ship, causing severe shock damage. The outer hull was opened up and some of the frames cracked; *Illustrious* was limited to 19 knots. She arrivd at Rosyth, for what was to have been a four-month refit, on 27 June 1945. Planned improvements would have included more accommodation (at the expense of the after 4.5in guns: as had been suspected in 1935, upper gallery deck gun positions cramped accommodation), and she would have been fitted as a flagship. The after Oerlikons would have been replaced by single 2pdr guns. However, with the end of the war and the need for a new generation of naval aircraft, it was decided on 19 September 1945 that she would be employed as a trials and training carrier, replacing the escort carrier *Pretoria Castle*. The long refit was completed in June 1946.[22] When the ship emerged, she had six 8-barrel pom-poms, but only eighteen single Oerlikons, all in her stern galleries, and seventeen single and two twin 40mm guns.

Illustrious ended the war as the only British fleet carrier without a low-altitude air-search radar; she had a Type 272 surface search set, but the others all had 277s. During her postwar refit, then, a US SM-1 radar replaced the 4.5in director atop the bridge, and a 293M target indicator was fitted, as well as VHF D/F. A prototype 960 air-search radar replaced the existing 281M. The after 4.5in guns were retained.

As part of the 1945–46 refit, the flight deck was again rebuilt, this time being extended forward about 5ft. Overall length was now 748ft 6in, and usable flight deck length 740ft. *Victorious* was also refitted, but probably not HMS *Formidable*. *Victorious* was listed in 1945 as 750ft 6in long. Effective flight deck lengths were listed postwar as 743ft 6in for *Formidable* and *Victorious*, and 747ft 6in for *Illustrious*, but the *Formidable* figure may represent planned rather than actual improvement.[23]

Illustrious remained operational, primarily for trials and training, until September 1954, being refitted in 1947 and again in 1950–51. In 1947 she carried five 8-barrel pom-poms, seventeen Bofors guns, and sixteen Oerlikons. Her catapult was again modified. In her final configuration, all the pom-poms were removed, the ship being armed with two twin 40mm Bofors, the nineteen single 40mm, and six Oerlikons aft, plus the sixteen 4.5in guns. Postwar service included an emergency troop-carrying run to Cyprus in 1951, during the Canal Zone crisis that November, and from time to time the ship participated in full-scale exercises such as 'Mainbrace,' in September 1952.[24]

Formidable was hit fore and aft by two 1000lb bombs on 26 May 1941 during the Crete operations, and severely damaged underwater. Like her sister ship, she received emergency repairs at Alexandria and then was refitted at Norfolk, from 26 August – 29 November 1941. It was later said that she had suffered permanent hull distortion due to the shock effects of these hits. A spall from one of the flight deck hits travelled down and penetrated her centreline machinery space. *Formidable* emerged from her Norfolk refit with ten Oerlikons added to her anti-aircraft battery.

She was refitted at Rosyth from 21 September to 13 October 1942 and then at Belfast from 29 November 1943 to 31 March 1944. She emerged from this latter refit with one fewer 8-barrel pom-poms, but also with one 4-barrel pom-pom, twenty twin 20mm, and fourteen single 20mm guns. This was the ship's last recorded refit. At the end of the war she had all six 8-barrel pom-poms, plus five single power-operated 40mm guns, seven single 'Boffins' (40mm), eleven twin and twelve single 20mm.

Formidable was hit by Kamikazes on 4 and 9 May 1945, but was not put out of action. In one case it took her five hours to repair damage to the point where she could operate aircraft; the other put her temporarily out of action. However, on 18 May she suffered an accident; a Corsair landed-on while the after lift was in the down position. Bouncing over the wires, it fell down into the hangar, and its cannon began to fire. The hangar was burned out.

The ship was considered unfit for further combat service, but

22 By this time light displacement had increased from the design figure of 22,840 tons (22,440 as built) to 25,940 tons, and deep load from 28,620 (28,210 as built) to 31,630; draft increased (freeboard decreased) 1.8ft, and GM was reduced by 16 per cent. It was estimated at the time that aircraft and their associated equipment accounted for 350 tons of this 2520 ton increase; structure for 990 tons, splinter protection 85 tons, armament 50 tons, and petrol and flooding water (for extra tankage) 300 tons. Figures and data on refits from D J Lyon, 'HMS *Illustrious*' (Warship Profile No 10, 1971), and from J D Brown, 'HMS *Illustrious*' (Warship Profile No 11, 1971). Most but not all of the data originally came from the Ship Covers.

23 The 748ft 6in and 740ft figures are taken from the Profile, and is almost certainly based on official data. The postwar effective flight deck lengths are taken from the 1947 official handbook on British aircraft carriers.

24 In this operation she carried a mixed British-Dutch air group, comprising 824 Squadron and No 4 Squadron Royal Netherlands Navy (with a total of twenty Fireflies), and 860 Squadron Royal Netherlands Navy, with eight Sea Furies.

Above, left and below left: *The two* Implacables *were the ultimate development of the* Illustrious *design. As completed, they included several of the modifications applied to earlier ships: Type 277 on the bridge top (with the high-angle director located on deck forward of the bridge). HMS* Indefatigable *is shown in February 1944 and in 1945 (overhead view). Neither ship ended the war with her full complement of six 8-barrel pom-poms, the after lower mount on the starboard side being removed. In* Implacable *it was replaced by a 4-barrel pom-pom sponsored out below flight deck level. A second such weapon was mounted to port, and a third, sponsored out on the starboard side below the foremost 8-barrel pom-pom, was added before the end of the war.* Indefatigable *only had the port side 4-barrel pom-pom. These ships were the last two British fleet carriers to retain the Type 72 aircraft homing beacon.*

she ferried liberated Allied POWs from Japan to Australia, and then made two round trips carrying British servicemen home from Australia. *Formidable* returned home in November 1946 and went into reserve in March 1947. Of the three ships, she was clearly in the worst condition, partly because she had not been refitted since early 1944. By 1946, her boiler superheaters all needed retubing (a six-month job), and by 1948 she was good for only 21 knots, and then only with great care.

She was therefore the first of the type to be discarded post-war. Because she was so clearly unfit for further service unless drastically rebuilt, she was an early candidate first for modernization (see Chapter 15) and then for alternative uses.[25] She was laid up unmaintained in 1948, and discarded in 1953, partly because the cost of refitting as a usable carrier (including replacement of electric wiring) was considered excessive.

By October 1941 *Victorious* had eight Oerlikons in addition to her designed light anti-aircraft battery. She was bombed in the Mediterranean during the Pedestal convoy, 12 August 1942, but the bomb broke up on her flight deck armour and bounced over the side. She was refitted at Norfolk from 1 to 30 January 1943, when seventeen single Oerlikons were added and operated during the following year with the US Pacific Fleet. Eighteen single 20mm guns were added at Pearl Harbor

25 For a proposed missile cruiser conversion, see my *Postwar Naval Revolution* (Conway Maritime Press, London 1987).

Above: *HMS* Illustrious *was rebuilt postwar as a training and trials carrier, with the extended bow evident in this 1946 photograph. Her obsolete Type 79B radar was removed, and a new Type 960 replaced the Type 281B on her stub mainmast. Also visible here are some of the 40mm guns which replaced her pom-poms.*

Left: *A Seafire F.47, in fact the first of the type with power-folding wings, takes off from HMS* Illustrious, *probably during deck trials in May 1948.*

Below: Implacable *in 1948, with Barracudas on deck. They were then the standard British carrier-based ASW aircraft.* CPL

Victorious *displays most of the standard late wartime electronic modifications in this July 1949 photograph: Type 277 atop her bridge, with a Type 283 barrage director before and below it. The heavy tripod foremast, originally built to take the homing beacon, carries a Type 79B air warning radar, with its 'hayrake' IFF interrogator below the platform, plus VHF radio antennas (the short dipoles, Type 87) and an IFF transponder (the twin cones). The mainmast carries the shorter-wave Type 281B air-search radar and a Type 293 (the 'cheese'), each with its own IFF interrogator. Single Bofors guns mounted forward of the bridge helped make up for the loss of the 8-barrel pom-pom replaced by the high-angle director visible forward of the bridge. The square coils on the bridge face were for medium-frequency radio direction-finding (MF/DF). CPL*

from 9 March to 8 April 1943, for a total of forty-five. Before she left the Pacific, two quadruple and two twin Bofors were installed. One 8-barrel pom-pom was later removed, and by April 1944 the Oerlikon battery had been changed to twenty-three twin and fifteen single guns (she was refitted at Liverpool from 4 January to 3 February 1944 and from 17 February to 4 March 1944). At the end of the war the two twin 40mm had been replaced by two single power mounts and seven 'Boffins' and the Oerlikon battery had been reduced to sixteen twin and thirteen single mounts.

Victorious took two Kamikaze hits (which holed her flight deck) on 9 May, but she remained operational. She later had to spend a month being repaired. She was officially placed in reserve in 1947, but served in the Home Fleet Training Squadron 1947–50. She was rebuilt at Portsmouth in 1950–58 (see Chapter 15).

Indomitable was completed with six 8-barrel pom-poms and eight Oerlikons. On 12 August 1942 she was bombed during the Pedestal convoy operation (when HMS *Eagle* was sunk). Seven dive-bombers, each carrying a 500kg (1100lb) SAP bomb approached from astern, releasing their weapons from 1500ft in 70-degree dives. There were two hits and three near misses. The first hit struck the flight deck to starboard of the forward edge of the forward lift, where there was no armour. It

Table 7–8: Inclining Experiment Data, HMS *Indefatigable*, January 1944

Condition	Deep	Light
GM	6.91 [7.65]	4.06
GZ (hangar intact)	4.82 [5.43]	3.27
Angle (degrees)	57.5 [45.5]	34.5
Range	>90	77
GZ (hangar free flooding)	3.52	3.08
Angle (degrees)	32.5	32.5
Displacement (tons)	32,101 [28.968]	26,125

Note Numbers in square brackets refer to 1939 design.

left a 14in hole in the 60lb flight deck plating, penetrated the 10lb upper gallery deck, and burst just above the upper hangar deck (having travelled 16ft). The resulting fire, including a petrol fire, was controlled within 40 minutes. The second hit was on the centreline abaft the after lift, again outside the armoured portion of the deck. It penetrated the 14lb flight deck plating and the 10lb upper gallery deck, bursting just above the upper hangar deck in a torpedo body room. The resulting fire fortunately did not ignite the torpedo warheads in their protective mantlets.

The first hit blew out the side of the ship between the lower gallery deck and the gallery deck, making a 20 × 12ft hole in the upper gallery deck and a 20 × 28ft hole in the upper hangar deck. The radius of splinter damage was about 30ft. The forward lift was canted up 5ft on its starboard side, and this had to be reduced to a 2ft 6in arch on the centreline so that the ship could resume flying off her aircraft. The second hit blew a large hole in the flight deck, the edges of which had to be burned away to remove an obstacle to landing-on; this left a 56 × 40ft hole between the longitudinal bulkheads. The upper gallery deck hole was 12 × 20ft, the upper hangar deck hole 18 × 16ft.

Of the near misses, the first carved a groove in the lower edge of the bulkhead around a portside pom-pom director. The explosion destroyed plating over an area of about 16 × 12ft. A second struck the sea 25ft from the port side about amidships, and blew in the ship's side over a length of about 48ft and a width of about 30ft, flooding wing compartments over a length of 104ft (760 tons of water were taken aboard and the ship listed 8 degrees). The third bomb exploded in the sea off the port quarter and had little effect, although its shock did unship the two rudder woodlocks.

Immediately after the attack, the ship reduced speed and turned to reduce the wind on the two fires. Remarkably, despite damage to the lifts, the after lift was still able to work at half speed immediately after the attack. This was attributed to the design requirement (which had been expensive to fulfill) that the lift work even if its transmission gear was substantially misaligned.

The ship was repaired at Liverpool from 30 August 1942 to 11 February 1943. She emerged with eight twin and two single Oerlikons.

Indomitable was torpedoed during a German night torpedo attack at Salerno on 11 July 1943. The torpedo hit her port side amidships as she turned hard to port to evade, the heel bringing her side well down. Thus it struck the lower edge of her belt armour, about 4ft 6in below her main deck level. One plate disintegrated, fragments passing through the intervening longitudinal bulkhead and piercing the 60lb boiler room protective bulkhead. The torpedo made a 28 × 25ft hole in her outer plat-

Above and right: Indefatigable *as a training ship, 1950 (aerial view) and November 1951. Most of her light weapons had been landed. The Type 72 was landed, but no YE beacon was installed, since the ship was not expected to operate aircraft (note the deckhouse right aft on the flight deck).* CPL (above)

ing, and the fragments a 6 × 8ft hole in the 60lb bulkhead.

Probably largely because the ship was already heeling when she was hit, she soon took a 12½ degree list. The lessons of the *Ark Royal* were heeded: officers counter-flooded immediately, without waiting for further orders. The port boiler room flooded and was put out of action, but the centre boiler room (which had been shut down when it was filled with steam from the port room) was soon restarted. Within three-quarters of an hour, the carrier was steaming at 14 knots, and the next day, en route to Malta for repairs, she operated aircraft.

Temporarily repaired at Malta, HMS *Indomitable* was sent to Norfolk for repairs from 31 August 1943 to 15 April 1944. Upon her return to the United Kingdom approved alterations and additions were carried out at Rosyth from 3 May to 16 May 1944. Her light armament now included two quadruple and two twin 40mm guns, plus twenty twin and sixteen single 20mm guns. En route to the Pacific Fleet, she was docked at Bombay from 3 November to 16 November 1944.

Indomitable was hit by a Kamikaze on 4 May 1945 which broke up on her flight deck and went over the side without affecting her fighting efficiency. At the end of the war she retained the US-type Bofors guns, adding twelve single power mounts and one Boffin, her Oerlikon battery having been reduced to twelve twin and twelve single guns.

Like her half-sister ships, *Indomitable* had her usable flight deck extended in wartime. She gained 65ft aft, and was lengthened at the end of the war, from 745ft to 753ft 11in. At that time her effective flight deck length was 745ft 6in.

Postwar, *Indomitable* was used for trooping, then refitted 1948–50 for further service, joining the Home Fleet in 1950. She was Home Fleet flagship in 1951, and flagship of the Heavy Squadron in 1952–53, operating in the Mediterranean

in 1953. On 3 February 1953 she suffered a petrol explosion just outside her hangar near the damage control position on the starboard side abaft her island. It wrecked ventilation trunks to her machinery control room and starboard evaporator room, and blew out part of her side. She was repaired with concrete to participate in the 1953 Coronation Review, but was never rebuilt, going into reserve on 5 October 1953.

Indefatigable was hit by a Kamikaze at the base of her island on 1 April 1945. She was back in action within half an hour, but later repairs to her island took almost a month (2 April to 1 May 1945). At the end of the war *Indefatigable* was flagship of the British Pacific Fleet carriers. She ferried liberated prisoners of war back from Japan to Australia, then made a trooping voyage between Australia and Britain. Upon her return in December 1945 she was reduced to reserve (trooping arrangements were removed 24 December 1946 to 11 January 1947) and then reduced to reserve at Portsmouth (1947–49). She was then refitted at Devonport as a training ship (without aircraft). From 1950–54 she served in the Home Fleet Training Squadron (as Flagship in 1951), going into reserve in 1954.

Of the six armoured carriers, only *Implacable* avoided all battle damage, because she arrived in the Pacific after the end of

HMS Indomitable *as modernized postwar, shown in March 1951. Note that the 4.5in director has finally been moved from the top of the bridge structure to the flight deck, replacing a multiple pom-pom. Note, too, that the island structure has been extended forward. The aircraft forward are Sea Hornets and Firebrands.*

Below: Implacable *on 12 May 1952, when her Type 72 had finally been replaced by a YE. By this time she was a training ship, and her light weapons were cocooned. The weapon in the sponson immediately below the foremost 8-barrel pom-pom is a single Bofors gun.*

Left: *Unmodified after 1945, HMS* Formidable *was the first of the armoured carriers to be broken up. She is shown in 1952, stripped for disposal. Note the waveguide for the Type 293 microwave radar which had been mounted on her stub mainmast. The stub carrying her YE beacon is not clearly visible, because at this angle it is hidden by her foremast. Note the lattice mast (forward of the island) built to carry her VHF DF, and the tilting radio masts. There were several abortive proposals to rebuild the ship, initially as a jet carrier, and then as a missile cruiser.* CPL

the Okinawa campaign. She had been delayed by serious weather damage (sustained in operations off the Norwegian coast in December 1944) and was repaired at Rosyth between 15 December 1944 and 10 March 1945. The Kamikaze attacks were beginning, and DGD ordered two 4-barrel pom-poms mounted. He proposed that they be fore and aft of the island, but instead one was to port, on a sponson amidships. A third was later added. *Implacable* was the only one of the six big fleet carriers to have her light armament augmented in Britain against Kamikaze attack; all the others were already in forward areas. Available weapons were the 4-barrel pom-pom, a single (ex Coastal Forces) pom-pom and the single 40mm, the last two

replacing twin Oerlikons on a mount-for-mount basis.

Implacable served as Home Fleet deck-landing training ship in 1946, and participated in a Mediterranean exercise in 1947. She was Home Fleet flagship 1949–50 (refitted from 6 September to 15 November 1948), and was used for Jet Fighter Evaluation Unit trials. In 1951 she was reduced to a non-flying training role, serving as Flagship of the Home Fleet Training Squadron in 1952. At this time plans called for her reconstruction (see Chapter 16). In 1953 she transported troops to the Caribbean, and in 1954, after the reconstruction programme had been abandoned, she reduced to reserve and was paid off for scrapping the following year.

Both ships were initially armed with six 8-barrel pom-poms and thirty-seven Oerlikons. By the end of the war, one of the pom-poms had been removed. *Implacable* had three 4-barrel pom-poms, four single Bofors, seventeen twin and seventeen single Oerlikons. Her sister ship *Indefatigable* had only one 4-barrel pom-pom, but five single 40mm and five Boffins, plus fourteen twin and twelve single Oerlikons. These batteries were somewhat reduced postwar; in April 1946 *Implacable* had eight single Bofors and four Boffins, plus eight twin and fourteen single Oerlikons. Her sister ship had six single Bofors and five Boffins, plus six twin and seven single Oerlikons.

In 1945 these were the only British fleet carriers still equipped with the Type 72 beacon; all the others had the US-supplied YE instead.

Above and below: *Postwar,* Indomitable *was modernized, her bow rebuilt (as in* Illustrious*) and her island modified, with two Type 277Q pencil-beam radars and her high angle director moved down onto the flight deck to displace one of the two pom-poms before her bridge. Note also the new twin Bofors on the hangar deck level abaft the bridge. The detail view is dated 26 January 1953, the overall view 19 March 1952; both were taken at Malta. CPL (below)*

Table 7-9: British Fleet Aircraft Carriers of World War II: Final Design Characteristics

	Ark Royal	Illustrious	Indomitable	Implacable
LOA (ft)	800	740	753 11	766 2
LWL (ft)	725	710	710	730
LBP (ft)	685	673	673	690
BWL (ft)	94 9 1/8			
BEXT (ft)	112	106 9	116 3	141 5
Depth (ft)	83 6	67 9	73 9	70 11 1/2
Flight deck dimensions (ft)	797 × 96	740 × 95 9	751 × 95 9	760 × 102
Hangar dimensions (ft)	568 × 60	456 × 62	416 × 62 × 14	456 × 62 × 14
	452 × 60	—	208 × 62 × 16	208 × 62 × 14
Lift dimensions (ft)	46 × 25	45 × 22	45 × 33	45 × 33
	45 × 22	45 × 22	45 × 22	45 × 22
	45 × 22			
Catapults	2	1	1	1
Displacement (tons) std	22,000	23,207	23,080[3]	23,460
Deep displacement (tons)	27,700	28,619	28,216	28,968
Deep draught, mean (ft)	27 4	28 2	27 9	26 7
SHP	102,000	111,000	111,000	148,000
Speed, deep (knots)	31	30	30	32
Trial shp				149,000
Trial speed (knots)				31.89
Trial displacement (tons)				31,240
Endurance at 12 knots (nm)	4300	14,000[1]	13,000[1]	11,300[4]
Oil fuel (tons)	4443	4854	4517	4693
Petrol (gallons)	100,000	50,660	70,000	96,230
Complement	151/1630	121/1155	142/1450[3]	1390[3]
Stresses				
fwd, hogging	7.6	4.7	5.07	5.38
keel, hogging	4.0	4.5	4.06	5.2
at (tons)	24,710			24,359
fwd, sagging	5.6	2.8	2.95	3.34
keel, sagging	3.8	4.1	3.96	5.0
at (tons)	24,260			26,676
Weights (tons)				
Hull	13,651	12,724	12,969	13,235
Protection	2854	4941	4299	3645
Machinery	2468	2464	2471	3128
Armament	1042	997	997	1074
Aircraft equipment	1629	1186	1448	1503
General equipment	1382	2266	1328	1428
RFW	252	187	187	262
Oil fuel	4443	4854	4517	4693
Deep load	27,721	28,619	28,216	28,968

1 Endurance at 10 knots.
2 As inclined initially, light displacement was 23,526 tons and deep displacement was 29,084 tons, the latter about 860 tons over the design figure. This was due largely to improved equipment, modified structure, and permanent ballast.
3 As completed in 1941, compared to a design feature (1938) of 136/1256 (including 94/433 FAA). In 1946 war complement was 215/1731.
4 At 14 knots.
5 As designed; by 1945 complement was 180/1745.

8

The Interwar Fleet Air Arm

1 The weight penalty was much more important than the additional drag, as drag cost relatively little speed at a given power. Fighters were withdrawn from cruisers and capital ships in the late 1930s precisely because, in combat, they probably could be used only once and then ditched (some might land on the fleet's carriers). This in turn made it impossible for the pilots to maintain their proficiency, and because each ship carried very few there was no opportunity for training in tactically meaningful units. Note, however, that the one-shot catapult fighter was revived in World War II for trade protection (see Chapter 9).

THE DEVELOPMENT OF the Fleet Air Arm between 1918 and 1939 was prey to several conflicting considerations. First, the fleet required large numbers of aircraft to perform several quite different missions. Existing carriers generally could not support the required numbers, so that there was substantial pressure to combine somewhat conflicting roles in a single aircraft. Similarly, naval planners had to place a substantial number of fleet combat aircraft, such as fighters and reconnaissance types, aboard capital ships and cruisers, to be catapulted off in battle. This requirement that they be suitable for catapulting in turn limited their acceptable maximum weight and, by extension, their performance.

Virtually all interwar naval aircraft were designed with alternative float and wheel undercarriages. This was largely so that their pilots could practise in peacetime, flying from whatever waters in which their ships might be anchored. Provision for floats exacted a weight penalty, particularly if the aircraft had to be able to manoeuvre or bomb while on floats. This was quite apart from the drag penalty of the floats themselves; it was assumed that in wartime most aircraft would fly, even from catapults, in wheeled form.[1]

The squeeze on carrier space intensified as aircraft technology developed, since more modern aircraft tended to be larger (so that carriers could not accommodate as many) and to demand more fuel (which could not easily be provided within the limited protected volume of existing ships). Treaty restrictions, both on total carrier tonnage and on the tonnage of individual ships, aggravated matters further, as the preceding chapters show.

Finally, the experience of the Abyssinian crisis showed that the fleet required mobile support, even in a European war. Efforts in that direction, particularly the construction of HMS *Unicorn* (see below), can be seen as forerunners of the much

larger effort required when the fleet went to the Pacific in 1944–45.

THE BASIC AIRCRAFT ROLES were reconnaissance (R), to find and shadow the enemy's fleet and, later, to provide early warning of the approach of his aircraft; ASW reconnaissance; torpedo attack (T), either to force the enemy fleet to action or to prevent its escape; level (and later dive-) bombing (B); spotting (S), to make surface gunfire fully effective; and fighting (F), to deny the air over the battlefleet to enemy spotters, to protect the fleet's spotters, and to help the striking force penetrate enemy air defences. The Fleet Air Arm tried to amalgamate several functions: S/R, F/R, and, in the famous Swordfish, TSR (actually four functions: torpedo attack, level bombing, spotting, and reconnaissance).

Reconnaissance was the first essential. An Admiralty paper written in 1924 gives some idea of what was required.[2] It divided reconnaissance into screen and contact roles. Screen reconnaissance would be based on sector patrols by amphibians equipped with good long- (over the horizon air to ship) and short- (air to air and spotting) wave radio. On sighting the enemy fleet, the amphibian would make her first report and return to the carrier as soon as she was relieved. Similar sector scouts would intercept her report and support her until relieved, then return to the carrier. Unsuited to contested reconnaissance, they could now be used as spotters, protected by fleet fighters.

Then the carrier aircraft would try to keep in contact with the enemy (contact reconnaissance), the staff paper laying down five to nine separate reconnaissance stations which had to be maintained.[3] Because the contact reconnaissance aircraft would probably have to operate outside the zone protected by fleet fighters, they might have to fight for their information. This was the origin of the Admiralty requirement for a

2 Filed in AIR 5/300, on fleet reconnaissance aircraft.

3 Five stations were required during the approach: observation of the enemy battlefleet, extended lookout on the enemy left and right flanks, observation of enemy battlecruisers, and observation of enemy carriers. Nine stations were required during battle itself: observation of enemy battle fleet*, extended look-out ahead of the enemy**, extended look-out ahead of own forces**, observation of enemy battlecruisers*, extended look-out on the unengaged bow of the enemy**, observation of enemy destroyers* (which might be preparing a torpedo attack behind a smoke screen), extended look-out on the disengaged bow of the fleet**, observation of enemy aircraft carriers*, and support of observation of the enemy fleet.* Here a single asterisk denotes an action observation aircraft, a double asterisk an action look-out. Action observation aircraft reported general alterations of enemy course or formation; destroyer flotillas moving out to attack, firing torpedoes or releasing gas or smoke; movements of enemy carriers, aircraft, torpedo-bombers, and motor torpedo boats; and torpedo firing by any other enemy units. Action look-outs reported submarines ahead of the fleet or steering to attack; mines or minelayers operating ahead of the fleet or the carriers; motor torpedo boats or remote controlled motor boats (a German weapon in 1917–18 off the Flanders coast) away from the enemy fleet; and the approach of reinforcements. There was a serious problem of radio congestion (too few channels, too many users).

HMS Courageous *displays the prototype Type 72 aircraft homing beacon atop her new tripod mast in this 5 March 1937 photograph. The beacon did not obviate the requirement for a navigator, but it did increase the aircrew's margin of error in returning to their carrier, and so (in theory) it could markedly reduce losses in sustained long-range reconnaissance. The greater the allowable margin of error, the longer the effective range to which carrier aircraft could expect to fly. The Royal Navy, like its American and Japanese contemporaries, believed that the air attacker would enjoy such enormous advantages that longer search and strike range could easily be decisive. Ironically, an electronic relative of Type 72, air-search radar, greatly reduced that advantage and so reduced the value of the extreme search and strike range Type 72 was intended to provide. The antenna was enclosed in a radome in the hope that foreign observers would not be able to estimate its wavelength (and therefore its frequency). As long as that information remained secure, Type 72 emissions would probably not be intercepted and the set could be used even under conditions of nominal radio silence. Similarly, the antennas of early wartime centimetric radars, such as Types 271 and 272, were enclosed in radomes not for weather protection but to conceal their frequencies.* CPL

fighter/reconnaissance aircraft (F/R), a fast two-seater with long-wave radio only (to communicate back to the fleet), with two guns, and with an endurance of about 2½ hours at full speed.

There was also 'spasmodic' reconnaissance, reacting to some external information, by one aircraft (relieved as necessary). For example, a scout could be sent out 200 miles on a line of bearing determined by fleet D/F.

Current Atlantic Fleet tactical orders envisaged continuous reconnaissance by one to four aircraft in daylight, and it was believed that with three large carriers the fleet could soon easily maintain six reconnaissance aircraft in the air for five days in succession.

Spotting was extremely important. The British concluded quite early, and maintained throughout the interwar period, that their carrier torpedo-bombers could not, themselves, sink

large capital ships.[4] They considered that only powerful ship-delivered weapons, primarily heavy shellfire, could sink enemy capital ships. Spotting was expected to make such fire effective at long range and in poor weather. On the other hand, only torpedo-bombers could attack an enemy fleet in a defended harbour.[5]

From about 1933 on, the Admiralty showed increasing interest in dive-bombing, as the best means of accurate delivery against small and highly manoeuvrable ships.[6] Dive-bombing was also particularly attractive as a means of neutralizing enemy aircraft carriers, which some in the Fleet Air Arm considered their primary targets. British observers seem to have been impressed by US demonstrations. The Fleet Air Arm distinguished between three forms of dive-bombing: shallow (glide bombing, in later parlance), relatively steep, and terminal velocity (T/V) or nearly vertical. This interest resulted in the only fundamentally new classes of aircraft ordered in quantity between about 1930 and the outbreak of war in September 1939, the fighter (FDB) and torpedo dive-bombers (Skua, Albacore, and Barracuda). Otherwise, aircraft were ordered either to amalgamate existing roles or as direct replacements for earlier types.

The British fleet had to be defended while at an unprepared anchorage. It would rely largely on floatplanes carried aboard

4   The aerial torpedo warhead was 440lbs of TNT, compared with 750 or even 1000 for a ship- or submarine-launched torpedo. In 1940–41 British aerial torpedoes failed to sink the French battleships *Dunkerque* and *Strasbourg* and the German *Bismarck*, in each case inflicting severe (and tactically crippling) but not fatal damage. On the other hand, they did sink three Italian battleships at Taranto in November 1940.

5   A special Committee on Harbour Attack was formed in 1928. About this time a special radio-controlled super-torpedo was developed specifically to penetrate enemy harbours and to attack ships inside,

controlled by a torpedo-bomber. In 1936 the Mediterranean Fleet Air Orders included specific instructions for setting torpedoes to attack in shallow water (for example, in Taranto harbour).

6   By 1931 it was already accepted that high-level bombing was unlikely to be effective, as it required a rigid formation approach at high altitude (but within anti-aircraft range), making the bombers relatively easy fighter targets. In November 1933 RAA suggested that the Fleet Air Arm adopt dive-bombing to the exclusion of high-level bombing, even though the RAF had just developed a new automatic bomb sight.

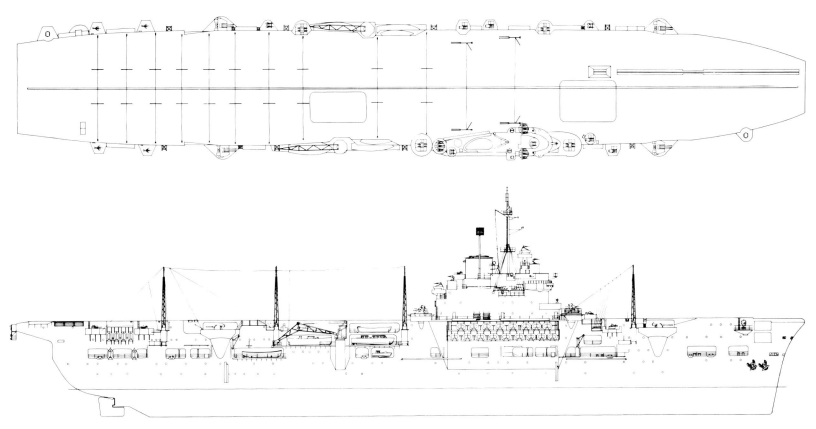

battleships and cruisers, although carrier aircraft on floats were expected to help. Through the mid-1930s, too, there was some feeling in the fleet that dispersing aircraft to the battleships and cruisers could help reduce the impact of losing any one of the very few available carriers.[7]

These requirements were equated to numbers of aircraft. In June 1927, for example, a specially constituted staff committee estimated that the fleet required 110 fighters, seventy-four, seventy-five, and seventy-eight T/B, and the resulting total of 337 was formally approved by the Board. This represented the total capacity of the existing carriers plus a new fifty-plane carrier (238) plus ninety-nine aircraft aboard cruisers and capital ships. At this time the estimate for scouting was sixty S/R, with another fifteen for such subsidiary operations as anti-submarine patrol, and the total of 184 fighters and F/R was based on air defence and escort requirements. The number of T/B was determined by remaining fleet aircraft capacity, rather than by any tactical doctrine. However, on the basis that it would take twenty-four to inflict serious damage on a capital ship, reductions below seventy-two could not be accepted.

In about 1929, calculation showed that 100 S/R were required to search out to 180nm. Once action was joined, the same aircraft could conduct action observation. Spotting would be conducted by battleship aircraft, but the carriers would accommodate six reliefs. Finally, the distant anti-submarine screen would consist of six aircraft, and the carriers would have to provide six reliefs for continuous operation. This made 118 S/R in the fleet.

Analysis showed that the minimum effective T/B strike would be three flights of six aircraft each (eighteen), and it was assumed that at least eight attacks (144 aircraft) would have to be mounted. All 144 T/B would have to be accommodated aboard carriers. Six flights of fighters would be required either to escort the fleet's striking force or to deal with the enemy's; four more flights would be required to patrol over the battle-fleet, and another four over the carriers. This amounted to fourteen flights, or eighty-four aircraft. More fighters might be

HMS Unicorn. *She originally had a Type 72DM aircraft homing beacon on her foremast, but it was later replaced by a US-supplied YE on a stub mast stepped on her funnel, as shown here. The unusual overhang aft was incorporated into the design to handle a special aircraft lighter.* ALR

needed to gain air superiority during the approach and the battle, but they might be accommodated aboard cruisers and capital ships.

That made the total of carrier-borne aircraft 346, for the main fleet alone. If it was assumed that 20 per cent of the carriers would always be absent, then the total for all carriers rose to 433, which far exceeded existing accommodation, 188 aircraft (fifty-two aircraft in each of *Courageous* and *Glorious*, thirty-six in *Furious*, for a total of 140 in modern ships, plus eighteen in *Eagle* and fifteen each in *Hermes* and *Argus*). At this time the Fleet Air Arm operated 142 aircraft at sea, and hoped to have 225 in first-line deployed service by December 1936. The problem was that, if the size limit was about sixty aircraft per carrier, even five large ships (to treaty limit) would accommodate only 300 aircraft.

In 1931, an Admiralty analysis showed that the Fleet would require 405 tactical aircraft, 62 per cent above the existing total capacity of 250 aboard six carriers (three of very limited capacity). Catapult aircraft aboard battleships and cruisers had to make up the difference.[8]

The Royal Navy had two choices. It could continue to build

7   In January 1934 the First Sea Lord observed that only three carriers would be available to accompany the main fleet to the Far East. A Mediterranean fleet exercise, QK of 1932, showed that the loss of a single carrier would be disastrous. Against this, it was argued that aircraft catapulted from the battleships and cruisers might not be recoverable. The other argument for placing large numbers of aircraft aboard capital ships and cruisers was that they might have to operate independently, as in the case of the battlecruisers. This concept was important for *carrier* aircraft design because it was largely responsible for the float requirement imposed on those aircraft. By August 1931 fleet cruiser policy was to carry wheeled F/R in wartime; ships protecting trade routes would carry a new light reconnaissance type floatplane (L/R, the Fairey Seafox). Proposed capital ship policy was to provide one S/R (on the quarter-deck) and one fighter (on the turret), on the theory that each ship should carry her own spotter. However, the C-in-Cs feared that the complications of carrying a three-seater on a quarter-deck catapult made the scheme impractical. The solution was a heavy turret catapult.

8   The Royal Navy could not buy many more carriers because of the treaty, and it could not cram many more aircraft into its existing carriers because of its operating practices. In 1928 the Naval Staff argued, moreover, that on a cash basis it was much less expensive to add catapults than to build new carriers, since the cost of the catapult-carrying ships had already been borne. At that time it estimated that a hundred catapult aircraft could be added for cost of thirty-three aircraft aboard a new carrier. The tactical fallacy was that these one-shot (probably unrecoverable) aircraft were much less valuable tactically, since they could not support sustained action. Furthermore, they could not really practice in peacetime, and so probably would not have been effective in wartime.

Table 8-1: Aircraft Attributes, 1924

	Reconnaissance		Spotter	Torpedo
	I	*II*		
Amphibious	no	yes	desirable	no
Armament	none or 1 gun	good defensive	good defensive	torpedo, 2 guns
W/T	long range	long range	short wave	R/T[2]
Endurance (hours)	3½	5–6	4[1]	2½–3
Range (nm)	500	500	350	min 300
Seats	2	3 or 4	4	2
Speed (knots)	about 150	85–90	80–90	min 85

1 Based on effective spotting endurance of personnel
2 Either one of the torpedo-planes should have long-range R/T, or the flight should be accompanied by an aircraft (preferably reconnaissance) with a long-distance set.

Table 8-2: Carrier Aircraft, 1936

	I		*II*			*III*		
	GP	FF	TSR	DBR	FF	TSR	FDB	
Ark Royal	60	12	24	36	12	48	24	
Courageous	42	6	18	24	6	36	12	
Furious	30	6	12	18	6	24	12	
Eagle	18	—	9	6	—	12	—	
Hermes	12	—	6	6	—	12	—	

Note Glorious would have had the same aircraft complement as *Courageous*. This list is from a draft Staff Report on naval air doctrine, compiled early in 1936, and included in papers used to press for naval control of the Fleet Air Arm (ADM 116/3724).

large carriers, each of which might have limited accommodation but each of which would be able to operate effectively in rough weather; or it could opt for a larger number of smaller carriers, say 13,500-ton ships like USS *Ranger* (CV 4) then under construction. In 1931 the choice was posited as six of 22,000 tons or ten of 13,500. Typical air complements were estimated as thirty T/B, twenty-five S/R, and eighteen fighters (total seventy-three) for the large ship or eighteen T/B, fifteen S/R, eleven fighters (total forty-four) for the small. Thus the six large carriers could, in theory, accommodate 438 aircraft, the ten small ones 440.

The US Navy actually chose the small-carrier option in about 1926, on much this basis, later reversing towards larger ships. For the Royal Navy, the small carrier seems never to have been a viable option. The surviving papers strongly suggest that none of the participants in the argument believed that the Treasury would ever provide ten small carriers, although the government might be induced to build up to treaty limits in a smaller (hence less expensive) number of large ones. Ironically, given British carrier operating practice, the number of aircraft estimated for the large ship was grossly optimistic.

The alternative approach was to reconsider the number of aircraft the ship would have to operate simultaneously. While the fleet cruised, the carriers would have to maintain continuous reconnaissance and anti-submarine patrols. The carrier would also have to be able to launch a torpedo-bomber attack at any time, to respond to a target report. These requirements equated to simultaneous operation of two flights (twelve aircraft) of S/R and one of fighter-reconnaissance (F/R). She would also have to be able to launch a T/B attack (three flights, eighteen aircraft) at half an hour's notice, and one or two flights of fighters at immediate notice.

These were theoretical numbers; before 1931 the Royal Navy operated its carriers singly, and had no real experience of concentrations of aircraft. Appointed in July 1931 as the first RAA, Rear Admiral R G H Henderson conducted multi-carrier operations, with special procedures for flying off, forming up, and co-ordinating squadrons from several carriers. As a result, in 1939 the Royal Navy considered itself more experienced than any other in multi-carrier tactics. Ironically, it was soon spread so thin that these tactics did it little good.

Henderson was also responsible for establishing a squadron organization (twelve aircraft each) in May 1933, to supersede

the flights (six aircraft) which up to then had been the largest tactical units of the Fleet Air Arm. This coincided with the rise of mature torpedo attack tactics: flight attack (later called sub-flight) and loose formation (later called sector), the former for self-defence against fighters, the latter against heavy anti-aircraft batteries and where surprise could not be achieved. Both were dive attacks.

Experience of practice torpedo attacks led in turn to the development of massed formations with fighter escorts and, after Henderson's appointment, to their extension to two and later three carriers. This development in turn changed the role of the two-seat naval fighter (F/R). The F/R was conceived as an armed reconnaissance plane, capable of fighting its way through enemy fighters. However, the new two-seat fighters of the middle and late 1930s were strike escorts, their endurance and performance tied to strike aircraft characteristics.

By 1934, with the TSR in prospect, the Admiralty could hope to simplify the Fleet Air Arm, reducing carrier complements to TSR and FDB (fighter dive-bombers). RAA wanted the 2:1 ratio changed to 3:2, that is, more fighters; the Tactical School suggested instead that it should be 3:1. These figures applied to a fleet of six carriers, four of which would accompany the main fleet, for example, to the Far East. The carriers would be responsible for all reconnaissance, for the striking force, and for fleet air defence. Spotting would be left to the capital ships themselves. Cruiser aircraft had to be left out of the calculation because it was not clear how many cruisers would be available to the main fleet, considering the need for trade route protection. Each capital ship would therefore be provided with her own TSR, capable of extended reconnaissance or bomb or torpedo attack, plus a quarter-deck catapult for one TSR and two F/R or three F/R (that is, Skuas on floats, capable of limited reconnaissance and spotting).

RAA considered two disparate cases: a fleet opposed by enemy carrier-based aircraft, and a fleet attacked by a land-based air force. In the first case, which corresponded to the Tactical School concept, the best defence was clearly a pre-emptive attack on the enemy carriers. In the second, a decisive pre-emptive attack was clearly virtually impossible, since the carrier aircraft might not even be able to find the land bases; in this case the more F/R, the better.

Even in the carrier against carrier case, the pre-emptive attack might fail, and the fleet might require protection by fighter patrols assisted by sector patrols. Interception and fighter defence exercises conducted in 1932–34 showed that a defending formation could expect to intercept a raid about 50 per cent of the time, and that the defenders had to outnumber the attackers to achieve even this rate. The minimum defending formation seemed to be twelve fighters, to keep effective lookouts and to execute effective fighter tactics. Exercises showed that a superiority of 3:1 was needed to defeat an attack by multi-seat attackers; any lesser concentration would probably no more than hinder it. Even odds would probably result in the destruction of about a third of the attackers.

At least two fleet fighters were needed to maintain one in the air at all times.

Thus the fleet required a combination of a striking force for pre-emption and a defensive fighter force. RAA proposed making one of the two big carriers a dedicated reconnaissance ship, using thirty-six TSR. The remaining sixteen aircraft would work in three watches, accompanying the search aircraft most likely to make contact and carrying reduced crews and bombs for early attacks on the enemy carriers.

The other carriers would be loaded with FDBs and TSRs in equal proportions, the FDBs to attack the enemy carriers, the TSRs his heavy ships. Thus the new carriers would have

UNICORN
Gr. Britain - CVL
1943

Unicorn is shown newly completed, in 1943. Although nominally a light carrier, she was entirely unrelated to the later light fleet carrier (Colossus class) design.

thirty-six FDB and thirty-six TSR. *Courageous*, the dedicated reconnaissance carrier, would carry only TSRs; *Furious* would carry eighteen TSR (T/B Striking Force) and eighteen FDB (dive-bombers and defensive fighters), so the total for the fleet would be 142 TSR and ninety FDB. *Glorious* would carry thirty-six TSR and sixteen FDB, for general-purpose operation on a foreign station or relief to another large carrier.

All of this translated into the scale of operations the main fleet could maintain: the torpedo-bomber strike force would consist of $7\frac{1}{2}$ squadrons, ninety aircraft; the dive-bomber force could be up to $7\frac{1}{2}$ squadrons, ninety aircraft; the defensive force would be built up from the dive-bombers, plus $2\frac{1}{2}$ squadrons (thirty-two aircraft) from the capital ships. Reconnaissance would be conducted by twelve aircraft, accompanied by five advanced bombers working in three watches; or any combination from the fifty-two aircraft aboard the reconnaissance carrier. A reserve reconnaissance force of thirty-six aircraft could be obtained by reducing the torpedo strike force to $4\frac{1}{2}$ squadrons (fifty-four aircraft). Finally, action observation would be conducted by twelve TSR from the battleships, plus survivors of the carrier reconnaissance force.

The one great defect in this scheme was the special character of the reconnaissance carrier, which might, after all, be sunk.

In May 1934 the Tactical School at Portsmouth reported its own analysis. In contrast to RAA, it supported existing policy, as codified by the two principal C-in-Cs in 1927, that the main objective of the air striking force should be the enemy battle-fleet. Since it was believed that battleships could not be sunk by bombing (whether level or dive), the TSR would remain the primary striking weapon; the FDB could not compete. Moreover, the School considered air interception too unreliable to depend upon. Better to assume that the enemy carriers survived, and to rely on massed anti-aircraft batteries.

Existing analysis showed that forty-eight aircraft were the minimum to maintain an all-round search at sea for 12 daylight hours. This number would also provide ASW patrols and night shadowers.

Again, the standard assumption was that the main fleet would include four carriers, each with an average of sixty aircraft. It seemed reasonable to assume that each could range eighteen aircraft at one time, so that the striking force could be seventy-two TSR. War game rules allowed one hit for six aircraft, six hits to sink or disable a battleship. These rules made allowance for casualties to the attacking force on passage, and also for the effect of evasive action by the target force. Thus the striking force could expect to sink or disable two battleships, or to seriously reduce the speed of at least four. It seemed unlikely that equivalent bomb damage could be inflicted by existing weapons or methods.

The carriers could accommodate both forty-eight TSR for reconnaissance and two striking forces of seventy-two TSR, a total of 192 TSR. This would leave forty-eight FDB to complete the total of 240, for a ratio of 4:1.

This was too few fighters, since it was still necessary to achieve air superiority in the battle area, and to fight off enemy spotters. Therefore the School recommended a ratio of 3:1, which could be achieved by reducing the second strike to sixty TSR, a difference of only twelve TSR.

According to the official aircraft tactical instructions, issued in July 1933, 'the best defence of the fleet against air attack lies in offensive action against the enemy's air forces at the earliest possible moment,' that is, in sinking or neutralizing his carriers.[9] This was much the same as contemporary US doctrine. Defence against those enemy aircraft which did appear would be mounted at three levels: an air defence force consisting of fighters assisted by air patrols; gunfire; and evasive manoeuvring. Fighters could patrol over the fleet when attack was expected, and their first object would be to break up and disorganize approaching formations.

This was much the same as later standard doctrine, except that the prewar Fleet Air Arm lacked radar for early warning. Lookouts aboard a ring of surface ships would provide early

9   ADM 186/96

warning of aircraft flying below cloud cover. The 1933 doctrine called for the fleet to establish an outer air patrol of six S/R or other two-seaters, each in a sector, about 10 or 20nm from fleet centre, communicating with the Admiral and the senior carrier officer (and, until 1936, with the fighter force commander), flying above cloud cover. The fighter force itself would remain concentrated, and would patrol close to the fleet itself, engaging the enemy bombers as a formation.

Given a limited number of aircraft within the fleet, the question was how to divide the defensive effort between fighters and massed anti-aircraft guns. As RAA, Henderson advocated fighter defence: he observed that in World War I 95 per cent of air casualties were to air fighting. Gunfire might force aircraft to higher altitudes, but it was unlikely to do much execution. In 1932 he wrote that the Royal Navy had far too much faith in its new high-angle fire control system (HACS) – which in fact performed quite poorly in World War II. At this time interceptors were considered to be of limited use on land (this was the era of 'the bomber will always get through') but Henderson argued that there would be fewer attackers at sea, that the fleet screen would provide 18 to 20 minutes warning, and therefore that, if they were given freedom of action right up to the pom-pom screen, the fighters might have 5 minutes or more to harass enemy formation. They would therefore completely defeat high-level bombers and harass torpedo- and dive-bombers far more effectively than high-angle (long range) fire, particularly since the British HACS was designed specifically to deal with level bombers maintaining constant height, course, and speed. The fighters should also have a greater morale effect.

The problem was insufficient warning time. Naval fighters could not maintain continuous patrols, due to their limited numbers and short endurance. As aircraft became faster, warning time shrank. Henderson himself came to advocate defensive armour and carriers with all-strike air complements (the *Illustrious* class). After Munich it was commonly believed that shipborne fighters would be useful primarily against enemy shadowers (which were, after all, necessary if the enemy was to deliver successful massed attacks). At this time exercises showed that fighters often could not intercept incoming aircraft. Only in 1938–39 did it seem that the situation could reverse. Radar could detect attackers far enough away to provide a useful degree of warning. The new 8-gun fighters were so lethal that a few of them could inflict significant losses on an incoming enemy force. These considerations explain a growing fleet interest in defensive fighters just before the outbreak of war (see Chapter 10). There was not yet anything like the fighter control exercised in wartime.

AIRCRAFT DEVELOPMENT depended very largely on engine development. Several ambitious aircraft failed because satisfactory engines could not be obtained. Conversely, in several cases the appearance of a new generation of engines led to the appearance of a new generation of aircraft. Aero engine development was particularly crucial to naval aircraft, because the requirements were so exacting. For example, the prewar two-seat fighter (the Hawker Osprey F/R) became a practical proposition only because of the appearance of a new supercharged liquid-cooled engine, the Rolls-Royce Kestrel. By the late 1930s several advanced engines were being designed specifically for British naval aircraft.

At any particular point of development, maximum power per cylinder of a piston engine was fairly well fixed.[10] Basic improvements, for greater power per cylinder, included higher compression ratios (achieveable with better materials and higher-octane fuels) and supercharging for better high-altitude performance and generally to get more air (for fuller combustion) into the cylinder.[11]

To achieve greater total power, the engine designer had to add more cylinders at a cost in drag and in extra weight. The two basic configurations were radial, in which the cylinders were spread out around a short central crankshaft, and in-line. In theory a radial engine developed greater drag, but it could be air-cooled (and thus without the extra drag of a radiator) because all of the cylinders were close to the nose of the aircraft. In-line engines, most commonly vees, presented much less frontal area and therefore imposed less direct drag, but long ones (with many cylinders) could suffer from torsional vibration. One solution was to link two vees in an *X*. All in-line engines had to be liquid-cooled, so all carried with them some form of radiator drag.

The Fleet Air Arm generally preferred the air-cooled radial because it was smaller and cheaper. A smaller engine made for a smaller aircraft, which could be more manoeuvrable, could climb more steeply, and could take off in a shorter distance. It would need smaller floats (since the engine was shorter), was easier to maintain, and needed no special provision for tropical

Table 8-3: *Unicorn* designs

Scheme	A	B	C	C'	D
LBP (ft)	525 [535]	670	520	545	495
LWL (ft)	555 [555]	700	550	575	525
LOA (ft)	610 [572 3]	755	615	640	550
BEXT (ft)	88 [74 8]	90	90	90	80
Std displacement (tons)	13,900 [13,910]	18,080	14,050	14,800	10,985
Draught (ft)	17 6 [19 6]	18 3	18	18 6 (18 9)	16 6
Freeboard (ft)	61 6 [60]	60 9	58 9	56 4 [56 6]	50 1
Draught, deep (ft)	20 6 [22 6.5]	20 3	22	22 2	20
SHP	20,000 [20,000]	12,000	37,000	40,000	20,000
Speed (knots) std	21.5	17	24	24.75	
deep	20 [20]	13.5		24	20.75
Fuel oil (tons)	2500 [2045]	2000	2750	3000	2500
Endurance at 12 knots (nm)	6800 [5150]	4000[1]		7000[1]	4000[1]
Complement, war	1000 [500]	1000		976	930
peace				680	
Petrol (gallons)	21,000 [14,500]	40,000	21,000	36,500	21,000
Armament					
4in	8 (400rpg) [6(270rpg)]	—	8 (400rpg)	8 (400rpg)	—
4.5in	—	8 (329rpg)	—	—	8
Pom-pom (8-barrel)	2 (1800rpb)	4 (1800rpb)	2 (1800rpb)	3 (1200rpb)	4
.5in (quad)	—	4 (2500rpb)	—	—	
Aircraft					
Spread	8 [6]	8	7	7	7
Folded	21	42	20	20	20
Boxed	21	—	21	21	6
Weights (tons)					
General equipment	780 [630]	850	773	780 {770}	773
Aircraft equipment	1544 [70]	1750	1172	1250 {1250}	1072
Machinery	790 [1560]	550	1260	1370 {1370} 790	
Armament	324 [—]	500	330	350 {350}	500
Protection	812[3] [200]	1780	835	350 {950}	—
Hull	9650 [11,450]	12,650	9680	10,060 {10,050}	7850
Std displacement	13,900 [13,910]	18,060	14,050	14,450 {14,750}	10,985

Data in square brackets are for HMS *Argus*, for comparison. Data in braces are the legend approved for HMS *Unicorn* in January 1939.
1 Endurance at 13.5 rather than 12 knots.
2 Single 4in guns, not mounted in peacetime when *Argus* functioned as a Queen Bee tender.
3 Of the 2in plating on the flight deck, ½in is carried as hull structural weight.
4 This design did not have a flush deck; this is freeboard forward (41ft 4.5in aft).

10 The usual measure is power per cubic inch of displacement, but aero engines were limited in the number of cylinders (by the complexity of valve arrangements and by the need to cool each cylinder), so their designers tried to get as much as possible out of each. Engine displacement is also commonly measured in cubic centimetres and in litres (1000 cubic centimetres); 1 litre is equal to 61.025 cubic inches. Thus a 2800cu in engine (such as the US R-2800) has a displacement of about 45.9 litres.

11 The development of the early British liquid-cooled supercharged engines made the F/R possible. The Air Ministry rejected the proposed F/R Specification in 1925 on the ground that no engine could give sufficient performance.

In the Pacific, Unicorn *performed her designed aircraft support role, although she also functioned as a spare flight deck. The US-supplied aircraft (Hellcats and Avengers) on her deck wear the special Pacific roundel, which incorporated a US style white bar, and was intended to avoid confusion with the red Japanese rising sun.* FAAM

operation. At least in the United States, the Navy tended to argue that an air-cooled engine was inherently more reliable, since a liquid-cooled engine could be disabled by cooling failure, and also less vulnerable, since there was no radiator to be hit. Moreover, Fleet Air Arm experience in hot climates convinced the Royal Navy also that the air-cooled engine was more reliable. However, it was easier to build more cylinders into a liquid-cooled engine.[12]

In 1918 the only lightweight engines were rotaries, air-cooled single-row radials in which the cylinders themselves spun with the propeller. They were inherently limited in power because they had to spin the weight of their cylinders as well as that of the propeller. The only alternative for greater power was an in-line liquid-cooled engine, which, however, was much heavier. Wartime floatplanes, such as the Short 184 and the Fairey Campania, used such liquid-cooled engines, as did the Cuckoo.

The 450hp Napier Lion was in effect the end-point of this line of development.[13] Aside from their greater inherent power, liquid-cooled engines offered lower fuel consumption and thus were attractive for long-endurance aircraft such as fleet spotters and reconnaissance planes. This advantage gradually declined postwar, and by the 1930s the best air-cooled engines actually enjoyed better fuel economy.

The postwar successor to the rotary was the conventional radial engine, which combined light weight and relative simplicity (due to air cooling) with greater power (more cylinders). Most radials employed only one row of cylinders, and suffered from considerable drag. With the introduction of the Townend and NACA cowls in 1927, a good air-cooled installation could begin to match the drag of a closely-cowled liquid-cooled engine.

The major British naval radial engines of this period were the Armstrong-Siddeley Panther, capable of about 565hp, and the Bristol Pegasus, initially rated at about the same power.[14] However, the Pegasus improved over time, so that production versions were rated at 800hp by 1936, and at 1065hp by 1939.

By the end of the 1920s, the best air-cooled radial engines weighed little more than liquid-cooled engines (without their radiators and coolant) per horsepower, so that water cooling imposed a weight penalty of about 50 per cent. However, through the 1930s, it was argued that better liquid-cooled engines could be as light as air-cooled types, by reducing radiator weight and drag (in part by using new coolants with higher boiling points) and by increasing the power output per pound of engine.[15] One key argument was that a liquid-cooling system could dissipate any amount of heat the cylinders could produce, whereas air-cooled engines were limited by the fin area per

12   The Admiralty was actually responsible for the development of the first high-powered British radial engine; on 5 April 1917 the Air Board issued an Admiralty-inspired Specification for a new 300hp fighter engine to be not over 42in in diameter. At this time the Royal Navy was also sponsoring development of the Bentley rotary, then planned for 150hp but ultimately capable of 230. The Brazil-Straker Mercury (unrelated to the later Bristol Mercury) engine won the competition. However, a private venture engine, the ABC Dragonfly, was adopted instead. It was a failure, and production was cancelled in 1918 after 1147 had been made. This made it impossible for several aircraft planned for production in 1919 to achieve their designed performance. A third radial in this class, the Royal Aircraft Factory Raf 8 of 1916, was developed postwar into the successful Armstrong-Siddeley Jaguar, which in turn made the development of the Flycatcher possible. The Jaguar became the standard British fighter engine of the early 1920s. It is possible that the 1917 Specification was actually based on the Raf 8 design The practical maximum for a one-row radial was then nine cylinders (as in the Dragonfly); the Raf 8 had fourteen in two rows. After World War I, Brazil-Straker was renamed Cosmos Engineering; it produced the two-row Mercury and then a single-row (nine cylinder) 300hp engine, the Jupiter. Development proved extremely expensive and Cosmos failed; the Jupiter was taken over by Bristol, and by late 1921 was rated at 385hp (400hp maximum), compared to 320/360hp for the Jaguar. The later military Jupiter VI was rated at 480 hp maximum at sea level. Jaguar and Jupiter represented the effective upper limit of early British radial engines of this period. See R Schlaifer, *The Development of Aircraft Engines* (Harvard University Press, Cambridge, 1950), pp125ff

13   From a naval point of view, the most important wartime liquid-cooled engine was the 200hp Sunbeam Arab, which powered the Sopwith Cuckoo. Other Sunbeam engines (225, 240, 260hp) powered Short 184s. The 275hp Sunbeam Maori powered some Fairey Campanias and late-production Short 184s. In 1918 the most powerful liquid-cooled engine in British service was the 360hp Rolls-Royce Eagle VIII, a V-12. It powered later Fairey Campanias, IIICs, and IIIDs. A scaled-up version, the Condor, was under development; it achieved 525hp on test. Its main postwar competitor, the Napier Lion, had 12 cylinders in a W arrangement, one bank being vertical between the two arms of a V, and quickly displaced the Eagle. The Lion powered most heavy British naval aircraft of the 1920s, eventually producing almost 600hp in developed form.

14   The Panther was a two-row (14-cylinder) engine initially producing 525hp; it seems not to have been capable of much growth. Armstrong-

Siddeley also produced a larger 14-cylinder engine, the 800 (later 920-)hp Tiger (originally Jaguar Major), which powered the Seal. The Pegasus was, in effect, a direct descendant of the Jupiter, by way of a short-stroke version (Mercury) designed specifically for Schneider racing. The Pegasus of 1932 was originally designated Mercury V, and employed Jupiter-type cylinders with major improvements. Displacement was 1753 cu in. The Mercury (1520 cu in) itself was produced as a fighter engine, and appears in several Specifications of the time.

15   In particular, Rolls-Royce developed improved engine and cooling installations, and so was able to reduce radiator weight by about 50 per cent between 1936 and 1940. This company seems to have been unique in designing engine installations as well as engines proper. Merely raising the boiling point of the coolant drastically reduced radiator area, hence drag; for example, a glycol radiator had only a third of the surface area of a water radiator.

Folded width was an important limit placed on naval aircraft. From a ship design point of view, the narrower the lift, the less it detracted from the strength of the flight deck, which formed the upper flange of the hull girder. Narrower aircraft could also be stowed in greater numbers. In the latter case, folded wing span was more important than total folded width, since the tailplane of one aircraft could project over the body of another. Folded Albacores are shown aboard HMS Indomitable, *1943. CPL*

cylinder. In addition, in-line engines were easier to run at higher speeds, and it was easier to cool hot spots in their cylinders to prevent pre-detonation and thus permit operation at higher pressures.

Thus, throughout the 1930s liquid-cooled engines enjoyed considerable advantages in power output (for example, per cubic inch of cylinder displacement). Air-cooled engines required about one-third more displacement per unit power. It was, therefore, much easier to build high-powered liquid-cooled engines, and they in turn benefited from low frontal section. The first modern high-powered engine of this type was probably the American Curtiss D-12, actually begun during World War I. It inspired Rolls-Royce to design the Kestrel (Falcon X and then F.XII), which powered the new generation of Fleet Air Arm fighters of the early 1930s, the Nimrod and Osprey.

Experience with the Kestrel and with the Schneider racers led Rolls-Royce in turn to the Merlin and then the Griffon.[16] The latter was designed specifically for the Royal Navy; indeed, after the British aircraft programme was centralized in the Ministry of Aircraft Production, development almost stopped

because it was considered a special-purpose engine.

The Merlin moved British aircraft into the 1000hp class. This may not seem so much more than, say, a Taurus, but the Merlin enjoyed much lower drag and was much more compact, so that it made possible a new level of aircraft performance, typified by the Spitfire. On the other hand, the Spitfire enjoyed sparkling performance because it was a very small aircraft, and it was small largely because the RAF did not require long endurance or a second crewman. Because the Navy required both, it took about 2000hp (that is, a Griffon) to reach the same performance level. High performance was finally achieved in wartime due to a combination of much more powerful engines, such as the Centaurus, and radical relaxation of naval requirements (see Chapter 10).

By 1930 it seemed that a single-row radial would be limited to about 1800cu in (up to nine cylinders), a figure well within the range of liquid-cooled engines (the Merlin displaced 1650cu in). Any increase in power, to match the new liquid-cooled engines, required more cylinders, hence at least one more row. By this time work on cowlings was showing how the rear rows could efficiently be cooled.[17] In the United States, this trend led to twin-row radials, perhaps most prominently (for naval purposes) the Wright R-2600 (fourteen cylinders) which powered the Avenger and the Pratt & Whitney R-2800 (eighteen cylinders), which powered the Hellcat and Corsair.[18]

Rolls-Royce tried to combine the low frontal area of an in-line engine with the simplicity of an air-cooled type in its Exe, apparently intended primarily for the Royal Navy.[19] The Exe was chosen to power the Barracuda torpedo-bomber, but had to be cancelled in 1939 so that the firm could concentrate on Merlin. This left the field to more conventional radials.

16   The Griffon was conceived as a Merlin with 36 per cent more displacement, carefully designed so that it would be no longer than a standard Merlin, and thus so that it could be fitted to airframes designed for the smaller engines. Work began in January 1939 and production in March 1942. At that time the Griffon produced 1720hp at sea level, compared to 1230hp for a Merlin 46.

17   At this time it was not altogether clear that an efficient two-row radial could be built. The two-row Jaguar (1512cu in) had been a successful fighter engine, but the single-row Jupiter (1753cu in) proved more successful from 1927 on. Both produced about the same output, which suggested that two rows were not necessarily better than one.

18   The largest US wartime service engine was the two-row R-3350; the numbers in US designators gave the displacement in cubic inches. In 1942 Pratt & Whitney produced the 28-cylinder (four-row) R-4360, which was producing 3500hp by 1945. It is significant here because during World War II the Royal Navy considered buying it to power a new generation of single-engine attack aircraft (see Chapter 13).

British carriers had radio direction-finders to assist in air navigation and in air control; in the former case, the ship transmitted bearings to her aircraft. This VHF/DF is shown aboard HMS Implacable, postwar. CPL

Bristol developed sleeve valves specifically for compact two-row radials. The company's first application of such valves was the single-row Perseus, which powered the Skua.[20] The Taurus, which powered the Albacore, was the company's first production twin-row radial (fourteen cylinders, 1550cu in, initially 1065hp in 1938, and later 1130hp). The ultimate Bristol radial was the eighteen-cylinder Centaurus (3270cu in). It first ran, at 2000hp, in July 1938, and a supercharged version delivered 2375hp late in 1942. The Centaurus was, in effect, the British equivalent of the most powerful wartime US engine, the R-3350, and it delivered the same sort of very high power: 2520hp for the wartime production version, and 3220hp in a postwar fuel-injection version. It powered the Sea Fury and the Fairey Spearfish torpedo-bomber.

By the late 1930s new in-line engines were under development: the Rolls-Royce Vulture (essentially two Kestrels in X configuration, totalling 2590cu in), and the Napier Sabre (H-configuration, 2238cu in). The Sabre was planned to replace the Merlin as the standard British fighter engine.[21] It encountered development problems, and in the case of the Firebrand it had to be replaced by a Centaurus radial.

The effect of the war emergency was to focus the three primary high-power engine builders on the development of existing types rather than on wholly new ones. As a consequence, Britain had no equivalent of the US R-4360, which powered the late-war generation of US single-seat attack aircraft; for a time it even seemed that Britain would seek to build the R-4360 under licence. New engine designs began about 1942, but in 1944 the Ministry of Aircraft production decided that this work should cease in favour of concentration on the new jets and turboprops. Only the Rolls-Royce Eagle (twelve cylinders, 2808cu in, 3500hp) survived (if briefly), to power the initial version of the Wyvern strike fighter. Another Rolls-Royce project, the Crecy two-stroke 12-cylinder engine (about 2000hp), was tested in 1941, but never entered mass produc-

tion. The Rolls-Royce Pennine, another very powerful engine planned for Spearfish strike bombers, was cancelled. Napier was able to build a big hybrid diesel/gas turbine, the Nomad, which was planned for one version of the post-World War II Blackburn (GR 17/45) ASW aircraft.

For Fairey, the effect of cutting off high-powered engine development was to focus interest on more ingenious ways of using existing engines, the ultimate result (see Chapter 13) being the dual powerplant of the Gannet ASW aircraft.

The newer, more powerful, engines required more fuel, and this had a direct effect on carrier design requirements. By the mid-1930s, aircraft were expected to burn an average of about 30 gallons per hour (see Chapter 6). By 1938, the theoretical requirement was for a carrier to accommodate enough fuel to fly her aircraft for one month (60 hours for a TSR, 45 for a fighter). In 1938, the requirement was set at 35 gallons per hour. For *Illustrious* this amounted to thirty-three aircraft (twenty-four TSR and nine fighters), or 64,575 gallons, compared to a designed stowage of 50,000 gallons of petrol. *Ark Royal* required 116,500 gallons (forty-two TSR and eighteen fighters), against a designed stowage of 100,000. The older carriers were much worse. At this time HMS *Indomitable* and the 1938 carrier, HMS *Implacable* (each with thirty-three TSR and twelve fighters) required (at 35 gallons per hour) 88,200 gallons compared to a planned stowage of 70,000.

With twelve TSR, *Hermes* required 25,200 gallons but stowed only 7000 (plans called for her petrol stowage to be increased to 13,000 gallons, but this appears never to have been done). *Courageous* and *Glorious* required, in theory, 103,950 gallons (thirty-six TSR and fighters each), against 34,500 available. Thus even with the planned modifications *Hermes* would carry only 52 per cent of the required fuel load, *Eagle* only 39 per cent, *Furious* (the worst) only 30 per cent, and *Courageous* only 33 per cent.

In May 1938 DAM pointed out that the new torpedo-bomber (Barracuda) scheduled for service in 1941 would have a 1000hp engine, and would probably average 35 to 40 gallons per hour. Later aircraft would have 1500hp engines, and would probably consume over 40 gallons per hour. He therefore wanted the standard raised, particularly for the new carriers, to at least 75 per cent of a month's consumption. This came to 51,000 gallons in *Illustrious*, and 75,600 gallons in *Indomitable* and *Implacable*. DAM hoped that 5000 gallons could be added in *Illustrious* and 6000 in *Indomitable* and *Implacable*. For the older ships, he hoped that fuel could be traded off against petrol, to add 1400 more gallons (above the 13,000 planned) in *Hermes*, 7000 in *Eagle* (at the cost of 100 tons of oil fuel), 19,000 in *Furious* (at the cost of 300 tons of oil fuel), and 25,000 in *Courageous* and *Glorious* (at the cost of 375 tons of oil fuel).

These were major sacrifices. In July 1938 the Admiralty approved adding 6000 gallons to *Hermes* (for a total of 13,000) at the cost of 80 tons of oil fuel. Detailed analysis showed that, because of the awkward shape of existing fuel tanks, very little could be done for the existing big carriers. The loss of 150 to 200 tons of oil fuel would buy only 10,000 gallons of petrol in *Courageous*. Moreover, to construct extra petrol tankage would be very expensive and very time-consuming. It appears that the proposed changes were dropped under the pressure, first of the Munich Crisis, and then of war itself.

As for carriers under construction, only *Ark Royal* already met the new standard (relaxed to 75 per cent of monthly consumption). Nothing could be done for *Illustrious*, as the design was far too tight. *Indomitable* was increased to 75,160 gallons (tanks 95 per cent full), which approximately met the new standard (75 per cent of 100,800 was 75,600 gallons). It was

19 The Rolls-Royce Exe was an air-cooled 24-cylinder engine, the cylinders being arranged 90 degrees apart; in effect, then, it was a six-row radial (four cylinders per row). Conceived in 1935, it ran at 920hp in September 1936, and later at 1200hp. It was planned for the Barracuda, but cancelled in 1938 when priority shifted to Merlin production.

20 Production Perseus rating was 905hp, and the wartime Hercules was in effect a double Perseus (fourteen cylinders, 2360cu in). The Aquila was a smaller 9-cylinder single-row sleeve-valve engine (500hp, 1934); it never went into production, but was considered for several naval aircraft.

21 The Vulture (2592cu in) used a similar arrangement but was liquid-cooled; it ran in 1937, but had to be abandoned due to excessive failures. It is probably best known as the powerplant of the Manchester bomber, the failure of which led to development of the Lancaster (four Merlins in place of two Vultures). The Sabre was conceived in 1935. It consisted of two side-by-side opposed-piston (flattened-out vee) engines, each with twelve cylinders, for a total of 2238 cu in. It ran in 1937, and was tested at 2200hp in 1940, but was so complex as to be unreliable until 1944.

Left and below: Unicorn *supported the Common-wealth carriers in Korea. She is shown moored in a Japanese port, and under way off Korea. The ship also per-formed shore bombardments in Korea, with her 4in guns.* FAAM

possible to do much better in the 1938 carrier (*Implacable*): 82,000 gallons (these ships were completed with a capacity for about 95,000 gallons).

PERHAPS THE FOUR most characteristic constraints on British naval aircraft of the interwar period were a limit on dimensions (largely to fit carrier hangar and lifts), a limit on all-up weight (chiefly for catapulting from non-carriers, but later for carrier lifts, accelerators, and arrester gear), a limit on take-off (for catapulting) and landing speeds, and a limit on deck run to take-off.

At first, fighters had to be able to fly from capital ship turret platforms and from rotating platforms aboard cruisers. This imposed a limiting deck run of 47ft (generally in a 20-knot wind).[22] Later, after the turret platforms had been replaced by catapults, British carrier aircraft were required to take off in about 20ft (with the same wind over deck), so as to leave sufficient deck space abaft the first aircraft taking off for aircraft ranged on deck for a massed strike.

The usual limit on take-off speed was 55mph, and later 55 knots. Approach speed also had to be limited, initially because aircraft had to be able to stop within a fraction of total deck length. Later, when arrester gear was introduced, the decelera-tion it applied was limited, so that higher entry speed translated into a longer pull-out. Again, ship dimensions limited the acceptable pull-out of the wires, which was reflected back as a limit on stall speed (typically about 55 knots). Short take-off and a low stall speed together tended to require a large (hence high drag) wing or wings, and a limit on overall span encour-aged the Admiralty to prefer biplanes. More generally, the overall performance envelope of an aircraft, that is, the ratio of maximum to minimum flying speed, is limited; the lower the minimum speed, the lower the maximum. Widening the enve-lope to achieve better maximum speed requires special inge-nuity on the part of the designer.

As a further complication, within a limited all-up weight (6000lbs for the 1920s and early 1930s, then 8000 and then 9000lbs just before the outbreak of war), substantial fuel (for long endurance) had to be carried. This left only a limited weight for a more powerful engine, no matter what the state of engine development. In wartime, for example, the Barracuda could not be fitted with a new and much more powerful Grif-

fon engine until sufficient weight had been saved elsewhere in its airframe.

One more constraint deserves mention here. The Royal Navy tended to equate an observer/navigator with really long-range operation, on the theory that a pilot could not expect to navigate precisely enough. This may have been partly a conse-quence of RAF control: many pilots were necessarily RAF officers with very limited naval training, but all the observers were naval officers specially trained to navigate over the sea. The Royal Navy, moreover, was very unwilling to rely on electronic navigational aids, since their operation would reveal the presence and position of the fleet. Navigational standards were quite high: in 1936 it was expected that the error, after a 400-mile flight, would be no more than about 12 miles, within which a pilot should easily find his carrier visually.[23]

Thus long-range torpedo attack required the second seat introduced in the Ripon, and it was prewar practice for two-seat Ospreys to lead single-seat Nimrods. Similarly, during World War II the Short Sturgeon was designed partly to lead

22 Turret platforms imposed a weight limit of about 3000lbs.

23 As reflected in Meditteranean Fleet Air Orders of that date.

Unicorn *at Malta, on her way home (note the paying-off pennant), 5 November 1953.*

the new single-seat strike fighters to their targets.

Until the late 1930s the chief means of homing aircraft was two-way medium-frequency radio, which was easy to intercept and which was, therefore, susceptible to direction-finding (D/F). An aircraft unable to find its carrier could transmit, the carrier could use its own D/F gear, and then could transmit homing bearings.

In 1933, however, the Admiralty Signals Establishment (ASE) conceived something better, a rotating beacon which an aircraft could pick up. It had to be directional, which meant that it had to operate at relatively high frequency; this at the time required considerable technical sophistication. The first trials were conducted at Southsea Castle in May 1933, using a 3.5 metre transmitter driven by a silica magnetron, and directed by a parabolic reflector consisting of half-wave rods. An aircraft found that the beam was 45 degrees wide at a range of 15nm, and the required range, 50nm at 2000ft, was easily attained. The next step was to go down to shorter wavelengths (even higher frequencies), since the shorter the wavelengths the easier the installation aboard a carrier. In June, ASE tried 2.75 metres, and then 2 metres, and then, at the end of the year, 1.5 metres; this last test was delayed because special tubes (valves) were needed to transmit on so high a frequency. However, 1.5 metres made for a 6ft reflector which was acceptable in a ship. DSD concluded that the beacon was very practical, and that it would have to be installed above any other masting, since any metal structure near it would distort the beam.

The beam was designated Type 72. Installation aboard carriers, during their long refits, was approved in January 1935, HMS *Courageous* being test ship. Her captain feared that the appearance of the beacon would make its principle and approximate frequency obvious to any enemy observer, who would then be able to build the proper D/F equipment. He suggested, therefore, that the beacon be camouflaged to resemble a director, and a radome was therefore built around it. This radome

was later applied to all Type 72 installations. The same principle, to deny to the enemy knowledge of the frequency and nature of an electronic installation, probably explains the use of radomes for the wartime 271/272/273 series of centimetric surface search radars.

There was one problem. Carriers were also being fitted with HF/DF gear, which also had to go atop masts. The only solution was to fit a mast running through the radome, and this was duly planned for HMS *Illustrious* and later carriers (with the D/F loop atop the mast, with MF/DF loops between it and the radome). Until the new version of Type 72 became available, only the two-masted carrier *Eagle* could be fitted with HF/DF.

Type 72 did not do away with the need for the navigator; the pilot still had to come within 40 miles merely to pick it up. However, it did relax restrictions on carrier manoeuvre, and it did make night operations, which the Royal Navy favoured, much easier, because pilots could not be expected to see their carriers at any distance at night. Moreover, because it was a line of sight system, Type 72 could be used under conditions of radio silence.[24]

IN 1918 THE MAJOR British naval aircraft were the Sopwith Camel fighter and the two-seat Sopwith 1½-Strutter (and its derivatives), which served both for reconnaissance and for spotting. The only British aircraft designed specifically for carrier operation was the Sopwith Cuckoo torpedo carrier. Although in theory it could carry a bomb load equal in weight to its torpedo, in fact it was not equipped for accurate bombing.

At the end of the war the Camel was being replaced by the new Snipe fighter, but the latter proved less adaptable to naval use, and the Camel was retained. In 1920 the Air Ministry decided that the Nieuport Nighthawk would be its next fighter, and a navalized form, the Nightjar, was issued to the Fleet. However, its engine proved defective, and the Camel was retained for the time being.[25]

24 Radio silence was intended to prevent a distant enemy (that is, well beyond the horizon) from detecting and locating the fleet by radio interception and D/F. It therefore applied to high-and medium-frequency radio, but not to higher frequencies which propagated only along the line of sight, that is, only to the horizon. Thus wartime formations under radio silence could still communicate ship-to-ship and ship-to-air using VHF and later UHF radio (such as the US TBS), but they could not use long-haul HF radio to communicate with their bases. VHF was originally difficult to manufacture, and until after the Battle of Britain it was limited in British service to the RAF. The major British naval VHF set, Type 87, was an adapted RAF type.

25 Nightjars saw some overseas service in 1922, during the Chanak Crisis, when No 203 Squadron (RAF) operated them from HMS *Argus.* They were replaced by Flycatchers in 1924.

The Fairey Flycatcher was the first British carrier fighter designed specifically for that role. It was the first occasion on which the Royal Navy found itself unable to adopt standard RAF fighters for shipboard use; over the next six decades, the Navy would shift back and forth between specialist and adapted fighters. The Flycatcher is sometimes described as the last gasp of the Sopwith single-seat floatplane fighter formula, extending from the Sopwith Schneider to the Sopwith Baby and then, through licence production, to the Fairey-built Hamble Babys.

By late 1920, then, it was Navy policy to adapt standard RAF fighters for naval use. At this time most of the fighters were aboard battleships and cruisers rather than carriers, and pilots stationed aboard such ships had to spend most of their time ashore, keeping up their skills by flying practice. There was no clear estimate of how many fighters the fleet would need, partly because this depended on the scale of opposition. Moreover, fighters seemed comparatively easy to adapt to ship use because of their small size. The Admiralty reasoned that the considerable fighter strength of the RAF provided a reserve against which it could draw to meet variable, though generally

large, requirements. Thus it planned to use the standard RAF day fighter.[26]

In fact adaptation of standard land-based fighters proved unsuccessful. A Specification (6/22) had to be issued for a specialized ship fighter, which became the Fairey Flycatcher. It in turn succeeded only because the Jupiter radial engine became available.[27] A specification for a replacement was drafted in 1925 and issued in 1926.[28] Several unsuccessful prototypes were built, but the Specification could be met only after the advent of the Rolls-Royce F.XII (Kestrel) engine. The Hawker Nimrod was chosen in 1930.[29] It was a great advance on earlier types, and introduced R/T (radio-telephone) into British naval service.[30]

The wartime 1½-Strutter was clearly obsolete in 1918, and a new aircraft, the rotary-engined Parnall Panther had been selected to succeed it. This entered general service in 1919 and remained until 1924. Although not specifically designed for deck landing, it was considered satisfactory.

The Panther was a wheeled aircraft. During the deliberations of the Postwar Questions Committee it became apparent that many naval officers favoured an amphibious reconnaissance aircraft. They argued that such an aircraft might well miss its

26 Policy described by Admiral Chatfield, then ACNS, in a report of air progress for the Board, 10 March 1921 (ADM 1/8602/52).

27 It had almost too long a take-off run for turret launching. The alternative, the Plover, was considered inferior except for its weight and take-off. As first described in March 1923 the next fighter (armed with one .303in and one heavier gun) would be too heavy to fly from light cruiser platforms; Vyvyan (Coastal Area) suggested that a smaller fighter, perhaps launchable even from a destroyer, be developed. The Air Ministry refused, considering it unwise to multiply

types. Moreover, tests seemed to show that the Flycatcher could indeed take off from a capital ship platform. The design called for either a Jaguar or a Jupiter engine, first being tested with the former. It was adopted on the first production aircraft because they had to be rushed out to equip HMS *Eagle*. AIR 5/243.

28 The Flycatcher had to be retired when the Fairey IIIF, which was actually faster, entered service as a standard spotter/reconnaissance type.

29 Specification N.21/26. The Nimrod itself was designed as a private venture (originally named Norn),

Specification 16/30 being drafted around it. Nimrod II was produced to Specification 11/33. Submissions to the original Specification included Fairey's Flycatcher II (a new design despite the name). Admiralty requirements were (Flycatcher data in parentheses): 150mph or more (128 at 5000ft), endurance 3½ hours at reduced speed plus ½ hour at sea level (1½ hours at 5000ft plus ½ hour at sea level), ceiling 18–20,000ft (19,000ft), armament two guns with at least 600 rounds each, consider making one .5in (two .303, 1500 rounds total); dimensions 35ft (29) span × 23ft (23ft 1in) × 14ft 9in (9ft 4in); weight up to 400lbs (3029lbs). Since this was to be a turret

fighter as well as a carrier fighter, it had to take off within 47ft (wind over deck 20 knots). Flycatcher II could achieve 137mph at sea level and 150 at 10,000ft, but had poor take-off performance; the fighter powered by a supercharged Mercury or Falcon X was expected to make 150mph at sea level and 168 at 10,000ft. Nimrod actually made 195mph at 14,000ft, and service ceiling was 26,000ft, but endurance was only 1.65 hours. Note the emphasis on the large gun; according to the FAA, the Admiralty supported air-to-air gunnery between wars, and it rather than the Air Ministry insisted on development of the reflector sight, for accurate deflection shooting.

30 The R/T requirement was based on Mediterranean Fleet exercises. In Exercise M.D. of 15 September 1926, a Bison successfully guided a Flycatcher flight to attack an 'enemy' carrier 25nm away, and guided them home again. NAS also considered R/T essential for any type of massed air tactics, for instance fighter attacks on enemy torpedo-bomber formations. Prearranged tactics would be ineffective if the enemy formation broke up unexpectedly. R/T was expected to be effective 25 to 30nm from a ground station, or at a range of 3nm air to air (in 1936 the Nimrod was credited with a radio range of 50nm). The problem was weight; a two-way R/T weighed about 100lbs, and naval fighters were already burdened with special equipment such as a floatation bag (40lbs) and an R/L tube (presumably to drop flares) with six bombs (20lbs). Moreover, the Admiralty wanted the new fighter to have one .5in gun in addition to the usual .303 (the RAF used twin .303s). The heavier gun and its ammunition were expected to add 48lbs. These were not trivial weights; unless there was some compensation, the R/T was expected to cost 2mph, 1500ft in ceiling and half an hour of fuel supply.

carrier at the end of a long overwater flight, and thus that the amphibious feature was essential to guarantee the pilot a chance of surviving. Moreover, reconnaissance flights would have to be sustained over a substantial period, until the enemy's fleet had been spotted and defeated. The British fleet could not afford substantial losses of such aircraft during that period. Other types of aircraft would be launched only during a fleet action, and so could more reasonably risk loss in the water. As a result, the Fleet Air Arm procured the Seagull, a three-seat amphibian powered by a Lion engine. It was slow (80 knots) and very difficult to deck-land, and served only aboard HMS *Eagle* (1925–27).

The other, more successful, three-seat reconnaissance aircraft of this period was the Fairey IIID, which entered service aboard HMS *Hermes* in 1924, and served until 1931. It was designed as a wheeled aircraft, but had an alternative float undercarriage.[31]

During the summer of 1919 fire control from aloft became more sophisticated, and the two-seaters became inadequate because a single observer could not spot, code, send and receive signals and adjust his radio. A third man, a radio operator, had therefore to be carried. A DH9A bomber was modified at Donibristle to carry two passengers, and proved much more effective. Several such aircraft were used during the 1920 Fleet Gunnery Exercises. They proved unsuited to carrier operations (due to their high landing speed and relatively insensitive controls) and their wings could not fold. Further conversions, designated Westland Walrus, were given detachable wings for hangar stowage. However, they never served afloat.

On the basis of wartime experience, the Air Ministry asked for a fourth crew member, a defensive gunner: surely an enemy would try to disrupt the vital spotters. The Ministry therefore issued a Specification (3/21) for a four-seat spotter, leading to construction of the Blackburn Blackburn and the Avro Bison.

By 1921, the Cuckoo seemed dated; torpedo attack tactics had developed sufficiently to justify a better type. A 1921 Specification (9/21) resulted in the Blackburn Dart, which was also a single-seater.[32] Attacks had to be made at very short range, so the aircraft had to be manoeuvrable, to avoid either colliding with the target or with other aircraft attacking, with it, in close succession. Conversely, saturation attacks required that the bombers fly off in very close succession. The lifts of the new carriers were designed specifically to lift spread torpedo carriers so no time would be lost unfolding wings on deck.

The Fairey Seal, the successor to the IIIF (originally designated IIIF Mk VI) was the last British spotter-reconnaissance aircraft; it was replaced by the Swordfish, which could also deliver heavy bombs or a torpedo. Like other contemporary British naval aircraft, it could operate on wheels or floats. The Seal was the last of a series begun with the Fairey III in 1917.

In 1923 the Air Ministry issued a Specification (21/23) for a longer-range torpedo-bomber, requiring a second crewman to act as navigator. It could also therefore carry out reconnaissance. This aircraft emerged in 1926 as the Blackburn Ripon, essentially a redesigned Dart.[33]

Thus by 1924 there were four distinct types of naval aircraft. Although no firm estimates had yet been made of requirements for fighters or torpedo carriers, carrier space was clearly very limited. Late in May, therefore, the Director of the Naval Air Section (NAS) proposed some amalgamation of types. This was potentially valuable on two quite distinct levels. First, the same aircraft could be used for two purposes, as long as they did not have to be carried out simultaneously. For example,

31 Specification 38/22. A specialized fleet reconnaissance Specification was issued in 1922 (37/22), resulting in construction of the Fairey Ferret, which might be considered in effect the Fairey IIIE. It certainly did not match the Reconnaissance I requirement, since maximum was about 132mph at sea level. Details from H A Taylor, *Fairey Aircraft Since 1915* (Putnam, London, 1974). Issued in May 1923, 37/22 called for a three-seater (pilot, observer/navigator, gunner) powered by a Jaguar engine, with a Vickers .303 forward and a Lewis gun on a Scarff ring. Minimum acceptable speed was 108 knots (124mph) at 10,000ft, and landing speed was not to exceed 40 knots (46mph). Folded dimensions were not to exceed a length of 37ft, a width of 14ft (unfolded span was not to exceed 48ft for a monoplane, or 40ft for a biplane), and a height of 17ft 6in. Minimum endurance was 4½ hours. This Specification in turn was superseded by 1/24, which emphasized seaworthiness. It was conceived as a floatplane convertible for deck landing. Requirements included a speed of 98 knots at sea level, or 88 knots at 10,000ft, with a service ceiling of 15,000ft as a landplane; as a seaplane, it would make 87 knots at sea level or 80 knots at 11,000ft. This idea was superseded by the fast S/R typified by the Fairey IIIF.

32 Specification 9/21 was superseded by 32/22 (Dart production). The earliest postwar Air Ministry torpedo-bomber Specification (1919) revived the wartime project for an aircraft to carry the heavy 18in torpedo, after the Blackburd and Shirl had proved unacceptable. Blackburn developed the Swift as a private venture. In 1921 the Air Ministry issued Specification 3/20 for a carrier torpedo-bomber, ordering three modified Swifts (with span reduced by 2ft 11in) capable of carrying either the lightweight Mk IX or the heavier Mk VIII torpedo (or two 520lb bombs under its wings). The Air Ministry also ordered a prototype of the Handley Page Hanley (HP.19) to this Specification. Although the Hanley was not adopted, the company modified it as a two-seater (Hanley III), this version receiving the Air Ministry name Hendon. It was defined by Specification 25/23, for an interim aircraft pending production of more advanced two-seaters to 21/23 (Dart replacement). A Hanley variant was also proposed to 37/22, for the new fleet spotter.

33 Production was to Specification 2/29. A radial-engined derivative, the Baffin, was produced to Specification 4/33. The second seat may have been intended for a bomb-aimer. In October 1923, discussing a proposal that torpedo-bombers carry heavy (520lb) bombs, an Air Staff memorandum noted that although the Dart could carry two under exceptional circumstances, it could not be an effective bomber because the pilot had his hands so full with piloting and attack that he could not even operate his R/T. He also had no navigator. A two-seater could usefully carry alternative loads of torpedo or bombs. The existing Bison and Blackburn spotters could carry 500lb bombs, but had too poor a downward view for bombing. At this time the Air Ministry rejected a specialized naval bomber on the ground that the bomb was a weapon of opportunity, and hence should not be allowed to crowd out more essential types of naval aircraft. AIR 9/2. Note, that all these aircraft should be distinguished from contemporary RAF *land-based* torpedo-bombers.

long-range reconnaissance was needed before the battle, but not during it, whereas spotters were needed only during the battle. Thus the development of a dual-purpose spotter-reconnaissance aircraft would actually reduce carrier stowage requirements. Second, even if distinct spotters and reconnaissance aircraft had to be maintained, any reduction in the sheer number of types of aircraft in the Fleet Air Arm would simplify maintenance, and it would also lengthen production runs and thus reduce costs.[34]

NAS thought it unlikely that the fighter role could be combined successfully with any other, since the essence of fighter performance was speed and manoeuvrability. Moreover, any new type could not fly successfully from the platforms of battleships and cruisers. The other types, however, might usefully be amalgamated. He listed the chief attributes of the non-fighter types (see Table 8-1).

NAS considered the Type I reconnaissance aircraft, prototypes of which were then on order, unacceptable because, fast as it might be, it could not hope to evade enemy fighters. In any case its reconnaissance would be spasmodic at best. The torpedo carrier sacrificed fuel, W/T, speed, crew and defensive armament, and so did not really seem compatible with any other type. This was a good judgement, as Dart performance proved inadequate.

That left the spotter and Type II reconnaissance aircraft; NAS recommended development of a new combined type, which would be designated S/R. However, the S/R actually brought into service was closer to Type I, the poor performance of the Seagull and the four-seat spotters leading to demands, in 1925, for what became the Fairey IIIF, which had three seats.[35] The IIIF entered service in 1927, and by 1930 it had reached its weight limit (due to additional W/T, buoyancy, and navigation equipment). A replacement specification (12/29) was issued in 1930.[36] It was filled by the Fairey Seal, in effect a redesigned IIIF powered by a radial engine.[37]

The fast reconnaissance or reconnaissance-fighter (F/R) idea was not quite dead. In December 1924 Admiral Dreyer asked the Air Ministry to develop one, partly on the strength of recent exercises in the Mediterranean. They seemed to show a need for both the new S/R *and* an F/R . The Air Ministry considered the F/R idea unrealistic: since the end of the war it had been trying without success to build a useful long-range fighter. One solution was to give it a very high ceiling, so that enemy fighters could not reach it, but in this case it could not see enemy ships through cloud cover. In any case, high ceiling might buy very little in future if all aircraft were to be supercharged.

A Specification (22/26) was issued in 1926, but in the absence of a suitable powerful low-drag engine the aircraft proposed to meet it all failed. Only the advent of the new Rolls-Royce F.XII (Kestrel) solved the problem, the Hawker Osprey being chosen in 1930 and entering service in 1932. It was described as a reconnaissance fighter (F/R), but the Specification referred almost exclusively to the reconnaissance function. It was, therefore, designed as a floatplane which could be converted to wheeled operation.[38]

Admiralty policy followed a suggestion from C-in-C Mediterranean in September 1931 that ultimately the two-seat F/R should take over all naval fighter work, since normally either over the horizon navigation or W/T (Morse radio), each requiring a second crewman, was required.

Meanwhile the two-seat torpedo-bomber, the Blackburn Ripon, appeared. Performance was limited (90 knots, 3½-hour endurance) because the Lion was still the only really powerful engine available. However, the design was accepted in order to gain experience with a two-seater. The Ripon entered service in

The Fairey IIIF combined spotting and reconnaissance roles with high performance: it was much faster than the standard fleet fighter, the Flycatcher. Over 350 three-seaters were built for the Royal Navy, and a two-seat version was built for the RAF. The IIIF first flew on 19 March 1926; it served aboard carriers in 1928–36, and was not declared obsolete until early 1940.

1928, and within two years it had gained 400lbs (for a total of 7750). Orders were limited due in part to limited pilot vision and very moderate performance, but also because of the 1929 fiscal crisis.

In 1929, however, a new 800hp engine was in prospect and a new torpedo-bomber Specification was issued, for an aircraft to carry the new Type K (2000 rather than 1500lb) torpedo. The

34 This type of dual-purpose operation can confuse the historian. For example, the US Navy of the late 1930s and World War II used the same type of aircraft as a scout and as a dive-bomber. However, both roles were required, so US carriers had separate scouting and bombing squadrons. Many observers thought that they had double strength dive-bomber units. Later, fighter and fighter-bomber units used the same aircraft, but trained quite differently and so could not easily be amalgamated.

35 Designed to Specification 19/24, the IIIF was built to 36/26 and 37/26. A modified version (Mk IVB) was designed to Specification 3/31. One problem in the design was that the same aircraft had to accommodate both the long-wave reconnaissance radio and the short-wave spotting set. Long-wave was suited to reconnaissance because the aircraft was far from the fleet; used for spotting, it would give away the position of the fleet. Hence the requirement for short wave for spotting. Short wave also provided more channels. Owing to the bulk and weight of existing short-wave sets, the same aircraft could not carry both, though it could be wired for both, and they could be made interchangeable. S/R endurance was calculated so that the reconnaissance aircraft could send her contact report in time for torpedo-bombers to be launched. In 1925 effective torpedo-plane attack range was about 100nm, so the S/R required a radius of action of about 200. In practice, at this time, reconnaissance aircraft

were used to lead torpedo-planes to targets more than 15nm away. The scout was not part of the torpedo formation, which broke off and manoeuvred once it had sighted the enemy fleet. After the attack, the torpedo-bombers and their fighter escorts would form up and return to the carrier, again led by the scout (report from C-in-C Mediterranean of air work, summer, 1924). This practice explains the need for a second (navigator's) seat in the torpedo-bomber, as forming up after the attack was difficult at best. Of the two Mediterranean carriers at this time, HMS *Eagle* preferred the unitary S/R, *Hermes* the division into two types, the reconnaissance aircraft having floats and sacrificing performance to seaworthiness. C-in-C Mediterranean wanted a three-seater which could bomb when the third crewman did not fly. One argument was that patrols in themselves would not be opposed, so that high performance would not be too important.

36 The Air Ministry initially offered a new 800hp engine, but the resulting aircraft would have weighed 8500lbs, and therefore would have been too heavy to catapult. The Admiralty had, therefore, to retreat in several requirements, including bomb load. The resulting Specification was issued in 1931: maximum weight was about 6000lbs and the aircraft was to be launched by catapult at 60 knots and to land at 48 knots. Required maximum speed was 135 knots at 8000ft, and endurance was 6 hours, with tankage for 8 hours. The bomb load (reconnais-

sance) was 200lbs, and a 250lb bomb could be added as an overload, with 500lbs of bombs or petrol as an alternative load.

37 Produced to Specifications 17/32 and 11/34. It was a navalized Gordon. The prototype was actually designated Fairey IIIF Mk VI.

38 The F/R was conceived at a conference on 10 December 1924 chaired by the Deputy Chief of Air Staff and attended by ACNS; this led to a design proposal in June 1925. The Air Council originally resisted the idea on the ground that performance would be insufficient to justify it. However, it also noted that the new Fairey Fox demonstrated that a carefully designed low-drag two-seater could achieve fighter-like performance. The original Specification offered the designer either the Mercury radial or the Rolls-Royce Falcon (F.X) liquid-cooled engine. Maximum wingspan was 37ft, and the Specification required at least 120 knots at 15,000ft, with a service ceiling of at least 26,000ft (Mercury) or 23,000ft (Falcon). The aircraft was essentially a reconnaissance type with limit self-defensive weapons (one fixed Vickers and one Lewis gun); it could also carry eight 20lb bombs underwing. Because it was expected to operate mainly on floats, the Osprey had no floatation bag. The Osprey was derived from the land-based Hart light bomber (itself inspired by the Fairey Fox), which was designed in 1926; it entered service in November 1932 and was withdrawn in 1939.

39 Span could be up to 50ft (23 folded) and length up to 44ft; all-up weight with torpedo could be 9300lbs, and maximum speed 132 knots at 4000ft. Endurance was to have been 6 hours (with tankage for 7). Landing speed had to be less than 55 knots.

40 M.5/28, superseded by M.1/30. The three prototypes were the Blackburn B-3, the Handley Page H.P. 6, and the Vickers Type 207, all large two-seaters. Instead, the Fleet Air Arm called for a third seat (so that its aircraft could spot for gunfire as well as attack), the TSR (torpedo-spotter-reconnaissance). It combined the new S/R requirement (S.9/30) with the torpedo-bomber requirement, as S.15/33. In effect, the third seat was traded off against the heavier torpedo of M.1/30. Both Fairey and Gloster built S.9/30 prototypes. S.9/30 requirements were: maximum dimensions, 46(18) × 37 × 14ft 9in, speed at 8000ft at least 140 knots, and landing speed 50 knots, with a fixed forward-firing machine-gun and a Lewis gun in the after cockpit. Alternative underwing bomb loads were three 150lb or five 100lb plus eight 20lb; or one 500lb plus four 250lb. The engine was a water-cooled Kestrel. It seems likely that the key to conversion to a TSR was the advent of a new lightweight air-cooled engine, first the Panther VI and then the Pegasus. Fairey's TSR was a private venture, and it is possible that the S.15/33 specification was written because Fairey demonstrated that it was practicable. Gloster converted its S.9/30 submission into a Kestrel-powered TSR, and Blackburn's B-6 (which became the Shark) was also a private venture. It was powered by an Armstrong-Siddely Tiger 14-cylinder radial engine.

Navy was willing to accept a larger, heavier aircraft, and to waive catapult and float requirements.[39] Prototypes were ordered from Handley-Page, Blackburn, and Vickers, for completion in 1932.[40]

Instead, under the pressure of limited numbers, interest turned towards amalgamation of the S/R and a torpedo-bomber (TSR) carrying the standard weapon (S.15/33). Both Blackburn and Fairey offered private-venture proposals, which entered production as the Shark and Swordfish, respectively.[41] Unlike previous torpedo-bombers, these aircraft had the three seats required for successful spotting, with the spotter remaining behind on attack missions. They were described as 'four-purpose' planes, capable of torpedo attack, level bombing, spotting, and reconnaissance (TSR). With the advent of a successful TSR (replacing both T/B and S/R), carrier air complements could be limited to only two types, a two-seat F/R replacing both Osprey and Nimrod fighters.

Thus far the main driving forces in aircraft development had been the need to conserve numbers (within limited carrier capacity) and improving engines. In the early 1930s, however, a new factor, dive-bombing, emerged. It was not immediately obvious to what extent this technique could be applied to various Fleet Air Arm aircraft. Clearly a fighter could be stressed to dive-bomb; the first British naval dive-bomber was the Osprey (F/R) replacement, the Blackburn Skua, which was designated a Fighter Dive Bomber (FDB).[42] The Skua was intended to replace not only the Osprey (which had insufficient endurance), but also the obsolete single-seat Nimrod.

The Skua was limited to a 500lb bomb; this was acceptable because it could be brought into service relatively quickly. The more distant goal was a dive-bomber capable of attacking with a 1000lb bomb (as in contemporary US aircraft). This might be a specialized dive-bomber reconnaissance (DBR) or, even better, it might be combined with torpedo attack in a general-purpose (GP) bomber. In the event that the GP bomber could be built, the FDB could be discarded in favour of a specialized Fleet Fighter (FF).[43] However, in the event the DBR proved unsuccessful, it might be necessary to eliminate the FF in favour of increased numbers of FDB.

There were, then, three possibilities in 1936, shown in Table 8-2: the GP could succeed, or it might be necessary to have both TSR and DBR, or the DBR, too, might fail.

Dive-bombing made fighter defence more important. In 1934 C-in-C Home Fleet wrote that fighters were the only effective defence against such attacks, but that the Home Fleet had only eighteen of them, all aboard carriers. He wanted as

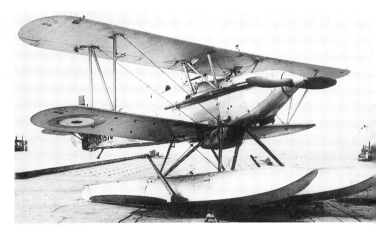

The Hawker Nimrod was the high-performance fleet fighter bought after the Fairey IIIF made the Flycatcher clearly obsolete. One reason all interwar British naval aircraft had alternative float undercarriages (as shown) was that, using them, pilots could practise flying when their carriers anchored in foreign waters. They could not fly off or land on without the wind over deck generated by an underway carrier.

The Blackburn Dart, a single-seat torpedo-bomber, was the postwar successor to the Cuckoo. The first entered service in 1922, and production ended in 1927. The last did not leave first-line service until 1933, partly because limited finances slowed purchases of the intended two-seat successor (the Ripon). The Dart was declared obsolete in April 1935.

41 Shark production was to Specification 12/34, and further development to 13/35; production of later versions was to S.19/36 and 31/37. Swordfish development was to Specification 38/34. Reportedly the TSR concept was initially suggested by the officers of HMS *Courageous*. The requirement was for an all-up weight not to exceed 7800lbs, with a cruising speed of at least 100 knots and a landing speed not to exceed 50 knots as S/R; endurance was 6 hours for reconnaissance and 4½ as a torpedo-bomber. Maximum folded dimensions as a floatplane were 18ft (17ft preferred) width × 44ft × 14ft 9in height. It was hoped that ultimately the TSR on floats could be catapulted carrying a torpedo. Armament was one 1500lb torpedo or 1500lb of bombs, plus one Vickers gun and one Lewis gun (600 rounds each). It seems likely that the Swordfish was ultimately chosen over the Seal primarily because Blackburn's limited

production capacity was needed for Skuas.

42 Designed to Specification 0.27/34. Work on an Osprey replacement began in November 1933. Unlike the lightly-armed Osprey, it was to have useful striking power in the form of dive-bombing capability. Initially DNAD wanted it to be able to dive-bomb in both wheeled (terminal velocity bombing) and float (glide bombing) form. It would function primarily as a fighter from carriers, but primarily as a strike or reconnaissance aircraft from cruisers, for example, on trade routes. D of TD considered these requirements contradictory, and pressed for development of two separate types, a two-seat fighter and a strike/reconnaissance aircraft for cruisers too small to take TSRs. The original specification listed maximum dimensions as 40ft span (16ft folded) × 36ft length × 14ft height. In fact span had to be increased

to 46ft (16ft 2in folded), but length remained within the stated limit. Design work was complicated by the catapult requirement, initially 5500lbs at 50 knots (later 6000lbs at 50 knots). Initial Air Ministry estimates showed that the only suitable engine within the weight limit, the Aquila II, would make for a maximum speed (with bomb) of only 179mph, compared to 174 for the Osprey. With a more powerful Pegasus III, the aircraft would be much heavier – 7210lbs – but faster (209mph at 14,500ft). The Admiralty considered the fighter dive-bomber so important that it was willing to give up floats altogether (saving 250lbs on the basic airframe). As issued in December 1934 the Specification called for an endurance of 3 hours carrying a 500lb bomb, or 5 hours at most economical speed. As built, the Skua was powered by a Perseus XII engine, achieving 225mph at 6700ft, with an all-up weight of 8230lbs. Development de-

tails are from ADMI/10103. Development was delayed early in 1936 when RAE tests with a spinning model showed that the fuselage had to be lengthened, from 33 to 36ft. The decision to order the first 150 was made on 24 March 1936, the prototype flying on 9 February 1937.

43 The original fleet fighter was apparently the Blackburn Roc turret fighter, developed in parallel with the Skua to Specification 0.30/34. In theory the Roc's four-gun power turret could traverse to track and hit passing enemy aircraft, compensating for the aircraft's own very limited performance. The concept was not unlike the much more recent one of putting performance in air-to-air missiles rather than in the aircraft carrying them. Rocs helped defend Scapa Flow in 1940, and were valued for their long endurance; the theory of their weapon had not yet been tested. They were withdrawn

from active service in August 1941 and never served at sea. Because they did not have to be very manoeuvrable, Rocs could easily be stressed to take floats. By 1937, although fighters were no longer being planned for cruiser operation, they were to have been kept aboard capital ships. Thus in August 1938 plans called for three Rocs each aboard *Malaya*, *Warspite*, *Queen Elizabeth*, and *Valiant* (with space for four); three each (space for four) aboard the battle cruisers *Renown* and *Repulse*; and one (space for two) aboard *Rodney*. Ultimately all fighters would go aboard carriers, with only amphibians, TSRs, or F/S aboard capital ships. Development of the Roc was protracted, and in September 1938 the Air Ministry tried to have it cancelled as a mediocre aircraft. The Admiralty view was that the RAF coveted the Boulton & Paul turret production line, which it wanted for Defiant day fighters. ADM 1/10103.

many aircraft as possible in all types of ships, with means of rapid launching; each future capital ship should carry five or six, and each cruiser not fewer than four. This never happened, but it indicates the thinking of the time.

A parallel idea developed at this time, 1935–36, was the three-seat fighter-spotter (F/S). It was to have replaced the TSR or Osprey aboard battleships and cruisers. During and immediately before the battle, the F/S would attack enemy spotters and protect friendly ones; it would also spot for friendly fire. Since spotting required the F/S to remain steady, it would be armed primarily with a power turret. Presumably the manoeuvrability of the turret would help make up for the unmanoeuvrability of the aircraft itself. A Specification (S.9/36) was issued, but no F/S was built.[44]

The GP actually materialized, as the Fairey Albacore. It was designed as a combined dive-bomber and TSR.[45] Its companion fleet fighter or F/R was the Fairey Fulmar which, unlike the Skua, had no major strike role.[46] By late 1937 it seemed likely that the new fleet fighters (as yet not in service), the Roc and Skua, would have insufficient performance, and the Fulmar was conceived as an emergency (and interim) replacement, pending development of a better fleet fighter. As its Specification was being drafted (February 1938), it became clear that, even though the Fulmar was based on existing designs, it could not be ready before the end of 1939 (first deliveries were actually made in June 1940, the prototype having flown the previous 4 January).

Thus should the Skua and Roc indeed fail, the Fleet would be entirely without a modern fighter for at least two years. Even if the Roc and Skua succeeded, fighters would not be available in sufficient numbers; the forecast showed only sixty-seven of the

134 required by the end of 1938.[47] War was clearly imminent and the only way to get anything approaching modern performance was to adopt an RAF fighter, which became the biplane Sea Gladiator. This was a temporary expedient, not the beginning of a single-seater policy, although the Fleet saw matters somewhat differently. In 1939, when supplying Gladiators to HMS *Courageous*, the Admiralty promised Skuas to guide them. The ship's captain refused the Skuas on the ground that he did not want so many distinct types of aircraft aboard. He also seems to have flound Gladiator performance attractive, and this in turn contributed to the general wartime adoption of single-seaters (see Chapter 10).

The successful design of the Albacore proved that the GP idea could work, but it incorporated obsolete biplane technology. The Admiralty therefore also called for a more modern (higher-risk) GP, which became the Fairey Barracuda.[48] Although the Barracuda was capable of spotting, it was designated a TBR, torpedo-(dive) bomber-reconnaissance.

In July 1936 DNAD listed two new aircraft types to be ordered under the 1937–38 Estimates: an autogyro for reconnaissance, which might be flyable from battleships and cruisers without requiring a catapult (S.22/38); and a night shadower for carrier operation. The latter would have to be able to fly for long periods (not less than six hours at economical speed plus one at full speed) very silently at very low speed, and to have a good downward view.[49] The Specification (S.23/37) was issued in October 1937, and two prototypes each ordered from Airspeed and General Aircraft. In theory the night shadower would take over from a reconnaissance aircraft which found the enemy fleet in daylight; it would need less performance because

44 The F/S was first proposed in March 1935 as a replacement for TSRs and Ospreys on battleship and cruiser catapults. It was conceived as the first heavy British naval monoplane, and was originally included in the 1936 programme. However, the Admiralty ordered it cancelled in November 1937, a 1939 requirement (S.24/39) being substituted under the new designation SOR (spotter-observation-reconnaissance). The Admiralty view was that existing (1937) technology was not sufficiently advanced to meet this requirement; by 1939 remotely controlled power turrets promised some protection against intermittent fighter attacks without excessive sacrifices in other directions. In 1936 the F/S could weigh up to 8500lbs on floats, maximum dimensions being 46ft (16ft folded) span × 40ft × 17ft 6in (on catapult), with an minimum endurance of 5 hours at 100 knots, or 3½ hours at maximum speed. Stall speed would be 56 knots or less, and maximum speed was to be as high as possible at 10,000ft. At this time a crew of two, with twin rear guns, was considered adequate. The Specification actually issued called for three seats and power guns. An F/S version of the Barracuda was proposed, but not built. The Roc was not suitable because it had only two seats, and thus could not accommodate a spotter, though it may have inspired the original proposal. The F/S designation was changed to SOR largely to avoid Treasury criticism of simultaneous development of three types of naval fighter (fixed gun, turret, and SOR). The SOR designation moved the aircraft into the TBR class. However, there was still some hope, in August 1939, that a wheeled version could help defend TBR formations.

45 The new TSR Specification was M.7/36. The Albacore was built to S.41/36, for a Swordfish replacement. The Albacore was one of the first types built without ordering competitive prototypes, in an effort to bring it into production as quickly as possible to replace the Shark and Swordfish. This was also why the Admiralty rejected Fairey's alternative monoplane design; it wanted to minimize technical risk. Requirements were issued to Fairey on 26 June 1936. The design actually began as a DBR because it was thought that a division between DBR and TSR might make it possible to build one of the two as a monoplane. When Fairey could not produce a satisfactory monoplane DBR, the two types were combined, and a draft TSR specification which had been issued to other manufacturers was withdrawn. The monoplane would have been 40mph faster, but there was some fear that it would be difficult to handle on deck in high winds, and it would have been too large to bring up spread from the hangar. Although floats were required, they had to be usable only from sheltered water. Requirements included a speed of at least 156 knots (180mph) at two-thirds power, endurance of six hours at 120 knots or more at 2000ft, and range with bomb and torpedo of 600nm at 6000ft at 120 knots. Take-off was to have been within 200ft (wind over deck 20 knots), although this was difficult to achieve. In the event, Albacore production was delayed partly by problems with the new Taurus engine and partly, according to the Air Council, by Fairey's desire to prolong the more profitable Swordfish production line. These notes are based on AVIA 46/137.

46 This was despite the fact that the Fulmar was derived from a failed light bomber, which Fairey had designed to RAF Specification P.4/34. Fulmar development was to 0.8/38. Work began in December 1937, when the Admiralty had decided that a Skua replacement was urgently needed; they were already expected to have unacceptably poor performance. Staff Requirements were drafted the following January, and an existing design (suggested by the Air Ministry) adapted for quick production. Thus the Fulmar was always considered an interim design. The original Staff Requirements had to be relaxed somewhat to reflect P.4/34 characteristics. Ultimately they called for a maximum speed of at least 230 knots at 10,000ft, and a stall speed (engine off and fully loaded) of not more than 56 knots. Take-off distance was initially to have been 225ft (20 knots wind over deck), but that had to be relaxed to 240ft. Designed roles were air fighting and shallow dive-bombing (with two 250lb bombs underwing); the aircraft was not stressed for dive-bombing with flaps down. These notes are based largely on AVIA 46/141.

47 Deficiency figures are from AVIA 46/142.

48 To Specification S.24/37. An advance letter was issued on 7 October 1937, and tenders were received 7 March 1938 from Westland, Fairey, Blackburn, Hawker, Supermarine, and Bristol. Fairey was considered best, and Blackburn worst; the Supermarine proposal, which employed variable-incidence wings, was considered too experimental. The Supermarine design was, however, built for experimental purposes, as the

Type 322 'Dumbo,' flying in February 1943. Hawker and Westland incorporated experimental features of considerable naval interest, but the Air Ministry refused to tie up their design teams. The Specification called for either a Bristol Taurus or a Rolls-Royce Exe engine. All-up weight could be 10,500lbs in carrier version or 11,000lbs on floats. Maximum cruising speed had to be at least 185 knots, and stall speed 58 knots. Carrier take-off distance was relaxed to 225ft at 20 knots wind over deck. The reconnaissance mission was 6 hours of flight at 2000ft and 120 knots (plus a quarter-hour for take-off). Alternatively, a special reconnaissance mission might use extra tanks for 8 hours at 120 knots or more. The bomb/torpedo mission was 600nm at 6000ft at 156 knots or more (plus a quarter-hour for take-off). The bomb load was 1500lbs (three 500lb SAP or GP), and the aircraft had to be stressed for a 70-degree dive. The key to the Barracuda design was a Fairey flap which could provide high lift at positive angles of incidence and high drag (as a dive brake) at negative angles of incidence, with little overall change of trim. Thus in theory a diving Barracuda could drop a torpedo at an angle of incidence favourable to air flight. In practice, this meant that the Barracuda had to be trimmed down by the nose to dive, and that merely pulling in the flaps (dive brakes) did not bring the nose up. Thus a Barracuda pilot, having dropped his bombs, had to trim up his aircraft before trying to pull out of his dive, a time-consuming process because it entailed turning a trim wheel. Many were lost before this problem was discovered. Notes on development are from AVIA 46/138.

49 The draft Specification called for a stall speed not greater than 45 knots; maximum speed could be as little as 100, though not less than 90 knots. Economical speed would be no more than 60 knots, and the aircraft would operate at about 2000ft. Span would be limited to 50ft for carrier operation, and there was the usual requirement to take off in 200ft with a wind over deck of 20 knots. DNAD envisaged a three-seat pusher, the observer in front of and below the pilot, the radio operator (with plotting arrangements) sitting behind the pilot. The Specification stated that the operational value of the aircraft would depend on its ability to fly slowly and under full control without loss of height; its value would be greatly reduced if this exceeded 35 knots (later amended to 38). The prototypes actually built were powered by four small engines. Night shadowing was the only practical means of holding a target for night torpedo attacks. Shadowers would take off at dusk and, provided contact was not lost, could call in night torpedo attacks to home on flares they dropped. The specialist night shadower was requested because existing reconnaissance aircraft (such as the Fairey IIIF and Swordfish) were not considered altogether satisfactory in this role. The Walrus amphibian was found to be best in 1937 tests. The prewar FAA stressed night attacks, which explains a requirement in 1935 that its aircraft have autopilots.

The Ripon was the two-seat successor to the Dart. Given a navigator, it could attack at much greater ranges. The Ripon first flew on 17 April 1926, and it entered squadron service in August 1929. Performance was limited because the Lion, the engine installed in the Dart (albeit in a more powerful version), was still the only suitable engine.

Below: *The Blackburn Baffin, which replaced the Ripon from January 1935 onwards as the standard British two-seat torpedo-bomber, was essentially a Ripon with a more powerful air-cooled engine; the prototype was designated Ripon V. Like the Ripon, the Baffin was limited to reconnaissance and torpedo attack. From 1930 on the Admiralty had two choices: it could develop a new generation of more powerful two-seaters to deliver much heavier torpedoes, or it could amalgamate the T/R and S/R categories, reducing the total number of aircraft the fleet required. Given the inherent limits of British carrier capacity, the choice was inescapable, and the last Baffins were withdrawn from squadron service in December 1936.*

it would be difficult to shoot down at night, and its presence would reduce the load on the conventional TSRs, since at most two night shadower sorties would suffice to track an enemy fleet through the night until an attack could be mounted at dawn.

Meanwhile, the Air Ministry pressed the Navy to adopt what it termed 'clean' monoplanes, paticularly twin-engined types, for Fleet service. The chief advantages of such aircraft were reliability and better forward view; against this had to be put greater folded width, greater weight for the same performance, greater fuel consumption for a given load, range, and speed, worse view for the observer (except in a high-wing configuration) and a greater maintenance load (for example, in engine stowage and in personnel). In particular, it seemed

unlikely that any twin-engine aircraft could come within the 18ft folded width required for it to fit the 62ft hangars of the new carriers. Hangar width would have to be increased to 64ft to allow for a more likely folded width, 19ft. All of these figures entailed very tight fits, the aircraft moving on side-tracking skates inside the hangars. DNC argued against any increase in hangar width, on the ground that it would make for much larger carriers outside the 23,000-ton treaty limit.[50]

Despite the Admiralty's view that there was much to lose and little to gain in opting for twin engines, the Air Ministry included a twin-engine monoplane TBR (S.30/37) in the 1937 experimental programme. Two designs (by Short and by General Aircraft) were submitted the following year. The Admiralty estimate was that they would be no more than 20 per cent more reliable than a single-engine type, and their estimated performance was little better than that of the single-engine Fairey monoplane TBR (which became the Barracuda). One had a superior bombing view but was inferior for spotting or formation work; the other was inferior except for the pilot's view ahead. Each would cost 40 per cent more than the single-engine type, and folded width could not be reduced below 18ft or 18ft 4in, compared to 13ft 6in for a single-engine type.

Perhaps most important, the single-engine TBR was already at the weight limit for catapults and lifts and for rapid man-handling. Thus adding 15 per cent more weight (in a twin-engine TBR) would be a disproportionate burden on overall ship design and operation. The Admiralty felt that the limited available experimental funds might better be spent on an experimental single-engine aircraft incorporating features more valuable to the fleet, such as a variable-incidence wing and possibly a tricycle undercarriage. The Air Ministry was sympathetic, and the Supermarine 'Dumbo' TBR was ordered, on the understanding that it was too experimental to be considered a potential operational type.

In September 1937 DNAD proposed four new types for 1938: two fighters (one forward-firing and one with a power turret), a new boat amphibian, and a new single-engine three-seater (Barracuda replacement or F/S). These Specifications were not actually issued until 1939.

The two fighters were, respectively, Skua and Roc replacements, N.8/39 and N.9/39.[51] They would exploit the new

50 The chief effect was to convince DNAD that future designers could not be limited by hangar width, that the Royal Navy should aim at the widest possible hangars. However, that was impossible in a closed-hangar design. The maximum which could be realized without major sacrifice was 64ft, and DNAD wanted it adopted. *Illustrious* began with a 60ft width, then went to 62ft at a cost of 50 tons (ordered October 1936), and another 2ft were expected to cost another 60 tons. This had to be rejected because weight was not available.

51 These two Specifications replaced N5/38 and N6/38, respectively; they were issued on 21 June 1939. Operational height was 15,000ft, and minimum acceptable speed 275 knots (270 knots for the turret fighter); required endurance matched that of the strike aircraft, 6 hours at 120 knots at 15,000ft, plus 15 minutes of combat at sea level. Specified maximum all-up weight was 900lbs (but there was soon some question as to whether it could be relaxed to 10,500lbs), and maximum dimensions were 50ft span (13ft 6in folded) × 40ft length × 13ft 6in height. The turret fighter would be armed only with a four-gun Browning turret (4000

rounds). For a time the Admiralty hoped for a six-gun turret, or for a cannon turret. The two were theoretically equivalent in that the turret and the fixed guns (plus ammunition) weighed about the same. The turret fighter was to be suitable for catapulting from battleships and cruisers (maximum acceleration 2.25 g, end speed 66 knots). Take-off run (as a wheeled fighter) was set at 200ft, and stall speed at 58 knots. Early in 1939 the Admiralty hoped for a speed of 300 knots, but none of the alternatives drawn up by the Air Ministry was that fast (the Hercules fighter was best, at 290 knots). In view of the very real danger of exceeding the weight limit, the Air Ministry offered a smaller and lighter version powered by a Merlin (278 knots for N5/38, 268 knots for N6/38, the turret fighter, against 254 knots then estimated – grossly optimistically – for the Fulmar). The Merlin alternative was actually an improved Fulmar; the Admiralty rejected its lower performance, and the Hercules was then favoured. At this time the Fifth Sea Lord considered 10,500lbs the absolute upper limit on a naval fighter. There was also some question as to whether a larger wing (48 instead of 46ft maximum span) might be acceptable.

56 The 20-knot figure seems to have been a minimum for operating Queen Bee drones.

57 It seems likely that this is what Henderson actually had in mind.

58 For seventy aircraft (100 less twenty write-offs and ten repairable crashes), operating an average of 60 hours per month.

59 These are April 1938 figures. In November 1937 the assumption was that the ship would carry out 120/240/360 hour overhauls eight at a time, three, four, and five days (respectively) per overhaul, so that in two months she could rotate through all 100 aircraft. In some versions of the calculation, it was estimated that three days would be required to erect a boxed airplane. A later estimate was twelve repairs (four days each), thirty 120-hour inspections (two days each), thirty erections (two days each), and thirty-five modifications to stored aircraft (one day each), a total of 203 aircraft-days per months, or about seven aircraft unfolded each day. All of these figures ruled out conversion of the two oldest and worst carriers, *Eagle* and *Hermes*. It was estimated that *Eagle* could accommodate three spread and eight folded aircraft, without providing any shop space. *Hermes'* hangar was too low, and she could accommodate only three spread aircraft.

60 In Scheme B, of 3320 tons of protection, 1775 tons went into 2in plating on the hangar roof and on the roofs and end of the 4.5in magazines; 1140 tons into 1½in hangar walls, 110 tons into 4in magazines sides, 25 tons into bullet-proof plating, and 270 tons into the underwater longitudinal bulkhead (1½in 'D' quality steel).

twenty boxed aircraft per month to make up for wastage (write-offs).[59]

The Staff considered and rejected Henderson's proposal that most aircraft be carried in boxed form, on the ground that folded aircraft, which could be made available much more quickly, would not take up much more space. It also rejected the arguments for higher speed, D of P arguing that at 13.5 knots the ship, which would inevitably resemble a carrier, would clearly be an auxiliary. DTD argued that the maintenance role would be so important that the ship probably would not be permitted to go to sea. Aircraft would generally be brought aboard by means of two self-propelled lighters or pontoons (10 knots, about 20 tons), which the ship would have to carry.

DTSD wanted four rather than two pom-poms, and DNO wanted larger numbers of 4.5in rather than 4in guns; he considered a broadside of four inadequate. The Staff considered Henderson's level of protection inadequate, and added 1½in hangar sides and a longitudinal bulkhead on each side for underwater protection.[60]

Carrier support would include providing a pool of pilots and observers to make up for wartime losses. They in turn would have to keep up their flying skills, presumably flying amphibians supported by the depot ship. Similarly, the depot ship might well operate a detached port security ASW squadron, so she would require ASW bombs (200). Petrol (40,000 gallons) would be needed for proficiency flying, for ASW patrol, and to run up engines for testing. The depot ship would also have to function as a radio (W/T) base ship. Scheme A provided only limited radio facilities. Its draught, moreover, seemed excessive (the Staff wanted 18ft at most).

The Staff Requirements implied a very large ship of fleet carrier dimensions, Scheme B of Table 8-3. Several alternatives were offered. In A.1, speed was increased to 24 knots (adding 10ft on the waterline, standard displacement increasing to 14,600 tons); in A.2 a second lift was added, at the expense of one spread and one folded position, and hangar side armour (1.5in) and underwater protection were added. Cost increased by £200,000, compared to £2,250,000 for A. B would cost £3 million. In B.1, a second lift was added, and the folded aircraft capacity reduced from forty-two to thirty-three (LWL was reduced to 670ft). Power was increased to 20,000shp to match

The Shark was Blackburn's version of the multi-function (TSR) aircraft. Like its rival the Swordfish, it began as a private-venture design, and the prototype B-6 flew on 24 August 1933. Sharks entered squadron service in 1935, but were withdrawn in 1938, although some were being used for training in Trinidad as late as 1944. The Shark apparently fell victim to the need to standardize to one type of TSR, when the Swordfish was chosen. This situation was much like that of the post-1945 US Navy, which chose the Skyraider over the attractive Martin Marlin, not so much because of some defect in the latter, but because the service could not operate two aircraft in exactly the same class. In the case of the Shark, the desperate need to build Skuas may have precluded continued Shark production.

A, primarily in the interest of better ship-handling. Net saving was £30,000. In B.2 aircraft capacity was reduced yet again, to a minimum of six spread and thirty folded (630ft) with two lifts. Speed was held to the 13.5 knots depot ship standard, and total estimated cost was £2.8 million. These studies showed that boxed stowage really did save ship size.

First Sea Lord (Admiral Chatfield) ruled in April 1938 that the ship should not exceed 14,000 tons, which effectively killed Scheme B. At this time ACNS(A) approved stowage limited to six spread aircraft, two aircraft being unfolded, and twenty-one folded aircraft, and DNC notes of a Sea Lords meeting showed that the ship would almost certainly have a full flight deck and a speed of 24 knots. Hangar side protection, which had been quite costly in Scheme A.2, would probably be eliminated, but the ship would need some underwater protection (against the 440lb charge of an aerial torpedo). The 4in armament seemed satisfactory.

Henderson asked for Scheme A modified for greater speed, accepting some reduction in shop size to shorten the ship. It would have two lifts, although the forward lift would have to be so close to the accelerator that it would have to be in the up position when the latter was used. This became Scheme C (Table 8-3). Scheme D was an austere (clearly non-carrier) alternative proposed by ACNS, lacking horizontal protection as well as arrester gear. Scheme D incorporated an accelerator and one lift, as well as a heavier gun battery. It would have cost

The Avro Bison was a specialized spotter. When it was designed, the assumption was that the spotter himself could not operate the radio relaying gunnery data back to the firing ship. The Air Ministry argued, persuasively, that such aircraft would be subject to attack, and therefore that they should carry defensive gunners. Counting the pilot, then, the spotter aircraft needed a crew of four. Beyond that, spotting required an excellent view; note the large portholes and side window. Bisons entered squadron service in April 1923, replacing the Westland Walrus, and they were replaced by Fairey IIIFs in 1929.

The Skua answered two quite different requirements. It replaced the existing two-seat biplane fighter, the Osprey. At the same time, it was the first British naval dive-bomber, the means of developing dive-bombing tactics. In this latter role it was notably successful in 1940, its exploits including the destruction of the German cruiser Königsberg *and damage to the French battleship* Richelieu *at Dakar. The Skua was withdrawn from production because the later Albacore torpedo-bomber took over its dive-bombing role, and the companion Fulmar fighter took over its fighter role. Blackburn apparently found the Skua difficult to manufacture; the Royal Navy had to buy single-seat Sea Gladiators to fill the gap due to late deliveries. The Sea Gladiators did not, however, represent any central decision to revert to single-seat fighters. That came only later.*

£2,250,000, compared to £2.5 million for Scheme C, which was clearly the better bargain.

In May, Henderson pointed out that, unlike other depot ships, this one showed no ammunition capacity for the ships she was supporting. He called for a new study, Scheme C', to incorporate two-thirds of the capacity of an *Illustrious* class carrier (twenty-eight torpedoes, 120 tons of bombs, and 40 tons of pyrotechnics). Ordnance had originally been omitted on the ground that sufficient weapons were aboard the aircraft carriers themselves, and that it was important to keep the new ship as small as possible. It seems likely that Henderson now insisted on stowage in the expectation that the ship might be needed as an operational wartime carrier. The cost was 25ft more length and 800 tons, the extra flight deck length being considered advantageous.

Scheme C' could easily be converted into a small carrier capable of operating twenty aircraft (two Albacore squadrons) in wartime. The final Staff Requirement based on Scheme C' therefore showed carrier-scale endurance (at least 7000nm at 13.5 knots), and 50,000 gallons of petrol. DNC protested that 48,000 would suffice to fuel all the aircraft on board for a month, and that ships under construction carried only 75 per cent of a month's full consumption. Scheme C provided 21,000 gallons, and DNC proposed 25,000. Ultimately Scheme C' showed 36,500 (plus 1800 gallons of paraffin).

The Staff asked for two accelerators forward, but had to settle for one as the cost in terms of maintenance hangar space proved excessive. The required weapons load had risen to thirty torpedoes, 240 250lb SAP bombs, and 240 100lb ASW bombs. Hangar clear height was subject to some controversy, the 20ft of the upper hangar having been required to allow for installation of float undercarriages. However, a trial in HMS *Pegasus* showed that 18ft 6in would suffice. To reduce displacement, 16ft 6in was accepted as sufficient for normal maintenance; anything more could be done on the flight deck, using the cranes. The Staff Requirement showed this latter height for both hangars (the lower one had initially been only 16ft high). The ship was built with an upper hangar to accommodate seven spread aircraft (324 × 65 × 16ft 6 in) with shops forward and component stowage aft; and with a lower hangar for twenty folded aircraft (360 × 62 × 16ft 6in). She could also carry

61 It was possible to reduce the planned 160lbs (4in) to 140lbs, and the planned 120lbs to 100lbs, that is, adding 40lbs to the whole of the vertical sides of the magazines. Protection was revised again in November 1938, the forward magazine being reduced to 80lbs plating worked in panels between the flanges of the stiffeners to the existing protective bulkhead (which was now 55lbs); the after magazine side was 100lbs. It was estimated that ¾in (30lb) NC deck armour would keep out a 6in shell at 10,000 yards, 1½in (the minimum to keep out splinters) at 15,000, and 2in at 17,000. DNC proposed that the forward part of the magazine crown be 2in thick, the after part 1½in, the extra plating being applied to areas not in the shadow of flight deck armour.

62 It was argued, tortuously, that since the ship was not really a carrier, she would have to be considered a capital ship (the only classification left), and would be prohibited as a capital ship displacing less than 17,500 tons. Henderson certainly wanted the other treaty powers to consider her an auxiliary.

fourteen or fifteen boxed aircraft. As a training carrier, the ship would have sufficient hangar stowage for thirty aircraft. However, additional cabins would have been required to accommodate men actually to operate two Albacore squadrons. Parts stowage, including fifty spare engines, was about four times that built into the large fleet carrier *Ark Royal*.

The design showed two self-propelled lighters, one in a recess under the after round-down, lifted by a gantry, and one which could be lifted onto the flight deck, by the port (15-ton) crane. The starboard crane (7-ton) plumbed the after lift, and so could place aircraft with damaged undercarriages onto it. The unusual hull form aft, to accommodate the lighter, required special wind tunnel work.

E-in-C initially called for four generators, comprising two steam units in the engine rooms and two diesels at the ends. The Staff Requirement reduced this to four steam generators, two of which were to be as far as possible from the engine rooms (for survivability), and an outfit of four 350kW turbo generators was approved late in October 1938.

This was a large and costly maintenance ship, and throughout June and July 1938 DNC tried to reduce its size. One possibility was to count the underwater protection bulkhead as part of the magazine protection against shellfire.[61] The 2in full-width (378 × 90ft) flight deck armour was retained, and the lift platforms were built of 1in armour steel.

In December 1938 CNS asked for more guns, at least twelve 4in. This would have brought the ship out of the auxiliary category, as defined by the London Treaty. It is not clear why that was a problem, as the treaty included no limit on the total number of British carriers, and as the repair ship was well inside the unit limit of 23,000 tons. It seems more likely that the Board feared that the Treasury or Air Ministry would have counted the ship against the total number of carriers the Admiralty wanted.[62] Quite aside from any treaty problem, there was very little space for extra guns, four twin mounts representing a practical limit.

It was possible to add a third 8-barrel pom-pom, but DNC could not provide the fourth requested by ACNS to allow for equal fire on both sides, without guns firing across the flight deck. Moreover, magazine stowage could not be increased, so that each pom-pom barrel could be provided with only 1200 rounds, rather than the standard 1800.

Drawings and a legend were presented to the Board in January 1939. At this point Henderson gave up his fight, and the ship was classed as a carrier. This in turn led to demands for a

During World War II, the Swordfish was adapted specially for anti-submarine warfare. This meant the detection of surfaced subarines or of their periscopes or snorkels, and the attacking weapons were depth bombs (to hit the U-boat as it dived after spotting the aircraft), rockets (to hit the U-boat before it could dive), and homing torpedoes. This Mark III shows a large centimetric surface-search (ASV Mk X) radar between its undercarriage legs. It also carries the dipole antennas of the earlier longer-wave ASV radar splayed out from the two forward interplane struts. Four rockets were carried under each wing. Outboard of the rocket rails on each wing are flare racks. The earliest ASV radars became standard on Swordfish by the end of 1941, and a Swordfish first tested rockets on 12 October 1942. Short-wave (centimetric) radar was important because it was more difficult for the Germans to detect or to counter, and because it could detect small objects, such as periscopes and snorkels.

Below: *The Fairey Fulmar was adapted from an unsuccessful light bomber. As such it could hardly be expected to match high-performance enemy aircraft. However, like other British naval fighters of the interwar period, it was intended primarily to escort strikes, rather than to beat off enemy bombers. Its origin seems to have been the perception that, with the success of the Albacore torpedo dive-bomber, the carrier fighter no longer had to be a dive-bomber. Therefore something more satisfactory than the Skua (which had encountered considerable delays in development, and which was therefore already obsolescent) could be built. The Fulmar was conceived as an interim step before the advent of a much more powerful engine, the Navy-sponsored Griffon, made a truly satisfactory fighter (which became the Firefly) possible.*

The Blackburn Roc was a premature example of an idea which now makes much more sense, that it is easier to put high performance into a weapon than into the platform carrying it. In the case of the Roc, the weapon was a power gun turret, and its supporters believed that the turret could manoeuvre quickly enough to make up for the aircraft's very limited performance. It could therefore, for example, protect spotters against enemy fighters. The Roc was almost certainly the basis of the fighter-spotter idea of the late 1930s, and it was expected to operate from capital ships and cruisers. Rocs were assigned to the defence of Scapa Flow in 1940. They never served at sea, although they were designed as carrier aircraft.

more powerful armament of 4.5in guns, which could be accommodated in the 4in positions, the gallery deck being lowered 3ft to keep them clear of the flight deck. Since 4.5in guns were in short supply, they would have to come from a depot ship under construction, and several candidates were identified. These weapons were power-worked; DEE wanted six (rather than four) 350kW generators. He had to settle for five 400kW units, as very little space was available. Similarly, DEE could not go above 400kW per generator, as this would have required a larger ring main and new switch gear, entailing unacceptable delays. The ship grew by 165 tons. Late in February 1939 the Board decided to retain the original 4in battery, and not to ask for the fifth turbo generator. However, the ship was redesigned for four 4-barrel pom-poms (1800 rounds per barrel).

The other major revision at this time was streamlining of the island structure for better air flow. This actually increased space available for pilots' ready rooms. Shop space was insufficient, the final design showing shops in place of the projected torpedo stowage.

The Board approved the Legend and drawings on 30 March 1939; the maintenance ship was ordered from Harland & Wolff and laid down on 29 June 1939 as HMS *Unicorn*. Henderson's idea bore fruit: by February 1941 it seemed likely that she would be completed as a carrier rather than a maintenance ship, and the Board so decided on 25 April 1941. She was completed on 12 March 1943, and operated as a fighter carrier, supporting the Salerno invasion that autumn. She was later converted back into an aircraft maintenance ship, supporting the British Pacific Fleet in that guise. That was possible partly because, even as a carrier, *Unicorn* retained a core of maintenance capability, about a third of her designed capacity.

At the end of the war, *Unicorn* steamed home from Australia, going into reserve in January 1946. She was refitted and reactivated in the summer of 1949 for service in the Far East, supporting the light fleet carrier *Triumph* based at Singapore. Instead of returning home as planned in 1950, she remained in the Far East to support British and Australian carriers operating in Korea. This service included ferrying replacement aircraft from Hong Kong. She also served as a troopship, and at times bombarded North Korean positions with her 4in guns. The ship returned to Devonport (and to reserve) on 17 November 1953. Although modernization (as a replenishment carrier) was considered, it was never carried out, and she was listed for disposal in 1958 (broken up beginning in June 1959). See Chapter 15 for details of this proposal.

Largely because it, rather than its planned replacement, the Albacore, was in production at the outbreak of war, the Fairey Swordfish executed such classic British naval torpedo attacks of 1940–41 as the strike on Taranto and the attack on the Bismarck. Here a Swordfish drops its torpedo during practice in English waters, 1939. Collection of George L Dant, via USN

9

Trade Protection

1   In the Royal Navy the application of the word auxiliary to a carrier was unfortunate, since it implied service in the Royal Fleet Auxiliary (RFA), a Merchant Navy adjunct to the Royal Navy. For example, when HMS *Dasher*, an escort carrier, joined a convoy, her captain had to explain that she was a warship, manned by the Navy. In October 1942 DNAD proposed that these ships be designated escort carriers, as that was their primary role. At this time the auxiliary carriers were broken down into three classes, A (20 knots, twenty-five aircraft), B (18 knots, fifteen aircraft), and C (16 knots, ten aircraft).

2   It is true that even in World War I the Germans managed to operate U-cruisers in American waters. However, given treaty restrictions on the size and number of pre-World War II U-boats, the British could reasonably imagine that the Germans would not dilute their effort by sending boats very far afield. Until June 1940 U-boats were also limited in patrol endurance by the very long transit around northern Scotland to their Atlantic patrol areas. The situation changed dramatically in 1940, when the Germans obtained Atlantic bases and then when their own mobilization programme greatly enlarged the U-boat fleet. As long as the U-boats were confined to the area around the British Isles, aircraft based on the coast could deal with them reasonably well. These considerations explain the short endurance of the corvettes, which had been designed before the outbreak of war, and the urgency of the programme of longer-range escorts (such as the River class frigates) pursued after the situation changed.

THE INTERWAR ROYAL NAVY had to plan both to fight an enemy main fleet and to protect trade on a worldwide scale. Because its resources were always limited, and because it was believed that the strength of the British main fleet might well deter an enemy from attacking, the interwar building programme, apart from some cruiser construction, emphasized the main fleet role. Trade protection therefore had to depend largely, though never entirely, on preparations for mobilization, for example, for the conversion of existing fast liners into armed merchant cruisers.

Thus, when trade-protection carriers were urgently needed during World War II, they had to be improvised on merchant hulls. Because British shipbuilding capacity was badly stretched, most wartime British trade-protection (escort) carriers were obtained from the United States, which mass-produced them. Because the Royal Navy found itself chronically short of fleet carriers, it had to use its trade-protection carriers in other roles, most notably to support landing operations. These ships were initially designated Auxiliary Aircraft Carriers, and then Escort Carriers (CVE, in US parlance).[1]

PREWAR STUDIES emphasized two quite distinct threats to trade: submarines and surface raiders. World War I experience seemed to show that a combination of convoying and shore-based aircraft could deal with the submarine threat, which would be concentrated around the British Isles.[2] Aircraft were essential because even if they sank relatively few U-boats, they could radically reduce U-boat mobility by forcing submarines off the surface. Once U-boat operations had extended beyond a few hundred miles offshore, continuous coverage by shore-based aircraft lost much of its effectiveness, and carriers had to make up the difference.[3]

Armed merchant raiders were expected to operate on a worldwide scale, and the chief problem would be to find them within the vast spaces of the oceans. Given the very limited distance over which a surface ship could search, aircraft were essential, and small carriers were the obvious solution. However, the effect of the Washington Treaty was to limit the British carrier force and so to preclude the construction of specialist ctrade-protection carriers. Even after the limit lapsed with the London Treaty of 1936 the need for main fleet carriers precluded the construction of specialized trade-protection ships. The conversion of suitable merchant ships into trade-protection

carriers was a natural extension of the usual plans for wartime armed merchant cruisers.

It was quite clear that to deal with surface raiders, armed merchant cruisers should be equipped with aircraft so that they could search large ocean areas, and also that the Royal Navy would have to improvise air stations in remote areas (in effect, movable but not fully mobile aircraft carriers). This latter consideration led to the seaplane carrier project described at the end of this chapter.[4]

The German successes of 1940 added a third threat to open-ocean shipping by bringing air bases to the coast of Europe.[5] In 1940 the main threat was presented by long-range FW 200 (Condor) maritime bombers. Not only could the Condors attack ships directly; they could also find convoys and bring U-boats to bear. Although really effective anti-aircraft weapons

3   A carrier operating with a convoy could keep U-boats from shadowing beyond the effective range of the surface escorts. This alone sufficed to negate wolfpack attacks, at least until the advent of very fast snorkel U-boats in 1945. From 1943 on, moreover, ASW carriers were used offensively, to attack U-boats located by code-breaking and HFDF.

4   In 1939 the Royal Navy planned the immediate conversion of fifty armed merchant cruisers, to be followed by another twenty-four (sometimes stated as twenty-five) later on. The rate at which ships could actually be converted depended in part on how fast heavy catapults could be provided, and peacetime stocks of aircraft were scaled to match likely wartime aircraft and catapult production. Of fifty armed merchant cruisers actually commissioned by the Royal Navy, only eight actually received catapults and cranes. In addition, two or three Australian armed merchant cruisers carried aircraft, although it is not certain that they had catapults. The British ships had turntable catapults removed from County class cruisers when the newer athwartships catapults were fitted, and they were generally limited to light reconnaissance aircraft (Seafox, later King-

fisher). Data from A Hague, 'Armed Merchant Cruisers,' in R Osborne, ed, *Conversion for War* (World Ship Society Monograph No 6, 1983). Prewar Admiralty papers show that heavy catapults capable of launching such heavy amphibians as the Walrus had been planned for these ships, particularly for those earmarked for the calm waters of the East Indies.

5   There had already been some studies of air attack on shipping in a world war, probably inspired by the problems of war with Italy in the Mediterranean. Minutes of a meeting of the Committee of Imperial Defence in December 1937, for example, included the observation that merchant ships sailing in convoy might be particularly subject to air attack, and hence that independent sailings might have to be adopted, which in turn would make ships much more vulnerable to submarines. These minutes do *not* suggest that a fighter carrier in convoy might solve the air attack problem, perhaps because at the time it seemed unlikely that fighters could effectively protect a fleet at sea. That became practical only after radar and radar fighter control had been introduced. The Royal Navy did, however, develop a variety of specialist anti-aircraft escorts for convoys.

HMS Audacity, *the first escort carrier. The aircraft on deck are American-supplied Grumman Martlets (later renamed Wildcats). Another emergency trade protection measure, a CAM ship, is visible in the background. The boom in the bow was probably a paravane fitting, which could be swung back down to the forefoot.*

might neutralize them in the first role, they could operate quite effectively from beyond surface anti-aircraft range in the second. Only carrier-based fighters, then, could deal with such 'shadowers.'[6]

As noted in Chapter 2, some World War I armed merchant cruisers were equipped with aircraft; indeed, the line between the crudest carriers and the best-equipped armed merchant cruisers was indistinct. Aircraft were already being used to search for enemy surface raiders. In 1926 this idea was extended, and the Admiralty proposed to the Air Ministry that wherever possible future armed merchant cruisers should be equipped with aircraft. The issue of trade protection was reviewed in 1931, with the proposal now that some ships be fitted with a catapult (sufficient to launch 7000lb aircraft) and a landing-on deck (with arrester gear) abaft the funnels.[7] DNC was asked for proposals in November 1932. Outline arrangements were prepared for a variety of ships, from 14,000 to 20,000 gross tons, and from 15 to 20 knots. In each case a hangar and lift were provided, the landing-on deck (285 × 65ft to 300 × 80ft) being equipped with three arrester wires. Estimated conversion time was nine to twelve months.

Any such design was awkward, in that special arrangements had to be made to transport aircraft from landing-on deck to hangar to catapult. Moreover, as in World War I, it must have seemed likely that landing-on abaft a superstructure would be difficult at best. When the Staff reviewed the DNC proposals in

March 1934, it suggested that converted trade-protection ships be made flush-decked. Funnel gas had always been a problem in flush-deck carriers, but provision of a large island would greatly complicate conversion; the solution would be to select diesel-powered ships for conversion.[8] In November 1934 the Controller approved a suggestion that this matter be raised again in 1936.

The Ethiopian crisis intervened, and the issue of conversion was revived in November 1935, presumably as an alternative to specially-built trade-protection ships (see Chapter 7). This time definite requirements were laid down. Ships would be diesel-driven, of the highest possible speed, of 10,000 to 20,000 gross tons. Endurance would be at least 6000nm at 14 knots, comparable to that of a contemporary British battleship. They would be fitted with a full-length flight deck, at least 70ft wide, with arrester gear and lifts, beneath which a hangar would accommodate twelve to eighteen aircraft. Armament would be the usual carrier battery as then understood, 4.7in dual-purpose guns and pom-poms.

In February 1936 DNC prepared conversion plans for two typical merchant ships, *Winchester Castle* (20,000 gross tons,

6   However, shadowers were not the only means by which U-boats could find targets in the open ocean. After 1941 the Germans relied heavily on code-breaking and other forms of signals intelligence, placing patrol lines of U-boats across likely convoy paths. Thus the elimination of the condors could not in itself neutralize open-ocean U-boats. On the other hand, because the U-boats had to be centrally directed, and because the boats of the patrol lines had to communicate back to the central command, the U-boat force itself was vulnerable to signals intelligence, both radio-direction-finding and code-breaking. This in turn made it possible for carrier- and shore-based aircraft to hunt down individual U-boats outside convoy battles. For typical U-boat tactics, see J Rohwer, *The*

Critical Convoy Battles of March, 1943 (Ian Allan, London, 1977).

7   No original paper on this subject seems to have survived. The 1931 date is from the unpublished DNC history of World War II naval construction. The paper, which appears not to have survived, was M.01647/31. A Cabinet history of prewar naval requirements gives the November 1932 date. It seems likely that the proposal derived directly from the newly-developed arrester gear; see Chapter 6. The relevant paper, which seems not to have survived, was NAD.253/32, discussing the possibility of fitting catapults, landing deck and arrester gear in armed merchant cruisers on the outbreak of war.

8   It was only at about this time that fast diesel liners appeared. *Winchester Castle* and *Union Castle* were sisters, completed in 1930 and in 1931, and capable of 18 knots. *Brittanic* and *Georgic* were even larger (about 27,000 gross tons, 712ft long, 18 knots, delivered in 1930 and 1932). The Union Castle line built serveral other large diesel liners just before the war; *Winchester Castle* and *Athlone Castle* (about 25,500 gross tons, 725ft long, 20 knots) were delivered in 1936, and *Capetown Castle* in 1938 (27,000 tons, 734ft, 20 knots).

Table 9-1: Early British Escort Carriers

	Audacity	Activity
LBP (ft)	434 9	475
LOA (ft)	467 3	513
Beam, moulded (ft)	56	66
Depth to flight deck (ft)	59 9	64
Displacement, deep (tons)	10,230	14,250
Mean draught (ft)	21 7	25 2
Flight deck dimensions (ft)	453 × 60	498 × 66
Hangar dimensions (ft)	—	87 × 59
Lift dimensions (ft)	—	42 × 20
SHP	5200	12,000 (2 shafts)
Speed (knots)	14.5	18
Generators	4 × 200kW	4 × 220kW
Endurance (nm)	12,000 at 14.5 knots	15,000 at 16 knots
Oil fuel (tons)	649	2015
Petrol (gallons)	10,000	20,000
Complement	210	50/325
Armament		
4in	1	1 twin
20mm	2	4 single, 10 twin
2pdr	4 single	—
Stability		
Light displacement (tons)	8200	10,870
GM	2.7	3.9
GZ angle (degrees)	4.1(49)	3.8(43.5)
Deep load (tons)	10,200	14,250
GM	3.3	4.3
GZ angle (degrees)	4.2(48.5)	3.4 (39.5)
Ballast (tons)	3000	1600

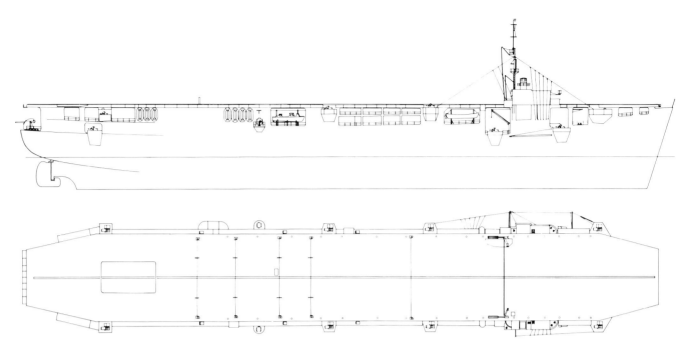

HMS Activity. *Note the substantial control positions on* both *sides of the flight deck. The signal deck and navigating bridge were to* port. ALR

631ft) and *Waipawa* (12,500 tons, 516ft). DNC suggested further that suitable ships be earmarked and their structural plans obtained so that preliminary design work could proceed. That April, the Controller approved studies of four passenger ships; by December DNC had prepared outline designs for conversions of *Brittanic, Winchester Castle, Warwick Castle, Reina del Pacifico, Dunvegan Castle,* and *Dunnottar Castle. Brittanic* was not recommended for conversion, but the other ships appeared suitable. Due to the press of other design work (connected with British naval rearmament), DNC could not pursue this work further before the outbreak of war.

However, DNAD developed provisional staff requirements in March 1937, a Staff conference was held in July 1937, and in April 1938 the Controller decided the matter should be pursued further, but with low priority. In January 1939 it was decided *not* to proceed as 'all money likely to be available is required for more important services.' Nor was anything done on the outbreak of war, as these conversions would have taken about twelve months.

WHEN THE GERMANS reached the European coast, both in Norway and in France, in June 1940, they gained airfields from which a wide variety of bombers could attack British shipping, both coastal and open-ocean. Throughout the autumn of 1940 both the Admiralty and the Air Ministry sought countermeasures. For work within a few hundred miles of the coast, the Air Ministry suggested equipping ships as mobile equivalents of its own sector control stations, with their own radars and with radios to control shore-based long-range fighters. Further out, this would be impractical; not only would the fighters have insufficient range, but they could not arrive on station quickly enough to intercept enemy aircraft. The ideal solution would be a cruiser with both radar and a catapult-borne fighter; next best would be a lesser ship still combining radar and catapult.[9]

The Deputy Chief of the Air Staff, Air Vice Marshal Sir Sholto Douglas, suggested that 400 merchant ships each be equipped with a catapult and two or three fighters.[10] This was much like the prewar Navy practice of placing fighters aboard capital ships and cruisers. In that case, fighters launched in battle would either land aboard a carrier or ditch. In the convoy case, it might be argued that since enemy aircraft would probably be encountered within a few hundred miles of land, in theory a fighter with long-range tanks could hope to return to some base. In practice that was clearly very difficult, and the greatest defect of the system was that no one was very anxious to waste a pilot. Therefore captains were always reluctant to launch their aircraft without very clear warning, that is, without actually seeing an enemy aircraft.

For the catapult fighter, the Air Ministry suggested the Sea Gladiator, to be succeeded by a new wooden (hence expendable) fighter, the Miles M.20. The Admiralty offered the new Bank class anti-aircraft ships as radar fighter control ships, perhaps fitted with standard RAF radios and radars (CHL). For its part, the Air Ministry suggested as a further refinement that each ship be fitted with a catapult and equipped with two or three interceptors.

Unfortunately, suitable catapults were in short supply; in November 1940 the Admiralty had only five heavy catapults and three light ones, the latter not powerful enough to launch modern fighters.[11] The only available catapult ship was HMS *Pegasus*, formerly *Ark Royal*, which had been built before World War I as the first British carrier. She was assigned to duty training catapult pilots for battleships and cruisers. VCNS assigned her to catapult fighter duty on 23 November, and she was immediately provided with three Fulmar fleet fighters and despatched to escort a Gibraltar convoy, sailing on 3 December 1940. This work was so urgent that she had to be fitted with a modified ASV (airborne surface search) radar (286P) in place of the more desirable long-range air search type (79). Experience soon showed that the ASV radar did not suffice.

The Air Ministry still wanted large numbers of convoy protection fighters, and late in November it suggested placing short

9   These proposals were made at an Admiralty–Air Ministry meeting on 13 November 1940. Coastal Command suggested that a VHF-equipped radar control ship could make Beaufighters effective out to their maximum range, about 375 miles from the coast. The fighter would be directed for the first 125 miles by a shore station, and it would pick up the ship's VHF emissions and home on them. The effective radius around the ship would be 125 miles, for a total striking range 375 miles, about the limit of Beaufighter range. The issue of timely arrival, which has generally bedevilled attempts to use shore-based aircraft to defend ships, seems not to have been raised.

10   The Douglas proposal was described within the Admiralty as the 'Woolworth' scheme (that is, mass produced and inexpensive). This seems to have been the first use of the term, which was later applied to the escort carriers in general. The original Air Ministry proposal was to use a very cheap wooden fighter (the M.20) carrying neither radio nor dinghy, but capable of delivering a 250lb bomb against a submarine or surface raider.

11   The heavy catapult (23 to 60 tons) could launch up to 12,000lb aircraft, at 55 to 70 knots; the unmodified Hurricane weighed 6670lbs. The light catapult (16 to 20 tons) could launch a 5500lb aircraft at 50 knots. In 1940 five British firms were equipped to manufacture catapults, but two were fully occupied, one was probably occupied, and the other two would be slow to provide new catapults. A new austere design would be needed for quicker production, and that itself would take three months to perfect. Some work could be saved by using steel tube (from the United States) in place of forgings, but this had a lead time of twelve months. Supply directly from the United States was rejected because US catapults were not suited to the arrangement of catapult spools used by the Royal Navy.

HMS Avenger *was the first production escort carrier. Her loss, in November 1942, led to drastic modifications to escort carriers in British service. This photograph was taken before the ship was handed over to the Royal Navy.*

take-off decks aboard tankers. Meanwhile the Sea Gladiator was soon rejected as an interceptor, leaving the existing Hurricane and the projected M.20 as the only realistic candidates. The latter flew, but it never entered production.[12]

Hurricanes could operate from conventional carriers, because they could take off in 350ft (with the usual 20-knot wind over deck).[13] However, this meant that they could not take off from a short platform on the bow of a relatively slow tanker. There was also some problem in using a Hurricane fitted with the usual pair of 44-gallon long-range tanks. For example, pipes from the tanks passed through the gun bays, and were therefore probably a fire risk. This was no problem if the pilot could drop his tanks, but in theory he would have to retain them throughout combat in order to fly home. It also seemed unlikely that the tanks could be stressed to withstand combat aerobatics or even catapult launching. Even so, the Hurricane was clearly the most likely candidate for any catapult fighter force.

Meanwhile, DNC urgently investigated conversion of a Bank class auxiliary anti-aircraft ship (HMS *Springbank*, not yet completed, was the only one available) into a fighter catapult ship.[14] Unfortunately no heavy catapult was immediately available, and the Admiralty was reluctant to delay conversion. The chief alternative, a heavy catapult on a tanker, could not really be satisfactory because of the tanker's low freeboard.[15] The Douglas scheme was, therefore, rejected because sufficient catapults could not be provided in time, because it would tie up too many pilots and because it would interfere with cargo handling. Installation of a conventional naval catapult would have taken about three months.

One alternative was to divert a small number of heavy catapults, either from existing warships or from future construction, and install them aboard selected naval auxiliaries, which

would then be designated Auxiliary Fighter Catapult Ships. They would be specialist units, with full radar and fighter direction equipment. Installations would be limited to ships already in naval service, to avoid exacerbating the existing shortage of merchant shipping.

Ocean Boarding Vessels (OBVs) were chosen: first *Maplin* and *Patia*, and then *Ariguani* as well. *Springbank* and the first two were built by Harland & Wolff, *Ariguani* by Jeffries, Avonmouth.[16]

The other alternative was a simpler and cheaper means of assisted take-off. DAM suggested rockets; with rocket assistance, for example, a Hurricane might take off in 150ft with 20 knots of wind over the deck. This in turn could make the short flying-off deck practicable. A very simple rocket catapult was built at Farnborough, with tests beginning shortly before the

---

12   The M.20 had been built at the express order of Lord Beaverbrook, the Minister of Aircraft Production, as a cheap mass-production fighter. The catapult-ship version would have been built without an undercarriage, presumably landing by ditching. It would have been powered by a Merlin III engine removed when a Spitfire was re-engined.

13   Stall speed was 60.9 knots, only slightly higher than the accepted figure for carrier aircraft. Carrier suitability had, in effect, been proven earlier in 1940 when unmodified Hurricanes landed on HMS *Glorious* off Norway.

14   Only *Springbank* could be fitted, because only she had adequate stability (since she had been given additional rock ballast). Her sister *Alynbank*, which was already in service, was not considered stable enough to take even a light catapult. The main effect of the catapult was to limit the arcs of X

twin 4in gun mount. Ten sister ships were not taken over by the Admiralty; the very similar *Foylebank*, also converted into an anti-aircraft escort, was sunk soon after completion, on 4 July 1940.

15   Freighters did not seem satisfactory. Typical positions above the holds would be too low in the ship (the catapult had to be at least 20ft above water), and the catapult had to clear the ship's capstan. It was also essential that the catapult should not interfere with cargo handling. In many ships it seemed that the only practical position was athwartships, but then the ships would have to manoeuvre to place one beam towards the wind, and she could not use her own speed to help launch her aircraft. A Ministry of Shipping representative to the Admiralty conference discussing catapult ship alternatives (on 12 December 1940) feared that ships might be too lively to use their catapults when they were lightly loaded.

16   OBVs were, in effect, small armed merchant cruisers, intended to intercept merchant ships, including blockade runners, in distant areas. They were under naval control (and so did not detract further from merchant shipping resources), but were smaller and generally slower than armed merchant cruisers, and therefore represented less of a drain on effective cruiser strength. For an account, see A Hague, 'Ocean Boarding Vessels,' in R Osborne, ed, *Conversion for War* (World Ship Society Monograph No 6, 1983).

HMS Archer, *the first American-supplied British escort carrier. She was a somewhat improved version of USS* Long Island. *The original merchant ship superstructure is clearly visible amidships. Unlike the US ship, the British carrier had her control positions relocated to the deck edge forward. The aircraft visible on deck are two Swordfish and a Wildcat.* FAAM

17   The rocket catapult consisted of a pair of 75ft rails, the aircraft being accelerated at 3.5 g by thirteen electrically fired 3in rockets. Note that this was considerably higher than the acceleration then imparted by accelerators aboard British carriers.

18   The first ship had ASV (Type 286P), the next two RAF CHL, and the next seventeen 286P.

19   A total of 249 Hurricanes were converted, thirty-five in an initial batch, followed by 214. F K Mason, *The Hawker Hurricane* (Aston Publications, Harvest Hill, 1987). According to Mason, the Hurricane was selected because it was already in use as a trainer by the Royal Navy, so that some Fleet Air Arm pilots were already trained to fly it. The Spitfire I, which was then obsolescent, was ruled out because its flaps interfered with catapult attachment.

end of 1940. By late January they were clearly successful; moreover, the new catapult could be built in only three weeks. This solved the catapult bottleneck.[17]

Meanwhile, the Admiralty decided to assign the athwartships catapult intended for the heavy cruiser *Kent* to HMS *Springbank*. The next two catapults would be those intended for the cruisers *Glasgow* and *Liverpool*, but by late January 1941 they were no longer needed: the three later naval conversions all had rocket catapults. All four naval conversions were designated Fighter Catapult Ships.

It was now also possible to convert substantial numbers of merchant ships. The policy was to convert large new freighters of about 9000 tons while still under construction, to avoid holding up ships already in use. Large hulls were required, to give 85ft between bow and foremast, the catapult firing somewhat off the centreline. One would sail with each transatlantic convoy. By way of contrast, the naval catapult ships (each carrying two aircraft) were intended to spend most of their time in the air attack danger zone, escorting convoys between Britain and Gibraltar. Merchant catapult ships were later (after March 1942) assigned to convoys to northern Russia (which were subject to considerable air attack), and to Gibraltar, particularly for the invasion of North Africa.

The merchant ships were not commissioned into the Royal Navy; they retained their civilian status, carrying only small fighter direction teams. They were, therefore, equipped with air search radar, which in 1941 was in very short supply,[18] and they were designated CAM (Catapult Aircraft Merchant) ships. A few carried Fulmars, but most carried Hurricanes modified for catapult launching and designated Sea Hurricane IA.[19]

By late April 1941, twenty-nine merchant ships had been earmarked, and the first, *Michael E.*, was nearly complete. She sailed with Convoy OB327 in May 1941. The original figure of 400 such ships was dropped, but there was some brief discussion of building 250: 200 to be equipped by the RAF, and fifty by the Royal Navy. This figure was cut to fifty on 1 April 1941, and thirty-five merchant ships were actually con-

verted. They were supported by a pool of 200 Sea Hurricanes in Britain. Since the single Hurricane on board would be expended in each engagement, a replacement pool of 100 Canadian-built Hurricanes was built up in Canada.

The first operational launch of an expendable fighter was from HMS *Pegasus*, on 11 January 1941; the intruding FW 200 evaded attack but the Hurricane pilot landed successfully after being launched 250nm from the Irish coast. A series of Fulmar launches, up to June 1941 failed to catch escaping Condors, and the first success came with a Sea Hurricane flown from HMS *Maplin* on 2 August 1941. None of the CAM-ship Sea Hurricanes succeeded in intercepting a Condor during 1941, although it seems likely that their presence did deter German attacks and even observation.[20]

Overall, the catapult pilots saw little real combat, partly because captains were reluctant to expend them until enemy aircraft came quite close. Thus, of 170 round trips by CAM ships between May 1941 and the end of the programme in August 1943, only eight aircraft were launched, achieving six kills, damaging two enemy aircraft and driving off three. One RAF pilot was killed. The high rate of engagement was achieved because aircraft were launched only when targets were immediately at hand. Of the special Navy catapult ships, *Pegasus* (one to three Fulmars) made three operational launches, intercepting one aircraft and driving it off. *Springbank* launched her Fulmar twice, achieving two interceptions (in both cases the aircraft was driven off). *Ariguani* (one Fulmar, later one Hurricane) launched twice (one interception, in which the target was damaged), and *Maplin*, the last of them, made three launches for three interceptions, achieving one kill; another was shot down by the convoy. *Maplin* was the only Fighter Catapult Ship to continue operations until 1942, being withdrawn in July.[21]

A proposal in February 1943 that Swordfish be placed aboard CAM ships was rejected because anti-submarine patrol was anything but a one-shot operation; it was vital that the aircraft be able to return to the launching ship for re-use.[22] This made the MAC ship the only suitable convoy platform.

One intermediate idea deserves mention: in July 1942 the Admiralty considered building helicopter platforms on merchant ships. It appeared that the new US R-4 helicopter could carry small shaped-charge anti-submarine bombs. The R-4 turned out not to be able to carry a sufficient load, and the project had to be abandoned the following year, though not before the Royal Navy had tentatively ordered 500 of an improved model, the R-5.[23]

EARLY IN DECEMBER 1940 DAM, Captain M S Slattery, suggested an alternative, an extremely simple carrier, to be

20   There was only one operational CAM-ship launching during 1941, from *Empire Foam* on 1 November; her aircraft drove off an FW 200 which was making a bombing run. Two other CAM ships were present in this convoy, and in some as many as four were present.

21   HMS *Patia* was sunk at anchor and so was never operational. Of the others, HMS *Springbank* was torpedoed on 27 September 1941 and subsequently sunk while derelict; HMS *Araguani* was seriously damaged by a torpedo during 1941 and had to be withdrawn. HMS *Maplin* was then given two more Hurricanes (for a total of three), but she was withdrawn from service by the end of June 1942 and returned to trade.

22   However, the idea seems initially to have been to use the Swordfish to drive off or sink a trailing submarine, that is, to act as a submarine interceptor. Surface escorts could not deal with U-boats trailing a convoy from beyond the horizon, because even when they swept towards the U-boats, they could spend only a very limited time away from the convoy. Given 1942-43 technology, only a carrier could sustain the anti-trail mission.

23   The R-5 (Sikorsky S-51) was actually built in Britain postwar. Britain received small quantities of wartime R-4 and R-6 helicopters, but they did not have sufficient lifting capacity for the combination of two men, electronics (at least MAD and a radio), weapons (at least one and preferably two 110lb AS bombs), and fuel (for endurance).

Table 9-2: Auxiliary Carrier Requirements, February 1942

Standard	A	B	C
Max speed (knots)	20	18	16.5
Endurance (nm)	15,000	15,000	max possible
Aircraft, total	25	15	10
Aircraft in hangar	16	12	4
Lifts	2	1	1
dimensions (ft)	45 × 34	45 × 34	42 × 20
capacity (lbs)	15,000	15,000	10,000
Flight deck dimensions (ft)	550 × 70	550 × 70	450 × 60
Catapult	fit	fit	if practicable
Arrester gear (wires/barriers)	6/2	6/2	4/1 (and 1 safety wire)
Crane	yes	yes	if practicable
Petrol (gallons)	75,000	50,000	33,000
Armament	2 twin 4in	2 twin 4in	1 twin 4in
	4 pom-pom (plus Oerlikons)	4 pom-pom	4 pom-poms
Asdic	yes	yes	yes

Note No original dated copy of this table has been found; it is taken from the World War II DNC History, which is not footnoted. There is some evidence that it was issued in draft form late in February 1942.

equipped with six Hurricane land-based fighters. It would be no more than a flat deck on a merchant ship hull, with simple arrester gear (two wires) and a barrier, but without any hangar.[24] This degree of austerity would make quick conversion possible; Slattery made no reference to prewar work on more elaborate conversions, and indeed he seems to have had in mind a merchant ship which would continue to carry cargo, in effect a MAC ship as later conceived (see below). He called her an Auxiliary Fighter Carrier. At an Admiralty conference on shipping air defence measures on 12 December 1940, the Ministry of Supply representative commented that the idea was attractive, but that it was too complicated to use the ship both for cargo and for aircraft. She therefore became an Auxiliary Aircraft Carrier, the first of many escort carriers.

The need was very urgent, so formal requirements were stated on 12 December, and a merchant ship, chosen for OBV service, was allocated for conversion on 2 January 1941.[25] She was the former German refrigerator ship *Hanover*, taken as a prize in the West Indies as she tried to run the British blockade. Renamed *Empire Audacity* and then HMS *Audacity*, she was converted by Blyth Drydock and Shipbuilding. The design was assembled extremely quickly; advance information was provided to the builders on 17 January, final information following on 7 March. The ship, which was designated an Auxiliary Aircraft Carrier, was completed on 26 June, and her trials on 7 July 1941. A second conversion was ordered and then cancelled: Admiralty Tanker 1044.[26] In January 1941 the Admiralty sought further *Audacity*-type conversions, as well as the four 'Castles' designed prewar, but was turned down at Cabinet level on the ground that fast cargo ships were needed too badly to be spared for trade protection.

The *Audacity* conversion was extremely simple. All structure above the shelter deck was removed, and a flight deck (without hangar or lift) was built. Unlike the flight decks of all earlier

British carriers, it was a superstructure rather than a strength deck, and therefore incorporated three expansion joints. The ship's side between hull and flight deck was plated in and the diesel exhaust was led out the starboard side. Platforms were built about 4ft 6in below the flight deck on each side for ship control and signalling.

Because HMS *Audacity* was expected to be the first of numerous merchant conversions, a special simplified arrester gear was designed for her, consisting of two wires (for 9000lbs at 55 knots), with an additional safety wire and a barrier. Six aircraft could be carried on deck, leaving sufficient length for a take-off run. The only protection was splinter plating around exposed control and gun positions. Given so simple a conversion, the ship naturally retained much of her prewar character below decks, with the air crew being accommodated in the former passenger cabins. Many of her personnel, including her engine room staff, were Merchant Navy seamen with T.124X articles serving with, but not in, the Royal Navy. Details of the conversion are given in Table 9-1.

HMS *Audacity* proved extremely successful, first as a fighter carrier (outperforming all the catapult ships combined, because her recoverable fighters could patrol) and then as an anti-submarine escort, carrying Swordfish.[27] Even before she had been completed, the Admiralty was seeking more such carriers. The conversion of the four Castle class liners was revived, but it had to be rejected because the ships were too valuable for trooping duty. Instead, on 20 January 1941 the US Navy was asked to act as design agent for six further ships, to be built in US yards. Remarkably, the US Navy independently developed a somewhat similar design at about the same time, using the standard Maritime Commission C3 hull in its diesel-powered version.[28] The US design differed from HMS *Audacity* in that it incorporated a short hangar (with a lift) aft, as well as an H.II catapult. She also carried much more petrol, about 83,000 gallons. British drawings of an improved *Audacity* were sent to the United States on 4 February; it was only at this point that the Admiralty learned of the parallel US project.[29]

The improved *Audacity* would have had an island and better aircraft arrangements (a hangar large enough to accommodate four stripped Swordfish and one spread Swordfish undergoing repair or maintenance, a 42 × 20ft lift, four to six wires strong enough to arrest a landing Barracuda and one barrier). Survivability features would include subdivision (and buoyant cargo) so that the ship could survive a torpedo hit, high-capacity pumps, and horizontal protection against dive-bombing over the vitals. Required armament was one twin 4in gun aft, plus six twin power-operated Oerlikons and eight single mounts. Weapons would include ninety depth charges and ten torpedoes, the latter to protect a convoy against a surface raider. The ship would have six radio receivers and radar.[30]

The Admiralty also wanted six more elaborate carriers built, based on the *Winchester Castle* design. On about 20,000 gross tons, they would have a flight deck about as long as *Audacity*'s with a hangar for up to six folded Swordfish, and a narrow lift. Six fixed-wing fighters would be carried on deck in a permanent deck park. This was actually inferior to what the US Navy expected to achieve on about half the tonnage, and it was rejected.

In April and May 1941 the US Navy requisitioned three C3 hulls, one already in merchant service, for conversion as what were then called BAVGs (British auxiliary carriers). Work on the first, HMS *Archer*, began even before the Lend-Lease Act had been passed. She was commissioned in November 1941, after only six months and one day. Of the other five ordered for the Royal Navy, *Charger* (BAVG 4) was retained by the US Navy for training, and HMS *Tracker* (BAVG 6) was completed

---

24 Slattery's memorandum, which emphasized the threat of the FW 200 and subsequent long-range aircraft both for direct attack and for 'shadowing,' was dated 5 December 1940 (AM. 8136/40). No copy has been found.

25 Formal requirements included provision for six fighters, TSR, or TBR, with bombs for six TSR and eighteen depth charges. There would be a hangar, with a 35 × 16ft lift. A 450 × 60ft flight deck would allow for a 360ft take-off run. Minimum accepta-

ble speed was 14 knots, with more desirable so that aircraft could take off in winds of less than 10mph. Navigation would be from positions below the flight deck on either beam. Required petrol capacity was 10,000 gallons (and 700 gallons of oil), and armament was one 4in dual-purpose gun plus four twin .5in machine-guns. The ship would have four transmitters and receivers, and radar. These requirements, which HMS *Audacity* did not quite meet, are quoted from the Cabinet history of British naval requirements, 1939–41 (CAB 102/536).

26 NAD Secret Office Aquaint listing the programme, December 1940.

27 She initially carried six Martlet I (Wildcat) fighters, in place of the projected air group at four fighters and two Swordfish, the theory being that there were so few ships with good anti-aircraft protection that four fighters might well be expanded on the outbound convoy run, leaving the ship unprotected on her return.

28 After World War II, the Admiralty Historical Branch investigated the question of whether HMS *Audacity* had inspired the US programme. The records showed that although the responsible senior US naval constructor, then-Captain E L Cochrane, had visited DNC Department at Bath, his visits (1 and 2 October and 15 to 27 November 1940) had preceded the conception of *Audacity*, which in turn was entirely independent of prewar work on converted merchant ships. The US Navy, too, had developed elaborate prewar plans for merchant ship conversions, though for offensive use rather than for trade protection, and it, too, had been forced to abandon them because conversion would have been too lengthy a process. For details, see my *US Aircraft Carriers: An Illustrated Design History* (US Naval Institute, Annapolis, 1983). The origin of the US CVE seems to have been a request in October 1940 by President Roosevelt himself for a converted carrier for convoy-protection (ASW). By December 1940, when the design was being developed within the Navy Department, one requirement was that the ship being converted have a sister ship which could be transferred to Britain. Two C3s, *Mormacland* and *Mormacmail*, were selected for conversion early in January 1941.

29 From US naval officers attending a conference in London, 26 March 1941, called to discuss further conversions. The proposed British conversion would have accommodated six Swordfish on a hull substantially larger than that of a C3; the US Navy argued that its C3 conversion was far superior.

30 CAB 102/536, quoting TSD 13/41 (undated).

31 These US designations may cause some confusion. The original US designation was AVG (BAVG for British), for general-purpose aviation auxiliary (a cover title); it was changed to ACV (auxiliary carrier) and then to CVE (carrier, escort). I have used CVE because it is much more familiar.

32 *Tracker* may have been delayed by being used to test alternative workshop and control space layouts; she was laid down on 3 November 1941 and completed for trials in January 1943. The first of the US series, USS *Nassau*, was completed on 20 August 1942.

33 In November 1941 it appeared that the Royal Navy would receive its first six ships by March 1942, but would have to wait until 1943 for six more. After Pearl Harbor the US Navy requisitioned all C3s and tankers suitable for conversion to escort carriers. By February 1942 the Royal Navy expected to receive nine of the next twenty-four C3s, plus the six already arranged (*Archer* series), plus eight more. In fact one ship of the first series (*Charger*) was retained and the Royal Navy received ten of the FY42 series. In March the Admiralty sought US agreement to complete fifteen tankers as British escort carriers, beginning in March or April 1943, in addition to the ten FY42 carriers.

to a modified steam-turbine design.[31]

HMS *Archer* followed the US prototype *Long Island* in that she retained the freighter bridge structure amidships, the bridge wings projecting under both sides of the flight deck. Unlike the *Long Island*, her hangar followed the sheer and camber of the original freighter hull.

The four US protection conversions (HMS *Avenger*, *Biter*, *Charger*, and *Dasher*) were to have been identical, except that their engines were Doxford rather than Sulzer diesels. In each case two engines were geared to a single shaft through electromagnetic clutches. All experienced some machinery trouble, *Archer* herself being particularly unfortunate in this regard. She was laid up as a stores ship in August 1943 and turned over to the Merchant Navy in March 1945 as *Empire Lagan*, serving as an aircraft transport. Her near-sister USS *Long Island* had a similar fate, although she remained officially in US naval service. The only other British diesel C3 conversion to survive the war, HMS *Biter*, was returned to the United States on 9 April 1945 and transferred to France as *Dixmude*.

These ships all had a single flight deck catapult on the port side, a US-type H.2 rated at 12,000lbs at 47 knots (7000lbs at 60 knots in *Archer*). Because the catapult was designed only for tail-down operation, it could not launch standard British aircraft.

All four diesel carriers were initially armed with three 4in guns, plus six .50 calibre Colt machine-guns (presumably the standard US Navy water-cooled weapon) and ten Oerlikons. The US guns originally fitted were replaced by British-pattern Mk Vs in the autumn of 1942. By October 1943 both surviving ships, *Biter* and *Archer*, had four twin power Oerlikons in place of four of her original single mounts. In addition, HMS *Archer* had two twin Bofors in place of her Colt machine-guns.

HMS *Tracker* was different. She was built on an incomplete

The first US-supplied steam-powered escort carriers could be distinguished externally by their British-type radar. This is HMS Stalker, *15 January 1943.*

steam C3 hull, which was much faster (18.5 compared to 16.5 knots). Because the hull had not been built up to the bridge level, she could have a full-length hangar (with two lifts) and a wider flight deck. A small island was erected forward of amidships. This configuration, which reflected British experience, in turn became the standard for US escort carriers. The island as accepted for HMS *Tracker* was also installed aboard HMS *Avenger*, HMS *Biter* and HMS *Dasher*, replacing the underdeck bridge wings of HMS *Archer*.

In July 1941 the Admiralty asked for six more C3 conversions, intending to operate them as fighter carriers. However, C3 hulls were in short supply, and the request was turned down within a week, leaving the Admiralty to seek six conversions at home. This time a small hangar and a lift were required, and the preliminary design was completed in November 1941. Long-lead items, such as lifts, were ordered in December (see below).

By this time the United States had entered the war, and the US Navy had gained control of all new merchant hulls. Acquisition of twenty C3s for conversion was approved before the end of December 1941. Four more were requested, but hulls were not available, and four fleet tankers had to be substituted. Five of these hulls were further advanced than HMS *Tracker*, and eleven of the late 1941 ships actually preceded her into service.[32]

HMS *Tracker* became, in effect, the prototype of forty-four more C3 steam conversions built under the US FY42 and FY43 programmes (forty-eight were planned for this period). Of twenty actually built under FY42 (CVE 6–25), half were assigned to the Royal Navy.[33] For a time it was suggested that all twenty-four FY43 ships be converted tankers rather than C3s, but this proved impractical. The US Navy also bought a specially-built CVE, the smaller *Casablanca*, and for a time it seemed that the two navies would share both classes. However, in the interest of standardization, the Royal Navy received all but one of the FY43 C3s (which became the CVE 31–54; CVE 31, *Prince William*, was retained), and the US Navy received all the *Casablancas*. Thus US CVE deliveries to the Royal Navy came to thirty-eight ships (*Archer*, three production diesel ships, *Tracker*, ten FY42 and twenty-three FY43).

For a time it seemed that mass-production *Casablanca* ('Kaiser') class carriers would be assigned to the Royal Navy, with the Admiralty requesting in November 1942 that the planned allocation of twelve FY43 C3s be changed to five C3s and fourteen Kaisers.[34] This was approved, but a week later the Admiralty pressed unsuccessfully for another dozen. By the following May it was clear that the Kaisers would not appear nearly as quickly as expected, and after some discussion the Admiralty agreed late in June 1943 to exchange its Kaisers for an equal number of C3s.[35] Later the US Navy provided four more FY43 C3s, for a total of twenty-three in British service. This made a total of forty-two British escort carriers, including

OFFICIAL PHOTOGRAPH
NOT TO BE RELEASED
FOR PUBLICATION
NAVY YARD MARE ISLAND. CALIF

RESTRICTED

STALKER (ex-ACV15)
Gr. Britain – ACV
(BATTLER Class)
(Jan. 15, 1943)

527-43   (ACV15).
45° OFF CENTERLINE.
SAN FRANCISCO. CAL. JANUARY 15. 1943

34 At least three ships were definitely assigned: CVE 56, CVE 59, and CVE 62 would have been named *Ameer*, *Atheling*, and *Begum*, respectively, the class being designated Ruler. Details from 'Particulars of H.M. Ships,' April 1943 edition. These ships became USS *Liscombe Bay*, *Mission Bay*, and *Natoma Bay*. Compared to the C3 conversions, they had longer flight decks and a greater fuel capacity (83,000 gallons).

35 The proposed transfer of Kaisers did have one byproduct. Examination of their plans showed that numerous changes would be necessary, yet the mass-production technique admitted none while the ships were being built. The Admiralty therefore asked the British Admiralty Delegation in Canada to consider modifying the ships in Vancouver. Although ultimately only C3 conversions (which, like the *Casablancas*, were built on the US West Coast) were transferred, the new modification arrangements did reduce the time lag between transfer and completion to British standards. A commercial wharf was converted, so that three ships could be handled at one time, each ship taking six weeks.

Most of the US-supplied escort carriers were identical to their US Bogue *class counterparts. HMS* Reaper *is shown off Hampton Roads, on 14 October 1944, with a deck load of Corsairs for delivery to the Royal Navy. She later served as a fighter carrier and aircraft transport in the Pacific. Escort carriers were unique among British warships in carrying only numbers, and not pendant letters superior, on their sides, US-style.*

six British conversions and excluding three losses.

British requirements were much larger. By December 1942 the long-range British programme called for eighty-three escort carriers by 1946 (for details of the logic behind this programme, see Chapter 13). The Admiralty could expect to have forty by April 1944, including the elderly *Argus*, HMS *Activity*, the five British 1942 conversions, and US-supplied ships, with another six US ships scheduled for delivery by June 1944. D of P had pressed for ten more British conversions, but his argument had been rejected.[36] One of the wartime Miscellaneous Carrier Covers (DNC records) includes an undated series of Staff Requirements for a conversion which seems intermediate between Type C (*Activity*) and a MAC ship. Six cargo liner conversions appear to have been envisaged; the Staff Requirements are reproduced as Table 9-6, which may well refer to the D of P proposal.

In May 1943 the Admiralty officially stated that it needed fifty-two escort carriers; it seems likely that this reduced figure was acceptable because about thirty merchant ships were being converted to Merchant Aircraft Carriers (MACs) for Atlantic duty (see below). The Admiralty presumably expected the US Navy to make up the remaining difference of ten carriers. In August however, the Allied ASW Survey Board reported excessive delays in bringing British escort carriers into service, and shortly afterwards the US Navy decided that no further carriers beyond those already earmarked could be made available, partly on the ground that the Royal Navy lacked sufficient men to operate them.[37]

By this time escort carrier engine room and supply departments were largely manned by Merchant Navy men (T.124X), and aircrew and aircraft themselves were scarce. Of fifteen

escort carriers delivered after August 1943, nine were employed only for training or to ferry aircraft. No further conversions were carried out in the United Kingdom, although the record is too sketchy to show that the Admiralty abandoned its attempt to build up to a greater force. By 1944 the Admiralty was aware that escort carriers would have to be decommissioned to release men to the new light fleet carriers, and plans were being made to run down the escort carrier force.

In British parlance, the three production diesel ships were the *Avenger* class, the FY42 ships were the *Tracker* class, and the FY43 ships were the *Smiter* class. Although the last two classes were very similar externally, they differed considerably internally. Typical characteristics of US-supplied escort carriers are given in Table 9-3; see below for a discussion of later design development and modification.

THE EXPERIENCE OF SEARCHING for hulls suitable for conversion (to armed merchant cruisers as well as to carriers) led, in the autumn of 1941, to a proposal to design merchant ships specifically suited to completion as auxiliary carriers.[38] Such a ship would have to be relatively fast for a merchant ship, capable of sustaining at least 16.5 knots and reaching 18, yet preferably diesel-driven. To provide a sufficient flight deck she would have to be 480 to 500ft long, with a 68–72ft beam. Survivability demanded a completely water-tight deck about 8ft above the deep waterline, with transverse bulkheads water-tight up to the water-tight deck and sufficient water-tight subdivision for

36   ADM 1/12164, on the British escort carrier programme 1942–46 in light of the US refusal to build MAC ships. The D of P paper was P.D. 0229/42, for conversion of cargo liners completing during 1943. At this time there was some hope that the Royal Navy would receive a share of future US CVE construction (*Commencement Bay* class).

37   By the end of August 1943 five of the twenty-two British Lend-Lease carriers had been in combat, five more following by the end of Sep-

tember 1943. Nine of the sixteen US Navy escort carriers had been in combat. If British ships commissioned (in the United States) during June, July and August 1943 (and therefore hardly delivered) are eliminated from the total, the British had received thirteen carriers by August 1943.

38   M.O.12267/41 (undated, but probably 5 March 1942) comments on the draft Staff Requirements paper, in the Miscellaneous Carrier covers (National Maritime Museum).

Table 9-3: American-Supplied Escort Carriers

	Avenger	*Smiter*
LBP (ft)	465	
LWL (ft)	492	
LOA (ft)		492
Beam, moulded (ft)	69 6	69 6
Beam, extreme at flight deck (ft)		108 6
Depth to flight deck (ft)	42 6	
Displacement, deep (tons)	13,305[1]	15,160
Mean draught (ft)	27 3	25 5
Flight deck dimensions (ft)	442 × 69 6	450 × 80
Hangar dimensions (ft)	190 × 47 × 16	260 × 62 × 18
Lift dimensions (ft)	42 × 34	2 (42 × 34)
Catapult	H.2 (7000/60)[4]	H.4 (16,000/74)
SHP	8500	
Speed (knots)	16.5	
Generators		
Endurance		
Oil fuel (tons)	—	3160
Diesel oil (tons)	1600[2]	130
Petrol (gallons)	36,000	43,200
Complement		
Armament		
5in/38	—	2 single
4in	3 single	—
40mm	—	8 twin
20mm	10	14 twin, 7 single
.5in mg	6	—
Stability		
Light displacement (tons)		9170
GM		1.9
GZ angle (degrees)		(44)
Deep loads (tons)		15,160
GM		3.7
GZ angle (degrees)		(48)
Ballast (tons)	1500[3]	1000–1300

1 On arrival in UK.
2 Plus 1700 as cargo; fitted to fuel destroyers at sea.
3 Added on arrival in Britain. Original GM was 1.67ft fully loaded. Buoyancy drums were also fitted over the ballast in the wing deep tanks.
4 Load in lbs/end speed in knots.
5 As surviving ships were modified; originally 75,000 gallons.

the ship to remain afloat and remain stable with any three compartments flooded up to the waterline.

The associated draft carrier Staff Requirements (TSD 1533/41) were circulated in a paper of 21 October 1941. They included diesel power, a speed of not less than 18 knots in average weather (deep load, six months out of dock), with an endurance of not less than 15,000nm at 15 knots, and twin-screw manoeuvrability. The hangar would have to be large enough for twelve aircraft, including six non-folding fighters; this in turn required a large (45 × 33ft) lift rated at 15,000lbs. The flight deck would be at least 550 × 75ft, with a cordite-operated catapult (since ship hydraulic power would be limited at best). Magazine capacity would include twenty-four torpedoes. Armament would be at least two twin 4in dual-purpose guns (250 rounds of anti-aircraft and 100 of anti-ship ammunition per gun), four predictor-controlled pom-poms (1800 rounds per barrel) for four-cornered fire (two forward and two aft), and as many Oerlikons (1800rpg) or similar as possible. As in the Staff Requirements written earlier in the year, consideration was to be given to providing deck armour against dive-bombing over machinery spaces, magazines, and bulk petrol stowage, and the best possible underwater subdivision was required.

All of this seems to have been considered somewhat excessive. Instead, three parallel sets of requirements, for three standards of conversion, were developed (see Table 9-2).

That such large numbers would be forthcoming from the United States was by no means immediately obvious. Given the success of HMS *Audacity*, Coastal Command suggested early in November 1941 that the goal should be to provide an escort carrier for every convoy, or thirty in all. As the war proceeded, the requisite number expanded to take advantage of

the versatility of the basic design. At this time, it was estimated that an improved *Audacity* would take nine months to convert, compared to six for *Audacity* herself and twelve to fifteen for the more elaborate *Winchester Castle* conversion. Unfortunately the most suitable candidates for conversion other than fast passenger ships, fast refrigerator ships, were in great demand.

Late in November 1941 the Board decided on a new programme of six more austere (*Audacity*) conversions and nine more US (*Archer* class) conversions. The former corresponded roughly to the Standard C conversion which the Naval Staff had just defined. The latter were the US FY42 ships. The incomplete cargo liner *Telemachus* was taken over at the Caledon Shipbuilding Co in January 1942 and converted (see Table 9-1 for particulars). She differed from HMS *Audacity* in having a small island, hangar and lift. Decks below her upper deck were made water-tight to improve her protection against underwater damage. Flight deck arrangements were more elaborate, with two arrester wires for a 15,500lb aircraft at 60 knots and two for 15,500lb at 55 knots, plus a safety wire and a barrier. As in HMS *Activity*, the only splinter protection was around exposed topside positions.

The other five austere conversions did not materialize, and it is not clear from surviving records whether specific ships had been chosen. Certainly early drafts of the British 1942 shipbuilding programme showed no escort carriers at all. However, in March 1942 the decision was taken to convert two existing armed merchant cruisers and two large merchant ships (*Winchester Castle* type), one of which would be the liner *Georgic*. At this time it seemed likely that the United States could be convinced to convert fifteen tankers into escort carriers for the Royal Navy, so the programme totalled thirty-five ships (five British, including *Audacity*, fifteen C3, and fifteen tankers). As before, the liners were too valuable to convert, and they were soon dropped from the programme. Of the two armed merchant cruisers, only *Pretoria Castle* was converted. Of the other three planned conversions, two were merchant ships under construction (*Nairana* and *Campania*) and one was a conversion of a completed ship. The completed ship, *Carnarvon Castle*, was later replaced by a third ship under construction, Swan Hunter Hull 1667, which became HMS *Vindex*.

Pretoria Castle was the largest British escort carrier; she was employed throughout World War II for trials and deck-landing training. She generally followed Standard B (presumably *Georgic* would have been Standard A), and conversion consisted of stripping her down to the hull, making C deck continuous as the hangar deck, and building up a hangar and flight deck. Although her side was plated in, the flight deck was not the strength deck, and expansion joints had to be fitted.

The six flight-deck arrester wires were rated at 15,500lbs at 60knots. *Pretoria Castle* had a twin-track CII catapult rated at 14,000lbs at 66 knots.

Protection, in the form of 40lb (1in) MS (mild steel) plating, was fitted over the bomb room and magazines, and around the steering gear. Note that even in so large a ship the ideal of protecting the machinery could not be realized. See Table 9-4 for particulars.

Nairana and *Vindex* were requisitioned so early in the course of construction that major changes could be made. The merchant ship design was followed up to the upper deck, except that decks were made water-tight, water-tight bulkheads were added fore and aft, and some scantlings reduced. The shell plating was carried up to the flight deck, which was a strength deck, as in larger British carriers. However, unlike other British ships, this one used the entire width of her hangar for aircraft stowage, fore and aft access being arranged at the upper deck level (that is, below the hangar deck).

Both were fitted to handle 15,500lb aircraft, *Nairana* having eight and *Vindex* six arrester wires (plus a safety wire). Both ships had cordite catapults similar to that in *Pretoria Castle*.

As in the case of *Pretoria Castle*, both were protected with 40lb MS plate over 4in magazines and bomb rooms; they also had buoyant cargo (empty drums) to help reduce the effect of torpedo hits. The ships were also arranged so that all living spaces were on the 2nd deck and above, that is, at least 9ft above deep waterline.[39]

Campania generally followed the *Nairana* design, but she was completed with four arrester wires, which proved insufficient. She was the first British escort carrier to have an Action Information Organization (AIO, CIC in US parlance), and in 1944 was considered the best-equipped British escort carrier from an electronics point of view.[40]

Campania, *Nairana*, and *Vindex* all spent their entire operational lives in the Arctic, being fitted for night flying and for fighter direction.[41] *Campania* had the distinction of being the only escort carrier retained postwar by the Royal Navy. She was converted in 1950–51 as a floating exhibition centre for the Festival of Britain and then supported the 1952 British nuclear test series. At that time she was classified as a ferry carrier; she was stricken in 1955.

Nairana was transferred to the Royal Netherlands Navy in 1946 as that Service's first carrier; she was renamed *Karel Doorman*.[42]

THE ROYAL NAVY took delivery of its US-built escort carriers while this programme was being carried out. In general the Admiralty considered that they required substantial modification. The first three production diesel ships (*Avenger*, *Biter* and *Dasher*), which were designated the *Avenger* class, were designed to a two-compartment standard for buoyancy but not for stability. About 1000 tons of ballast was therefore added, plus buoyancy drums in the wing deep tanks, the latter to keep the ship from listing excessively if torpedoed.

HMS *Avenger* experienced some difficulty in operating Hurricanes given her low speed and short flight deck, but the flight deck was lengthened to 438ft (and rounded down aft) upon her arrival in Britain.[43] Petrol stowage was reduced to 29,000 gallons (but by 1944 it had been increased to 36,000).

This, however, was a relatively minor problem. On 15 November 1942 HMS *Avenger* sank (practically disintegrating) after one torpedo hit. A special inquiry found that numerous bombs and depth charges had been stowed against her side, and that at least some of them had been detonated by splinters due to the torpedo hit. The Admiralty ordered all British escort

VINDEX
Gr. Britain - CVE
(NAIRANA class)
Nov. 1943

VINDEX
Gr. Britain - CVE
(NAIRANA class)
Nov. 1943

Above and top: *HMS* Vindex, *a British converted escort carrier, in November 1943. Note the two radar lanterns, one atop her mast (presumably housing a Type 277), and one just above her bridge.*

carriers modified so that all bombs and depth charges were at least 10 to 15ft inboard; this was done by working in a 1in longitudinal bulkhead on either side of the ship. Even then, some magazine crowns were above the waterline. The US Navy introduced similar modifications to its own ships.

The other shocking loss was the explosion of HMS *Dasher* in the Firth of Clyde on 27 March 1943. The ship had just completed flying her aircraft, all but one having been struck down into her hangar, and two Swordfish were being fuelled. The carrier suddenly exploded with the audible 'pouff' characteristic of a petrol vapour explosion rather than of bomb or depth charge detonation. The explosion vented through the after bulkhead of the engine room low down, up through a large hatch just forward of the lift well, up and through the ship's side to starboard via the FAA messdeck, and presumably through the bottom in several places. All light and power failed immediately (the emergency diesel generator cut in, but failed after 20 seconds), the lift was blown into the air, the after end of the flight deck was visibly damaged, a violent fire started in the after end of the hangar, the engine room also began to burn, and the ship flooded rapidly from the forward engine room bulkhead to her stern. She listed to starboard at about 10 degrees and then settled quickly by the stern, sinking in about 8 min-

39 This caused some crowding, and it was impossible to provide Merchant Navy (T.124X) personnel with a civilian standard of accommodation. This had not been a problem in *Activity* and *Pretoria Castle*.

40 Official data (*Particulars of H.M. Ships*) for April 1944 and October 1945 show the same armament for all three British escort carriers. However, *Campania* was reportedly fitted with a fifth 4-barrel pom-pom in mid-1944.

41 They were preferred to the US-built welded CVEs on the theory that some plating might well suffer brittle cracking in extremely low temperatures. The joint between riveted plates would tend to stop cracks from spreading, but a crack can (and, in some celebrated cases, did) spread

over a considerable area of welded hull. D K Brown, 'The Development of the British Escort Carrier,' in *Warship 25* (January 1983).

42 In 1943 the Dutch government in exile asked Britain for what it called a light carrier, to be manned as soon as the Netherlands were liberated. The Admiralty was then disputing American claims that it could not man its allotted CVEs, so it was reluctant to transfer any of them to other friendly nations. It did provide the Dutch with two MACs, and then postwar with HMS *Nairana*.

43 The figure given does not include the short round-down at the after end of the deck or the short rounded portion forward. Total length was probably 440ft. The early CVEs were delivered with 410ft flight decks.

Table 9-4: Type B Escort Carriers

	Pretoria Castle	Nairana	Campania
LBP (ft)	560	498 3	512
LOA (ft)	594 7	528 6	538
Beam, moulded (ft)	76	68	70
Depth to flight deck (ft)	78	72 7	68
Displacement, deep (tons)	23,450	17,200	15,970
Mean draught (ft)	29 1	25 8	22 10
Flight deck dimensions (ft)	560 × 76	502 × 66	515 × 70 6
Hangar dimensions (ft)	354 × 46 × 17 6	231 × 61 × 17 6	198 × 63 6 × 17 6[1]
Lift dimensions (ft)	45 × 39	45 × 34	45 × 34
Catapult type	C.II	C.II	C.II
SHP (shafts)	16,000 (2)	10,700 (2)	13,250 (2)
Speed (knots)	18	16	18
Generators	4 × 450kW	4 × 245kW	5 × 300kW
	2 × 200kW	1 × 200kW	
	1 × 50kW		
Endurance (nm)	16,000 at 16 knots	13,000 at 15 knots	17,000 at 17 knots
Oil fuel (tons)	2430	1655	2229
Petrol (gallons)	76,000	52,000	52,000
Complement	86/580	85/554	85/554
Armament			
4in	2 twin	1 twin	1 twin
20mm	10 twin	8 twin	8 twin
2pdr	2 quad	4 quad	4 quad
Stability			
Light displacement (tons)	19,900	14,500	13,000
GM	1.97	2.75	3.85
GZ angle (degrees)	4.54 (7)	4.38 (53.5)	4.62 (45)
Deep load (tons)	23,450	17,200	16,000
GM	3.8	4.8	4.95
GZ angle (degrees)	5.4 (48)	5.8 (57)	5.62 (46.5)
Ballast (tons)	2500	3000	1620

1 With extension 25 6 × 47.

utes. Only the captain and 148 out of a crew of 526 were saved.

The Board of Inquiry noted that there was a 1in diameter hole between the petrol stowage and the main shaft tunnel, and that there were probably also several other openings below. Men had been working in the after depth charge stowage, immediately abaft the petrol compartment, and it was thought that a man smoking in the shaft tunnel, or throwing a lit cigarette down from the FAA messdeck (and into the petrol control compartment below) had ignited the vapour. Another possibility was a spark from the hangar lighting system, which was not up to the magazine standards imposed in British fleet carriers.

Precautions were immediately taken. The trunk between engine room and shaft tunnel was sealed off permanently, existing magazine and petrol regulations were ordered enforced more rigorously, and smoking on messdecks over petrol stowage was prohibited.

For the longer term, the *Dasher* accident emphasized what the Royal Navy considered the unsafe design of the US escort carriers, in which petrol was stowed in bulk. As an interim step, petrol stowage was reduced from the original 75,000 gallons to about 44,000 (36,000 was considered but rejected as a limit).[44] Tanks not required for stowage were filled with water and their petrol pipes were blanked off. Hangars and petrol control compartments were fitted with artificial ventilation so that fumes could not build up in either. Standard British-style asbestos fire curtains were fitted in hangars to contain fires which did occur. Wiring and internal lights were removed from the petrol control compartment with exterior light boxes (as in British-built carriers) substituted. Doors to the funnel uptakes were made gas-tight, and the door between the engine room and the shaft tunnel sealed. Finally, the petrol line carried outboard on the hull was fitted with a protective casing.

As a longer-term policy, it was decided that British escort carriers would be fitted with Admiralty-type petrol stowage, consisting of cylindrical tanks in compartments flooded with water.

In both cases, the Admiralty response was a major conver-

sion which had to be carried out after delivery, since US production-line techniques did not admit major changes to plans once a design had been frozen. The official US view was that HMS *Dasher* had exploded not because of faulty design (US escort carriers were not rebuilt), but because British operating practice, which reflected different (the British would say inherently safer) petrol stowage arrangements, was too casual; the seamen assumed too wide a margin of safety.

The British view was that wartime experience showed that American escort carriers were too easy to sink: USS *Liscombe Bay* disintegrated after taking one torpedo a year after the loss of HMS *Avenger*. By way of contrast, several British *Smiter* class escort carriers survived severe underwater damage. *Slinger* was mined in February 1944, spending most of the rest of the year out of action; *Nabob* was torpedoed by *U-354* on 22 August 1944 (and written off); *Thane* was torpedoed by *U-482* on 15 January 1945 (and written off). *Nabob* was particularly notable for surviving a lengthy voyage from the Norwegian coast back to Scapa Flow despite a hole about 30 × 30ft below her waterline aft. She even managed to fly off and recover a night anti-submarine patrol of two Avengers. The two carriers were written off because they were beyond economical wartime repair (by an overburdened British shipbuilding industry), not because they had been irreparably damaged; note that they were not discarded until after the end of the war. Moreover, by 1944–45 so many escort carriers were available that the effective loss of two of them was of little moment.

The *Tracker*s were faster than the diesel carriers due to their steam powerplants, and they were also better subdivided, with nine main transverse bulkheads up to the main deck and two to the lower deck. Unfortunately the actual production of the geared turbines was contracted out, and the ships required substantial engine repairs after sea trials. As in the *Avenger*s, the *Tracker*s all had H.2 catapults suitable for US-type aircraft, such as the Wildcat (Martlet) fighter and the Avenger torpedo-bomber. They could not catapult the existing British Swordfish, however, which meant that although the latter could take off and land at relatively low speed, it was actually more limited operationally than the heavier and faster Avenger.

The Admiralty demanded very substantial changes in the steam CVEs. Petrol stowage was reduced and rearranged. As part of protection against petrol vapour explosion, hangars were fitted with inductor ventilation, and the electrical system modified to avoid sparking. An extra bomb room was fitted, and protective bulkheads worked around both bomb rooms and around the depth charge stowage. However, unlike the British-converted escort carriers, the US-built ships were never provided with magazine armour. To improve the aerodynamics of the flight decks the escort carriers were fitted with a 2ft 6in round-down aft, and in many ships they were also lengthened to increase the available take-off run.[45]

The *Tracker*s were completed with two 4in guns (both aft, compared to two forward and one aft in *Avenger*s), four twin 40mm guns and ten Oerlikons. As in the *Avenger*s, the 4in guns were replaced by British Mk Vs, and by October 1943 four of the single Oerlikons had been replaced by twin power mounts. At that time *Searcher* had six twin and nineteen single Oerlikons, *Battler* had eight twin 20mm and two single mounts, *Fencer* had eight single mounts, and *Ravager* 17. By April 1944 only *Fencer* and *Tracker* still had the original four twin power Oerlikons; *Hunter*, *Stalker*, *Battler*, and *Attacker* each had eight. Many single Oerlikons had been landed, so that *Fencer* had seven, *Tracker* still had the original four twin power Oerlikons; *Hunter*, *Stalker*, *Battler*, and *Attacker* each had eight. Many single Oerlikons had been landed, so that *Fencer* had seven, *Tracker* had nine, *Hunter* and *Attacker* had four, *Stalker*, *Battler*, and

44 *Biter* was actually reduced to 38,000; she seems to have been unique. A 40,000-gallon capacity was proposed in 1943. In principle the diesel carriers were to have been reduced to about a quarter of their originally designed capacity, but this was not done. In the steam carriers only one petrol tank was retained, the remainder being filled with water. In 1945 petrol stowage in the surviving steam carriers was 50,480 gallons in HMS *Slinger*, 48,000 in *Emperor*, 34,860 in *Begum*, 44,000 in *Pursuer*, 43,176 in *Striker*, 52,800 in *Ravager*, 41,000 in *Searcher*, 44,600 in *Tracker*, 45,400 in *Hunter*, and 44,800 in *Stalker*. Data from *Particulars of H.M. Ships*, October 1945 (corrected to 30 September), ADM 234/76.

45 Changes to *Smiter* class escort carriers are described in ADM 1/14798. The diesel carrier flight decks were all originally 410ft long, increased to 438ft, and to 442ft in HMS *Biter*. Steam carriers had 450ft flight decks, lengthened to 450ft. Flight deck lengths are effective lengths, excluding rounded portions fore and aft. These figures are from the semi-annual volumes of *Particulars of H.M. Ships*. However, the 1945 British carrier handbook stated that escort carriers had 438ft flight decks, modification increasing this figure by 17ft, that is, to 455ft. The extra 5ft may represent round-downs fore and aft.

Attacker each had eight. Many single Oerlikons had been landed, so that *Fencer* had seven, *Tracker* had nine, *Hunter* and *Attacker* had four, *Stalker* had six, and *Battler* had two. In October 1945 the standard close range battery was two 4in, four twin 40mm, eight twin and a variable number of single Oerlikons. However, *Pursuer* had four, and *Striker* six, single 40mm guns, probably 'Boffins.' The latter had no twin 20mm at all, the single 40mm replacing twin 20mm mounts. She had four single 40mm; *Pursuer* had six twins and six singles. *Ravager* had no twin mounts at all (and only ten singles). Except for *Searcher* (ten) and *Fencer* (four), the others had the standard twin Oerlikon battery. Single Oerlikons also varied: *Chaser* (four), *Searcher* (fifteen), *Fencer* (seven), *Tracker* (ten), *Hunter* (four), *Stalker* (six), *Battler* (two), *Attacker* (four).

The *Smiters* were delivered with standard US weapons: two 5in/38 aft, plus eight twin 40mm and 27 Oerlikons. Table 9-7 lists other anti-aircraft weapons in October 1945. Unlike the *Trackers*, the *Smiters* were delivered with H.4C catapults rated at 16,000lbs at 73.8 knots. In 1945, however, these catapults were temporarily limited to 7000lbs at 60.8 knots; HMS *Pursuer* had Mod I, which was rated at 10,000lbs.

Because the Royal Navy had so few conventional fleet carriers, the Admiralty saw the escort carriers as general-purpose ships. In addition to their ASW role, they would provide fighter support for amphibious operations (for which purpose they were described as assault carriers) and for convoys operating in the face of enemy air as well as submarine attack (as in the run to Murmansk). The Admiralty therefore wanted to install carrier-like control facilities (AIO and Aircraft Direction Room, ADR), and British radar and communications equipment. Thus *Avenger* and *Tracker* class carriers had British Type 271 and Type 79/279 radars fitted upon arrival in the United Kingdom.[46] *Smiter* class carriers were delivered equipped with US SG and SK radars. Ships subject to the complete modification package were also Arcticized.

All this took time, typically six to twelve weeks to make up defects after trials, then two weeks for passage to Britain, seven weeks in a British yard and then five to six to work up. HMS *Battler*, the first of the *Trackers* to be delivered, took ten weeks in a British yard. The US Navy considered the total of twenty to twenty-seven weeks excessive, and during 1943 delays in bringing British escort carriers into service became a source of friction, hence the August 1943 recommendation that the US Navy take over the next seven CVEs allocated to the Royal Navy.[47] The Admiralty counter was twofold. First, it emphasized the need for the modifications, particularly those suiting the carrier to wider service (for example, to supplying fighters to support amphibious operations). Second, the Admiralty offered to reduce modification time, essentially by refitting the ships at the same time that post-trial defects were made good. As noted above, the Admiralty could not really bring escort carriers into service much more quickly because crews, including air crews, could not be trained more quickly.

Ideally, the Admiralty would have modified all its CVEs. However, this was not possible in practice, and the class split in three. The most austere were the Trade Protection or convoy ships. They were fitted with HF/DF, on a mast forward of the bridge, and their Action Information Organization was optimized for surface or anti-submarine action. Some were Arcticized for northern Russia convoy operations. They carried composite squadrons consisting of fighters and torpedo-bombers.

At the other end of the spectrum, Assault Carriers, or CVE(A), were intended primarily to provide fighter support for amphibious operations. Their Action Information Organization was designed to support air interception and close air support, and they carried two fighter squadrons (twenty-four

Table 9-5: MAC Ships

	Empire Maccalum (Grain)	Empire Mackay (Tanker)
LWL (ft)	425	460 (LBP)
LOA (ft)	444 7	479 6
BWL (ft)	57 9	61
Depth to flight deck (ft)	54 6	58 8¾
Displacement, deep (tons)	13,000	16,967
Mean draught (ft)	24 6	27 2¾
Flight deck dimensions (ft)	424 6 × 62	460 × 62
Hangar dimensions (ft)	142 × 38 × 24	—
Lift dimensions (ft)	42 × 20	—
SHP	3300	3300
Speed (knots)	12.5	11
Generators	2 × 125kw	2 × 30kw
		1 × 35 kw
Petrol (gallons)	5000	5000
Complement	107	122
Armament		
12pdr	1	1
40mm	2	2
20mm	4	6

aircraft). In theory they would operate in pairs, one carrying fighter-bombers and the other general-purpose fighters.

Fighter carriers, to protect convoys against intense air attack, were a related sub-type: *Pursuer*, *Searcher* and *Atheling* were converted specifically to support Gibraltar convoys. The mixed Trade Protection squadron proved sufficient for this duty, and these ships were used instead as Assault Carriers, although *Pursuer* did some escort work.

The other specialist Assault Carriers actually converted as such were *Attacker*, *Hunter*, *Stalker*, *Pursuer*, *Searcher*, *Thane*, *Emperor*, *Khedive*, *Ameer*, *Empress*, *Speaker* and *Ruler*, in order of entry into front-line service.

Intermediate between the two cases was the General Purpose CVE, which could operate either fighters or TBRs (generally Avengers), and which was employed primarily in the Bay of Bengal operations in 1945.

Carriers not converted to Admiralty standards were used for training (*Ravager*) or as aircraft transports (*Patroller*, *Reaper*, *Slinger*, *Trouncer*, *Arbiter*, *Rajah* and *Ranee*). Several were selected for CVE(A) conversion in 1944, *Trouncer* becoming a CVE(A) flagship.

BRITISH ESCORT CARRIERS participated in the invasion of North Africa, but the CVE(A) concept was first really applied at Salerno in September 1943 (Operation Avalanche). Experience there showed that CVEs themselves were not satisfactory flagships, and it seemed that only cruisers could be altogether satisfactory.[48] The British assault CVE flagship seems to have been conceived on much the lines of the contemporary US amphibious flagship (AGC), with the flagship taking over much of the force's fighter control responsibility both for defence and for attack.[49]

The cruiser HMS *Royalist* was converted for the Indian Ocean operations then planned for early 1944.[50] She had the armament and armour to protect herself against air and light surface attack and, moreover, her 5.25in battery could help protect her CVE charges. Cruisers with 6 or 8in guns were rejected because their guns would have been wasted in the CVE group offshore, though valuable for surface cover and for shore bombardment. The chief objections to *Royalist* were, first, that the eastern fleet was short of cruisers for general-purpose duty and, second, that she was badly cramped, with her own complement plus the CVE flagship unit, which latter included an Army liaison staff. In any case, operations on the planned scale, perhaps involving half the British escort carrier force, would require more than one assault flagship.

Thus some alternative was sought. The natural choice was a

46 All the *Trackers* also had a tilting radio mast on the starboard side, abaft the island. At least *Battler*, *Chaser*, *Fencer*, *Striker*, *Pursuer* and *Tracker* had HF/DF on a mast forward of the bridge, also on the starboard side.

47 This seems to have been partly a bluff; the US Navy, too, lacked sufficient crews for seven more escort carriers.

48 ADM 1/17193. HMS *Euryalus* served as CVE flagship at Operation Avalanche, but she was barely adequate, having had special fighter direction equipment fitted at Alexandria just before the invasion. She was not available for the Indian Ocean operations because she was due for a long refit after 2½ years in the Mediterranean. Another alternative, the Canadian armed merchant cruiser *Prince Robert*, was rejected because she was vulnerable and because she lacked anything approaching the required radar outfit.

49 The AGCs were slower than contemporary CVEs. The British equivalent to the AGC, the LSH (Headquarters ship), lacked fighter control radar and facilities, and was also slower than a CVE.

50 She was flagship of a CVE(A) group which left England in mid-January 1944: *Attacker*, *Hunter*, *Stalker*, *Pursuer*, *Searcher*, *Emperor*, *Fencer* and *Nairana*.

NAIRANA
Gr. Britain - CVE
(NAIRANA class)
Jan. 1944

Right and below right: *HMS* Nairana, *January 1944*.

NAIRANA
Gr. Britain - CVE
(NAIRANA class)
Jan. 1944

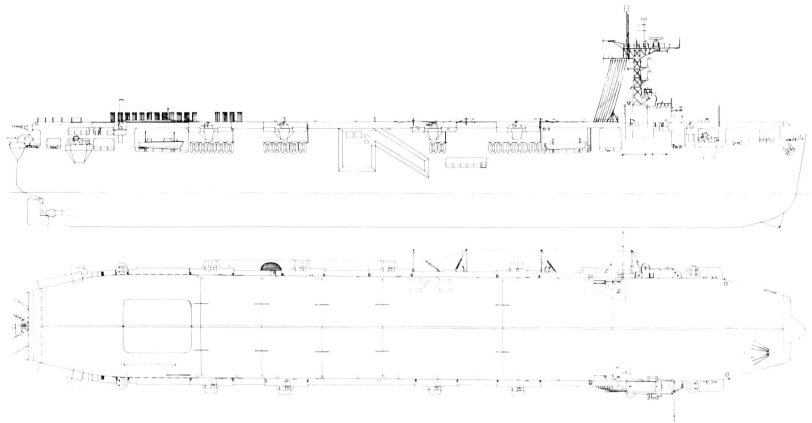

HMS Nairana. *Although the plan shows a radar lantern (for Type 271) atop her bridge, Type 277 was also fitted, with a Type 242 IFF interrogator immediately above it, on the lattice mast. The masthead carried a Type 293 for short-range (gunnery) air search, with a wind-speed and direction indicator and transmitter before it. Above were a Type 281B air search antenna, with its Type 243 interrogator above. Horizontal dipoles below the masthead served Type 251M (port) and 253 (starboard) IFF transponders, and the twin vertical cones on the after side of the mast served Type 252. The mast also carried a US-supplied YE aircraft homing beacon, and Type 87 VHF radio dipoles (vertical, abaft the mast). The folding masts carried the long wires of a Type 89 HF radio installation. Other notable features are the mushroom steam jet in the bow (to starboard), to indicate wind direction to the pilot, the deck signal panels (for visual signalling to aircraft) on the port side well abaft the island, and the dipoles projecting aft abaft the round-down of the flight deck. All were associated with blind landing: Type 92 outboard, and three for Type 257 (BABS, the Blind Approach System) inboard, two (angled outboard) for transmitting and one for receiving. At the after end of the flight deck, note the small sponsons on either side for depth charge ready-use stowage. In this side view, note that the diagonal projection is the donkey boiler funnel casing. The larger rectangular projection is the motor room exhaust casing.* ALR

rebuilt CVE, the only question being how quickly it could be converted. Initial studies were depressing. In June 1944 DAWT suggested that three US-supplied *Smiters* be converted.[51] The best candidates seemed to be ships still requiring long refits in the United Kingdom. Early in July D of P agreed that three CVE(A)s should be fitted as flagships while refitting in England. At this stage it seemed likely that the CVE flagship could retain full carrier facilities.

Even so, requirements were fairly elaborate; the flagship

required much more radio capability (including six VHF circuits for air control), an Admiral's bridge with good all-round vision (the existing bridge was not nearly large enough, and had only three positions affording a foward view), and a greatly enlarged action information centre and operations room, plus accommodation for substantially more staff.[52] Radar requirements were a 277 height-finder and a 281 for long-range air search, although there was some hope that the US-supplied SK air search set would prove effective enough to retain. All of this was much more than the US Navy seemed to need, and there was some fear that it would take far too long. In particular, DNC could not enlarge the carrier island in a quick refit.

The project did not die, because there was no really satisfactory alternative. The only other carrier possibility, a light fleet carrier, was far too valuable for such an assignment. There were too few cruisers, and also too few suitable merchant ships. By late 1944, moreover, the Board decision to stabilize first line aircraft strength at 1800 (later reduced to about 1600) made it likely that several CVE hulls would become surplus in the new year, providing they could be withdrawn from ASW and also providing that the rate of losses remained low. Two ships could, therefore, be withdrawn for full conversion towards the end of 1944.

HMS *Campania*, which had better radio, radar, and aircraft plotting facilities than any other escort carrier, seemed the best candidate. In September there was, then, some hope that if she were released from the Western Approaches in October or

51 Only *Smiters* were considered at this time, because in the earlier *Trackers* the accelerator compartment occupied space on the gallery deck which would be needed to expand the Operations Room. Moreover, there were already plans for enlargement of the *Smiter* bridge, and fitting of the required Type 277 radar on the compass platform had already been approved for HMS *Slinger*. In this ship the standard compass, lookouts, and air defence position were removed from the existing compass platform to a new one built above the after end of the bridge. The space below could be enclosed and a radar plot built inside. If necessary, the existing compass platform could be extended aft, and the new compass platform could be extended abaft the mast.

52 DRE considered existing radio facilities aboard the US-supplied CVEs inadequate for even the CVE(A) mission. They had eleven dipoles (including whips), eleven wire transmitter aerials, and aerials for sixteen receivers. DRE estimated that three dipoles, one wire transmitting aerial and three receiving aerials would have to be added, at a considerable cost in effectiveness of reception and transmission (due to mutual interference). The existing CVE had four VHF circuits plus the ship-to-ship TBS; HMS *Royalist* had six circuits plus TBS. In HMS *Royalist*, five VHF channels were used for beach cover high altitude, assault carrier cover high altitude, beach cover low altitude, close air support, and army reconnaissance. The sixth circuit was for communication between fighter directors. There was some question as to whether so much centralization was either necessary or wise, since it would tend to overload the flagship and to reduce the other carriers merely to flying aircraft on and off, letting their own fighter directors go stale. The counter-argument was that even with decentralization, the CVE group Admiral might well want to work all six circuits.

November, she could be in service in the Indian Ocean by February 1945. The second choice was a *Smiter* CVE(A), the third a *Smiter* earmarked for Trade Protection. D of P suggested *Patroller*, *Rajah* or *Shah*, all of which were scheduled for CVE(A) conversion, and all of which he hoped could be ready in time for operations in the summer of 1945.

Unfortunately, full conversion was so extensive that DNC estimated it would take eight months.[53] Thus *Campania* would not be available in the Far East until the autumn of 1945. The alternative was a much more austere conversion, limited to two months. That would provide only some additional radio circuits, accommodation for a flag officer, and some improvement to aircraft direction facilities. There was also some question as to how many *Smiter*s the Royal Navy could afford to convert,

Vindex as the first fully operational Dutch carrier, Karel Doorman. *Note the stub lattice supporting a Type 277 antenna, and the mast further aft carrying a VHF/DF antenna.*

given the heavy demand for new assault carriers for 1945. However, *Campania* was ruled out because her island structure was too small to convert; replacement of the island would have been a major, and unavoidable, job.

Although the *Smiter* also had a small island, it could easily be enlarged to provide a simple Admiral's bridge, one deck below the existing open bridge and about 6ft above the flight deck (about 14 × 6ft). Unfortunately there was no space in the island for a bridge plot, so the Operations Room had to be used instead. The gallery deck could be rearranged to provide suitable accommodation for additional staff officers, the only important limitation on space under the flight deck being a requirement to leave a space at least 8ft wide on the centreline to provide a clearance of 17ft for access to the forward lift. To accommodate the required twelve wireless transmitters and twenty receivers the ship needed a second transmitting office (the existing squadron office) and an additional receiving office, which could be built in the hangar roof alongside the enlarged coding and cipher office. Space was available for the Aircraft Direction Room (a 20 × 15ft space plus 9 × 11ft extension into the former Mk II radar room), for the Operations Room (24 × 13ft 6in), and for the adjacent Army Liaison Room (15ft 6in × 13ft 6in). No 1 barrier would have to be unrigged to provide sufficient space under the flight deck.

Masting would be no great problem. The ship needed an additional seven Type 87M radio aerials and two TBS aerials; they would be carried on two masts about 15ft high, angled outboard at 45 degrees and arranged to top up when the ship had to go alongside. Other aerials would be on a fixed mast

53 As discussed at Bath (DNC Department) on 19 September 1944, the flagship conversion would have required installation of a new island, extended forward and 5ft wider (13ft in all, extending over the flight deck). The new island would comprise an open navigation deck and compass platform, with the 13 × 16ft bridge plot beneath the compass platform (and visible to those on it); a 13 × 13ft Admiral's bridge on the same level as the bridge plot and forward of it; an RCM (ECM) space limited to anti-missile measures; a sea staff office; the bridge mess; and the Admiral's, Captain's, Navigator's, Flag & Staff Officers' sea cabins. S1 pom-pom and its director would have been eliminated. The ship would require two masts, one on the island and another 60ft abaft it. The forecast would carry the radar aerials and radio transmitter aerials, the mainmast the receiving aerials, Y aerials, and signal flags. Mainmast yards would project inboard more than 20ft above the flight deck. Two hinged radio masts would be fitted on the port side, 60ft apart. The existing YE homing bacon would be retained, and the existing 277 radar moved forward away from the foremost if possible. VHF D/F would be fitted on a hinged mast foward. The Aircraft Direction Room (ADR) would be extended 8ft aft into the existing pilot/observer Ready Room; the remainder of that Ready Room would become a new Operations Room. The existing TAG (telegraphist-air gunner) Ready Room would become an Army Liaison Office. A new deck would be built into the forward end of the hangar to take the Y office and the second VHF transmitting office. The existing Torpedo Body Room would become the Admiral's quarters. The action information spaces would be airconditioned if possible, using self-contained units.

Table 9-6: Escort Carrier Conversions Planned, probably late 1942

	Type C (Activity)	Proposed Conversions (Cargo Ships Medium Speed)	MAC (Grain) Ships (Grain Ships, Low Speed)
Function	convoy protection ————————		
	A/S and A/A	A/S and A/A	A/S only
Speed (knots)	18–19	15–16	11
Endurance (nm)	12,000	approx 8000	approx 6000
Seakeeping	ocean going ————————		
Manoeuvrability	twin screw	4 twin/single	single screw
Bridge	island, navigation and signal bridges —————		island, navigation bridge only
Compasses	1 magnetic, 2 gyro ———————————————		1 magnetic, 1 gyro
Echo sounding	fitted	to be fitted	not fitted
Bottom log and tactical plot	not fitted	to be fitted	not fitted
Machinery	diesel	4 diesel, 2 steam	diesel
Damage control	no special arrangements ————————		
Cold weather arrangements	North Atlantic service ———————————		no special arrangements
Heating arrangements to living spaces	steam	living spaces	merchant ship only standards
Accommodation	RN standards for RN, T.124 for T.124	all RN	RN standards for RN T.124 for T.124
Stores (days)			
refrigeraterated	40	50	not known
dry	120	120	(probably 60)
vegetables	21	21	
Fresh water	distiller fitted	bulk stowage ————————————	
Fuel for escorts	—	—	
Aircraft	6 FF, 6 TBR	6 FF, 4 or 6 TBR	4 TBR
Lift	42ft × 20ft, 10,000lbs ————————————		
Flight deck dimensions (ft)	492 × 66	450 × 62 6 min	390–400 × 62
Arrester wires	4	4 to be fitted	4
Trickle wire	1	1 eventually if needed	—
Barrier	1	1 eventually if needed	—
Hoisting arrangements	Portable derrick (to be fitted)	—	—
FDO	fitted	reduced requirements	not fitted
Night flying equipment	fitted	not fitted	fitted
Link trainer	fitted	not fitted	not fitted
Photo facilities	fitted	not fitted	not fitted
Torpedo facilities	fitted	not fitted but space available	not fitted
Aircraft ammunition	for 10 F or 6 F and 4 TBR	for 10 F or 6 F and 4 TBR	for 4 TBR
Aircraft repair shops			
ERS	not fitted	shops as	not fitted
MWS	not fitted	*Activity*	not fitted
elect & inst	fitted		not fitted
W/T & R/F	fitted		not fitted
battery charging	fitted		not fitted
Petrol (gallons)	20,000	20–24,000	5000 in two tanks,
	in flooded compartments ———————————		not flooded
Oil (gallons)	1400	1400	
Armament	1 twin 4in	1 twin 4in (no director)	1 12pdr
	6 twin 20mm	10 single 20mm[1]	4 single 20mm
	8 single 20mm		2 Bofors
	30 PAC		
Searchlights	2 36in	2 24in	—
Asdics	fitted	to be fitted	—
Smoke making equipment	fitted	propose not to fit	—
Protection	to exposed personnel only	to exposed personnel, bomb & DC rooms	to exposed personnel only
Buoyancy drums	in unoccupied spaces	in unoccupied spaces (cargo required)	—
Mine protection	DG, P/Vs	P/Vs	P/Vs
W/T	main and standby on H/F, M/F; H/F R/T on 1 line, VHF on 1 line; M/F DF simultaneous reception on GL during R/T transmit	as for grain ships rather than *Activity*	merchant M/F transmit, H/F transmit
RDF	WA (281), WS (272) IFF	WS only	251 beacon
Electrical generators	4 220kW (2 in motor room, 1 fwd, 1 aft)	[2]	
Subdivision	each cargo space divided by WT transverse[3] bulkhead	no extra	no extra
Bombs, DC, etc	for 8 TBR	for 10 TBR	for 4 TBR

1 Single Oerlikons on platforms capable of taking twin power-worked Oerlikons if necessary.
2 Max additional dynamo power proposed for installation; not more than 2 × 200kW recommended, but provision made for four dynamos.
3 Subdivision doubtful due to progress of ships.

54 In many cases MAC crews painted the words 'Merchant Navy' in place of 'Royal Navy' on the Swordfish TSRs on their ships.

55 The US OS2U Kingfisher spotter was considered but rejected for this duty.

about 54ft abaft the island on the starboard side; it would also be used for flag hoists and a new flag deck built in the walkway between the two batteries of Oerlikons. The Y (signals intercept) office (12 × 12ft) would be built on the gallery deck inboard of the new mast. RCM (countermeasures) would be provided if possible, in two 8ft square offices and using aerials on either side of the island.

The existing MF D/F antenna had to be removed to clear the Admiral's view, but VHF D/F, a required class improvement, would be fitted. The only important radar modification would be the addition of a Type 277 height-finder, plus a Type 253 beacon and a G-band interrogator (Type 940).

Additional permanent ballast (300 tons) would be added to compensate for the new topweight.

DNC observed that the work was considerable but considered it practicable in the time available, twelve weeks, though he might not be able to air condition essential spaces in that time. The conversion had to be done by a large shipbuilder, where the ship could come alongside. This restricted the choice to Harland & Wolff, some of whose men would be released from work on the troopship *Georgic* in December 1944. In fact work could not begin until considerably later.

It was preferable to convert a *Smiter* which had not yet been refitted in the United Kingdom for first line service. Existing CVE(A)s could not be converted, because they had the same priority as the flagships. In October 1944 the most likely candidates were *Trouncer* (due to arrive in the UK early in November), and *Ranee* (due late in October). *Trouncer* was already surplus to General Purpose requirements, and she already had many of the radios a flagship would require.

On 12 November 1944 it was approved that HMS *Trouncer* would be fitted as an Assault Carrier Flagship, to be taken in hand at Harland & Wolff in mid-March 1945. Meanwhile HMS *Royalist* was modernized (also as a carrier flagship) at Alexandria.

BY FEBRUARY 1942 it was clear that escort carrier production

HMS Pretoria Castle, *the largest British escort carrier, which served as a trials and training carrier.* CPL

would not meet the Allied goals for Atlantic trade protection in 1943. Moreover, some escort carriers would be needed to provide fighter protection against a renewed German air threat, on convoys between Gibraltar and the United Kingdom. Others would be needed to protect convoys to Murmansk, which also had to pass close to German air bases. One way out of this problem was an even more austere carrier, which would be capable of nothing beyond limited ASW, a converted grain carrier with three or four Swordfish aboard. Unlike the escort carrier, this ship would retain her cargo capacity, handling her bulk cargo (grain or, later, oil) despite having a full flight deck atop her hull. Indeed, she would not be a commissioned warship; she was to be designated a Merchant Aircraft Carrier (MAC).[54] Austerity also demanded that she be able to function without a catapult; the MAC idea worked because the Swordfish could take off in so short a distance.[55] In its combination of a true merchant ship role and a convoy defence role, the MAC recalled the earlier CAM.

It was not immediately obvious that the MAC was feasible, and the proposal to convert two ships was not approved until June 1942. The draft requirement was for a 490ft flight deck and a speed of 14 to 15 knots, but the Controller of Merchant Shipbuilding and Repair (within the Admiralty) argued that these figures could not easily be met. In May, therefore, the project was revised so that it could be built on the hull of the standard 11-knot tramp then in production, which could carry grain in bulk. Tankers were the other obvious candidates. Unlike a tramp, a tanker could not easily incorporate a hangar, because this would have interfered with the complicated piping above decks.

The first two contracts were left early in June 1942, to the Burntisland Shipbuilding Co. They had 414ft flight decks and small hangars above their after holds, served by lifts originally ordered in December 1941 for the abortive repeat *Audacity* class. Electronics was limited to a surface search radar and communications. Unlike the escort carriers, the MAC ships were not ballasted. Even so, they sacrificed some cargo capacity in favour of petrol and other aviation stores. They were also provided with more powerful engines, 3300 rather than the original 2500bhp, so that they could maintain a minimum speed

of 11 knots (13 knots lightly loaded). The two prototypes lost about 28 per cent of their cargo deadweight, larger ships (by Denny and Lithgow) suffering only a 15 per cent penalty.

Tankers carried their petrol in Admiralty-type cylindrical tanks in their oil deep tanks. Grain ships had no analogous space, so their petrol tanks were above the waterline, off the hangar deck and near the depth charge and rocket stowage.

By early July, with two under construction, the Ministry of War Transport was asked for four more grain ships, and to consider conversions of other types of merchant ships. In October, twelve more (six grain ships and six tankers) were approved, and the programme was later extended to sixteen more ships (six new grain carriers, six new tankers, and four or six existing tankers).[56] However, of a planned total of thirty or thirty-two, only nineteen were completed, with two (*Gadila* and *Macoma*, both tanker conversions) manned by the Royal Netherlands Navy. The first ship, *Empire MacAlpine*, sailed with Convoy ONS9 on 29 May 1943, and the last ship entered service in June 1944. Typical MAC data are given in Table 9-5.

The Admiralty also approached the US Navy, for thirty MAC conversions, but in November 1942 this proposal was rejected.

Simultaneous with the MAC project, the conversion of six new cargo ships was proposed. Table 9-6 gives approximate Staff Requirements for both projects, probably as they were in June 1942.

SEVERAL LATER BRITISH STUDIES deserve mention here. One was a project in May 1944 to combine a 20-knot tanker (which was needed to support the fleet in the Far East) with an aircraft transport (which was needed to ferry aircraft there). It began with a requirement to transport 15,000 tons of boiler oil and 3000 of aviation spirit, the latter making the ship very vulnerable. DNC's view was that a large tanker could indeed be designed to operate a few fighters (say four or six), or that a large escort carrier could be designed to carry 3000 or 4000 tons of oil. After all, the MACs typified the former (but did not have requisite speed), and the US *Commencement Bay* class the latter. However, DNC cautioned that any attempt to operate substantial numbers would make for a very large ship, probably too large to function as a fleet oiler. On the other hand, tankers already carried large numbers of aircraft as deck cargo, and they might as well be folded on a flight deck. The design would, however, become substantially more complicated if a hangar were included.

At this time Lloyds estimated that a conventional 20-knot tanker carrying 18,000 tons of oil would be about 580 × 78 × 43ft (depth) × 34ft draft, with 20,000shp engines.

Two such tankers were already on order and were urgently needed; D of P was unwilling to alter them. However, the idea of providing flight decks for aircraft transport or even operation had been raised the previous year. DNC commented that any aircraft-carrying platform would have to be well above deck, to avoid damage in rough seas. It would necessarily become a flight deck, and would make for a larger ship. He estimated that to carry thirty aircraft of the new dimensions (30,000lbs, 48 × 27 × 17ft) the ship would have to be about 600ft long, and that the flight deck would inevitably complicate efficient oiling at sea. The project died. It can be seen as the last gasp of the MAC idea.

A second question was whether merchant ships could be designed for emergency wartime escort carrier conversion. The question was first raised in March 1945. By this time the end of the war was in sight, and the new construction programme was already being pruned to allow more effort for replacement of the enormous wartime losses. Soon, too, all of the useful US-

built CVEs would have to be returned. Surely the postwar effort could be used to buy insurance against future disaster? Clearly no converted merchant ship could be as good as a warship designed as such. However, it was also true that a *Colossus* class carrier took about thirty-two months to build, compared to six for *Audacity* and nine for *Activity*.

It was assumed that future CVEs would be limited to ASW operation, and that future ASW aircraft would approximately match existing ones. It followed that a future CVE should be 500 to (preferably) 600ft long (that is, about 20,000 gross tons), with a speed as high as possible (at least 17.5 and preferably 20 knots), and with sufficient stability to accept conversion, preferably without the ballasting required in wartime conversions. An important feature would be water-tight frames fitted approximately midway between each pair of main transverse bulkheads, so that on conversion water-tight bulkheads could be installed to divide each large hold in two. Similarly, it was important that the main accommodation deck be water-tight, in addition to the water-tight bulkhead deck.[57]

In May DNC pointed out, however, that hulls had never really been a problem. The best way to ensure that future CVEs could be produced rapidly enough would be to stockpile essential components: petrol tanks and equipment; distilling plants; generators; aircraft cranes; radio mast operating gear; hydraulic pumps; hangar spray pumps; firefighting equipment; electric cooking equipment; electric fans; refrigerating plant; domestic refrigerators; laundry equipment; water coolers; portable pumps; winches; aircraft lifts and equipment; workshop equipment; protective plating; buoyant cargo; air conditioning plant; structural steel for flight decks; radar and radio equipment; arrester gear; armament and control gear; power boats; and accelerator gear. The list is reproduced in full because it is a kind of check list of wartime shortages.

Given stockpiles of such equipment and standardized plans, any fast new cargo liner could be converted. It would, of course, help if it had excess electrical power, unusually good stability (especially when light), large fuel capacity and deep tanks for ballasting and trim, and unusually good compartmentation (with bulkheads carried as high as possible). Ideally, too, machinery would be mounted on shockproof bearers. However, most of these features were not essential; the only ones which really mattered were speed and seaworthiness. Unless these two features made economic sense, they could be secured only by subsidy. It was generally assumed that no such funds would be available, and all DNC could suggest was that the Admiralty might be able to influence the industry to seek increased speed, stability, and subdivision, though reasonable commercial arguments could certainly be adduced in their favour. Given a stockpile of conversion items, it would be possible to earmark ships, as had been done in the past for armed merchant cruiser conversion.

The final step was an Admiralty meeting in July 1945 attended by the Naval Architect to the shipping line Alfred Holt & Co, whose name was Flett. He pointed out that there was nothing approaching combined planning for British merchant shipbuilding, and indeed no mechanism to induce owners to take account of war experience; ships were being built on the assumption that there would never be another war. He believed, too, that the new Holt cargo ships, not over 500ft long and capable of only 18.5 knots, were typical of the largest British cargo liners likely to be built in the near future. Anything larger would be a refrigerated cargo or passenger ships. Unfortunately, liners were too valuable (as troopships) to convert. Flett also considered it unacceptable to improve water-tight subdivision by reducing hold size, as this would complicate cargo handling. However, in these days of welded ships, it

56 All of the tankers actually converted were of a standard type operated by the Anglo-Saxon Co.

57 One desirable feature not raised at this time was the elimination of cast iron fittings, particularly in hull valves and engine foundations. Cast iron cracks under shock, and after World War II the U.S. government subsidized ship-owners willing to forego its use. The Royal Navy also found that commercial-grade mild steel was brittle at low temperatures. Postwar British proposals to modernize war-built destroyers were subject to the criticism that they were vulnerable to shock, because their engine foundations were cast iron. However, the counter-argument was that the merchant ships they would escort shared this same vulnerability.

Above and left: Campania, *probably the best of the wartime British escort carriers, was the only survivor. She is shown in 1952, as headquarters ship for the first series of British nuclear tests.* CPL

HMS Campania, *postwar.* NF

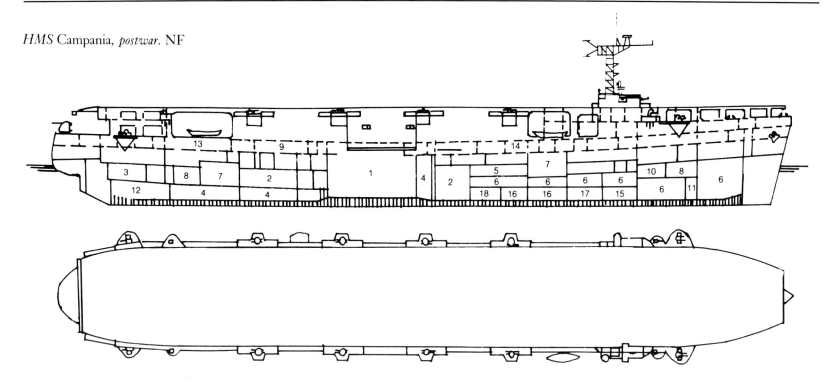

might be possible to do something towards improving the water-tightness of important decks.

Speed was determined by trade function, and it seemed unlikely that owners would be prepared to seek higher speeds. It would be possible, however, to provide better bilge keels. The Holt Line always provided ample rudder area and a good margin of power in the steering gear, which would probably be sufficient to cater for the increased wind area of an escort carrier, and Holt Line ships were always provided with ample stability. The trend was towards diesels for cargo ships and cargo passenger ships, and these ships usually had ample electric power because all the cargo winches were electrically driven. Flett doubted whether ship owners would be bothered with anti-shock fittings or would go to the expense of steel fittings instead of cast iron, although this could of course be done.

The conclusion, then, was that there was little hope of gaining any dividend from the expected postwar shipbuilding boom. It appears that some ships actually were earmarked, but little remains of any early postwar work on future CVE conversion.

BY 1946, THEN, there seemed to be no obvious way to provide sufficient carriers for trade protection. Only after 1953, when the new *Ark Royal* and *Hermes* class carriers entered service (and, therefore, when existing light fleet carriers could be reduced to second-class status) would the situation really improve. Even then considerable numbers of ships would still be needed upon the outbreak of any future war, which would surely begin with a massive submarine offensive against trade. Matters would, of course, be much worse if the war also involved a bomber offensive against shipping, because the new jet fighters made particularly heavy demands upon their carriers (see Chapter 15). In April 1946, therefore, D of P sought some alternative to the wartime CVE. He was also trying to develop an aircraft suitable for trade defence, and thus for flying from future improvised carriers. D of P's position was that he wanted to develop carriers capable of operating reasonably high-performance aircraft, rather than aircraft capable of operating from slow merchant ships.

It seemed unlikely that an impoverished Royal Navy could

built new trade-defence carriers. However, there were ten hulls available for future conversion: the ten existing British 8in cruisers. They were comparable in size to *Colossus* class light fleet carriers, and their speed and endurance were actually greater than that required for trade protection. For the present, all but *Kent* were required for the operating postwar Navy, but clearly all would soon be replaced by newer ships, and two were actually scheduled for laying-up in 1948. D of P suggested that on these hulls a 600 × 70ft flight deck could be built, over a hangar 17ft 6in high, with a 45 × 34ft lift capable of taking 20,000lb aircraft. The ship could probably accommodate thirty aircraft, including a deck park, and D of P hoped that conversion might take no more than a year. His scheme was to cut off all superstructure when a ship come into Category 3 reserve, preserving her below the upper deck for potential conversion. Essential equipment would be prepared in advance, and a standard conversion design maintained. Their high speed and excellent seakeeping would be particularly valuable. DNC considered that conversion would entail large stresses, but if it were done in a graving dock the problem would be solved. The ships would have to be blistered to about 71 or 80ft, and the increased beam carried up to the flight deck. Conversion might well take 18 to 21 months. Finally, DNC wondered whether the ships might be somewhat elderly for further high-speed running.

Nothing came of this proposal, but it indicates D of P's concern. The following year D of P proposed that the three suspended *Tiger* class cruisers be completed instead as carriers. He argued that they would be quite obsolete when completed (then scheduled for 1950–51, with much the original armament), and that the Royal Navy badly needed carriers. Surely it had enough cruisers without accepting two or three very badly cramped ones. In October 1947 DNC sketched a conversion in which they would be bulged to 75 or 80ft, carrying a 530 × 75 or 80ft flight deck and a 300 × 50ft hangar deck (twelve aircraft, each 48 × 20 × 20,000lbs) with one lift forward (34 × 34ft). The cruiser hull was very small, and to provide sufficient petrol, bombs and supplies for reasonable carrier endurance, one set of boilers and engines (40,000shp) would probably have to be removed. Deep displacement would increase from

58 The precedent for this estimate was a projected wartime (June 1942) conversion of the large World War I-built cruisers *Enterprise* and *Emerald*. The ships would have been stripped down to the forecastle deck and that deck continued right aft; they would also have been bulged from their existing beam of 54ft 6in to about 72ft, and that beam carried up to the flight deck. To provide internal space, the machinery would have been removed from the midships engine room and the boilers from X and Y boiler rooms; the two wing shafts would also have been removed, leaving 40,000shp. The ship would then have been able to carry petrol as well as much more endurance oil. DNC estimated that the flight deck would be 500 or possibly 530ft long × 72ft, with a small island forward of amidships and a hangar sufficient for eighteen standard folded naval aircraft (40 × 18ft; twenty-four of 44 × 13ft 4in), assuming only one lift, probably at the forward end of the hangar (and probably 44 × 22ft, perhaps 46 × 33ft). DNC estimated that design work would take three months and conversion eighteen to twenty-one months, much of it in dock. At this time (June 1942) it was believed that a light fleet carrier, which would have been much more satisfactory, could be built in about the same time, so the project was not pursued further. See Chapter 11.

59 The MAC papers survive because they were collected to support the Admiralty's refusal to subsidize the construction of merchant ships specially designed for wartime MAC conversion. This had been suggested by a British shipowner, Edmund H Watts, in December 1951. The Admiralty was unwilling to expend scarce funds on such a subsidy, and it pointed out that shipping faced several threats, only one of which (submarines) MAC ships could counter. Further, it appeared that Watts' ships would be available only in 1957, the year before it was expected that helicopters would begin to supersede most fixed-wing ASW aircraft. By 1953 the British government assumed, moreover, that they could prevent nuclear war by deterrence at least until 1959. By 1954 the entire issue of mobilization seemed moot, given the existence of thermonuclear weapons. The papers of the working party on the Watt scheme are in ADM 1/25633. For the decline of mobilization and trade protection ideas, see my *Postwar Naval Revolution* (Conway Maritime Press, London, 1987).

the designed figure of 11,000 tons to about 18,000 tons, draft would be about 25ft. The flight deck would still be too short to operate modern aircraft with 75 knots landing speed, as it would be almost impossible to get a satisfactory arrangement of catapult, wires, and barrier; most of the wires would overrun the barriers and the barriers would overrun the lift and catapult. DNC considered the result inferior to existing light fleet carriers, and closer to a fast escort carrier like HMS *Vindex*.[58]

DNC also commented that the US *Independence* class, converted from cruisers, were never satisfactory ships, and that converting a completed cruiser would be even more difficult.

Agreeing with yet another D of P proposal, DNC suggested that the best way to provide future CVEs would be to build fast merchant ships similar to the US C3s which had given such good wartime service. Reasonable requirements might be a speed of about 20 knots and a length of about 600ft, compared to 500ft and 14 to 16 knots for a ship built in 1945. Surely the government could arrange with shipowners to build say ten to twenty, and in that case a common conversion design could be developed.

IN 1949 ACNS, then Admiral R S Edwards, wrote a paper on the future fleet in which he proposed a new inexpensive ASW aircraft, in effect a Swordfish successor, for future escort carriers. It became the Seamew, and Edwards' idea led to the creation of an A/S Aircraft Working Party, to review the entire question of trade protection. It concluded that Britain needed sixteen trade-protection carriers, not counting deck-landing training and ferry requirements. However, the financial decision had been made to limit the Fleet Air Arm to a front-line strength of 600 aircraft, and this in turn left only enough aircraft for seven such ships. In 1950 the Royal Navy had six *Colossus* class carriers (one of which was lent to Australia) and could look forward to completing four *Hermes* class light carriers.

Under these circumstances, existing hulls sufficed. It was

Empire MacAlpine was the prototype MAC ship, a grain-carrier. The gallows at the bow were probably a paravane fitting. CPL

decided that the existing, obsolescent, *Colossus* class light fleet carriers (see Chapters 11 and 15) would be retained in Class C reserve after new *Hermes* class light carriers entered service. There was little point in designing new escort carriers or MACs. The Seamew was, therefore, designed within the limitations imposed by the *Colossus* class.

However, the situation changed again in 1951–52. First, the Board abandoned plans to modernize the existing fleet carriers, so that the *Hermes* class would have to operate in offensive task forces. This reduced the numbers available for trade protection. At the same time, it became obvious that in wartime the United States would supply aircraft sufficient to build up the Fleet Air Arm, so that the peacetime limit of 600 seemed less relevant. The Seamew and the new ASW helicopters could, it seemed, operate from simple converted merchant ships, similar in principle to the wartime MACs. Further small carriers would be needed for such roles as replenishment, ferrying, and deck landing training.

D of P therefore began a re-assessment of emergency carrier requirements. Existing British plans allowed for four (or perhaps five) light fleet carriers devoted to trade protection; D of P added some escort carriers and MACs. In wartime the Royal Navy would also complete the suspended *Majestic* class carriers (see Chapter 11). At this time the US Navy still had about fifty escort carriers in reserve, and it is possible that the Admiralty expected to take some of them over in wartime, as in World War II. No record of British escort carrier planning seems to have survived. However, considerable attention was devoted to future MACs.[59]

The initial estimate was nineteen MACs, that is, the number actually operated during World War II. However, by early 1953 the British mobilization plan showed a requirement for

Table 9-7: *Smiter* Class Light Anti-Aircraft Weapons, October 1945

	Single 40mm	Twin 20mm	Single 20mm
Reaper	—	14	7
Puncher	(6 twin 40mm)	16	7
Trouncer	14	—	7
Smiter	—	14	7
Rajah	—	—	27
Arbiter	4	20	7
Ruler	—	14	7
Queen	—	14	7
Speaker	—	14	7
Thane	disarmed after damage		
Ranee	—	14	7
Premier	—	14	7
Patroller	—	14	7
Shah	—	14	7
Nabob	disarmed after damage		
Khedive	—	8	15
Empress	—	14	7
Slinger	—	14	7
Emperor	—	4	23
Trumpeter	—	14	7
Begum	—	—	27
Atheling	—	—	27
Ameer	—	2	25

Note Single 40mm were probably Boffins in all cases.

twenty-one MACs to operate fixed-wing aircraft, plus twelve MACs to operate helicopters.[60] In each case, numbers were intended to provide one MAC ship with each convoy, assuming that it took three to keep one at sea at all times. The logic of the breakdown between fixed-wing and helicopter MAC ships was that only fixed-wing aircraft could operate reliably in the North Atlantic, whereas helicopters might well be usable most of the time in the calmer Central Atlantic, for instance, on the tanker convoy run between the Caribbean and the Azores. Moreover, it seemed likely that fixed-wing Seamews might often have to be launched by rocket boosters (RATOG), and it was by no means clear whether tankers (the only suitable MAC candidates on the Caribbean run) would be sufficiently protected from the effects of these boosters. On the other hand, existing helicopters burned petrol, whereas the Seamew burned much less dangerous jet fuel.

Dipping sonar helicopters had been under test for some time, and they were very promising. Perhaps their greatest advantage was that a ship operating them did not have to turn into the wind to launch and recover aircraft, and therefore needed little or no speed margin over its convoy. Aeroplane operation required a margin (usually estimated as 4 knots), and also entailed trick carrier manoeuvres to remain within the protective box of the convoy. From a shipbuilding point of view, helicopters would simplify any conversion, since they could use a garage-type hangar leading directly to a pad, with no lift.

In 1954, DNAD estimated that by 1958 helicopters would begin to replace conventional fixed-wing ASW aircraft. A fixed-wing aircraft might still be better in bad weather and as a snorkel detector, but the helicopter would be superior for screening and for underwater tracking and attack, and it would also be valuable for rescue work. At this time the austere ASW aircraft, the Seamew, was expected in 1956, and its helicopter successor, the Bristol 173 (which was not, in the event, accepted) in 1958. This left little room for any serious fixed-wing MAC design.[61]

Tentative Staff Requirements for both MACs were prepared during 1953. The fixed-wing ship had to achieve at least 14.5 knots, both in order to fly off the Seamew (from a 440 × 75ft deck) and in order to operate with a slow (11-knot) convoy. Minimum endurance was 4500nm at 14.5 knots deeply loaded and six months out of dock, and a hangar (with a minimum height of 17ft 6in) would house five Seamews, one of which

could sit on the lift (45 × 34ft, 18,000lbs). The ship would have to be able to communicate with other warships so that she could be integrated into the convoy escort.

The helicopters required a 120 × 30ft pad (stressed for 20,000lb aircraft) and a 55 × 34 × 17ft 6in garage hangar; more ideal dimensions would have been a 300 × 70ft pad (25,000lbs) and a 55 × 68 × 17ft 6in hangar, with a protected parking area (45 × 70ft, with a 20ft wind screen).

No equipment was procured in advance. Indeed, one fear was that any stockpile of electronics would soon become obsolete, and thus would be a liability to the entire programme. However, some merchant ships were earmarked, at least tentatively. In 1952 the Holt Line had eighteen to twenty suitable dry cargo ships, with five to eight more under construction. Similar ships were operated by the Clan Line (five) and by the Pacific Steam Navigation Company (three). The Anglo-Saxon Co operated forty-four suitable tankers (530 × 69ft 3in, 14 to 14.5 knots, 18,000 tons), and tankers were becoming larger and therefore more attractive.

Although the MAC project seems to have faded as British defence policy changed after 1954, the basic idea, that the merchant fleet would be a valuable source of emergency wartime hulls, remained and indeed may have had a decisive effect on British conduct of the Falklands War in 1982. In 1954 the MAC seemed less and less relevant, as it was by no means clear that organized manufacturing capacity would long survive in a Britain under even the moderate scale of nuclear attack which was then thought characteristic of a future major war. The British government increasingly adopted the view that such a war would be far too catastrophic to fight, and that resources should be devoted to a combination of deterrence and limited warfare (which was termed 'warm,' as opposed to hot or cold, war). In either case, the forces which counted were those in being, not those which might be mobilized within six months. This evolution culminated in the 1957 Defence White Paper, the effects of which are recounted in Chapter 16.

Nuclear war now (1988) seems so unlikely that it is again possible to imagine a protracted World War II-style non-nuclear conflict – in which MAC ships would once again be very useful.

ONE OTHER World War II trade protection measure deserves mention here: the revived seaplane carrier. As the Admiralty developed trade defence (both anti-raider and anti-submarine) reconnaissance requirements before World War II, it seemed likely that aircraft would be needed in remote areas, far from established aircraft or seaplane bases, such as the Mozambique Channel and the Caribbean. Given specialized seaplane tenders, amphibian bases could be established instantly in sheltered waters.[62] Because the seaplane carriers would not have to operate their aircraft at sea (but merely to transport them from point to point, and support them there), they could be much simpler than full-scale carriers. In effect the seaplane carriers provided strategic, but not tactical, mobility.

This idea was briefly tested in 1938, using the seaplane tender *Albatross*, which had been transferred by the Royal Australian Navy.[63] Given the success of this experiment, the British mobilization plan was amended to include four seaplane carriers, similar to those of World War I. However, no additional amphibious aircraft were bought or planned.

In April 1939 DNAD proposed a study to see how many aircraft an 8–10,000 gross ton ship could carry. He hoped for twelve operational and six spares, the minimum acceptable being six operational plus three spares. About 60,000 gallons of petrol would be needed, and shops would approximate those aboard HMS *Albatross*. DNAD hoped that complement could be minimized, since the ship would steam only rarely. CNS

Amastra was a typical tanker MAC-ship; much of her original superstructure can be discerned under her flight deck. This was inevitable, since space had to be left to work her piping.

wanted the ship to be as small as possible, something like the converted railway steamers (seaplane carriers) of World War I. DNAD considered this too small. Operational aircraft would be stowed in the holds fore and aft, and a small hangar (as in World War I ships) would be provided aft, mainly to take a spread aircraft for maintenance, but also perhaps to take folded aircraft. There would be no catapult, because the ship would operate in a harbour. This was expected to save considerable time and money. Similarly, the ship needed little armament.

When war actually broke out in 1939 there was insufficient shipyard capacity for all the requisite conversions, and the Board decided to defer the seaplane conversions for six months. It seemed unlikely that either personnel or Walrus amphibians would be available much earlier. Moreover, the projected conversion was relatively simple; it would take only three to four months.

Beginning in September 1939, DNC developed plans for a typical merchant ship, *Clan Campbell*; DNAD wanted the ship to operate at least six (later nine) amphibians (plus three – later five – in reserve). She would have a hangar aft (at least 40 × 80ft), primarily for maintenance, aircraft being carried in the holds (two of which had to have hatches 41ft long). Amphibian operation required several winches (maximum lift about 5 tons) and derricks reaching at least 25ft over the side. Flying and maintenance personnel would live on board, and the ship would need special arrangements for the bombs the aircraft would carry (two 250lb SAP or four 100lb ASW bombs each).

Finally, the ship had to have a deep tank in which Admiralty-type cylindrical period tanks (for at least 40,000 gallons) could be installed, the remainder of the tank being flooded.

Speed would be about 12 knots, and endurance about 4000nm. Other requirements were good dynamo power, two 'tween decks, and good subdivision.

It seemed likely that two ships would be converted at first, two more to follow later. At the beginning of January 1940, DNAD argued that there were many important places, such as the East Indies, the Greek islands and northern Norway and the Faroes, where seaplane carriers would be the only source of naval reconnaissance aircraft. By this time C-in-C America and West Indies badly wanted air reconnaissance in the Caribbean; he considered that employing two relatively inexpensive ships

60   A Naval Staff estimate showed eighteen dry cargo MACs operating as grain carriers on the North Atlantic run, to provide one for each HX and ON convoy, plus nine tanker MACs for the Caribbean, plus others.

61   The helicopter MAC requirement was deleted altogether in February 1954 due to limited availability of helicopters, but it is clear from the discussion that within a few years helicopters would take over entirely from fixed-wing ASW aircraft, as long as the bad-weather problem could be solved.

62   In about 1940 the US Navy hit upon much the same idea for ASW patrol of the American coast; a special patrol seaplane was authorized but not built.

63   HMAS *Albatross* was designed by the DNC Department specifically for the Royal Australian Navy, for trade protection in South Pacific waters. Australia could not have afforded a full-scale carrier; *Albatross* had hangar facilities and a catapult, and might be considered the true successor to the World War I seaplane carriers. She was transferred to the Royal Navy in part payment for the cruiser HMS *Apollo* (which became HMAS *Hobart*), having spent 1933–38 in reserve in Australia. Some consideration was given to converting her to a conventional carrier, but she was too small, and she operated as a trade-protection seaplane carrier off West Africa and in the Indian Ocean in 1939–41. At this time she had no catapult, one being fitted only during a refit at Simonstown in June–July 1941. With the completion of an airfield at Hastings in May 1941, she was no longer needed at Freetown, and she was refitted in the United States early in 1942 for service as a convoy escort, a sort of second-rate escort carrier, for the South Atlantic station, using her aircraft to destroy or at least keep down shadowing U-boats. However, experience at sea after the completion of the catapult in December 1941 showed that anything above wind force 4 entailed a definite risk to both aircraft and crew. Her captain reported that she could not be used at sea, and suggested that she could best be used as an Aircraft Depot Ship and Transport. By this time she was quite topheavy after her fuel had been burned; 10 degrees of wheel at 12 knots put the head of her recovery boom under water. She was assigned to the eastern fleet but was considered relatively useless, and in December 1942 she was proposed as an advanced base ship for flying-boats (for example, to maintain one squadron of nine RAF Catalinas for one month), for the expected Indian Ocean offensive. DNAD urgently wanted repair ships for forward areas, but her speed (21 knots) seemed wasted in this context. She was also proposed as an amphibious flagship. Ultimately the choice seems to have been to use her as a seaplane tender for amphibians providing local ASW protection of an advanced base. She already had much of the capacity required of an aircraft engine repair ship. She was brought back to the United Kingdom to be refitted for the projected Indian Ocean offensive (autumn 1944), and while at Portsmouth in the spring of 1944 she was used as a base for British landing craft, using her extensive workshops, berthed alongside the inactive French battleship *Paris*. At this time she was expected to recommission in May 1944, but she was held over for the work-up to D-Day. After having been torpedoed in August 1944 she was not repaired. Postwar she became the immigrant ship *Hellenic Prince*.

Seaplane tenders were a way of providing patrol aircraft in remote areas. HMS Engadine was to have been completed as an austere seaplane tender, but she served as an aircraft transport. The hangar aft and the heavy-duty cranes testify to her original role. She was broadly comparable to the early World War I seaplane carriers, although she was not intended to operate her aircraft at sea.

Below: *The Australian seaplane carrier* Albatross, *transferred to the Royal Navy in 1938, was initially used as a fixed seaplane base at Freetown. She was considered for service as a convoy escort, but it was soon clear that she could not recover her seaplanes while underway in most sea states. She was probably the closest World War II equivalent to the World War I seaplane carriers.* CPL

would save many others. D of P observed that even with the new carriers, the Royal Navy would still be far short of the desired total of fifteen, and that many of the existing ships were elderly and nearing the end of their service lives.

Late in February D of P argued that all four were badly needed, because the Royal Navy was so badly short of carriers, especially after the loss of HMS *Courageous*. By mid-October, D of ST and DNC were searching for two suitable ships, for service in the Caribbean and the Mozambique Channel. However, when the decision to convert was reviewed as planned in March 1940, the Admiralty had just ordered forty long-range flying boats (Catalinas) from the United States for much the same duty. They would probably be delivered at about the same time as the seaplane carriers, and shipping was, if anything, harder pressed than in 1939. HMS *Albatross*, at Freetown in West Africa, could probably be spared for other trade protection duty as a seaplane carrier. The decision, taken by the VCNS and endorsed by the Board, was not to convert any ships yet, but to renew the decision again in six months.

However, in June 1940 a second carrier, HMS *Glorious*, was lost, and with her the Fleet Air Arm lost an important measure of mobility. The seaplane carriers would help offset that loss, by transporting wheeled aircraft overseas to ports near airfields. They could also provide badly-needed patrol aircraft for the Caribbean and the Atlantic. In June 1940 the Board authorized the first two conversions: two Clan line ships, No 444, building at Greenock, and No 1356, at the Denny yard. The first was to be ready in about March 1941, the second by June. They were named *Athene* and *Engadine*.

As converted, they could stow nine operational Walrus amphibians and five spares: six in No 2 hold, three in No 4 hold, four in a new hangar aft, and one atop the hatch to No 2 hold forward. On the usual basis of 45 hours of flying time (and 35 gallons per hour) for each operational aircraft, stowage was arranged for 30,000 gallons of petrol. The air complement was later revised to ten Sea Otters (31,500 gallons). Stowage was provided for an equivalent bomb outfit (56 × 250lb, 210 × 100lb, 224 × 40lbs, and 1344 × 11½lb), but it was impossible to meet a new requirement for a catapult.[64]

As in other aviation ships, it would have been desirable to provide underwater protection and 2in armour over magazines (against 250lb bombs). However, the holds could not be subdivided, since they had to carry aircraft. All DNC could do was to continue as many water-tight bulkheads as possible up one

CAM ships were a desperate expedient, but they were used: this is Empire Faith. *Note the air search radar atop her foremast, with the lantern of a Type 271 surface search radar below that.*

more deck, to arrange ballast for stability, and to provide buoyancy drums as in an armed merchant cruiser, so that she would float with a 5ft freeboard when the two worst compartments were flooded. Two layers of 40lb MS (mild steel) were provided as umbrella protection to the crowns of the magazines. The hangar and aircraft holds were all fitted with water sprays.

The ships had already been stiffened for defensive armament, consisting of one 4.7in gun forward (400 rounds) and one 12pdr aft. D of P and DTSD wanted a broadside of four 4.7in, but DNC could only offer three (one on the side and two at the ends). In the end DNC provided two 4in guns (200 rounds each) and four close-range anti-aircraft guns (later two single 2pdr or two twin .5in on the hangar roof). These arrangements were complicated because the forward hatch had to be left free and the hangar occupied much of the deck space aft.

DEE asked for three 100kW diesel generators, since the ship would operate from anchor without using her boilers.

DNAD required an endurance of 400nm at 12 knots; DNC estimated that the ship could make 6000 with 10 per cent reserves. She had been designed to burn coal (1441 tons) and oil (889 tons), and had an unusual propulsion system, an inverted triple expansion engine exhausting into a low-pressure (Bauer-Wach) steam turbine. Because the coal in effect acted as ballast, the ship would need extra ballast if converted (as she was) to all-oil operation.

All of this took some time, and there was some consideration of a more limited conversion. However, it would not have saved much time, and it was dropped.

Both ships were reclassified as aircraft transports in April 1941, before completion, on the basis that they could easily be reconverted to seaplane carriers if so needed. In this guise they could stow forty Hurricanes. *Athene* may have served briefly as a seaplane carrier on the South Atlantic station.[65] In July 1944 the Admiralty decided that they should revert to the Merchant Navy, still as aircraft ferries, since then they could also carry some cargo. They are interesting here as they show just how much work was required even for the most austere aviation ship conversion.

64 When the project was revived in July 1940, the Naval Staff called for a light catapult from which a Seafox light reconnaissance float plane could fly. It would take off from the sea if heavily laden. DNAD asked about a heavier catapult, which could launch a Walrus. Although neither ship seems ever to have been fitted with a catapult, the description of HMS *Athene* sent to the C-in-C East Indies in March 1941 included one, presumably the heavy type.

65 Particulars of *Athene* as reported 6 March 1941 (for East Indies Station): 11,470 tons; 487ft LOA, 457ft LBP × 62.75 × 21.25ft (mean); 1000 tons of oil for 12,000nm at 12 knots (5800 at 16.5); three 4.7in BL guns, one 4in HA gun, four twin .5in. The ship was described as equipped with catapult and recovery gear (nine operational and up to three reserve Walrus amphibians), and capable of operating for one month away from base. On trials, on 6 October 1941, *Athene* made 17.24 knots on 8667ihp at 9897 tons, and 14.45knots on 4620ihp at 9904 tons. In December 1941 in the South Atlantic she was armed with one 4.7in BL Mk I, one 4in HA/LA QF A Mk V, four 2pdr Mk VIII pom-poms, and four Lewis guns. She had 980 tons of oil fuel and 146 tons of diesel oil aboard, as well as 656 tons of water (335 for the boilers). Service speed was 15.6 knots. At this time she had 1850 buoyancy drums aboard (481 over her forward magazine, 236 abaft her chain locker, and 1133 over her after magazine and 146 tons of her after peak tank). She was ballasted with 1455 tons of road surfacing (road metal ballast). By May 1943 both ships had Oerlikons (seven) and rocket projectors (UP and PAC) in addition to the armament described above. Typical stability data (probably for *Athene*): light condition, 8590 tons, GM 3.3ft, angle of maximum righting arm 50 degrees (range 88 degrees); deep load, 10,890 tons, 4.15ft, 51 (over 90) degrees.

10

Wartime Aircraft Development

THE BRITISH FLEET AIR ARM of the interwar period was designed to meet what seemed to be the single most difficult naval scenario, a war against Japan in the Far East, in which the British main fleet would face a carrier-equipped Japanese main fleet. It was tacitly assumed that an enemy's naval aircraft would have only a limited performance, since they would have been designed within the kind of restrictions which applied to British aircraft. Moreover, because they would be carrier-based, they would not be encountered in enormous numbers.

These expectations failed on several grounds. Until 1941 Britain fought land powers, Germany and Italy, and her ships were attacked only by land-based aircraft not subject to any sort of performance or numerical limitation. The prewar policy of buying only two-seat fighters had to be abandoned specifically because those aircraft could not deal with fast land-based bombers. On the other hand, one of the happy surprises of 1940–42 was that a few aircraft aboard a carrier could make an enormous difference even under such circumstances, either offensively (as at Taranto), defensively (as in several Malta convoys), or in the prewar role of finding and fixing enemy forces (as in the *Bismarck* action).[1]

It also turned out that the restrictions placed on British naval aircraft were uniquely rigorous. The Royal Navy required very limited stall (approach) speeds, partly because its arrester gear provided very limited deceleration (to reduce stress on airframes). Its requirement (at least up until 1940) that aircraft be capable of launch by catapult from battleships and cruisers equated to a requirement for very low take-off speed. All-up weight and overall dimensions were also very limited. It turned out that aircraft designed within these limits could not achieve very high performance, particularly as fighters. The US Navy accepted much looser limits, as a result of which its modern fighters, first the Wildcat and then the Hellcat and Corsair,

outperformed British aircraft available up to 1942. Fortunately these aircraft were also made available to the Royal Navy, filling a gap until British requirements could be radically revised.

In effect, the availability of American aircraft made up for the fact that the British did not really revise their requirements until 1942. Had they then ordered prototypes of a new generation of aircraft, the new generation would not have been available until 1945 or later. Instead, the Fleet Air Arm could use a combination of US and adapted RAF fighters, the strengths of each making up for the weaknesses of the other. US supply was also important because it made up for drastic British production shortfalls, and the RAF enjoyed priority almost continuously throughout the war.[2]

Another major factor in wartime development was that in 1939 the Fleet Air Arm found itself responsible for several roles not envisaged beforehand, most notably perhaps the air defence of fleet bases. Aircraft were based at Hatston in the Orkneys both to protect Scapa Flow and to support the fleet in the North Sea, and in this role they encountered fast German bombers. Further south, the RAF was using fast-climbing short-range single-seat fighter interceptors, the Hurricane and the Spitfire; at Hatston the Fleet Air Arm was limited to relatively slow fleet (escort) fighters, Skuas and Rocs. Quite aside from any purely carrier requirements, this situation led the Navy to seek high-performance single-seaters to supplement the existing series of two-seat fleet fighters.

At the same time, Coastal Command was revealed to be far too weak to meet its requirements, both for anti-submarine patrol and for shore-based reconnaissance in support of the fleet. At the outbreak of war, therefore, carriers were assigned to maintain anti-submarine flights. This turned out to be extremely dangerous; a U-boat narrowly missed HMS *Ark Royal* on 14 September 1939, and HMS *Courageous*, one of the three best British carriers, was sunk on 17 September. At this time many ships were sailing independently, and focal areas had to be covered. The carrier patrols ended after the loss of HMS *Courageous*, however, and naval aircraft were then employed only for the local ASW defence of naval forces or special convoys, or for ASW patrols ahead of the fleet. These patrols resulted in few attacks; they were designed to force U-boats down and thus to immobilize them.

For the other role, long-range fleet reconnaissance, the Fleet Air Arm was briefly provided with American-built Martin

1   This point requires some explanation. Total numbers of naval aircraft always seem pathetically small compared to land-based air forces. However, those air forces cannot be concentrated in any one place; their bases are not mobile, and they must cover a large area. Naval aircraft are concentrated, deriving their mobility from that of their carriers. Thus they may often achieve local superiority,

particularly if they can attack before the enemy has time to concentrate his more ponderous land-based force (as at Taranto). The other point to be borne in mind is that powerful warships are so expensive that they cannot be built in great numbers, so that by contributing to their loss (as at Taranto or in the *Bismarck* chase) a few naval aircraft could have a very substantial effect.

2   As a measure of the importance of US sources of supply, on 19 October 1941 the Admiralty estimated that between 30 September 1941 and 31 March 1943 it would need, from US sources, 1700 TSR, 150 light reconnaissance aircraft, and 1240 fighters, a total of 3090 aircraft. This figure was somewhat deceptive, in that it included 800 fighters and possibly also 1500 TSR intended to form pools of US naval aircraft in various strategic places (and thus really intended for US use should the United States enter the war). Even so, the total is impressive, compared to an expected British output (1 October 1941 to 1 July 1943) of 3779 Fleet Air Arm aircraft (2017 TBR, 972 fighters, and 790 amphibians). In fact MAP was unable to meet its production goals. The figures which follow compare the June 1942 MAP forecast of 1943 production with actual figures (in parentheses): TBR 2360 (1201), fighters 981 (375), total 3341 (1576). MAP announced in January

The Fairey Firefly was the culmination of prewar British carrier fighter ideas. In the Griffon, DAW thought he finally had an engine powerful enough to guarantee respectable performance despite the constraints of carrier operation, particularly the demands for great range and for very limited stall speed. He regarded the demand for a second seat as a very minor inconvenience, and hoped to prove this point by inviting the firms tendering for what proved to be the Firefly contract to submit alternative single-seaters (to meet similar range and low-speed requirements). A Firefly FR.1 is

shown. The rack under the engine cowling could carry an ASH surface-search radar. The externally similar NE.1 carried an AI radar in a similar pod. The later FR.4 carried its radar in a pod faired into its starboard wing, a similar pod in the port wing carrying extra fuel. A few aircraft were completed as night fighters (NF.4), but the Sea Hornet was the standard postwar British carrier night fighter. Although there were FR and NF versions of the next Firefly (Mk 5), most of these postwar aircraft were configured for ASW.

Maryland bombers, one of which, flying from Hatston, detected the sortie of the *Bismarck* in May 1941. Later the Navy took over operational control of Coastal Command, and during the war the Future Building Committee (see Chapter 13) proposed that this arrangement be made permanent, on the ground that maritime operations were really indivisible. The Navy's postwar failure to secure control of Coastal Command led, in turn, to RAF attempts to substitute long-range shore-based aircraft for anti-submarine carriers.

WAR EXPERIENCE LED to a series of changes in the overall programme for Fleet Air Arm aircraft development. In 1939 the policy was to limit carriers to strike aircraft and fleet (escort) fighters. The Skua and Swordfish were in service, the Fulmar and Albacore in production, and Specifications had been written for what would become their lineal successors, the Firefly and the Barracuda. In 1940, as will be related below, a

1943 that it would be unable to add capacity for naval types, forcing the Royal Navy to depend on the United States for nearly half its aircraft. Unfortunately, after December 1943 the US Navy found it more and more difficult to supply aircraft, citing the needs of the Pacific offensive. Except in the case of Corsairs, for which production greatly exceeded US needs, the US Navy supplied only sufficient aircraft to cover British wastage, not enough to supply new carriers entering service. The Corsair did not solve the problem because it could not operate from many British carriers. At this time the US position was that it had to build up 100 per cent replacement air groups (25 per cent for CVEs) as well as large shore-based formations. The British Admiralty Delegation to Washington com-

plained that, even though these requirements would soon be met, the US Navy still would not provide aircraft; the implication that the US Pacific offensive had absolute priority over British operations both in the West and in the Indian Ocean, was very disturbing. Monthly figures for the first six months of 1944 are shown below.

These figures are from ADM1/17095, referring to a Navy plea for higher priority after the end of the war

with Germany. The situation worsened in 1944, when MAP was ordered to reduce its labour force (to provide more troops for the invasion of Europe). The Admiralty share of these cuts included postponement of Firebrand production, the final abandonment of Swordfish production, and a reduction in the rate of Firefly production.

	Agreed June 1943	Scaled down for US Shortfalls	Offered December 1943
Wildcat	60	50	20
Corsair	60	53	118
Hellcat	40	40	13
Avenger	45	43	23
Helldiver	30	21	1

third type, the single-seat fighter, was added, initially for special operations and then as a means of countering high-performance bombers. However, war experience also showed that strike aircraft had to be escorted by long-range fighters, and in the British view long-range flight over the sea required a second crewman to navigate.[3]

In the autumn of 1941 the Board formalized the new series of carrier types, approving the formulation of Staff Requirements for:

(a) a single seat maximum-performance fighter solely for day defence of the fleet (Fleet Fighter - FF). To get sufficiently high performance, the fleet fighter would give up both endurance and navigational facilities, and therefore could not function as a strike escort;

(b) a two-seat night fighter, also suited for some daylight reconnaissance, for action observation, and as a strike force escort, to be designated Night Fighter-Observation–Reconnaissance (NFOR);

(c) a long-range TBR of maximum possible performance, not heavily armed, for long-range ocean reconnaissance and night shadowing.

The Board considered the strike escort particularly important for fighting the Japanese Navy, since naval strikes would surely encounter Japanese carrier fighter opposition.[4] This made it impossible to avoid having two distinct fighter types. Combining so many roles in (b) was not really satisfactory, but it was impractical to carry as many as four or five distinct types of aircraft aboard existing carriers. The hope was that developments in surface (ASV) radar would make it possible to adapt the two-seater for day reconnaissance without losing night fighter qualities.

Of the existing types of aircraft, the Firefly was clearly the candidate for NFOR adaption, using new air-to-air (AI) and air-to-surface (ASV) radars. This adaptation was expected to be extensive, and it would impair the aircraft's day fighting capabilities. Only a few could be adapted, as the fleet needed every day fighter it could get.

The Barracuda was the only candidate for (c), and it was already overweight. There was no hope of improving its performance, and its armament was considered inadequate. The only prospective improvement was in its radar, which would ultimately be a centimetric ASV scanning over 360 degrees, and displaying on a PPI scope. This would greatly improve its reconnaissance and night shadowing capability.

Naval aircraft policy was reviewed again in mid-1942, probably just after the Battle of Midway had demonstrated the vulnerability of American naval strike aircraft to Japanese naval fighters. It was now clear that the Barracuda could not survive in clear weather unless escorted, and that the escort role required a high-performance fighter; the two-seat night fighter could not suffice. The essential fleet aircraft roles seemed to be:

(a) a strike aircraft with sufficient armament and performance to fight after dropping its load;

(b) a maximum-performance fighter for fleet defence strike escort; in the latter case endurance had to match that of the strike aircraft;

(c) a reconnaissance aircraft capable either of fighting for its information or of evading fighters by its speed;

(d) a night fighter.

It was by no means clear how (b) was to be achieved, given the earlier demand for a second seat for long-range operation. Nor was it clear how the Navy was to avoid building an excessive number of separate aircraft types. One possibility was to adapt a two-seat fighter or dive-bomber as the fast reconnaissance aircraft, without sacrificing its facilities for accurate navigation and good radio aids to fighting qualities.

The Firefly seemed to be an attractive prototype for (a), and during 1942 an unsuccessful attempt was made to modify it to drop a torpedo. It was probably the earliest approach to the later torpedo-fighter concept, although in this case performance was limited because of the weight and space associated with the second crew member.

In the near term, there were still only two long-range production aircraft, the Firefly and the Barracuda. Neither turned out to be particularly amenable to major improvement, possibly because each was already at the upper limit of what could be achieved within the very tight design restrictions imposed by British carrier practice. That is, progress in long-range aircraft could not be achieved unless weight, stall speed, and probably dimensional limits were all relaxed. This relaxation in turn made it necessary to redesign both the new fleet carrier (which became *Ark Royal*) and the new light fleet carrier (which became *Hermes*); see Chapter 12 for details. Chapter 13 describes the new generation of heavier aircraft which were designed within the new limits.

Fortunately the single-seat fighter problem was much easier to solve. The fleet air defence interceptor, the Seafire (the navalized Spitfire), had a substantial margin for growth in performance, partly because it did not have to undertake the long-range strike escort role. For the latter, the Royal Navy was able to obtain US Hellcats and Corsairs, which had been designed for long range under much less restrictive carrier operating conditions.

Given the failure to improve either Firefly or Barracuda performance to any great extent, policy was re-evaluated in the spring of 1943. By this time the new British long-range carrier fighter, the Firebrand, was clearly a failure (see below). However, it was fast, and it could carry a heavy load. It was, therefore, a candidate for (b), carrying either bombs or a torpedo. The question then was whether the usual strike aircraft second crew member could be foregone. At this time the concensus was no single-seater could be altogether satisfactory, since it could not equal the performance of enemy single-seat fighters, and would labour under serious tactical disadvantages. The larger problem was FAA training (for navigation, attack, signal-

---

3   This was true even when homing beacons such as Type 72 were in use, since the beacons were effective only along the line of sight. They could save a pilot who found himself just beyond visual range of his ship, but they were of no value at ranges beyond about 50 miles. The prewar beacon receiver was not sufficiently reliable; single-seat fighter pilots considered 10nm its maximum range. A specialist radio receiver in a multi-seat aircraft could expect to receive Type 72 out to 40nm. The reliable alternative, for the ship to use her direction-finder and then home in the aircraft from beyond the horizon, required the ship to transmit on high frequency, which an enemy well beyond the horizon could be expected to pick up. Type 72 could be used in conditions of radio silence because it was limited to line of sight.

4   In air strikes on Kirkenes (by *Victorious*) and Petsamo (by *Furious*) during July 1941, twelve Swordfish and four fighters were lost to German fighters. The First Sea Lord asked whether strikes should not be escorted

by high-performance carrier fighters. The reply was that the two aircraft available, the Sea Hurricane and the Martlet, lacked sufficient navigational facilities. The Sea Hurricane also lacked endurance. Such fighters could rely on the strike aircraft for navigation outward bound, but the strike formation would break up during the attack, and the escorts would probably be lost on the way home, unless an efficient method of homing them to the carrier was found. It did not yet seem in prospect at that time. The US losses after the dusk strike during the Battle of Philippine Sea (June 1944) might be considers a case in point. Many escorts were lost, while others landed only after searchlights were turned on to guide them home. Presumably a standard of navigation for daylight operations in connection with a large (hence quite visible) fleet was grossly insufficient at night, or in connection with smaller numbers of ships. This was quite aside from the scale of escort required: the RAF had virtually abandoned daylight bombing because of the number of escorts required.

The Firebrand was the single-engine equivalent of the Firefly, and its performance proved to be limited: like the Firefly, it was designed for long endurance and for a low landing speed. As a consequence, it had a very large wing. This gave it a substantial lifting capacity, and inspired the development of the Firebrand as a torpedo fighter. A Mark I prototype is shown.

ling, etc). Even so, the single-seater was attractive. The new policy, then, was to develop both it and a new two-seat torpedo/dive-bomber.

In addition, despite improvements in shore-based reconnaissance coverage, there was still a distinct need for a new fast reconnaissance aircraft, which might not be related to the strike aircraft.

This increase in the number of aircraft types (at least interceptor, strike escort, one- and two-seat strike, and probably reconnaissance) was probably acceptable in view of the increased aircraft capacity of the new carriers.

By December 1944, British thinking had evolved further. The big US-built Corsair had proven extremely successful not only as a pure fighter but also as a fighter-bomber. It might therefore be better to use high-performance single-seaters for many types of operation previously executed to two- or three-seaters. On the other hand, the problems of pilot fatigue and navigation at very long range had not really been solved. The conclusion, then, was that the fleet needed a combination of fast torpedo-fighters and larger and slower multi-seaters. Given the same experience, the US Navy view was that really powerful single-seaters, such as the Douglas Skyraider, could take over the strike role altogether.

BRITISH PROCUREMENT and operations were much affected by the rapid growth of the Fleet Air Arm. The five-year expansion plan adopted in 1937 was to have provided 450 aircraft (on carriers and catapult ships) by 1942. The Navy had insufficient pilots even for this strength, and had to borrow about 150 from the RAF. It also had to institute a system of short-service pilot officer training, in which training time was cut largely by eliminating the naval part of pilot education. Flying training was provided by the RAF; the FAA official historian comments that, as a result, many British naval pilots received too much RAF indoctrination at a particularly impressionable point in their careers. Perhaps more importantly, because the prewar Fleet Air Arm was so small, early war losses, particularly in Norway, drastically reduced its overall effectiveness. For example, the standard of navigational skill, which had been very high in the prewar Fleet Air Arm, dropped dramatically during 1941. This lesson was so painful that after World War

II, when the FAA was again essentially a cadre, there were strong arguments that in any future war offensive action be postponed until the cadre could be properly expanded.

The prewar FAA organization included only enough first-line squadrons to man the existing carriers. The Admiralty soon found that carriers could not accommodate sufficient aircraft to meet all likely requirements, and also that really intense operations could wear out squadrons. Its solution was to form 'supernumerary' squadrons. In effect, each carrier would maintain some of its aircraft ashore, squadrons being exchanged so as to change the effective balance of the air complement of the carrier, to cater for defensive (many fighters) or offensive (many TBR) operations, or simply to replace worn-out units. The proposal for four single-seater fighter squadrons (see below) was probably the beginning of this idea.

The effect of the supernumerary idea was virtually to double the strength of the FAA, and thus to increase its demands for aircraft, since each supernumerary squadron had to be supplied with reserve aircraft on the same scale as each first-line squadron, 190 per cent. When this doctrine was applied to Spitfire supplies in the autumn of 1942, the Air Ministry protested vigorously, and the Navy was forced to reduce its plans. Supernumerary squadrons were reduced in number, to provide one for every two fleet carrier squadrons and one for every four escort carrier squadrons, and they would be supplied with only 100 per cent supplies, even though they were, in effect, front-line units. In late 1942 the new squadron structure was planned for 1944.

Few supernumerary squadrons seem to have been formed. By 1944 a new Fleet Air Arm expansion plan was being framed, in which squadrons were integrated into permanent US-style Carrier Air Groups (CAGs), which would be replaced on a unit basis to maintain a high level of air operations, with the carrier herself remaining on station. This was a radical step for the Royal Navy.

The plan provided two CAGs for each fleet carrier (Nos 1 to 6 for the *Illustrious* class, 7 to 10 for the *Implacable*s, and 11 and 12 for HMS *Indomitable*), and three for every two light fleet carriers (Nos 13 to 18 for the first four of the *Colossus* class). No reserves were provided for escort carriers. Nine (Nos 1, 2, 7, 8, 11, 13, 14, 15, and 16) had been formed in the Pacific by the end of June 1945. The CAG designation persisted in the post-war Royal Navy until February 1952, and in the Royal Canadian and Royal Australian navies until 1954, although after VJ-Day there was no longer any need for mass replacement of carrier aircrew.

In 1945, however, the British view was that although its own experience with CAGs had been very limited, US experience showed that they were essential in any sustained carrier air war.[5]

The original 1944 FAA expansion plan, designed for the period after the defeat of Germany and before that of Japan, was to provide sufficient aircraft so that every carrier could vary strength between two fighters per TBR and one fighter per TBR, as required. Each air group thus had more aircraft than could be embarked and operated efficiently. On the other hand, no replacement squadrons, apart from a few night fighters, Mosquitoes for special operations and air-sea rescue units, were contemplated.

In practice, the fleet did not need the versatility provided by the organization, so the carriers found their air establishments inflated and untidy. The assault carriers (see Chapter 9) were not needed in the numbers originally contemplated, but there were new requirements for replenishment and ferry carriers. Manpower was short, but there was an urgent call for replacement CAGs, on the US model.

The air plan was to stabilize at a first-line strength of 1605 aircraft, in theory by 1 October 1945 but more probably by 1 January 1946, given delays in ending the war with Germany. This was insufficient for CAGs on a US scale, but it was possible to reduce each carrier's air complement slightly to provide CAGs on the scale contemplated.[6] In each case, the balance chosen was two fighters for every TBR, with 25 per cent more aircrew than aircraft, to make up for fatigue and losses. Assault carriers would continue to have all-fighter air complements (twenty-four aircraft).

The assumed fleet composition was the six armoured carriers, twelve light fleet carriers, and eight assault carriers. *Illustrious* class carriers were provided with thirty fighters and fifteen strike aircraft, and the other three armoured carriers with forty-eight fighters and twenty-seven strike aircraft each. Light

With the failure of the Firebrand, the Fleet Air Arm urgently needed a modern interceptor. The Spitfire was the only available British-built airframe, and it was adapted. This is a Seafire IIC, essentially a navalized Spitfire V.

carriers would each have twenty-one fighters and twelve strike aircraft; in each case, this was slightly short of previous aircraft complements.[7] In addition, the fleet would have a few special aircraft: thirty-six night fighters and twelve photo reconnaissance fighters, for a total of 1086 fighter aircraft. There would also be twenty-four Mosquitoes for special operations, and thirty Sea Otters for air-sea rescue, for a total of 522 strike and miscellaneous aircraft. These figures include the planned replacement CAGs.[8]

The Royal Navy was not really prepared to support CAGs on this scale, nor did it have sufficient men, in the spring of 1945, to provide the required 25 per cent reserve. It would have to shift from a replacement pool system to group-for-group replacement while the British Pacific Fleet was almost continuously in battle. Finally, the new organization of Mobile Naval Air Bases (MONABs), patterned after that of the US Navy, would barely suffice. Even so, the CAG organization seemed so important that it was accepted, and implemented, within a few months.

In fact in 1939 first-line strength was 232 aircraft (fourteen TSR and three fighter squadrons). By 1945 it had increased to 1336 (twenty-three strike and fifty fighter squadrons). Similarly, at the outbreak of war there were four Naval Air Stations with about 190 secondary (training, for example) aircraft attached; in 1945, there were forty-five naval air stations with 2790 aircraft. All these figures should be distinguished from *production* figures. Aircraft did not last very long; wastage rates might be as high as 8 per cent per month, or even more in the East. Thus several aircraft had to be manufactured for every one in first-line service.

AT THE OUTBREAK of war the primary British fleet fighter was the two-seat Skua. A few Sea Gladiator single-seat fighters were in service to make up for slow Skua production, but their appearance did not indicate any intention to revert to single-seat fighters. An interim replacement programme was producing the next two-seat fighter, the Fulmar; the projected longer-term replacement was the N.8/39 fighter, which ultimately became the Firefly. There was a general feeling that the Fleet Air Arm was waiting too long for new aircraft, and that true modernisa-

5   The US Navy estimated that the efficiency of air crews dropped off after a few months of intensive operations, so that it was economical to replace a CAG after six months. Standard practice was to keep one or two spare groups right forward ready to embark, others in forward area completing training, and the rest in a rear area. This was a revolutionary idea for the Royal Navy, which in the past had always stressed the close relation between carrier and her aircraft.

6   Prior to the shift to CAGs, the *Illustrious* establishment was thirty-six Corsairs and twenty-seven Avengers, so that the ship could launch either thirty-six Corsairs and eighteen Avengers (2:1) or twenty-seven Corsairs and twenty-seven Avengers (1:1), or any other suitable combination. Similarly, the light fleet carrier establishment was thirty-six fighters and eighteen TBR to 21/12. Numbers were also made up by reducing the number of operating assault carriers from sixteen to eight and then to six, and General Purpose carriers from about six to two or none, depending upon the rate at which light fleet carriers were completed. The released escort carriers would be used for replenishment and ferrying. In January 1945 it was estimated that four to six CVEs would be required as ferry carriers. Unlike other ferry carriers, those in the Pacific required air staff, so that they could fly off the aircraft they carried, to land them aboard the combat carriers. The CAG scheme required two training carriers, one for reserve groups in advanced area and one for training pools in Australia.

7   For example, light fleet carriers could each operate about forty-two aircraft, whereas the new plan allowed them thirty-three. On the 2:1 scale they would require twenty-four fighters, in which case the total first-line strength would increase to 1662 aircraft.

8   This plan had to take account of reductions in US supplies (Hellcat deliveries were scheduled to end later in 1945), and of the build-up in Seafire production. Corsairs would be limited to the *Illustrious* class and to four light fleet carriers (total 306), and Hellcats to *Indomitable* and five assault carriers (plus the night fighters and photo aircraft, a total of 264). Seafires would total 516 (*Indefatigable*, eight light fleet carriers, and three assault carriers). All the fleet carriers would be equipped with Avengers (total 180), all the light fleet carriers with Barracudas (total 216). *Indomitable* and *Indefatigable* would account for seventy-two Fireflies, some of them night fighters, between them. Wildcats would be withdrawn entirely from service, although they might remain for a time aboard assault carriers in the Indian Ocean. Nor was there any allowance for the expected build-up of Firefly production; some Fireflies would replace Barracudas. One light fleet carrier, HMS *Ocean*, would be a specialist night carrier, with 1790 (twelve Fireflies) and 892 (twelve Hellcats) aboard. Two light fleet carriers would re-equip with Firebrands by March 1946. *Indefatigable* and *Implacable* would re-equip with Sea Mosquitoes beginning early in 1946, *Indomitable* with Seafires in mid-1946, and *Indomitable* and *Illustrious* with Firebrand early 1947. The light carriers *Colossus*, *Venerable*, and *Vengeance* would be re-equipped with Firefly fighters in mid-1946.

tion demanded that aircraft be ordered 'off the drawing board,' without flying competitive prototypes, and even at some technical risk. This new policy accounts for the Firefly and the Firebrand (see below).[9]

The new two-seat fighter (N.8/39) was conceived primarily as a strike escort, and thus required considerable endurance.[10] It was believed, too, that long-range operation required a substantial navigational capability as well as Morse code radio (W/T, or wireless telegraph), both entailing a second crew member. Initial submissions for the N.8/39 requirement were disappointing, and in December 1939 the tendering firms were asked to resubmit. In each case, they were to provide an alternative single-seat version for comparison.[11] The turret fighter

The Barracuda was the strike aircraft contemporary with the Firefly. It was conceived as a torpedo- and dive-bomber, somewhat analogous to the later US Helldiver (SB2C); compared to the US aircraft it suffered from insufficient engine power. This photograph shows prominent features required for two of its roles: the big Fairey-Youngman flap, below the wing, which doubled as a dive brake, and the large observation window, below the wing, for the reconnaissance role. The fairing protruding above the wing carried a wing-section locking plunger, and the V-shaped object folded up into the wing was an outer wing-section handling rail. This MK II was built by Blackburn.

requirement (N.9/39) was abandoned at this time.

Although these fighters were nominally comparable to contemporary RAF types, the combination of low stall and take-off speed and long endurance made them much larger. High performance required large, heavy, engines, but such installations might be impractical because overall weight was also limited. It was by no means clear that the presence or absence of the second seat would have much impact. At this time Rolls-Royce was developing the Griffon primarily for the Royal Navy; the RAF considered the Napier Sabre its next major fighter engine. The Griffon fell barely within the weight limit as understood in 1939; the Sabre seemed slightly too heavy.

By early December, DAM badly wanted higher performance, as existing naval fighters had failed to catch shore-based German reconnaissance, shadowing and attack aircraft. His solution was a drastic reduction in navigation and radio facilities; he now saw the two-seater as a single-seater with a second seat for elementary navigation and a Morse key, but he was reluctant to give up navigation entirely, because it seemed to be the key to long-range strike operation. Nor was he willing to increase stall speed beyond that of the Skua. War experience had already shown that there might actually be less wind over deck available that expected, as ships could not always turn out of formation to recover their aircraft. The take-off requirement had already been relaxed, and the all-up weight limit increased to 11,500lbs.

DAM hoped for production within eighteen months.

On 4 January 1940 a meeting on fighter policy, called by the Fifth Sea Lord, decided to adopt two-seat fighters, that is, to continue the existing policy.

Tenders for N.8/39 were compared at a conference at the Air Ministry on 5 January 1940. A Fairey two-seater seemed to be

---

9   The Fulmar and Albacore were also ordered 'off the drawing board,' but in both cases conservative design practice was followed in order to avoid technical risk. The Fulmar was a modified RAF light bomber, and the Albacore was a biplane, albeit rather different from the Swordfish. By way of contrast, the Firefly and Barracuda were conceived as state-of-the-art high-performance aircraft, although both suffered while under development.

10   Specification N.8/39 was first drawn up in February 1939, and it was issued in June 1939 in conjunction with N.9/39, a parallel turret fighter. Dimensional and performance requirements were the same, except that N.9/39 was designed for catapulting from battleships and cruisers, N.8/39 being a pure (accelerator or free take-off) carrier aircraft. These Specifications were originally N.5/38 and N.6/38. Limiting dimensions were 40 × 50ft (folded: 13ft 6in, with 11ft preferred) × 13ft 6in. The aircraft would make its best speed at 15,000ft, a minimum of 275 knots; endurance matched that required for the new strike bomber, 6 hours at not less than 120 knots at 15,000ft, or 3 hours at maximum power for weak fuel mixture (whichever was greater), plus 15 minutes at maximum power at sea level. Stall speed was not to exceed 58 knots with engine off, and take-off with 20 knots of wind over deck was not to exceed 300ft. The catapult (battleship/cruiser) requirement was to take off at

66 knots after experiencing a maximum acceleration of 2.25g. Armament would consist of eight .303in guns (4800 rounds total) or four 20mm cannon (total 240 rounds). Notes to the Specification show a comment that increased ammunition was considered more important than more (say, twelve) guns. The Specification demanded for the observer a sufficient view for good look-out below on either side; he had to be able to take navigation bearings from either beam to right astern through the maximum possible angle of depression (at least 70 degrees). This would have entailed a canopy extending out into the slipstream.

11   The main changes were a reduction in fuel tankage to 4 hours (with additional tankage available for two more as an overload), and acceptance of a higher stall speed (65 knots at ⅔ engine power, with ⅓ fuel remaining). Maximum speed would be maintained for only 10 minutes at sea level in the 4-hour endurance case. Minimum speeds were 300 knots (350mph) for the two-seater and 330 knots (385mph) for the single-seater; the Admiralty hoped for 310 knots in the two-seater. The Fulmar, the first production example of which flew on 4 January 1940, was rated at 230 knots. Probably the most important change was that the observer's view was no longer so important; his canopy was not to disturb the cross-section of the fuselage. AVIA 15/2739.

the most attractive conventional design. For the single-seater requirement, Supermarine offered what amounted to a Griffon-engined Spitfire. It was rejected for its poor deck-landing view. Blackburn proposed partial-span 35 per cent chord high-lift flaps and spoiler ailerons, which promised much higher wing efficiency, so that its fighter could afford a higher wing loading; this in turn allowed it to use a smaller wing, with less drag. The Air Council considered this experimental feature so promising that it wanted the Navy to order twenty-five Blackburns in addition to a larger order for a conventional fighter. As submitted in December 1939 the Blackburn proposal incorporated a Hercules engine and fixed (though streamlined) undercarriage.[12]

The net result of the submissions was to show that the extra seat imposed a relatively small cost in performance, only about 25mph in maximum speed, which confirmed the judgement of 4 January. On this basis the Board approved an order for 200 two-seaters, now designated N.5/40, as a long-term policy. These aircraft became Fairey Fireflies. Note that the Firefly depended on a new engine, the Griffon, for its performance.

In the interim, the Admiralty still needed a few high-performance aircraft for special purposes, particularly for the protection of its bases.[13] The suggested interim solution was to navalize the Spitfire. On 29 January 1940 the Board approved a policy of continuing Fulmar production for the present, seeking fifty folding-wing (and hooked) Spitfires beginning in July, and buying 200 Fireflies (to be ready by the end of 1941). This policy was approved by the First Lord, Winston Churchill, on 21 February.

In January, the Technical Sub-Committee of the Fleet Air Arm Advisory Committee informally discussed the proposal for fifty navalized Spitfires, and the Air Council was formally asked for these aircraft in February. On 12 March it was reported that these aircraft, which had been expected in July, could not be produced before October 1940 or even January 1941. The RAF was reluctant to spare any Spitfires, and there is some indication in the records that this judgement was somewhat contrived, the Air Ministry trying to make the Fulmar as attractive as possible so as to soften the blow. It was, however, reasonable in view of the need to build up the home defence fighter force. By April the RAF clearly could not afford to spare any Spitfires at all. The First Lord, Churchill, agreed to forego any navalized Spitfires so as not to interfere with the fighter defence of Britain.

The short-term problem remained. On 27 April the Fifth Sea Lord proposed to form four squadrons (forty-eight aircraft) of single-seat fighters, possibly obtaining them from the United States so as to avoid reducing RAF resources. The VCNS approved, but it was some time before the First Sea Lord could add his own approval. These aircraft were Grumman Martlets (later re-named Wildcats), and they first entered service in September 1940.

This left the longer-term issue of two- versus one-seat fighter aircraft.

At about 310 knots (352mph), the revised two-seaters were about 35 knots faster than the earlier submissions, but DAM argued that they could not be further improved within the FAA limits. A single-seater could use its weight margin for a more powerful engine, and revised figures showed that it might be 30 to 35mph faster (390 versus 355mph at 18,000ft and 382 versus 345mph at 25,000ft).

Since the planned two-seaters were barely fast enough to pursue existing British bombers, surely they would be outclassed when they entered service eighteen months hence. DAM expected German escort fighters to be even faster, and had reason to believe that the Germans would soon introduce bombers supercharged for maximum speed at 25,000ft. Since the engine of the N.8/39 would be supercharged to 15,000ft, its engine power, and therefore its speed, would decline above 18,000ft. The single-seater would still retain a speed margin. DAM argued, then, that the two-seater could not meet the new stated requirement, to deal with enemy shore-based reconnaissance aircraft, bombers and escort fighters. It might be argued that high-level bombers could not hit manoeuvring ships (although they certainly could damage fleet bases), but high-altitude reconnaissance aircraft and shadowers were a real threat.

This left three choices. Some two-seaters could be built specially for high-altitude operation, using two-speed blowers, though this would still leave them with insufficient speed. The two-seater decision could be reversed, but this would leave the fleet without long-range fighters (due to limitations in communications and navigation) and would entail delay. Finally, both types could be produced in parallel. Writing in March 1940, DAM liked this course best. A production lot of the Blackburn single-seat fighters proposed in December could be ordered, with orthodox wings so that they would present no great technical risk.

DNAD was unenthusiastic, although he observed that single-seaters accompanying two-seaters could put their superior speed to considerable tactical use once enemy aircraft were in sight. Single-seaters certainly would be valuable defending fleet bases. He therefore approved the production order, providing it did not affect production of the more flexible two-seaters. Single-seaters might be embarked on carriers for special operations, sometimes replacing TSRs and sometimes replacing two-seaters; they would also be used to defend fleet bases (as, for example, was 804 Squadron at Hatston). DNAD therefore proposed production of four squadrons of single-seaters (forty-eight aircraft) plus appropriate spares (another forty-eight, that is, 100 per cent). This order would be large enough to gain the Navy a source of fighter supply independent of the Fairey Firefly line.

For his part, DAM remained unconvinced that the relatively slow two-seater could deal with bombers, particularly given the experience at Scapa Flow.[14] He considered attacks on Scapa analogous to attacks on carriers, in which the enemy would fly straight for the target and the interceptors would have to meet him midway. DNAD later pointed out that the situation at Scapa was more like that elsewhere in the country, where fighters made flanking attacks. Even so, he admitted that the experience had shown that speed was sometimes very valuable. However, DNAD argued that all experience confirmed that the second crewman – the navigator – was essential for long-range navigation. He was soon confirmed in this by successful Skua attacks on Norway, mounted from Hatston. For example, sixteen Skuas managed to reach and sink the German cruiser *Königsberg* at Bergen at extreme range after flying through a

12   An alternative was a modified version of the new RAF fighter, the Hawker Tornado (which was powered by the new Rolls-Royce Vulture engine). Study early in 1940 showed, however, that it would have required substantial redesign, including a larger wing to reduce wing loading from 42.5 to 35lb per square foot, to achieve the specified stall speed. This still ft open the possibility of modifying an existing single-seater, which in turn explains the navalized Spitfire proposal.

13   Although the naval Spitfires were then conceived primarily as a means of base defence, the Admiralty wanted them navalized so that they would not come under the statutory prohibition against owning purely land-based aircraft (which was why the RAF retained Coastal Command). Navalization was justified on the ground that they might have to be flown overseas to defend advanced bases, but it does not seem that sustained carrier operation of Spitfires was envisaged at this time. They did not come close to fulfilling naval requirements as then understood.

14   After an attack on Scapa Flow on 16 March, C-in-C Home Fleet asked that his Skuas be replaced by Spitfires. He considered the Hurricane (320mph at 17,500ft) too slow to deal with the German Ju.88 (310mph at 16,000ft). DNAD had argued in December 1939 that such figures could not really be applied to the defence of the fleet at sea. In that case the bombers would have to come directly towards their target, at reduced speed (for accuracy) and at relatively low altitude. Even from the furthest point in a patrol 10 miles from the fleet, a fighter section at 300mph could deploy behind a bomber at 300mph providing the latter was reported at 25nm; the fighters were equipped with radios, and there was a system of report-passing equal in efficiency to destroyer night manoeuvring procedure, which would be quite easy to provide. DNAD also considered the 300mph bomber cruising speed unrealistically high. This was before the advent of long-range fighter direction DNAD made the revealing comment that the objective in any case would be to inflict a punitive toll on the bombers rather than break up their attacks.

The Hawker Hurricane was adapted for naval use as a stop-gap, Grumman being unable to supply enough Wildcats (originally named Martlets in British service). Adaptation to naval service was limited to provision of an arrester hook (shown) and catapult spools.

weather front, then found their way home, landing with their tanks almost empty.

Up to this point the Admiralty and Air Ministry had competed for aircraft production resources, with only relatively informal co-ordination. On 10 May 1940, with air attack on Britain imminent, a new Ministry of Aircraft Production (MAP) was created to achieve maximum efficiency. Although nominally it was intended to meet both RAF and naval requirements, the MAP was primarily concerned with the needs of the RAF. At this time they were clearly paramount; on 20 May the MAP formally stated that the RAF would have precedence. That delayed several new naval aircraft, although types already in production, such as the Fulmar, were not severely affected.

There seems to have been little question within the Admiralty Air Departments that contemporary RAF fighters (that is high-performance single-seaters) could operate from carriers; the issue was really whether their limited endurance and the lack of a second crewman were tolerable. Senior officers afloat were apparently less convinced. However, during the evacuation of Norway in June 1940 a squadron of Hurricanes successfully landed aboard HMS *Glorious*, even though they had no tail hooks. This apparently deeply impressed C-in-C Home Fleet.[15]

A memorandum of 21 June from the new First Lord to the Board suggested that 100 Blackburn single-seat fighters, now designated N.11/40, be ordered. The Board approved this on 12 July, with the proviso that none be requested until MAP production capacity became available. Development of this fighter, which was later named Firebrand, was delayed by problems with the Sabre engine. The parallel RAF Typhoon, which had a higher priority, encountered similar delays.[16]

Experience in 1940 showed that high-performance single-seat fighters were much more badly needed than had been expected, particularly to defend the fleet at sea against shore-based aircraft. The fleet was too often out of range of friendly shore-based fighters. All of the existing fleet fighters (Skua, Sea Gladiator and Fulmar) were outclassed by the standard Ger-

man fighters (Me.109 and Me.110), although they were somewhat more manoeuvrable. They were faster than the standard Italian CR.42, but the Fulmar was less manoeuvrable.

Bombers were proving difficult to intercept, because the fleet fighters were too slow, and moreover climbed too slowly, and because they lacked efficient voice radio.[17] The Skua was slower than most German bombers, and its four .303in guns, which had been impressive enough when it was designed, were not lethal enough. It could only overtake the Italian SM 79 and the German Ju.88 in a shallow dive. The Fulmar, which was initially used mainly in the Mediterranean, was effective against Italian shadowers and against the slower Italian bombers, but its margins of speed and climb rate were insufficient for successful interception. However, its battery of eight .303in guns, the heaviest then in use in the fleet, was effective.[18]

The Firebrand would not be available for some years. Given the pressure on RAF fighter stocks, the only realistic option was to order American naval fighters.[19] As it happended, following the Fall of France, existing French aircraft contracts were transferred to Britain; the Admiralty was offered eighty-one fixed-wing Grumman fighters, which it named Martlet (they were renamed Wildcats, to conform to US nomenclature, in January 1944).[20] Because they had fixed wings, they could not fit the lifts of the modern carriers and would therefore have to park permanently on deck. However, by the late summer of 1940 the need for single-seat high-performance fighters was obvious and urgent, and the Martlet was gladly accepted. They were delivered between July and December 1940 (ten were lost at sea), but they required extensive modification as their Wright Cyclone engines proved unreliable.

The Martlet first entered British service with 804 Squadron at Hatston (protecting Scapa Flow) in September 1940, replacing Sea Gladiators, which themselves had replaced Skuas and Rocs. The First carrier squadron (No 802) was formed for the new escort carrier *Audacity*, which had no lift and thus had to park them on deck anyway, and by August 1941 two more were planned, one for HMS *Ark Royal* and one for one of the six escort carriers then being converted in the United States. They were not formed, the aircraft being used for training and tactical trials, pending arrival of Martlet IIs with folding wings. Thirty more sent to Alexandria as a fighter pool for any carriers operating in the Eastern Mediterranean, and to augment

15 They landed aboard *Glorious* rather than *Ark Royal* because her lifts were large enough to take them below, and thus to clear the carrier's deck for operational flying. However, photographs taken the day before *Glorious* was sunk show these RAF Hurricanes ranged at the after end of the flight deck.

16 Thus on 30 January 1941 MAP announced that no N.11/40 could be built for the Navy until Sabre production had established a surplus over Typhoon requirements. The Admiralty replied that only three would be needed, for prototypes, since production would not begin until 1942, and on 7 February MAP promised two Sabres for prototypes. At this time the Admiralty asked that the order be increased from 100 to 300, to achieve a peak production of twenty-five to thirty per month. At MAP suggestion, the Admiralty agreed to consider an adapted version of the Typhoon as an alternative, but this was rejected in March. The MAP agreed, and in April it instructed Blackburn to proceed with the first fifty aircraft, and with the balance of 250 when raw material was ordered (July 1941). At this time the prototype was expected at the end of 1941, and the first squadron in the autumn of 1942. The prototype actually flew on 27 February 1942.

17 According to the official FAA history, ADM 234/383, pilots tended to open fire at excessive range, partly because they could not easily overtake their targets, but partly also because they were unprotected, for instance by armour glass windscreens.

18 A table in the FAA official history (Vol I) shows 100 Skua engagements against German aircraft during 1940, thirty-six against Italians, and sixteen against French, for a maximum of thirty-three Skuas operational. Sea Gladiators (fifteen aircraft operational) had forty-eight engagements, and Fulmars (thirty-seven aircraft) sixty-seven. Both Fulmars and Sea Gladiators made a high proportion of kills, but few were fighters. Skua victories were limited by its low speed and slow climb, but even the Fulmar found it difficult to catch Italian SM 79 bombers. The official historian suggested that 20 or 30 knots more might have made a great difference. He considered that firepower accounted for much of the Fulmar's superiority; he attributed the success of the Sea Gladiator to its manoeuvrability.

19 It is possible that by June 1940 the Admiralty had already ordered 100 Grumman fighters, and that the ex-French aircraft preceded them only because the Admiralty were willing to accept a delay so as to have then fitted with folding wings. The Air Ministry considered and rejected the aircraft which became the Martlet I in about January 1940; the British option (for what became the Martlet II) was exercised officially on 7 October 1940. Grumman company files include no correspondence between January and October, but a British file dated 7 July 1940 lists 100 Martlets already on order, with another 150 soon to be added.

20 The Admiralty also obtained twenty-six Brewster Buffaloes originally ordered for Belgium. Eighteen were shipped to Alexandria (without crews) late in 1940 or early in 1941 as a reserve of high-performance carrier fighters, to be embarked for special operations. Six (possibly not among those at Alexandria) went to Suda Bay, Crete in March 1941 with 805 Squadron, in the fleet base defence role.

RAF fighters defending the fleet base at Alexandria. Although carriers had been withdrawn from the Eastern Mediterranean, this role was considered so important that more Martlets were shipped directly from the United States to Alexandria.

Tactical trials showed that the Martlet was more manoeuvrable than the Hurricane I, was faster up to 15,000ft, and climbed better.[21] It introduced the Royal Navy to the .50-calibre Colt machine-gun, four of which armed the Martlet I.[22] In August 1941 the Martlet was considered the best available naval fighter, pending production of the Firebrand. The Admiralty asked for 450, and was promised an initial shipment of 250. Unfortunately, deliveries were nine months late, and did not begin until September 1941.[23]

Another interim fighter was therefore needed; it would have to come from the RAF. Early in 1941 the Air Ministry was rebuilding RAF fighter strength to make up for the losses of the Battle of Britain, and it was concentrating on Spitfires, all production of which the RAF was absorbing. The Admiralty therefore asked for Hurricanes, which were considered acceptable for naval service. The type had already been earmarked for CAM service, so further modification for carrier operation was less onerous. The Prime Minister, Churchill, ordered the Air Ministry to provide a few really fast fighters for the carriers, and 270 Hurricanes were released between February and May 1941. As in the case of the Martlet, the Hurricane's wings could not fold; it had to go aboard ships with unusually large lifts. Initially, therefore, one squadron was assigned to HMS *Furious*, with a second planned for HMS *Indomitable* (whose forward lift had been enlarged while the ship was under construction). Half a squadron was assigned to the naval catapult ships (CAM ships had RAF aircraft).

Hurricane I performance was insufficient; in August the Admiralty asked for either Hurricane IIs or Spitfire IIIs. In September 1941 following a directive by the Prime Minister ('the aircraft carriers should have supreme priority in quality and quantity of suitable types'), the Admiralty asked for 400 current Spitfires, with fixed (non-folding) wings but with

arrester hooks. A Spitfire VB successfully deck-landed aboard HMS *Illustrious* late in 1941. The Air Ministry could not spare 400, and the Admiralty agreed to accept 250, initially forty-eight hooked Mk V(B) (Seafire IB) armed with two 20mm cannon and four machine-guns, and then 202 hooked and spooled (for accelerators) Mk V(C) which could be armed with four 20mm cannon (Seafire IIC). In fact, in an effort to improve take-off performance, these aircraft were limited to two 20mm cannon and four .303in machine-guns. There was some hope, which proved vain, that they could be built so that two more 20mm guns could be fitted for special operations or when the aircraft were shore-based. Even with the weight reduction, their take-off performance was too poor to permit service aboard escort carriers. Deliveries of Seafire IB began in June 1942, with six assigned to each of *Formidable*, *Illustrious* and *Victorious*. Because they could not be folded, they had to be carried as a permanent deck park, their tails on outriggers.

The take-off problem limited escort carriers to Hurricanes and Martlets. During the North African invasion, the Hurricane II (four 20mm guns) showed that it could fly from escort carrier decks, thanks to its large wing. By this time it could no longer deal with fast German shore-based aircraft, but it was valued for its capability against many slower German aircraft and many shadowers. It therefore remained in British naval service, although numbers in service did not increase after late 1942.

At this point both Firefly and Firebrand should have been ready to enter service, but unfortunately such was not the case. The Firefly was delayed, first, by MAP refusal to order its Griffon engine solely for a naval aircraft. When that had been resolved, 300 more (for a total of 500) were ordered in February 1941, with the prototype scheduled to fly at the end of 1941 (it actually flew on 22 December) and the first squadron forming in the autumn of 1942. Design and production planning, however, were delayed by the company's work on the Albacore and Barracuda bombers. Firefly development was further delayed by the crash of one of the two prototypes. However, production prototypes were completed during 1942, and a total of 800 (500 Mk I, 200 Mk II, and 100 Mk III) aircraft were on order by mid-1943.

Even so the delay was unfortunate in that the Firefly was the only candidate modern carrier night fighter; existing air-to-air (AI, or Air Interception) radar required a dedicated operator, although the US Navy was experimenting with a pilot-operated set. Conversion of existing Fulmars was undertaken to provide both training aircraft and an emergency capability.[24]

The Firebrand story was sadder. As DAM had said, it was essentially a single-seat equivalent of the big Firefly, and as a result it was large, heavy and unmanoeuvrable. It was also too slow; its measured speed (345mph) was 40mph below expectation and 15mph slower than that of the Seafire IIC. The big Firebrand wing did promise superior load-carrying, perhaps as a dive- or torpedo-bomber, but hardly as a fighter. Later, in March 1943, the Firebrand was rejected as an escort fighter because Firefly performance was closer to that of a bomber, and because the US-supplied Corsair performed better overall.

By July 1942, then, the Seafire, the improvised single-seater, was clearly the best British-built fighter. The US Navy could not release Martlets as quickly as expected once the United States entered World War II, so in July 1942 the Admiralty requested 500 more Spitfires (to replace Fireflies and Firebrands) and 250 Hurricanes (to replace an expected 250 Martlets).[25] This was unpopular with the Air Ministry, which was trying to build its own forces while delivering 2400 modern fighters to the Soviet Union. The Air Ministry cut the requirement by 267 aircraft by taking over some shore respon-

---

21 The Martlet was rated at 280 knots, compared to 230 for the Fulmar and 195 for the Skua; at this time the Hurricane was rated at 280 knots and the Spitfire at 300. However, endurance at maximum speed was only ¾ hour for the Spitfire, and 1 hour for the Hurricane, compared to 2¾ hours for the Martlet, and 2 hours for Fulmar and Skua. At economical speed, Fulmar endurance was 6 hours (to match strike forces), and Skua and Martlet were similar; Hurricane endurance was 4¼ hours, and Spitfire 3½ hours.

22 The Fleet Air Arm found the Fulmar's eight .303s reliable but barely adequate in killing power. Opinion within the FAA was divided as to whether the increased hitting power of the .50 was worth its lower rate of fire and the reduced number of rounds (for example, 1000rpg in a Fulmar, compared to 400 in a Martlet, for half the number of guns). Experience, particularly against shadowers, showed that the Martlet was more effective. In 1940 the RAF was fitting a few 20mm guns to its fighters, but none in naval service; they were tried in at least one Fulmar. At least some late-production Fulmars (sometime after August 1941) and all Fulmars converted to night fighter were armed with four .5in guns. By August 1941 Fulmar observers, previously entirely unarmed, had each been provided with a Thompson sub-

machine gun (ADM 1/11980 of 1 August 1941). Some aircraft had a single Vickers K gun in the rear cockpit. During the spring of 1942, all Fulmars were ordered equipped to carry one 250lb bomb or 500lb bomb or an overload tank, for low-level or shallow dive-bombing.

23 The Martlet II, corresponding to the US F4F-3A, was powered by the more reliable Pratt & Whitney Twin Wasp, and it was armed with six .5in guns. The first ten (of 100 delivered) had non-folding wings and four rather than six guns. Of the other ninety, fifty-four were shipped to the Far East, some being lost at sea. The Martlet III was similar, but had fixed wings, and comprised ten British-ordered and thirty Greek-ordered aircraft. A total of 220 Martlet IVs (F4F-4) were supplied under Lend-Lease, followed by 312 Wildcat (rather than Martlet) Vs (FM-1) and 340 Wildcat VIs (FM-2). In the Mk VI the original Cyclone engine was re-introduced. The Martlet V and Wildcat VI had four rather than six .5in guns, to improve performance against Zero fighters. These delivery figures probably do not include Wildcats which the US Navy placed aboard HMS *Illustrious* and HMS *Formidable* when they left US yards after damage experienced in the eastern Mediterranean was repaired.

24 Work on the Fulmar NF.II, with AI.VI radar, began late in 1941. At least 100 were fitted, fifty for training and fifty to provide an emergency pool of carrier night fighters. They were armed with four .5in guns, with armour-piercing ammunition required specially for stern attacks. The first converted fighters joined No 784 Squadron (night fighter training) in the spring of 1942, and the first fully operational aircraft were scheduled for completion in May 1943. In the event, the programme was much delayed; the AI.VI radar was considered inadequate at low altitude, where most night interceptions would occur. Even so, Fulmar night fighters carried out successful operational trials in the escort-carrier *Campania*, which had been fitted specially for night fighter control, in the spring of 1944.

25 These official figures do not quite match. By 1942, 500 Fireflies and 200 Firebrands, presumably in addition to development aircraft, were on order. The official decision to replace Firebrands with Seafires was made on 14 August 1942, but it seems to have been expected. The aircraft would be manufactured by Westland in lieu of Barracudas (which would be transferred to Blackburn), and 262 aircraft would, it was hoped, be produced up to the end of 1943.

26 A total of at least 167 Seafire IBs (one prototype and 166 production aircraft) were converted from Spitfire VBs. Orders for Mk IIC comprised 523 Mk IIC (some completed as Mk III) from Westland and 464 Mk IIC from Supermarine; another sixty were cancelled in January 1943. Orders for Mk III were: 750 from Westland (some cancelled) and 300 from Cunliffe Owen. In all, 373 Mk IIC (prototype plus 372 production aircraft) and either 1218 or 1250 Mk III were built. Of the later Griffon types, there were 390 Mk XV, 234 Mk XVII, fifty-one F.45, twenty-six F.46 and ninety F.47. Data from E V Morgan and E Shacklady, *Spitfire: The History* (Key Publishing Ltd, Stamford, 1987) and from C F Andrews and E B Morgan, *Supermarine Aircraft Since 1914* (Putnam, London, 1987).

27 In all, 1699 Merlin-engined Seafires were built, 166 of them being converted Spitfire Vs. A total of 110 Spitfire IIs were designated LIIC, powered by a low-altitude Merlin with cropped wings. In others, Merlin 32 engines replaced the original Merlin 46, for better high-altitude performance. The next step in Seafire development was Mk XV, powered by a Griffon engine, with the tail of a Mk XII. It was soon succeeded by Mk XVII, which had a bubble canopy. These Mark numbers were chosen to avoid duplication with the Spitfire series, and an entirely different series was chosen for Seafire versions of the redesigned Spitfire 21.

28 It was estimated that the Typhoon I (11,010lbs) would require 620ft to take off in a 20-knot wind (454 with 30 knots); the Tempest II (Centaurus, 10,550lbs) would take off in 515ft (385). Both stalled at about 78 knots. Maximum speeds were, respectively, 348 knots at 21,000ft and 370 knots at 18,600ft. Ranges at most economical speed were, respectively, 536 and 596nm.

29 The Fleet Air Arm received ninety-five F4U-1s (Corsair I), followed by 510 Corsair IIs (F4U-1 with raised canopy), 430 Corsair IIIs (Brewster-built F3A-1, used only for operational training), and 937 Corsair IVs (Goodyear-built FG-1 and FG-1D; another forty were cancelled at the end of the war). Corsair II and IV were the main combat versions. Hellcat deliveries were: 252 Mk Is (F6F-3) and 930 Mk IIs (F6F-5). Of the Hellcat IIs, seventy-four were Hellcat NF IIs (F6F-5N). Unarmed photo-reconnaissance Hellcat PR IIs and camera-equipped FR IIs (similar to F6F-5Ps) were apparently converted by the Royal Navy. The proposed British name, Gannet, was never used in practice. At the end of 1944 the British expected one-third of their new Hellcats to be night-fighting F6F-5Ns. A quarter of all Hellcats were to be modified for the FR role.

sibilities, and the Admiralty cut another 169 by accepting 100 per cent reserves for the supernumerary squadrons in lieu of 190 per cent. This reduced the Admiralty requirement to 234 of the most modern fighters, plus eighty for training, a total of 314.

This was a considerable reduction. On 1 July the MAP programme showed 462 Seafires already projected (but 260 of which the Air Ministry had not yet agreed to release; the other 202 were from the previous order for Seafire IIC), plus 262 Firebrands, a total of 724 aircraft. Beyond the earlier order for 202 Seafire IIC, the Admiralty wanted another 239 in lieu of Firebrands, and 234 more, a total of 675, not including eighty obsolete Spitfires and Hurricanes for training. On 29 September the Admiralty revised its requirements for modern RAF fighters. It wanted 492 Seafires (229 non-folding and 143 folding), but only 120 Hurricane IIC, for a total of 612 aircraft. In fact 400 Seafire IICs were built.[26]

Once the Seafire had been chosen as the standard British-built single-seat naval fighter, redesign with a folding wing became essential, since only a folding Seafire could be stowed below in all the fleet carriers. This was Mark III, essentially a Seafire II with manually-folded wings. Production began in April 1943, and over 1200 were built.[27]

There was one possible Seafire successor, the heavy Hawker fighter which the RAF had developed as a Spitfire successor: the Typhoon and its lighter-weight relative, the Tempest. Although a suggested Sea Typhoon had been rejected (as an alternative to the Firebrand) in April 1941, in December 1942 RAA suggested that a Typhoon be hooked for trials. The original Sea Typhoon had been rejected because it required massive modification to meet the 4-hour cruising endurance and the take-off and loading requirements imposed in 1940. In the interim, the Spitfire, which clearly did not meet these requirements, had been accepted. The minimum modifications were installation of an an arrester hook and a 4-blade propeller, and in January 1943 the Admiralty asked for one of each for deck trials. The Fifth Sea Lord cautioned that because the Typhoon itself showed no great performance improvement over the Spitfire, little could be hoped of a Sea Typhoon. On the other hand, unlike the Spitfire, Hawker fighters were very strongly built (particularly in their undercarriage), and the pilot's view was excellent. 'These are cart-horses, pulled along by immense engines; the Spitfire is more a racehorse.' They did land at very high speeds, and they were at nearly the upper limit of carrier aircraft weight. At Boscombe Down in 1941 a naval pilot testing the Typhoon reported that it would be difficult to operate from a carrier because of its long take-off run, high stall speed and poor view; it was not nearly as controllable as a Spitfire at stall speed. The Firebrand would be a better deck-lander.[28]

The RAF considered the Typhoon a good bomber-destroyer but a poor dog-fighter. However, the Typhoon did seem to go some way towards combining the 'umbrella fighter' (interceptor) and the long-range escort. DNAD supported the test proposal on the ground that the Fleet Air Arm could not go very far wrong by keeping up with the RAF.

In the event, the Typhoon IB (DN 419) allocated for preliminary trials crashed (on 8 February 1943) due to engine failure, and the only existing Tempest was still in Hawker hands. However, the Navy's interest in these fighters probably led Hawker to offer the Navy a developed Tempest, the Sea Fury, as an interceptor/escort; see Chapter 13.

Contemporary with the Seafire were two US high-performance long range naval fighters, the Corsair and the Hellcat.[29] The US Navy had chosen the big Corsair in 1940 as the successor to the Wildcat, emphasizing its very high speed. Unfortunately, early carrier trials were unsuccessful, and Cor-

Except for a few high-performance fighters, carrier aircraft all had to fold for stowage. Very large aircraft had large wings, and folding schemes could be complex. This folded Barracuda II was photographed in the autumn of 1944. Note the handling hoops under the wings, necessary because the wings were so high (to give the observer an excellent view), and the radar masts (for long-wave ASV radar) above the wings, inboard of the locking posts.

sairs were made available to the Marine Corps – and to the Royal Navy – from early 1943 onwards. The first unit formed was No 1830 Squadron, on 1 June 1943. Although there were some initial difficulties, the Royal Navy found the Corsair entirely acceptable; many had their wing tips clipped by 16in so that they would fit British carrier hangars. The Corsair proved that a single fighter could be built to perform all the fighter roles: fleet air defence (interception), escort, and single-seat attack.[30]

The Hellcat was designed as an alternative to the Corsair, and although it had a somewhat lower performance, it was much better suited to carrier operations. The US Navy was therefore reluctant, at first, to release many Hellcats to the Fleet Air Arm. From 1944 on, with an improved Corsair in squadron service aboard US carriers, the situation changed and Hellcats became available in quantity. The clearest evidence of this shift is the difference between the number of early Corsairs and early Hellcats transferred, compared to the difference between late models (Corsair IV versus Hellcat II).

THE OTHER GREAT wartime fighter development was radar control of interception. There was little expectation, before the advent of radar, that carrier-borne fighters could intercept incoming enemy bombers. As aircraft speed increased, warning time became tighter, and no carrier could accommodate enough fighters to maintain a standing patrol. As much as any other factor, this explains why the Royal Navy could not emphasize performance in its fighters. The approach to higher performance, in 1939–40, was initially associated not with the defence of the fleet at sea, but rather with radar-directed interception in defence of fixed fleet bases.

30 The Fleet Air Arm considered the Corsair the better dive-bomber of the two, because the Hellcat tended to become tail-heavy in a prolonged steep dive with its undercarriage down (as an improvised dive brake).

Fighter direction entailed several distinct steps. First, targets had to be detected at maximum range, largely by radar. Second, this information had to be collated in some form usable by fighters. The fighters then had to be directed. Each step involved radio (or wireless telegraphy) technology, and several steps risked detection by enemy intercept receivers.

British naval fighter direction practice derived in large part from the techniques developed before the war by the RAF. It was first put into practice during the second phase of Norwegian operations, beginning on 24 April 1940, with cruisers providing radar warning to the carriers *Ark Royal* and *Glorious*.

Approaching aircraft were tracked either by a cruiser's radar or visually by the controlling ship. Lack of reliable ship-to-air voice (that is, pilot-operated) radio (R/T) made control difficult. Not only did the single-seat Sea Gladiators depend entirely on voice radio, but Skuas used for fleet air defence generally flew without the radio operators who would have received Morse messages. Ideally, fighters would have been controlled by carriers, but none of the carriers in Norwegian waters had radar. Because Morse radio (W/T) was the only reliable means of communicating with aircraft, the tendency was to send all messages to two-seaters by both R/T and W/T.

An Admiralty circular of 20 July 1940 summarized the new fighter control system developed in Norway. In this system, the director ship was the one with the best radar, not necessarily the carrier. This decentralization, and the relatively small number of search radars aboard individual British ships, made it natural for the Royal Navy to exchange radar data between ships in company.[31] At this stage W/T, which could be used efficiently only by two-seat fighters, was preferred. The RAF equipped its single-seaters with VHF R/T.

Fighter direction was developed more fully in the Mediterranean, particularly after four radar-equipped ships (*Illustrious*, *Valliant* and two anti-aircraft cruisers) arrived at the end of August 1940. The combination of radar and Fulmars launched by HMS *Illustrious* was strikingly effective against Italian bombers, although the Fulmars could not drive off shadowers.

The RAF fighter direction system was not adopted in complete form and was not adopted at all until early 1941, when HMS *Ark Royal* was equipped with a fighter direction plot and an efficient R/T set, with an RAF officer on board to assist. Since the ship was never fitted with any type of radar, presumably she depended on her consorts for radar data. There was no means of radar height-finding. Although the ship proved quite successful, it was clear that aircraft needed a better R/T and a better means of homing (that is, air navigation). The

experience of night attacks showed the need for air-to-air radars.

From 1940 on, carriers were fitted with radars, initially relatively broad-beam low-frequency types such as 79 and 281. Much work went into improved plotting devices for better air control, leading to the development of a long-persistence display tube, the Skiatron.[32] The emphasis, however, was on an information-processing *organization* within a ship (or, in extended form, within a force); the British term was Action Information Organization (AIO). In mature form, by 1943, the AIO employed an Air Operations Room, an Air Direction Room (ADR), and a Radar Filter Room, all of which were logical developments of the earlier Fighter Direction Office. The Air Operations Centre directed all aircraft, both anti-air and anti-surface (or ASW). For example, escort carriers used AIO techniques to direct their aircraft against distant submarine contacts, and the AIO effectively navigated the aircraft.[34] In wartime fleet carriers, the Air Operations Centre was typically located on the upper gallery deck near the island, which removed offices from the island to leave space for more ready rooms, as well as more radio and radar.

HMS *Indomitable* received the first fully-developed AIO, employing not only the broad-beamed sets (79 and 281 combined to obtain full coverage), but also a 277 for low cover and height-finding. A combination of PPI (for 227) and skiatron allowed as many as ten plots to be told per minute, and a prototype vertical plot proved quite successful. By 1945, all British carriers other than HMS *Illustrious* had this combination of radars, including a height-finder (in some cases, the US SM-1 in place of the British Type 277).

Like contemporary US CICs, this system was designed to deal with a limited number of simultaneous raids. Off Okinawa, when the British fleet met Japanese tactics designed specifically to overcome it, the flexibility of the *fleet* AIO organization proved particularly effective. Small groups of Kamikazes split up upon being intercepted (or when expecting interception), evading to make track and identification as difficult as possible. They also tried to follow strikes back to the carriers. Some cruisers were used as pickets, to give advance warning of low-flyers and to assist in early identification. Two cruisers were fitted with YE homing beacons so that returning strikes could form on them and return to the carriers along a prearranged lane, while the cruiser 30nm from the main body tried to identify any hostile aircraft trying to mix with the returning group. Battleships tracked all nearby friendly patrols by a combination of radar and dead-reckoning, contributing to the success of the controlling fighter centres. Even so, some attackers penetrated, and anti-saturation measures were a major theme in postwar British (and US) naval air development.

From a constructional point of view, fighter control presented two problems. First, ships with very little potential space for masting had to accommodate multiple antennas, all of which required something approximating an all-round view. Internally, the same ships had to accommodate large air control spaces. British carriers mounted their radar antennas primarily on their islands, and inevitably they were damaged by funnel gas heat. HMS *Indefatigable* apparently encountered particular difficulties, partly because of the revised Staff Requirement (late 1942) for two rather that one air search (air warning) sets. The two had to have sufficient vertical separation, but this brought one of hers so deeply into the funnel gases that it was destroyed.

The other radar problem was low-level coverage, which required a special narrow-beam set, Type 277 or the US SM-1. In 1945 two new sets, 980 and 981, were in prospect. The *Ark Royals*, the first British carriers designed specifically for radar, had two sets of antennas for all-round coverage, but this made

31   In 1943 British official doctrine was to avoid breaking radio silence by radar reporting until a raid, as opposed to shadowers, was detected. However, the Royal Navy placed much less emphasis than the US Navy on avoiding breaking R/T silence for fighter direction (on HF radio, which could be detected beyond the horizon). This was partly because surprise (preserved by radio silence) was so important in carrier-carrier combat, whereas carriers were easily located in areas such as the Mediterranean or off the Norwegian coast. Moreover, the Japanese were known to operate a very efficient radio direction-finding network. The US solution was technological: to use VHF radio, a line-of-sight system not detectable beyond the horizon. Depending heavily on radar contact reporting within a force, the Royal Navy devoted a radio channel to this purpose. Lacking such a channel, the US Navy preferred to concentrate numerous radars in one carrier, which would direct her own aircraft. US procedure was to use the UHF (line-of-sight) TBS sets for initial reports. As soon as a raid was detected, the OTC ordered reports shifted to the HF Warning Net (medium frequency), all by R/T. Both nets carried other traffic; the Royal Navy considered their system of having separate fleet and radar reporting channels simpler and more efficient. These notes are based on the report of HMS *Victorious*, August 1943, after working up with US fighter controllers in preparation for operations with the US Pacific Fleet.

32   Until quite late in the war, British naval radars, such as Type 281, did not rotate continuously, and did not feed PPI (map-like) scopes. Using a skiatron, an operator could compare returns from one direction, the displays of which would persist after the radar had turned away, with returns from another. In effect the skiatron was an intermediate step between a one-dimensional display (A-scope) and a fully two-dimensional (range and bearing) display (PPI).

33   CVE aircraft direction teams successfully controlled aircraft against submarines. When the aircraft flew beyond the radar horizon, they were tracked by dead reckoning, the aircraft measuring local winds and passing this data back to the fighter direction office, thus enabling the latter's FDO to carry out in full the navigation task formerly done by observer.

34 Albacore production was curtailed in 1940 (with 800 delivered) to release capacity (at Fairey) for the Barracuda and Firefly. Swordfish production was transferred to Blackburn in December 1940, and thus was not. This was quite apart from any admirable qualities enjoyed by the Swordfish.

35 This was a matter of some wartime debate, the US-supplied Avenger being much more robust and also much faster. Wartime ASW tactics required co-ordinated attacks by strafing fighters and by bombers. In the case of the Swordfish, because the fighters were so much faster, they had to be held on deck pending a contact, which made for a considerable delay while the Swordfish found U-boats and then reported back. Fighters could accompany Avengers from the beginning. Moreover, because of its greater speed, the Avenger could attack contacts at a greater range, a capability particularly important during the hunter-killer operations mounted in 1943 and afterwards. On the other hand, the Swordfish could operate in weather conditions completely beyond the Avenger's capability (in the Arctic, HMS *Victorious* considered the limit to be a Force 7 wind). It could also operate from very austere carriers without catapults (such as MAC ships), although such ships could still accelerate aircraft by RATOG.

for a massive island which consumed flight deck area. The alternative, to mount all the antennas on a 'merry go round' turning around a single massive mast, was considered in 1945 but could not then be realized.

Homing and blind landing were two other important wartime developments. The British Type 72 beacon was gradually superseded by the US YE/YG, which was lighter and more reliable, and which could be received at a greater range.

Blind landing was vital to escort carriers operating in the Arctic, where conditions could be so bad that a landing aircraft might not be seen from the bridge. They were also essential if fleet carriers, providing the main air defence of the fleet, were to overcome attacks by enemy bombers equipped with radar. This became a particularly important theme postwar.

Escort carriers were fitted with a Blind Approach Beacon System, Type 257, which could be received by multi-seat aircraft carrying standard ASV radars (Mk IIN and Mk XI). An

Having unavoidably locked itself into aircraft of 1936–39 vintage, the Royal Navy was fortunate, during World War II, to have access to American naval aircraft using the more powerful engines which only became available a few years later. The US aircraft, moreover, reflected a different philosophy of carrier operations, and the combination of British and American aircraft made for considerable flexibility in British operations. A US-supplied Avenger torpedo-bomber is shown aboard HMS Indomitable, *at the end of 1944 or very early in 1945, in the East Indies, with Hellcats in the background. The Avenger was considered much superior to the Barracuda as a torpedo- and glide-bomber, but it did not solve all the Royal Navy's problems, because it could not dive-bomb. The Royal Navy hoped to obtain US Helldivers, but their appearance was delayed by severe development problems. Once they became available, the US offensive across the Pacific required all of them. Note the omission of the red centre on the wing roundel of the Avenger, a measure taken in the East to avoid confusion with Japanese aircraft.*

aircraft using it could expect to come within 200 yards of the carrier's stern, and, under conditions of no drift (that is, no cross-wind), directly up the centreline of the deck. ASV IIN could receive the signal at about 8nm, and it was used with the British IFF (Type 251M) for homing. It was first used aboard HMS *Biter*, in the Atlantic.

Type 93, an aural (W/T) counterpart for fighters, entered production in mid-1945. It could be used by all naval aircraft fitted for beacon reception. In theory, such equipment indicated a narrow approach path.

Once the pilot was on this path, he could be talked down to within sight of the DLCO's bats, using a precision radar. Both the US and the Royal Navy experimented along these lines in 1945, the British using an ASV Mk XI with an inverted antenna and a specially expanded PPI display giving precise bearing at short range. This idea was first tried aboard HMS *Vindex*. In production form, it was designated Type 961. Both Type 93 and Type 961 were planned for the first British night carrier, HMS *Ocean*.

AT THE OUTBREAK of war, the primary British strike and reconnaissance aircraft was the Swordfish, with the Albacore entering production. The Barracuda was under accelerated development, having been ordered off the drawing board specifically to provide the Fleet Air Arm with a modern aircraft. Thus the Albacore might be seen as an intentionally transitional type, analogous to the Fulmar interim fighter, and it did not last very long either in production or in service.[34] The Swordfish survived in production until 1944, and in service until 1945, primarily because it was well suited to small wartime escort carriers and MAC-ships.[35] This was particularly true when it was relatively lightly loaded, with only a surface search (ASV) radar and anti-submarine rockets. Carrying a full strike load (torpedo and fuel), the Swordfish needed a long deck run.

Early war experience confirmed the prewar estimates that substantial numbers were needed for reconnaissance. This problem was compounded because until late in the war the Royal Navy could not concentrate carriers as it had expected to. The carriers had to be dispersed, first to hunt down German raiders, then to provide forces simultaneously in the North Sea and the Mediterranean (and later in the Indian Ocean and the Pacific), and finally because of the heavy fleet carrier losses suffered in 1940–42, which were not really made up until 1945. Thus it was never possible to mount the mass torpedo strikes contemplated by prewar tacticians.

Unopposed, Swordfish reconnaissance was considered effective to 170nm or 180nm.[36] However, when enemy air opposition did appear (as at Dakar in 1940), something of much higher performance was required, and Skuas were substituted. This was quite apart from the issue of strike escort, since a low-performance reconnaissance aircraft could not evade enemy fighters by, for example, diving to very low altitude or manoeuvring violently, as a strike aircraft could.

This experience confirmed the wisdom of the prewar requirement that two-seat fighters (which were, after all, desig-

36 This was less than rated range. Rated Swordfish strike range, operating from a carrier with auxiliary tanks in place of the observer, was 360nm, and from an airfield (which would provide a longer take-off run) 450nm. The Skua was rated at 550nm carrying one 500lb bomb. Maximum effective ranges were much shorter: Swordfish attacked *Scharnhorst* from the airfield at Hatston at 240nm; to attack Taranto from HMS *Illustrious* they flew 180nm; Skuas flying from Hatston attacked the German cruiser *Königsberg* at Bergen, 280nm away. The difference was due in part to lower than rated air speed (endurance was really in hours, not miles), and partly due to the need for margins against navigational error. For example, Skua pilots preferred to carry 250lb bombs so as to allow a greater fuel margin at very long range.

nated reconnaissance fighters) should be able to carry out reconnaissance. However, as noted above, in the new F/R, the Firefly, observation (that is, reconnaissance) capability had to be sacrificed for performance. To the extent that a solution was possible, it had to be found in surface-search radar carried by the high-performance aircraft. Throughout much of the war, work proceeded on a combination sea-search/air-to-air radar which would make the Firefly a dual-purpose F/R and night fighter. It was ultimately unsuccessful; the best that could be done was to build sets with many common components.[37]

There was still some hope that a higher-performance strike aircraft, the Barracuda, could carry out successful reconnaissance in the face of the enemy. As noted above, this hope faded well before the Barracuda entered service, and the Firefly thus became a primary reconnaissance aircraft. Note that tactical reconnaissance at sea against a moving target had to be distinguished from strategic photo reconnaissance conducted against fixed land targets, for example in preparation for strikes. The latter could be conducted by specialized single-seaters, the former only by multi-seat aircraft accommodating a specialist observer (either visual or radar).

Barracuda development was unfortunate in its timing. The basic design was approved in 1938, and 250 aircraft were ordered in March 1939. In October 1939 the Exe engine, for which the Barracuda had been designed, was cancelled so that greater industrial effort could be devoted to the more important Merlin; Barracuda production had to be suspended pending redesign. The Merlin was approved for production aircraft in March 1940, but the Battle of Britain intervened; fighters had absolute priority and Barracuda production was suspended again in June 1940. It was resumed as soon as the danger had passed, in September. Even then there were delays because fighter production had priority for tooling, for example, for dies for forgings.

By this time the Barracuda was clearly the only acceptable future British carrier strike bomber; 250 were ordered from Blackburn in January 1941, and 300 more (from Boulton Paul) in February; another 300 (from Westland) were ordered in May 1941. This dispersal was necessary to make efficient use of the British aircraft industry, but it imposed a heavy co-ordination load on the design firm, Fairey, and thus helped delay the project.[38] CNR later stated that the basic problem was a lack of forethought, drive and energy on the part of Fairey management.

The prototype flew on 7 December 1940. It was soon apparent that when the flaps were set for diving the aircraft buffeted because their disturbed air stream hit the low-set tail; it was necessary to move the tailplane up, and a redesigned prototype flew only on 29 June 1941. The prototype also suffered from instability of aileron controls, and then from bad carbon monoxide contamination in its cockpit. Major modifications were needed. After the design was finalized, the target date for the first squadron was autumn 1942. In fact, however, during the already-protracted development period substantial weight had been added, so that early production Barracudas performed inadequately. Thus a second round of redesign (which produced the Mk II) was necessary before the aircraft could enter service.

Improvements included not only weight reductions but also a new engine (Merlin 32 instead of Merlin 30).[39] The Barracuda Mk II could carry an ASV radar (Mk IIN), but could not carry both a torpedo and the new all-round-vision centimetric ASV (Mk XI). Thus production had to be split between a strike version and a night reconnaissance/ASW version, the latter (Mk III) with the better radar. By mid-1943 the Barracuda had been cleared to take off at 14,250lbs, but anything

above 13,900 was undesirable, as handling deteriorated drastically.

Radical improvement could come only from a new and much more powerful (Griffon) engine, but given the restriction on all-up weight, this installation would be possible only if substantial weight were saved. It would be worthwhile only if drag could be reduced drastically, and up to mid-1943 an attempt was made to redesign the Barracuda. It turned out that neither complete internal rearrangement nor removal of underwing and under-fuselage racks saved enough drag to justify total redesign. Instead, some equipment was deleted to allow for the Griffon. Because time was so limited, the major changes in the new Mk V were a new wing (with 4ft more span), a stronger airframe, a better electrical system, and the required new engine mount. The rear gun and third crewman were eliminated, armament being reduced to a single forward-firing machine-gun. There was also some increased tankage, as existing Barracudas could not make the desired range.[40] The redesign study also led to weight-saving modifications of production aircraft.[41]

The Barracuda was limited as a torpedo-bomber, in that its weapon could not be fitted with an air tail allowing release at relatively high speed; it had to make do with a box tail. This may explain why Barracudas apparently never dropped torpedoes in combat. Late in 1943 the torpedo strong points under the fuselage were modified to allow the Barracuda to dive carrying a single 1600lb US-type armour-piercing bomb.[42] Unfortunately there was no bomb crutch, so the maximum dive angle was limited to 60 degrees (to avoid the possibility that the failing bomb would strike the propeller). This in turn effectively limited attacks to ships in harbour, and the Barracuda is now best known for its attacks against *Tirpitz*, using the heavy bomb in 1944.[43]

There is no question that the Barracuda was disappointing, but it was no disaster. Its closest American counterpart was, not the very successful Avenger, but rather the unloved Helldiver. It seems fairest to consider the Barracuda, like the Firefly, a victim of very tight limits on aircraft size, weight and low-speed behaviour.[44] By 1942 it seemed that these limits were altogether intolerable, and after they were broken much better aircraft could be designed. Some of the oddity of the Barracuda's appearance can be blamed on the Admiralty's insistence on the reconnaissance function (hence the high wing and the big windows under it, and the lack of an internal bomb bay), and this in turn can be blamed on the limited aircraft capacity of British ships.

The Barracuda also had its wartime supporters. It was considered much superior to all US naval aircraft in navigational

---

37 True dual-purpose radars of this type have only recently come into service.

38 Total production amounted to thirty Mk Is, 1688 Mk IIs (675 by Fairey, 1013 by the other firms), 1052 Mk IIIs (460 by Fairey, 392 by Boulton Paul), and thirty Mk Vs (out of 140 ordererd); the Mk IV was the Mk V prototype, a modified Mk II, and a projected Mk VI was not built. The original intention was that the Mk III should account for only 25 per cent of total production. The improved Mk V, with APS-4 radar, was expected to replace both Mks II and III.

39 The major sources of increased all-up weight were increased structural weight due to the raised tail-plane, an Admiralty requirement that a third crew member be carried at all times and not omitted, as in earlier

TBRs, when a torpedo was carried, and provision of radar and IFF. This increase required use of the new Merlin 32 engine. Other major modifications to the Barracuda before it entered service included provision of twin guns aft (in a new mounting), flame damping exhaust pipes, a bulkhead behind the pilot (which cured tail buffeting below critical speed due to disturbed airflow inside the fuselage), provision of a special torpedo air tail for high speed attack, arrangement to carry 1000-2000lb series bombs and mines (requiring new crutching positions and new strong points), and additional wing fuel tanks, the original fuel system being inadequate to meet range requirements. Further modifications (a new 'Rose' gun mount aft, actual provision for the heavier bombs, and provision to fire rockets) were put in abeyance so as not to delay production.

40 In 1943–44 reported operational radius was only 180–200nm in home waters, and only 125nm in the Indian Ocean, although it appeared that in the latter case careful flying could increase it to 160–175nm. None of these figures was considered even remotely satisfactory. Greater range would provide not only direct tactical advantages, but it would also allow a pilot to fly shorter distances at less efficient altitude (but at a better altitude from a tactical point of view, for instance at sea level).

41 By 1945 many Mk IIs were being stripped of their rear armament, and having their crews reduced to two. In this form they could carry either a torpedo or an additional 116-gallon fuselage tank.

42 There is some evidence that the first aircraft modified to carry the 1600lb bomb were specifically for the *Tirpitz* attack, but plans for this modification (which also catered for the 1000lb GP bomb) were ready (and had already been approved) in June 1943. Deletion of the bomb carriers under the wings was proposed for Mk V as a considerable aerodynamic improvement. The bomb carriers would be repositioned under the fuselage. Because any arrangement of bombs under the fuselage would limit the dive angle to 60 degrees, some form of displacer crutch would have been necessary. This idea was rejected because it would have entailed considerable structural alterations to the fuselage, including provision of two bearer beams to carry the bomb carriers; this would have delayed production. It was estimated, moreover, that no more than three bombs of any size up to 500lbs could be accommodated.

43 As designed, the Barracuda would have carried lighter bombs under its wings, and it could then dive at any angle. The Barracuda turned out to be a poor dive-bomber due to heaviness of control and a tendency to skid (hence to miss) in a steep dive with the air brakes on. It was more satisfactory as a steep glide-bomber. Barracudas proved much pleasanter to fly carrying one large bomb than three smaller ones, two under the wings.

44 In October 1940 the Director of Scientific Research (MAP) estimated the effects of these limitations on a Sabre-powered TBR. He estimated that any new TBR should have an all-up weight of 17,000 to 19,000lbs, compared to the 11,500 approved as an upper limit in 1939. His three cases were:

(a) no restrictions at all, maximum take-off run 300ft
(b) 57ft span and 55ft length, no limit on folded width
(c) existing case, 50ft × 40ft and 13ft 6in folded

	(a)	(b)	(c)
Reconnaissance			
Wing loading			
lb/sq ft	23.5	39	51
Take-off run, ft	220	410	630
Stall speed, knots	54	66	79
Max speed at			
10,000ft, knots	240	248	254
Torpedo-bomber			
Wing loading	26	42.5	55
Take-off run	300	550	790
Max speed, at			
10,000ft	227	231	234

Long range case

Wing loading	25	42	56
Take-off run, ft	265	530	820
Max speed, knots	238	245	250

In each case of a longer take-off run the only solution was to increase lift coefficient during take-off, that is, by something like a variable-incidence wing. The span in (a) would have been about 70ft, 40 per cent over limit.

45   These aircraft were initially known as Tarpons, but soon renamed Avenger to conform to US Navy practice. Deliveries: 402 Avenger Is (TBF-1), 334 Avenger IIs (TBM-1, the General Motors-built equivalent), and 232 Avenger IIIs (TBM-3 and -3E); another seventy Avenger IVs were not delivered due to the end of the war. An improved Mk V version, with stronger wings, was scheduled for production in 1946. The Avenger reppeared in British service postwar as AS 4 (100 TBM-3Es delivered 1953–54, eighty of them modified to suit British requirements).

46   For its part, the Admiralty sent an early Barracuda to the United States in hopes the US Navy would adopt it and then mass-produce it; it could then be supplied back to Britain under Lend-Lease. The only important wartime example of such adaptation was the Merlin engine, although other large-scale licence-production programmes (such as one for Mosquitoes) came close to fruition. Standard RAF aircraft were produced in Canada and in Australia.

facilities, and in 1943 the Admiralty claimed that it was much easier to fly at night, an important consideration given an evolving British preference for night attacks.

AS IN THE CASE of fighters, in 1940 the Admiralty had to turn to the United States for strike aircraft. Its situation was complicated by the divergence between US and British carrier operating practice. Because US carrier aircraft complements were so large, the United States developed torpedo- and dive-bombers as distinct and separate types. As noted in Chapter 8, the British had been forced to amalgamate the two, first in the Albacore and then in the Barracuda. They were most unwilling to forego dive-bombing; like the US Navy, the Royal Navy considered it the most promising means of hitting rapidly manoeuvring ships. On the other hand, only the torpedo seemed capable of actually killing large warships.

In the absence of the Barracuda, and with the Albacore clearly too slow, the Admiralty sought a Skua replacement. It obtained fifty Vought Vindicators (SB2U, renamed Chesapeake in British service), originally ordered for France, as rough Skua equivalents. The much better Douglas Dauntless (SBD) appears not to have been on offer. There was some hope that the Chesapeake could be flown from escort carriers, but it required too long a take-off run, and had to be relegated to training. It did, however, offer some insurance until better strike aircraft became available.

There was as yet no truly satisfactory American torpedo-bomber, the Admiralty rejecting the existing Douglas Devastator (TBD). A much better torpedo-bomber, the Grumman TBF Avenger, was then under test, and in 1941 200 were ordered under Lend-Lease specifically to equip escort carriers.[45] Because the US Navy built specialized dive-bombers, the TBF was not stressed for diving bomb or torpedo attacks, and could only drop its weapon in level flight. It was expected to outrange and outrun the Barracuda.

The Admiralty therefore still sought an American equivalent of the full TBR. The new Curtiss SB2C Helldiver seemed to be the only option. Designed primarily as a heavy dive-bomber, it could also carry a torpedo. Britain therefore requested Helldivers under Lend-Lease, their priority rising as the Barracuda programme encountered worse and worse delays. Thus the initial failure of the Helldiver was a particular disappointment to the Admiralty. Once its faults had been overcome and production had been resumed, moreover, the US Navy could not spare it in any numbers. The single squadron formed (No 1820) had to be disbanded after a few months because there was no prospect of further supplies either of aircraft or of spare parts. By that time, 1944, Barracudas did provide the dive-bombing capability the Admiralty needed.[46]

The balance between Avenger and Barracuda actually changed over time. In December 1943 the Avenger was assigned primarily to escort carriers as a torpedo- and glide-bomber. Aboard the fleet carrier *Victorious*, it was replaced by

Grumman's Wildcat (Martlet) first demonstrated to the Admiralty the value of a high-performance single-seat naval fighter. The earliest Martlets were taken over from a French order. Here one is tested over the Grumman plant at Bethpage, 27 July 1940. It is in British colours, but note the French-style fin stripes. Grumman History Center

Barracudas capable of steep glide-bombing. By this time Avengers had shown by far the highest proportion of kills in the Battle of the Atlantic, using a form of glide-bombing to drop their depth charges.

A year later, however, Barracudas had largely been replaced by Avengers aboard fleet carriers, Barracuda IIs being retained aboard light fleet carriers and Barracuda IIIs aboard some General Purpose CVEs

CONSIDERABLE EFFORT went into improving torpedoes for higher altitude and higher speed release (largely by fitting special air tails), so that a torpedo-bomber could attack at greater range. A new Mk XI torpedo was designed specifically for the Swordfish, to replace the World War I-type Mk VIII, which imposed unacceptably low altitude and speed limits. Mk XI in turn was replaced in 1939 by Mk XII, which could be dropped at up to 150 knots, and at altitudes of up to 200ft.[47] It could also be gyro-angled, and therefore could be launched at an offset angle, so that the bomber did not need to fly directly at its target. Mk XII also introduced a duplex (magnetic and contact) detonator which, in theory, made it much more lethal. As in other navies at this time, the magnetic detonator proved unreliable, and was withdrawn from service.[48]

Wartime effort was concentrated on developing torpedoes which could be dropped at higher speeds and at greater altitudes. The Monoplane Air Tail (MAT) greatly extended the range at which torpedoes could be dropped. A gyro pilot in it controlled the gliding flight of the weapon, so that it could be dropped reliably as much as 3000 yards from the target. MAT was developed by Miles Aircraft, and it remained in production at least as late as 1947. This project was also known as TORA and VOX. By late 1943 Mk XV had been cleared for an entry speed (not a release speed) of 215 knots, the goal being a release speed of 250 knots at up to 1000ft. The later Mk XVII, which was ready in 1945, was designed for release at 300 knots. The step beyond that was to toss-bomb the torpedo, using a special sight, to remain out of anti-aircraft range. This was pursued postwar as the Bootleg.[49]

Torpedoes were dangerous to fire, because even in diving attacks they had to be delivered at short range. During World War II, however, they achieved the highest hitting rate of any British naval weapon, 224 out of 615 fired in action.[50]

The largest bomb in service in 1939 weighed 500lbs, chosen because the next larger size, 1000lbs, which only a Swordfish could have carried, was not expected to be any more effective against an armoured deck. Lighter bombs could be delivered in greater numbers, to greater effect, and many ships carried 250lb bombs. Only in 1942 was it discovered that these weapons had

A hangar aboard HMS Indomitable *illustrates one of the major constraints on British naval aircraft designers. These Seafires, which could not fold, were stowed diagonally. The hangar itself was divided into three bays by fire curtains, and its ends (at the lifts) were closed by armoured doors. The doors had to be closed off to complete the protection of the hangar, but this could not be done quickly. Since carriers tended to fly their aircraft during action, then, they were vulnerable to hits penetrating the unarmoured decks and lifts outside the protected hangar area, and the effects of such hits would pass through the open armoured doors. This problem was a consequence of the drastic change in carrier operating ideas between 1936, when the armoured carriers were designed, and 1940, when they entered service. Later armoured carriers of the* Ark Royal *class, intended to keep operating their aircraft during air attacks, were designed with power-operated armoured doors, open only when needed to accept aircraft from the lifts.*

---

47 As a result, a torpedo-bomber could fly higher and could evade more radically. Because the standard British delivery manoeuvre was a shallow dive, higher altitude and greater speed translated into greater delivery range and therefore into greater immunity for the torpedo-bomber.

48 It was credited with the effectiveness of the attack at Taranto, although four torpedoes exploded harmlessly before passing close enough to their targets, and another was a dud. On the other hand, the *failure* of the duplex detonator saved HMS *Sheffield* in 1941, when inexperienced pilots mistook her for the *Bismarck*.

49 Bootleg was a 20in jet-propelled torpedo, 150in long (1730lbs, including a 575lb warhead), which

would be toss-bombed at 300 to 500 knots at a range of 5000 yards. In the water it would run 750 to 1000 yards at a depth of 30ft and at a speed of 70 knots, using a proximity detonator to explode under a target's keel.

50 A box score for 1940, reprinted in the official FAA history (Vol I), shows sixty-two torpedo attacks at sea, with 6.5 per cent confirmed hits, and 6.5 probable, for six ships damaged, and two aircraft lost. For torpedoes against convoys at sea, the figures are nineteen dropped, 29.1 per cent confirmed and 10.7 per cent probable hits, two ships sunk, one probably sunk, no aircraft lost. For torpedoes in harbour: thirty-six dropped, 41.8 per cent confirmed hits, 6 probable, for fifteen ships sunk, ten damaged, and two aircraft lost. In dive-bombing attacks at sea and

in harbour, 229 bombs were dropped, the number of hits was not known; seven ships were sunk, thirty damaged (plus eight slightly); losses of aircraft were not recorded. Prewar doctrine had emphasized mass torpedo attacks, but even up to 1941 the greatest number of aircraft in any torpedo strike was fifteen. It was estimated that they would make only two to three hits, as against the four to five required to sink or neutralize a heavy ship. Hitting percentages in 1940 confirmed prewar estimates, but the official historian noted that the proficiency of both British pilots and of enemy anti-aircraft fire seemed below the expected prewar standard. He felt that torpedo-bombers might well have sunk one or two enemy capital ships at sea had their pilots been better practised.

too little effect against ships to be worthwhile; from late 1942 on, they were replaced by 500lb MC bombs suitable against both ship and shore targets. In 1939–40 there was also a 20lb anti-personnel bomb, but it was considered ineffective.

At this time the other major naval air anti-ship weapon was the 'B' bomb, a buoyant weapon designed to be dropped ahead of a ship, rising to explode against its bottom. The B bomb seems to have originated with DNC Department about 1924, and it was gradually developed throughout the interwar period. A few were actually employed against German canal traffic in 1940, and from 1942 on an improved version was issued to aircraft carriers. In theory, aside from a heavy torpedo, the B bomb was the only aerial ship-killer. In practice, pilots disliked it and did not believe that it could be delivered accurately enough; although aboard British wartime carriers, it was not used in combat, and it was discarded postwar.[51]

Rockets were introduced during the war, initially to enable aircraft to attack U-boats from beyond the range of their fire. Solid (armour-piercing) 25lb heads were used. Later, they provided fighters with very substantial anti-ship firepower, usually in the form of 60lb HE/SAP, 'F' (fragmentation), or even shaped-charge warheads. In 1945 the Royal Navy was testing a much larger rocket weapon, 'Uncle Tom', with a 550lb HE/SAP warhead (out of a total weight of about 1050lb), to attack large ships underwater, and also against land targets. Plans called for a limited number of Avengers to be modified to carry two each. Postwar, Uncle Tom became Red Angel, a rocket 11.75in in diameter and 129in long. Out of a total weight of 1055lbs, 88lbs was high explosive (which would correspond to a much greater total warhead weight). Effective range was 5000 to 6000 yards, depending on aircraft speed (for example 5250 yards when droped at 400 knots from 2000ft, attaining an entry velocity of 1500 ft per second).

There were also special air-dropped depth charges and, from 1943 on, the American-developed Mk 24 'mine', actually an ASW homing torpedo. The Fleet Air Arm also dropped conventional mines.

As the British fleet began to concentrate on land targets towards the end of the war, its bomb inventory changed to include both large general-purpose weapons and 500lb cluster bombs. Small bombs, such as the 100lb, became important once more, since they could be spread over relatively large areas.[52]

Dive-bombing, which had been so important in prewar thinking, went into decline as the Skua was withdrawn from service after 1940. Although the Albacore was, in theory, a dive-bomber, it received little publicity in this role. Thus the official Admiralty publication for airmen was able to announce, in 1942, that dive-bombing was being revived with the planned introduction of the Helldiver.[53] It would be synchronized with torpedo attack, for maximum disruptive effect on anti-aircraft gunners, using 1000lb (British MC or US GP) or 1600lb (US AP) bombs. At about the same time high-level bombing was formally abolished as a Fleet Air Arm mission. Later, after the failure of the Helldiver, the FAA used its fighters as steep glide-bombers.

51 The problem was that modern fast attack aircraft and fighters carried their weapons underwing, and thus could carry no more that two B bombs each, which seemed a poor return on their size and cost. The argument in favour of retaining the B bomb was that it provided the Firefly with a useful anti-ship weapon, at least until large anti-ship rockets were cleared for use. The counter, that it was not worth retaining a large stock of more or less passé weapons, was decisive.

52 The 500lb MC bomb Mks VI, VII, IX, XIII, and US GP AN M64 were introduced, but unfortunately it was decided in May 1945 that a modified form of the US AN M64 A1, of which large quantities had been received in the UK, was unsuited for naval service. Attempts were made to cluster British 20lb HE bombs and 30lb incendiaries, both of which were

in RAF service; development for the Royal Navy was complicated by the need for safe stowage aboard ship, and also for a robust container for shipment abroad. The 30lb cluster bomb had to be abandoned because the bomb's shape made economical clustering impossible. Attempts were also made to cluster the US AN M69 6lb incendiary and the AN M40 23lb parachute-fragmentation bomb; in each case the problem was that the cluster had to be filled with fused bombs.

53 This was partly a matter of changing definition. Prewar dive-bombing often meant attack at a 45-degree angle, with bombs dropped at 1000 yards slant range against a capital ship, that is at a height of 2120ft. After 1943 it was defined as diving at a 60-degree or greater angle; in this sense the only Royal Navy dive-bomber in service in 1940 was the Skua. Attack at lesser angles was glide-bombing. A bomber

diving steeply enough could hit small targets quite accurately, but could not accurately drop a 'stick' of bombs; a glide-bomber could. The Helldiver was vitally important to the Royal Navy because, in 1942, it was the only available aircraft which could dive-bomb at over 65 degrees, and thus which could emulate the very successful US techniques demonstrated at Midway.

11

Emergency Fleet Carriers

BRITAIN BUILT NO new fleet carriers during World War II; the six completed in wartime were all prewar ships, and the two entirely new ones laid down during the war were completed well afterwards. This did not mean that the Admiralty disregarded the importance of carrier air power. Quite the contrary. Keeping in mind the limits of British shipbuilding resources, the Royal Navy devised a relatively simple light fleet carrier, one of the few entirely new major warship designs started during World War II and leading to completed ships before the end of the war. While these ships were being built, the Future Building Committee greatly increased British naval goals for carrier construction, with the class expanding from an initial four ships to sixteen. Remarkably, although they were designed as a war expedient (and perhaps for an operational lifetime as short as two years), three of these *Colossus* class carriers remain in active service, greatly modified, more than forty-five years after having been laid down.

THE CONSTRUCTION of the light fleet carriers connected two quite distinct eras in British naval thinking. They began as an extension of the prewar idea that capital ships, the basis of seapower, should carry some of their own fighters. This was partly a consequence of limits on overall British carrier capacity, but it partly also responded to a demand that capital ships be more self-contained. Once the demands of war had fragmented the unitary British fleet, the capital ships could no longer count on substantial fighter cover. Moreover, it was soon obvious that anti-aircraft fire, unsupported by fighters, could not protect capital ships within reach of enemy shore-based aircraft. In December 1941 these considerations came together in a proposal for a small fighter carrier specifically to escort capital ships. It might have been considered an anti-aircraft equivalent of the classic destroyer, clearly an adjunct to the battleship. However, when the light fleet carriers built to realize this idea were actually completed, their aircraft were not only the fighter defence, but also the main striking power, of the fleet. In many circumstances the battleships were the anti-aircraft escorts.

The British fleet operated or planned to operate combat aircraft, such as fighters, from its capital ships and cruisers throughout the interwar period (see Chapter 8). The primary objection was always that these aircraft could not be recovered after they had been launched; if wheeled for maximum performance, they could either land on a carrier or ditch; if on floats, they would sacrifice performance, perhaps fatally, and in any case they probably could not land safely in any sea. One obvious solution was to provide the capital ships or cruisers with some kind of rudimentary landing-on deck, so that it could function as a self-contained unit. The object was not to replace fleet carriers; rather, the self-contained unit would reduce the defensive load on the carriers. Alternatively, the capital ship or cruiser could operate independently, using its aircraft for reconnaissance and even for long-range strikes.

Until 1936, the naval treaties made such capital ships unattractive. Each navy had to live within fixed total and individual battleship and carrier tonnages, and any flight deck would inevitably reduce the firepower a given hull could carry. Thus to adopt hybrid designs would be to accept a substantial reduction in either total fleet gun power or total fleet airpower. However, with the Treaty of London in 1936 the total ('global') tonnage restrictions lapsed.

It was also no longer clear, at least in Britain, that future naval forces would always be concentrated. In 1936 analysis of the naval problems of a war with Germany showed that the fleet would have to be split into hunting groups to find and destroy the German pocket battleships. Hunting would require aircraft, both to find the German ships and to slow them sufficiently to bring them to battle. One possibility was to build a class of hybrid battlecruiser-carriers, and a sketch design was prepared.[1]

No such ship was included in the new construction programme; even though Britain was no longer limited by treaty, her resources were definitely finite, and so she could not afford anything but the most efficient fleet, in terms of guns and aircraft per ton or per pound spent. Even so, the hybrid idea seems to have circulated fairly widely. In 1939, for example, several students at the Admiralty's Greenwich school of naval architecture produced hybrid designs as their student projects. Such sketch designs had, of course, no official standing, but knowledge of their existence tended to encourage those interested in such ships.[2]

For its part, the Fleet seems to have been uneasy at the abandonment of the previous policy of carrying fighters aboard capital ships and cruisers. During 1940 it became evident, at least in Norway and in the Mediterranean, that massed fleet anti-aircraft guns often could not deal with heavy attacks by land-based aircraft. Fighters were needed, but there were only a

1   This design is mentioned in the official FAA history, but details have not come to light. It was not mentioned when the hybrid idea was revived in 1940–41. The idea of a *cruiser*-carrier was not new, having received some considerable publicity in connection with the London Naval Conference of 1930. At that time the US Navy proposed what it called a 'flight deck cruiser' partly to obtain more carrier tonnage using an unregulated category of warship. Several hybrid cruiser-carriers were designed, and one was very nearly built. See my *US Cruisers* (US Naval Institute, Annapolis, 1984). In 1933 DNC reportedly developed a sketch design for a cruiser-carrier, but the Board rejected it, partly on the ground that it wished to avoid initiating construction of a new and dangerous type of warship: the cruiser-carrier would make a very effective commerce raider. In 1936 the idea of a *capital ship*-carrier was fairly novel, although there had been private speculation about the possibilities of such a ship as early as 1923, for instance in Sir George Thurston's article on experimental capital ships in *Brassey's Naval Annual*.

2   Such student projects did, however, reflect the view of the professor, at that time Sir Victor Shepheard, who served as DNC from 1952 to 1958.

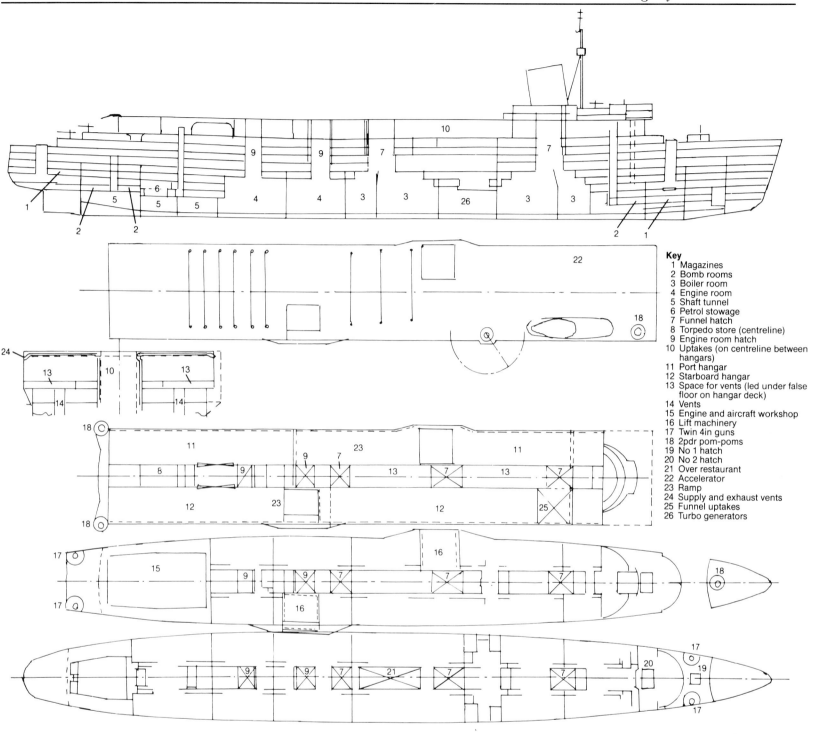

Key
1 Magazines
2 Bomb rooms
3 Boiler room
4 Engine room
5 Shaft tunnel
6 Petrol stowage
7 Funnel hatch
8 Torpedo store (centreline)
9 Engine room hatch
10 Uptakes (on centreline between
    hangars)
11 Port hangar
12 Starboard hangar
13 Space for vents (led under false
    floor on hangar deck)
14 Vents
15 Engine and aircraft workshop
16 Lift machinery
17 Twin 4in guns
18 2pdr pom-poms
19 No 1 hatch
20 No 2 hatch
21 Over restaurant
22 Accelerator
23 Ramp
24 Supply and exhaust vents
25 Funnel uptakes
26 Turbo generators

very few carriers; they could not always accompany the battle-ships. The fleet was already split between the North Sea and the Mediterranean, and by June 1940 two of the best of the seven existing carriers had been sunk.

In October 1940 DAM put the case for reversing this policy by providing new capital ships with aircraft which would be launched by accelerator and recovered on short landing decks. DAM thought, for example, that ten fighters could be accom-modated in the hangar aboard a *King George V* class battleship, and that a short flight deck could be accommodated between the fore and aft turrets, perhaps with a hangar below it. DNAD was sceptical; surely the sacrifice in battleship features would be excessive, and surely air operations in a small space would be much more difficult, and much less efficient, than DAM imagined. He suspected that a few fighters, though effective against shadowers, would do little against massed bombers.

The final version of the plan to convert the liner Queen Elizabeth *to a carrier, with an offset island, in 1942. The funnel uptakes would have been trunked together, as shown, on the hangar deck, splitting about half the total length of the hangar. What is most striking about these plans is just how little carrier capability so massive a hull provided. This was typical of merchant ship conversions.* NF

However, D of P (then Admiral C L Daniel) rather liked the idea, seeing the fighters as longer-range anti-aircraft weapons. The idea was sent to DNC in Bath, subject to a requirement that the hangar accommodate two spread aircraft at a time for maintenance, and that a hatchway with crane would be an ade-quate substitute for a lift. DAM protested that this apparent simplification made the entire scheme impractical, as any deck stowage would complicate the arrangement of the flight deck.

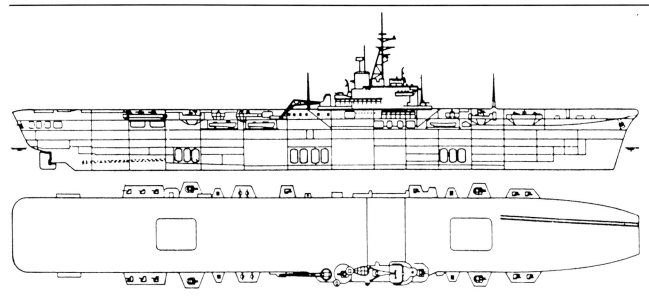

The internal arrangement of a typical war-built light fleet carrier, in this case a Majestic, *showing the pairs of engine and boiler rooms and the aircraft fuel stowage (vertical cylindrical tanks).*

DAM's idea had been to provide a deck just long enough for a free take-off should the accelerator fail. With the barrier up, there was room for a short deck park (DAM estimated two Barracudas and three Fireflies), but this meant that without a lift the ship could operate only five aircraft (plus another landing-on). Moreover, any aircraft on deck would be subject to gun blast. This made the lift and the hangar essential, and the revised requirements sent to DNC on 11 January 1941 showed a lift, a hangar for twelve fighters and two spotters; and the longest possible flight deck (minimum 320ft) on 45,000 tons, with eight 15in guns in four turrets or nine 16in in three turrets.

DNC's report in March 1941 was not encouraging, but D of P persisted. Discussion within the Naval Staff brought out the fundamental problem of such a ship: air operations were incompatible with effective battlefleet gunnery; carriers usually turned into the wind to launch and recover their fighters. The take-off (but not the landing-on) problem could be solved by using an accelerator to launch all aircraft. Battleships needed wide firing arcs, and their guns would surely blast aircraft on a flight deck.

A committee was formed to study the problem, and DNC provided a variety of sketch designs in July (see Tables 11-1 and 11-2). He found that none carried enough aircraft to make much of a difference, either defensively or offensively (for instance by forcing an enemy to accept battle). As the number of aircraft increased, the ship turned into a cruiser-carrier and then into a small carrier with a substantial gun battery, what DNC called an 'aircraft destroyer'.

Moreover, the aircraft were extremely expensive in terms of gunpower. DNC preferred separate carriers and battleships. A squadron of five carrier-battleships, 225,000 tons, would carry only thirty aircraft and thirty 15in guns – compared to three *Lions* and three *Indomitables*, roughly 200,000 tons, with twenty-seven 16in guns and 135 aircraft.

As the idea was discussed further, two distinct schools of thought emerged. One preferred ships ('aircraft destroyers') built primarily, almost solely, to·carry fighters protecting the accompanying capital ships. The other wanted dual-purpose ships (battleship- or cruiser-carriers) with fairly large numbers of aircraft on board. DNC sketched examples of both types.

Since aircraft destroyers would be needed in some numbers they would have to be relatively inexpensive. DNC's aircraft destroyer was based on the new escort carrier *Audacity*. She was given sufficient protection to survive destroyer attack, and a torpedo battery enabling her to damage a large enemy ship encountered at short range at night or in thick weather.

Not surprisingly, the small aircraft destroyers had insuffi-

cient aircraft facilities. On 8350 tons, Design B had an obstructed flight deck and a single lift, but a clearer flight deck (Design E) cost an alternative machinery arrangement more vulnerable to underwater attack. These problems could be solved by adding tonnage (and cost: Designs C and D), but even they were not entirely satisfactory. DNC considered them less satisfactory, as cruisers, than a conventional 8in gun cruiser.

The parallel series of battleship-carriers was also unsatisfactory. Design practices entirely satisfactory in carriers (such as uptakes adjacent to an unprotected hangar) were unacceptable in a ship designed to survive heavy bombardment. Moreover, the sheer size of the hangar surface made it impossible to protect on the necessary scale.[3]

Thus both ends of the spectrum were unacceptable. A dual-purpose ship could be built, but it could never be efficient. DGD went further: 'the functions and requirements of carriers and of surface gun platforms are entirely incompatible ... the conception of these designs (the increased silhouettes and superficial vulnerability and decreased A/A armament of which has been insufficiently noted) is evidently the result of an unresolved contest between a conscious acceptance of aircraft and a subconscious desire for a 1914 Fleet ... these abortions are the

Venerable, 1 May 1945. She, Colossus *and* Vengeance *could all be recognized by the pom-pom directors sponsored out above their bridges.*

3   In much the same way, it is difficult to provide enough weight to armour the large magazines and combat control spaces of modern warships. Carriers were the first surface warships in which volume was more important than weight; battleships were practicable because most of the components which had to be armoured were relatively compact.

Table 11-1: DNC Proposals for Dual Purpose Warships, July 1941

	Cruiser Carrier A	Cruiser Carrier B	Battleship Carrier	Aircraft Destroyer B
LWL (ft)	670	690	800	560
Breadth of hull (ft)	83	83	112	66
Mean draught at std displacement (ft)	22	22 3	29 10	15 7
Std displacement (tons)	18,900	20,000	44,750	8350
Deep displacement (tons)	23,000	24,500	51,000	10,550
SHP	120,000	120,000	130,000	80,000
Speed (knots)	30.75–32.25	30.75–32.25	28–29	31–32
Oil fuel (tons)	3600	3750	4350	1800
Endurance on trial (nm)	11,000 at 16 knots	11,500 at 16 knots	14,750 at 10 knots	8300 at 16 knots
Armament	2 triple 8in, 1 DCT	3 triple 8in, 2 DCT	2 triple 15in	
	6 twin 4in HA/LA	6 twin 4in HA/LA	8 twin 5.25in	4 5in HA/LA
	2 HACS	2 HACS	4 HACS	2 directors
	3 4-barrel pom poms	3 4-barrel pom poms	8 8-barrel pom poms	
	3 directors	3 directors	6 directors	
	10 Oerlikons	8 Oerlikons		10 Oerlikons
	2 triple 21in TT	2 triple 21in TT		4 twin 21in TT
Protection (above water)	½in NC belt to main deck abreast machinery and magazines; 1in D splinter protection on sides forward and aft; 4in NC main deck over magazines, 2in over machinery; main bulkheads 1in.		13in belt abreast magazine; 6in main deck over magazine, 5in over machinery; bulkheads, barbettes, gun-houses as in *Lion*	2in NC belt to upper deck abreast magazine and machinery, 1in NC on upper deck
(under water)	boiler rooms separated; engine rooms separated; WT subdivision separated		sandwich bulge, ½in bulkhead BRs and ERs	BRs, ERs separated
Aircraft	10 fighters, 4 TBR	10 fighters, 2 TBR	12 fighters, 2 TBR	12 fighters
Flight deck dimensions (ft)	380 × 80	340 × 80	500 × 73	520 × 80
Hangar space	for all aircraft carried —————————————————————————————— for 6 fighters			
Lifts	two 45 × 33ft, 45 × 22ft —————————————————————		45 × 33ft, 45 × 22ft	One 43 × 33ft
Petrol (gallons)	30,000	23,000	35,000	20,000
ATOG	yes	yes	yes	yes
Barriers	1	1	1	1
Wires	4	4	6	6
Remarks	In both, uptakes awkward; airflow rather disturbed around after end of flight deck		Uptakes dangerous; projections outside hull	Many erections on starboard side of flight deck

results of a psychological maladjustment'. By this time there was a new D of P, and no one on the Staff wanted a hybrid. The subject was therefore dropped in October 1941.

However, the aircraft destroyer idea was not entirely forgotten. If anything, the basic idea of an inexpensive fighter carrier must have seemed more valid. The main effect of the hybrid studies was to show that the requirements for such a ship had to be very carefully drawn to keep it both effective and affordable. In particular, British shipyards and the associated industries were already much too badly pressed to build new fleet carriers very quickly, yet by November 1941 the Royal Navy had already lost three of its seven prewar ships. The three new armoured carriers had a nominal aircraft capacity only about 56 per cent as great as the lost capacity. Escort carriers were coming into service, but they were too slow to operate with modern (or modernized) capital ships.

Because the new carrier *Indomitable*, working up off Bermuda, ran aground and had to be repaired, the battleship *Prince of Wales* and the battlecruiser *Repulse*, the remnant of the main fleet, had to be sent to the Indian Ocean without any carrier consort. Their loss made it painfully obvious that fighter carriers would be indispensable for future operations within range of enemy land-based aircraft. Given current experience in the Mediterranean, and the striking demonstration of the loss of the two capital ships to land-based bombers so far from home in the Far East, it seemed likely that in future such exposure would be the rule rather than the exception. Fighter complements aboard fleet carriers were already being increased, but Britain lacked the capacity to build new fleet carriers quickly.

The idea of a special fighter carrier was revived in December 1941. Carriers were not the only major ships in short supply; the Royal Navy also lacked fast capital ships, since the only new ones on order, *Vanguard* and *Lion*, were not due until 1944–45, if then. The Deputy Controller therefore suggested a new equivalent of the 'large light cruisers' of World War I, which he described as a 'Woolworth' (cut-rate) capital ship.[4] To ACNS(W), writing on 16 December, this really raised the question of whether the same principle could not be applied to

other types of ships, given limited British building capacity. In particular, if the Japanese carrier force penetrated the Indian Ocean, the Royal Navy would need its own carriers to hunt them down.

D of P observed that two major lessons of the war were the paucity of fast capital ships capable of bringing enemy capital ships to action (as demonstrated, for example, in the *Bismarck* operation) and the ever-increasing need for aircraft at sea (as demonstrated by the hybrid ship idea). He rejected the 'Woolworth' supercruiser as neither sufficiently heavily armed nor sufficiently protected. Moreover, it could not stand up to Japanese control of the air, as the *Repulse*, which had much the same sort of protection, had just shown. The carrier would be a very different proposition, so important as to be worth massproducing. He envisaged conversion of existing hulls, as was done with escort carriers. Unfortunately there was a bottleneck in high-powered machinery, so it seemed unlikely that a new ship could be much better than a fast merchant ship. ACNS(H) agreed; modern capital ships were clearly in a class by themselves, and could be met by older ones only on a 2:1 basis. Britain lacked anything remotely like the industrial capacity needed to build modern battleships in such numbers. However, 'Woolworth' carriers seemed very attractive, provided their cost and complexity could be held down.

A quick staff study followed. There were three possibilities: the existing *Audacity* type to protect convoys; a merchant ship type capable of operating TSRs, small bombers and land-type fighters; and a fighter carrier to protect the battlefleet.[5]

The third alternative was not really satisfactory, but the *Prince of Wales* disaster had demonstrated that battleships could not rely on their own weapons, and, moreover, that shore-based aircraft (which could mount sustained saturation attacks) could achieve remarkable ranges. The hybrid ship was one ideal solution, but it was impractical. Since fleet carriers could not be built quickly enough, each battleship or pair of battleships would have to be attached to a small fighter carrier. This was DNC's aircraft destroyer idea reborn.

The basic requirements were a flight deck long enough for

4 It would use existing weapons, two twin 14in or 13.5in, and armour would be limited to 3in–4in deck and 6in–8in belt. Speed would be 29 knots. The Deputy Controller hoped they could be built in two years or less by keeping all features as simple as possible and avoiding frills of any kind, including aircraft.

5 The second type did not materialize, but it may explain British interest in escort carrier conversions of medium liners. It could provide offensive power against ships and shore targets. As envisaged in December 1941, it might transfer aircraft to an armoured carrier just outside the range of shore-based aircraft, and the strike aircraft could be recovered by the unarmoured carrier after refuelling aboard the armoured carrier. This concept was discussed by the War College just before the war in connection with attacks on the Japanese coast. It would be useful in hunting down and killing raiders, and it might operate as a ferry carrier to support amphibious operations.

Above and right: *The light fleet carriers were extraordinary successes: designed as an interim measure, to last only until the end of World War II, some of them remain in active first-line service four decades later. This is HMS* Triumph, *the last ship of the class, newly completed, in May 1946. Note the YE homing beacon on a stub mast on her funnel; other ships of the class had theirs on fore topmasts.* Ocean, Theseus, *and* Warrior *had similar stub masts. In the aerial photograph, only the base of the mainmast (carrying a 281BQ antenna) is visible.*

the latest fleet protection (that is, high-performance) fighters, a hangar for fifteen or twenty-four fighters, speed comparable with a *King George V* class battleship, a few low-angle guns, and a maximum anti-aircraft battery.

These ships were badly needed, and it seemed best to convert some existing hulls. The most likely candidates were the old cruisers *Frobisher* and *Hawkins* (the latter under refit); or perhaps a fast minelayer (*Abdiel*) or a D class cruiser.[6]

ACNS(F), ACNS(W), Fifth Sea Lord and D of P met informally to discuss this project. They agreed that conversion characteristics would be:

- minimum flight deck dimensions of 450 × 60ft
- a hangar for at least fifteen fighters (but TSRs would sometimes have to be carried in place of some fighters)
- short-range weapons only, except for one heavy aircraft gun
- 25 knots was desirable, but less would be accepted

The three alternatives were a cruiser (*Hawkins*) conversion, a liner (*Winchester Castle*) conversion, or a new ship, the 'Woolworth' carrier. Although the requirements applied specifically to a conversion, they also indicated what would be needed in a new carrier.

The outline of requirements was dated 26 December 1941. On 30 December, the Controller instructed DNC to design an altogether unprotected carrier with a speed of 25 knots, to carry at least fifteen fighters, as a battleship escort. Although it was not so stated at the time, the idea seems to have been to accommodate the highest-performance aircraft available, that is, fixed-wing (non-folding) RAF fighters such as the existing Spitfire or the new Typhoon. Certainly provisions made in the design by mid-1942 (deck length and lift size) were justified specifically on that ground.

Quick construction was the most important consideration;

the Controller suggested a hull to merchant ship standards with cruiser machinery (half the plant designed for HMS *Bellerophon*, a cruiser whose construction had been suspended, rated at 40,000shp).

This ship would require little armament and no armour; underwater protection could be provided by filling hold spaces with buoyancy drums. Except for her speed, then, she was conceived as an *Audacity* with a hangar. However, within a few weeks the ship was described as an 'intermediate aircraft carrier' (between the escort and fleet categories), at a cost of £1,740,000, something less than half the cost of a fully armoured fleet carrier. Average cost was actually £2.5 million, in each case exclusive of aircraft; the ships grew considerably more sophisticated during their early design phase.

The result was an outstanding success, the *Colossus* class.

DNC ordered a quick feasibility study, and then turned the problem over to Vickers-Armstrong, as his design staff was already fully committed, and Vickers had both merchant and warship design experience. The firm agreed, and DNC supplied what amounted to tentative Staff Requirments. Progress was very fast: the first sketch design was submitted on 14 January 1942, for review by the Controller and the Naval Staff. At

6   Thornycroft later proposed a small carrier based on the *Abdiel* hull. It was rejected as too small to be worthwhile. As had been demonstrated in the past, 10,000 tons was about the lower limit for a viable carrier.

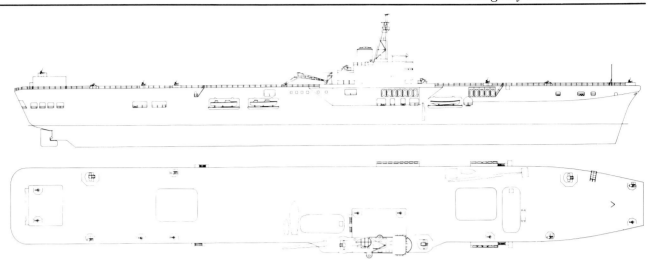

this point Vickers estimated that the ship could be built in twenty-one months, which must already have seemed somewhat long.

The staff required some additions, the ship grew, and a new sketch design was reviewed on 23 January. Further alterations were now made, and a somewhat larger ship was submitted for Board approval. In particular, the flight deck was made long enough for Typhoon fighters, which were then being considered for naval service, to make rolling take-offs. Estimated building time was now twenty-seven months, uncomfortably close to that achieved prewar for much superior fleet carriers.[7] At this stage the ship met the proposed Staff Requirements, except that she lacked any assisted take-off gear. DNC suggested that this was acceptable, given the lengthened flight deck, but that the ship might be designed for later installation of a simplified catapult. However, when the design was submitted to the Board in February 1942, VCNS and ACNS(W) both insisted on a catapult, and one was incorporated in the Staff Requirements written (essentially after the fact) in July 1942.

The carrier was essentially unarmoured, apart from splinter protection for some exposed personnel; and it had no conventional side protective system. A torpedo hitting amidships would necessarily flood one or probably two compartments. To limit the effect of such a hit, the ship was much better subdivided than a merchant ship, and her two machinery units well separated. Summarizing the design in December 1942, the DNC, Sir Stanley Goodall, described her as better protected against underwater attack than a cruiser, except that she had only two screws, and therefore might be immobilized by a hit close to one of them.

Finally, in so small a carrier much more than usual had to be concentrated in the unprotected island; not only ship and aircraft control, but also a good part of the short-range battery control.

The First Lord, Sir A V Alexander, approved construction of the class on 11 March 1942; Treasury approval was to be sought for three. He was, however, disturbed by the constant additions to what had been conceived as an extremely austere design. Surely it was essential that the ships be built as quickly as possible, as stop-gaps pending the construction of satisfactory new armoured carriers? Thus he conditioned his approval on reduction of the building time to twenty-one months; 'if necessary, everything which is not vital should be omitted...'

Early in March 1942 the D of P drew up two tables; one to show how an austere concept had grown into a sophisticated, if unarmoured, carrier (Table 11-4), and the other a detailed comparison between the Staff Requirements as initially proposed by DNC and the requirements as amended by the Staff (Table 11-5). Together, they are an excellent illustration of the

HMS Perseus *as completed as an aircraft repair ship, 1945. The deckhouse aft housed spare aircraft engines, an oxygen producing plant and an oxygen cylinder filling and stowage room. Boats, including a 48ft aircraft lighter, could be stowed on deck just abaft amidships, served by the large crane just abaft the island. The built-up structure inboard of the island housed, among other things, a large crew recreation space and cinema, and an awning could be rigged over the remaining width of the former flight deck. A second 48ft aircraft lighter could be stowed on deck just forward of the forward lift, served by a 15-ton crane mounted to port.* ALR

usual upward pressure on the designer, as it is exerted even in the most desperate period of a war.

As a result of the attempt to prune back the growth of the design, the docket for Board approval of the design, which was dated 26 February 1942, was side-tracked by yet another review of the design, this time in the interest of simplification. As no formal Board approval had been given, a new docket had to be prepared in July 1942, with a new Staff Requirement (reflecting the design as it was at that time).

The Deputy Controller held a conference on simplification on 5 May 1942. Since the ship was being built to merchant ship standards, eighteen to twenty-one months was surely a reasonable building time. Visiting Newcastle, he discussed the design with the Walker Yard, which was being asked to build the ship in two years. The yard manager considered this quite impossible, unless requirements were relaxed further.

He wanted to eliminate hangar fire curtains and water sprays, which involved considerable labour (but also made for a considerable measure of survivability). The argument was that an accidental fire could be put out with chemical extinguishers and the ordinary fire hose system, whereas massive damage, for instance by shellfire, would surely wreck the curtains and hangar sprays. The usual ring main for electric power distribution would be replaced by a pair of switchboards, on merchant ship lines, each switchboard being fitted on the centreline, for maximum protection. Circuit breakers would be eliminated in favour of simple fuses, and all duplicated electric feeds would be eliminated, except those to the steering gear. The diesel generating plant would be halved.

The yard wanted the 4in guns eliminated, too, because this would eliminate their magazines, hoists, fire control and personnel. Similarly, it proposed that the pom-poms be hand-worked, which would eliminate both much wiring and their directors – as well as much of their effectiveness in combat. Similarly, the manager proposed that the 44in searchlights be replaced by 20in units, that degaussing be cut drastically and asdic and acoustic mine countermeasures eliminated altogether.

7   *Illustrious* was completed in about thirty-six months. However, a war-built ship, *Impacable*, took about sixty-six months.

HMS Theseus, *in October 1946, shows a Sea Vampire on deck, with a massive Barracuda abaft it and, apparently, Seafires (including a late type with contraprops) aft. The light fleet carriers were valued postwar because they could accommodate interim aircraft too large for the lifts of the armoured carriers, and because they were relatively inexpensive to operate. They could not, however, be modified to operate the very heavy aircraft projected from 1943 onwards.*

These and other suggested simplifications were considered at the meeting:

(a) Two large lifts were essential, but each was being fitted with two sets of electrical machinery. They were cut back to a single set per lift. The lifts were 45 × 34ft, dimensions chosen specifically to allow for existing types of fixed-wing RAF fighters.

(b) Hangar spraying and fire curtains were clearly essential, but fire curtains were arranged for hand operation only.

(c) The range-finder director for the 4in guns was deleted, leaving only the barrage director, and eliminating considerable wiring and one radar set. The two twin 4in guns aft were retained, but there was considerable discussion of reducing the number of 4-barrel pom-poms (seven) to four (as in HMS *Unicorn*, of comparable size) or five. Any such reduction would save considerable electrical work because the associated director and its radar would be eliminated. On the other hand, an additional close-range weapon could be mounted in the position vacated by the high-angle director abaft

the funnel. On 20 May the armament was set at two twin power-controlled 4in HA guns controlled by barrage director; six 2pdr RP50 Mk VII (4 barrel) pom-poms each controlled by a Mk IV director with radar, and ten twin power-operated 20mm canon. The pom-poms were arranged for four-cornered fire from the gallery deck, plus one at each end of the island. Of the 20mm guns, one was forward on each side, and two were sided both amidships and aft, all being at the gallery deck level.

(d) The two 44in searchlights were retained but their controls simplified.

(e) Degaussing coils were simplified.

(f) Asdic was omitted.

(g) Radio had already been reduced to a minimum.

(h) Generating power was reduced by omitting the two 200kW diesel sets planned for the platform deck, leaving two 400kW steam generators and two 200kW diesel sets.

The Deputy Controller approved this list, but wanted some way of controlling the 4in guns aft to beat off night destroyer or E-boat (MTB) attacks. The proposed solution was a target designation system with an associated barrage director. As for the lighter weapons, there was a proposal to replace all the pom-poms with twin Bofors (Hazemeyers or STAAGs), and to add three more.

By June 1942 it was clear that the limiting factors were hull and machinery, and that they would impose a minimum building time of two years. The Deputy Controller had to admit that, as far as hull and machinery were concerned, the design was as simple as possible, possibly even too simple as regards

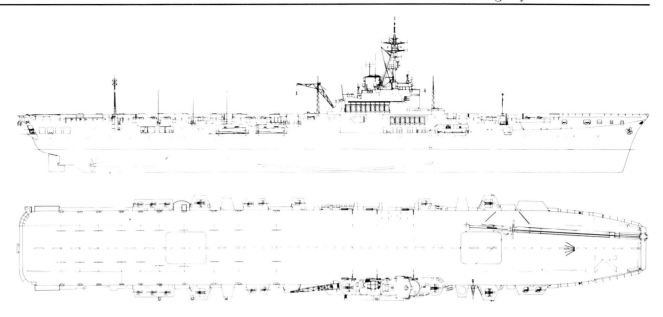

underwater protection. Machinery alone would probably dictate a building time of two to three and a half years, and no improvement could be expected short of retreating to an 18-knot escort carrier.

Even so, the search for simplification continued. Late in July DNE suggested some new approaches:

(a) Limit the prospective life of the ship to 1945 or the end of the war, whichever came first. This would simplify the supply of materials and fittings, since there would be no need to ensure durability or to make allowances for corrosion. Moreover, inconveniences of all kinds which would otherwise be unacceptable to the crew might be tolerable for the 'duration'.

(b) Limit full speed to a minimum, say 24 knots six months out of dock in the tropics. This would discount the need to work to a high strength/weight ratio; more easily obtainable materials could be used.

(c) Confine provision for efficiency in the machinery to a narrow speed range, say 20 to 24 knots. This would make for good endurance at the assumed operational speed with the simplest possible machinery, and without cross connections.

(d) Limit defensive armament to anti-aircraft weapons (20mm and 40mm and 2pdr guns), thus eliminating much magazine work, control gear and personnel.

(e) Eliminate secondary control positions and accept permanent subdivision of duplicated equipment to prevent complete breakdown; this covered a mass of piping, gearing, spindles and electric leads. DNE argued that these represented less of a combat safeguard than was commonly imagined, since the connections were likely to be put out of action. Complete subdivision of engines, steering gear, armament, and pumping, flooding and fire arrangements might actually be better.

(f) Use existing designs for machinery and other equipment.

(g) Eliminate as far as possible provisions made primarily for comfort and convenience.

Most of these ideas were in fact followed, and it was at this point that 4in guns disappeared from the design.[8] As a result, the July 1942 Staff Requirements called for six 4-barrel 2pdrs (as before), eleven quadruple 20mm, and two twin 20mm Mk V (powered), twin 20mm to be fitted in place of the quadruple mounts until the latter became available.

HMAS Sydney *(ex HMS* Terrible*) was completed to virtually the original* Majestic *design in November 1948. Note the two 277Q pencil-beam radars, fore and aft of the funnel. She was never further modernized, and ended as a fast troop transport, supporting Australian troops in Vietnam.* ALR

At this stage it was assumed that the ships would carry twenty-four aircraft, eighteen of them in the hangar and six in a permanent deck park. Stowage was provided for 96,000 gallons of petrol, almost twice the load of an armoured-hangar carrier. The July 1942 Staff Requirements showed 75,000 gallons, and stowage was cut back to 80,000 gallons (four tanks eliminated) in March 1943.

The statement of the 1942 Staff Requirement included a claim that deck protection over the machinery spaces, magazines and bulk petrol stowage had been considered and rejected as impracticable, but the Ship's Cover shows no evidence of any such proposal.

Most of the development of the design from 1942 onwards was in the direction of larger air complements. Thus late in 1943 the DNC Department had to provide for more aircraft and for the men to man and to service them, alternatives ranging from forty-eight even to fifty-four mixed aircraft, or sixty fighters. The planned eighteen TBR and six fighters required a total of ninety officers and 899 ratings, and standard growth factors brought that to ninety-two and 992. Table 11-6 shows the terrifying consequences of really large air groups.

These huge numbers were adopted because the existing armoured carriers, particularly *Illustrious* and *Victorious*, had successfully operated large permanent deck parks. One possibility, then, was to take over part of the hangar forward of the lift for additional accommodation. The maximum deck park was probably twenty-eight Seafires, and in that case the ship could accommodate twenty-four Barracudas and twelve Seafires (folding), or twelve Barracudas and thirty-four Seafires. However, the deck park required a fleet-carrier-size deck handling party, ninety men, who would themselves have to be accommodated. These figures were approved in principle by the First Lord on 2 December 1943. The new complement was set at 120 officers and about 1216 ratings.

By June 1944 there was fear that requirements for increased accommodation would affect completion dates. It was not so much the increase in total numbers as the change in the distribution among officers, chief petty officers, petty officers, and ratings, due to differences in the standards of accommodation each

8   It appears, however, that the decision was taken to extend the flight deck to the greatest possible length, to increase available take-off and ranging length. The longer deck and the elimination of the 4in guns in favour of two quadruple Oerlikons was formally approved only in March 1943.

Table 11-2: Aircraft Destroyers, July 1941

	E	C	D
LWL (ft)	560	680	650
Breadth of hull (ft)	66	76	76
Mean draught at std displacement (ft)	15 8	17 6	17 9
Std displacement (tons)	8400	13,400	13,450
Deep displacement (tons)	10,600	17,500	17,000
SHP	80,000	90,000	90,000
Speed (knots)	31 – 32.5	31 – 32.5	30.75 – 32.25
Oil fuel (tons)	1800	3200	3000
Endurance on trial (nm)	8300 at 16 knots	13,000 at 16 knots	11,500 at 16 knots
Armament	4 5in HA/LA	4 5in HA/LA	4 5in HA/LA
	2 directors	2 directors	2 directors
	10 Oerlikons	12 Oerlikons	12 Oerlikons
	4 twin 21in TT	6 twin 21in TT	6 twin 21in TT
Protection (above water)	2in NC belt to upper deck abreast magazines and machinery	2in NC belt to forecastle deck abreast magazines and machinery	2¼in NC belt to forecastle deck and machinery
	1in NC on upper deck	1in NC forecastle deck	1in NC on forecastle deck
(under water)	BRs adjacent	BRs separated	BRs separated
	ERs adjacent	ERs adjacent	ERs separated
Aircraft	12 fighters	10 fighters, 2 bombers ———————————	
Flight deck dimensions (ft)	530 × 60	630 × 66	600 × 66
Hangar	for 6 fighters	for all aircraft carried ———————————	
Lifts	45 × 33ft	two 45 × 33ft ———————————	
Petrol (gallons)	20,000	23,000	23,000
ATOG	yes	yes	yes
Barrier	1	2	2
Wires	6	6	6
Remarks	In all designs, considerable projections on starboard side outside the ship proper		

required. With eighteen TBRs and thirty-four Seafires aboard, for example, there would be 111 officers and 1188 men; with twenty-four of each type, 118 officers and 1164 men. Accommodation was now being arranged for 123 officers and 1236 men, which sufficed but did not provide for the 25 per cent aircrew manning margin then being demanded. Emergency measures included subdivision of the mess, placing additional officers' bunks in existing cabins, and even providing camp beds.

In 1945, *Colossus* had aboard 142 officers and warrant officers (plus six officers without cabins), 244 chief petty officers and petty officers, and 949 ratings, a total of 1341. At that time provision was made for 146 officers, 287 petty officers, and 977 ratings.

THROUGHOUT 1942 THE ROYAL NAVY became more and more uncomfortably aware of its desperate need for carriers, and the orders for light carriers grew. In mid-January D of P estimated that thirteen to twenty were needed with the fleet, plus forty on trade routes (one for each convoy plus about ten to hunt down raiders), plus two for training, a total of fifty-five to sixty-two compared to the 1940 estimate of fifteen (seven with the fleet, seven on the trade routes and one for training) or fourteen in 1936 (eight with the fleet, five on trade routes and one for training). Although the greatest expansion was due to the convoy requirement (see Chapter 9), the fleet requirement had approximately doubled, and merchant conversions would not do. It appeared that two 'Woolworth' (light fleet) carriers could be built in twenty-one months by using the engines built for a cancelled cruiser. ANCS(W) suggested that at least six 'Woolworths' be built to fill the gap before any new armoured carriers could be completed.

Early in February the Admiralty hoped to build two fleet carriers and three 'Woolworths' under the 1942–43 programme. Any further carrier construction would have to be at the expense of *Lion* class battleships, fleet carriers, or cruisers.

HMS Triumph *at Malta, with a* Firefly *and a* Walrus *amphibian on deck. British postwar carrier air groups typically included one Sea Otter for search and rescue; these aircraft were replaced by Dragonfly helicopters after 1950.*

Light fleet carriers used much the same building slips as cruisers. The 1942 programme included four light fleet carriers as well as two fleet carriers. Three light fleet carriers were ordered before the beginning of the 1942 financial year. Some expenditure was deferred by using existing cruiser machinery.

Then the Future Building Committee was formed (see Chapter 13). Its analysis showed that the shortage of carriers was even worse than had been imagined, much worse than any shortage of cruisers. Against a requirement in January 1944 for sixteen fleet carriers, the Royal Navy would have only four modern and three old fleet carriers (equivalent to four 48-aircraft fleet carriers). Every two light fleet carriers were equivalent to one more fleet carrier; thus the two fleet carriers and

four light fleet carriers of 1942 would effectively double the total British force.

Early in August the First Lord asked for nine more light carriers. As compensation, four cruisers, one minesweeper, and two civilian cargo liners would be cancelled.[9] Of these nine carriers, one could be completed at the end of 1944, six in the first half of 1945, and the other two in the second half of that year. At this time the first three were expected to complete in the first half of 1944, and the fourth ship, which was ordered later, in the first half of 1945.[10]

The Air Ministry was unenthusiastic, since it was already resisting Admiralty demands for fighters to equip the existing carriers. However, the First Lord prevailed, and the programme grew to thirteen light fleet carriers.

In September 1942 the First Lord approached the Cabinet for more light fleet carriers. Harland & Wolff had sufficient capacity for two more (having already been allocated four). A third was allocated to the Royal Dockyard at Devonport.[11] The final programme, sixteen light fleet carriers, was expected to cut the projected 1945 shortage of carriers to 37 per cent.

The last six ships (*Majestic*, *Hercules*, *Leviathan*, *Magnificent*, *Powerful*, *Terrible*) were rearranged primarily to accommodate the new centralized messing system. On 13 September 1945 they were redesignated the *Majestic* class. None was ever completed for the Royal Navy, though five of the six were eventually completed for foreign navies (two for Australia, two for Canada, one for India).[12] Other relatively minor modifications increased *Majestic* class design displacement by 550 tons. Estimated weights in October 1945 are shown in Table 11–9.

STRUCTURALLY, THE LIGHT FLEET CARRIERS followed merchant ship practice, the flight deck being the strength deck. They were designed to a four-compartment flooding standard, but during construction some concern was expressed about merchant ship-style hatches in their decks. To improve resistance to underwater damage, spaces about 340ft long at the waterline (covering magazines, machinery and bomb rooms) were fitted to stow buoyancy drums, as in escort carriers. The machinery itself was of the unit system, in two large machinery spaces (two boilers, one 500kW turbo generator, and one main turbine each) separated by two spaces 24ft long, containing auxiliary machinery and the petrol tanks. In addition, there

In 1949, HMS Vengeance *shows an unusual mix of aircraft: a Sea Fury fighter, a Firefly, a Firebrand strike fighter and two Sea Otters aft, and a Dragonfly helicopter forward. As the first Dragonfly squadron was only formed in 1950, this must have been a test machine. The unusual complement may have been aboard for Operation Rusty, the Arctic carrier tests of 1949.*

were two 200kW diesel generators on the centreline of the main deck; a third diesel generator (180kW) was later fitted.

The island was carried on two transverse bulkheads; there were no fore and aft bulkheads below the line of the island plating, and no continuous bulkheads ran up through the island. As a result, all the heavy masses of the island, including the mast and struts, were suspended within or above the island, and not structurally connected to it. There was some feeling that this arrangement contributed to the vibration which plagued early ships of the class.

Electronically, the class was unfortunate in that its role changed during the period of design, while requirements radically increased. In 1942, radio requirements were completely met by providing one transmitting room and one set of hinged masts on the port side. Fleet carriers typically had duplicate arrangements port and starboard. Revised Staff Requirements issued late in 1944 showed what amounted to fleet carrier standards. This was late in the construction of the class, and in November 1944 it was agreed that the question of starboard hinged masts would have to be taken up separately. DNC offered hydraulically-operated masts, but the necessary hydraulic machinery could not be obtained in time. The extra masts would also have interfered with gun arcs.

No extra masts were fitted, but in May 1946 ASE suggested that whip aerials be fitted to the *Colossus* class. They might even be preferable to the earlier type of hinged mast, and by this time they had been approved for the starboard side of the *Majestics*.

Ships were fitted with two long-range air search sets, Type 79B and Type 281B (Type 281BQ in later units), one height-finder, Type 277 (which was also the surface search set), and with a short-range precision radar (Type 293, on the aft side of the mast) to assist in aircraft traffic control. A proposal to fit a missile jammer (Type 651) was cancelled in November 1944, but a special intercept direction finder (for 'Y' operation: RU 1

9   PREM 3/322/10

10   In fact the first ship, HMS *Colossus*, completed only in December 1944 (thirty months from laying-down); four ships (including one converted for aircraft maintenance) completed in the first half of 1945, then two more in the latter part of that year, and the last three during the first half of 1946, for a total of ten. To the extent, then, that the design was specially prepared for quick production, it was a failure. However, that failure was probably largely due to the immense overall load on British wartime ship-building rather than to excessive sophistication in the light carrier design.

11   Since the fall of France, no new construction had been allocated to the Royal Dockyards, due to the danger of air attack. Now this danger had abated, and it was estimated that a ship laid down early in 1943 could be completed twenty-seven months later. The available ship at Portsmouth could not have accommodated a light carrier, so a cruiser was ordered from that yard, reducing the 1942 cruiser cancellations from four to three.

12   On 29 December 1945 it was decided that three *Majestics* (*Leviathan*, *Powerful*, and *Terrible*) should be completed subject to the sale of two, or if possible three, *Colossus*-class carriers to foreign governments. Meanwhile work was to proceed slowly so that they could be cancelled if no sale materialized. On 29 January 1946 *Hercules* was substituted for *Majestic* as one of the ships to proceed at a slow rate of construction.

or RU 4) would be fitted.

C-in-C British Pacific Fleet was much impressed by the US SM-1 height-finder, and wanted it fitted in place of 277. For a time that was approved for the last eight ships, but by mid-1945 it was clear that this would impose unacceptable delays. At this time the war with Japan was expected to last until mid-1946, and the decision was to fit SM-1 only to HMS *Ocean*, after her sea and flying trials. Other ships would be fitted only if they required major repairs after battle damage, and that turned out not to be the case.

HMS *Ocean* was refitted at Cammell Laird as a night fighter carrier.[13]

By July 1945 the next generation of British naval radars was clearly in sight: Type 980 for precision two-dimensional search and Type 981 for height-finding. Although these sets never entered production, they were modified postwar as the ubiquitous Types 982 and 983. The new standard carrier air search radar outfit would consist of a new long-range set, Type 960 (roughly comparable to the existing 281), 980, and 981. Twenty ship sets were ordered, for delivery beginning in March 1946, sufficient for the new *Ark Royal* and *Hermes* classes, and for the last three light fleet carriers, *Leviathan*, *Majestic*, and *Hercules*, scheduled for completion in May, June, and September 1946. To avoid delaying ships which might otherwise be available for the Pacific War, only the last ship could be held back for fitting with the new radars.[14] This was not, in fact, done because *Hercules* was suspended at the end of the war.

These ships had two 45 × 34ft lifts, designed for a 15,000lb working load, with a 36-second working cycle. To save construction time each was fitted with one rather than the usual two sets of machinery.

There were eight arrester wires on four Mk 8 units (15,000lbs at 60 knots). The first ships to complete found this inadequate, and two more wires were fitted as ships became available. There were also two safety barriers.

The approved battery was six 4-barrel pom-poms, eleven quadruple and ten twin hand-worked Oerlikons.[15] It is not clear whether any ships were completed in this form; in at least some ships (certainly HMS *Glory*) twin power-worked guns replaced the quadruples, and single Oerlikons replaced the planned twin mounts. By the end of September 1945 the approved battery was six pom-poms, plus eleven standard single 40mm guns and ten 'Boffins', the latter replacing the twin hand-worked Oerlikons. While under construction, HMS *Ocean* had five twin and two single 20mm replaced by seven single 2pdrs, leaving

HMS Glory *at Malta, in about 1950. Note that her mainmast, which normally carried a Type 279 long-wave-length radar, has been retracted. This arrangement made servicing easier.*

her with six twin and eight single 20mm guns. They in turn were replaced by twelve single 40mm (in late September 1945). In April 1946 the standard battery was six quadruple 2pdrs and nineteen single power-worked 40mm guns.

It is not certain which ships had all nineteen guns. In June 1950 this battery was confined to *Triumph* and *Vengeance*; *Glory* had eighteen 40mm, *Ocean* had fifteen, *Theseus* had seventeen, and *Warrior* had fourteen.[16]

THE FIRST TRIALS of HMS *Colossus* were in December 1944.

13   The refit was scheduled for 18 August to 16 November 1945. It included SM-1, Type 961 for carrier-controlled approach, relocation of Type 293; installation of Type 93; installation of FV 5 rather than FV 4 HF/DF, and installation of Asdic 149 A/S in place of 132VS; the after 100kW diesel generator was connected to the ring main.

14   There was some interest in an interim policy of fitting only one of the two new radars, the Type 981 height-finder, but the displays designed for the new sets could not easily be adapted to work with existing ones, and the narrow-beam Type 980 was needed to direct Type 981 onto a target. In effect 980 and 981 operating together were equivalent to a single very long-range pencil-beam set, a super 277 or SM-1.

15   Ammunition stowage was 1800 rounds per barrel for pom-poms and 2400 per barrel for Oerlikons. Bomb stowage, based on eighteen TBR and thirty-four fighters, comprised thirty-six 2000lb AP bombs, 216 500lb SAP bombs, seventy-two 500lb MC bombs, 216 100lb A/S bombs, and thirty-three torpedoes.

16   Data from US ONI manual on the Royal Navy, July 1950, based on British handbooks.

HMS Theseus *shows the standard British postwar fighter, the Hawker Sea Fury, in 1950.*

Her island, mast, and some sponsons vibrated, and had to be stiffened. Hull vibration was strongest just abaft the after lift. Several other ships experienced much the same problem, which was largey cured in *Ocean* (in August 1945) by additional stiffening (at the SM-1 position on the island, at the after gun sponsons, and at the other minor positions). There were still problems in the island structure, and further stiffening was required, as the ship still vibrated when her starboard shaft ran at a critical rate, about 180rpm. However, the last of the class, HMS *Triumph*, was essentially free of vibration through her whole speed range. The crucial improvement was apparently the elimination of the S.2 director, which overhung the compass platform.[17]

Trials performance of the first four (and the last) ships is listed in Table 11-8.

The captain of HMS *Colossus* reported after her trials that she handled well, considering her lack of power; she was quick on her helm and in calm weather turned satisfactorily at rest. Astern power was sufficient for normal manoeuvring, but there was little to spare in an emergency. She was very lively in a seaway, but did not roll heavily, and showed little tendency to heel even at full speed under full helm. On the other hand, he found the bridge arrangements inadequate. The view from the CO's position at the Pelorus was very limited, and with the overhanging pom-pom director platform and the HF/DF bracket he could not see what was going on overhead without walking out of the wing doors. The charthouse was far too small, particularly as it was the only place the captain could privately discuss most secret matters over a chart; there was hardly working space for one officer, and standing room for only three. Unfortunately space in the island was so limited that there was no obvious remedy.

As reported by HMS *Venerable* in September 1945, the ship was inclined to pitch considerably in a head sea or swell of any strength, due to her fine lines forward and light tonnage. She was also lively in any beam sea, and thus could not match fleet carrier operating capability in rough weather.

Habitability was also a serious problem, as might have been expected in such cramped ships.[18]

THE LIGHT FLEET CARRIERS were very important to the postwar Fleet Air Arm. They were relatively inexpensive to operate, and they had somewhat better aircraft arrangements than the surviving armoured carriers. The first four, *Colossus*,

HMS Ocean was converted into a night fighter carrier soon after completion. The outward marks of conversion were a US-supplied SM-1 radar (atop the island) and the associated extra structure at the forward end of the island.

Glory, *Vengeance* and *Venerable*, reached the British Pacific Fleet in 1945 to form the 11th Carrier Squadron.

Since all the ships were relatively small, and since they could not be spared from operational service, major modernization was never a realistic option. They were therefore earmarked for trade protection duty. Even that, however, required some improvement, since the main postwar trade protection aircraft (such as the Gannet and a moderate-performance jet fighter, initially a Vampire and later a Sea Venom) were substantially faster and heavier than their wartime predecessors. These required flight and hangar decks and lifts strengthened for a dead weight of 24,000lbs and a landing load of 20,000lbs.[19] Arrester gear would have to be brought up to Mk 8 (Mod) standard. During 1949 *Glory*, *Theseus*, and *Vengeance*, the three ships temporarily in reserve, were fitted with the modernized arrester gear, the simplest of the minimum modifications.[20]

17 A modern analysis suggests that the vibration was a combined torsional/bending mode, a weakness at the after lift opening affecting the island through a lower arm. Because she was completed well after the war (in May 1946), *Triumph* had such peacetime features as tiling in her washplaces and heads, and side scuttles for main deck and higher compartments.

18 According to the DNC World War II history.

19 Lift modification would require extra motors and new shafting. It was estimated in May 1950 that lifts would be completed in the ships a year after the necessary contracts were placed. If motors were taken from the *Majestic* class, the time could be reduced to six months. The existing 45 x 34ft lifts were big enough to take both the Gannet and the Vampire: 20,000lbs was the limit unless entirely new lifts were built, and 20 to 24,000lbs was the limit to which decks could be strengthened (a four-month job) rather than replated (a much larger job)

20 The strength limit for unmodernized (but slightly modified) light fleet carriers was 18,000lbs, corresponding to a landing weight of about 16,000. By late 1948 five sets of modified arrester gear had been manufactured, two for the Commonwealth carriers (*Terrible* and *Magnificent*) and three for HMS *Glory*, *Triumph*, and *Vengeance*. Three more sets were later ordered for the remaining three *Colossus*-class ships. Modification time was about four months. More stiffening was required to operate aircraft at an all-up weight of 20,000lbs. There were proposals for lift improvements using equipment which had been manufactured for the suspended *Majestic*-class carriers and by taking equipment from the *Hermes* class. *Glory* was refitted at Devonport, mid-January to mid-June 1949 (delayed by departure of RAN personnel for HMAS *Sydney*), *Theseus* at Rosyth April until the end of July, and *Vengeance* in the autumn of 1949.

Warrior was first modernized in 1952–53; note her enclosed bridge, her new lattice foremast, and her two Type 277 radars. These photographs were taken at Malta in 1954, the starboard side and overall view on 24 February and port side on 17 April. Note that her pom-poms have been replaced by more modern twin Bofors, and that the long-wavelength Type 279 air search radar has been landed. The aircraft aft are Fireflies, and a Sea Fury is barely visible abeam the island.

Ocean and *Triumph* followed in 1951.[21] At this time it seemed that an adequate radar suit would consist of three 277Q, one 960, one 293Q, and one carrier-controlled approach radar (961, later deleted). The existing BH 3 catapult could launch a 20,000lb aircraft at 66 knots (thus, a Gannet with 10 to 14 knots of wind over the deck). However, a Vampire would require 38 knots (modifications could reduce that to 29). It seemed likely, then, that Vampires would require rocket assistance, a common procedure during World War II. The Mk 8 (Mod) arrester gear could accept Gannet and Vampire at, respectively, 20 and 25 knots wind over the deck.

At this time the *Hermes* class was expected to come into service in 1952–54, and the six big armoured carriers were all scheduled for modernization. Plans called for the *Colossus* class to reduce to Category C reserve as the new light fleet carriers were commissioned, and for trade-protection carriers to be maintained as a mobilization reserve.[22]

Colossus was transferred to France on 6 August 1946 (as *Arromanches*) upon her return from the Pacific Fleet. *Venerable* returned to Britain in April 1947 and was sold to the Royal Netherlands Navy on 1 April 1948, as *Karel Doorman*.

Glory returned from the Far East in 1947, and was immobilized between October 1947 and February 1948; she then refitted at Devonport, not recommissioning until 1949 and then deploying to the Mediterranean. Her bridge was rebuilt and her mix of single Bofors and pom-poms replaced by sixteen single 40mm. She was recommissioned in December 1950, and relieved HMS *Theseus* in Korea (April–September 1951, February–May 1952, and November 1952–May 1953). She operated against terrorists in Malaya in 1953, arriving at Portsmouth on 8 July 1953. She reduced to trooping and ferry carrier duties in 1954, and was reduced to reserve in 1956.

Ocean was trials carrier in 1945, when a Vampire made the first jet landing on her deck on 3 December. A total of fifteen landings and take-offs were made during a two-day period. At this time HMS *Ocean* was the only available carrier in home waters, the larger ships remaining in the Far East. She then served in the Mediterranean, including a period as a supply ship during the Palestine crisis (1946–48); she provided air cover for the withdrawal of British troops from Palestine. She was flagship (air) of the Mediterranean Fleet in 1949. From June 1949 on she served as a troopship for the Mediterranean and the Far East, after which she was refitted for carrier duties early in

21   At this time one set of new lift motors (of four originally ordered) was still on order, and there were suggestions that the ship's refit should be extended so that her flight deck could be stiffened and the new motors installed. *Ocean* could then easily be cleared to operate the Gannet and perhaps also US-supplied aircraft in wartime.

22   Retention of the *Colossus* class was specifically recommended in February 1950 by the same A/S Aircraft Working Party which drew up initial Staff Requirements for an aircraft which could fly from an unmodified light carrier, the Seamew (see Chapter

15). Unfortunately the Seamew could not be ready before 1957, at the time the target date for British readiness. In May the Working Party suggested that Gannets could actually be flown from unmodified ships, providing required strength factors were somewhat relaxed. It was understood that the US Navy had cleared the war-built *Casablanca*-class escort carriers to take Skyraiders (which were roughly equivalent to Gannets). The limiting factor in lifts was their motors; surely they could be geared to lift a greater weight more slowly. DNC felt that existing decks were probably good for 17,000lbs but that aircraft would inevitably grow beyond that figure.

56). During this period she was occasionally used for trooping. *Theseus* served as an improvised helicopter carrier at Suez in November 1956. She reduced to reserve upon her return in December, and was sold in 1960 for breaking up.

Triumph was initially trials ship for twin-engine aircraft, replacing HMS *Illustrious* while the latter refitted during 1948. She served as flagship (air) in the Mediterranean 1947–48, and in 1949 was sent to Malaya to help suppress the Communist insurgency there. She was the first British carrier in Korea in 1950. Upon her return home she tested the first British angled deck, which had been painted on her axial one (1951); aircraft made touch-and-go landings. She was then converted into an Officer Cadet Training Ship in 1953, serving until 1955 (when she was replaced by a destroyer and two frigates). In 1956 she was ordered converted into a heavy repair ship, the work being done at Portsmouth in 1958–65. Upon completion she relieved HMS *Hartland Point* at Singapore. This service included support during the Indonesian confrontation (1966) and the Beira (anti-Rhodesia blockade) patrol in 1972. She was refitted in 1972, and paid off at Chatham in 1975, being sold and broken up in 1981–82, the last light fleet carrier in the Royal Navy.

Warrior was lent to the Royal Canadian Navy upon completion in March 1946 and was returned early in 1948 after completion of HMS *Magnificent* for Canadian service.[23] She was fitted with a flexible deck at Portsmouth (1 March – 30 September 1948), commissioning for British service (for flexible deck trials) in November 1948. The deck was removed in June 1949, and *Warrior* went into reserve. She was recommissioned in July 1950 as an aircraft transport and troopship, to the Far East and to Cyprus (July 1951). She was then refitted at Devonport (April 1952 – October 1953).[24] In February 1954 she relieved HMAS *Sydney* in the United Nations force monitoring the Korean cease-fire, and then helped evacuate refugees from North Vietnam. After arrival at Devonport in December 1954 she was taken in hand for a further refit (completed August 1956), becoming the only Royal Navy *Colossus* class

HMS Ocean *at Malta, 1952 (starboard side) and 31 March 1953 (port side), the latter showing her SM-1 replaced by a British Type 277Q. In both cases, note that the after (long-wavelength) air search radar has been eliminated, leaving a stump mainmast, and that the pom-poms have been replaced by twin Bofors.*

1951. She rejoined the Mediterranean Fleet and then, having been replaced by HMS *Theseus*, went to the Far East for Korean operations (May 1952 – November 1953), returning to the United Kingdom early in 1954. She was then refitted as a training ship. With HMS *Theseus*, she served as an improvised helicopter carrier at Suez in November 1956. In 1957 she was flagship of the Training Squadron of the Home Fleet. That December she went into reserve, and she was sold with *Theseus* in 1960.

Theseus was flagship (air) in the Far East in 1947, and flagship of the Third Aircraft Carrier Squadron in 1948–49. She was employed in night jet trials in mid-1950, and relieved HMS *Triumph* in Korea (1951–52). In 1952 she was flagship of the Heavy Squadron, Home Fleet. She was refitted as a training ship in 1954, replacing the fleet carrier *Implacable* as flagship of the Training Squadron of the Home Fleet (1955–

23   The Canadian Navy acquired these carriers for two reasons. First, the Royal Navy encouraged its expansion to make up for gaps in its own manpower. Second, by September, 1943 the Canadian Naval Staff was determined not to end the war with only a small-ship navy. In January 1943 the Canadians tried to get four escort carriers to work with the four Canadian escort groups, but that was precluded by the terms of Lend-Lease. Instead, Canadian seamen manned the escort carriers *Nabob* and *Puncher*, but the Royal Navy furnished their air groups. The Canadian Naval Staff proposed in September 1943 that two light fleet carriers be acquired as part of the Canadian contribution to the Pacific War. The Admiralty offered HMS *Ocean* and *Warrior*. HMS *Vengeance* was initially proposed to replace the badly damaged *Nabob*, but she was expected to enter service before sufficient Canadian seamen would be ready. Then *Ocean* or *Warrior* was offered to replace the escort carrier *Puncher*, and then *Ocean* and *Warrior*. There were some problems; the Admiralty had hoped that the Canadians would man 30 per cent of the Pacific escorts as well as some repair ships. The Canadian government offered 13,000 men and the two light fleet carriers, and also refused to contribute to British operations in the Indian Ocean (that is, to the reconquest of Burma and Malaya). In November 1944, the Board finally approved transfer of the two light fleet

carriers. However, due to manning problems the RCN could accept none before September 1945, and that eliminated HMS *Ocean*. The offer shifted to HMS *Warrior* and *Magnificent*, which were expected to complete in September and November 1945. The carriers were formally offered on 14 January 1945, the Canadians having the right to purchase them later. However, by the summer of 1946 it was clear that Canada could not afford to operate two carriers. This decision was formalized as part of the 1947 Canadian defence cuts. As a result, HMS *Warrior* was returned to Britain when HMS *Magnificent* (renamed *Powerful*) became available. At that time, the public excuse was that *Warrior* was not really suitable for Canadian service, not having been Arcticized. J D F Kealy and E C Russell, *A History of Canadian Naval Aviation, 1918–62* (Naval Historical Section of Canadian Forces HQ, Ottawa, 1965).

24   She was fitted with a new lattice mast carrying a Type 293Q short-range air search radar and her YE beacon, and a second Type 277 replaced the pom-pom at the after end of her island. The small mainmast abaft her funnel carried her Type 281BQ with its IFF. All pom-poms were eliminated; two at the ends of the island were suppressed altogether, the other four replaced by twin Bofors. Her single 40mm battery was increased to twenty guns.

Right and below right: Vengeance *as a ferry carrier, in 1953 (photos taken 30 January and 1 February). The aircraft on deck are naval types cocooned for preservation while en route. The forward island extension carried a pom-pom director.*

carrier with an angled deck, with some of the portside sponsons suppressed. Her hydraulic catapult was modified to 20,000lb capacity, and a mirror sight and blind landing radar were installed. She also received a US SPS-6C air search radar. Her only subsequent important operational service was as flagship of the squadron supporting the first H-bomb tests in the Pacific, and she returned home in February 1958 to go into reserve. That July it was announced that she would be transferred to Argentina (renamed *Independencia*); she sailed from the United Kingdom on 10 December 1958, after a minor refit.

Vengeance served briefly in the Mediterranean before joining the British Pacific Fleet, and returned to Britain on 13 August 1946. She was employed on six weeks of cold-weather trials in the Arctic (Operation Rusty, for which she was refitted 3 May – 1 September 1948) in 1948–49,[25] was flagship of the Third Aircraft Carrier Squadron (Home Fleet) in 1950–51, and then ferried troops to Korea (and aircraft to Malta) during 1952. She was refitted in 1952–53, during which she was transferred to the Royal Australian Navy on 13 November 1952 pending completion of HMAS *Melbourne*; she actually sailed in January 1953. She returned on 12 August 1955, and was then sold to Brazil (transferred 14 December 1956 and renamed *Minas Gerais*), being rebuilt at Rotterdam in 1957–60.

ON THE GROUNDS that *Hercules* would be held back to be fitted with modern radar, DACR proposed in July 1945 that her flying arrangements also be modernized to bring her up to *Hermes* class standards as far as possible, that is, to be able to operate the new generation of naval aircraft. The rest of the class might follow.

This was the first approach to the vital postwar question of carrier modernization (see also Chapter 15). The decision, late in 1942, to radically relax limitations on carrier aircraft divided the British carrier force into limited and modern ships, the armoured fleet carriers and the *Colossus* class light fleet carriers all falling into the limited category.[26] This was of little moment in 1942, when very large numbers of modern carriers (ultimately the *Ark Royal*, *Hermes* and *Malta* classes) were in prospect. In 1945 the question was only one of modernizing a large existing fleet so that it would not become prematurely useless. However, within a year many of the modern ships had been cancelled, and the question was really one of assuring the viability of the British carrier force as a whole.

Unfortunately, the *Colossus* design had been fairly tight to begin with. It appeared that lift and accelerator capacity could not be increased, the flight deck could not be widened (to take longer-span aircraft), and fitting *Hermes* type arrester gear would reduce clear hangar height. It seemed likely, as early as 1945, that the *Colossus* class would replace existing escort carriers as future convoy escorts, or fighter or assault carriers. This in turn squeezed out the CVEs (see Chapter 9).

The Controller formally raised the question of *Majestic* class modernization in September 1945. At this time it seemed likely

that the first three ships (*Majestic*, *Magnificent* and *Terrible*) could be completed for service. The three less advanced ships, *Leviathan*, *Powerful* and *Hercules*, would be completed only up to the stage at which they could be towed away for preservation. When resumed they would be completed to the modernized design.

It had to be accepted that such ships could never operate aircraft up to the new 30,000lb limit. The minimum acceptable aircraft weight was 20,000lbs, with entry and launch speeds of 75 knots. Existing lifts could be modified to take a 20,000lb load (including the working party), with enlarged (50 x 34ft) platforms. They could also be altered to take 20,000lb aircraft (plus working party), but this would take longer. A new arrester gear design would be required, but the existing catapult could be modified, with a single track. A 20,000lb aircraft crane could be fitted on the port side, but it would be subject to sea damage there.

It seemed likely that *Hermes* class requirements for radar, radio, armament and AIO could be met, albeit at a cost in topweight.[27] The initial modernization plan called for twin

25   Operation Rusty demonstrated the limitations of conventional materials in the Arctic: HMS Vengeance received a very serious brittle-fracture crack in her flight deck, causing considerable worry among British constructors.

26   Modernization of the *Colossus* class light fleet carriers, to handle the new aircraft, was studied in May 1943, but was found to be impractical. That was why the *Hermes* class was designed.

27   A reduction in GM, in the light condition, from 4.9ft to 3.05ft, seemed acceptable. By filling oil fuel tanks with water as fuel was burned, the ship could maintain a GM of 5.46ft or more (average action condition). Previous British practice had been to leave oil tanks empty as fuel was burned; the US Navy tended to fill them with sea water. Speed in deep condition with a clean bottom would be reduced from 25 to 24.5 knots, and six months out of dock in temperate waters, to 22.5 knots (in the tropics, to 20.55 knots).

Bofors in place of the six pom-poms, for a modernized accelerator of improved performance, for new radio equipment, for new radars (277Q, 960, and 293), and for increased generator capacity. The aircraft-handling improvements, which required new equipment, were left for a second phase.

A tentative modernization plan added 510 tons, so that the modernized *Majestic* would displace 1060 tons more than a *Colossus*, losing 1.01ft in GM. Stresses would increase by about 5 per cent.

The new aircraft would require much more fuel; the goal was 100,000 gallons of petrol and another 100,000 gallons of paraffin (jet fuel). Hull volume was limited, and petrol stowage could not be increased. Paraffin could only be stowed at the expense of petrol, oil fuel or magazine space.

Modern radar could be fitted on a lengthened and widened

HMAS Sydney *(ex HMS* Terrible*) showed few differences from the original* Majestic *design, the chief visible improvement being the provision of two Type 277 radars, for all-round coverage. Note the absence of the mainmast characteristic of the* Colossus *class, and the different bridge face. Pom-poms were replaced by twin Bofors. This photograph was taken on 11 July 1953.*

island: 980/981 forward (with 277 pointing aft to fill in the blanked area astern), 960 (with 281 aerial), 293, and 961 (or its successor, 962). An additional hinged mast would have to be erected aft for HF/DF, and two more hinged radio masts (starboard side) would be required.

The island would also be enlarged to provide better aircraft direction arrangements, including the two-level ADR/Operations Room then planned for the new carriers. The enlarged island had to be cantilevered over the side so as not to encroach more than 3ft more onto the flight deck.

The six existing 4-barrel pom-poms would be replaced by twin Bofors, and supplemented by fifteen single Bofors (two replaced by the new crane on the port side). Thus all Oerlikons would have been replaced by power-worked single Bofors.

One 100kW diesel generator in the hold amidships would be replaced by a 400kW steam turbo generator and a second 200kW diesel generator added to the unit forward (absorbing mess space for fifteen men).

Accommodation would be slightly reduced, from 147 officers to 143; additional space could only have been provided at the expense of mess space.

At the end of the war two ships, *Magnificent* and *Terrible*, were earmarked for the two major Commonwealth navies. The other four were candidates for cancellation and scrapping. They were obsolete (because they could not operate the new 30,000lb aircraft) and savings were desperately needed. The Admiralty argued that they would still be needed for trade

Table 11-3: Legend, Light Fleet Carrier, 1 February 1942

LBP (ft)	630
LWL (ft)	682
LOA (ft)	682
Beam, extreme (ft)	80
Draught, at std displacement (ft)	19
Std displacement (tons)	14,000
Draught, deep (ft)	23
Freeboard (ft)	42 9
Fuel oil (tons)	3000
Endurance (nm)	8500 at 20 knots
SHP	40,000
Speed, deep (knots)	25
Complement	1054
Petrol (gallons)	96,000
Lube oil (gallons)	7000

Armament

Twin 4in	4 (400rpg)
4-barrel pom-pom	6 (18000rpb)
Twin Oerlikon	10 (2400rpg)
Torpedoes	32
Depth charges	108

Aircraft

TBR	18
FF	6
Bombs	
2000lb AP	36
500lb SAP	216
500lb MC	72
250lb B	108
40lb GP	360
Incendiary	204

Weights (tons)

General equipment	1200
Aircraft equipment	610
Machinery	1110
Armament	695
Hull	10,085
Margin	300
Std displacement	14,000

route protection and as fighter carriers; even if they were completed, the Navy would be five carriers short of its planned postwar fleet. The Board also argued that stopping the four ships would throw shipyard workers out of work, and that, since about two-thirds of the total building cost had already been expended, the saving would be small. The First Lord reluctantly agreed to continue the ships for the Royal Navy, in hopes of selling one *Colossus* to the Netherlands (negotiations were already under way late in 1945) and one or two to France. It was hoped that the income from this sale would pay for completion of two *Majestics*. In the event, the sales went through, but the ships were suspended anyway, and completed only for other navies. For a time work on HMS *Majestic* was also suspended, but she was rebuilt (for the Royal Australian Navy) beginning in 1949.

Although the Royal Navy never completed and modernized the *Majestics* several of them were rebuilt for Commonwealth navies. These ships showed what could be achieved in a relatively simple, small hull. Moreover, most or all of the design work on these Commonwealth ships was a DNC responsibility.[28] These ships fall into two groups. *Terrible* and *Magnificent* were completed to the final *Majestic* class design and transferred to Australia and to Canada. *Majestic*, *Powerful*, and *Hercules* were all drastically rebuilt to handle jets; all were given steam catapults, for example. They can be compared to the two Dutch reconstructions of *Colossus* class carriers, the *Karel Doorman* (later the Argentine *25 de Mayo*) and the *Minas Gerais* (for Brazil).

DNC maintained a current modernization plan for ships of this class remaining incomplete. In June 1950 the major items planned for HMS *Majestic* were:

28 As attested by the existence of Ship's Covers for each conversion. Several of these Covers have not yet been released, but all are shown on the current consolidated list at the National Maritime Museum, Greenwich.

HMS Glory *returns to Britain after Korean War service, 1953.*

Glory as a ferry carrier at Malta, 24 September 1954. The ferry carrier role was vital as long as aircraft could not easily be flown over very great distances. It declined with improvements in jet endurance and with the rise of air-to-air refuelling. For the Royal Navy, ferrying became less important as overseas commitments were cut after 1957, and as fixed garrisons were replaced by a limited number of carrier task forces.

Triumph as a cadet training carrier, 27 October 1954, with some of her armament removed and the rest cocooned, and with a Sea Balliol trainer visible on deck.

- new arrester gear and barriers (for 20,000lb aircraft landing at 87 knots)
- new lifts (54 x 34ft; 24,000lbs)
- stronger flight and hangar decks (to handle 24,000lb aircraft, and land 20,000lb aircraft)
- a more powerful crane
- a rearranged island with modernized AIO arrangements,

a second 277Q (in place of the twin Bofors at the after end of the island), and a carrier controlled approach radar (Type 961)
- island and mast strengthened to reduce vibration
- ready and enlarged briefing rooms re-sited nearer the island
- petrol stowage increased from 80,000 to 130,000 gallons
- increased air conditioning capacity, improved ventilation, improved accommodation
- 400kW diesel generators in place of existing 200kW sets
- modernized bomb rooms
- Type 149 Asdic

Also under consideration, but not yet formally approved, were a 105ft steam catapult and air casing for the boilers (as protection against gas attack).

In 1950 the Canadians asked that HMCS *Magnificent* be modernized from 1952 on. She would arrive in the second half of 1952, and a modernized *Colossus* class carrier (that is, one with stronger deck, lifts and arrester gear) could be lent to Canada in her place. However, no steam catapult could be available until April 1954, and it would take about six months to install. In November 1950, then, the Admiralty suggested that *Magnificent* not be taken in hand until then. Canada opted to buy a new hull and have it totally rebuilt.

Terrible was purchased by Australia in 1948 and transferred in 1949; she was renamed *Sydney*. She participated in the Korean War, becoming training carrier in 1957 and a troopship in 1962, largely to support Australian troops in Vietnam. Australia bought HMS *Majestic* in 1949; she was rebuilt in 1949–55 and was renamed HMAS *Melbourne*, serving as a carrier until mid-1982. In December 1950 the RAN was informed that a steam catapult would be available at the end of March 1954, and that three more, not yet earmarked, would be completed in May, July and September. By July 1951 the Australians wanted steam catapults for both their carriers, but in fact HMAS *Sydney* was never rebuilt at all.

HMS *Magnificent* was completed for the Royal Canadian Navy in 1946–47. She participated in several NATO exercises, and carried the Canadian peacekeeping force to Suez in December 1956. She was then returned to Britain, arriving in Portsmouth on 14 June 1957, to be replaced by the extensively rebuilt *Powerful*, renamed *Bonaventure*. The latter had been sold to Canada in 1952, when a scheduled modernization of HMCS *Magnificent* was cancelled. She was commissioned in Belfast on 17 January 1957. *Bonaventure* was extensively refitted in 1966–67, but she was then discarded, after a Canadian defence review, in July 1970.

Hercules was sold to India, and completed to a modified design in 1961, as INS *Vikrant*.

Leviathan was never completed, and her hull was broken up from May 1968 onwards.

The first full modernization, then, was of HMAS *Melbourne*. She was fitted with a steam catapult and a 5½ degree angled deck, to operate the standard postwar trade protection aircraft, Gannets and Sea Venoms. The ship was rebuilt again in 1967–69, when her flight deck was strengthened and new Dutch Signaal radars fitted.

HMCS *Bonaventure* also had a steam catapult, but her deck angle was 7½ degrees. She had US radars and operated American trade protection aircraft (Trackers and Banshees, later Trackers and Whirlwind helicopters). She was armed with eight US-type 3in/50 guns.

Like the Canadian carrier, *Vikrant* has a 7½ degree deck and a

Table 11-4: Development of Light Carrier Requirements

	Controller Requirements	DNC Proposal	After Bath Meeting 14 January 1942	After Controller's Meeting, Whitehall, 23 January 1942	March 1942
Flight deck dimensions (ft)	450 × 60	600 × 75	663 × 78 ————	————————	665 × 80
Speed (knots)	25 ———				
Aircraft	at least 15 fighters	15 FF or 15 TSR	18 FF or TSR in hanger, 6 aircraft on flight deck, 4 aircraft stripped	18 FF or TSR, 6 aircraft on flight deck	18 FF or TSR (13 of new SIS dimensions), 6 aircraft on deck
Hangar height (ft)		14 6	16 6 ————		
Armament	1 HA gun	2 4in aft	4 4in aft	4 4in aft ————	————————
		2 4in fwd ———			
		4 4-barrel pom-poms	5 pom-poms	6 pom-poms ————	————————
		8 Oerlikons	10 Oerlikons	6 twin power-worked Oerlikons ————	————————
		2 4in directors	1 4in director	7 pom-pom directors ————	————————
Directors				8 FAM projectors ————	————————
Endurance (nm)		6000 at 20 knots ————			
		17,500 at 10 knots ————			
Arrester gear		6 wires, 145ft pullout, 11,000lb at 60 knots ————			
		1 trickle wire ————			
Lifts	2 45 × 34ft, 15,000lb ——	1 barrier	2 barriers ————		
ATO gear		not required	required ————		
Crane		not required	required ————		
Wireless masts		hinged, hand-worked	————————		carrier type
Torpedoes		27	32 ————		
Protection		none	machinery, petrol, magazines ————		none
Petrol (gallons)		40,000	75,000 ————	————————	100,000
Bomb lift		not required ————		required ————	————————
Ship dimensions		610ft LBP × 70ft beam	630ft LBP × 78ft beam	630ft LBP × 80ft beam ————	————————
Deep displacement		17,000 tons	18,000 tons ————		
Time to build		18 months	21 months		
Complement		600 ————		750 ————	————————

Note: Both electric plant and island structure were changed at the Controller's Meeting.

steam catapult; however, she was completed with British radars (originally 293Q, 277Q, 960, and 963 for carrier-controlled approach).

Left: *HMAS* Melbourne, *as initially completed, in 1955.*

BY MID-1943 A FURTHER modified light carrier design was being considered. Although the war was far from over, there were already suggestions that the 1942 light carriers would be used as troop transports at the end of the war in Europe, presumably to move troops to the Far East. The DNC, Sir Stanley Goodall, suggested that any conversion would have to be done very quickly, preferably by building a deck into the hangar. If sufficient time could be spared, petrol tanks could be replaced by cold and cool rooms, or stores. The lifts would be retained

HMCS Magnificent, *the first Canadian* Majestic, *at Port Said, Egypt, at the end of her career, in 1956. She had just ferried the Canadian part of the United Nations peace-keeping force, and would soon be returned to Britain. Note the de Havilland Otters at the after end of her flight deck. She saw no further service, although she was not broken up until 1965.*

to move baggage, etc.[29]

This note is interesting in that it is the only reference to what might be considered passenger service in the whole of the *Colossus* covers. It has sometimes been suggested that the light fleet carriers were deliberately designed for later conversion to peacetime passenger service, but that seems very unlikely. Rather, Vickers was instructed to build the hulls to merchant standards for quick construction. The degree of subdivision would have made liner conversion difficult and expensive.[30]

There were also other proposals for conversion. By early 1944 it was clear that the British Pacific Fleet would badly need new aircraft maintenance ships equivalent to HMS *Unicorn*, (see Chapter 13 for the reasoning); the two candidates were an American-supplied escort carrier and a *Colossus*. The escort carrier would be equivalent to one-third of a *Unicorn*, the light fleet carrier to one-half. The new British Pacific Fleet would need up to three *Unicorn* equivalents by the end of 1945, that is, nine escort carrier hulls or six light fleet carrier hulls. By this time the

Table 11-5: Changes Made in the Intermediate Carrier Since the First Design (March 1942)

	DNC Draft Staff Requirements	Present Staff Requirements
Flight deck dimensions (ft)	600 × 75	665 × 80
Aircraft	18 fighters or 18 TSR	18 Fighters or TSR plus 6 aircraft on FD
Hangar height (ft)	14 6	16 6
Armament	4 4in HA/LA	4 4in HA/LA
	4 4-barrel pom-poms	6 4-barrel pom-poms
		1 8-barrel pom-pom
	8 Oerlikons	6 twin power-worked Oerlikons
	2 4in directors	1 4in director
		2 4in barrage directors
	4 pom-pom directors	7 pom-pom directors
		8 FAM projectors
		(all directors RPC)
Arrester gear	6 wires, 60 knots, 11,000lbs	6 wires, 60 knots, 14,000lbs
	1 trickle wire	
	1 safety barrier	2 safety barriers
Assisted take-off	not required	required
Aircraft crane	not required	required
Wireless masts	simple hand-worked hinged booms, aerials run from main mast	hydraulically-worked type masts; cannot fit original scheme with a crane
Torpedoes	27	32
Asdic	not required	required
Petrol (gallons)	40,000	100,000
Electrical generators	3 300kW SSTG	2 400kW SSTG
	2 150 kW diesel	4 200kW diesel
Island	three decks 12ft wide	four decks 16ft wide
Bomb lift	not required	required
Complement	600	750–800
Estimated time to build	21 months	27 months

Note Increased number of aircraft, and increased main and secondary batteries, entailed considerable increases in ship and aircraft ammunition stowage, etc.

29 Letter from Sir Stanley Goodall to Sir Charles Lillicrap, his successor, 5 August 1943, in the *Colossus* class Cover.

30 The three remaining hulls (*Hercules*, *Leviathan* and *Powerful*) were not included in the British long-range fleet programme as it was drawn up in mid-1949. In July 1949 DNC was asked for proposals for disposal, one possibility being coversion to emigrant ships for the Australian trade. They could be converted to one-class ships, but substantial plumbing, electrical and joinery work would be required. The scantlings were light by Lloyds standards, but DNC thought Lloyds could be induced to accept them

with draft limited to 24½ft (2500 tons of oil, for 4500nm at 22 knots). DNC produced a sketch design based on a recent P&O liner. He believed that the ships could be transferred to the Ministry of Transport subject to return for carrier conversion in an emergency. At the same time, a new study of ASW aircraft showed that wartime conversion of merchant ships might be difficult and that light fleet carriers might represent the minimum acceptable future trade-protection ships. The three hulls were therefore retained incomplete for possible completion in a future emergency. They became truly surplus again when the mobilization concept was abandoned in 1957.

Above, right and below: *HMS* Warrior *was modernized as a trials and training carrier 1955–56, but sold as part of the 1957 defence economies. The glow visible in the view from ahead was due to her mirror landing sight. she was very unusual in being equipped with a US SPS-6 air search radar, which figured in many contemporary British projects. The two surface views are dated 17 October 1956. The ship was disarmed as a training carrier; after her transfer to Argentina she was rearmed and a US-type quadruple 40mm gun was mounted forward of her island. FAAM (right)*

Above and right*: The Royal Canadian Navy also had a rebuilt Majestic, HMCS Bonaventure. The photograph of her island was taken on 24 October 1958, and shows her with a US SPS-8A height-finder and a stub lattice for an SPS-12 air search radar. The larger photograph shows her as refitted, with the height-finder removed (because she no longer carried fighters requiring control), and a new SPS-501 air search radar (SPS-12 electronics and a Dutch high-gain antenna) atop the stub latttice. The small dome atop the tall lattice mast was a Tacan aircraft navigation beacon. Tacan replaced the earlier beacons because it could give a pilot his range and bearing, so that it helped him navigate to targets designated by the ship.*

Table 11-6: Consequences of Increased Air Complements, as Estimated in January 1944

Aircraft	Officers	Men	Total
18 TBR + 6 fighter	90	899	989
estimate on this basis	92	992	1084
Available accommodation	96	1027	1123
18 Barracuda + 34 folding Seafire; deck park 28 Seafire:			
	111	1168	1279
18 Barracuda + 34 folding Seafire, deck park 9 TBR, 15 FF:			
	110	1181	1291
24 Barracuda, 24 folding Seafire, deck park 6 TBR, 18 FF:			
	118	1164	1282
59 folding Seafire, including deck park of 28:			
	92	1227	1319
If the DNC proposal to use the forward hangar extension for accommodation were followed:			
ordinary carrier	120	1216	1336
assault carrier, with 59 Seafires	96	1262	1358

Notes The 120-officer case (design as an ordinary carrier) was short 11 men for 59 Seafires, but otherwise covered all requirements. The ship's galleys as installed could cater for 1700 men, and the worst case was 1227. However, the wardroom galley was arranged to cater for 90 men and in the worst case there were 118.

Bomb stowage would have to be increased by a third to provide the proper proportion for 24 TBR, but existing bomb rooms could not take the extra weapons. Extra bombs could only be accommodated by converting a pom-pom magazine to take small bombs. This would leave only one pom-pom magazine, and supply to the guns would be inconvenient. Similarly, the single belt-filling room (to load machine-gun ammunition onto belts for aircraft) would hardly suffice for 59 fighters, but there was no obvious position for a second belt-filling room.

first four ships (*Colossus, Glory, Vengeance,* and *Venerable*) were too far along to convert, but the next four (*Edgar, Mars, Warrior,* and *Theseus*) were viable candidates. Given an early enough decision, two ships (one unit) could be available at the end of 1944, followed by another in April 1945 and the third in the latter half of 1945. Another alternative, to build a new specialist ship, was rejected because it would have taken too long, even if shipyard capacity could be made available.

In the event, the light fleet carrier conversion was chosen. Ships selected well before completion could be altered internally, and time (up to two months) would actually be saved, because considerable electrical work and piping could be omitted, particularly if endurance was reduced to that required of a conventional fleet auxiliary (5000nm at 12 knots). HMS *Edgar* and HMS *Mars* were chosen, and renamed *Perseus* and *Pioneer,* respectively.

THE LIGHT FLEET CARRIERS were a response to a larger desperate need for carriers. One other project of this period seems worth describing: a plan to convert large fast ('monster') liners, including the two *Queens*.[31] The idea seems to have originated with the First Sea Lord, Admiral Dudley Pound, in mid-April 1942, that is, at the high point of Japanese expansion into Southeast Asia and the Indian Ocean. It seemed impossible to bring bombers to bear against Japan. The big liners seemed unsuited to any kind of fleet operation, but they were so large that surely they could launch large bombers, which then could land in friendly territory.[32]

DNAD suggested several possible operations:

(a) bomb Japan, aircraft land in China
(b) bomb Singapore, aircraft land in Australia
(c) reinforce an area with large numbers of fighters or light bombers
(d) Support combined operations

The candidates were the two *Queens* (29 knots loaded), the elderly *Aquitania* (25 knots), and the modern *Mauretania* (22.5 knots).[33] Conversion would eliminate a great deal of weight, and so might add 3 knots to a ship's speed. Given the experience of escort carrier design and conversion, the work could

31 Draft plans are in ADM 1/11940.

32 Pound's memorandum predated the Doolittle Raid on Tokyo, which was much the sort of operation he was describing, by a few days; it is not clear whether Pound knew in advance of the US operation.

33 At this time, the largest liner conversion contemplated was the diesel-powered *Georgic,* 683.6 × 82.4ft; estimated speed as a carrier was 21 knots.

The second Australian carrier, HMAS Melbourne, *was much more thoroughly redesigned, with an angled deck and a steam catapult. She is shown at Pearl Harbor on 11 June 1958. The detail view was taken at Malta, 26 March 1956, when she was ferrying cocooned Sea Venoms home. The Sea* Venom *itself was originally designed specifically for Australia, because the heavier night-fighters planned for the Royal Navy could not operate from the two Australian carriers. The* Melbourne *reconstruction was planned by the British DNC Department.*

HMS Leviathan, *the only* Majestic *class carrier never to have been completed, is towed to the breakers. She shows the island as designed; all ships of this class completed for foreign navies were considerably modified. Boilers and turbines form this ship were installed aboard the Dutch* Karel Doorman *when she was repaired, after fire damage, for sale to Argentina as* 25 de Mayo. *Reportedly there was some interest, in the 1960s, in completing her as a commando ship.*

probably be completed in no more than twelve to fifteen months. Large US-type lifts (45 x 45ft) could be installed in such huge hulls.[34] It turned out that the liners were roughly comparable to large warships in manoeuvrability and in acceleration, and so could probably function as large unarmoured fleet carriers or as aircraft transports.

Because British industrial capacity was limited, DNAD hoped that the United States could be convinced to undertake the work. In Britain, only three yards, John Brown, Harland & Woolf and Cammell Laird even had the necessary facilities, not to mention the necessary surplus capacity.

The alternative would be an austere conversion reminiscent of Beatty's late-World War I proposals. A flying-off deck could be built forward and aircraft stowed amidships and aft, wheeled around the funnels (which would be left in place) to take off; landing-on would probably be impossible.

Further study showed that, like later projected British super-carriers, the monster carriers could not dock in many places, particularly in the British Empire. It would, in fact, be so difficult to repair the ships in the event of damage that they would have to operate within about 3000nm of the North American or British coast in 1942, and within a similar distance of the Australian coast in 1943.

It also turned out that, despite their huge hull size, the monster liners would not be particularly spectacular carriers. Having built both *Queen*s, the John Brown yard was asked to study their conversion. It seemed unlikely that the other two candi-

Table 11-7: Inclining Experiment, HMS *Colossus*, 4 November 1944

	As Inclined	Deep	Average	Action	Light	STD
Displacement (tons)	12,210	18,040	16,540		12,820	13,190
Mean draught (ft)	19 7.25	23 2.9	21 9.7		17 6.5	18 6.25
GM (FS)	5.86	8.6	7.53		4.94	5.43
GM (solid)	6.1	9.07	8.33		4.94	5.29
TPI	79.4	88.4	86.3		79.31	80.9
GZ (a)		5.65	5		2.84	
GZ (b)		5.66	5		2.84	
Angle (a)		36.5	37.5		36	
Angle (b)		37.5	37.5		36	
Range (a)		74	70		58.5	
Range (b)		>90	>90		59.5	

Key (a) Hangar free flooding (b) Hanger intact

Table 11-8: Trials of *Colossus* Class Carriers

	Displacement (tons)	SHP	Speed (knots)
Colossus	16,200	38,290	25.32
Vengeance	17,000	39,780	24.3
Venerable	14,650	39,520	25.6
Glory	15,900	39,980	25.23
Triumph	15,640	39,648	25.17

Table 11-9: *Majestic* Class Weights (tons)

	Colossus (as built)	Magnificent (October 1945)
Hull	6650	6670
Incidentals	1030	1070
General fittings (including ballast)	1800	2035
Main machinery	1100	1100
Auxiliary machinery	120	132
Aircraft equipment	1010	1120
Stores, provisions, fresh water	1330	1330
Lube oil	40	40
Oil fuel	3196	3196
Diesel fuel	284	284
Reserve feed water	130	130
Petrol	272	280
Water round petrol	818	863
Deep condition	18,040	18,590

34   Large lifts were attractive because they could bring up fighters very quickly to launch more of them in a very short interval; three folded fighters could share a single lift.

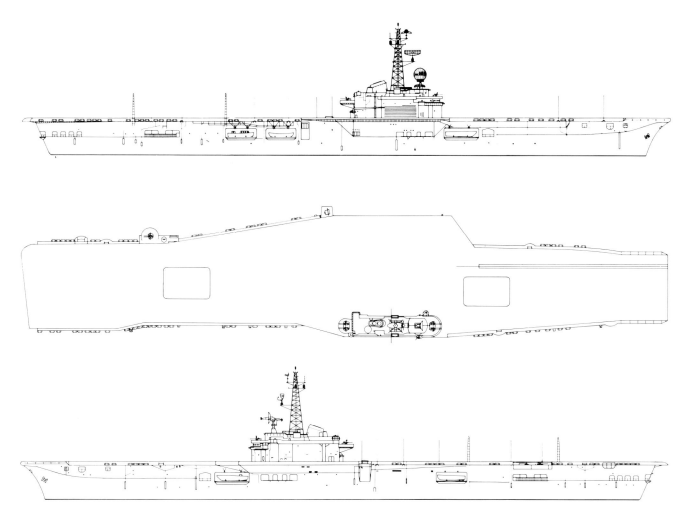

The Brazilian Minas Gerais (*ex HMS* Vengeance) *was rebuilt in the Netherlands (by Verolme, Rotterdam) between mid-1957 and December 1960; she emerged with an 8½-degree angled deck, a steam catapult, new lifts, and strengthened arrester gear. She was armed with US-type 40mm guns (two quadruple mounts around the island, and one twin aft). The radars were also of US types: an SPS-12 for air search, and a big SPS-8B mounted directly atop the island,* for fighter control. The surface search radar was SPS-4. Later she was fitted with a prominent bridle catcher in her bows, and she was refitted in 1976–81. Improvements included a data link for co-operation with Niteroi *class frigates, and replacement of SPS-12 by a new SPS-40B. The big SPS-8B was removed in 1984. The ship has always operated ASW aircraft; plans to buy twelve Skyhawks, announced in 1984, were cancelled early in 1985.*

HMCS Bonaventure (*ex HMS* Powerful), *the Canadian version of the fully-modernized* Majestic, *in about 1961. She was armed with four twin US-type 3in/50guns.*

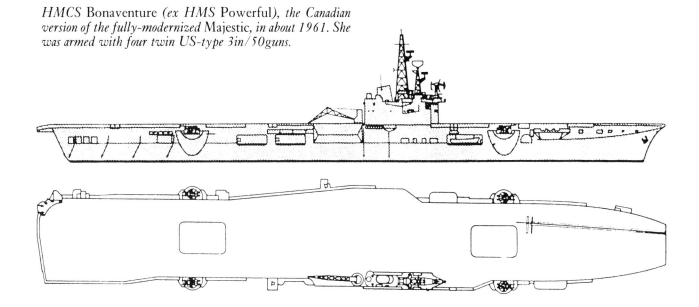

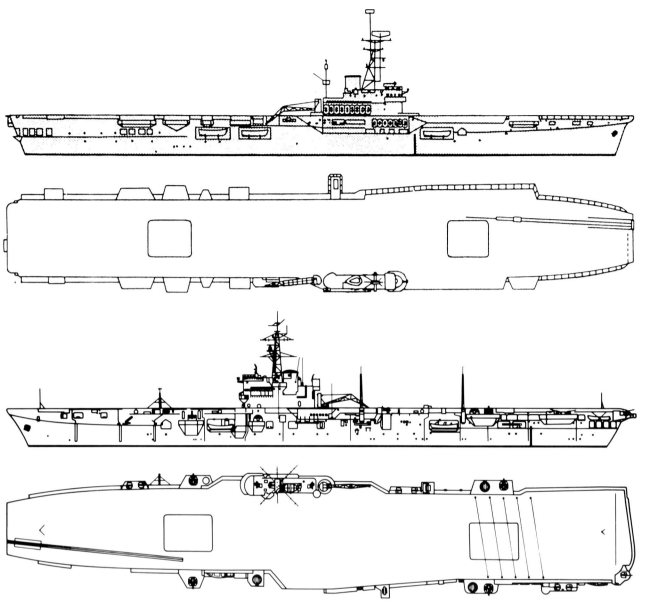

Left: *Foreign navies tried to extract all the potential growth in the light fleet carrier design. This is the French Arromanches (ex HMS Colossus), as a training ship, in about 1962. The 4-degree angled deck was fitted during a 1957–58 refit, and all guns were landed in about 1962. She was refitted again as an ASW carrier in 1968.*

INS Vikrant (ex HMS Hercules). Note that her steam catapult overlaps her forward lift, whereas in other modified ships it is shorter. The ship was rebuilt between April 1957 and March 1961. Armament was four twin and seven single 40mm, and the air complement was ten Seahawks, four Alizes, and two light Alouette helicopters. She was modernized between 1979 and January 1982, with new boilers, engines, CIC, and Dutch radars (DA-05 and LW-08). Armament was seven single 40mm. Another refit (December 1982 to February 1983) adapted the ship to operate Sea Harriers, but no ski-jump was fitted; the ship still operates Alize fixed-wing ASW aircraft. An IPN-10 combat data system was installed in 1985. In 1986, her air complement was six Sea Harriers and nine Alizes.

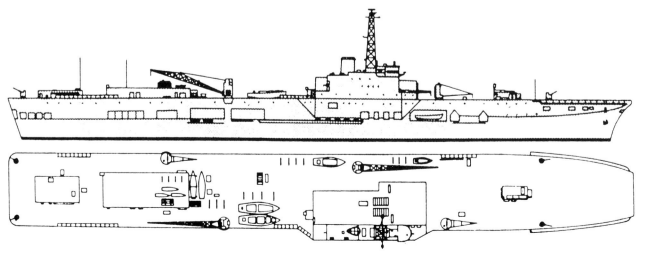

Left: *HMS Triumph as a heavy repair ship in about 1968.*

Left: Melbourne *in her final configuration, in the mid-1970s, with a Dutch LW-02 long-range air search radar atop her bridge, replacing one of the two Type 277s. It was initially mounted at the masthead (1965). The other 277 was retained for a time, but was later removed, and the after 277 was replaced by a US SPN-35 carrier-controlled approach radar, in the big radome. The dome at the top of the lattice mast is a Tacan aircraft homing beacon, and the two domes below are probably for ECM. Note the prominent bridle-catcher forward, and the A-4 Skyhawk attack aircraft on deck, opposite the S-2 Trackers. The ship was extensively refitted specifically to operate A-4s and S-2s in 1967–69, the flight deck being strengthened. The catapult was modified in 1971, when the prominent bridle catcher shown was added. The stub mast forward carries her UHF/DF antenna, a fitting common to many British carriers. The UHF or VHF direction-finder was much more a means of locating friendly aircraft (which now use UHF, and once used VHF radio) than an ESM device.*

Below*: The Dutch-modernized 25 de Mayo (ex Karel Doorman, ex HMS* Venerable*), about 1974. She was rebuilt by Wilton-Fijenoord in 1955–58, emerging with an 8-degree angled deck, a steam catapult and strengthened deck and lifts. As rebuilt, she had twelve single 40mm guns, reduced to nine by this time (one abaft the island, and two to* port had been removed*). Her deck part was enlarged to accommodate three more aircraft in 1980. A British CAAIS action automation system was later installed to allow the ship to co-ordinate with the ADAWS-4 data systems aboard the two Argentine Type 42 destroyers.*

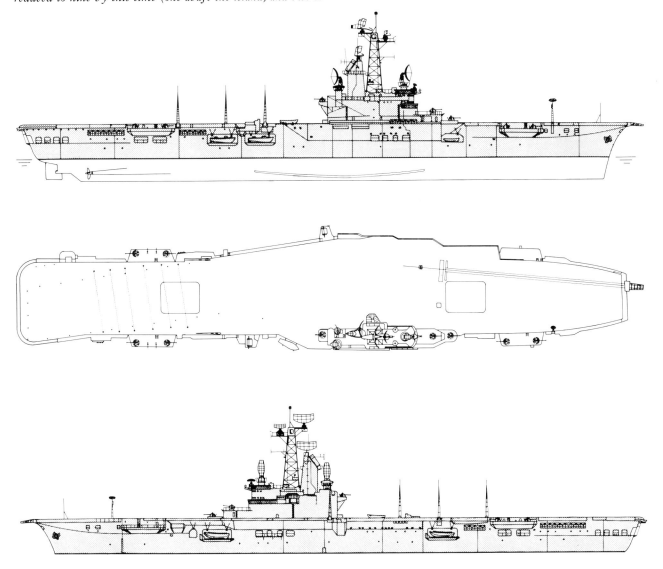

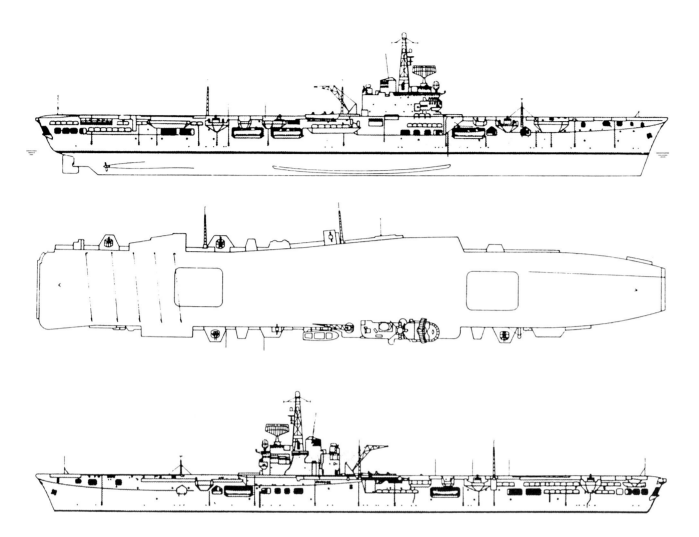

HMAS Melbourne *(ex HMS* Majestic*) as refitted (with flight deck extensions) in 1969. The radar abaft her funnel was a US supplied SPN-35 for carrier-controlled landing, and it was later enclosed by a radome.*

dates would be suitable, due to their insufficient stability.

The John Brown sketch design for the *Queen Elizabeth* showed all of her uptakes trunked into a single centreline funnel forward, with sufficient space aft for flying-on.[35] Particulars are given in Table 11-10. It proved impossible to provide 45 x 45ft lifts. The Fifth Sea Lord wanted a third lift, and wanted each one to be on the starboard side, and John Brown found that this

Table 11-10: *Queen Elizabeth* **as a Carrier 1942**

Hull dimensions (ft)	1025 OA × 118 × 38
Maximum width (ft)	143 6
Flying-off deck dimensions (ft)	
port side	500 × 63 6
starboard side	500 × 47 6
Displacement (tons)	72,000
Speed (knots)	29 (normal) 31.5 (maximum)
Endurance (nm)	9000 at 25 knots[1]
Aircraft	60 folded TSR (40 × 18ft) or 84 folded TSR (44ft × 13ft 6in)
Petrol (gallons)	120,000
Armament	4 twin 4in, 5 8-barrel pom-poms
Hangars	2 (each 672 × 45 × 16ft)
Accelerators	2
Arrester gear	6 wires, 2 barriers
Lifts	

1 Reduced to 6000nm when recalculated. The original figure was based on trial performance; fuel capacity was 7919 tons, and with a clean bottom the ship burned 750 tons at 25 knots.

would not cause undue delay. A new sketch design prepared early in June showed stowage for fifty-four large or seventy-two small TBR, a loss of six small aircraft (40 x 18ft). This left a clear flight deck, but it was only 730ft long, 10ft shorter than that of HMS *Illustrious*. The sheer size of the ships had given the false impression that large aircraft could easily be embarked. In fact the hangar dimensions (45ft wide and 16ft high) did not allow for anything larger than existing naval types (except land-based fighters).

The builder estimated that actual conversion would take about six or seven months – once plans and prefabricated material were assembled, a process which would probably take another nine months, for a total of fifteen or sixteen months.

ACNS(W) finally killed the project later in June, pointing out that the employment of these two very valuable troopships was the subject of a specific Anglo-American agreement that could not lightly be disturbed. Nor was he sure that they would be worthwhile operationally. First Sea Lord concurred, and the papers were filed as a hedge against possible further carrier losses. They were circulated within the Future Building Committee, which was then seeking other fleet carrier alternatives.

35 Wind tunnel tests were ordered, as the aerodynamic problems of such   an arrangement were well understood.

12

The Last Carriers

THE LAST CONVENTIONAL BRITISH CARRIERS, *Ark Royal* and *Hermes*, were both deeply affected by new aircraft requirements adopted late in 1942. *Ark Royal* began as a modified *Implacable*, and by early 1942 she was a radically different ship. The final wartime version of the design, however, was determined by the new aircraft limits. The *Hermes* class was more radically affected. It was conceived as a second-generation light fleet, that is, austere, carrier. The *minimum* hull requirements imposed by the new aircraft forced it up into the full fleet carrier category.

For some time the Admiralty had been uncomfortably aware of the crippling extent of the prewar and early wartime aircraft limits. Investigation by the Future Building Committee (see Chapter 13) showed that some radical relaxation was needed.

At the end of 1942, the Joint Technical Committee drew up a series of recommendations for naval aircraft:

- take-off distance could be up to 500ft (rather than 350ft) with 20 (rather than 27) knots wind over deck
- all future carrier aircraft would be fitted for rocket-assisted take-off (to overcome accelerator limits)
- folded width could be up to 27ft, on the ground that aircraft could be staggered for more efficient hangar stowage[1]
- maximum allowable span was increased from 50 to 60ft[2]
- all aircraft had to fold and unfold within a maximum height of 20ft 3in (the height of the lower hangar in HMS *Ark Royal* between the beams)
- clear hangar height was increased to 17ft 6in (to follow US practice), so the maximum height tail-down was increased to 17ft
- maximum weight was increased from 11,000 to 30,000lbs[3]
- stall speed was increased to 75 knots, so that arrester gear would have to accommodate a 30,000lb aircraft landing at that speed, and future accelerators would have to launch a 30,000lb aircraft at 75 knots

Since future naval aircraft might well be launched primarily by accelerator, the JTC recommended that the new *Ark Royal* have two separate sets of accelerator machinery (for quicker launching). The new catapults, moreover, would launch by the US two-point system, which simplified design and allowed

them to launch US aircraft without modification. The catapult (cruiser-battleship) requirement would be discarded.

The new requirements were intended to apply to *Ark Royal* and later fleet carriers, and as far as practicable to light fleet carriers expected to complete from 1946 on. This mandated a new design for the *Hermes* class.

These were radical changes. The immediate prewar limits were 11,000lbs, 300ft take-off at 20 knots, and 50 (18ft folded) × 40 × 13ft 6in. Recently the length limit had been relaxed to 44ft, the span increased to 58ft, and the weight to 20,000lbs; take-off had been relaxed to 350ft, and stall speed to 58-60 knots. The new 500ft requirement was acceptable because, with their round-downs flattened, existing fast carriers could accommodate fair numbers of aircraft abaft that mark. An *Implacable*, for example, could range seventeen 50 × 40ft aircraft with their wings spread, nineteen if all but the first six were folded.

THE LAST CONVENTIONAL BRITISH CARRIER was HMS *Ark Royal*, also the culmination of armoured carrier development. She was initially conceived (see Chapter 7) as an *Implacable* modified to reflect war experience, but by October 1941 an entirely new and much enlarged design had been developed. The *Implacable* design had been constricted by treaty, and *Ark Royal* might be considered intermediate between a treaty carrier and an entirely unlimited ship (*Malta*), equivalent in some ways to the US *Essex* class. However, because she was designed about two years later, and because the Royal Navy had been at war since 1939, she reflected more of the lessons of combat. Subsequent criticism of the much larger *Malta* and 1952 designs suggests that *Ark Royal* was also the largest carrier which the Royal Navy could comfortably operate, given the inherent limitations of existing harbours and dockyards.

The draft 1940 Supplementary Programme included a new armoured flight deck carrier, essentially a repeat *Implacable* (to make for quicker production). Compared to *Implacable*, the Staff wanted better protection (against a 500lb SAP bomb delivered by dive-bomber from 3000ft instead of against a 500lb general-purpose bomb) and more aircraft. The latter was much easier to achieve with the standard aircraft width reduced from 18ft to 13ft 6in. Aircraft could therefore be stowed four rather than three abreast. However, the complement could not be increased from the forty-eight of HMS *Implacable* to sixty-four,

1   The previous limit, 18ft, had been chosen so that three aircraft could be stowed abreast in a 62ft hangar. However, the Firefly, nominally designed for a folded width of 13ft 6in, had a 16ft tail – which did not interfere with stowage nearly four abreast, much depending on whether the tailplane passed beneath the rest of the aircraft. Stowage space could be gained by staggering aircraft, or by placing them nose to tail; the JTC emphasized that aircraft were anything but simple boxes to be stowed alongside each other.

2   Span was determined by flight deck width abeam the main obstruction, the island structure: 69ft in HMS *Illustrious*, and 85ft 9in in *Ark Royal*. The JTC argued that if 50ft was satisfactory in HMS *Illustrious*, surely 65ft could be accommodated in 85 to 90ft. At this time the Naval Staff wanted a four-gun turret in future TBRs, and Westland had designed one with a 60ft span. Length would increase to 48 to 50ft, and the JTC suggested that the lifts of the *Ark Royals* be lengthened to 50ft.

3   The 11,000lb limit had been imposed in 1938; 30,000lbs was needed to accommodate the expected turret TBR. At this time Douglas was building a huge torpedo-bomber (TB2D) with a maximum weight of over 30,000lbs. The JTC argued that ships completed in 1946 would have to last about a quarter century, and that anything less than 30,000lbs would be absurd in 1971.

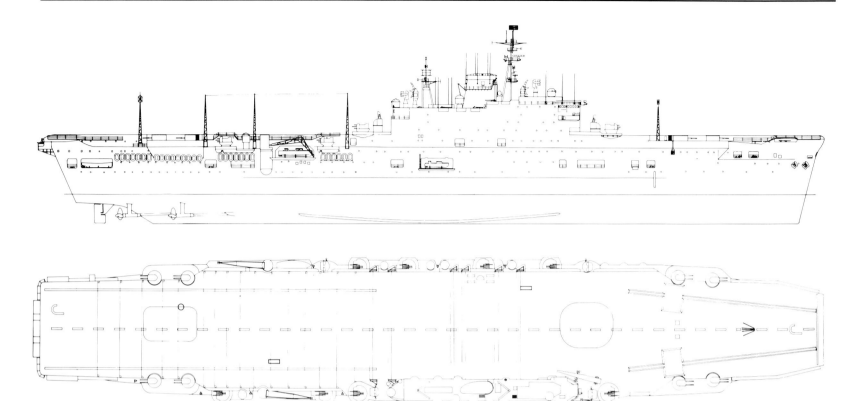

HMS Eagle as completed, to much the 1946 design. The big radars atop the island, fore and aft of the funnel, are Types 982 and 983. The forward tripod carries a YE aircraft homing beacon at its head, with a ship-to-ship (TBS) dipole at the after end of the platform below. The fore end of this platform was earmarked for a television antenna, probably for ship-to-ship transmission of radar plots (a technology developed by the Royal Navy in 1944–47). Below it was a Type 253P IFF transponder, and below that was a platform carrying a Type 293Q short-range (gunnery) air search radar and a Type 242Q interrogator for the Type 960 long-range air search radar. Below this was a platform carrying the Type 242M interrogator for the 293Q, and also a Type 251P transponder (a small horizontal dipole). Below that was a navigational radar, probably Type 974. The after tripod carries a Type 960 long-range air search set, topped by its Type 940 interrogator, with a Type 87M VHF R/T above that. The very small dish alongside the pom-pom director (CRBF) at the after end of the top of the island is a Type 961 for carrier-controlled blind landing. The coil on the forward face of the bridge carried a medium-frequency radio direction finder (MF/DF). The lattice mast forward of the bridge carried VHF/DF; the lattice mast at the after end of the flight deck carries a HF/DF at its head; the other masts carry a long-wire HF radio antenna. The emergency rudder forward is not shown in this drawing. ALR

because extra accommodation had to be found within the limited hull volume of the original ship. DNC proposed to obtain this space by shortening the lower hangar from 208 to 150ft. On the other hand, any substantial increase in deck thickness would reduce stability, and would have to be compensated by widening the ship, which would complicate matters further.

Other desirable improvements were provision for the larger forward lift (45 × 33ft) so that non-folding aircraft could be carried, revised bomb stowage, increased gasoline stowage, a 10ft wider flight deck and an increase of at least 6in in clear hangar height. All of this was possible. Detailed analysis

showed that the depth of the beams under the flight and upper hangar decks could be reduced by the required 6in. This ship would have displaced about 23,200 tons.

DNC also developed alternative, completely new, designs at this time, details of which have been lost. On 10 February 1941 the Controller approved the DNC's modified repeat *Implacable*. It would also incorporate some vital modifications which had since been made to HMS *Implacable* herself: the HA directors were concentrated on the island, the flight deck was extended on the port side and the magazine crowns were increased from 3 to 4in. About ten days later DNC was asked to fit a wider lift aft, and this also proved practicable. In March 1941, therefore, DNC asked the Board for permission to place an order for the slightly modified repeat *Implacable*.

No order was placed, however. The urgency of the project was thus removed, and it was no longer necessary to hold the design to something close to the original *Implacable*. In the course of 1941, too, war experience, particularly the loss of HMS *Ark Royal*, showed that the existing designs were inadequate. In particular, diesel generators became attractive as insurance against the loss of steam power (two would replace two steam generators), the machinery spaces had to be better subdivided, and DNC was asked for greater beam for greater stability. In November 1941 the new carrier was still nominally a repeat *Implacable*, but the resemblance was less obvious.

Meanwhile DNC developed parallel designs for a new carrier. The Staff wanted the forward lift, as well as the after one, to serve both hangars, and the Fifth Sea Lord pressed for a thicker flight deck. In August 1941 the Controller asked for studies to reflect these ideas. DNC offered two alternatives with 4in flight decks (see Table 12-1). Scheme A had a small lower hangar, as in *Implacable*; the larger Scheme B had a full lower hangar, and had to be beamier to make up for the extra topweight involved. In a third alternative, Scheme C, the flight deck armour was reduced to the 3in of HMS *Implacable*; this showed that the longer lower hangar was effectively equivalent to an extra inch of flight deck armour. By this time the enlarged lower hangar was accepted as a necessity. However, the Staff still wanted some further schemes of protection, in which flight

Inboard profile of Eagle *as completed.* ALR

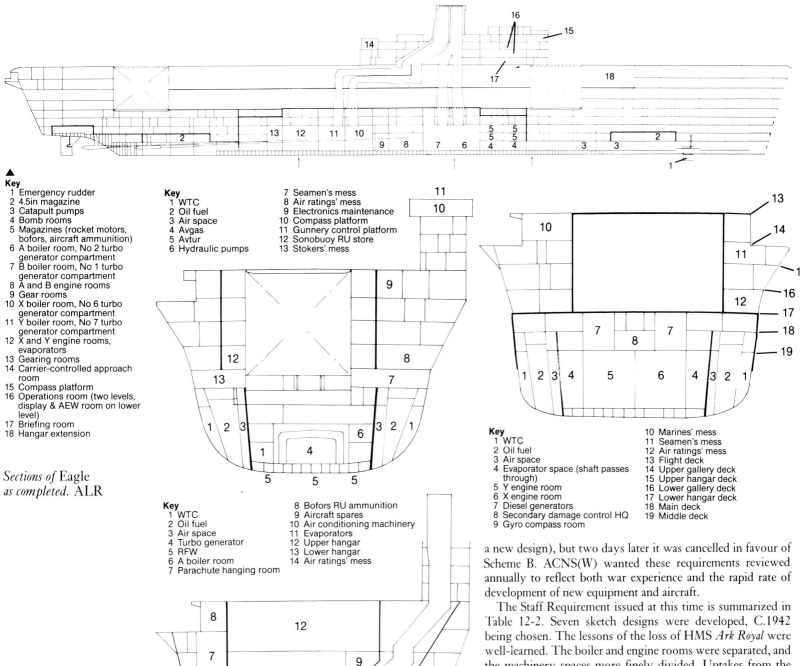

Key
1 Emergency rudder
2 4.5in magazine
3 Catapult pumps
4 Bomb rooms
5 Magazines (rocket motors, bofors, aircraft ammunition)
6 A boiler room, No 2 turbo generator compartment
7 B boiler room, No 1 turbo generator compartment
8 A and B engine rooms
9 Gear rooms
10 X boiler room, No 6 turbo generator compartment
11 Y boiler room, No 7 turbo generator compartment
12 X and Y engine rooms, evaporators
13 Gearing rooms
14 Carrier-controlled approach room
15 Compass platform
16 Operations room (two levels, display & AEW room on lower level)
17 Briefing room
18 Hangar extension

Sections of Eagle *as completed.* ALR

Key
1 WTC
2 Oil fuel
3 Air space
4 Avgas
5 Avtur
6 Hydraulic pumps
7 Seamen's mess
8 Air ratings' mess
9 Electronics maintenance
10 Compass platform
11 Gunnery control platform
12 Sonobuoy RU store
13 Stokers' mess

Key
1 WTC
2 Oil fuel
3 Air space
4 Turbo generator
5 RFW
6 A boiler room
7 Parachute hanging room
8 Bofors RU ammunition
9 Aircraft spares
10 Air conditioning machinery
11 Evaporators
12 Upper hangar
13 Lower hangar
14 Air ratings' mess

Key
1 WTC
2 Oil fuel
3 Air space
4 Evaporator space (shaft passes through)
5 Y engine room
6 X engine room
7 Diesel generators
8 Secondary damage control HQ
9 Gyro compass room
10 Marines' mess
11 Seamen's mess
12 Air ratings' mess
13 Flight deck
14 Upper gallery deck
15 Upper hangar deck
16 Lower gallery deck
17 Lower hangar deck
18 Main deck
19 Middle deck

4   Experiments (1941) suggested that a single bow rudder was as effective as a single stern rudder of the same area, but that a small bow rudder reduced tactical diameter so little when used in conjunction with a stern rudder that it was worthwhile only as a means of making up for battle damage. Further tests showed that a 50sq ft (rather than 28) bow rudder would reduce tactical diameter by 10 per cent. A 56 sq ft rectangular bow rudder was eventually adopted (May 1943). Each of the twin stern rudders had an area of 170sq ft.

deck armour would be traded off against citadel (main armoured deck) armour; they are listed as Schemes D and E.

Late in September DTSD came out in favour of the full double hangar ship with 4in flight deck armour, B. Work on the design, which became the basis of the 1942 carriers, began on 9 October 1941. On 28 November approval was formally given to proceed with the improved repeat *Implacable* of the 1940 Supplementary Programme (which by now was virtually

a new design), but two days later it was cancelled in favour of Scheme B. ACNS(W) wanted these requirements reviewed annually to reflect both war experience and the rapid rate of development of new equipment and aircraft.

The Staff Requirement issued at this time is summarized in Table 12-2. Seven sketch designs were developed, C.1942 being chosen. The lessons of the loss of HMS *Ark Royal* were well-learned. The boiler and engine rooms were separated, and the machinery spaces more finely divided. Uptakes from the forward and after groups of boilers were widely separated so that a single underwater hit was unlikely to flood both. The uptakes from each boiler room were also well separated. Air intakes to the boilers were taken from both the port and starboard sides of the ship.

The ship's beam was increased, both for greater stability and for wider (hence more effective) underwater side protection. Magnetic mines and non-contact torpedoes threatened the ship with under-bottom damage; all main transverse and longitudinal bulkheads were taken down to the outer bottom to localize the effects of such damage. DNC offered a small retractable auxiliary rudder forward, presumably a response to the effects of rudder damage in the *Bismarck* action. It was actually fitted, but proved ineffective and was removed early in the ships' careers.[4]

In addition, the design provided increased protection against fire from astern, and the armour over the citadel was extended to protect the diesel generators on the main deck aft. The lower

Right, below right and bottom: *HMS* Eagle *was completed to the original 1946 design. In these photographs, the triple cheese antennas serve Type 982 radars; they were soon replaced by the familiar hayrakes. Note also the US-type Mark 37 high-angle directors, fitted with British Type 275 radars. The overhead view and the port side view were taken in 1951; the other two were taken in Malta in 1953 (the detailed view of the island is dated 13 February 1953). In the view from aft, the aircraft on deck are the Royal Navy's first standard jet fighters, Supermarine Attackers, with piston-engined Fireflies for ASW. Note the HF/DF antenna on a mast right aft, with VHF/DF forward. Although the light guns may appear to be pom-poms, they are in fact postwar sextuple Bofors (Mk 6 mountings).*

strake of the external armour belt was made non-cemented to make fragmentation less likely; large pieces of armour had been forced into HMS *Indomitable* by an underwater hit.

Torpedo protection was by the usual multi-layer system, a liquid layer being sandwiched between two voids, with a 100lb (2½in: two 50lb layers) inner or holding bulkhead. In *Ark Royal*, however, 35 and 25lb plating had to be used to consume existing supplies of plating.

Structurally, the ship used more welding than any previous carrier, particular attention being paid to welded connections to the inner bottom.

The original hull form was similar to that of the earlier carriers, with a round stern. Model tests showed that a square transom would save 3 per cent at maximum speed (31.5 knots), and about 1 per cent at lower speeds. Haslar therefore recommended that the ship's length be increased by 20ft, her transom area increased to 4.5 per cent of her midship section, her prismatic coefficient be reduced (to 0.55), her waterline forward be reduced, and a bulbous bow applied. These suggestions proved impractical, but the area of the transom was increased (to 6 per cent) so as to increase propeller separation lengthwise. A new model made to the modified lines (April 1942) showed that the transom was too large. When the beam was increased in November 1942 a further model was made, and tank tests showed that ehp would increase by about 7 per cent, both at 20 and 31 knots. The final hull form showed a prismatic coefficient of 0.562, block coefficient of 0.552, midships coefficient of 0.982, and waterplane coefficient of 0.696.

Considerable effort went into improving steering performance, largely to avoid torpedoes and bombs. Experience of actual attacks showed that a quick initial turn was more valuable than a tight turning circle, and twin rudders were provided. At this time there was considerable feeling in the Royal Navy that US ships with twin rudders could consistently out-turn their British counterparts. DNC pointed to the disadvantages of past twin rudders: vibration, increased resistance, and a considerable loss of speed when rudders were put over. Tank tests showed that vertical twin rudders did indeed make for a fast initial turn, but that high initial speed was the most important factor. It also turned out that a ship with a centreline rudder of the same total area would out-turn one with twin rudders, but of course it was easier to provide more area with twin rudders. Twin rudders (and a small retractable bow rudder) were provided.

The sketch design was approved on 11 March, and the Board approved the legend on 3 September 1942 (see Table 12-3). Compared with *Implacable*, the new design was much more survivable, due to its better underwater protection, the dispersal of the main machinery, and the adoption of diesel generators. The uptakes were more widely separated and the large side openings reduced in number and their positions raised further above water. The flight deck was thicker, and there were more

Centaur *as completed to the 1947 design.* ALR

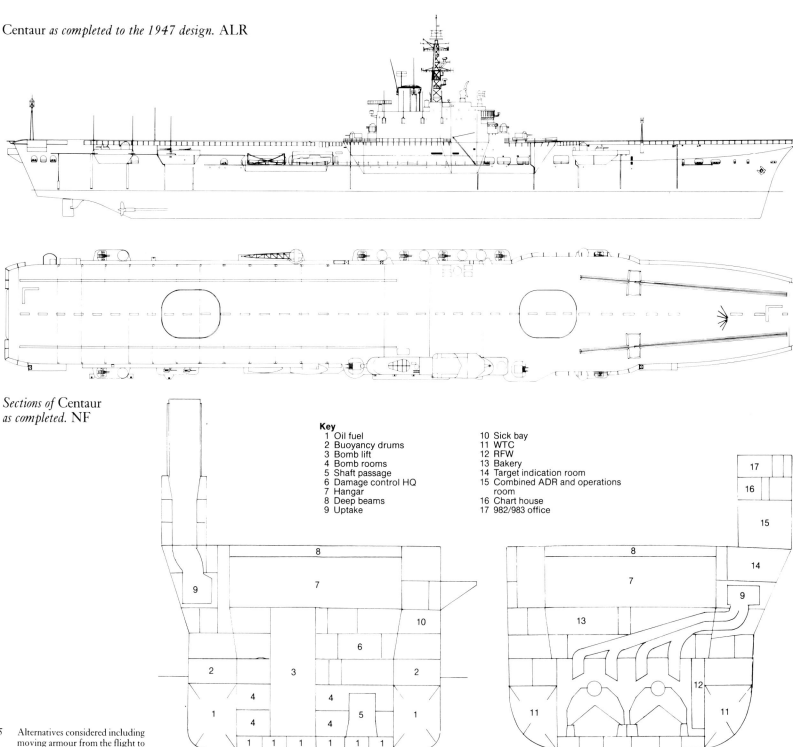

Sections of Centaur
as completed. NF

Key
1 Oil fuel
2 Buoyancy drums
3 Bomb lift
4 Bomb rooms
5 Shaft passage
6 Damage control HQ
7 Hangar
8 Deep beams
9 Uptake
10 Sick bay
11 WTC
12 RFW
13 Bakery
14 Target indication room
15 Combined ADR and operations room
16 Chart house
17 982/983 office

5 Alternatives considered including moving armour from the flight to the citadel deck to reduce topweight without increasing beam. In the end, to minimize delay, the main longitudinal protective bulkhead was not moved. Instead, the increased beam went into oil fuel tanks, the air spaces on the port side remaining the same (4ft), but increasing to 5ft 2in on the starboard side. This helped balance the asymmetric weight of the island. The layout of the hull below the lower hangar deck changed very little, but above that deck the hangar bulkheads were straightened to increase the clear hangar width to 67ft. To support the wider hangars, the deep beams under the upper hangar deck had to be deepened from 2ft 6in to 2ft 9in. Plating under the flight deck armour was reduced from 60 to 40lbs to reduce topweight. The hull was refaired and the transom reduced somewhat.

automatic anti-aircraft weapons with more directors. The flight deck was also considerably longer, with larger lifts (both serving both hangars), and more arrester wires. Finally, with the end of the treaties, there was no longer any need to avoid margins, and the new ship was designed with a 150-ton margin at flight deck level.

The 1940 Supplementary ship became HMS *Ark Royal*; in addition *Audacious* (later renamed *Eagle*) and *Eagle* were ordered under the 1942 programme, and *Africa* under the 1943 programme. *Eagle* had to be transferred from Swan Hunter to Vickers (Newcastle) after the beam of the ship was increased (17 November 1942). Work on *Eagle* was suspended in January 1946, and on *Africa* on 12 April 1947, with *Audacious* renamed to remember the earlier carrier of that name. Ultimately *Ark Royal* and *Eagle* were completed to a modified

design, each serving for about two decades. They were the largest carriers built by the Royal Navy.

The most important changes could be traced to aircraft. By late 1942 the Royal Navy knew that it would have to rely heavily on US-manufactured naval aircraft, which were all designed for 17ft 6in hangars. The new carriers would be too cramped; on 6 December the Board approved an increase of clear hangar height to match the US standard, which made for 6ft more hull depth. The increased topweight was compensated by 4ft more beam (total 112ft 8½in), which in turn made construction at Swan Hunter impossible.[5] Estimated design speed fell to 31.5 knots (deep and clean) or 29.5 knots six months out of dock in the tropics. Standard displacement was now about 32,500 tons.

By this time, too, the Future Building Committee (see Chap-

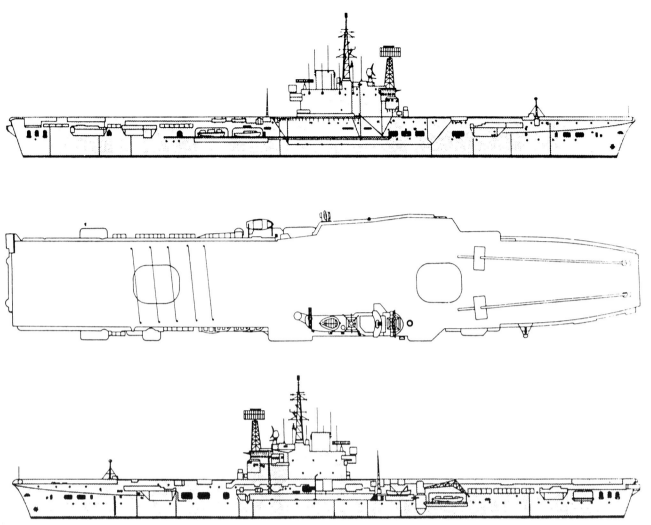

HMS Centaur *as completed in 1953, typical of the three* Hermes *class light fleet carriers completed to the 1947 design.*

ter 13) was reviewing British naval aircraft policy. The 1942 carrier had been designed to operate 20,000lb aircraft (launched at 66 knots and arrested at 60). Staff Requirements were amended late in November 1942 to allow for 30,000lb types, which had to be launched and arrested at 75 knots.[6] The aircraft crane load was set at 25,000lbs. Hangars would be fitted with side tracking gear for efficient movement of aircraft. The design originally allowed for eight wires and three safety barriers, but in May 1943 the Fifth Sea Lord ordered heavier (Mk X) arrester gear, and sixteen wires and four safety barriers; the arrester gear prototype was tested at RAE in 1944.

The catapults were initially to have been of the standard British two-track trolley type. These were not suited to American aircraft, however, and in 1943 the JTC recommended that a US-type two point tail down system be substituted.

The lifts had to be lengthened to 54ft (March 1943), and the forward one moved back about 50ft, to make space for an aircraft repair shop at the forward end of the hangar.[7] In May, the forward lift was widened to 44ft. The after lift could not be widened because this would have interfered with the ammunition hoists nearby. Again, larger (and heavier) lifts were needed both to operate the new American aircraft and to cater for likely future growth. The larger lifts in turn filled space planned for accommodation, and to compensate the lower hangar extension was eliminated and the lower gallery deck built in.[8]

Aircraft tracking gear was approved in 1946 as part of the

modernization of the design.

The most radical change to the hangar was the provision, in 1946, of sufficient ventilation to allow eighteen aircraft to run up simultaneously. The British closed hangar had always been criticized on the score that aircraft could not be warmed up until they reached the flight deck. With the demise of the *Malta* open hangar design, it seemed more important than ever to provide such facilities in a closed-hangar carrier. This was accomplished by using high-capacity direct exhaust fans.

At the same time that the aircraft requirements were increased, November 1942, bomb lifts were enlarged to take 2000lb weapons, and the scale of bomb stowage revised, based on an air group of eighteen fighters and forty-two TBR. In 1943, however, the Royal Navy adopted a policy of permanent deck parks, so the ship could (in theory) accommodate forty fighters and forty TBR, or fifty-six fighters and twenty-eight TBR. Because the overall size of the ship was fixed, however, there could be little increase in accommodation (to make up for up to seventeen more aircraft) and no increase in protected bomb or petrol stowage.

The problem was further complicated as more types of air weapons appeared. In 1945 DAWT called for flexible weapon stowage, the bins of which the ship's staff could easily convert to stow any type of bomb, bomb cluster, or rocket warhead, so that the ship could easily vary her weapon mix to suit changing operations. This policy in turn essentially eliminated any need for ready-use (that is, unarmoured) air weapon stowage, as any weapon could be stowed near any bomb lift. Weapons were divided into three categories (large, medium, and small, nomi-

6   The decision on future aircraft weight was taken on 30 September 1942, at a meeting of the Future Aircraft Carriers Sub-Committee. Minutes seem not to have survived, but this seems to have been a joint Anglo-American figure, the Royal Navy accepting that it had to be able to operate American-supplied aircraft for the foreseeable future. According to the DNC History (World War II naval construction), the ships were completed with decks strong enough to take 40,000lb aircraft, although lifts were balanced for 35,000lbs because it was thought that aircraft would not grow to this weight for some years. At this time (about 1950) the standard limiting dimensions for British naval aircraft were 48×27 (folded) $\times 17$ft (full span could be 60ft). The ships were completed with two BH 5 catapults (140ft 9in stroke, 30,000lbs at 75 knots or 14,000 at 85) and with Mk 10 arrester gear (30,000lbs at 75 knots or 20,000lbs at 91 knots); maximum pull-out was 172ft.

7   This answered a standard criticism of the British closed hangar, that there was no protected space where aircraft could be welded, or where power tools could be used. The repair space was shut off by the lift from the protected hangar, which therefore could still be subject to magazine-like safety regulations. In addition, because the repair space was out of the flow of hangar traffic, aircraft could be spread for repair without slowing operations. Special ventilators allowed engines to be run up for testing.

8   In addition, because the forward lift was wider, the armoured doors sealing it off from the protected hangar had to be in four rather than in two sections.

Table 12-1: Carrier Sketch Designs

	Implacable	A	B	C	D
Flight deck armour	3in	4in on 1½in ————— (equiv to 4½in)		3in	1½in
Deck over citadel	1½in-2½in	————————— 6			6in
Beam (ft)	95 0½	100	104 6	100 ————	
Displacement (tons)	23,500 ————————		27,000	25,000	26,500
GM	4.85 ————				
Hangar armour	1½in ————————		2in ————		
Depth (ft)	71 ————————		80 ————		
Draught (ft)	22 9	23 2	23 6	22 11	24 5
Speed, deep (knots)	32.5	31.5	30.5	31.5	30.5

nally 2000, 1000, and 500lbs), and in September 1946 it was decided that each of thirty-six strike aircraft would be provided with nine loads (one large, or two medium or four small weapons).[9] Flexible torpedo stowage (for sixty standard weapons) could accept the new large-diameter (30in) weapons then under development, as well as proposed small-diameter (10.5in) types.

Larger aircraft also needed more fuel, and space for protected stowage was particularly difficult to find. The original requirement was 103,000 gallons of petrol, in three groups of cylindrical pressure tested tanks (drum stowage). The tanks were separate from the hull, and they sat within flooded compartments. This was safe but inefficient. Not even the increase to 115,000 gallons could really satisfy the needs of the enlarged air group, especially after the deck park had been introduced. In 1945 the Staff raised the requirement to 500,000 gallons, so that the ship could operate jet aircraft.[10]

Fortunately turbine fuel (avtur) had a relatively high flash point and so could be stowed unprotected, like oil fuel. However, when the ships were completed many operational aircraft still needed petrol, so some protected stowage had to be provided. The choice was to carry as much petrol as possible (165,000 gallons), the balance being avtur in tanks originally provided for oil fuel. Even this increase required a change in petrol tanks, to American-type saddle tank (displacement) bulk storage.

More and larger aircraft needed more flight deck space, but at the same time the anti-aircraft battery had to be improved to meet a growing air threat. This involved both fire control for the heavy (4.5in) weapons and an enlarged light anti-aircraft battery. The latter competed with the aircraft for space, since mountings along the edge of the flight deck generally required cuts into it.

Existing British anti-aircraft directors, of prewar design, were ineffective. In 1943, therefore, it was decided to fit these ships instead with the much more effective US Mk 37 directors, adapted to control 4.5in rather than 5in guns. DGD wanted a diamond arrangement allowing guns firing across the flight deck to be controlled, but this proved impossible because the Mk 37 allowed only for convergence in one line, for example when A director controlled A and/or B groups. DGD therefore had to adopt the same four-cornered arrangement as that of the guns. Because the width of the flight deck was increased to 112ft, however, B and Y directors were limited to the port side only and thus could not control their guns when firing across deck. A and X directors would control these guns when firing cross deck in an emergency, that is, when A and X batteries were out of action.

In July 1946 the design was further modified, four MRS3 (medium-range) directors being added so that each 4.5in mount could be independently controlled. The mounts were separated so that their barrels could not collide when they were under independent control.[11]

The feeling in 1942–43 was very much that British carriers

9   At this time stowage was provided by 10-gun ammunition loads for each of seventy-five aircraft.

10   The requirement was initially stated as 350,000 gallons of petrol plus 100,000 of paraffin or diesel fuel (that is, jet fuel). In addition the ship was to accommodate at least 14,400 gallons of lubricating oil (up to a maximum of 34,000). DTSD wanted 360,000 gallons of petrol, based on eighty aircraft flying 1½ 4-hour sorties each per day for five days at 150 gallons per hour. Lubricating oil was to be 10 per cent of aircraft petrol and avtur. These figures could not be met within the limited volume of the ship. For a time it even appeared that DNC could not provide the necessary separate pumping facilities for petrol and avtur.

11   In 1945 the 4.5in guns were changed from fixed to separate ammunition, to increase their rate of fire. However, a later proposal, to use Mk 7 mountings (as in the *Darings* and in the abortive *Malta* class) was not adopted.

sacrified aircraft facilities for armament, particularly light armament; in 1943 USS *Midway*, with her very narrow island and wide (112ft) flight deck, was often used to exemplify superior practice. *Implacable* was considered a particularly bad example, and at the time of her launch (December 1942) it was tentatively decided to straighten the flight deck edge of the new carrier, fit a continuous walkway along it, and fair in the ship's side to avoid or reduce sponsons. When this modification was adopted for the class in March 1943 the permanent structure had to be limited to a width of 126ft at upper gallery deck edge level to clear fixed cranes at the Cammell Laird slip; the Panama Canal limit was 135ft.

Applied to a ship launched with her island in place, the Cammell Laird limit implied that the outer face of the island would be 63ft from the centreline, and therefore that the inner face would be 42ft off centre. By January 1944 the island had been lengthened substantially, and flight deck area could be restored only by shifting it outboard. The solution was to launch the ship before fitting the island structure; it could then be 4ft 6in outboard.

In September 1943 the FBC decided to compromise on a 107ft flight deck in *Ark Royal*; it was widened to 112ft in April 1944. At the same time the light battery was reviewed. In November 1942 the sextuple Bofors, then in the early stages of development, was suggested as an alternative to the currently standard 8-barrel pom-pom. By September 1943 the Bofors was considered twice as effective as the pom-pom on a barrel for barrel basis. By April 1944 single Bofors were to replace the previous Oerlikons, giving the ship a single-calibre secondary armament. By this time the policy was explicitly to sacrifice armament for flight deck configuration but, within this policy, to provide the maximum anti-aircraft battery. When MRS was applied to the 4.5in battery, it had to replace some of the single Bofors guns, the number of which was reduced from twelve to eight. The ships were completed with eight sextuple, two twin and twelve single Bofors.

The design of the island was particularly complicated because radar and the associated AIO (CIC) were changing so rapidly. It was lengthened in 1944 and a second radar mast provided, but even in 1945 mast design was still uncertain.

Table 12-2: Staff Requirement for the 1942 Fleet Carrier

Standard displacement 27,600 tons

Beam 104ft

Speed 29.5 knots deep 6 months out of dock in tropics (design speed 31.5 knots)

Endurance not less than 6000nm at 24 knots

High speed of turn and small turning circle

Flight deck to be as long as the design of hull permits with 4in NC armour

Space for 72 aircraft (44ft × 13ft 6in × 13ft 6in folded), with operational arrangements for 60

Two full-length hangars; clear height 14ft 6in and minimum width 62ft

Two lifts (45 × 33ft) each serving both hangars, working load 20,000lbs

115,000 gallons petrol

16 4.5in HA/LA in BD mountings

4 HADTs and HA/LA calculating positions

8 8-barrel pom-poms each with its own predictor

Flight deck: 4in NC armour

Side: 4½in NC armour

Hangar sides: 2in NC plating where exposed, otherwise 1½in

Protected against near misses and 1000lb contact charge

Sufficient electric power available to fight the ship against aircraft attack without steam. Total electric generating power should if possible be evenly divided between steam- and diesel-driven generators.

As far as practicable, accommodation to be arranged to give ready access to action stations.

To be fitted as a flagship.

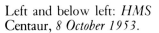

Left and below left: *HMS* Centaur, *8 October 1953.*

HMS Centaur *shows her interim angled deck, 1954. Note that whip antennas have replaced the tilting masts and long wires of earlier British carriers. Although not visible here, two tilting masts were retained on the port side. The lattice mast aft carries a HF/DF antenna.*

Table 12-3: Legend, 3 September 1942

LPB (ft)	720
LOA (ft)	790
Beam (ft)	108 8¼
Std displacement (tons)	31,600
SHP	152,000
Speed, deep (knots)	31.5
Generators	4 turbo, 500kW
	4 diesel, 500kW
Oil fuel (tons)	7000
Endurance (nm)	6000 at 24 knots,
	6 months out of dock
Complement, as flagship	2178, incl 15% supernumerary
Petrol (gallons)	115,000
Aircraft lube oil (gallons)	7600 in 3 groups,
	fwd and aft
Armament	16 4.5in DP
	8 8-barrel pom-poms
	75 18in aircraft torpedoes
	252 Mk VIII depth charges
	24 A mines
Aircraft	69 (44ft × 13ft 6in × 13ft 6in) or
	57 (40ft × 18ft × 13ft 6in)
Catapults	2
Arrester gear	8 arrester wires
	1 trickle wire
	4 fwd arrester wires
	3 safety barriers
Aircraft cranes	2
Lifts	2, 45 × 33ft, serving both
	hangars, 20,000lb
Hangar dimensions	412 × 62 × 14ft 6in clear height
Protection	
side	4½in NC
magazine side and end	4½in C
crown	4in NC
hangar side and end	1½in NC
flight deck	4in NC on two ¾in DW decks

Funnel uptakes from top of citadel to flight deck splinter proof.
Underwater protection against 1000lb contact charge; wing oil tanks worked by water displacement system.

Although island dimensions as such did not change after 1944, shape and internal layout were still quite fluid. Ultimately a two-deck combined Operations Room and ADR was adopted. The island arrangement was quite controversial, and it was settled only in November 1945 (subject to the proviso that minor changes could still be made) only because further delay would have slowed construction.

In 1943 these ships were ordered Arcticized. Insulating asbestos was sprayed under decks and on exposed bulkheads,[12] and living spaces, offices, and working spaces were provided with steam air heaters. Steam heat was applied directly to fresh water tanks, exposed control positions, and exposed machinery, including the catapults. De-icing compound was applied to the flight deck. The general goal was to maintain 70 degrees F inside when the outside temperature was 10 degrees F.

NUMEROUS CHANGES ACCUMULATED between the approval of the Legend and the end of World War II. On 13 September 1945 the Deputy Controller suggested that the design be reviewed so that it could be brought up to date. A new legend incorporating changes to date (see Table 12-4) was prepared. At this stage the only major new items were the increased aviation fuel and lubricating oil stowage, the aircraft transporting gear in the hangars, increased protection for the island (40lbs DW around important cable trunks), and an additional LP room to serve the new armament.

A few further items were proposed after completion of the 1946 Legend:

- six safety barriers were fitted instead of four, the extras being spares (replacement of damaged barriers in action was not always practicable), and the cost was three single Bofors
- improved water-tight integrity was provided above the lower hangar deck, to protect the ship even at steep angles
- a self-protection sonar was added
- sonobuoy stowage, maintenance and testing facilities were specified, for a total of 500 buoys (seventy-two ready-use).[13]
- radar modernization was specified, generally in line with the systems planned for the *Malta* class, including carrier-controlled approach (Type 961) and an airborne early warning (AEW) terminal.

The intention overall was to bring the *Ark Royals*, which were definitely being built, as close as possible to the *Maltas*, which would quite possibly be cancelled. It seemed that nothing could be done to provide a side lift, but the *Arks* would

HMS Centaur *as refitted, 7 May 1954. The very small thimble radome at the after end of her island was a Type 961 carrier-controlled approach (blind landing) radar.*

12 This practice, common in war-built ships, later caused severe health problems. At present, reportedly, about one man dies each week in the dockyard towns as a result of the spraying.

13 The basic torpedo stowage was sixty conventional (Mk XVII 18in) anti-ship torpedoes, but arrangements were to be made to substitute forty ASW homing torpedoes (Dealer). The difference in numbers was attributable partly to the additional workshop and other facilities required by Dealer.

Right, below right and bottom: *HMS* Centaur *was refitted during the spring of 1954 with an interim (5½-degree) angled deck. This involved moving the arrester gear and barrier, removing three twin port side 40mm mounts, and repainting the flight deck. She is shown on 25 February 1955 (broadside view, operating with the US Sixth Fleet in the Mediterranean), in 1956, from aft, and on 28 November 1958, from overhead. These three views span a drastic change in British naval aircraft: in 1955, the ship was equipped with piston-engined Sea Furies and Avengers; in 1958, after a major refit (September 1956 to September 1958) she operated jets: Sea Hawks. At this time she was fitted with steam catapults, and the sextuple Bofors abaft her island was landed. Note, too, the installation of a Type 963 blind-landing (CCA) radar in the aerial view replacing the small dish of a wartime-developed Type 961. The overhead view also clearly shows the starboard mirror landing sight, just abaft the crane abaft her island.*

be able to handle much the same aircraft, and they would accommodate the same new radars and much the same AIO arrangement. However, nothing could make a 40,000-ton carrier into a 60,000-ton carrier, and this was most painfully evident in the case of aircraft fuel. By 1945 it was already obvious that *Ark Royal* carried far too little, less than two days' worth by existing standards. Fortunately jet fuel could easily be stowed outside the citadel, but in 1945 it was not yet clear what fuel would be required for jets.

NEARLY ALL THE MODICATIONS added weight, but the power remained unchanged at 152,000shp. On trials in April 1951 *Eagle* made 30.53 knots on 156,630shp at 44,250 tons, which might be equated to 29.6 knots deep (49,950 tons) and clean. The corresponding endurance, six months out of dock, at an average action displacement of 48,700 tons, was 4500nm at 24 knots. Turning trials showed that the ship behaved well, even in strong winds, despite her considerable sail area. Tactical diameter at 30 knots and 35 degrees rudder angle was 847 yards.

Stability data for HMS *Eagle* (as completed) are given in Table 12-5. The ship came out about 4000 tons heavy as completed, and detailed calculations showed that about 1400 tons was hull incidentals and about 1100 general fittings including pumping, flooding and draining, radio and radar. Armament and ammunition accounted for another 400, and permanent ballast (due to topweight growth) for 600 tons.

Because she was being completed somewhat more slowly, *Ark Royal* became a candidate for three major modifications. First, her completion date was altered to fit the steam catapult schedule; she became the first British carrier so fitted. The forward lift had to be moved aft to clear the long catapults.

The second modification was a deck-edge lift. The wartime *Malta* had been designed with two deck-edge lifts (see Chapter 14), and the staff had just tried unsuccessfully to get such a lift into the new carrier reconstructions (see Chapter 15). The wartime logic still seemed valid; Pacific operations showed that reliance on a forward centreline lift precluded high-intensity operations. Aircraft landing had to be moved forward, eventually covering any centreline lift. This left no way to move damaged or unfoldable aircraft which had just landed from the parking area of the flight deck forward of the barriers. In the worst case, the carrier might be unable to recover all her aircraft, or she might have to suspend landing operations while striking down an aircraft aft. The deck-edge lift was also useful as a means of transporting aircraft between flight deck and hangar while flight operations were going on.

As proposed to the Board in August 1950, it would serve the upper hangar only (the lower hangar had insufficient freeboard). Because considerable structure had to be provided around the opening in the ship's side, the opening (to a 17ft 6in hangar) was only 16ft 6in high. Clearing space for it required new and somewhat tortuous (hence less efficient) leads for the port downtakes to A and B boiler rooms, and access from the port side to these boiler rooms and to an auxiliary machinery room was through the lift machinery compartment. About 2800sq ft of hangar had to be surrendered, as well as two port side sextuple Bofors (one single Bofors was moved, and space was cleared to mount a second).[14]

The Board approved the new third lift.

At about this time, too, RAE (Farnborough) proposed a new flight deck configuration, the angled deck (see Chapter 15).

---

14 It was difficult to provide sufficient shear strength around the side lift, and the structural solution adopted in HMS *Ark Royal* (developed by K J Rawson, RCNC) was novel. Rawson used the then-new photo-elastic technique, in which a plastic scale model of the structure was used to estimate stresses, as his primary tool.

HMS Centaur, *in 1956, with an angled deck. Note that her after 982 antenna has been replaced by a hayrake, while the forward antenna is still a triple cheese.*

Table 12-4: *Ark Royal* Legend, 1942 and 1946

	Legend 26 July 1946	Original Legend 3 September 1942
LBP (ft)	720	720
LWL (ft)	750	750
LOA (ft)	803 9	790
Beam (ft)	112 8½	108 8½
Depth (ft)	86 2	79 11½
Displacement (tons) deep	46,000	40,200
standard	36,800	31,600
Petrol (gallons)	103,00	115,000
Aircraft diesel oil (ASF) (gallons)	279,00	–
SHP	152,000	152,000
Speed (knots) std	31.5	32
deep	30.5	31.25
Oil fuel (tons)	6510	7000
Endurance at 24 knots (nm)	5000	6000
Complement	2715	2178
Armament		
Guns	16 4.5in	16 4.5in
	8 sextuple Bofors	8 8-barrel pom-poms
	2 twin Bofors	12 20mm Oerlikons
	12 single Bofors	
18in aircraft torpedoes	60	75
Depth charges	160	252
A mines	24	24
Protection		
Armour	unchanged except plating under armour on flight	
	deck (1in DW) and protection to island 2 × 2in DW69	
Bulge width (ft)	19	17
Aircraft	40 TBR + 40 FF	69 (44 × 13 6 × 13ft 6in)
	or 28 TBR + 50 FF	57 (40 × 18 × 13ft 6in)
Bombs for	40 TBR + 40 FF	42 TBR + 18 FF
Aircraft ammunition for	28 TBR + 56FF	24 TBR + 36 FF
Accelerators	2 30,000lb, 75-knot	2 20,000lb, 66-knot
Arrester wires	16 30,000lb, 75-knot	8 20,000lb, 60-knot
Barriers	4 30,000lb, 75-knot	3 20,000lb, 60-knot
Weight (tons)		
General equipment	2700	1850
Aircraft equipment	3150	1980
Machinery	3580	3260
Armament	1330	1220
Armour and protection	6240	6020
Hull	20,240	17,430
Fuel	6510	7000
RFW	270	260
ASF	930	–
Water protection to petrol	700	630
Board margin	–	150
Deep displacement	46,000	40,200

Ark Royal *as completed, with side lift and steam catapults, and with the early (triple cheese) Type 982 radar antennas. Note the 'flyco' ('pri-fly' in US terminology) built out from the side of the bridge, and not at the after end of the island as in US practice.*

Left, below left and below: Ark Royal *was completed with steam catapults, an interim angled deck and a side lift. The angled deck did not originally extend over her port forward sponson, but the 4.5in guns there were removed during a short post-completion refit, in 1955. This increased accommodation. At this time the 40mm gun mounting forward of the island was removed, and the operations room enlarged. She is shown in July 1957 at Norfolk, USA, for the International Naval Review that year. Beside the usual British radar (a Type 293 cheese), IFF transponders, and radio antennas, the mast carries what appears to be the then-standard US suit of ESM antennas, one in a radome and the other, unshielded, below it. Note also that the lattice mast is angled to the carrier's centreline. Unlike* Eagle *in 1951–53,* Ark Royal *had no HF/DF, because her aircraft all use VHF radio (with a VHF/DF forward on the starboard side). The aerial view shows a mix of British and American naval aircraft: two Cougars and two Banshee single-seat night fighters at the bow, three Seahawks forward of the after lift, and two Gannets and two Wyverns at the stern.*

Although, there was no hope of any major reconstruction so late in the building process, *Ark Royal* was completed with an interim 5½ degree angled deck, the port side being extended slightly and the forward port pair of 4.5in turrets blanked over. There was some objection, for example to widening the ship, but the new configuration was clearly worthwhile. It appears to have been proposed first for *Ark Royal*, but first installed in HMS *Eagle* during a Devonport refit (June 1954 – February 1955). In the latter case the two forward port 4.5in turrets were retained, one sextuple 40mm mounting and a Mk 37 director being landed.

The angled deck actually made the somewhat awkward deck-edge lift much less valuable, because it moved the parking area back abaft of the forward centreline lift to the triangular area to starboard of the landing line. The deck-edge lift was eliminated during a Devonport refit (July 1958 – September 1959). At this time the two starboard forward 4.5in guns were removed, together with the single Bofors around the island; at the end of the refit she carried thirty-two Bofors. A platform for flight deck vehicles was built around the outboard side of the island. The two after port side 4.5in guns were removed during the next refit (February – November 1964), together with two sextuple and one twin Bofors, leaving sixteen such weapons.

Eagle was substantially modernized in 1959–64 (see Chapter 15), having been refitted from November 1955 to April 1956. *Ark Royal* would have followed, but her full modernization was cancelled when the Labour Government decided, in February

Left and below left: Ark Royal *as completed in 1955, before her angled deck was extended forward to blank off the two forward port 4.5in gun mounts. Note that their director lay directly in the line of the landing (and bolting) path. The side lift filled space which, aboard, HMS* Eagle, *could be devoted to light anti-aircraft weapons. Therefore she was completed with five (rather than eight) sextuple Bofors (one on the flight deck forward of the island, one on the starboard side aft, and three on the port side), two twin Bofors (in the after gallery), and three (rather than nine) single mounts. Very large numbers of light anti-aircraft weapons were difficult to maintain and to man in peacetime, and this problem was exacerbated as more and more men were needed to maintain increasingly complex aircraft: ships had only so much accommodation space. As a result, and quite apart from changes in likely air targets, both in the Royal Navy and in the contemporary US Navy the large wartime anti-aircraft batteries declined sharply during the 1950s.*

1966, to end British carrier aviation. Instead, she was refitted and given an interim modernization (October 1967 – February 1970) to operate the Phantom fighters the Royal Navy had bought.

THE LIGHT CARRIERS projected for the 1943 programme were the first to be affected directly by the new JTC directives. Initial studies showed that a *Colossus* could not possibly be modified to operate 30,000lb aircraft, and the new design was necessarily a compromise between the goal of quick commercial-style construction and the need for substantial size and strength. Draft Staff Requirements (Table 12-6) were prepared in March 1943. Growth was inevitable, given the new relaxed take-off constraints (27 knots wind over deck and a 500ft run).

Perhaps the clearest proof that size was due entirely to a change in aircraft characteristics is that the 1943 carrier was designed to operate the same number of fighters and TBR as the 1942 light fleet carrier (see the 1943 Legend, Table 12-7).

By 1943 many British naval officers were too aware that previous restrictions on aircraft size, incorporated in earlier carrier designs, had left their fleet painfully inferior. Thus the 1943 ships seemed to be an opportunity to gain essential margin against unforeseen future developments. This choice turned out to be very fortunate, since they allowed for the early part of the postwar jet revolution.

Moreover, given the large number of light fleet carriers already under construction, there was little point in accepting mediocre new ships merely to get aircraft to sea. It seemed likely that, by the time the first 1943 ships commissioned, at least fourteen *Colossus*-class carriers would be in service. Under these circumstances the claims of quality could supersede those of quantity.

As the ship grew to accommodate the new and prospective aircraft, it became logical to improve protection and armament. Thus, although there were no specific requirements for protection, DNC proposed a 1in longitudinal bulkhead throughout the length of the citadel for splinter protection, armoured boxes (1in sides and 2in crowns) over the magazines, a 1in deck over machinery spaces and petrol compartments, and 1in vertical

Ark Royal *after her post-completion refit, 1955, showing the extended angled deck.*

British carriers were designed to cross-deck American aircraft, partly because it was assumed that in a protracted war the Royal Navy would have to rely partly on the large US aircraft industry to make up for early losses, and to provide for expansion. Here, in 1957, Ark Royal operates US Skyrays and Demons; two of her Gannets are visible at the after end of the flight deck.

Table 12-5: Stability Data, HMS *Eagle* as Completed

	Deep	Light
GM	7.08	2.85
GZ max (intact hangar)	6.52	4.3
Angle	42	47
Range	79	61.6
GZ max (hangar flooded)	5.8	4.2
Angle	37	40
Range	64.2	59.5
Displacement (tons)	49,950	39,500

Note Design GM was 8.6ft deep (45,720 tons)

Left: Eagle *on 18 July 1955, showing her new angled deck. Note that although the forward port 4.5in gun mount roofs formed part of the deck, the guns were not removed. Note also that the single 40mm guns shown had been cocooned; in peacetime the ship did not carry enough men to operate or maintain them. The port forward Mk 37 director had to be removed, together with one of the Mk 6 sextuple Bofors (note the empty platform almost directly under the funnel in this picture) and its local director.*

armour over the side, bulkheads abreast the machinery, and gun positions. Underwater protection would match that of the *Colossus* class.

Note also the new heavy battery, far more powerful than that of the *Colossus* and approaching that of a fleet carrier. DGD considered it essential.

DNC submitted a sketch design on 29 May 1943 (see Table 12-7). Expected construction time was two years and nine months, compared with less than two years aimed at in the *Colossus* class.

The basic design of the ships compromised between merchant ship (*Colossus* class) and warship practice. The transverse frames, for example were of bulb angle type. Except for the flight deck, longitudinal protective bulkhead, middle deck over machinery, and lower decks over petrol and other vitals, the hull was built of mild steel. Welding was used extensively.

Protection was limited to 80lb (2in) NC armour over magazines and bomb rooms, plus splinter-proofing elsewhere. As in the earlier light fleet carriers, underwater protection relied mainly on transverse bulkheads, although in these ships there were also 1in wing bulkheads on each side. They were intended to keep out near-miss bomb splinters, and to reduce flooding effects. The ships were designed to a six-compartment standard amidships, and a five-compartment at the ends. To increase accommodation, DNC provided a middle deck.

E-in-C was anxious to avoid designing a new powerplant. The machinery therefore was half a set of *Ark Royal* engines

HMS Eagle *shows her interim angled deck (which blanked out the forward port 4.5in guns), in 1956. She had not yet been fitted with steam catapults. The aircraft on deck are Gannets alongside the island, Seahawks and three Sea Venoms along the deck edge to port, and Wyverns and Skyraiders (for airborne early warning) aft. The Skyraiders are in dark (US Navy) paint, the others in standard Fleet Air Arm colours (extra dark gray above, sky below). FAAM*

HMS Albion *as completed, with an angled deck, on 4 June 1954. The aircraft aft are two Vampire trainers and a Firefly.*

Right*: HMS* Albion, *1954, showing her new interim angled deck, mirror landing sight (port side, with the source lights also visible, further aft), and two single 40mm guns right aft. The small cheese antenna on the after part of her island is a Type 961. It could direct a pilot in bearing but not in elevation, and thus was not a true blind-approach system.*

Right and below right: *The other two ships of the original class were completed with interim angled decks.* Bulwark *is shown on 26 November 1954 (aerial view) and on 29 January 1960, apparently little changed (but in fact serving as a helicopter carrier). She was not refitted as a carrier because after 1957 she was clearly surplus to the much-reduced first-line carrier force. The change most visible here was the elimination of the after Type 982 radar antenna. In the aerial view, the aircraft are a Sea Vampire trainer and a Firefly. Note the VHF/DF in the 1954 view, and the UHF/DF which replaced it in 1960.*

Table 12-6: Outline Staff Requirements for the 1943 Light Fleet Carrier, 2 April 1943

	1943	1942
Speed (knots)	25, deep, 6 months out of dock; approx 28.5 clean	25, deep, clean
Hangar width (ft)	62	52
Lifts	54 × 34ft, 30,000lb	45 × 34ft, 15,000lb
Flight deck dimensions (ft)	at least 700 × 90	690 × 80
Aircraft	24 of new type (30,000lb)	24 of existing type (15,000lb)
Wires, barrier, accelerator	30,000lb, 75-knot	14,000lb, 60-knot
Torpedoes	32 18in or 21in or 22 4in	32 18in
Armament	4 twin 4.5in BD	—
	2 sextuple Bofors (or 8-barrel pom-poms)	6 4-barrel pom-poms
	10 twin Bofors ('Busters')	
	11 quad Oerlikons	11 quad Oerlikons
	up to 12 twin Oerlikons	8 twin Oerlikons

DNC Estimates

Dimensions		
LBP (ft)	650	630
BWL (ft)	90	80
Draught, std (ft)	21	19 6
Std displacement (tons)	18,000	14,000
Complement	about 1400	1050
Estimated cost (£m)	2.75	2 (Vote VIII)
Time to build	2 years 9 months	2 years 3 months

Table 12-7: Sketch Design for the 1943 Light Fleet Carrier, 29 May 1943

	1943 Design	1942 Light Fleet Carrier
LBP (ft)	650	630
LWL (ft)	685	650
LOA (ft)	736	691
BWL (ft)	90	80 6
Displacement, std (tons)	18,000	14,000
Draught, std (ft)	20 3	19
Depth (ft)	70 7	61 9
Displacement, deep (tons)	23,800	
Draught, deep (ft)	24 8	23
SHP (2 shafts)	76,000	40,000
Speed, deep (knots)	29.5	25
Oil fuel (tons)	4000	3000
Endurance at 20 knots (nm)	6000	6000
Complement	1400[1]	1054[2]
Petrol (gallons)	80,000	80,000
Lubricating oil (gallons)	7000	7000

Armament

Twin 4.5in	4	—
Sextuple Bofors	2	—
4-barrel pom-pom	—	6
Twin Bofors	10	—
Quad 20mm	7	11
Twin 20mm	4	8
Torpedoes	32	32
Depth charges	108	108
Aircraft	18 TBR and 6 FF or 24 FF	

Weights (tons)

General equipment	1300	1200
Aircraft equipment	1530	610
Machinery	1720	1110
Armament	800	695
Protection	300	—
Hull	12,000	10,085
Margin	350	300
Displacement	18,000	14,000

1 Excluding supernumeraries.
2 Including supernumeraries.

Right and above right: Albion *at Malta on 27 January 1956 (starboard side) and 22 January 1957 (port side). In the 1957 view, note that the sextuple Bofors abaft the island has been replaced by a crane, although its director remains. The Sea Venom aircraft on deck had probably participated in the Suez operation the previous November.*

Below: HMS Eagle, *newly completed, is shown in March 1952. Note the Firebrand strike fighters aft, soon to be replaced by Wyverns.*

HMS Eagle *in 1957, with Wyverns and Sea Hawks on deck, and with the mirror landing sight clearly in view abeam the foremost Wyvern. Presumably the Sea Venom night fighter overhead is a bolter which has just missed its approach to the angled deck. Note the single Bofors forward, and the big sextuple Bofors gun mounts on the gallery deck. These weapons and their directors were gradually eliminated, partly because of their declining value against jet aircraft, but partly also because the limited accommodation aboard ship was required for men to maintain the increasingly complex aircraft; there just were not enough berths left over for those serving and maintaining the light guns.*

Eagle *rigged for air operations in 1959, with jet blast deflectors up behind each catapult and the rescue helicopter, ready to launch, between the catapults. The aircraft lined up along the deck are Sea Hawks and Sea Venom night fighters, with early warning Skyraiders (painted dark blue) and ASW Gannets (in conventional British naval colors) aft. The ship was just about to decommission for her long modernization.*

Below and below left: Eagle *was extensively modernized in 1959–64, when the big Type 984 radar was fitted. All her light anti-aircraft guns were removed; they were replaced by six quadruple Seacat launchers, two of which replaced the forward starboard 4.5in guns. The two after 4.5in guns on each side were retained.* FAAM

Table 12-8: *Hermes* Class as Built (1947 Design)

LBP (ft)	650
LWL (ft)	696 9
LOA (ft)	736
BWL (ft)	90
Beam, extreme (ft)	120 6
Depth (ft)	70 7
Displacement (tons) std	22,471
deep	27,015
Draught, deep (ft)	27 2½
SHP	76,000
Speed, clean (knots)	28.5
Endurance at 20 knots (nm)	6000
Oil fuel (tons)	4083
Flight deck dimensions (ft)	732 9 × 84 (min, at fore end)
Hangar dimensions (ft)	381 × 62
Lifts	2 54 × 44ft, 35,000lb
Arrester gear	Mk 11, 30,000lb, 75-knot[1]
Accelerators	2 BH V, 30,000lb, 75-knot
Aircraft	50[3]
Armament	2 sextuple Bofors
	8 twin Bofors
	4 single power-operated Bofors
Directors	10 CRBF[4]
Complement (peace)	227/1596
Weights (tons)	
Hull and protection	12,402
General fittings	2514
Machinery	2109
Armament and ammunition	358
General equipment	1583
Aircraft equipment	2352
Oil fuel and lube oil	4133
Avgas and water	573
Avcat	666
RFW	175
Permanent ballast	150
Deep displacement	27,015

1 Or 20,000lb at 91 knots
2 With 3 pumps, so that 1 aircraft could be launched every 40 seconds from each
   catapult.
3 2 bomb rooms, one above the other on the hold and platform decks; maximum bomb
   lift load, 4000lbs. Stowage sufficient for 9 loads for each of 26 strike aircraft, each 2
   1000lb or 4 500lb bombs; plus 32 18in torpedoes, 2000 3in rockets, and ammunition
   sufficient for 10 loads for 50 aircraft (316,000 rounds of 20mm).
4 Close Range Blind Fire

Table 12-9: Designed Stability, *Hermes* Class (1947 Design)

	Light	Full Load
GM	3.7	7.07 (liquid)
GZ (angle)	3.33 (38)	5.62 (40)
Range	60.5	74.5
Displacement (tons)	20,029	27,015

HMS Ark Royal *in February 1960, with Sea Vixens and Scimitars aboard. At this time her only forward-firing anti-aircraft weapon was the twin Bofors forward of the island, on the flight deck.*

At Okinawa on 21 June 1962, Ark Royal *showed the effects of a long refit (July 1958 to December 1959). The deck-edge lift was removed, together with the two starboard forward 4.5in mounts, the single 40mm guns around the island, and the forward Mk 37 director. Note the twin 40mm mount installed forward of the island; another was fitted on the port side of the island just abaft the funnel. The forward Type 982 was replaced by a new long-range air search radar (Type 965), but the Type 960 on the mainmast was retained. Note the replacement of the VHF/DF by a UHF/DF (forward of the twin 40mm mount) to reflect a shift in aircraft radio frequency, and the replacement of the old YE homing beacon by the masthead Tacan (Type 957 in British service). A new CCA radar, not visible here, was installed during a short refit in 1961. The aircraft on deck are Scimitars and Sea Vixens, with Wessex ASW helicopters aft.*

Probably because Centaur *was the only one of the original three ships fitted with steam catapults, she was retained longest in service as an aircraft carrier. She is shown in December 1962, with a Tacan atop her lattice mast. When it was fitted, her Type 960 long-range air search radar was moved to a light tripod mast.*

and boilers, consisting of two (rather than four) units, each comprising a boiler room and an engine room. There were also four diesel generators and four turbo generators, each of 400kW. As in the *Ark Royals*, all generators were intended for sustained use, and there were no emergency generators as such. Dispersion was expected to protect them. The diesel generators were in individual compartments (two forward and two aft); dtwo turbo generators were in the engine rooms and two in the boiler rooms.

The Future Building Committee suggested several improvements:

(a) increased close-range armanent:
  (i) fit additional twin Bofors, three port and one starboard, in lieu of quadruple Oerlikons
  (ii) mount additional Oerlikons fore and aft
  (iii) move the port side boats down one deck and mount Oerlikons above them
(b) increased lift width

The Board saw these ships as supplements to future heavy armoured carriers, and feared that they were too complex and too expensive. The First Lord felt dissatisfied with the concept, and was not prepared to agree to construction without Cabinet approval. He wanted the ships reconsidered. The Controller ordered the design developed as though approval had been granted, and eight ships were ordered on 12 July 1943.

Given so large a hull, there was a natural temptation to use it more fully. The nominal aircraft complement was increased to twenty-four bombers and sixteen fighters (aircraft equipment weight increased 320 tons), the lifts were widened (from 54 ×

Below: Ark Royal *in about 1966, with a Gannet landing. The 'thimble' radome at the after end of her island was the Type 963 carrier-controlled approach radar fitted in 1961. The ship was refitted from February to November 1964, one of the two twin 4.5in mounts being removed from each after sponson. At this time, too, the ship was left with only two sextuple and three twin Bofors (the mount on the starboard side of the stern gallery was removed). Within a short time all the sextuple mounts had been removed (as is evident here), together with the twin mount forward of the island. The Fresnel lens (successor to the mirror) landing sight is visible above the flight deck on the left hand side of the photograph.* FAAM

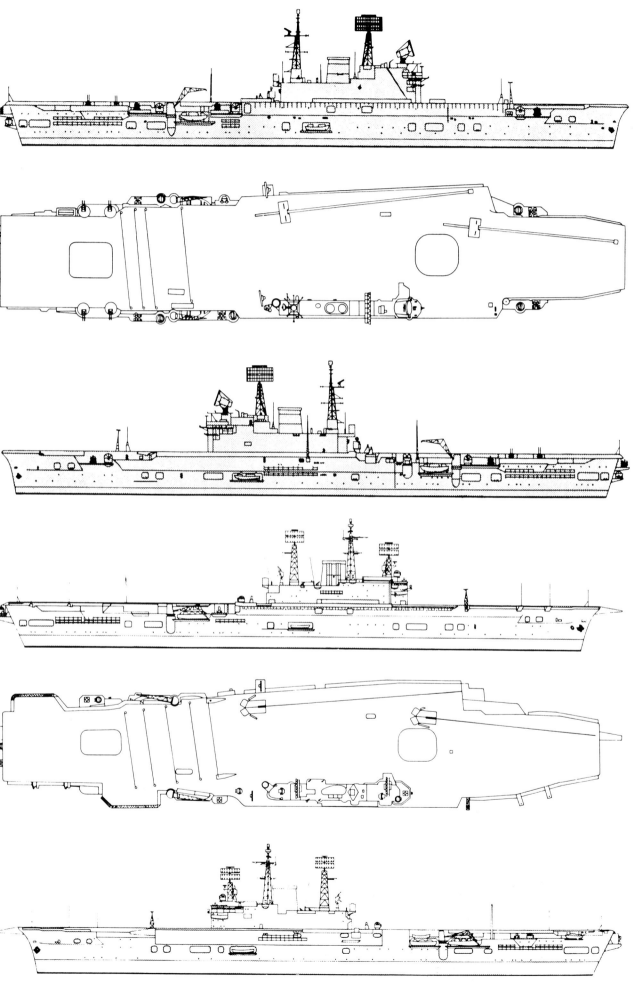

Left *HMS* Eagle *as modernized, in about 1968, showing her waist catapult and her Type 984 radar. Note the big mattress of the Type 965, which was used as a back-up for the less reliable (but much higher performance) 984. A further, relatively small, modernization to handle Phantoms had to be abandoned due to a fiscal crisis in 1972–73.*

Left: *HMS* Ark Royal *in her final configuration, as modified to operate Phantoms, in 1971. This drawing shows the modernization as planned, and therefore includes three Seacat launchers aft which were not, in fact, installed aboard the ship. The bow projection is a bridle catcher to retrieve wire bridles used in catapulting.*

Ark Royal *in her final form, refitted to handle Phantom fighters. These views were probably taken in 1971, soon after the completion of her final refit. She had been completely disarmed and the Seacats for which she was fitted had not in fact been installed. Note the long bridge extension out over her flight deck, reminiscent of that in HMS* Courageous *three decades before. The radars were two Type 965, two Type 983 (height-finders), and one narrow-beam Type 982; the Type 963 thimble-dome was retained, but a more capable SPN-35, in the big radome abaft the island, was installed.*

A US A-7 lands aboard HMS Ark Royal *in a cross-decking exercise on 13 April 1976. The small dish atop the bridge, installed in 1973, was for satellite communications.*

Below and below left: Ark Royal *in 1976, at the end of her career, operating Phantoms and Buccanneers.*

34ft to 54 × 44ft, at a cost of 80 tons), guns were added (four twin 40mm and some 20mm, at a cost of 80 tons), and machinery weight increased 80 tons.[15] This was a total additional weight of 560 tons, but the original design incorporated a 350-ton margin. DNC resubmitted the design in January 1944, at 18,310 tons with a 100-ton margin.

The sketch design was eventually approved formally in February 1944, and the final design and Legend in March.

There must have been a shrewd suspicion, even in 1943, that many of the ships then being ordered would never be completed, and that the postwar fleet would be glad to get anything approaching a fleet carrier capable of operating modern aircraft. This was certainly what occurred.

At the end of the war, four out of the original eight ships were cancelled.

As in the case of the *Ark Royals*, construction slowed drastically after the war, and numerous changes had to be made. A new design was prepared in 1947 (see Table 12-8). It introduced such new standard features as centralized messing, better accommodation and peacetime amenities. Additional accommodation was provided by filling in the after hangar extension, reducing the aircraft complement by three. A second accelerator added forward may also have reduced hangar length, the final figure being 381 rather than 501 ft.[16]

Space was provided for 100,000 gallons of jet fuel (middle distillate aircraft fuel), at the expense of 403 tons of fuel oil, the total being reduced to 3492 tons.

The island was redesigned to accommodate the new type of two-level AIO introduced in the *Ark Royal* design. At this time the planned radar fit comprised a long-range air warning radar (960), a gunnery air search radar (293), and two pairs of 277Q pencil-beam radars, each pair acting as a three-dimensional air control set. The ships were completed with one Type 983 height-finder and two Type 982 precision two-dimensional air search radars in place of the 277s. As compensation for the increased weight of the island, the aircraft crane was moved from the starboard to the port side.

The 4.5in gun battery had to be omitted, presumably to reduce manning so as to reduce overcrowding.[17] The first three ships (*Albion*, *Bulwark* and *Centaur*) were completed to much this modified design. They could not be held back for installation of steam catapults. However, the first of the class, HMS *Centaur*, was taken in hand almost immediately after completion for installation of an iterim (5½ degree) angled deck (February 1954); three twin port side Bofors were removed. Two BS 4 (139ft) steam catapults were fitted during a major refit from September 1956 to September 1958.[18] *Albion* would have been the next ship, but she fell foul of the 1957 defence policy review which sharply limited the British carrier force.

Albion and *Bulwark* were completed with interim angled decks, but were still too early to receive steam catapults. Neither was refitted. Instead, they were both converted to Commando (helicopter) carriers, again in line with the new 1957 policy (see Chapter 17).

HMS *Hermes*, the name-ship of the class, was further redesigned to incorporate such new features as an angled deck, steam catapult, and the new 984 integrated radar. This design is described in Chapter 16.

Ark Royal *island, 1977, showing the satellite communications dish, one of the 965s, and a Type 983 height-finder. The cones on the side of the island, visible above the 'flyco', are hooded spotlights for night operations.*

15 Armament was increased to two sextuple Bofors, fourteen twin Bofors, one quadruple 20mm, eighteen twin 20mm, and two single 20mm.

16 It was originally feared that the second catapult would reduce armament to two sextuple, four twin, and four single Bofors, but eight twins were retained.

17 Unfortunately the Ship's Covers for this class have not yet been released, and therefore this must be surmise. Most of the details are taken from successive DNC memoranda for the Board (including a description of the 1947 design), and from the June 1943 sketch legend (Table 12-7) preserved in a book of collected DNC legends at NMM. The 1946 papers on elimination of the 4.5in battery appear

not to have survived, but in 1947 manning was a major issue. The ships were designed for 1540 men, and at one time a complement of 1952 was suggested. By 1947 the designed complement had reached a compromise figure, 1752.

18 In approving this very limited modernization, the Board commented that the ship was very severely limited; due to insufficient hangar deck strength, armed aircraft had to be held on the flight deck, and she had only rudimentary protection against nuclear fallout and chemical attack. However, it was better that she should be available in two years than to aim higher and accept a very long refit such as that of HMS *Eagle*. (Board Minute 5001, 3 May 1956). Staff Requirements for the 1956-58 refit were dated 9 March 1956.

13

The Future Building Committee

IN EFFECT, the *Ark Royals* were the last carry-overs from the prewar building programmes. By 1942 it was clear that naval warfare had changed drastically, and that the overall shape of the British fleet had to be re-thought.[1] A Future Building Committee, chaired by the Deputy First Sea Lord, was therefore set up in July 1942. ACNS(W) served as Deputy Chairman, and the committee included as permanent members representatives of the Controller, Director of Plans, DTSD, DGD, DNC, DNAD, and DACR.

Because the most radical change was in the role of aircraft, the Committee spent a great deal of its time on carrier and naval aircraft characteristics. To some considerable extent it seems to have been constituted specifically to reverse what many in the Royal Navy saw as backwardness in naval aviation. At the very least the Committee was responsible for the enormous increase in the British carrier programme, which produced the *Ark Royals*, most of the light fleet carriers, and the *Maltas* (see Chapter 14). It was also responsible for the new generation of naval aircraft which began to appear in 1944–45. Earlier aircraft had been conceived either as successors to older types or as answers to specific tactical problems. The Committee tried instead to re-think the fleet's air needs as a coherent whole.

Perhaps as importantly, because it was the only organization within the Admiralty charged with the overall review of British naval requirements, the Committee became responsible for decisions on many central issues of ship and aircraft design and construction policy. In March 1943 its Aircraft Design Sub-Committee was split off as a separate Naval Aircraft Design Committee, but the two organizations worked very closely together and are treated as one in this chapter. The Future Building Committee itself was disbanded in 1945, but it was soon reconstituted as the postwar Ship Characteristics Policy Committee, a title which better expresses one of its main contributions. The Naval Aircraft Design Committee survived the war.

The Committee began by estimating British naval requirements as they would exist in January 1944. It accepted the classic main fleet strategy; what was new was that strike aircraft were now considered the longest-range main fleet weapons, albeit weapons limited by weather. As in the past, the main fleet was defined by its ability to destroy or neutralize any enemy main fleet, while itself enjoying a sufficient degree of invulnerability. The painful lesson of recent warfare was that any future

main fleet would need a combination of defensive fighters and striking forces in sufficient numbers to achieve decisive results. Prewar ideas survived, and the report noted that the final decision could be achieved either by more aircraft or by battleships, the latter being more economical in some circumstances.

Security still seemed to require a combination of enough battleships to match those of an enemy, but this now had to be supplemented by a larger and more efficient air arm.

At this time the German battleships *Scharnhorst* and *Gneisenau* had just escaped through the Channel, Malta was still under siege, the Eighth Army was on the defensive in Egypt, the Germans were advancing in Russia, and the Japanese had just been defeated at Midway, with unknown consequences. Although neither of the European Axis powers yet had aircraft carriers in service, it seemed reasonable to imagine that the Germans would have their *Graf Zeppelin* by 1944. The British Home Fleet, in the north, was badly stretched to cover convoys to northern Russia, the Eastern Fleet had been forced (largely by a lack of air power) to withdraw through the Indian Ocean, and Force H was stationed at Gibraltar.

The Committee reviewed requirements fleet by fleet. To simplify calculations, it worked in terms of standard 48-aircraft armoured fleet carriers (such as HMS *Implacable*) and standard escort (auxiliary) carriers (twenty-four aircraft each). Light fleet carriers were, in effect, fast escort carriers.

The Home Fleet would generally operate outside a line about 100nm from enemy North Sea shores, as within this area sufficient carrier fighters could not be provided to guarantee the safety of naval units from German shore-based aircraft. Elsewhere in the North Sea, about 100 fleet air defence fighters might be required. There were fewer airfields in the north, although fleet fighters might have to escort strikes. The maximum weight of an enemy attack would probably be fifty aircraft, with ten or fifteen more likely, and the fleet would need eight fighters on CAP (supported by a total fighter complement of thirty-two).

If the Germans did complete *Graf Zeppelin*, she would probably carry forty strike aircraft and no fighter escorts; they could be dealt with by twenty fighters, six on CAP, the rest on deck alert. A total of thirty fighters would suffice.

The Home Fleet would, therefore, need thirty to thirty-six fighters for all operations other than prolonged ones near the Norwegian coast. It would need about 100 fighters either in

that case or in the case of North Sea operations, which might be considered extraordinary.

The standard reconnaissance for a typical Home Fleet operation would be two searches a day by twelve aircraft, continuous ASW patrol by two, and an allowance for shadowing, relief spotting and action observation. This would be covered by thirty-six aircraft.

A striking force of eighteen aircraft at one time would suffice for the three or four heavy ships the Germans were considered likely to coordinate. At least two waves would be required, but once the enemy was located the search requirement would be reduced.

Thus total search and strike requirements would amount to about sixty TSR. Allowing 50 per cent aircraft reserves for refit, the fleet would require a total of ninety TSR and forty-five fighters, 135 aircraft in three fleet carriers.[2]

The Home Fleet was also responsible for the Russian convoys. They could not be run if the scale of air attack increased, but the existing level could be handled by at least two large escort carriers per convoy, a total of four (two convoys) plus two refitting, or six altogether.

The Eastern Fleet had already been badly battered, and British resources could not build it to the level of the Japanese navy. However, it seemed reasonable to expect that by January 1944 the US Pacific Fleet would have reached parity with the Japanese. The British target was to be able to balance 50 per cent of the Japanese Fleet, in the expectation that the Japanese could not deploy more than half their fleet against either enemy. The estimated Japanese carrier striking force was four carriers (150 strike aircraft with fifty fighter escorts), which would require a defending force of 125 British carrier fighters (150 aboard the carriers). This large force would also suffice against any realistic scale of shore-based attack.

Because it placed so much emphasis on the need for more naval aircraft, the Future Building Committee was largely responsible for the immense mid-war carrier programmes. HMS Warrior *was one of the results. She was completed for the Royal Canadian Navy, and then returned to the Royal Navy when HCMS* Magnificent *was completed. From the British point of view, the individual Commonwealth navies were part of a larger joint Royal Navy, so these were actually transfers within the larger entity.*

Reconnaissance requirements would expand in the large areas of the East, and the enemy would probably be more dispersed. The fleet would also be further from its bases and hence would need a greater margin for serviceability. The Committee estimated that sixty reconnaissance aircraft were needed. A full-scale fleet action was possible, hence although for operational reasons no single striking force would need to exceed thirty-six TSR, at least four waves would be required, making 144 TSR. If the reconnaissance aircraft made up one wave, then 108 other aircraft were needed, and the fleet required a total of 168 TSR. With 50 per cent refit allowances this made 225 fighters and 252 TSR, a total of 477 aircraft, that is, ten carriers.[3]

In addition, the Committee suggested four mobile units, each consisting of one auxiliary carrier and one cruiser, to protect convoys and to hunt raiders. Once offensive operations began, more convoys would be run, and six such units would be needed.

Enemy shore-based aircraft made the Eastern Mediterranean dangerous for heavy units, and the Committee estimated that the minimum acceptable cover would be three armoured carriers (150 fighters). Because such coverage would be so difficult to arrange, it suggested that any East Mediterranean carriers be provided by temporary detachment from other fleets.

2   Even larger figures could be produced. A revision of the future fleet paper in October 1942 showed eight fleet carriers in the Home Fleet. The estimated requirement was a total of 110 fighters and eighty bombers, plus a strike force of forty fighters and sixty bombers in northern waters, or to cover the Atlantic approaches if the main fleet was otherwise engaged, equal to six carrier loads, plus fifty fighters and ten ASW bombers for the north Russia run (four escort carriers).

3   When the paper was revised in October, the Eastern Fleet requirement was cut back to five fleet carriers, with five support carriers (twenty-four aircraft each) to reinforce the seaborne air forces during action, that is, to make up for wastage. However, given the vast distances and the lack of bases, the fleet would also need five special aircraft repair ships (*Unicorn* type) and six special fast (20-knot) oilers carrying fuel and aviation spirit.

On the other hand, Force H had proven valuable both in the Western Mediterranean and in the Eastern Atlantic. Since it still seemed possible that the Italians would eventually operate from Spain or even from Gibraltar, the Committee estimated that Force H should be at about the same strength as the Home Fleet, three large carriers.

One escort carrier was required for each North Atlantic convoy, a total of twenty-one (with nine more refitting at any one time). In the South Atlantic, the chief roles were anti-raider and anti-blockade runner, using groups like those in the Indian Ocean (one auxiliary carrier and one cruiser). The Committee wanted three such groups, with a fourth refitting.

These were terrifying figures; they came to a total of sixteen fleet and forty-nine auxiliary carriers (of which the United States might be expected to supply eight for the North Atlantic). In January 1944 Britain would have only four modern fleet carriers (three carrying only 36 aircraft each) and three old ones (*Eagle* had not yet been sunk) equivalent, together, to perhaps four modern fleet carriers, (each carrying 48 aircraft). Within the next eighteen months, two more fleet carriers (*Implacable*s) and four light fleet carriers would be completed, equivalent to another four 48-aircraft fleet carriers, a total of about half of what was needed.[4] About thirty-two escort carriers would also appear, and they would help the overall situation but not the main fleets. By way of contrast, the cruiser situation was more hopeful. The total requirement was sixty-two and the Royal Navy had forty-four modern units and seventeen old ones, with eight more under construction for completion in the near future. Since a light fleet carrier was approximately equivalent to a cruiser in terms of shipyard effort, these figures justified a decision to cancel projected cruisers in favour of small carriers.

These numbers tended to grow over time. Table 13-1 shows the version submitted in November 1942: twenty-two fleet carriers, nineteen light fleet carriers, and eighty-three auxiliary carriers. The light fleet total had already been revised downward, with two rather than three for training (nineteen rather than twenty-one), and the escort carrier figure upward, from seventy-five to eighty-three. Much more striking, however, was the jump from sixteen to twenty-two fleet carriers.

Note the requirement for five aircraft maintenance ships (*Unicorns*), primarily for the Eastern Fleet.[5] By January 1944 Britain expected ultimately to maintain about 1000 aircraft, not including trainers or reserves, in the East, which would have to be supported by workshops sufficient for 120 per month plus replacements of 150 per month from Britain or, in the absence of maintenance facilities, 270 per month from Britain. This equated to three engine repair and three airframe component repair ships, not to mention maintenance of airframes proper, which could be carried out either ashore or afloat (aboard special ships). Repair ashore was not acceptable, because the aircraft would have to be transported thousands of miles to Australia, or else back to massive mobile bases on US lines (which the British could not expect to produce). By this time there was no question of duplicating the expensive *Unicorn*, but a 17,000-ton ship, capable of maintaining forty aircraft at a time, was sketched. Three CVEs (airframe, engine and airframe component repairs) could function as a repair group, equivalent to a *Unicorn*; at least three such groups (nine CVEs) would be needed. Alternatively, two converted light fleet carriers were considered equivalent to a *Unicorn*. The Fifth Sea Lord wanted specialized ships built; he thought two would be available for operations in 1946.

Three CVEs could be converted to provide one interim group, but on 1 February 1944 the Controller rejected this option as impractical. Two of the 1942 light fleet carriers, *Pio-*

neer and *Perseus*, had not yet been laid down, and they were ordered completed as maintenance ships, on an urgent basis (see Chapter 10 for details). Specially built ships would have been better, but it was not clear what existing projects could be cancelled to provide the necessary labour and slip space.[6]

Given its point of view, it was not surprising that the Committee wanted the largest hull under construction in Britain, the battleship HMS *Vanguard*, completed instead as a carrier.[7] At this time, July 1942, the Committee estimated that Britain needed twelve battleships, against which she would have nine (some of them nearing the end of their useful lives) plus *Vanguard* by January 1946. There would, however, be only ten carrier equivalents, against a required sixteen, and the Committee argued that the carrier was the real core of the Fleet. The First Sea Lord felt otherwise, and HMS *Vanguard* became the last British battleship.

To a limited extent, fleet carriers could be replaced by light carriers on a two-for-one basis; this partly explains the increase in the light fleet carrier programme. Even so, by January 1943 the Royal Navy had only four armoured and two unarmoured fleet carriers, though a large light fleet carrier programme was in hand. The Committee estimated that by January 1947 there would probably be only five armoured carriers (assuming one armoured carrier lost each year). Even worse, early in 1943 it was estimated that to achieve the required balanced fleet by 1948 would require an 80 per cent increase in the output of all the major warship yards, an impossible figure.

Overall, until the carrier deficiencies were made up, British fleet commanders would be unable to carry out offensive operations, particularly in the Indian Ocean. The earliest Committee reports seem to have influenced the Board to increase the 1942 light carrier programme from four to nine ships, in August 1942, at the expense of cruiser construction. Ultimately the 1942 programme included two fleet carriers (in addition to *Ark Royal* of 1940) and sixteen light fleet carriers. Unfortunately, the British shipbuilding industry was already badly stretched. At the beginning of 1944 one of the three fleet carriers was scheduled for completion in 1946 and the other two for 1947. Of the light fleet carriers, two were scheduled for 1944, eleven for 1945, and three (two of which would be completed as aircraft maintenance ships) for 1946.

The conversion of the two light fleet carriers to aircraft maintenance ships was a gesture in the direction of the five *Unicorns* the expanded carrier fleet would require. Neither had the capacity of a single *Unicorn*, but the hulls were available and the ships clearly would become surplus when the much superior 1943 light fleet carriers (*Hermes* class) entered service.

On the other hand, the British had learned painfully that carriers could not deal with overwhelming numbers of high-performance land-based fighters. In 1940, for example, the Mediterranean Fleet had often operated within 100nm of enemy bases. In mid-1942 it hesitated to operate within 350nm, and convoys within such ranges were thus endangered. There was some prospect that the effective range of land-based air attack might double within a few years, driving the fleet further out to sea. Thus some within the Committee, particularly Admiral Lyster, the Fifth Sea Lord, wanted the Navy to

---

4   The Royal Navy seems to have been shocked by the sheer size of the concurrent US building programme, which reflected the difference in the two countries' industrial bases. Late in 1942 the Assistant Naval Attaché to Washington reported that the US Navy planned more than 100 carriers of which thirty-six were First Line: thirteen *Essex*es, nine *Independence*s, ten repeat *Essex*es (CV 31–40), four larger fleet carriers with armoured flight decks, sixteen ACVs (converted merchant ships), twenty-five repeat ACVs (30–54), about fifty new-type ACVs to be built on P1-type hulls. The US plan (which was not successful) was for thirteen of the new First Line carriers and all the ACVs to be in commission by the end of 1943; eight more First Line carriers were due to complete in 1944.

5   *Unicorn* was designed to support three armoured 36-aircraft carriers, so that in theory she could support two and a fraction 48-aircraft ships. The six fleet and four light carriers of the Indian Ocean Fleet (as projected in 1942) would equate to eight full fleet carriers, and would require the four operational *Unicorn*s of the 1942 future fleet.

6   The Fifth Sea Lord considered the light fleet carriers too valuable to convert, but recognized that there might be Lend-Lease complications in converting US-supplied ships for a role other than that for which they had been supplied. Conversion of HMS *Argus* was seriously considered but rejected, on the ground that she would provide little more capacity than a CVE, and with a narrower hangar.

7   In reply, in July 1942, DNC suggested general arrangements similar to those of the 1942 carrier (*Ark Royal*). The design could be completed in six months, and the ship would probably be completed at the end of 1945. Some armour would have to be re-rolled and some plates scrapped, and much would depend upon detailed Staff Requirements. The original powerplant would be used, and armament would match that of the 1942 carrier. On 28 September the First Sea Lord decided to complete the ship as a battleship, but the Committee retorted that she was being built with elderly ordnance, which would be fifty years old at the end of her expected lifetime in 1966.

PIONEER (ex-MARS)
Gr. Britain - CVL (R)
(COLOSSUS Class)
Feb. 1945

More naval aircraft required logistical support as well as carriers. The Future Building Committee was responsible for the decision to convert two light fleet carriers into aircraft repair ships. HMS Pioneer, *newly completed in February 1945, is shown.*

concentrate on very large land-based aircraft; with the new power-operated turrets, it appeared that even a very un-manoeuvrable aircraft could protect itself reasonably well. This argument failed, in its most extreme form, because although the bomber might be an effective offensive weapon, it could not efficiently defend shipping against air attack. However, the Committee did find shore-based reconnaissance and strike bombers attractive, and it therefore pressed for the Navy to take over long-range maritime aviation from the RAF.

The shore-based aircraft would generally have to be supplementary, partly because there could never be enough of them close enough to hand. A sufficient concentration of carriers could move with the fleet; the bombers could not. This was, and is, the central argument for sea-based as opposed to land-based aircraft to work with a fleet.[8]

Carriers, then, were the core of the British fleet. This was not altogether welcome; the First Sea Lord (Admiral Sir Dudley Pound) argued that in the past the core of the fleet had been a capital ship which could be defeated only by another capital ship. He considered carriers a very soft core indeed; in November 1942 the US fleet had not a single fully serviceable carrier. If the carrier were indeed the core of the fleet, then it had to be hardened.

The replies were instructive. CAOR pointed out that battleships were much more vulnerable than might be imagined. Meeting a carrier at long range, a battleship would be hit and crippled long before it came within gun range. Thus it, too, was at best a rather soft core. Carriers were still too soft, but they were hardly the most vulnerable. In August 1942 a subcommittee (DNC, DTSD, DNAD, CAOR) had been set up to consider the protection of future carriers. DNC argued strongly in September for a combination of two heavy armoured decks, one the flight deck and one over the machinery.[9] During the autumn of 1942 the Committee pressed strongly for the extra 4ft of beam in the new carrier (*Ark Royal*, see Chapter 12), both to allow 4in flight deck armour and to improve underwater protection. It still wanted more hangar side armour to defend against fast bombers striking at low levels.

The Committee's interest in carrier protection led it to propose the use of diesel aero engines, whose fuel would not present any risk of explosion. Unfortunately MAP had suspended

work on such powerplants for the duration, and the Committee's protest (November 1942) had no effect. However, the idea was sound; jet fuel (which is much like diesel fuel) finally eliminated the gas-vapour explosion threat. This in turn greatly simplified postwar carrier design and operation, as fuel no longer had to be carried in specially protected and isolated compartments. For the present, the situation became, if anything, more complicated, as the new (1943) fighters required special higher-octane fuels.[10]

D of P took a different view of carrier protection. Carriers were the primary means of forcing an action. A superior British naval force could destroy the enemy's air defences and follow up to destroy his remaining ships. Even an inferior British fleet would have to destroy the enemy's long-range artillery – his aircraft – in order to avoid a crippling action. Carrier vulnerability was being overemphasized because carriers were so scarce, not because they were inherently soft. Sufficient numbers of fighters would in fact solve most of the problems. Because they did not carry a heavy weight of guns, modern carriers could be superior to modern battleships in deck protection, and equal in underwater protection.

The Committee took these ideas to heart, and from 1943 to 1945 it pressed for larger and more capacious – and harder – fleet carriers. Its advocacy of these principles in November 1942 seems to have shaped the *Ark Royals*. The chief requirements for the *Maltas* were also very much an expression of its ideas. On 23 November 1942 the Committee decided that future carriers would carry no more than sixty aircraft (which would have made repeat *Ark Royals* acceptable) and that the existing standard of 30 to 31 knots would be retained.

However, the conditions on both of these requirements drove carrier size up to the limit of British building facilities, to produce not repeat ships but the much larger *Maltas*.

First, the 60-aircraft figure was interpreted as hangar capacity, though by February 1943 the Royal Navy was commonly using deck parks. The Future Building Committee recommended that permanent deck parks be incorporated in future carrier designs, and that flight decks be laid out to allow for easy handling and parking. Deck parks in turn made for many more aircraft per carrier; *Victorious*, for example, was rated at thirty-three to thirty-six, but carried fifty-one in temperate waters. More aircraft required more personnel. DNC claimed a standard margin of 15 per cent in accommodation, but this tended to be consumed by post-design modifications.

Second, the aircraft were becoming much larger. Future types (see below) would probably be 48ft long, and they would not fit 50ft lifts. DNC could offer two 54 x 44ft lifts in a new design, but not three, and any increase in width would be

Table 13-1: Future Fleet (First Interim Report, November 1942)

	CV	CVL	CVE	BB	Cr	DD
Home Fleet	6	—	4	3	9	36
North Atlantic Trade Protection	—	—	30	—	—	—
Force H (mid-Atlantic)	2	—	—	1	2	12
South Atlantic	—	6	10	—	3	14[1]
Indian Ocean (Main Fleet)	6	—	—	2	7	30[3]
Indian Ocean (anti-raider, convoy)	—	4	15	—	3	14
Total Operational	14	10	50	6	24	106
Training	—	2	4	—	—	—
Total	14	12	54	6	24	106
With allowances for refits	22	19	83	9	50	191

Note The report also called for 300 submarines. Operational auxiliaries: 4 *Unicorns*, 7 aircraft replenishment ships (*Athenes*), 8 special oilers (20-knot), 25 16-knot oilers. With allowances for refits, this equated to 5 *Unicorns*, 10 aircraft replenishment ships, 10 20-knot and 40 16-knot oilers. Note also that the October 1942 version of the report showed 42 cruisers and 162 destroyers.
1 3 of the CVL and all 10 CVE were for convoy escort.
2 Allowances for refits: availability will average 65 per cent for carriers for all types, 70 for BB, 65 for cruisers, 64 for destroyers.
3 Two of the fleet carriers for reinforcement.

8   The Committee did not make the other important argument, that an aircraft based several thousand (or even several hundred) miles away could not be relied upon to be in position to deal with a sudden emergency, such as a surprise air attack or an unexpected submarine attack.

9   At this time his department was experimenting with a combination powerplant combining two 'tractor' screws forward with two shafts, to reduce vulnerability to hits aft.

10   The higher the octane, the scarcer the fuel. Thus the carrier designers had to plan for two fuels, standard aviation petrol for strike aircraft, and 120 (later 150 or even 170) octane for high-performance fighters.

difficult as long as the flight deck was used as the strength deck. He questioned the need for such equipment, as he doubted that the 48ft figure would ever be reached.[11]

A third factor was tactical. By early 1944 the Fifth Sea Lord had become convinced (largely by reports of US operations in the Pacific) that a carrier had to be able to fly off her entire air complement in one continuous operation. This required an open hangar and US-style deck-edge lifts, and it led in turn to the final *Malta* design (see Chapter 14).

The 30-knot speed was needed to fly off aircraft in a flat calm. Alternatively, it could be argued that with catapults and other assisted take-off devices, the requirement for high carrier speed, and hence for escort speed, could be relaxed. The strongly expressed counter-argument was that every knot of carrier speed helped the aircraft designer seeking higher performance in his aircraft. There was, after all, a relationship between maximum speed and stalling (take-off and landing) speeds. This relationship could be relaxed somewhat through special devices such as reversible-pitch propellers or brake parachutes (for landing with limited wind over the deck). In theory, this issue could be settled only by operational experience with the 25-knot light fleet carriers; earlier war experience, however, certainly showed the value of speed. The Fifth Sea Lord (Rear Admiral D W Boyd) recalled that existing carriers with nominal 30-knot speeds were actually rather slower. Because HMS *Illustrious* was effectively limited to 28 knots in 1940, at Taranto her Swordfish required longer deck runs, which in turn limited the number which could be ranged on deck. He wanted future carrier speed to be equal to that of US carriers (33 knots) or the German *Graf Zeppelin* (34 knots).

DNC suggested that a lengthened *Ark Royal* could make the newly required 33-knot trial speed, and he developed that design as an alternative to what became *Malta* (see Chapter 14). However, other factors led to the demand for a much larger ship.

Even so, the Committee was an early proponent of the catapult as the primary means of launching aircraft. Its studies of future naval aircraft (see below) revealed the extent to which performance was limited by the need to make rolling take-offs in the available wind over deck. The heavier the aircraft, the longer the rolling take-off and consequently the smaller the space available for deck parking – and the smaller the effective strike. Ultimately the whole deck would not suffice. In mid-1943, when the Committee wrote about them, rolling take-offs were still preferred because they could be made more quickly. The Committee saw, however, that in future assisted take-offs might actually be made more quickly, particularly if two or more catapults could be arranged to fire one after the other. Carrier tactics might change radically.

This was prophetic: by 1945 catapults were indeed the primary means of launching heavily-loaded naval aircraft. They made mass strikes by such aircraft possible. Wartime catapult development also made early carrier jet operation practical (though jets soon required several generations of new catapults).

In 1944-45 the Committee was concerned with future aircraft requirements, which would shape the big carrier (HMS *Malta*, see Chapter 14) then in the design stage. Under the Committee's pressure, the most modern land-based piston fighters had been adapted to naval service, within the constraints imposed by existing carriers. A Mosquito was successfully deck-landed in April 1944, and in November 1944 a Spitfire XXI, a type not yet in full RAF service. The third prototype Hawker Fury, the newest RAF piston interceptor, was the prototype for the navalized Sea Fury, and the Hornet, the fastest British twin-engined conventional fighter, was adapted for naval use.

Unfortunately, it was by no means clear that conventional carriers could realize anything like the full potential of the next generation of aircraft, the jets. In September 1944 the Committee's Aircraft Design Sub-Committee recommended that effort should be concentrated on a jet interceptor, and by that December there was some hope that such an aircraft would be available for deck trials in the autumn of 1945.[12] It was already clear that such a fighter would demand catapult-only launching and that no other aircraft could be within 30ft of it when its engine opened up to full power.

However, it was also clear that jet operation offered considerable advantages. There would no longer be a propeller requiring ground clearance, and in December 1944 the Sub-Committee proposed that future naval aircraft be designed without undercarriages, to land on soft (flexible) decks. This proposal led directly to postwar experiments, culminating in successful deck trials aboard the light fleet carrier *Warrior* (see Chapter 15), but ultimately the idea was dropped.

For the present, conventional design practice would have to be followed. Ships already under construction (*Hermes* and *Ark Royal*) would suffice for existing aircraft, but only a very large carrier would allow naval aircraft to grow to their potential. Much the same argument was being made in the United States at the same time, but the record does not suggest any interchange of views between the two navies. The Fifth Sea Lord himself pressed the argument for the largest carrier a British yard could build, or a British drydock maintain; there was even serious consideration of building a new dockyard on the Clyde to support a very large new carrier.

Fighters were no great problem, and all could probably be operated by a large light carrier such as HMS *Hermes*. Strike aircraft were a different proposition. Up to 1945 the pressure had been for increased individual performance (range and payload), on the grounds that even a few aircraft would probably penetrate weak defences. However, this seemed to be changing, and in future large numbers of fast aircraft (albeit of limited range), probably carrying 2000lb loads, would be needed, supported by long-range reconnaissance aircraft. The longer the reconnaissance range, the better the chance of achieving surprise and maintaining the initiative in battle. Surprise would also be valuable in shore strikes, as it would make counter-strikes against a carrier force less likely.

By 1949-50 jets and twin-engined night fighters would be in service. The use of catapults would allow most of the flight deck to be used for parking. High-lift devices might allow a fighter of given performance to be smaller, but the requisite level of performance would surely continue to rise, so aircraft would continue to grow. Moreover, it was possible that jets might be difficult to land, and hence might need very long decks.

A large carrier would also benefit from many economies of scale, for instance in propulsion and accommodation. These arguments were tempered by problems of limited slip and drydock size; in the end the Board's tentative decision was to build a large carrier, but not quite as large as the one Fifth Sea Lord wanted (see Chapter 14).

The Committee also spent much of its time comparing US and British carrier practice. The US Navy depended much more on arrester gear, since it used large deck parks. Typical US fleet carriers had twenty-nine wires (including, however, some at the bow), compared to eight in British ships. Moreover, US arrester gear was designed for much harsher deceleration than British. The Committee suggested that British carriers could, with advantage, have more arrester wires. The Committee also preferred the US-type crash barrier, which was supported from the deck, to the British type incorporating stan-

11   In fact the longest World War II-era British naval aircraft, the Fairey Spearfish, was 45ft long. Postwar jets were much longer, for example 55ft 7in for the de Havilland Sea Vixen.

12   The first British carrier jet landing was by a converted Vampire land-based fighter, aboard HMS *Ocean*, on 3 December 1945.

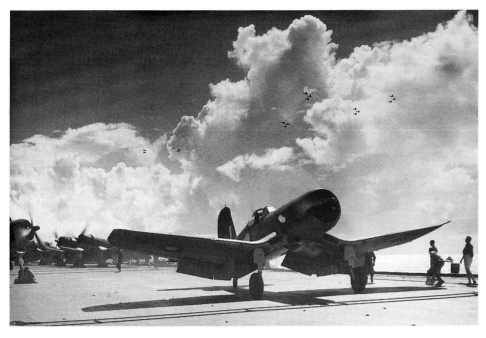

The wartime Royal Navy could afford to adopt short-range RAF interceptors because the United States supplied longer-range fighters suitable for escort work. These Corsairs are shown aboard a British fleet carrier in 1944. The double wire in the foreground is a crash barrier.

13   Plus twenty-five fleet and seventeen intermediate destroyers, forty-eight submarines (six to be built in HM Dockyards), one Depot Ship, and eighty-three twin- and forty-five single-screw Corvettes (already approved in addition to 1940, 1941, 1942 programmes).

14   Their underwater protection was designed to resist 750lbs of TNT, but the new Japanese aerial torpedo dropped by shore-based aircraft was rated at 867lbs.

chions: bombs or depth charges underwing could hit the stanchions in a crash. It was also the Future Building Committee which pressed for standardization between the two navies, for example in hangar clear height (17ft 6in in US ships, as little as 14ft in British).

THE 1943 BUILDING PROGRAMME was the first subject to detailed Committee review (in November 1942). It initially included a single cruiser, but this was deemed impractical; it was better to spread three among the three available firms, so that at least one would be built in time. However, the Committee considered the existing design obsolete, and was unwilling to perpetuate it with three more. It concluded that no cruisers should be built in 1943. DNC suggested four fleet carriers and nine light carriers (of which three might be completed as Aircraft Repair Ships).[13] At this time the fleet carrier was *Ark Royal*, and the extra beam would preclude Swan Hunter from building it. However, the Committee hoped that capacity could be traded off between cruisers and carriers at Swan Hunter and at Vickers (Walker Yard).

The matter was submitted to the Board for decision, and the programme was set at four fleet carriers (one of *Ark Royal* type, the others much larger, the *Malta* class, to fit the three available large-ship slips), and eight light fleet carriers of enlarged design

Table 13-2: Available Slips, 1945

March 1945
4 cruisers (1 vice *Tiger* if cancelled)
7 Battle class
4 Weapon class
September 1945
6 cruisers (1 vice *Tiger* if cancelled)
1 fleet carrier or battleship
14 Battle class
9 Weapon class

Two slips would thus be left available and, on these and other large warship slips as they become empty, competition would lie between cruisers, fast oilers and aircraft maintenance ships.

(*Hermes* class). Early in 1944 it appeared that one of the 1943 fleet carriers might complete in 1948, another in 1949, and the completion dates of the last two were uncertain. Of the light fleet carriers, two were expected to complete in 1946 and two in 1947, the completion dates of the others being uncertain. Most of the work was actually done postwar, and this under very different conditions, and none of these dates proved even remotely realistic (the 1943 fleet carriers were never completed).

By March 1943 the official British forecast was that the war against Germany would end during 1944, and against Japan in 1946. Only fleet carriers already under construction could, therefore, be ready in time to fight Japan. CAOR pointed out that new light fleet carriers could still be completed in time, and that two should be built for every 1943 fleet carrier, say six at the cost of three fleet carriers. The only drawback to this policy of building only light fleet carriers for the moment was that no fleet carriers might be built in future. CAOR somewhat naively imagined that postwar Boards would be sufficiently resolute to overcome this problem.

He also had to bear in mind that the core of the Navy would be considerably softer if it consisted only of unarmoured light fleet carriers. The new *Ark Royal* (the 1942 fleet carrier) was expected to operate $2\frac{1}{2}$ times as many aircraft (fifty-seven to sixty-nine as against twenty-eight), more easily and efficiently, and was both much faster and much harder (CAOR estimated that she could take three times as many hits before suffering equivalent damage). She could also develop equally effective fire against three times as many enemy aircraft, not to mention the effect of her 4.5in guns, which the light carrier lacked altogether.

CAOR estimated that a light fleet carrier could spoil a quarter of an enemy attack (three-quarters of the attackers would penetrate); the corresponding *Ark Royal* figure would be the cube of $\frac{3}{4}$, $\frac{27}{64}$, so that it would take about seven times the air effort to achieve the same degree of penetration. If one *Ark Royal* was considered equivalent to three, then an enemy would have to expend $\frac{7}{3}$ the air effort to put an equivalent British force out of action.

The Chairman considered it unrealistic to accept the official forecasts. The war might even end in an armed truce, and in any case Britain would have to retain her maritime status postwar. The US Navy was building very large carriers (the *Midways*), and without comparable ships the Royal Navy would surely be reduced to a secondary role either at the end of the war (in the Pacific, where loss of face mattered) or postwar. The existing six prewar-designed armoured ships carried too few aircraft, could not operate the newer types then being designed, and could not stand up to existing underwater weapons.[14] Nor could they be standardized with the latest US ships in the Pacific. Fast large carriers were essential to operate sufficient numbers of future naval aircraft.

The 1944 Programme came up for discussion in December 1943. By this time very few large slips were available; D of P listed what could be laid down (see Table 13-2). At this time the British government believed that the war would not extend beyond 1947, so that only ships completing before the end of that year could contribute to it. Any beyond that point would have to be justified by the need to assure the postwar position of the British Empire as a first class maritime power.

The need for carriers was still urgent. The British shipbuilding industry, however, was already so badly stretched that much of the programme approved in 1943 had not yet been laid down. D of P suggested that some of these ships be shifted to the 1944 programme; see Table 13-3. They had to compete with two other programmes: more LSTs were needed, and as

The Sea Mosquito began as an interim test aircraft, to prepare the way for the Short Sturgeon. Tests were so successful that it became a preferable alternative to the Sturgeon as a long-range carrier strike bomber. Performance was so impressive that in the autumn of 1944 the Admiralty saw in carrier-based Mosquitoes a means of offering something American carriers could not match. This is a TR.33, the first production version, with American-supplied ASH radar. The prototype flew on 10 November 1945, and the original contract for ninety-seven was cut to fifty. They served with No 811 Squadron at Ford from August 1946 to July 1947. The TR.37, six of which were built, was a developed version with a larger sea search radar (ASV.XIII) in the nose. These aircraft were quite distinct from the twenty-four RAF Mosquito IVs (and three PR XVI) of 618 Squadron, intended for a carrier-based strike against the Japanese fleet, using a spinning bomb (the Highball). On 31 October 1944 the Squadron sailed for Australia aboard the escort carriers Fencer *and* Striker, *arriving at Melbourne on 23 December. It was, however, disbanded in July 1945 and its 125 Highballs were destroyed, largely because of fears that the weapon's unique design would be revealed in combat.*

the war shifted to the Pacific a large fleet train had to be created. In addition, many ships had to be refitted for service in the Far East.[15]

D of P proposed that the 1943 fleet carriers be postponed because they would absorb much of the available capacity. The fleet would receive more aircraft faster if the light carriers already on the slip were accelerated. He therefore approved suspending the laying down of *Malta* and *New Zealand* to the fourth quarter of 1944 and the second quarter of 1945, respectively, with *Gibraltar* and the smaller *Africa* postponed until the work could be undertaken without delaying the completion of urgently required ships which might actually be ready in time. D of P also pointed out that to build all four would consume capacity required for the two new battleships the Admiralty then planned. Later in February 1944, therefore, the first two were postponed to some time in 1945, and the last two deferred altogether. Matters would become even worse if (as occurred) a

follow-up LST programme was approved. In fact none of the 1943 fleet carriers was laid down, partly because the design adopted in 1943 was rejected in mid-1944 and then completely recast, no approved design existing at the end of the war (see Chapter 14).

Similarly, limits on British shipbuilding capacity, particularly those imposed by the ongoing LST programme, made it impossible to lay down four of the eight 1943 light fleet carriers, even though they were clearly much more satisfactory than the 1942 ships. *Bulwark* and *Arrogant* had to be delayed to the first and second quarters of 1945 (when more capacity would become available), and *Monmouth* and *Polyphemus* postponed until their construction would not conflict with other work.

By this time considerable thought was being devoted to the special problems of war in the East. Carriers would have to operate far from their bases, that is, far from the sources of aircraft supply. The Prime Minister, Winston Churchill, suggested a 'feeder ship' which could supply eight or ten carriers, but this was impractical. The First Sea Lord considered it best, as a short-term policy, to provide relief squadrons aboard relief assault carriers (escort carriers) complete with their fighters for self-defence. Other expedients, such as ferry carriers or carriers used as stepping stones for self-ferrying aircraft, were rejected as sometimes but not always useful. There were also some abortive studies of carrying aircraft aboard large fast tankers, perhaps with flight decks.

A year later matters had changed yet again. With the end of the war clearly in sight, D of P framed policy in January 1945 to release as much building capacity as possible to reconstruct the British merchant fleet, which he considered essential for economic recovery. Warship building would be treated as a cushion to ensure full employment in the industry. He suggested that all four 1943 carriers (three *Maltas* and *Africa*) be deferred altogether, particularly in view of uncertainties concerning the value of such massive ships. The three 1942 fleet carriers (*Ark Royals*) would be built, together with four of the eight planned 1943 light fleet carriers (the other four being deferred). This was much what happended, except that one of the remaining 1942 fleet carriers was later cancelled. Unfortunately the fleet and light carriers interfered with civilian construction (for example, of liners), and they could not be pushed

15 For example, the 1943 programme was disrupted partly because LCT production had to be assigned to warship yards. This was not uniquely a British problem; the US Navy also had to choose between landing craft and escorts.

Once restrictions on carrier aircraft size had been dramatically relaxed, the Fleet Air Arm could adopt large twin-engine types. This Sea Hornet day fighter is shown aboard HMS Implacable, *postwar.*

forward nearly as fast as the Royal Navy might have liked.

This in turn raised a serious question. Only the 1942 fleet carriers and the 1943 fleet and light carriers would be able to operate the new heavy aircraft expected to enter service about 1946–47 (Sturgeon, Spearfish and Wyvern), not to mention the jets which would follow. Survivors from among the six older armoured carriers and the fourteen light fleet carriers would be limited to existing types of limited performance, such as the American-supplied Hellcat, Corsair and Avenger and the British Seafire, Firefly and Barracuda. The older ships would have either to be restricted to fighters or else rebuilt at considerable expense. It seemed unlikely that the nation could afford to build further new carriers soon after the end of a very costly war.

This made the surviving modern carriers, the three *Ark Royal*s and the four 1943 light fleet carriers, particularly important. D of P assumed that they would suffice for the postwar fleet, so that the *Malta*s could safely be deferred pending operating experience, and until the yards were less congested.

Even in January 1945 there was some fear that the larger

carriers would never be built, so that after the war the Royal Navy would find itself without any carriers embodying the very latest ideas. Alternative possibilities were to build one carrier to a modified (and smaller) *Malta* design; or to redesign some or all of the deferred four light fleet carriers (*Hermes* class), or to complete all eight of the *Hermes* class to the existing design. In the end, only six ships were completed, but all to more or less modernized designs.

THE COMMITTEE CONDUCTED a parallel study of naval aircraft requirements. Its interim report (February 1943) shaped British naval aircraft policy for the remainder of the war.

The first essential was very long-range (3000nm) open-ocean reconnaissance, and the Committee recommended a very large multi-engine shore-based aircraft. Although it might be bomber-sized, it could not be a converted bomber, because it would operate mainly at relatively low altitude and at low speed (200 to 250mph), relying on a 100nm radar, with which it could sweep 4000 square miles per hour in a straight run, or 80,000 square miles (about 1 per cent of the North Atlantic) in a 20-hour sortie.

Such strategic reconnaissance would have two roles. First, it would guide the fleet into position for combat. Second, it would guide other land-based long-range strikes, perhaps by a related heavy blind-bomber (to avoid fighter opposition). Because strategic reconnaissance could not be continuous enough to guide strike aircraft, particularly in the face of enemy air opposition, the fleet would need its own short-range search capability.

The ideal solution was a very fast short range-aircraft roughly comparable to a Mosquito, relying on evasion for survival. It would normally be carrier-based, although in some circumstances it might fly from shore bases against nearby coasts (for instance Norway).

The actual strikes, at ranges up to about 500nm, would be made by a twin-engined carrier-based bomber, using conventional bombs and torpedoes, rockets, B bombs, and spinning weapons.[16]

The Committee initially concluded that neither the strike nor the reconnaissance aircraft could be escorted effectively, since heavy long-range fighters probably could not compete with short-range interceptors.[17] This amounted to total rejection of the standard large two-seat F/R, typified by the Fulmar and Firefly. Eliminating these necessarily large aircraft, in turn, would free relatively scarce hangar and deck park space for more strike aircraft. The other major fighter type was the interceptor, typified by the Seafire, intended to fight nearly directly

Table 13-3: Projected 1944 Programme (January 1944)

2 1943 fleet carriers, approved but not laid down, to go into this programme
2 1943 fleet carriers, delayed, to be postponed
2 1943 light fleet carriers, delayed, to be included in this programme
2 1943 light fleet carriers, delayed, to be postponed [[included]
5 5.25in cruisers [6in cruisers]
22 destroyers [fleet type]
20 A class submarines [deleted]
5 sloops (3 reinstated from 1941 and 1942)
2 aircraft maintenance ships in lieu of 2 1942 light fleet carriers
2 20-knot fleet tankers
6 1500-ton capacity fleet attendant tankers
6 3000-ton capacity fleet attendant tankers
32 MTBs

Note Changes to 10 February are shown in square brackets.

The 20-knot fleet tankers were later deleted because there was no building capacity. They would have taken longer to build than standard commercial tankers.

over the fleet. It required, above all, a high rate of climb, since at least some of the interceptors had to be launched on warning of the approach of enemy aircraft. The accepted fighter tactic was to maintain such aircraft on combat air patrol (CAP) stations over the fleet, but limited endurance on such patrols was quite acceptable. Interceptors were needed even if escort fighters could be abandoned. From a ship point of view, they took up much less space (per aircraft) and consumed less fuel per mission.[18]

The best existing US naval fighters, the Hellcat and Corsair, more nearly approximated the prewar British escort fighter concept, except for the absence of a navigator. Like the Firefly and Fulmar, they had been conceived as strike escorts, albeit within less constricting requirements for take-off, landing and all-up weight. Thus there was no suitable US alternative to a British-developed carrier interceptor. A US Hellcat (F6F-5), for example, had a combat radius of 340nm, and climbed at 2980ft per minute. The Seafire LIIC climbed almost twice as fast, at 4380ft per minute, but its combat radius was only about 140nm.[19]

The Committee laid down that, from now on, carrier interceptor fighters should be the equals (in performance) of their land counterparts. This was actually quite radical; although the Seafire III, just entering service, approached this ideal, existing naval fighters such as the Fulmar were much slower than their land-based counterparts.

Some carrier fighters would have to operate at night, as within a few years a radar-equipped enemy would be able to detect and strike ships at night or in bad weather; indeed, within about five years, attack under such conditions might be the rule rather than the exception. Presumably the night fighter would be a modified carrier bomber without bombs or armour. To be truly effective, it had to have two engines (to leave the nose free for a large radar dish), and two crew members (to allow for a dedicated radar operator). Unfortunately, existing carrier lifts were probably not large enough for high-performance two-seat fighters.[20] They could not be enlarged because that would entail larger cuts in strength decks. This argued for a British equivalent of the new US single-seat night fighters, with their relatively small (but convenient) wing-mounted radars. This was acceptable on an interim basis, since neither the Germans nor the Japanese had demonstrated a capability for mass attacks at night or in bad weather.

The sheer number of fighters required was also an important consideration, both for future carrier design and to determine just how small fighters had to be to fit existing ships in sufficient quantity. At first (January 1943), it appeared that fighters could usually be limited to about a quarter of all carrier aircraft. British practice was to group carriers tightly (with a separation of 2nm) for mutual support, up to four carriers operating together.

Contemporary US practice was to keep carriers at least 10nm apart, too far for mutual support. The US Navy provided each fleet carrier with two fighter squadrons (thirty-six aircraft) for a combination of self-protection and strike escort. By April, the Committee reluctantly concluded that, whatever its ideal practice, the Royal Navy would have to assume that its carriers might often be separated, and therefore that each carrier would have to provide enough fighters (thirty to thirty-six) to protect itself. Because this was an absolute, rather than a proportional, requirement, it had particularly unfortunate implications for ships whose capacity, even counting a permanent deck park, was only fifty-one aircraft. Thus much larger carriers, such as *Malta*, became much more attractive.

The total elimination of escort fighters was soon recognized as a future ideal rather than a near-term possibility. Existing strike aircraft could not survive without escorts, and some existing fighters (particularly the Hellcat) were still suited for escort duty. A new RAF long-range fighter (F.12/43, the de Havilland Hornet), seemed suitable for medium-term escort requirements. By September 1943 this requirement was considered important enough for the Fifth Sea Lord to call for the design of a naval version to begin as soon as the RAF design was complete, and before the prototype flew. This saved considerable time, and the prototype Sea Hornet (N.5/44) flew on 19 April 1945, less than a year after the RAF prototype (28 July 1944). It promised the necessary range, the RAF claiming (in 1943) 1150 miles at economical speed, and 1500 with drop tanks. De Havilland claimed (correctly) that it could solve the problem of folding wooden wings, but its design staff was very hard-pressed; the first Sea Hornet prototype had a hook but fixed wings. There was one other problem: the Hornet was so clean (to reach high maximum speed) that it was expected to land-on much faster than had hitherto been accepted, at 85–90 knots, and there seemed to be no hope of achieving a lower speed without extensive redesign.

The interceptor problem was more urgent: the existing Seafire III was being outclassed by new German fighters. The only near-term possibility was a navalized version of the new Griffon-engined Spitfire, the Seafire XV (N.3/43), since the Spitfire was the only British interceptor in production. For 1944 the Committee proposed the laminar-wing Spitfire XXI (tentatively named Victor, and later renamed Spiteful).[21] It became the Seafang (N.5/45). Beyond 1944, the choice would be determined first by the RAF's choice of a Spitfire successor. The Committee expected jets to enter naval service in about 1946 or 1947.

---

18 Standard British doctrine (as expressed in the 1942 handbook on naval air warfare and in the 1947 Fighting Instructions) was to maintain CAPs over a fleet. However, it was always recognized that CAPs would have to be replenished by ready aircraft on deck, so that this practice may have been closer to what would now be considered reliance on deck-launched interceptors (DLI). Any reliance on DLI would make fast climb speeds essential. By way of contrast, a properly-directed CAP fighter could in theory be stationed above the incoming bombers, diving (preferably out of the sun) to attack them. With limited-endurance interceptors sustaining a CAP required frequent launching and recovery, which was particularly onerous when the fleet was steaming with the wind. During the Pedestal (Malta convoy) operation of 1942, for example, HMS *Indomitable* had to turn into the wind thirty-seven times in one day, in the course of launching and recovering seventy-eight sorties. This was a large number for the Royal Navy, but in one day at Tulagi, three US carriers launched a total of 230 sorties, though these numbers were probably not comparable, because the US carriers would have launched more aircraft at any one time. These figures are taken from a 1943 British report on multi-carrier operations, suggesting that frequent turns for launch and recovery would complicate carrier operating formations. According to J D Brown, *Carrier Fighters* (Macdonald & Jane's, London, 1975), British carrier fighter interceptor tactics initially placed the aircraft in a holding circle before vectoring them out, but by 1941 aircraft were typically launched and im-

mediately vectored to make flank attacks on their targets. Brown equates this change with improvements in the skill of the fighter directors, but it would also correspond to a shift from relatively slow long-endurance aircraft (Fulmars) which could orbit at relatively low cost, to deck-launched higher-performance interceptors such as Sea Hurricanes and, later, Seafires. For the Pedestal convoy in August 1942 the plan was to maintain a CAP of fast-climbing Wildcats (Martlets) at medium altitude, with the slower-climbing Hurricanes above them (so they could dive on their targets); during the most dangerous period, eighteen fighters would be maintained in the air at all times, and another eighteen ready on deck for DLI. If attack was imminent, another twelve fighters would be flown off, for a total of forty-eight, from three carriers (*Eagle*, *Indomitable* and *Victorious*). At Okinawa in 1945 British practice was to use a section of Seafires at low level, a section of Seafires and one of slower-climbing Hellcats or Corsairs at middle level, and one of Corsairs at high level, with further ready aircraft on deck. This was described as a 'stacked' CAP.

19 The US Navy produced only one true interceptor during the war, the Grumman F8F Bearcat, which climbed at 5610ft per minute, but had a combat radius of only 216nm (with a drop tank). Hellcat radius was also with a drop tank. Clean, the Hellcat could be out-climbed by the FM-2 Wildcat (developed F4F-3; it climbed at 3600ft per minute), but it was much faster in level flight. US figures are from standard BuAer Aircraft Characteristics Charts.

20 For the short term, the only available twin-engine night fighters were the Beaufighter and Mosquito. The Beaufighter would be too high (when folded) to fit several existing carriers, although the future *Ark Royal* could accommodate it. The Mosquito would fit, but its wooden construction did not seem to allow for wing-folding. In the event, that particular problem was solved.

21 The Griffon-engined Spitfire 21 was an entirely different aircraft.

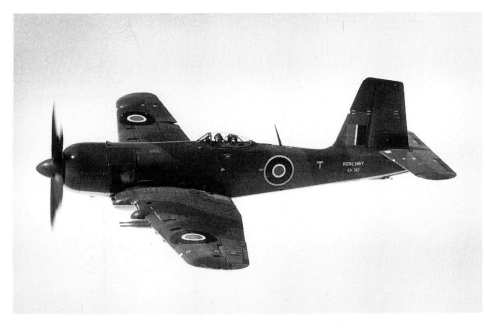

Although it was not part of the Future Building Committee's integrated strike aircraft programme, the Firebrand survived as a strike fighter. This is a TF.5, the final production version. About forty of the earlier TF.4s (of which a total of 102 were built) were modified to TF.5 standard (with horn-balanced elevators and longer aileron tabs), and sixty-eight more were built. Firebrands served with Nos 813 (Illustrious, Implacable and Indefatigable) and 827 (Eagle) Squadrons. A much-modified development flew as the Blackburn Firecrest, and a further development, to S.10/45, was never built: the Wyvern offered much better performance.

22   The Seafire XV and navalized Spitfire XXI were unique among British-built fighters of this time in having weapons of other than 20mm calibre.

23   MAP estimated that the Hawker fighter would climb to 20,000ft in just over 5 minutes, and that it would achieve a maximum speed of 437mph at 21,000ft. Folland estimated that its fighter would make the climb in just under 5 minutes, and that it would achieve 469mph at 20,000ft at an all-up weight of 11,042lbs (compared to 11,140lbs for Hawker). There was some hope, later in 1943, that an Exe 45-engined Folland would make 500mph. The other prospective advantages of a navalized F.19/43 were reduced folded height (the folded height of the navalized Hawker Fury had to be reduced from 15ft 10in to 15ft 9in) and longer endurance. MAP and the Admiralty tried to expedite the Folland design by linking that firm with English Electric, but the combination failed. By early 1944, moreover, the Folland fighter's width could not be brought within 21ft 4in, and in other ways the design no longer seemed so promising. It had to be killed when the Air Ministry decided to drop it. At that time estimated characteristics were: all-up weight, 11,237lbs, span, 36ft 6in (21ft 4in folded) × 35ft 10½in × (within) 13ft 6in; speed, 375mph at sea level, 225mph at 20,000, 480mph at 26,000ft; endurance, 1.9 hours (190 gallons), 3.7 hours with 90 gallons in drop tanks. Endurance figures allowed for warm up, take-off, climb to 20,000ft, 15 minutes combat there, and 20 minutes at the most economical cruising speed at 2000ft while loitering to land. The navalized Folland was liked for its longer endurance and its lower folded height.

The Committee's scheduling proved rather too optimistic. In September 1943 the Seafire XV prototypes were delayed, first flying only in 1944. The Spiteful was expected late in 1944, and its laminar wing was credited with an improvement of 25 to 30mph. There was some question as to whether the small Supermarine design team could develop a naval version quickly enough. One alternative was a navalized Spitfire XIV, which could achieve about the same speed with its non-laminar wing, but which would not be as good at high altitude. At this time Supermarine was producing 100 Mk XIVs with two-stage supercharged Griffon engines (which could not go into a Seafire XV), and 400 conversion kits to convert Merlin-powered Spitfire VIIIs into Mk XIVs. In the event, the Griffon Spitfire was redesigned as the Spitfire F.21.

By February 1944 the highest priority was being accorded the Seafire XV, first deliveries of which were expected in July. Unlike contemporary RAF fighters, it would have only two 20mm cannon (and four .303s, which might later be replaced by .50s).[22]

For the future, the laminar-flow Spiteful seemed too risky (although it might be revived later). Instead, the decision was to tool up for a navalized version of the Spitfire F.21 as soon as the German war ended. Its folded width of 19ft 4in would have to be accepted, as any reduction would also reduce its performance, but any means possible would be used to reduce folded height from 15ft 11in to 15ft 9in. Interceptor performance was so important that fixed wings might be acceptable in early aircraft. With successive modifications, this became Seafire 45 to 47.

Draft Staff Requirements for the 1943 Supplementary Programme Single-Seat Carrier Fighter (the Seafire replacement) give some idea of naval priorities. First, it had to fit carrier hangars, so height was limited to 17ft tail-down, with 14ft (for *Implacable* hangars) preferable. Maximum height while being folded and spread was 20ft. Rolling take-offs were still the rule, so the new fighter had to take off (with 27 knots wind over deck) within 500ft (to leave space aft to range aircraft). Maximum landing speed was 75 knots at two-thirds full power, a figure set by existing arrester gear.

A normal interception sortie would involve no more than 1¾ hours at maximum economical cruising speed (out and back) at 25,000ft (that is, a combat radius of about 130nm or less at 150 knots), and 15 minutes of combat at 15,000ft, the fighter being vectored to dive at incoming attackers. The design would,

however, allow for two self-sealing drop tanks providing another two hours' endurance (say 150nm more combat radius) at maximum economical crusing speed. The designer was to aim at the best possible performance up to 25,000ft, and at a service ceiling of not less than 35,000ft. Since it was possible that carriers might have to deal with high-altitude shadowers or attackers, the design had to incorporate an alternative engine suitable for combat at 35,000ft and allowing for a service ceiling of 42,000ft.

The staff preferred an air-cooled radial engine to existing liquid-cooled types.

Armament would be the usual quartet of 20mm cannon (150rpg on average) arranged for a combat range of about 500 yards, and the fighter would be armoured against 20mm AP rounds at 400 yards.

Electronic requirements included the usual VHF radio-telephone, IFF, a homing beacon receiver – and night fighter radar, if a suitable type could be developed.

Formal studies were submitted by Fairey, Hawker, Folland, Boulton Paul, Westland and R T Youngman (sponsored by Fairey). The best of the conventional proposals, which could be ordered off the drawing board, were Hawker (a new Tempest, which became the Sea Fury) and Folland variants of their proposed new RAF interceptors, to Specification F.2/43 and F.19/43, respectively.

Some of the other firms offered much more radical possibilities, a mixed piston-jet powerplant, a buried engine, and a pusher. Analysis of the unconventional submissions suggested that mixed propulsion (propeller for cruise, jet for take-off, climb and combat) might be promising. Both the buried engine and the pusher promised superior pilot view, both for fighting and for deck landing. Variable incidence wings and tricycle undercarriage were also attractive, but they added too much structural weight, about 2 per cent in each case. Whatever their promise, the unconventional designs carried considerable technical risk, and could not be ordered without prototyping. Therefore they could not enter service nearly as quickly as the more conventional designs.

Of the two best conventional proposals, Folland promised somewhat better performance, but it lacked sufficient production resources.[23] The choice, then, was either Hawker (which was not very much inferior), or to join the Folland design team to a large production firm. In either case, the Navy would enjoy the production advantages of joining in a large RAF production run. In the event, only the Hawker fighter was built. Prototypes of the Folland were ordered, but they never materialized.

However, by mid-1944 the policy of adapting RAF fighters was being re-thought, and ACNS (A) called for a new specially designed naval fighter.

Throughout, fighter production was a problem because naval fighters had an operational life of, at most, eighteen months. Thus the requirement was about 140 per month, but constant changes (due to very rapidly changing technology) made this difficult to achieve in practice. Planned peak Seafire production was about 125 per month, for example, but it was never attained. In order to achieve an average rate of 140 per month, CNR hoped to obtain capacity for 210 per month in 1944.

ECONOMY OF SCALE demanded that, apart from the very long-range aircraft, the ideal carrier should operate the same types (reconnaissance and short-range bomber) as the shore bases. Whether this was practical depended on such factors as flight deck length, carrier speed and catapult capacity. The US Navy officially considered the 50,000-ton *Midway* the minimum carrier in which such a goal could be met, and it urged the Royal Navy not to be afraid of sheer size. This advice directly inspired the *Malta* design (see Chapter 14). It appears that the 30,000lb limit on aircraft weight adopted at about this time was an expression of the same goal.

An unexpressed aspect of this policy was that the Royal Navy depended so heavily on US aircraft that it could not really afford to build ships unable to operate future US types. As an example, the British designers had to stiffen their arrester gear to match US practice.[24] Similarly, the hangars in new British carriers had to be enlarged to match the standard American clearance of 17ft 6in (see Chapter 12 for the effects on the *Ark Royal* design).

The two big shore-based aircraft (reconnaissance and strike) could not be developed during the war, particularly since the Royal Navy did not have statutory authority to control such types (it exercised only operational control over Coastal Command, and relinquished that control postwar).

However, the Committee's programme of long-range unescorted carrier-based strike and reconnaissance aircraft did shape future naval development. A series of design studies showed that torpedo-bombing, dive-bombing and reconnaissance could not be reconciled in a single high-performance design, partly because three crewmen were required. Therefore the unitary torpedo/dive-bomber/reconnaissance class (TBR) represented by the Barracuda had to be abandoned in favour of separate reconnaissance-bomber (primarily reconnaissance) and strike aircraft. In particular, it turned out that a pure reconnaissance aircraft would have an all-up-weight well below that required for a twin engine TBR or TDB (torpedo dive-bomber). Draft staff requirements were sent to the Ministry of Aircraft Production for:

– Reconnaissance (and torpedo) bomber: 22,000lbs, 46ft length, span 60ft, folded width 27ft, to have twin engines if desired (almost certainly required). It should be a three-seater, to carry a 21in torpedo or two heavy bombs and to be able to glide-bomb up to 50 degrees angle. It should have power-worked .5in rear armament if possible. Such aircraft could go only aboard the *Ark Royal* and the 1943 light fleet carriers, if the latter were modified. Aircraft weight was deliberately kept below the 30,000lb limit to allow for growth.
– Dive-bomber: 18,000lbs, 42ft length, span 56ft, folded 18ft. It could have twin engines if desired, but a single engine was preferred. It should be a two-seater carrying one 1600lb bomb in a vertical dive, armed (if possible) with a .5in power turret, on the understanding that limits on space and weight might preclude full power operation. This aircraft would be able to operate from *Unicorn* and the *Implacable* class as well as the new carriers provided folded height was kept to 13ft 6in. This was differentiated from the reconnaissance bomber

because dive-bombing was not considered compatible with reconnaissance (which did not require high stressing or dive brakes, but did require an elaborate radar).

The reconnaissance and strike aircraft would have to work together, so they had to have very nearly the same cruising speeds, at least 150mph.

Both aircraft were to have a range (fully loaded) of at least 900nm and 1500nm with auxiliary tanks and a limited load. Reconnaissance range was increased to 1000nm in May 1943.

This programme was soon rearranged. By April 1943 it was clear that the reconnaissance aircraft did not have to be large enough to carry a torpedo. The dive-bomber was combined with the torpedo-bomber because, although the dive-bomber was built around a 1600lb bomb, it could probably easily carry an 1800lb or even 2200lb (21in) torpedo, particularly if the extra weight were regarded as an overload for stressing, though not, of course, for take-off. This seemed logical: torpedoes were dropped in a dive, though accelerations were less severe than in dive-bombing. Dive-bombing was the primary role, because in 1943 it seemed by far the best way to hit manoeuvring ships, due to its inherent accuracy. On the other hand, it might be necessary to build alternative dive-bombing and torpedo attack versions of the same aircraft.

The two alternatives (as understood in April 1943) were a single-engined two-seater (18,500 to 21,000lbs) with a maximum speed of at least 300mph, and a twin-engined version (26,000 to 27,000lbs) which might be about 25mph faster. Requirements for the reconnaissance bomber, which would have to work with the strike bomber, were deferred until after the firms had submitted their proposals for the dive-bomber and torpedo/glide bomber/reconnaissance aircraft (mid-April 1943). Cunliffe Owen, Blackburn, Fairey and Folland submitted design studies.[25]

Fairey submitted the two best studies, single and twin-engined aircraft, both of which depended on an experimental device, power-operated full-span flaps, for lateral control. Spoilers would be used when the flaps were retracted, and thus had limited movement. Fairey also relied on reversible-pitch propellers instead of conventional dive brakes. The official evaluation was that such unconventional features were necessary if an aircraft so tightly limited was to achieve high performance.

The real question, then, was whether to adopt the twin engine design. With twin Merlins, it would take off at 26,000lbs, which was uncomfortably close to the design limit of 30,000. Maximum speed would be about 350mph at 19,000ft, and it would cruise at an acceptable 165mph. Powered by any existing British engine (Griffon, Centaurus, or Sabre), the single-engined Fairey would be underpowered. However, much more powerful engines would soon be available: the Rolls-Royce Exe 45 or the American Pratt & Whitney R4360.[26] The Exe would begin with no more power than the Centaurus, but promised 3000hp; the R4360 already delivered 3000hp but was larger and heavier. In either case, although the single-engined Fairey would begin at 20,000lbs and 310mph, it could probably be developed to achieve about 340. Because it was much lighter, it allowed for much more development, and it could also be stowed more easily aboard a carrier. It was chosen as 0.5/43, the Fairey Spearfish.

The Navy ordered few major changes to the design, principally a blister canopy (with reduced fuselage depth) and slightly greater folded width (20ft). It was cleared to carry internally every known form of torpedo (including the big British 21in), and most bombs up to 2000lbs (using the ejector only for the largest). The provision in the original design for carrying two 250lb bombs underwing was eliminated. Ex-

24 British practice was to stress aircraft to 2 g for landing, whereas standard American practice was 3.5 g (the 'controlled crash').

25 The projected performance of the dive-bomber was disappointing; CNR blamed a lack of suitable British engines. The most powerful existing types, the Griffon (2000hp) and Centaurus (2400–2500hp), hardly seemed powerful enough for a 20,000lb bomber. CNR was impressed by the new generation of US 3000hp engines, such as the R4360–12, which were scheduled for new US naval bombers such as the Curtiss XBTC-2. ACNS(A) proposed in April 1943 that Britain should obtain drawings of any good US design (such as the XBTC-2), and build it under licence. He hoped that a new British bomber could be designed around the XR4360-12. The BTC never entered production, but another aircraft of much the same kind, the Douglas Skyraider, was extremely successful.

26 Interestingly, the Exe 45 was a 45-litre air-cooled in-line sleeve-valve development of the original smaller-capacity Exe which had been designed for the Barracuda.

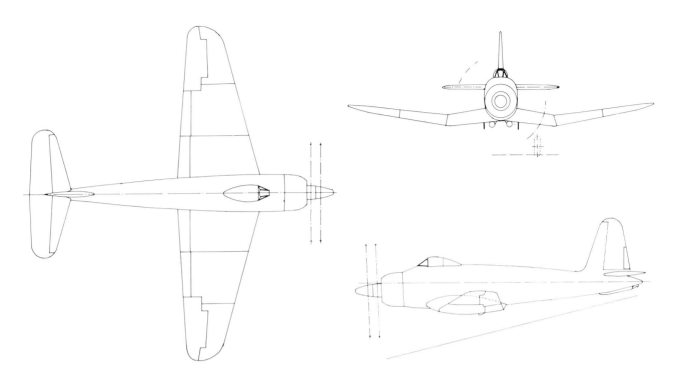

pected speed was 350mph with the Exe 45. Six prototypes were ordered.

The Fifth Sea Lord was not entirely happy with the heavy two-seat bomber; he considered it too slow and therefore too vulnerable. Given the general philosophy of unescorted strikes, he wanted a bomber fast enough to survive in the face of defensive fighters. Really high performance could be achieved only by eliminating the second crewman and his turret. This first-class single-seater would be both dive- and torpedo-bomber. It would work with a high-performance reconnaissance aircraft.

Fortunately in April 1943 just such an aircraft was about to fly: the experimental Blackburn Firebrand torpedo fighter. The Firebrand might be considered the opposite (that is, non-systematic) pole of aircraft development. Conceived as a carrier interceptor, it had been abandoned in 1942 due to its poor performance. A prototype converted to carry a torpedo turned out better than expected, so the Royal Navy decided to resume the original order for 300, now as torpedo-carrying fighters with Centaurus engines. The resulting aircraft did not have the range the Committee wanted, but it was too attractive to abandon. In June 1943 CNR agreed that as soon as experience was gained with the Firebrand, development of an improved single-seat torpedo-carrier would be pressed forward. This somewhat offhand process led (see below) to the development of the Western Wyvern (N.11/44), which, ironically, was one of the few survivors of the wartime programme.

Although the single-seat attacker enjoyed higher performance, there was a general feeling that its pilot would find very long-range navigation difficult. Therefore even the Fifth Sea Lord agreed that a two- or three-seater would have to lead a formation of such aircraft to their distant target.

Defenders of the two-seat Spearfish argued that even the single-seater could not compete successfully with high-performance radar-guided interceptors, and that power-operated guns could offer a great deal, particularly in a coordinated formation. It also seemed likely that two-seaters would enjoy overwhelming navigational and radar advantages, particularly at night or in poor visibility.

The result was that both the conventional (two-seat) torpedo/dive-bomber (Spearfish) and the single-seat torpedo

The Blackburn S.10/45, the final development of the Firebrand concept. It was a Firecrest redesigned to take the Napier Nomad engine. Blackburn adopted the Nomad after development of improved versions of the Centaurus had been cancelled. The engine and its radiator were quite heavy, so the Blackburn designers adopted a Napier proposal, placing the radiator in the nose and the engine behind the pilot. this moved the centre of gravity aft to a more acceptable position (although there was some criticism that it was now too far aft). They claimed an additional advantage; a pilot view nearly as good as that in a twin-engine aircraft. This would be particularly important for rocket attacks, for instance with the new 'Uncle Tom.' Despite its very different appearance, the Firecrest and its S.10/45 successor were structurally similar to the Firebrand, and thus were not really stressed either for dive-bombing or for the new turboprop engines. The S.10/45 was already inferior to the new Wyvern in level speed, although it could climb faster and could take off in a much shorter distance. It was cancelled in 1945 because it appeared to offer too little room for further growth. This drawing, taken from a Ministry of Aircraft Production file on technical policy relating to the Blackburn single-seat attack aircraft, did not indicate the dimensions of the aircraft, but they must have been very similar to those of the Firecrest.

fighter (Firebrand and then Wyvern) were developed.

The other major element of the programme was the reconnaissance bomber. It could carry bombs, but only if this was without detriment to the primary reconnaissance mission. Carrier stowage required that weight be limited to 24,000lbs (with 20,000 preferred), that folded height be kept to 17ft and folded width to 27ft (with 18 preferred); maximum length (to fit) was 45ft and span, spread, 60ft. As in the new fighter, the maximum take-off run (with 27 knots wind over deck) was 500ft, and landing speed 75 knots (to suit arrester gear).

Range was auxiliary tanks would be no less than 1500nm (without, 900nm at 150 knots).

Design requirements included a surface-search radar with all-round scan and PPI display (for the observer), plus provision

Table 13-4: Naval Strike Aircraft, July 1945

	Fairey Tandem (N.16/45)	Wyvern (N.11/40)	Spearfish (0.5/43)	Sturgeon S.11/43
Span (ft)	52 (20 folded)	44(18)	60(20)	59 11(20)
Length (ft)	42 6	39 4	45	44 7
Height (ft)	17 4 (15 6 min)	15 9	17(15 8)	16 2¾
Engine	2 RM 17SM	Eagle	Centaurus 17	RM 14 SM
	1960 shp T/O	2700[5]	2525[6]	2200[7]
Boost (lbs)	25	12	8½	27½
Guns	4 20mm (150rpg)	4 20mm	4 .5in (150rpg)	2 .5in (300rpg)
Torpedoes	1 2000lb	1 2097lb	1 1950lb	—
Bombs	—	—	1 1600lb	up to 1000
Rockets	—	8	16	8
All-up weight (lbs)	23,200 (2000lb torpedo)[1]	21,102 (2097lb torpedo)	21,600[1]	21,800[8]
Wing loading	55.8	60.4	40.8	38.9
Drop tank (gallons)	1 × 220	2 × 90	270[9]	180[9]
Speed (mph)	343/SL[2]	332[3]	269[10]	325[11]
	368/5250ft	377/10,000ft	285/5000ft	340/5000ft
	402/18,000ft	429/23,000ft	301/16,000ft	377/17,750ft
Take-off (knots)	75	74	94	90
Stall (knots)	67	66	82	78
Approach (knots)	74	72.5	90	86
Take-off run at 27 knots (ft)	675	850	520	285
Endurance after combat (hours)	2.4	3.01	3.85	3.35
Combat radius at sea level (nm)	290	315	345	302
With fuel (gallons)	460	490	388	430
Climb (ft/min) normal	1500	1500	1720	2400
combat	2320	3450	2110	4000
Service ceiling (ft)	30,000	32,800	25,200	34,100

1 Photo-reconnaissance version 23,560lbs with 165-gallon tank
2 Clean: 435mph at 18,000ft; cruising speed 248mph at 15,000ft (photo version 250mph at 15,000ft).
3 Clean: 455mph at 23,000ft; cruise 287mph at 20,000ft
4 With 1600lb bomb
5 3260hp at 18,000ft
6 2310hp at 14,000ft
7 1890hp at 14,750ft
8 With 1000lb bomb
9 In bomb bay
10 Clean: 301mph at 16,000ft; cruise at 215mph at 15,000ft
11 Clean: 377mph at 17,750ft; cruise at 216mph at 15,000ft

for a big vertical camera (20in lens). The aircraft would depend mainly on speed for survival, but it would have at least one rear-firing .50 calibre or 20mm gun (300 or 120rpg, respectively). If bombs were carried, the standard maximum load would be only one 1000lb MC or SAP or one or two 500lb SAP or MC, or two to four depth charges. These light loads again emphasize the primary reconnaissance mission.

This was a very straightforward design problem, and there was even some hope that it might be lighter than the torpedo/dive-bomber. Fairey, Westland, Cunliffe-Owen, Armstrong-Whitworth, Blackburn and Short all submitted designs in July 1943, the last firm proposing both twin- and single-engined alternatives. CNR found Short's the best of the single-engine submissions, and the firm's twin-engine proposal the best of all. Its performance approached that of the Mosquito, and its weight (about 20,000lbs) allowed an ample margin for future development.

The Short design was so good that the Staff Requirement was re-examined to decide whether or not any rear gun was needed, given its high speed. Omitting the rear gun, moreover, made possible a much smaller (and therefore faster) aircraft. The folded width of the original design was increased from 18 to 19ft to allow greater width between the propeller tips. The Short aircraft was ordered as S.11/43, the Sturgeon, with Merlins (although later Griffons might be substituted). By March 1944 it was scheduled for use as a special photo type, and possibly also as a night fighter.

For a time it seemed that the torpedo-bomber would inevitably have two engines. To gain experience in twin-engine operation, DAW proposed that one of two standard RAF aircraft, the Beaufighter or the Mosquito, be carrier-landed. For a time he envisaged adaptation of one or the other, preferring the Mosquito for its higher speed and better dimensions, but by late 1943 the Spearfish had definitely been chosen.

The trials continued, with a hooked Mosquito successfully landing aboard HMS *Indefatigable* at maximum arrester gear

weight (20,000lbs) and taking off at its maximum weight (22,000lbs). These trials were so successful that DAW rethought his ideas; now a navalized Mosquito was an attractive future naval type. By July 1944 the Admiralty definitely envisaged Sea Mosquito squadrons; it asked for 200 for delivery in 1945 and 250 to follow in 1946. A few dual-control aircraft were requested, to provide flying experience leading up to the Sea Hornet and to the Sturgeon as well as for future Sea Mosquito squadrons. Meanwhile, given the success of the Mosquito flying from the *Indefatigable*, the RAF planned a surprise strike against Japanese fleet units, using its own Mosquitoes flown from a British carrier. The weapon would have been the High-ball spinning bomb. By late 1944 the wooden Sea Mosquito seemed to be an attractive alternative to the metal Sturgeon.[27]

For the short term, the only available British-built strike aircraft was the Fairey Barracuda, which was already badly overweight due to additions during it development. As recounted in Chapter 10, the only real US alternative, the Curtiss Helldiver, took too long to develop and then could not be made available in sufficient numbers. Thus the Committee had to approve production of the Barracuda Mk V, and the alternative (to split the type into lighter-weight pure dive-bomber and pure TBR not stressed for diving) had failed.

There was also the Swordfish. If the small CVEs and MAC-

27 The original Mosquito or Beaufighter TBR proposal dated from 11 March 1943; existing types would be used to avoid delays. DAWT observed that the Mosquito had a better performance, could probably be developed further, was easier to fly, was shorter (40ft 6in versus 41ft 6in) and lower (12ft 6in versus 15ft 6in and hence could be stowed aboard an *Implacable*). The Beaufighter already had a cleared torpedo installation, and had more internal space. The Mosquito was chosen. DAWT's later Sea Mosquito proposal is in ADM 1/16503, of 14 May 1944. He considered it most useful in the Eastern theatre as a fighter-bomber for long-range strikes against Japanese bases, harbours and oil installations; also for long-range photo reconnaissance. The Sea Mosquito could operate only from the two *Implacables*, as only those carriers could take 20,000lb aircraft. Sea Mosquito units would be formed a alternative armament (that is, air complements) for these ships, beginning with two fighter-bomber units (twenty-four aircraft each) and one photo unit (twelve aircraft), plus training and trials aircraft, an initial total of seventy-two. The question of a night fighter version would be deferred, although a Sea Mosquito would probably be better than a night figher version of the Sturgeon. D of P considered the project extremely important, because it provided the Royal Navy with a long-range strike capability the US Navy could not match. It would be even more important if the new anti-ship weapon (Highball) proved effective.

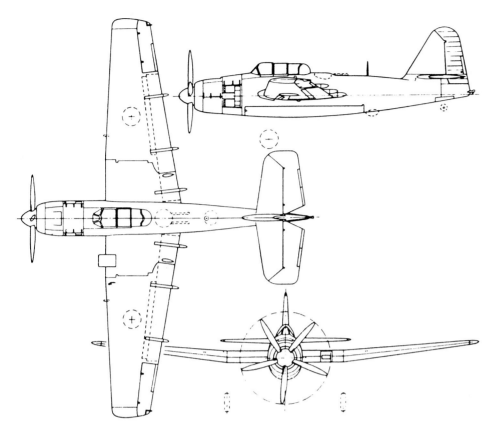

Fairey Spearfish.

ships were indeed to be a fixture of future naval warfare, some suitable aircraft would be needed. It would have to operate from small decks in all weathers, and would have to land at unusually low speed, yet carry a heavy load of depth charges and specialized equipment. Like a Swordfish, it would have to be so easy to fly that the pilot could afford to give minimum attention to controls at night and in bad visibility. All of these qualities ran against the trend of modern aircraft development, but they were clearly valuable. In July 1943, CNR suggested that the ideal solution would be a well-flapped cantilever biplane. Nothing was done, but the basic idea re-emerged in 1949 as the Seamew. In the absence of the Swordfish, the only available British-built general-purpose escort carrier aircraft was the Barracuda III, with its all-round sea search radar.

EARLY IN FEBRUARY 1944, it still seemed possible that the war with Japan would last into late 1947. Navalized RAF fighters were an acceptable short-term expedient, but ACNS(A) suggested that effort be concentrated on a new specialized naval fighter. Part of the reason may have been fear that, as maximum speeds increased, RAF fighters would have to land at higher and higher speeds.[28]

While Staff Requirements for a new long-range carrier fighter were being drafted, Westland proposed a new aircraft built around a buried Rolls-Royce Eagle engine. This was not entirely a private venture, since the company was clearly aware of the Admiralty's evolving needs, but it was in hand in advance of an actual Staff Requirement. The Committee found this procedure very attractive, since it saved considerable time; to the extent that a good commercial design met, or very nearly met, the Navy's needs, the staff requirements could be revised to reflect its characteristics. The new long-range fighter seems to have been the first example of this procedure (at least, the first in wartime), but there were later several others.

By this time the fully unescorted strike idea had been aban-

doned, even for the new fast aircraft. The new fighter, then, had to be able to reach the full range of the new Spearfish and Sturgeon at minimum formation cruising speed, which turned out to be about two-thirds of maximum speed, about 200 knots for the Sturgeon or 166 knots for the Spearfish. At these speeds their endurances were, respectively, 6 hours 25 minutes and 5 hours 35 minutes.

The new fighter would fly out (for $2\frac{1}{4}$ hours at 10,000ft) and climb to a combat altitude of 20,000ft using fuel in drop tanks, then drop them for 15 minutes of combat. Internal fuel would suffice for a $2\frac{1}{2}$-hour flight back, including 45 minutes at most economical speed (forming up after the strike and loitering before landing). In theory, the new engine would be so powerful that this kind of endurance would be compatible with a speed no less than that of the best existing interceptors, and with the best possible climb rate (though not the climb rate of those interceptors – hence the terminal climb to 20,000ft). Armament would be a minimum of four (20mm or 5in) guns (with six preferred), with sufficient ammunition for at least 25 seconds of continuous fire. Specified equipment included automatic navigation (to reduce the penalty of omitting the second crew member) and tail warning radar.

Meanwhile, DAWT was very interested in developing a new single-seat strike aircraft, although he still wanted the two-seater Spearfish; the Firebrand was not entirely satisfactory, because it was not stressed for dive-bombing. He therefore proposed a new single-seat carrier dive-bomber, similar in concept to the new US Navy aircraft such as the Martin Mauler and the Douglas Skyraider (neither of which had yet flown). He wanted a 350-400nm operational radius with a single large bomb (1600 to 2000lb), a torpedo as an alternative which could be waived if impractical, and possibly petrol in drop tanks. Dive angle would have to be at least 80 degrees. Maximum speed would be at 12,000 to 18,000ft, but the greatest need was for high speed at sea level, so the aircraft could escape after attacking. Armament would comprise two forward-firing 20mm guns, with good armour against attacks from astern.

CNR agreed that the gap in the current programme was a single-seat strike fighter, but wondered whether it had to be able to dive-bomb nearly vertically ('hell-dive' in British parlance, in reference to US practice). There was no question that dive-bombing was the best means of attacking carriers and lightly armoured ships, but CNR suggested that steep glide-

28   At this time MAP hoped the new laminar-flow Spitfire (that is, the Spiteful) would be about 30mph faster than a Griffon Spitfire (470mph at 30,000ft), but experience with such wings was very limited. Estimated stall speed was 100mph (87 knots), which CNR considered too great a jump from the landing performance of existing aircraft. More had to be known about the effect on the pilot of high deceleration loads (which would have to be imposed to stop the aircraft before it stretched the arrester gear wires into the barrier). There was also a suspicion that the laminar flow wing would add only 10, not 30, mph. By July 1945 the Admiralty considered the Sea Fury clearly superior to the existing Seafire 47, but hoped that the navalized Spiteful (Seafang) would be superior to both. This seemed likely to enter service during 1946. Moreover, cuts in RAF requirements made it possible for Supermarine to convert much of its capacity to naval fighter production. Supermarine was now enthusiastic about naval requirements, and it seemed likely that the Seafang would fold well outboard rather than inboard (folded width 27ft but height only 12ft 9in); it could then be stowed in the *Implacables*, which could stow neither the Seafire 47 nor the Sea Fury, due to their height. However, its increased width excluded it from the *Illustrious* class. Thus only the Seafang could permit the Royal Navy to dispense with the existing Seafire XVIII by 1947. A developed version (with an Eagle engine) was expected to make 456 knots (525mph) at 25,000ft using eight-blade contraprops compared to 391(450) for the Seafire 47 (21,000) and 417 (480) for the initial Seafang (six-blade contraprop) at 21,000. Max climb would be 6250ft per minute versus 5600 for the early version and 5250 for the Seafire 47. These were Supermarine estimates, which MAP considered overdrawn. After the Spiteful (and hence also the Seafang) was cancelled, the Royal Navy continued to buy Seafire 47s, which it considered inferior to Sea Furies, largely to keep Supermarine alive; it wanted the company to be able to keep developing the big interceptor, which ultimately became the Scimitar.

Throughout the war, the Royal Navy always had to consider whether to adapt RAF designs, or to wait for specialist naval types. The Future Building Committee favoured using RAF interceptors, the best of which was the Hawker Sea Fury. An early production FB.11, TF 956, is shown, in Korean War recognition stripes, as flown from HMS Theseus.

bombing might be as effective. A dual-purpose design could be developed: a really high-performance interceptor which, by carrying drop tanks, could also serve as a medium-range escort and which could carry an external load of one torpedo or large bomb, provided it did not need dive brakes and other attributes normally associated with 'hell diving'.

Alternatively, a single-set 'hell-diver' could be designed which could be a second-class low-altitude fighter, that is, which could not deal with first-class interceptors but could combat heavier attack aircraft.

The first, the fighter-bomber, would replace the Firebrand. As an escort, it would also replace American fighters, the supply of which was declining. CNR believed that the new generation of much more powerful engines would make it practicable. On 4 April the Committee agreed to include a Specification for a high-performance single-seat strike fighter in the new Naval Aircraft Development Programme. The Staff Requirement would be based on the Westland design. The second alternative, the single-seat 'hell-diver' and low-altitude fighter, would be translated into a Staff Requirement only if further studies showed that it was needed; it was soon forgotten.

Thus on 4 May the Admiralty formally asked MAP to develop, as a matter of high priority, a single-engine fighter with large internal tankage, to carry externally about 2000lbs of bombs or additional petrol.

Westland could not entirely meet the range requirement, but its design was so close to what was wanted that the Fifth Sea Lord ordered the Staff Requirements matched to it. By late 1944, the design had been developed so that it could be powered instead by one of the turboprops then under develop-

ment. It became the Wyvern, the standard British strike aircraft of 1953–58.[29]

This was one new requirement. By the late summer of 1944, MAP was drawing up a programme of new development projects for 1944–47.

CNR wanted three naval projects per year, to keep industry interested in naval requirements. He wanted a new fighter every year, so that the Royal Navy could keep up with land-based aircraft. There was, as yet, no naval interceptor in the 1944 programme. One was therefore needed for 1945, and for high performance, it would have to be a jet. Jets consumed their fuel much faster than piston aircraft, but, operating no more than 30 to 50nm from a ship, a jet could rely on drop tanks to remain on station. It could rely on its internal fuel supply for combat and for a quick return to the carrier. The committee agreed to have a company produce a design for a jet interceptor to see how it might fit naval requirements.

The second project would be a very fast combined strike-reconnaissance aircraft (Spearfish plus Sturgeon), powered, perhaps, by turboprops (for better performance but without paying the range penalty of jet engines).

By December 1944, the proposed development programme consisted of:

- A medium-range jet day fighter to replace the Hawker Sea Fury, to be developed as a combined RAF and Royal Navy project. Hawker was asked for a design. This became the postwar Sea Hawk.
- An experimental interceptor, possibly using a combination of a turboprop (or ducted fan) and a pure jet. Super marine was asked for a design. This project was redirected into a pure jet to use the new flexible ('sprung') deck, and ultimately emerged in very different form as the Scimitar.
- A long-range fighter/strike aircraft, already ordered from Westland as N.11/44 (Wyvern); it was also a possible Coastal Command strike aircraft, perhaps a replacement for the Bristol Brigand then about to enter production.

29 Dimensions were limited to 50ft span (18ft folded) × 40ft long × 15ft 9in; maximum speed desired was 500mph (434 knots) at 20,000ft, the designer to consider special measures for short bursts of speed for combat at 15,000ft and below. The aircraft had to climb to 15,000ft in 5 minutes with full tanks. It was to have a minimum turning circle; the designer could use landing flaps to reduce this on occasion. Best performance was to be at 10,000 to 20,000ft. The fighter would carry at least 75 per cent of its fuel in self-sealing tanks. It would cruise out to the target area at most economical speed (over a combat radius of 400nm) and climb to 20,000ft carrying drop tanks. Internal tankage would allow for 15 minutes of combat, return to the carrier, and 30 minutes loitering while circling to land at 2000ft. Since the aircraft would normally be catapulted off, a take-off run as great as 600ft was considered acceptable when it was loaded with strike ammunition. Primary strike loads: one 2000lb or 1600lb bomb, or two 1000lb or 500lb or clusters of small bombs not over 1000lb in weight, or one 18in Mk XVII torpedo (provision for gyro ranging) or Mk XV. Eight rockets were to be provided as a strike overload; in strike configuration the aircraft would use an external (wing nacelle) range-only radar.

30 Fairey was doing some work on a hybrid piston-jet version of the Firefly, and there was some hope that Miles might develop a similar aircraft.

31 Blackburn initially decided to go ahead with three prototypes. S.10/45 would have been powered by a Napier E.122 Nomad engine, and would have had a high-speed inverted gull wing with two strong points.

32 This was not a new idea; Fairey had proposed a double engine, the Fairey P.24 Prince, in 1935. This had consisted of two 12-cylinder vertically-opposed engines each geared to its own coaxial propeller, the combination flying in a Fairey Battle in June 1939. It was considered for the Hawker Tornado and was tested in the United States in 1942, but was not produced in wartime. The engine appears to have been intended to appeal to the Royal Navy, since it promised twin-engine reliability in a single-engine airframe, which could be flown with one engine shut down (because it would suffer no asymmetric forces).

33 The wording of the Minute describing the Committee action leaves it somewhat uncertain whether DAWT or Fairey made this suggestion; the Committee endorsed it (6 July 1945).

DAWT saw two gaps in the programme, a night fighter to follow the Firefly version then under development, and a 'hack' for the general-purpose CVE, to replace the existing Barracuda III. Though little was known of landing the Mosquito at night, DAWT suggested that it be adapted for night interception.

The Barracuda III replacement was deferred, although DNOR argued that in the next war convoy protection might well be the single principal naval role. In that case strike aircraft would not be too important, but many (probably about thirty) small carriers would be needed. The Fifth Sea Lord agreed that the Barracuda III replacement was needed, but work on this GR.17/45 requirement (which eventually produced the Fairey Gannet) seems to have begun only postwar.

Instead, the Committee recommended that work proceed on a medium-range day fighter or fighter-bomber, and on a new night interceptor. The alternatives for the fast night fighter were a Sturgeon development or a Sea Hornet development, the latter being chosen.

Thus in Februay 1945 the formal Navy aircraft development programme comprised:

(a) a general-purpose low-medium altitude fighter/bomber (catering for the escort role) to follow the Sea Fury, Spitfire XXI and Spiteful, and intended to get the best possible range

(b) an interceptor (probably jet)

(c) a long-range high performance escort fighter to follow the Sea Hornet (possibly using dual power or a reciprocating engine, to get best range)[30]

(d) a naval strike aircraft: a two- or three-seater to replace the Spearfish, and a single-seat high-performance aircraft as an alterntive to, or replacement for, the Wyvern

(e) a naval reconnaissance aircraft: a fast twin-engined aircraft to replace the Sturgeon in due course

(f) a new amphibian for air-sea rescue (the Seagull)

The turboprop Wyvern fulfilled both (a) and the single-seat requirement in (d); a prototype was ordered as N.12/45. Blackburn was already working on a Firebrand development as the Firecrest (S.28/43), and proposed further version, MAP initially agreeing to build prototypes to Specification S.10/45.[31] Unlike the Wyvern, these aircraft would have been able to operate from existing carriers, an important consideration for aircraft which might enter service in 1945–46. How-

ever, with the end of the war such second-rate aircraft were no longer worth developing. MAP initially persisted because Blackburn needed the work. However, the firm was soon assigned primary responsibility for the Barracuda III replacement (GR.17/45), and S.10/45 was killed off. The Wyvern was delayed, but this was no great problem as no new war was expected for some time (see Chapter 15 for an elaboration of this policy).

LATE IN 1944, in order to concentrate on jets and turboprops, MAP stopped development on new large piston engines, leaving the Eagle and Centaurus as the most powerful. Rolls-Royce was also developing a 24-cylinder air-cooled 'X' engine, the Pennine, though soon it would also be cancelled. A projected Bristol 28-cylinder radial engine and 32- and 48-cylinder in-line engines (by Napier and Rolls-Royce) were both cancelled.

Fairey had hoped to power later Spearfish with the new Pennine, with which it could achieve 330mph (compared to 300 with a Centaurus). In November 1944 the company proposed that, since none of the really powerful piston engines would probably materialize, the aircraft be redesigned with two Merlins (about 4000hp) in tandem, with the pilot sitting above one, and the other between him and the observer. Otherwise the aircraft needed no redesign, and in its new form it might achieve 350 or 360mph, while having much the same range as the single-engined Spearfish.[32]

Each Merlin would drive an independent (though concentric) propeller, each having its own throttle and its own fuel system, though the fuel systems could be interconnected so that the aircraft could cruise most of the time on one engine. The oil systems were entirely separate.

Advantages over the Sea Mosquito would include easier stowage and better deck landing (due to slower landing speed). It would be much easier to fly on one engine, and would enjoy many of the advantages of a twin without the drag of the second nacelle. Fairey claimed almost twin-engine reliability, but in some respects the tandem engines were not as good as conventional twins (if the aircraft suffered battle damage, the second engine might also be knocked out because it was so close to the first). The expected weight penalty was 2500lbs (total 24,000lbs).

Fairey also proposed using the tandem engines in a high-performance fighter/bomber. It would have no rear armament, but it could accommodate a small second cockpit for a radio/radar operator on an occasional basis. The firm hoped for 460mph as a fighter, and saw it as a possible successor to the Spearfish, if the tandem engine idea succeeded. CNR therefore encouraged MAP to order a prototype of this Fairey private venture as 0.21/44. Official consideration of the fighter-bomber project was deferred until it was more mature.

Fairey resubmitted its project in July 1945 (Table 13-4 compares Fairey's figures with contemporary British strike aircraft projects). The Committee accepted it (Specification N.16/45) as insurance against the possible failure of jet and turboprop engines, and particularly of the turboprop-powered Wyvern II (N.12/45).

The company was given the target of meeting four roles in one airframe: strike, escort fighter, fast reconnaissance, and night fighter. Apparently at DAWT's suggestion strike was chosen as the primary role, reconnaissance being selected as secondary, because it would not reduce strike effectiveness.[33] The escort fighter role was rejected as one in which the aircraft was unlikely to be efficient, and because crew training might prove difficult. Unlike a conventional twin-engine aircraft, the Fairey proposal could not accommodate a large radar in its nose, but a night-fighter conversion was still a possibility.

Table 13-5: Naval Jet Fighters, February 1945

	XFJ-1	XF6U-1	Jet Spiteful	TJ 6
All-up weight (lbs)	10,800	8675	11,000	10,400
Engine	TG 180	24C	B.41	B.41
Thrust (lbs)	4000	3000	4500	4200
Guns	6 .5in	4 20mm	4 20mm	
Rounds per gun	250	150–200	190	
Rockets	2 11.75	—	—	
Bombs			2 × 1000lb (later)	
Mil load (lbs)	1575	1560	1682	1750
Span (ft)	38 1	30 2 (18 10)	36 9	39 0
Height (ft)	14 2	13 8	9 5	
Internal fuel (gallons)	399	310	395	330
External fuel (gallons)	284	312	270	—
Wing loading	42.5	48.2	48.8	37.2
Maximum speed (mph/altitude)	537/SL	553/SL	575/SL	500/SL
	547/20,000ft	510/30,000ft	555/30,000ft	542/20,000ft
Approach speed (knots)	87	91	96	85
Rate of climb at sea level (ft/min)	5410	4880	5900	5210
Normal endurance (hours/speed)	1.8/420mph	2.9/— (20,000ft)	2.5/400mph (20,000ft)	1/—
Combat radius (st miles/mph)	316/346	323/369	375	148
Combat radius, maximum fuel	560/344	617/363	725	—
Take-off	550/27	795/27	820/27	640/27
(overload)	950/27	1670/27	—	—

The Westland Wyvern was the last of a series of single-seat strike fighters, all offspring of the successful attempt to save the Firebrand. They were closely related (in concept) to the US Navy's Skyraider, but were built in much smaller numbers because the postwar Royal Navy did not emphasize strike operations. This is a Wyvern S.4, the version which entered squadron service and which saw combat at Suez.

By this time trials in the Firebrand had shown that carrying a torpedo at high speed caused problems; DNDP (Director of Naval Aircraft Development and Production, MAP) suggested that either a new torpedo or an entirely new anti-ship weapon might be needed. Existing torpedoes could not be carried externally by any modern aircraft, even the Firebrand. The torpedo requirement was therefore abandoned, at least for the time being, saving 100lbs or more in sights, gyro angling gear, special carriage arrangements, etc. Since the aircraft was being designed to carry a 2000lb weapon under its fuselage, there would be no great difficulty in reviving the torpedo later.

The Vice Controller (Air) observed that if turboprops developed as fast as some hoped, the Fairey project would suddenly become outdated; DAWT found some hesitation in recommending it, as it would not be in service until 1948, by which time it would not be fast enough. DNDP replied that at present it was the best available in this class, and on that basis the Committee recommended it.

These fears were very realistic. By January 1946, turboprops were doing better than had been expected six to eight months earlier. Fairey was told to abandon its Merlin-powered strike

bomber in favour of a turboprop version. This time both engines were grouped side by side in the nose, each easily removed independently. Each still drove its own propeller through its own gear train, and one could be stopped while the other ran for long cruising endurance. Thus the aircraft could achieve the best possible fuel economy (no single turbine could give really good fuel economy except at a high percentage of full power). The staff requirement was revised to reflect this new design.[34]

As development continued, N.16/45 seemed less and less attractive. It was modified into a fast low-altitude two-seater, and weight saving expedients, such as the substitution of package guns for fixed armament, were suggested. However, it would enter service at least two years after the turboprop Wyvern, its performance was no better, and it was expensive and vulnerable. It was too heavy for the backseat operator to provide the pilot with warning early enough for him to evade attack. Moreover, war experience seemed not to bear out the need for a navigator in daylight air reconnaissance aircraft. If it was needed, the two-seat Sea Hornet was available. The Fifth

---

34 The Fairey brochure figures were: single-seat torpedo fighter; two Rolls Royce AP 25 (Tweed); span 51ft (20ft) × length 43ft 6in tail down × height 17ft (prop running, wing folded – 15 with prop stopped); all-up weight 23,100lbs; 545 gallons fuel; maximum speed 422mph at sea level (472mph without torpedo), 434mph at 10,000 (494), 429mph at 20,000 (490); approach speed 87.5mph (92.5 with torpedo); time to 10,000ft 2 min 6 sec; service ceiling 44,000; strike radius 427–480 st miles; 380ft/27 knots take-off; four 20mm (150rpg), one 2000lb torpedo. Endurance figures assume that a torpedo is carried at high speed from 50nm to the target. Landing approach speed assumes no torpedo but 2 hours supply of fuel. Strike radius is based on take-off and climb to 20,000ft, 115 miles at maximum speed at 20,000ft, with 30 minutes loiter at sea level before landing.

By the end of World War II, the British Government was firmly convinced that piston engines were obsolete, to the extent that several engines then under development were cancelled. Several new jet fighters were designed. They were, however, clearly immature examples of a rapidly-evolving technology, and as such were not considered worthy of investment postwar, when money was scarce. The Attacker, very much an interim design, was revived when the more mature Sea Hawk encountered unacceptable delays. One is shown aboard HMS Eagle *in 1952. The carrier's radars, like the fighter, represented the technology of 1945, delayed by unavoidable postwar economies.*

Sea Lord killed it off in the spring of 1947.

The novel double-turboprop engine installation survived, to appear in the Fairey Gannet anti-submarine plane built to Specification GR 17/45 (see Chapter 15).

HAWKER WAS ASKED to develop the joint RAF-Navy jet fighter, but Supermarine was arleady developing a simple alternative, a jet version of the Spiteful using the same wings and other important parts. It would be available much sooner than the Hawker, but it would also be much cruder. Supermarine submitted this proposal to MAP in July 1944, and that September the Controller of R & D of the MAP ordered three Jet Spiteful prototypes (E.10/44), one navalized, as an MAP (rather than Service) venture. Late in 1944 or early in 1945 the Naval Aircraft Sub-Committee asked RAE to estimate the characteristics of an uncompromised naval jet fighter, as a standard against which the Jet Spiteful could be compared.

RAE looked at pure jet, ducted fan, turboprop, turboprop with jet boost, and pure conventional powerplants. In February 1945 it concluded that any future high-performance naval fighter would have to be a pure jet, and that requirements for take-off, military load, and landing speed would have to be modified. Table 13-5 compares the Jet Spiteful, the RAE estimate (TJ 6), and two contemporary US naval jet fighters (as data were then known to the Royal Navy).

The Jet Spiteful was worthwhile because it would give the Royal Navy something approaching an operational carrier-capable jet fighter in the shortest possible time. There were too many unknowns for a realistic policy to be formulated. In April

1945 CNR hoped to try a Meteor III (which he considered unsuitable for carrier take-off and landing) aboard the trials carrier *Pretoria Castle* to investigate deck-handling and taxying. A Vampire was hooked for preliminary landings and take-offs.[35]

MAP was willing to buy twenty-four Jet Spitefuls (renamed Attackers) and eighteen navalized or semi-navalized versions, which would begin to appear in about April 1946. There was no question of producing this compromise aircraft in any numbers; Supermarine was developing a much better specialized naval interceptor, which ultimately became the Scimitar. However, it seemed prudent to go ahead with the interim Jet Spiteful even if only to study and overcome the problems of carrier operation of jets.

By August, DAWT's view was that if the navalized Jet Spiteful (E.1/45) proved successful, it would be worth ordering as an operational type. It could be operated only by carriers suited to 20,000lb aircraft (its high landing speed made up for its lighter weight in the arrester gear). Of the three, it could be stowed only in the upper hangars of two carriers, HMS *Indomitable* and *Implacable*, and it could not go down the lifts of the third, HMS *Illustrious*, which was then being modernized.[36]

Meanwhile, Supermarine worked on a fast undercarriageless jet fighter to use the proposed new flexible deck. In July 1945 it was intended to climb at 10,000ft per minute, and to achieve 680mph. Endurance was only one hour, far too little for CAP operation; it followed that the new generation of postwar jet fighters would have to rely on deck-launched interception (DLI), based on solid early warning, including airborne radar. It seemed possible that climb from the deck might even be faster if the endurance requirement were relaxed further. The RAF had much the same idea.

Attackers prepare to take off from HMS Eagle, 1952. Note the steam jet further forward, with its angled lines to indicate wind direction, a characteristic feature of British aircraft carriers.

35   Captain E M Brown, who made the first jet landings, claims credit for the first proposals for deck-landing trials of a jet fighter, sometime after mid-1944. The aircraft, LZ 551/G, arrived at Farnborough fully equipped with arrester hook, more powerful engine (2000lb thrust Goblin II), 40 per cent more flap area (by extending their chord and continuing them under the jet engine nacelle), extended dive brakes (by 8in), and an improved Pitot head on the port wing in place of one on the port fin, to measure performance at a lower stall speed. The carrier, HMS *Ocean*, was commanded by Captain Caspar John, who during the war had been Director-General of Naval Aircraft Design and Production (DGNDP) within MAP. He was later First Sea Lord. E M Brown, *Wings of the Weird and Wonderful*, Vol. 1 (Airlife, Shrewsbury, 1983). Navalized Vampires (Sea Vampires) were later used for training, but they had much too little endurance to be useful operational fighters. Two Meteor III fighters were hooked and made thirty-two landings aboard HMS *Implacable*. A Boscombe Down (A&AEE) report in 1950 described them as the best deck-landing jets tested to date.

36   Note that the Jet Spiteful Specification was experimental (E) rather than operational naval (N). The naval specification called for it to carry one 90-gallon drop tank and two 500lb bombs or two 1000lb bombs, as well as four 20mm cannon (150rpg). Service ceiling was not to be less than 40,000ft, maximum speed not less than 500mph TAS at all heights up to 30,000. With full tanks but no external bombs or drop tanks, take-off run was not to exceed 880/27 knots (assumes 4500lb thrust). Consideration was to be given to provision for underwing rockets in place of the two underwing bombs. A thrust spoiler (thrust reverser) was to be fitted, with its operating time not to exceed $\frac{1}{2}$ second, and interconnected with the throttle so that it could not be subjected to higher than cruising thrust. Folded width was not to exceed 29ft.

14

The Big Carrier: HMS *Malta*

1   The idea was to put the desired operational speed on a flatter part of the speed-power curve, rather than to operate at 33 or 34 knots. E-in-C suggested some alternatives. One was to use double reduction gearing (a novel development for the Royal Navy of the time) to reduce propeller revolutions, so as to keep the onset of cavitation further from the designed speed. Another was to reduce the boiler forcing rate and increase the number of boilers, to achieve maximum steam generating capacity – at the cost of more weight per rated shp and more personnel. All of this slightly misstated the argument, as the speed-power curve was a function only of hull size and form. The extra power was needed to boost the ship quickly to 30 knots. Design X was expected to make 33 knots (deep) on trial and 34.5 knots at standard displacement, but only 30 knots at deep displacement, six months out of dock in the tropics.

2   This did not even take into account the problem of supporting all that armour as a superstructure, which entailed further heavy structural weights in the *Midway* design.

BY LATE 1942 the Future Building Committee was prepared to consider new and much larger carriers. The Royal Navy badly needed not only more carriers, but many more aircraft. Since the number of slips – hence the number of carriers in any realistic programme – was limited, future carriers would have to be very large indeed. To some extent, too, British thinking was driven by observations of the US building programme (particularly of the *Midway* class) and, in 1944–45, of US carrier operations in the Western Pacific. The net result, which did not materialize due to the end of the war, was the *Malta* class, representing the upper size limit of British carrier design. Both of the later designs, the 1952 carrier (see Chapter 14) and CVA 01 (see Chapter 15) were of about the same size, and thus make interesting comparisons.

From the beginning, the question was whether to build another British-type closed-hangar carrier, or to switch to an American-type open-hangar design. The DNC, Sir Stanley Goodall, strongly favoured the closed hangar, and appeared to have won the argument in the autumn of 1943. However, the question was then reopened, largely on the strength of US experience in the Pacific, and the open-hangar design adopted. The arguments back and forth are a good measure of the advantages and drawbacks of the two types; when another large carrier was designed in 1952, it had a closed hangar.

The Future Building Committee first discussed broad Staff Requirements at its meeting on 23 November 1942. The primary issues were speed, protection, hangar height, accommodation, improved side protection to hangars and the balance between armament and clear flight decks. Improvement in any of these areas would drive the size of new carriers well above that of the new *Ark Royal*. On 21 December the Committee suggested that speed might be reduced below the usual 30 knots, in view of the development of catapults.

Unfortunately the requirement was not so much maximum speed as the ability to accelerate rapidly from cruising to launch speed. In mid-February the Fifth Sea Lord suggested that maximum speed actually be raised to 33 or 34 knots, specifically to achieve quick acceleration to about 30 knots (and also to guarantee 30 knots fully loaded in tropical waters).[1]

Higher speed implied much larger carriers. On 8 February the Committee accepted that the next class might be as large as 50,000 tons. This figure, which was a kind of natural limit for

British building and docking facilities, recurred in 1952 and 1960. DNC expected to achieve the new requirement of 33 knots by using very long hulls as well as much more powerful machinery.

The other main issue, as noted above, was whether to adopt a US-style open hangar. Goodall strongly defended the existing British practice of making the flight deck the upper strength member of the hull, and therefore of using a closed hangar. The Fifth Sea Lord, mindful of the greater efficiency of American carrier operations, pressed for a US-style open hangar which would form a superstructure over the hull.

The two principal arguments in favour of the closed hangar were that it was more efficient structurally and that it was less dangerous. The hull girder of a closed-hangar ship was inherently deeper and therefore the associated structural weight was less. Goodall claimed that much of the difference between HMS *Ark Royal* (32,500 tons) and USS *Midway* (a 35,000-ton closed-hangar ship) could be attributed to the difference in construction. Similarly, he estimated that the new 18,000-ton light carrier (*Hermes*) would displace about 19,000 tons if built with an open hangar. Moreover, US design practice accepted the much higher level of stresses entailed by using a shallower hull. Had the US Navy worked to British hull stress levels its carriers would have been substantially larger. Goodall saw evidence of the inherent efficiency of the closed-hangar designs in the greater weight they could devote to armour, both on the flight deck and over the citadel, deep in the ship.

Hangar protection was another consideration. By accepting double-level hangars, which were practicable only in closed-hangar ships, the British could minimize the exposed deck area. For example, each hangar in *Ark Royal* had a deck area of about 27,600sq ft, for a total of about 54,000 (the lower hangar was made slightly smaller by the recesses of the funnel uptakes). The contemporary USS *Midway* had a hangar floor area of about 50,000sq ft. However, the roof of the two-level British hangar had an area (to be protected) of only 27,600sq ft, whereas the whole of the 50,000sq ft in a *Midway* had to be armoured. Thus *Ark Royal* required only 1975 tons of 4in armour, whereas *Midway* required 3130 tons of 3.5in armour to protect the roof of her hangar.[2]

Aircraft in an open hangar were clearly vulnerable to blast, splinters, machine-gun fire and rockets, not to mention any water taken aboard in a seaway. Thus Goodall saw an inherent contradiction in the US *Midway* design, in which enormous sacrifices were accepted in order to place heavy armour on the flight deck, while the sides of of the hangar remained open and unprotected. The US Navy seems to have agreed; in 1945 BuShips stated that 5in gun mounts ranged along the sides of the hangar deck provided, in effect, some physical protection against Kamikazes crashing into the hangar from the side.

It was true that no practicable thickness of flight deck armour could keep all bombs out. However, a thick flight deck could resist small bombs, and so force an enemy to attack with a much smaller number of large ones – many or all of which might well miss, given limited bombing accuracy. Goodall argued, too, that an armoured deck caused bombs to burst far from a ship's vitals, whereas a bomb might well penetrate deep into an unarmoured carrier before exploding. Thus he could point to the case of the US carrier *Yorktown*, in which a single bomb penetrated the flight and hangar decks to burst just above the one armoured deck deep in the ship, and to the loss of HMS *Hermes*, sunk by large numbers of small Japanese bombs, while the armoured carriers had survived hits by much heavier ones.

British practice was to assign about half the total width of the ship to the hangar, the rest going into the side walls and into narrow open outer passageways on either side, from which the ship could be worked (for instance in harbour). American practice was to use the full width of the ship except where the base of the island, uptakes, ammunition hoists, etc had to pass through. As a consequence, where in a British carrier access from the hangar to the rest of the ship was through the hangar walls, in a US ship it was generally through hatches let into the hangar deck itself. Goodall argued that British practice was inherently much safer, because the petrol and other inflammable fluids in the hangar were automatically isolated, whereas in an American design they could easily flow down into the rest of the ship.[3] These arguments were made well before the great Kamikaze-induced fires of 1944–45.

Operationally, the great advantage of an open hangar was that aircraft could be warmed up in it, before they moved to the flight deck. This in turn could greatly increase the carrier's striking power, because it could launch more aircraft (both those on deck and those warmed up in the hangar) in quick succession. Goodall argued that with the advent of lubricating oil heaters, aircraft brought up cold from the hangar could be launched in about 5 minutes, rather than the 15 formerly required; in an emergency, aircraft with pre-heated oil could take off immediately. Even so, engines could be tested in an open but not in a closed hangar. As a subsidiary point, existing British carriers suffered from poor hangar deck ventilation.

The Fifth Sea Lord argued that, once penetrated, a closed hangar tended to magnify the effect of a bomb exploding in it. Goodall countered that a penetrating bomb would do worse damage to an unarmoured open-hangar ship, and that the hangar blast would not necessarily put the closed-hangar ship out of action. He planned to minimize the effect of bombs bursting in the hangar of any new carrier by breaking up its area with splinter bulkheads. Power-operated doors between the protected hangar and the unarmoured lifts at the ends would protect the hangar from bombs entering the latter.[4]

Two important points were not as yet evident. First, the open hangar allowed for a side lift. In February 1943 the US Navy was only beginning to use such lifts aboard *Essex* class carriers, and thus it was only beginning to appreciate their considerable virtues, among which the chief was that they allowed aircraft to be fed up into the launching area forward while others were recovered aft. Second, the large openings in US hangar sides made underway replenishment relatively easy.

Again, this was not yet well understood, but it would deeply impress British observers in the Western Pacific a year or so later.

There was also another important issue. For a given tonnge, British carriers tended to be considerably shorter than their American counterparts. The Americans accepted very high hull stresses because for them a long hull had a direct tactical value: the carrier air group was based on the numbers which could be ranged, ready to take off for a strike, on the flight deck. In British cariers, the air group was set by the area of the hangar deck(s) with, perhaps, an allowance for a limited deck park. Aircraft could be stowed three abreast in the hangar, but they needed more space on the flight deck.[5] As a consequence, whenever the air component of the Royal Navy demanded a longer flight deck, it had severe structural and size consequences. This was not so evident in the *Malta* class as in the abortive 1952 carrier, in which the British found it impossible on about 45,000 tons to provide a flight deck as long as that aboard a 30,000 ton *Essex*. This point was obscured because British closed-hangar carriers, particularly those with double hangars, had considerably greater hangar areas than American ships. They carried fewer aircraft because the basis for calculating aircraft numbers was so different.

The Future Building Committee did emphasize effective length of flight deck in its submission to the Board of September 1943.

EARLY IN FEBRUARY 1943 Goodall called for two parallel design studies, A and B. Design A would be about 850ft long on the waterline, driven by *Ark Royal* machinery. Goodall hoped that the increased length would give him the increased speed now required. It was, essentially, a longer and faster *Ark Royal*. Two alternative hangar configurations would be considered: (i) a single wide hangar with a long protected flight deck, and (ii) a double hangar with three lifts, divided up by transverse bulkheads. Alternative (i) would have protected sides and narrow external gallery decks for working the ship; it would be almost an American-style hangar, except that it would be closed. Hangar length would be increased about 100ft to match the area of the double hangar in *Ark Royal*. In both cases, hangars would be closed, the flight deck being the strength deck (as in earlier British carriers). However, special attention would be paid to hangar ventilation, so that aircraft could be started up in the hangar.

Accommodation would be provided below the flight deck and the hangar roof. Protection would include a 3in belt and underwater protection would be lengthened, compared to current practice, to include all petrol stowage. Many ships had been immobilized by propeller or rudder hits; Goodall suggested that secondary (bow) propellers be fitted, driven electrically from the ship's electric power circuit. There was also interest in an auxiliary bow rudder. The flight deck would be 4in thick, as in *Ark Royal*, and Goodall hoped for a 5in deck over the citadel. Armament would generally match that of the *Ark Royal* (but with more quadruple 20mm cannon), and not fewer than sixty large aircraft would be stowed on the hangar deck.

Design B was substantially larger, 900ft on the waterline (950 overall), and Goodall was willing to accept a maximum beam of 123ft. He expected that four shafts would suffice, but wanted his designers to investigate the desirability of using five. Otherwise Design B would generally match Design A, with any improvements in protection which could be achieved on up to about 50,000 tons (standard).

The 850ft design seems to have been dropped quite early. The Future Building Committee wanted something larger, and seems to have been willing to go to the limit of what could be

3   It could be argued that the Royal Navy had to fear a build-up of explosive petrol vapour, whereas this would present no problem in an open hangar. Several closed-hangar ships, including USS *Lexington* and the Japanese *Taiho*, were destroyed by hangar vapour explosions. Goodall argued that in US ships petrol vapour tended to penetrate below the hangar deck, for instance into mess decks and galleys; one DNC observer noted a pervasive smell of petrol below decks. Goodall argued that there was always a fire risk in a hangar filled with petrol-powered aircraft. The Royal Navy closed hangar operated under magazine regulations, and so was much less likely to suffer an accidental fire. Moreover, fire could spread more easily through hatches let into the hangar deck itself, whereas the Royal Navy hangar was specially designed to be isolated.

4   The Fifth Sea Lord had been particularly impressed by a hit on *Illustrious*. The hand-operated hangar doors were open and the blast from the lift well spread through them. Goodall argued that power-operated doors would have solved this problem, since they could have been closed whenever the lift was up, and quickly opened only when needed.

5   For example, at under 20,000 tons the prewar *Yorktown* was 824ft 9in long, compared to 800ft for the 22,000-ton *Ark Royal*. Presumably part of the reason was that light US flight decks could easily be extended fore and aft, whereas even in unarmoured British carriers the flight deck was a very substantial, hence relatively heavy, structure.

6   The US docks were South Boston, Roosevelt Roads, Puget Sound (Nos 4 and 5), Pearl Harbor (Nos 2 and 4), Bayonne, Norfolk, Philadelphia, Hunters Point, Brooklyn (Nos 5 and 6), and some floating drydocks. However, the carrier could not have docked at Brooklyn because she could not have passed under the Brooklyn Bridge, a restriction somewhat analogous to those applying to the Gladstone Dock at Liverpool.

built in Britain. In 1943 there were only three slips large enough, a fourth being suitable only after considerable improvement. Much the same considerations would have applied to almost anything larger than *Ark Royal*.

Thus by early April the designers were working on four studies (see Table 14-1), two with double (Design A) and two with single (Design B) hangars. Building facilities limited these ships to a maximum waterline beam of 114ft, a figure which was later somewhat relaxed. In these and later designs, overall width above the waterline was limited to 135 or 136ft, so that the ship could pass through the new (140ft) locks then being planned for the Panama Canal.

Ships this large could be accommodated in only a few British dry or graving docks, largely because a hard-pressed Admiralty had concentrated on ships rather than infrastructure during the period immediately before World War I, when ships grew so rapidly. Nor had there been money for new facilities postwar; the only major interwar graving dock was at the new Far East naval base, Singapore. By way of contrast, the US Navy invested very heavily in infrastructure, both immediately after World War I and just before and during World War II, so that many of its docks could have accommodated 50,000-ton carriers.[6] In 1943 the only available British installations were the big liner docks at Southampton (King George V) and Liverpool (Gladstone Dock), a floating dock, AFD 11 at Portsmouth, and the new AFD 35 (scheduled to complete in 1945). Abroad, there were large docks at Singapore, Capetown (to complete 1945), Sydney (to complete 1944), Esquimault, St Johns, Nova Scotia, and Quebec, plus a floating dock, AFD 23, at Trincomalee. However, it was difficult to manoeuvre very big carriers into floating drydocks, due to their overhang. This issue, whether big carriers were really practical to operate, would affect the later discussions of carrier size.

DNC wanted a minimum of 5in of armour on the citadel (main armour deck) under 4in of flight deck armour. He was offered both four- and five-shaft powerplants, preferring the latter because it provided a centre shaft less likely to be knocked out by a torpedo. This configuration had been recommended

Table 14-1: Large Carrier Studies, 6 April 1943

	A(i)	A(ii)	B(i)	B(ii)
LOA (ft)	950	950	950	950
LWL (ft)	900	900	900	900
Beam (ft)	122	118 6	114	114
Beam, maximum (ft)			135	135
Flight deck width abreast island (ft)			91	93 6
Protected length (ft)			446	465
Depth (ft)	91 3	91 3	78 4	78 4
Lifts			3	2
Hangar area (sq ft)			46,500	54,700
Displacement (tons) std	46,290	43,120	43,000	43,360
deep	54,500		53,000	53,440

Note A(i) and (ii) were double hangar and B(i) and (ii) single hangar designs.

after the loss of HMS *Prince of Wales*. Bow (tractor) screws were ruled out by the high required speed. Weight limitations made it impossible to provide more than 3in of belt armour (compared with 4.5in in *Ark Royal*). This was accepted on the assumption that bombs, rather than shellfire, were the primary threat. The combination of 4in flight deck (on 1.5in plating) and 5in citadel deck would keep out a 2000lb bomb dropped at 450ft per second (300mph) in a 70-degree dive. It would completely defeat 500 and 1000lb bombs dropped by similar dive-bombers. Similarly, it would defeat a 2000lb bomb dropped by a level bomber (at 200mph) from 8000ft, a 1000lb bomb from 22,000, and a 500lb from any height. The citadel-deck armour was later reduced to 4in reducing the keep-out height for a dive-bombed 2000lb bomb to 5600ft. Hangar sides at all stages of the design were 2in thick, which was considered equivalent to a 4in deck.

The two B designs differed in hangar and machinery arrangements, B(i) having three lifts and B(ii) two. In B(i) flight deck structure was slightly narrower, and the hangar was offset 4ft to port to balance the moment of the island. In B(ii) it was offset only 2ft, but the total available width was used more efficiently, so that the hangar was 100ft rather than 98) wide. Both designs showed two funnels, which were expected to entail the minimum loss of gallery and island deck area. In B(ii)

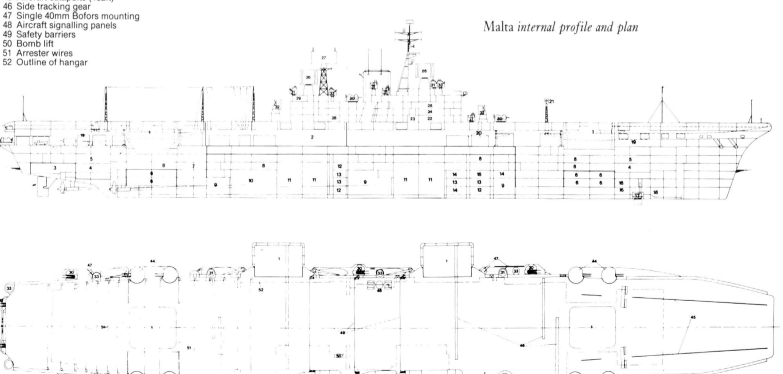

Malta internal profile and plan

the hangar bulkhead abreast the uptakes was twisted outboard instead of being pierced, for maximum continuity for strength. B(ii) was selected for further development.

Late in April DNC added a third study, Design C, essentially an enlarged *Ark Royal*. She was similar to B except for her double hangar. They are compared in Table 14-2.

All of these closed-hangar designs can be contrasted with a series of contemporary open-hangar studies. The first had a single hangar extending across the beam, with open sides, and with three lifts, including a midships deck-edge unit. The 4in hangar deck was the strength deck, and the flight deck was unarmoured. Other protection included 6in armour on the main deck and 2in bulkheads (with 4in on the flight deck) around the uptakes. The 220,000shp powerplant had five shafts. Displacement would have been 49,300 tons (standard) or 61,060 tons (deep load).

Protection was unimpressive, but difficult to improve. Scheme A showed 6in over the citadel (or equivalent to the lower hangar deck), a 3in strength deck being worked in 8ft 6in above it. All structure above that was discontinuous, fitted with expansion joints, and the hangar deck was unarmoured. The hangar deck was broken up by 2in bulkheads. The result showed stresses much beyond those standard in British practice, though comparable to American.

In scheme B, the depth of the ship was increased (from 53ft 6in to 58ft 9in) to reduce stresses, and the longitudinals in the double bottom increased from 1in to 2in in thickness. The result was too much topweight, even though the hangar deck was reduced to 2in. Displacement was 49,500 tons (standard) or 61,300 tons fully loaded. GM was 9.50ft in standard condition, or 12.99ft fully loaded, somewhat better than in the first version.

In a third version (C), beam was reduced to 112ft, as in *Ark Royal*. Standard displacement fell to 48,400 tons (60,000 fully loaded).

THREE OF THESE large carriers were ordered on 15 July 1943; *Malta* from John Brown, *Gibraltar* from Vickers (Walker Yard), and *New Zealand* from Cammell Laird. The Cammell Laird order was cancelled on 17 June 1944, and on 13 July Harland & Wolff was informed that *New Zealand* would ultimately be ordered from them.

In July 1943 no specific design had as yet been chosen. As none of the open-hangar designs was particularly exciting, Designs B(ii) and C were submitted to the Board on 17 July 1943. DNC found C more attractive, because it provided substantially more hangar area on 1700 tons less displacement. On the other hand, B(ii) had better access, because a complete upper deck extended across the ship under the hangar deck, so that access to spaces below it could be arranged along the centreline.

These were very large ships, and every effort had to be made to reduce their loads. Given existing scales of bomb loading, for example, an air group of 100 to 120 aircraft entailed large ammunition weight and volume, which was difficult to accommodate within a limited armoured box. In August 1943 DAWT and DACR agreed to reduce the total per bomber from seven to 4½ loads.[7] The big air group required proportionately large numbers of flight deck and hangar deck crew, so that total accommodation was badly squeezed; the estimated complement of Design C grew by 10 per cent (3000 to 3300) between May and July 1943, and the nominal aircraft load increased from seventy-eight to 108.

The Fifth Sea Lord, ACNS (Air), and other interested members of the Naval Staff met on 3 September to compare B(ii) and C, ultimately deciding in favour of C despite an early preference for the simpler single hangar, that is for B(ii), by

Table 14-2: Designs B(ii) and C, 17 July 1943

	B(ii)	C
LWL (ft)	900	————————————
LOA (ft)	950	——
Beam, moulded (ft)	114	——
Depth to flight deck (ft)	80 4	87 2
Std displacement (tons)	45,700	44,500
Std draught (ft)	27 9	27 2½
Deep displacement (tons)	56,300	55,100
Deep draught (ft)	32 8	32 7
SHP	190,000	——
Speed, deep and clean (knots)	32.8	33
Fuel oil (tons)	8500	——
Endurance (nm)	6500 at 24 knots	——————————
Armament	16 4.5in DP	————————————
	8 8-barrel pom-poms	
	32 twin 20mm	
Hangar area (sq ft)	54,000	62,000
Length of flight deck armour (ft)	468	422
Length of citadel (ft)	422	422
Protected area (sq ft)	47,600	55,000
Flight deck length (ft)	950	——
Lifts	2, 33 × 54ft	————————————
Catapults	2	——
Petrol (gallons)	130,000	——
Bomb lifts	3	——
Flight deck armour	4in	——
Hangar sides and divisional bulkhead armour	2in	——
Citadel armour	5in deck, 3in bulkhead and side belt	
Steering gear	5in crown, 3in and 1in side and end	
Underwater protection	against 2000lb charge—————	
Max hogging stress, flight deck (tons)	8.8	9.5
GM std	6.4	5.85
deep	10.20	9.76
Weights (tons)		
Hull structure	18,070	17,505
Hull incidentals, general fittings	5420	5620
Protection	11,955	11,087
Machinery	4150	4150
Armament	1307	1307
Aircraft equipment	2338	2400
Gen equipment	2000	2075
Displacement ex margin	45,240	43,996
Margin	452	440
Std displacement	45,692	44,436
Deep displacement	56,330	55,070

Notes Both had five-shaft machinery, using *Ark Royal* units (38,000shp each), to give a total of 190,000. The stress figures given compared with 6.5 tons in *Ark Royal* as then designed. Neither could be fitted with a midships lift, because this would have cut too much out of the strength deck, raising maximum stress to about 11.9 tons in the single-hangar ship, and even higher in the double-hangar, nor was it clear that such a lift could be accommodated amidships among the uptakes.

DAWT and DACR.[8] This decision was confirmed at a Future Building Committee meeting three days later. This meeting also agreed not to follow American practice in mounting guns at the extreme ends of the ship; to increase petrol stowage (from 130,000 to 150,000 and then to 195,000 gallons); to widen the flight deck (but maintain the width of the island at about 21ft), and to mount nine sextuple Bofors guns instead of the planned eight pom-poms.[9] Oil fuel stowage was increased from 8500 to 8600 tons. At this stage the ship had two funnels, and her island was already substantially longer than those of earlier ships (238ft versus 162ft in *Implacable* and 182ft in *Ark Royal*). It had to accommodate several new radars then under development.[10] The two funnels could not be trunked together because of the lead of the uptakes from the dispersed machinery; trunking would have eaten up valuable hangar space.

The Board approved Design C on 8 October 1943, and DNC began to develop a detailed design. Table 14-3 compares a mature version of Design C with *Ark Royal*, from which it was (in effect) descended, and with the US *Midway* design as then understood; various members of the Naval Staff constantly compared various versions of the 1943 carrier with the *Midway* design. The contemplated air group, which determined the ammunition load, was fifty-four TBR and fifty-four fighters, or thirty-six TBR and seventy-two fighters.

There must have been some fear that Design C was too large because, at the Controller's verbal request, developed sketch designs were requested of the largest carrier which could be

7   In both cases, single loads of 500lb SAP and 500lb HC bombs were carried. The change was to reduce the load of B bombs from one to a half load. In gross terms this was about a 35 per cent reduction in bomb weight and volume. Petrol stowage was based on five days of operation, each aircraft averaging one and a half sorties (total 7.5 sorties per aircraft), which did approximate seven bomb loads per bomber.

8   The single hangar imposed much less restriction on the folded width of each aircraft, and thus allowed for more future development (for instance, for designers to go from the allowed 20ft to 22ft). It allowed four abreast at even 22ft, whereas in Design C folded width had to be limited to 19ft, for rows of three. A roomier hangar made for easier (hence quicker) movement of aircraft, and the lifts had a shorter distance to travel. Design B also had a roomy full gallery deck under the flight deck, accommodating aircraft personnel near their places of work. Design C, however, had a greater total hangar area, and therefore could always be expected to stow more aircraft. It had more exits from hangars to lifts, which might compensate for B's roominess. Although C lacked a full gallery deck, its side galleries were roomy, and in the tropics they might not be as uncomfortable as a deck directly under the flight

deck – a point familiar to many US carrier sailors. In July 1943 the Naval Staff estimated that B would be able to stow twenty-four TBR (taken as large size, 44 x 22ft) and thirty fighters (Seafire size), compared to twenty-four TBR and sixty fighters in C, in each case excluding a typical deck park (twenty TBR and twenty fighters). These arguments convinced the doubters, although the issue of future aircraft design flexibility remained. The big new carrier was, after all, an opportunity to design much larger naval aircraft; one Staff commentator suggested that, if this opportunity was not taken, the *Ark Royals* might be quite large enough.

9   At this stage a close-range battery of eight pom-poms and thirty-four twin Oerlikons was shown, including two on the flight deck forward of the island, where the forward mounting actually interfered with aircraft ranging up to be fired from the starboard catapult. DGD suggested some alternatives: eight pom-poms, eleven single Oerlikons, and either twenty-eight twin Oerlikons or five twin Bofors Busters and twenty-one twin Oerlikons; or nine pom-poms and eleven single Oerlikons and either twenty-five twin Oerlikons or four Busters and twenty twin Oerlikons.

10   In March 1944 the list of radars was two air search (WA) sets, similar to 960 and 990, one short range air/surface search set (WS/WCH), similar to 295 (the planned successor to 293), one surface search (WS) set, appropriate gunnery sets, two IFF interrogators, one radar beacon (similar to 251M), and a blind approach system. Other major electronic equipment was HF D/F, two VHF D/F (one for ESM, known as 'Y,' and one for aircraft), four HF radio-telephone channels, eight VHF radio-telephone channels, two emergency VHF radio-telephone channels and an aircraft homing beacon. By way of comparison, in August 1944 the ship (Design X) was to have had four air search sets (including height finders), four surface search sets (with interrogators), eight search/fire control sets (including transponders), a radar homing beacon, a beam approach beacon, and DF on all three frequency bands (including ESM, anti-missile and anti-radar). Radio requirements were two MF transmitters (one high and one medium power), and fourteen VHF transmitters (ten for ship-to-air and four for ship-to-ship), aside from emergency sets.

Table 14-3: Designs C and X Compared with *Ark Royal* and *Midway*

	Design C	Ark Royal	Midway	Design X
LBP (ft)	870	720	861	870
LWL (ft)	900	750	900	900
LOA (ft)	950	795	968	947
Flight deck length (ft)	950	795	932	938
Beam, extreme (ft)	136	136	136	136
B(WL)	115 5½	112 8½	114 2¾	115 5½
Std displacement (tons)	45,620	33,000	45,000	48,400
Draught (ft)	27 11½	25 5½	28	29 3½
Freeboard (ft)	59 2½	60 8½	56 6	29 5¼
Draught, deep (ft)	33 4½	31 0½	34 0	34 7
Displacement, deep (tons)	57,300	42,400	56,000	60,000
SHP	190,000	182,000	212,000	220,000
Speed (knots) std	33½	32	—	34½
Deep	32½	31½	33	33
Fuel oil (tons)	8900	7400	10,210	8800
Endurance at 24 knots deep/dirty (nm)	6500	6000		6000
Complement, as flagship	2980	2580	3500	3300
Petrol (gallons)	195,000	103,000	230,000	190,000
Armament				
4.5in HA	16 (400rpg)	16 (400rpg)		16 (400rpg)
Bofors, sextuple	8 (1440rpb)	8 (1440rpb)		8 (1440rpb)
20mm, twin	34 (2400rpb)	30 (2400rpb)		40/50 (2400rpb)
5in DP, single			18	
40mm, quad			15	
20mm, single			54	
Torpedoes	90	75		68
Depth charges	324	252		180
A mines	24	24		
Hangar area (sq ft)	69,800	52,100	58,500	61,770
Flight deck area (sq ft)	90,100		100,000	102,000
(Figures below are 'worst cases' for which stowage is provided)				
Bombs	54 TBR/54 FF	42 TBR/36 FF		
Ammunition	36 TBR/72FF	24 TBR/54 FF		
Protection				
Side armour	3in NC	4½in C (4in C + 1½in NC)	7.6 STS	3in NC
Bulkhead	3in NC	4½in C	6.3 & 1 STS	3in & 2in NC
Magazine side	3in NC	4½in C		
end	3in & 2in NC	4½ C & 2 NC		3 NC
Hangar side	2in NC	1½in NC	—	—
end	2in NC	1½in NC	1 STS in hangar	—
Steering gear sides	3in NC	4½in C & 2in NC	6.3 STS	
Decks	5in NC & 4in NC	2½in & 1½in NC	2 STS (2 decks)	6in NC
Magazine crowns	5in NC	4in NC		
Steering gear crown	5 NC	4 NC		6 NC
Flight deck	4in NC on 1½in	4in NC on 1in	3.5 STS	—
Protective plating	¾in, ½in, ⅜in	¾in, ½in, ⅜in		¾in, ½, ⅜in
Underwater charge	2000lb	2000lb		2000lb
Weights (tons)				
General equipment	2380	1610		2520
Aircraft equipment	3290	2310		3500
Machinery	4370	3240		4515
Armament	1440	1300		1380
Armour, protection	10,610	6300		8506
Hull	25,180	18,070		27,505
Board margin	470	80		475
Std displacement	47,740	33,000	47,600	48,460

docked in No 10 dock at Devonport, and figures were submitted on 31 January 1944. This dock consisted of two docks lined up and merged into one, widened on one side only. It would admit a ship about 50ft longer than HMS *Ark Royal* (765ft LBP, 845ft on the flight deck). DNC estimated that eighty-seven aircraft could be operated, compared to eighty in *Ark Royal*, using wider hangars, and protection would approximate that of Design C. These studies are presented in Table 14-4. They are significant as an indication of the real limits imposed by existing British facilities, limits which would surface again later in the year and again in 1952.

THE BOARD'S 1943 DECISION was reversed later in 1944; the Fifth Sea Lord came more and more to prefer an American-style open hangar, on the basis that the crucial question was not how many aircraft were carried, but rather how many she could fly off in a single strike operation. This was generally phrased as a requirement that the carrier be able to fly on or off all her

aircraft in a single operation. Quick launching of the entire air group required that engines could be run up in the hangar, both for warming up and so that aircraft could taxi onto the lifts under their own power. This alone mandated an open-sided hangar, quite aside from the great advantages of deck-edge lifts. Mass take-off also required the largest possible flight deck, as wide as possible aft, so that as many aircraft as possible could be ranged aft to take off. Mass landing required the greatest possible width forward, to park aircraft as they were recovered. Together, these considerations implied a flight deck as close to rectangular as possible, with the minimum of indentations. To keep the deck clear, it would need a continuous walkway down its entire length.

DNC did not surrender easily. He investigated a closed-hangar design with a deck-edge lift, and also the extent to which the after end of the upper hangar could be opened so that engines could be warmed up. DNC found that the deck-edge lift would cut so deeply into the side of the ship (the vertical

Table 14-4: Carrier to Fit Devonport Dock

	Ark Royal	112ft	114ft
Length (ft)	720	765	765
LWL (ft)	750	820	820
Beam (ft)	112	112	114
Displacement (tons)	33,036	35,074	35,650
GM	5.9	5.0	6.5
Draught (ft)		25 6½	25 4
Displacement, deep (tons)	42,425	45,125	45,400
GM	10.2	9.3	10.5
Draught (ft)	31 6	31	30 7½
Speed, deep (knots)	31.25	31.7	31.7
Weights (tons)			
Structure	18,123	19,430	19,625
Protection	6391	6435	6510
Machinery	3380	3400	3400
Armament	1214	1214	1214
General equipment	2235	2515	2515
Aircraft equipment	1613	2030	2030
Margin	80	350	356
Std displacement	33,036	35,374	35,650

flange of the hull girder) that the flight deck could no longer be the strength deck, that is, that the hangar would have to be open. Warming up was another matter; DNC proposed that the after lift be split (one lift moving aircraft from lower to upper hangar, one from upper hangar to flight deck). Ten aircraft could warm up in the space between the upper lift and the stern. DNC argued that this would suffice, because most of the aircraft could be ranged on deck, warming up there. As the deck park emptied, the rest could be fed up quickly enough from the after lift, which would be moved as far aft as possible.[11]

The Fifth Sea Lord rejected these ideas and convinced the Board to reopen the question. Because the design was being reconsidered, on 27 April 1944 Vickers (Walker) was told to suspend orders for material. On 15 May 1944 the Board ordered DNC to produce a new design, with deck-edge lifts. This decision was formally approved by the Sea Lords on 19 May. The new version, which was submitted to the Board on 10 August 1944, became Design X (see Table 12-3). By arrangement with the Controller, a detailed design was developed and completed ready for submission, but it was never approved. Instead, a modified version was developed in 1945 (see below).

The new design was developed entirely without flight deck armour, on the theory that the open hangar sides would drastically reduce the value of any such protection. To DNC, this explained the lack of flight deck armour in US open-hangar carriers. US practice in the *Essex* class was to provide separate hangar and main protective decks, but this limited the protective value per ton of plating. Instead, deck armour in Design X was concentrated in a single 6in deck over the citadel, which DNC estimated would protect the vitals of the ship approximately as well as the combination of flight deck and citadel armour in the original closed-hangar design. Side armour was the corresponding thickness, 3in.[12] Underwater protection was based on war experience of damage due to near-miss bombs, but was also intended to defeat a 2000lb contact charge.[13]

The hangar deck was the strength deck, but DNC placed the 6in armour lower in the ship, arguing that the hangar deck was penetrated by too many hatches. The Fifth Sea Lord felt that this did away with many of the advantages of the open hangar, since a bomb penetrating the hangar deck would explode in an enclosed space, and thus with magnified effect.

The decision not to armour the flight deck was approved by the Controller and the Fifth Sea Lord early in June 1944. Later that month a meeting at the Admiralty to consider DNC proposals, chaired by Fifth Sea Lord and including DAWT, DACR and DNAC, decided that:

(a) As there would be no space between the deep beams overhead in the hangar and as in any case aircraft would have to taxi about the hangar, the swing of their propellers should come within the limiting height of 17ft laid down for the aircraft.
(b) The flight deck should be covered with wood.
(c) Four lifts should be fitted, two on the side; the Fifth Sea Lord later agreed that they would be on the port side.
(d) Two catapults were essential for quick launching of a massive deck-load strike.
(e) The four-cornered arrangement of 4.5in turrets should be employed as, compared with the American (*Midway*) design, it did not restrict the width of the flight deck.
(f) To avoid encroaching on the hangar, torpedoes should be stowed below.
(g) Hangar divisional bulkheads should not be fitted as they would obstruct the movement of aircraft.
(h) Only one of the three bomb lifts need go up to the flight deck.

The side of the hangar was open, to accommodate two 60 x 35ft deck-edge lifts (in addition to the two 54 x 46ft centreline units).[14] It was clearly desirable to limit the crash barriers to the space between the two lifts, so that the forward one could feed the two catapults, so the number of barriers had to be reduced to three from the four of HMS *Ark Royal*. This sacrifice was considered acceptable, partly because the fourth barrier (which was well aft) had been included in *Ark Royal* specifically to allow additional parking space in emergency. The design showed sixteen arrester wires.

Structurally, the new ship differed from earlier British carriers in that, since the flight deck was a superstructure, it had to be broken by expansion joints. The continuous length of the island was limited by the need for an expansion joint approximately amidships, and it was therefore split into two units on either side of the joint. DNC considered this an advantage for smooth airflow. In contrast with contemporary American practice, the fore end of the ship was plated in to withstand Atlantic weather. The US Navy would only follow suit about a decade later, although its big carriers were already suffering storm damage forward.

The new carrier was designed to accommodate 30,000lb aircraft, this being the limit set by the Future Building Committee. Because all future high-performance aircraft (particularly jets) would have to be catapult-launched, the two units at the bow had to provide both high end speeds (for heavy aircraft) and rapid-firing, a combination which complicated their design and increased their size and weight.[15] It then became important to specify how much wind over the deck could be added to the speed of the catapult; in August 1945 DNC proposed that the standard be within 3 knots of ship speed, no natural wind being taken into account.

This was the beginning of a major problem, as an end speed of 130 knots was suggested. In September 1945 RAE doubted that this speed should be assigned to any strike aircraft weighing over 20,000lbs, but DAWT wanted the full weight, arguing that the strike aircraft of the future would surely grow to meet whatever limit the ship imposed.

The acceleration a pilot could withstand set catapult length in terms of end speed. If the limit were taken as 5 g, the space between the expansion joint forward of the forward lift and the bow effectively limited end speed to 120 knots (the catapult was a few feet too long). It was impossible to move the lift, and therefore impossible to move the expansion joint. Since 130

11   If aircraft took off unassisted, a 500ft long area had to be kept clear forward, leaving space for about 50 to 60 per cent of the aircraft. Even larger numbers (ninety Fireflies or eighty Barracudas or eighty-four new fleet fighters or sixty-one new TBR) could be parked abaft the two catapults in the bow. DNC proposed that the deck park be fleeted forward as aircraft were launched, replenished from the after lift. A launch rate of 20 seconds equated to fifteen aircraft every 5 minutes, giving plenty of time for warming up aircraft fresh from the hangar. Assuming a lift cycle of 45 seconds (including 10 to load and 10 to unload) and a 20-second launch rate, the total number of aircraft launchable in a single strike would be the deck plus $^{20}/_{45}$ of the deck park (aircraft brought up from below while launching), or 44.5 per cent of the area of the deck park. Any greater hangar capacity could not be used to feed the single strike.

12   The 6in deck was expected to protect against a British-type 2000lb AP bomb (Mk III) dropped from 5800ft at 300ft per second (200mph), or from 4800ft at 450ft per second (300mph), or dive-bombed at 300mph from 3800ft (70-degree dive). Similarly, it could protect against the German 500kg (1100lb) SD bomb dropped from 16,800ft at 200mph, or from 15,600ft at 300mph, or dive-bombed from 13,500ft (300mph, 70-degree dive). Under these circumstances, 3in side armour provided equivalent anti-bomb protection. The same side armour could keep out 4.5in (55lb) SAP BC shells at 8700 yards, or 6in (112lb) SAP BC at 14,600lbs. The Staff Requirements called for the main deck to protect against a 2000lb bomb dropped from 3600ft, and for the side belt and magazine armour to protect against a 100lb rocket head at 1100ft per second. Note that it would take 6.9in to keep out a 4000lb bomb dropped from 5800ft.

13   This figure was frequently used at the time. However, in 1945 a caisson representing HMS *Malta* failed to defeat a 1000lb charge. As a result, expectations for the 1952 carrier were far more conservative.

14   It proved impossible to widen the deck-edge lifts to 48ft 6in. The original requirement was that all lifts should be at least 54ft × 46ft 6in.

15   The agreed launch rate was once every 20 seconds, that is once every 40 seconds per catapult. However, in September 1945 DACR argued that this was too slow, and that a large strike would take too long to launch. A 15-second launch rate had to be accepted. Although such timing was not critical for long-endurance piston aircraft, short-endurance jets were a very different proposition, the number of aircraft in a carrier strike ultimately being limited by the requirement that those launched be recovered before a new strike could go off.

The intended Barracuda re-placement, the Fairey Spear-fish, in flight during 1945. FAAM

Below: *The prototype Short Sturgeon Mk 1, pictured in June 1946. Like HMS* Malta, *both these aircraft fell victim to the changed require-ments of the Royal Navy in the post-war world.* FAAM

knots was wanted, E-in-C and RAE agreed on 6 g, with the accelerator usually set at 5 g (120 knots) for fighters; in 1945 RAE hoped that even 7 g would eventually be acceptable.

The 190,000shp of Design C was increased to 220,000, and a new four-shaft arrangement (with double-reduction gearing) was substituted for the earlier five-shaft plant. The critical factor seems to have been internal space: the five-shaft plant could only just be squeezed into the planned length of citadel. Any increase would make the ship larger and heavier, but that was unacceptable because she was already at the limit. The four-shaft plant was 49ft shorter, so that the citadel could be 20ft shorter while still accommodating all of the aviation petrol (20 per cent had to be stowed outside in the five-shaft design). Against this, the four-shaft ship would be slightly less manoeuvrable, propellers would be larger, and the loads on shaft brackets and stern tubes substantially greater.

During the discussion of Design X, DAWT suggested that future naval aircraft might well carry 4000lb AP bombs, and therefore that the carrier of the future should be protected against them. He also wanted this armour on the hangar deck, so that explosions could be vented properly. DNC estimated that it would take 7.5in of deck armour (1800 more tons) to defeat a 4000lb AP bomb. The Germans had just introduced a rocket-assisted 1400kg (3080lb) bomb; a ship would need 10.7in to defeat such a weapon dropped from 4000ft at 450ft per second at a 50-degree dive angle. The extra 1800 tons would cost 9.5in in draft, 0.3ft of GM, and a quarter-knot of speed, and the ship would find it more difficult to enter bases such as Portsmouth and Devonport or to pass through the Suez Canal.

Alternatively the protection might be rearranged, with heavy deck armour confined to the space between the holding bulkheads of the underwater protection system. Between the keel and the main (armour) deck, the holding bulkheads could be thickened to 3in, to form an armour box including the heavier, but narrower, armour deck. The external belt was eliminated as the armour on the holding bulkheads formed a deep belt to defeat diving rockets and bombs. This new arrangement allowed a thicker deck (6.9in) without any displacement penalty, and might be better than the earlier shallow belt against

steeply-diving rockets. Its main defect was that it could not prevent bombs from penetrating and damaging the torpedo protection from above. This new scheme was presented to the Controller on 14 October 1944. DNOR was asked to evaluate it by analysing carrier losses to date. By the time his paper was ready, on 9 March 1945, work was proceeding on a modified design, X1 (see below).

DESIGN X WAS VERY LARGE, and in October 1944 D of N (Director of Navigation) suggested that it was impractically so, and that in particular a Design X carrier would be unable to berth at Portsmouth and Plymouth. DNC was asked to produce two new designs, X1 and Y (see Table 14-5). Y was sized for Devonport drydock but had an open hangar.

D of N emphasized problems of manoeuvrability, for example in the Suez Canal (he was not sure the Canal Co would accept her at all), while oiling at sea (due in part to the side lifts), even while mooring. He rejected comparisons with large liners on the ground that warships and liners generally did not use the same ports, and that existing bases were very constricted. The large sail area of the ship would make matters considerably worse. ACNS(F) argued that smaller carriers would be easier to maintain (for instance, to dock) and could be handled more easily in constricted harbours. However, aside from the island, Design X had little more sail area than a US *Essex* or *Midway*. The sail area issue had been raised (and rejected) in connection with the old *Ark Royal*, which had about 92 per cent of the sail area of Design X, yet, with much shallower draft, she had manoeuvred well in harbour.

The Fifth Sea Lord countered that the largest possible carrier was needed to launch long-range strikes. Although the new light fleet carrier (*Hermes*) could also support 30,000lb aircraft, she could not fly off her full air group at one time, and the effective ratio of effort was up to 6:1 in favour of the large carrier. Existing light fleet carriers could barely operate existing aircraft, and a new fleet carrier would remain in service for twenty or thirty years, during a period of very rapid aircraft growth, both in performance and probably in size. As a result, requirements for landing and parking area would, if anything, grow substantially. DACR considered two deck-edge lifts

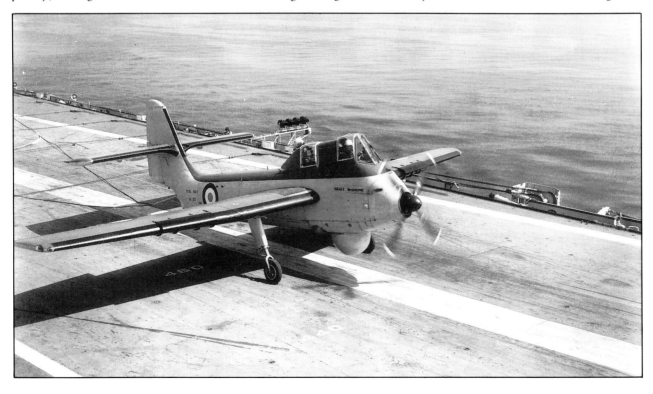

The short Seamew undergoing deck trials aboard HMS Bulwark *in 1955. FAAM (photograph courtesy D Joyce)*

Table 14-5: Alternative Designs: X, X1, Y

	X	X1	Y
LWL (ft)	900	850	750
Beam (ft)	115 6	115 6	112 5
Displacement (tons) deep	60,000	56,650	45,640
standard	48,400	46,500	36,740
Armour on main deck (in)	6	6	4½
Draught, deep (ft)	34 7	34 7	33 1
Speed (knots)	33	32½	31½
SHP	220,000	200,000	180,000
Hangar area (sq ft)	61,770	56,950	46,800
Hangar area per ton std displacement (sq ft)	1.275	1.225	1.275*
Hangar plus flight deck area per ton (sq ft)	2.08	2.01	1.885
Flight deck dimensions (ft)	936 × 122	856 × 122	790 × 119
Aircraft	90	83	62
Aircraft per 1000 tons	1.86	1.725	1.655

Notes Y design could only have one deck-edge lift; X and X1 would have two. Main armament is the same in all three. The secondary armament in X1 was reduced slightly and in Y the secondary armament was about 25 per cent less than in X.
*Originally 41,200sq ft (1.885sq ft per ton)

essential for efficient operation, and this fixed the minimum flight deck length at about 838ft.

The larger the ship, the more efficient the design in terms of hangar area or aircraft per ton; she could maintain high speed more easily (shp per ton); she could enjoy greater endurance (because she required fewer shp per ton to cruise); her longer flight deck would be more efficient; she would be more seaworthy; she would be more survivable; and she could more easily accommodate a large complement.

Overall, it was clear that the Navy would not receive any more carriers for some considerable time, so that it was wisest to build the largest (hence most flexible) possible ships.

DNC was formally asked for new designs on 27 February 1945, and the First Sea Lord decided that the 50ft difference between Design X and Design X1 might be a decided disadvantage in restricted harbours such as Malta and Gibraltar, but that the X designs were clearly superior to Design Y. Design X1 was therefore tentatively adopted. It was submitted to the Board on 12 April 1945, and worked out in detail in anticipation of final Board approval. A Board Minute of 31 August 1945 indicated that the sketch design and legend had been noted, but that consideration was postponed to a later date. Legend data are given in Table 14-6.

The project died in the run-down at the end of the war, when slips were required much more urgently to make up for wartime losses of merchant shipping. HMS *Gibraltar* was cancelled on 15 November 1945 and the other two ships followed on 21 December. It seems unlikely that any had been laid down.

Design X1 reflected the armour analysis submitted by DNOR. The main above-water threats were airborne weapons, bombs (both direct hits and near misses) and rockets. Clearly some enemy aircraft could carry powerful enough weapons to defeat any practicable thickness of armour, but the heavier the armour the larger the aircraft, and the fewer the potential attackers. Heavy armour, particularly high in a ship, was costly, especially since the overall size of the new carrier had to be limited so that she could be built and then docked, but it could not be eliminated altogether. A totally unarmoured carrier, for example, could be riddled by small rockets, which would probably cause fatal fires. Splinters from near-miss bombs could tear up the ship's side, and destroy her stability and buoyancy.

Protection also affected the internal arrangements of the ship. For example, a new cruiser being designed in 1945 had 'vertical' magazines, offering a minimum target to bombs falling at steep angles; this was a simple trade-off against the danger of providing a larger target to shellfire and rockets.

Early in 1945 ACNS(W) tabled a series of questions, asking whether the flight deck of an open-hangar carrier should be armoured. DAWT proposed that, subject to the primary con-

sideration that no single underwater hit should be able to put all power (propulsive or service) out of action, much less sink the ship, armour should be provided:

(a) on the sides against a 500lb SAP rocket (1500ft per second) and against the blast and splinters of near-miss bombs (1in down to the underwater protection)

(b) on decks, against a 2000lb HC (non armour-piercing) bomb and minor weapons (rockets, 30mm cannon, etc)

(c) on flight decks (2in) only for closed hangars (though 3in hangar deck armour would be useful in an open-hangar ship)

He liked the vertical magazines, and wanted protection against future weapons exploding under the keel – a problem which remains more than four decades later. DNC estimated that (a) would require 5in side armour, assuming the rocket was similar to a 500lb SAP bomb. Provision (b) required 2½in deck

Table 14-6: Characteristics of Design X1

LOA (flight deck) (ft)	897
Flight deck dimensions (ft)	888 × 121 9 (max)
Flight deck area (sq ft)	96,900
Hangar deck area (sq ft)	56,950
LWL (ft)	850
LBP (ft)	820
Beam, moulded (ft)	115
Depth (ft)	86 3½
Std displacement (tons)	46,900
SHP	200,000
Speed, deep, clean (knots)	32
	30 (six months out of dock)
Speed, std (knots)	33.25
Endurance (nm)	
temperate	7100 at 20 knots; 5600 at 24 knots
tropics	6000 at 20 knots; 5000 at 24 knots
Centreline lifts	2 45 × 46ft, 30,000lb
Side lifts	2 54 × 36ft, 30,000lb*
Wires	16 (8 units)
Barriers	3
Catapults	2 (new type)
4.5in	16
Bofors	7 (sextuple)
Citadel armour	
deck	4in NC
side	4in NC
Holding bulkhead	4in/3½in/2in
4.5in magazine	4in NC deck/4in C side/3in NC end
Steering gear	4in NC deck/3in NC side and end
Weights (tons)	
Hull structure	19,800
Hull equipment & general fittings	6100
Protection	8630
Machinery	4225
Armament	1530
Aircraft equipment	5900
General equipment	2445
Board margin	570
Std displacement	46,890
draught (ft) 29 7.5	
GM 8.42	
Lube oil	40
50 cal ammunition	5
Petrol & aircraft lube oil	655
Water round petrol	915
Fresh water	355
RFW	340
Oil and diesel fuel	7000
Full load displacement	56,800
draught (ft) 34 6.5	
GM 12.3/11.6	
Additional oil fuel	900
Max oil stowage displacement	57,700
draught (ft) 35	
GM 12.8/12.10	

*Reduced from 60ft of Design X to support the sides of the lift opening on main transverse bulkheads. This was acceptable to DACR because it would be necessary to side-track aircraft onto them.

armour, which would also defeat 30mm cannon and 25lb solid-head rockets delivered at dive angles of 40 degrees or less (3in would be required to defeat rockets fired in steeper dives). However, much more would be required to defeat SAP or even GP bombs. It would take 4in, for example, to defeat 2000lb GP and 500lb SAP bombs.

DNC suggested a compromise position, that the ship should be protected against light-case bombs and also against bombs small enough to be dropped in large numbers. Stability would limit flight deck armour to $3\frac{1}{2}$in, assuming no other deck armour apart from 4in over the steering gear. Probably, however, it would be better to armour the hangar or even the main deck, so that the ship could have a completely armoured box over her citadel. DNC favoured 4in cemented belt armour, which would protect against rockets up to and including the new US 5in HVAR (Holy Moses), and would probably stop larger rockets fired at oblique angles. It would also defeat destroyer guns (4.5in) at 5000 yards, and cruiser guns at moderate ranges. A carrier so protected would displace about 56,650 tons (deep). A 3in NC belt (56,300 tons) would defeat any near-miss bomb; $1\frac{1}{2}$in would suffice up to 500lbs.

For the future, the most likely developments were very large guided bombs, beyond the capacity of practicable armour, and large rockets which could strike directly under the waterline. The Navy was then experimenting with a large-calibre rocket, the Uncle Tom, which could be stopped by $3\frac{1}{2}$in of armour spread over the holding bulkhead of an underwater protection system. Although nothing could be done about the impact of a large bomb, the ship might survive if her internal bulkheads localized its damage.

DNC, then, proposed 4in armour on hangar deck, belt (up to hangar deck level) and steering gear. Outside the holding bulkheads, the armour deck was dropped down to the main deck level to simplify access into the ship from the hangar. The waterline was protected against splinters by $1\frac{1}{2}$in NC armour extending 40ft forward and 60ft abaft the belt, plus a $1\frac{1}{2}$in torpedo bulkhead. In addition there were 3in bulkheads, and $4\text{in}/3\frac{1}{2}\text{in}/2\text{in}$ armour was worked on the holding bulkheads of the underwater protection system. Transverse bulkheads within the citadel were 60lbs ($1\frac{1}{2}$in) DW splinter armour, to localize the effects of penetrating hits and to counter under-the-bottom hits. This would save 1350 tons compared to the original scheme (Design X).

ACNS(W) held another meeting early in March, where the Staff Divisions called for sufficient protection over the 4.5in magazines (which were outside the citadel) to keep out a 3000lb weapon (1500ft per second), whether bomb or rocket. DNC rejected any such requirement, as the necessary side armour would have been 15in thick, with 10in end bulkheads, for a total weight of about 7500 tons. DNC could minimize the deck or target area represented by the magazines by arranging them in double tiers; he provided 4in sides, 4in decks and 3in ends. The Staff argued that since there was not enough weight to keep out AP weapons, there was no point in protecting against anything but HC bombs.[16] This implied $2\frac{1}{2}$in side and deck armour, and now DNC wanted his $1\frac{1}{2}$in anti-splinter armour extended about 100ft fore and aft of the main belt.

The side protection system was rated at 1200lbs (at 10ft below the deep waterline), or slightly more for a deeper charge. This system represented a compromise between thin plating for elastic deformation, and armour sufficient to defeat diving rockets such as the Uncle Tom. In the final version of the design, the holding bulkhead was protected by a 4in belt tapering at the top to $3\frac{1}{2}$in and at the bottom to 2in.

While this protection was being developed, Kamikazes were crashing into British armoured deck carriers. ACNS(A) asked whether the new carrier should have flight deck armour, given its obvious combat value. This would have added considerable weight, and on 20 May 1945 the First Sea Lord rejected it. No practicable armoured flight deck was likely to defeat the bomb of the future; 'I consider it best to abandon it in this open hangar design, and treat the Japanese suicide bomber, against which it is a defence, as a passing phase.'

The 50ft shrinkage had other consequences. The side lifts were shorter; some form of power-loading was envisaged, using side tracking. One sextuple Bofors had to be sacrificed and DNC had to accept that DGD might not be satisfied with only seven mountings. There were, however, few alternatives; a mount abaft the island on the flight deck would have encroached on the landing area, and there was very little space on the hangar deck. All DNC could offer was two mountings (rather than one) each side on the sponsons at the after end of the hangar deck, but then it would be difficult to provide satisfactory firing and director arcs. The legend showed forty Oerlikon barrels, but that was only a bare estimate, and DNC's sketches showed no locations.

It was also difficult to provide sufficient directors. DGD wanted four long-range (LRS) directors, but this had to be reduced to two because no suitable locations could be found on the port side without interfering with the flight deck. The Staff Requirement also included four medium-range directors (MRS), but the forward MRS was badly wooded. DGD rejected a proposed two-LRS and four-MRS installation, asking that the eight 4.5in mounts be separately controllable, that is, that there should be a minimum of eight directors. DNC proposed four MRSs for the two forward batteries (A and B) and three aft (X and Y), one of which would have arcs on both sides. An eighth Bofors replaced one of the portside LRSs originally proposed.

ACNS(A) suggested early in May that some of this battery would have to be surrendered. The carrier would always be able to count on her consorts for gun defence. On the other hand, she could not be separated from her radars, and it might be necessary to rearrange islands and funnel to provide sufficient space and sufficiently free arcs. The Fifth Sea Lord suggested that the ship should be built as planned, with the understanding that the armament might later have to be reduced.

THE DNC, SIR CHARLES LILLICRAP, wrote XI's epitaph in May 1946. In the event another armoured carrier were desired, it would be unwise to adopt either B or C, because both had *Ark Royal*-type machinery. The future carrier, then, should have a closed hangar but Design X four-shaft machinery, which was an advanced highly superheated type. In any case a fresh design would be needed, 'for example, with our present ideas on accommodation, stores and aircraft fuel requirements we should not be able to promise such a large hangar even as was put forward for Design C'. Lillicrap was right; when a new large carrier was designed, in 1952, almost no reference was made to the 1943-45 studies.

It is, of course, difficult to avoid speculation on what might have been. *Ark Royal* and *Eagle* were large enough to be worth rebuilding during the 1950s and 1960s, but a *Malta* would have been much more flexible. A combination of, say, two *Ark Royals* and two *Maltas* rather than two *Ark Royals* and two or three *Hermes* would have presented Britain with a much more flexible force up to the 1970s—albeit at a much higher, perhaps unacceptable, cost in manpower and operation.

16 The argument was that it was use-
    ful to deter an enemy from using
    his really heavy HC bombs (which
    would otherwise be limited to land
    targets) against ships. It seemed un-
    likely that an enemy would manufac-
    ture really heavy AP or SAP bombs
    for anti-ship use.

15

Modernization and the Postwar Air Navy

EVEN MORE THAN IT HAD IN 1918, the Royal Navy found itself in 1945 with sharply contracted resources facing a technological revolution. Britain was effectively nearly bankrupt, and, as in 1918, she had to maintain a large standing army to maintain order both in occupied areas and in her Empire. Unlike 1918, the prospect of future war was very real, as Stalin's Soviet Union was clearly both hostile and aggressive. Because Britain desperately needed foreign exchange, the postwar British government had to emphasize civilian production for export. It also had to pay for massive social programmes which returning veterans considered their due.

All this meant that the large ship and aircraft programmes in train in 1945 had to be cut drastically to release manpower and industrial capacity. The situation in 1945 was quite desperate: during World War II Britain had survived on the strength of Lend-Lease supplies, abandoning virtually all civilian (and, more important, all export) production. Lend-Lease had been extended in the first place because by the spring of 1941 Britain had virtually exhausted her hard currency reserves. With Lend-Lease cancelled, then, the fiscal crisis inevitably returned. Aircraft spplied under Lend-Lease had to be destroyed, for example, not because of American pressure to do so, but because continued operation would have required a continued supply of spare parts, paid for in scarce dollars.

British heavy industry, which in wartime had been devoted entirely to military programmes, was an important potential postwar source of exports. Shipbuilders such as Vickers were encouraged to emphasize merchant ships over warships already under construction. Electrical draftsmen in particular were concentrated on civilian projects, again to the detriment of complex warships. Scientists left the wartime electronics industry. Aircraft companies also turned toward civil projects.

This was inevitable, and it was also justifiable. There was no question but that the perceived threat from Stalin was great, but there was a very real question of just how quickly he would, or for that matter could, act. If an early war was really likely, Britain could not afford to demobilize, and she would have to put the 1945 ship and aircraft plans into production. However, if war was not likely in the very near future, then it was pointless to maintain a large standing force and to produce weapons already obsolescent; better to cut operating and current production expenses in favour of work towards modernization.

The expectation was that the ongoing technological revolution, the jets, the missiles, the fast snorkel submarines and the nuclear weapons, would reach a plateau within a few years, probably a decade or so. Aircraft and weapons designed under war pressure in 1945 would be quite obsolete at that point, but it might be possible to anticipate the plateau if production were delayed until the mid-1950s. This was not an unreasonable reading of the situation. While new aircraft designed in the 1940s tended not to last very long in production (because they were soon outdated due to very rapid aerodynamic progress), those of the 1950s have lasted much longer.[1] In the 1950s it seemed likely that the next technological revolution, the replacement of almost all high-performance aircraft by missiles, would follow in the 1960s.

This course entailed a risk: if Britain found herself at war much before the late 1950s, she would have to fight with much the weapons of 1945, against opponents fighting with those of, say, 1950. Because technology was developing so fast early in the period, these newer weapons would be much superior. On the other hand, Britain could not afford to develop and then to produce two or three generations of aircraft and other weapons in a decade. If she mass-produced new aircraft in, say, 1952, she could not mass-produce their more expensive successors five years later without suffering severe economic consequences.

The British government of the day reasoned that the most likely enemy, the Soviet Union, had been so badly crippled that it could not contemplate war for some years; by 1947 the British Chiefs of Staff had agreed that 1957 would be 'the year of maximum danger' and therefore the target date for modernization. In 1948, the Admiralty adopted a nine-year modernization plan.[2] War was considered very unlikely before 1952, and then increasingly possible up to 1957. It seems likely that these dates reflected an official estimate that the Soviets would first obtain the atomic bomb in 1952, and that they could not face war until they had accumulated five years' worth of bombs.[3]

The effect of this post-1945 version of the old Ten Year Rule was that from 1946 on the Royal Navy and the RAF concentrated on designing the next generation of aircraft and missiles, maintaining only enough existing or interim models to develop tactics and maintain proficiency. Both seemed backward by comparison with the United States, but that was because the United States, with its much bigger industrial base (and with-

1   Cases in point are the F4 Phantom and the MiG-21. Some of the subsonic designs of the interim period, such as the Hunter, have also worn very well, partly because the aerodynamic goals of the 'ultimate' generation did not prove entirely worthwhile.

2   For a more complete discussion of postwar British strategy, see my *Postwar Naval Revolution* (Conway Maritime Press, London, 1987).

3   This seems to have been an agreed Anglo-American estimate. After the Soviet Union exploded her first bomb in 1949, the US government adopted 1954 (five years later) as the 'year of maximum danger'. The British could not, since all their plans were designed for modernization by 1957, and they had much less industrial leeway.

out large colonial army commitments) could afford to produce interim systems while developing better ones. Moreover, on the basis of past experience, the United States could be expected to supply some of its interim weapons in the event of an emergency.

Given the economic damage inflicted by World War II, the British government really had no satisfactory alternative. British aircraft of the period up to 1957 can be categorized as early, interim, and ultimate. The early projects were all wartime or immediately postwar designs, typified by the Supermarine Attacker and the Hawker Sea Hawk. The interim designs incorporated new aerodynamic ideas (such as swept wings) and new early postwar axial-flow turbojets; they include the Supermarine Scimitar and the Hawker Hunter. The ultimate designs were almost entirely dependent on postwar technology, and were not really conceived until the early 1950s. They included the Blackburn Buccaneer and the English Electric Lightning. Most of them were cancelled in 1957.

As it happened, Stalin acted earlier than expected, albeit on a strictly local and limited scale, first by seizing Czechoslovakia, then in the Berlin blockade, and then in Korea. Britain tried to mobilize, and found that, as forecast, she could not really afford the combination of weapons development and full production. As a result, she found herself mass-producing interim aircraft and associated systems, characteristic of a stage about half-way through the postwar decade, rather than waiting for what might be called ultimate ones. The cost of this mobilization in turn killed off most of the 'ultimate' aircraft.

The emphasis on aircraft is intentional. Compared to ships, aircraft could be produced much more quickly, and they generally also became outdated more quickly. Thus a British government looking towards 1957 could put off the mass production of new aircraft, but the carriers to operate those aircraft had to be built or modernized much earlier in the programme period. This is why the modernization of HMS *Victorious* was ordered well before the outbreak of war in Korea, whereas mass orders for new naval aircraft, such as the Scimitar, came only after mobilization had been ordered.

It turned out that Britain could not sustain the mobilization ordered in 1950, not so much for Korea as because many in the West feared that the attack in Korea was the beginning of a larger war. The situation was painful because it was so ambiguous. If indeed a major war was coming, then short-term economic sacrifice was well worthwhile, indeed, was mandated. However, Stalin did not have to follow up his Korean adventure with a larger war; Britain did not have the industrial strength to mobilize twice within a short period. Thus, if Stalin did not attack on a large scale within a few years, Britain would find herself armed with obsolete weapons and without the capacity to replace them. She could not, therefore, choose anything like mobilization on World War II terms. Instead, she had to sustain a high level of production within peacetime economic terms, which meant that exports had to be maintained, and military production balanced against the requirements of the export industries.

From 1952 on, then, successive British governments sought large defence economies. Their choices seemed bleak. Britain had to maintain garrisons throughout the Commonwealth, and therefore a large standing army. She also had to contribute her share of the Western standing force facing the Soviet Union. Finally, the air defence of the United Kingdom (ADGB) was a substantial drain. The situation was not entirely unlike that of the past (except that the main security threat to the Commonwealth was internal disorder due to subversion rather than direct invasion), but the required standing forces were much more expensive.

The naval jet age begins as a Vampire flies from HMS Ocean *on 4 December 1945. The Vampire was not really suitable as a carrier fighter, and it was some years before the Royal Navy could obtain the jet aircraft it needed. That was largely due to the conscious decision, in 1945–46, to eschew interim aircraft in favour of more fully developed types.* FAAM

At this time it was assumed that any war between the Soviet Union and the West would be protracted and intense. Its naval aspects would include massive submarine attacks on shipping, requiring the services of large numbers of escorts and of anti-submarine aircraft. It was inconceivable that Britain (or, for that matter, the United States) could maintain sufficient numbers of active warships to meet these demands. They had produced large numbers in wartime, however, and ships in reserve could be activated and, perhaps, subjected to interim modernization. On the other hand, wartime Allied naval forces would also have to deal with modern Soviet aircraft. No World War II aircraft or ship could be expected to do that. Thus naval aviation was inevitably a very expensive element of British naval planning, and therefore an attractive target for governments in search of economies.

The post-1945 Royal Navy, then, saw mobiliation as the only way of dealing with a possible war emergency: mobilization of men to operate existing if obsolescent reserve ships, mobilization of industry to refit whatever ships it could retain, and mobilization of industry to produce the modern naval aircraft it would need. To some extent it would also have to rely on the United States (particularly after US aid was resumed under the postwar Mutual Defense Assistance Program, or MDAP) for aircraft and for special equipment, such as radars.

The first break in postwar British policy came in 1952–53, when the Chiefs of Staff adopted a new Global Strategy based on nuclear weapons. The services could not agree on what cuts, if any, this might entail; it seems likely that the RAF demanded an increase for its V-bombers. The Royal Navy view was that a nuclear attack would probably be followed by a period of 'broken-backed' war during which it would be vital to protect

The steam catapult made modern jet carriers practical. It was tested aboard HMS Perseus, *shown here in July 1951. The aircraft are, fore to aft, two Sea Hornets, a Firefly (folded), a Short Sturgeon, an Avenger, and a Sea Fury. Note that the catapult track extends well abaft the forward lift. The modernization of light fleet carriers was limited because the steam catapults of operational ships could not extend so far aft, and thus could not develop very high end speeds.*

4   These arguments will be familiar as the basis of the current US maritime strategy. In 1952–54 the key for the Royal Navy was the requirement to contribute enough to Alliance operations to maintain a voice in Alliance (that is, US) councils. The RAF made an analogous argument for the V-bombers.

5   More generally, it could be assumed that no all-out war fought with the new thermonuclear weapons would last very long.

6   The experience at Suez (which might be thought of as the first British post-1945 approach to this kind of naval power projection) demonstrated just how weak existing British amphibious forces were while at the same time showing the potential for carrier-borne helicopter assault.

7   Of course the new policy did not sweep away all vestiges of earlier thinking. Technical policy decisions, for instance on standards of design and on standard threats against which weapons were designed, tended not be affected. However, overall force posture, determining, for example, the number of carriers or the fate of the reserve fleet, was very much determined by central strategy. To the extent that the technical decisions had a life of their own, they could be seen as hedges against policy disaster.

sea communications to the United Kingdom. The Commonwealth mission precluded any great cut in Army manpower.

Frustrated, the government demanded a second Defence Review, in 1953–54. This time the RAF argued that the Navy was spending too much on expensive carrier-based fighters and attack aircraft, and that it should cut back to ASW; then it argued that, given progress in fixed submarine surveillance systems, shore-based Coastal Command aircraft could take over much or all of the mission of the trade-protection carriers. The Navy's reply was that the big strike carriers were necessary as part of the NATO strike fleet. Like the main fleets of the past, the strike fleet would protect shipping by direct attacks on the Soviet fleet (including its naval air force) and by forcing the Soviet naval forces to concentrate their efforts against it, rather than against the more vulnerable shipping. It would cover the convoy escorts, which otherwise would be vulnerable to Soviet fleet units.[4]

In March 1954, however, D of P suggested an alternative, which became the basis of the new strategy announced in 1957. The period of relative safety might well last at least until the next, forecast, technological revolution, when missiles would be able to overwhelm existing national air defences. After that, the principal counter to major war with the Soviet Union would have to be a deterrent; D of P suggested submarine-borne nuclear ballistic missiles. This was a promise of major economies. ADGB could be dismantled, since it could not deal with nuclear missiles; the modern army could be cut down to a force capable of dealing with a very limited Soviet attack;[5] the big ASW mobilization plan could be scrapped, since a Battle of

the Atlantic Mk 2 would be most unlikely. Britain could concentrate on winning the 'cold war' in the Third World, mainly in the Commonwealth. This required mobile naval forces, such as cruisers and small carriers, and a large if lightly equipped army. Research funds could be directed away from aircraft, whose era was ending, towards the new missiles. Most important of all, D of P's strategy was clearly affordable.

It was not adopted at once, but it did form the basis for an internal Royal Navy policy review (Lord Mountbattan's 'Way Ahead' of 1955–56), and it fed into the major change adopted in 1957. This time the government was motivated not only to cut costs, but also to end conscription. This required that the army be roughly halved without cutting back the Commonwealth commitment; the solution was to place greater reliance on mobile naval forces. The carriers were now essential, not so much for their contribution to the NATO strike fleet or to wartime trade protection as for their ability to enforce British power throughout the world, particularly East of Suez. This new naval posture also explains the growing British interest in amphibious forces, particularly in helicopter carriers, after 1957.[6]

The new British policy also took into account the possibility that the army would have to land against real opposition. This in turn justified continued attention to naval strike aircraft, and to the sort of naval systems required for higher-intensity war. In addition, Britain still had the NATO obligation. The combination of the new strategy and the remaining NATO requirement explains the form of the final British full-size carrier design, CVA.01, which is described in the next chapter.[7] The new policy also explains why it was necessary to build up the mobile fleet support organization, for example by conversion of the light carrier *Triumph* to a repair ship. Given a very limited carrier fleet (the government offered only three active carriers, though the Admiralty tried for four), task forces could not be maintained on a global basis unless ships could have much or all of their maintenance done either on board or abroad. CVA.01, for example, was designed for an unusually high level of self-maintenance.

Victorious *as rebuilt, side view.* ALR

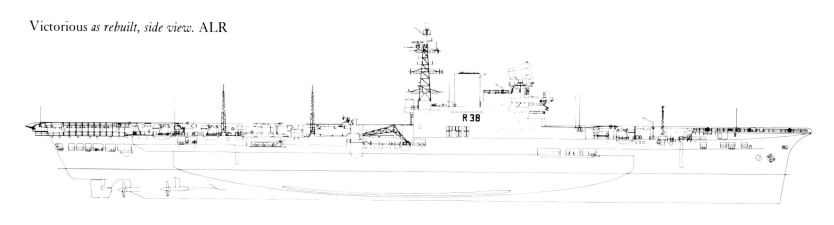

Victorious *as rebuilt, flight deck.* ALR

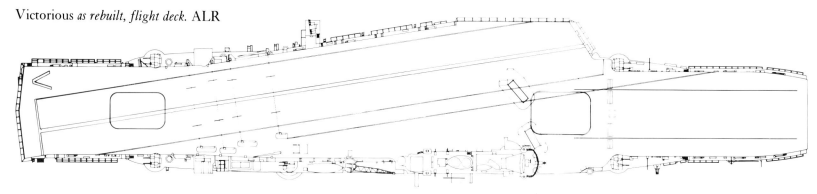

Victorious *as rebuilt, inboard profile.* ALR

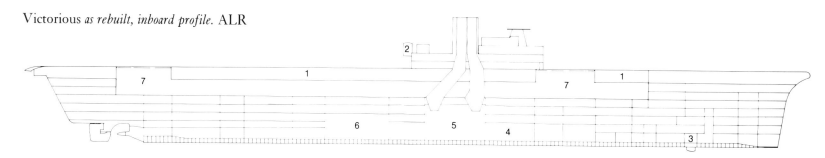

Victorious *as rebuilt, gallery deck.* ALR

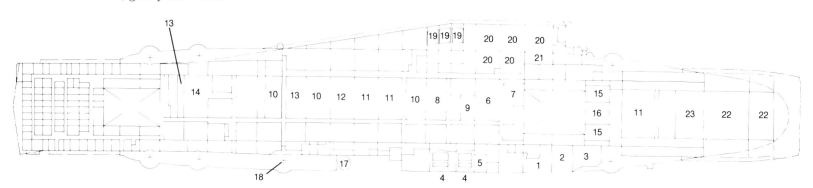

Victorious *as rebuilt, hangar deck.* ALR

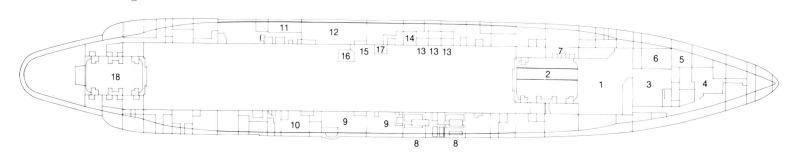

8   Unfortunately the report is not included in the Board Memoranda for 1947. It was accepted by the Board on 21 November 1947. This Board minute sanctioned preparation of reconstruction plans for HMS *Formidable* (later switched to HMS *Illustrious*) and for HMS *Majestic* (completed for the Royal Australian Navy), and sketch plans for both were submitted to the Board in 1949.

The next change in policy, again the result of a review caused by economic problems, was the final abandonment of the East of Suez commitment; this is described in Chapter 17.

THE RADICAL CHANGE in aircraft characteristics agreed in 1942 (see Chapter 12) divided British carriers into two categories: modern (*Ark Royal, Malta, Hermes*) and obsolescent (existing fleet carriers and 1942 light fleet carriers). In 1945 the Board decided, as a long term policy, to modernize the six big fleet carriers as far as possible. Because carrier modernization had to proceed in advance of aircraft design, it can be treated separately here.

A committee on carrier modernization, under Rear Admiral G N Oliver, was set up late in 1946. In mid-November 1947 it proposed that drawings immediately be prepared to modernize two fleet carriers and to bring all of the *Colossus* class up to modernized *Majestic*-class standards.[8] Long lead items (primarily new lifts and arrester gear) could be ordered under the 1948–49 programme. The steam catapult, production of which would determine the rate of actual modernization, was still in the future.

The modernization numbers were set by the capacity of the Royal Dockyards and by the requirement that the fleet should be modernized by 1957; by mid-1948 the plan was to modernize three fleet carriers and three rather than six *Colossus* class ships. The final pre-Korean War plan, the 'revised restricted fleet' of May 1949, showed a seventh modernization, a fleet carrier converted as a trials and deck-landing training ship. Although it was already understood that the 1942 light fleet carriers could never operate the new heavy aircraft, they were still valued as trade-protection or fighter carriers.[9]

Of the existng carriers, only the two *Implacable*s and the modernized *Illustrious* could handle 20,000lb aircraft (this relaxed weight limit had been introduced while the former were still under construction). None of the six fleet carriers could admit aircraft designed to the new hangar height (17ft 6in); the *Implacable*s had particularly low hangars. The *Illustrious* class also had very narrow lifts, and could not accommodate the new folded width limit of 27ft. In the later three ships, the forward lift (to the upper hangar only) could accommodate wider aircraft, but the after lift (to the lower hangar) could not. That was a particular problem for HMS *Indomitable*, whose lower hangar had the greater clear height.

The 30,000lb and 75-knot limits, which had seemed so far away a few years earlier, already seemed constricting. Although the new jet fighters were not very heavy (new strike aircraft might be much heavier), they would surely have to be launched by catapult, partly because jet engines provided relatively little effective power at low speed, hence needed long take-off runs. Their low-drag configurations probably would

make for much higher stall speeds, that is, much higher required catapult end-speeds and much higher entry speeds into arrester gear.[10]

Thus to operate jets three quite distinct problems had to be solved. First, more powerful catapults were needed; the existing BH V (30,000lbs at 75 knots) represented very nearly the limit of cable-and-sheave/hydraulic technology. Fortunately the steam catapult was already in prospect. Second, new and more powerful arrester gear was required. Third, pilots found it more difficult to react quickly enough to land at the new much higher speed, and some means had to be found to simplify this problem. This meant the angled deck and the mirror sight.

The new carrier technology – the angled deck, the steam catapult, and the mirror sight – appeared just as the first major carrier reconstruction, HMS *Victorious*, proceeded. This parallel development partly explains why this work was so protracted; similar considerations apply to HMS *Hermes*, which was completed two years later to a totally revised design. The advances made it possible for an 800ft carrier to duplicate the performance of a vast shore airfield. Because they came at a time of limited British resources, they were most fully exploited by the US Navy.

The new jet aircraft consumed much more fuel than their predecessors. To the extent that their fuel had to be protected, like the petrol of earlier aircraft, it had to be stowed within a very limited envelope within the hull. Jets did burn less volatile fuels, and at first it seemed that they could be stowed in ship fuel tanks.

In 1950, however, the Royal Navy had to abandon avtur because the US government, which would have been the chief source of supply in wartime, decided to standardize on petrol. At the time, special jet fuel was in little demand, and it was not expected to be available in sufficient quantity in wartime. Agreement was reached throughout NATO to use a new widecut petrol, avtag, as jet fuel. This was why HMS *Victorious* (see below) had to be redesigned to accommodate more petrol (which was then called avgas, as in the US Navy). The US solution was to mix paraffin, which could be stowed in double bottom tanks, with avgas to form an equivalent to avtag. In this way fuel endurance could be increased from 3½ to 7½ days. The alternative, in the early 1950s, was to use paraffin at sea and avtag ashore, accepting the need to adjust engines when shifting from one to the other. The Royal Navy settled on this solution, adopting a special high-flash-point jet fuel it called avcat.

Jets presented fleet air defences with new problems. Because attacking jets were faster, the defenders would be faced with a much quicker succession of targets. Wartime stand-off weapons, such as the German FX1400 and Hs 293, would find postwar successors, and using them aircraft could attack from

---

9   They were essential because it seemed unlikely that converted merchant ships (CVEs or MACs) could support modern ASW aircraft and trade-protection fighters. In 1946 the Naval Staff estimated that, eighteen months into a war, the Royal Navy would require twenty carriers beyond its existing building programme (twelve escort carriers, four replenishment carriers, and three training carriers, plus one spare). Unfortunately the most suitable merchant ships, fast (about 18-knot) liners, would be needed for other purposes. This left 14-knot merchant ships, and in 1946 the staff could not expect to requisition fifteen of them in wartime. The first British postwar naval plan, produced

in 1947 as a run-up to the Nine Year Plan, called for twelve light fleet carriers for trade protection (including some in hunting groups), plus four to replenish battle force carriers, four for training, and five spares. This was in addition to eight fleet carriers (the two *Ark Royal*s and the six existing ships, modernized). Against this requirement, the Royal Navy had four *Hermes* class carriers under construction, and six *Colossus* in service; the Commonwealth fleets would contribute their two, plus two more then proposed, for a total of fourteen. The proposed 1956–57 fleet included six new light fleet carriers (construction to begin in 1949) and eleven modernized ones (four *Hermes*, six *Colossus* and

HMS *Majestic*, then as yet unsold). Given economic realities, this programme had little chance of success; it was apparently the Board's opening move in the defence debate. One possibility raised at this time was to extend the deadline for modernisation to 1960. By May 1949 the projected 1957 wartime fleet was reduced to five fleet carriers (two *Ark Royals* and three modernized ships), plus one for deck training, the four *Hermes* and two older light fleet carriers in reserve Category C (to maintain the pre-*Hermes* total of six light fleet carriers). At this time the Admiralty was forced to admit that henceforth the Royal Navy alone would be unable to protect British maritime communications without

US military participation; the 1947 study had assumed that, as in 1941, the United States might assist Britain short of war. The 1947 and 1949 figures are from E J Grove, *Vanguard to Trident* (US Naval Institute, Annapolis, 1987). See also my *Postwar Naval Revolution*.

10   Existing arrester gear aboard fleet carriers was good for 20,000lbs at 63 knots; on modernized light fleet carriers, for 20,000lbs at 56 knots. The new gear on HMS *Eagle*, completed in 1952, was rated at 20,000lbs at 92 knots, and even it was not enough for the Scimitar.

Left and below left: *Nearly complete at Portsmouth,* Victorious *displays her massive Type 984 radar. The depth of the new gallery deck can be gauged by the filled-in area around each lift.*

11   It turned out that the wartime type of vertical plot was effectively limited to fewer than twelve targets. With twenty, its accuracy (required for fighter direction) was considered hopelessly degraded. Errors of 4 or 5nm were common in a twelve target plot, and some tracks were lost altogether because the sequence of individual radar contacts comprising them could not be distinguished from those comprising nearby tracks. Those running the plot tended to be entirely unaware of saturation. Much of the problem was due to the time lags inherent in the system: it was estimated that a target appeared on the face of the vertical plot about 20 seconds after it had been verbally reported, (that is, seen on a radar scope). At about Mach 1 (10nm per minute), this in itself was an inherent error of about 3nm. This was *control*, as opposed to interceptor, saturation, and it could not be cured by adding more fighters. Manpower was also a problem; *Ark Royal* required about sixty officers and ratings to run her AIO. Time lags were critical because fighters launched by a carrier would approach their targets more or less head-on, and the bomber would run in about 20nm while the fighters turned onto pursuit courses to attack (hence the importance of collision-course missiles). A fighter coming in from astern might take as much as 2.75nm to catch up. In 1948, the standard future threat was a bomber capable of launching an air-to-surface missile from 30nm from 50,000ft, or from 20nm at 35,000, or from 10nm at sea level (all of which figures tended to understate the threat a decade or so later). Fighters were expected to orbit over the fleet, and it was assumed that the intercept control system would require about 4 minutes of 'appreciation time' (detection to initiation of interception). On this basis the fighter would have to intercept a bomber at 50,000ft about 55nm from fleet centre. This would require initial detection (warning) at about 135nm, with precision intercept radars tracking the bomber at about 85nm. These figures explain the need for a new high-powered three-dimensional radar, 984, with a very high probability of detecting targets at long range in its multiple stacked beams.

12   This was a major contribution to countering staturation. Each fighter controller was limited by the rate at which he could calculate intercept paths (vectors). The alternative was loose or broadcast control, with the director giving the locations of the bombers and the fighters themselves calculating intercept paths on the basis of their known positions. In principle, broadcast control was the best counter to a saturation attack, since each fighter in the air could direct itself. Otherwise the number of intercepts was limited by the number of computers associated with the intercept radars.

On the other hand, the weight of the airborne computers was expected to reduce the performance of the intercepting fighters, and the machines could not be serviced in the air. Computers were expected to function much better in an air-conditioned space aboard ship than aboard a Mach 1 fighter. In the pre-automatic era, each intercept officer could be expected to control four simultaneous interceptions (three under World War II conditions). In a broadcast system, these officers would be replaced by bomber position reporters, but without a data link to the fighters, this reporting was itself a bottleneck. It was also easier to determine the relative positions of target and fighter (for intercept control) than to determine the absolute positions required for broadcast control; in the late 1940s the requisite ship and air navigation systems just did not exist. Broadcast control also became more complex as each fighter was given data about nearby targets in a mass raid. In either case, the efficacy of the system as a whole depended on the range of the air-to-air (AI) radar aboard the fighter, since greater AI range could make up for less accurate vectoring.

13 One major problem in AEW operation was the sheer number of aircraft required to give anything like gapless coverage far enough from the centre of the formation to be worthwhile. In 1946 it was estimated that the sort of antenna an aircraft could reasonably carry would probably detect aircraft at 500 to 3000ft at only 60 to 70nm. Sea returns interfered inside 40nm, so a force would need six AEW, each 50nm from the main body and 50nm apart, for all-round cover. Actually the aircraft would have to overlap. For 24-hour cover, a fleet would need fifty-four such aircraft (1:9 ratio). This was unacceptable. This problem in turn led to British interest in specialized radar pickets to provide what amounted to low-level cover for the fleet. The only other way to limit the number of pickets is to assume that the threat will appear along a particular axis. The other alternative was to station the AEW aircraft nearly above the ships, accepting relatively short-range coverage against low-fliers.

14 Although a considerable quantity of steam might be needed on a fluctuating basis, it was estimated that average steam consumption would actually be less than that of the hydraulic pumps of the previous BH V catapult.

15 It was possible to apply greater acceleration, but many existing aircraft were not strong enough. In 1949 it appeared that light fleet carriers fitted with steam catapults would be unable to launch Sea Hawks, Attackers or Wyverns unless the airframes were strengthened. Presumably this was done (at least in the case of the Sea Hawk; the Attacker was not strengthened, because it was only an interim aircraft), since the Indian Navy successfully operated Sea Hawks from INS *Vikrant*. However, in many cases catapult operation was marginal; during the Falklands War the Argentine Navy claimed that it could not launch heavily-loaded Skyhawks from its carrier because there was not enough natural wind.

greater distances. Similarly, an aircraft could loft a nuclear bomb from a considerable distance. On the other hand, because jets had such limited endurance, wartime Combat Air Patrol (CAP) tactics were no longer very viable. Instead, relying on their very rapid climb, jets would have to intercept from the deck (DLI – deck launched interception). This made it very important that a carrier be able to catapult off her aircraft without having to accelerate to high speed, or turn into the wind.

In 1948, experiments aboard a British fleet carrier showed that existing manual air control systems were easily saturated even by large numbers of propeller-driven attackers.[11] The British solution was automation, in the form of one of the earliest computer combat systems, the Comprehensive Display System (CDS). In theory, by maintaining track data internally, CDS could reduce the load on those feeding data from the radar or radars, and thus reduce their error rate. CDS was designed to be linked with a big three-dimensional radar, Type 984, and to maintain forty-eight tracks simultaneously. There was also a reduced 24-track version. Given digital radar information, computers associated with 984/CDS could calculate vectors for fighters to attack incoming bombers.[12] By the mid-1950s, 984 and CDS were essential elements of British carrier and battle group planning (the radar and CDS did not have to be aboard the carrier).

The wartime ideas of decentralization survived, and CDS was to have been accompanied by a digital plot transmission (DPT) system, by means of which all the major air defence ships of a group could share the same data. Although the specific DPT and CDS technology had little later application, the ideas these systems embodied contributed to later US Navy work on the present Naval Tactical Data System and its digital link (Link 11).

Type 984 itself was designed to provide air warning at 180nm, and to be precise enough data for fighter control at 90. Since it replaced three radars (960, 982 and 983), it made for a considerable reduction in top hamper. Unfortunately, like many contemporary electronic systems, 984 worked well but not often enough. It was first installed aboard HMS *Victorious* in 1956, and only two other carriers were fitted: HMS *Hermes* (1959) and HMS *Eagle* (1964). By 1964 a further new radar, the Anglo-Dutch 'Broomstick,' was in prospect, and so Type 984 did not figure in planning for the next British carrier, CVA.01.

Airborne early warning (AEW) was the other essential electronic element of fleet air defence. It was devised by the US Navy during World War II, the first carrier-borne aircraft (Cadillac I, an Avenger with an APS-20 radar) entering service in 1945. Early British postwar plans included an AEW version of the big Spearfish. Late in 1945 the Royal Navy decided not to buy the US system, but instead to develop an all-British one, presumably in line with the primary postwar policy (and to avoid expending scarce dollars). Both the RAF and the Royal Navy stated requirements late in 1945, but development could not proceed because of a lack of suitable scientists. Thus there was no British system in place or even in prospect in 1952, the United States supplying AEW Skyraiders (AD-4W) under the MDAP programme. The first of forty-five arrived in November 1951, each carrier operating a detachment of four. These aircraft in turn were replaced by Gannets, using the same radar; the last was retired in December 1960.

In the Cadillac I system, typified by the Skyraider, the aircraft acted only as an airborne radar station, supplying the carrier and her fighter controllers with a better radar picture, particularly of distant low-fliers. Because the APS-20 radar could not determine the height of an incoming aircraft, it was not considered a substitute for shipboard three-dimensional radars

and thus could not, in itself, be used for interception. The US Navy eventually took the next step and developed three-dimensional AEW radars. The equivalent British system, which would have been carried by a third-generation Anglo-French aircraft, died with CVA.01.[13]

THE STEAM CATAPULT was conceived in 1963 by C C Mitchell, who was then working for MacTaggart, Scott & Co Ltd, the primary supplier of British naval catapults. E-in-C was interested, but could not provide funds for a test. Presumably this was partly because really powerful accelerators were not then essential to carrier operation. Mitchell patented his invention in 1938, and in 1941 he joined E-in-C's Department. His interest in the slotted cylinder catapult was revived by reports, in the autumn of 1944, that German V-1s were being launched by a very similar device. Mitchell arranged to go to France in November 1944, and brought back enough German material to construct an experimental cordite slotted-cylinder catapult at Shoeburyness.

By this tme it was apparent that virtually all future high-performance carrier aircraft would have to be launched by catapult. Because it acted directly (the piston in the slotted cylinder drives the aircraft) without sheaves or pulleys, the new catapult could be much more powerful than any existing unit. It was also much simpler. The Admiralty decided to adopt slotted-cylinder catapults in 1946, and by 1948 plans for a test unit, BXS-1, had been completed. Their pistons would be driven directly by boiler steam.[14]

The BXS-1 prototype was installed aboard the maintenance carrier *Perseus* in 1951, and extensive trials (including 1560 launches) followed in 1951–52. This design then entered service aboard British carriers as BS 4. It was installed in several lengths, most commonly 151ft in fleet carriers and 103ft in modernized light fleet carriers. Length determined end-speed, since acceleration was fairly constant along the length of the catapult. This was unfortunate for the light fleet carriers, since for them maximum catapult length was determined by the distance between the forward lift and the bow.[15]

During her modernization in 1959–64, HMS *Eagle* was fitted with a new 200ft BS 5 catapult, rated at 105 knots end-speed for 50,000lbs. The next step, intended for CVA.01, was a catapult capable of launching 60,000lb aircraft at 150 knots (that is, suitable for Phantoms bought from the United States)

THE SECOND GREAT DEVELOPMENT was the angled deck. It was conceived at a Ministry of Aviation conference on means of using the new flexible flight deck on 7 August 1951. Captain Dennis Cambell, Assistant CNR, suggested that the deck should be angled, so that aircraft landing on it could be pulled off to one side to be set up for catapulting off. Lewis Boddington of RAE concluded that the angling idea could be extended to conventional aircraft, and indeed that it should be applied to the new carrier *Ark Royal*, then nearing completion. HMS *Triumph* was painted with an angled landing path for touch-and-go trials (complete conversion would have entailed moving her arrester gear).[16]

The angled deck removed the deck park from the path of a landing aircraft. There was thus no longer any possibility that a bolter would jump over the barrier to crash into the park. This

16 This account is based on Paul Beaver's *British Aircraft Carrier* (PSL Ltd, 1986); although no references are given, Beaver reproduces Captain Cambell's dated sketch showing a flexible deck canted to starboard. However, I am inclined to doubt Beaver's further assertion that the Admiralty refused to countenance any angled decks until after the US Navy had adopted this innovation in USS *Antietam*, as so much of the 1952 carrier work was based on angled deck configurations.

was critically important; as aircraft landed at higher speeds, they landed at flatter angles, and thus they tended to touch down further up the deck. Higher speeds also made for greater pull-outs, and thus an aircraft picking up one of the forward wires could easily still crash into the barrier. Moving the barrier forward was not really acceptable, because then the deck park would become too small. As modernized in 1952–53, for example, HMS *Warrior* was limited to a deck park of twelve aircraft because the last two arrester wires overran the barrier. The new *Eagle* was equally unsatisfactory.

In an angled-deck carrier, the deck park is the triangular area between the landing path and the starboard side. Forward of both are the forward centreline lift and the bow catapults, neither of which is encumbered by a deck park. This was particularly important for a Royal Navy which found deck-edge lifts (unencumbered by the deck park of a conventional axial-deck carrier) unacceptable in rough weather.

Quite aside from increased safety, angling also greatly increased carrier operating capacity. In 1952, DAW commented that angling had given the 20,000-ton *Hermes* class carriers much the same operating capacity as a 33,000-ton axial deck *Eagle*.

JET PILOTS HAD TO REACT very quickly when landing at over 100 knots. The combination of DLCO, hand signals and pilot could not be fast enough, since the DLCO had to sense the motion of the aircraft and make his signals before the pilot could even begin to respond. Lieutenant Commander Nick Goodhart, Captain Cambell's assistant, suggested a system by which the pilot could monitor his landing, and so could apply corrections instantly. It was a gyro-stabilized mirror; a light source abaft it was reflected back into the pilot's eyes.[17] Datum lines of red and green lights around the mirror showed whether he was

too high or too low, too far right or left. Air speed was also indicated by an audio tone, so that the pilot could continuously monitor the reflected light (the 'meatball') in the mirror. The earliest installations consisted of two mirrors, one to either side of the glide path, used together, but ultimately only one was required.

In effect, this returned to pre-1939 practice, with the pilot himself deciding whether he had snagged a wire. This still left open the possibility of incorrect judgement, and the aircraft might thus still crash into the barrier. In conjunction with the

Above and left: *HMS Victorious as completed, 1958–59. The VHF/DF mast is visible in its upright position in the stern view, taken 26 September 1958. The object visible above the flight deck aft is the port side mirror sight; note that there was also a starboard side mirror sight.*

angled deck, however, the mirror sight was extremely effective. Later the mirrors were replaced by Fresnel lenses, but Goodhart's basic idea, that the pilot should monitor his own landing to reduce time lags, continues to be valid. As much as the angled deck and the steam catapult, it made carrier landings by very high-performance aircraft possible.

THERE SEEMS TO HAVE BEEN general agreement that the first ship to be modernized should be an *Illustrious*. *Formidable* was laid up and required a long refit in any case, so she was provisionally selected for modernization. *Illustrious* was a deck landing training and trials carrier, and could not be spared, particularly as she was needed to test the new generation of naval aircraft. This left HMS *Victorious* as the only other candidate. In early 1951 the other two ships of the programme were HMS *Implacable*, followed by HMS *Indefatigable*, for modernization in, respectively, 1953–55 (to relieve HMS *Eagle* so that she could refit in 1956 with steam catapults) and 1954–57. HMS *Indomitable* was scheduled for a more limited modernization (1957) as the future deck landing training ship. At this time *Eagle* was scheduled for completion in August 1951 and *Ark Royal* in 1954, so that the full programme would provide the Royal Navy with five fleet carriers plus a semi-modernized deck landing training ship.

Of the light fleet carriers, HMS *Warrior* and HMS *Vengeance* were both scheduled for limited modernization (respectively in 1952–53 and 1953–54), the latter to go into Category C reserve upon completion. In their case, modernization would permit them to operate as trade-protection carriers, flying Gannets and Sea Venoms. The three *Hermes* class light fleet carriers of the original design were scheduled for completion in 1952–54, with *Hermes* to follow, to a modified design, in 1955. They would replace the *Colossus* class light fleet carriers *Theseus*, *Triumph*, *Ocean* and *Glory*, which would be discarded. Once *Hermes* had been completed, the other three would be refitted with steam catapults, so that they could operate modern aircraft.

The big modernization programme was stopped in 1952 with HMS *Victorious*, when it became apparent that reconstruction was too expensive. This left three large carriers which would never operate modern aircraft. Two of them, the *Implacables*, were decommissioned to provide men to commission HMS *Ark Royal*, and HMS *Indomitable* was not repaired after her explosion and fire (see Chapter 7).

The carrier fleet was gradually reduced through the defence reviews of the 1950s. The 1953–54 review (the Radical Review) forced the Royal Navy to choose between the two big (but non-operational) *Implacables* and three light fleet carriers, which were more valuable for trade protection. The two big ships were reduced to non-maintained reserve and the light fleet carriers converted for non-flying training in 1953–54 to keep them available for wartime mobilization. HMS *Glory* was retained as a ferry and trooping carrier.

The next step was to lay up the training and trials carrier, HMS *Illustrious*, which otherwise might have served throughout the 1950s. HMS *Warrior* was modernized instead as a less expensive replacement. Under the revised carrier strength adopted after the review, she would have become surplus when HMS *Hermes* entered service, but she was actually discarded earlier.

By 1955, planned British carrier strength was three modern fleet carriers and three modern light fleet carriers, HMS *Hermes* replacing HMS *Bulwark* upon completion. This sufficed to maintain five operational carriers. After the 1957 defence review, this fleet was cut again, to five modern carriers, sufficient to maintain four in active service. This allowed two of the

17 Goodhart wrote his paper on optical landing control in 1951; the mirror projected an optical guide path towards an incoming aircraft. He proved the concept using a secretary's pocket mirror and lipstick on a desk. When he walked towards the mirror keeping the image of the lipstick tip centred in it, his nose or chin would always hit the desk in the same spot. Goodhart reasoned that a pilot keeping the image of a light (equivalent to the lipstick) in the proper place on a mirror would always strike the deck in the appropriate place. Campbell formally proposed the idea to the United Kingdom Naval Aeronautical Research Committee in January 1952, and a test cast aluminium mirror (5ft 6in × 4ft) was installed 300ft from the after end of the flight deck of HMS *Illustrious* in November 1953 after land trials at Farnborough. The light source, eight 240-watt bulbs in a 20ft line, was 160ft further aft. This account is from '"Roger, Ball" – How It Started' by Vice Admiral D D Engen, USN (Ret), in *Tailhook* (Fall 1987). Admiral Engen, then an exchange pilot at the Empire Test Pilots School, evaluated the mirror sight for the US Navy in November 1953, flying a Sea Vampire 21. Engen strongly recommended its adoption, and the first US installation followed aboard USS *Bennington* in September 1955. The mirror was ultimately replaced by the Fresnel Lens (Projector) system, which uses a light source on the other (forward) side of the optics, but which follows the same principle.

18 The relevant ship's cover has not yet been released; this date is based on LCDR M Apps, *Send Her Victorious* (William Kimber, London, 1971); Apps appears to have had access to some official files. He describes DNC as having been 'invited to prepare designs' in February 1948. DNC always referred to a Board Minute of 21 November 1947 as the origin of the reconstruction design.

Table 15-1: HMS *Victorious* Reconstructed

	Legend, April 1950	As in 1957
LBP (ft)	673	
LWL (ft)	710	
LOA (ft)	768 6	778 3
BWL (ft)	103 3½	103 4
Beam, extreme (ft)	119	145 9
Deep displacement (tons)	33,000	35,500
Draught fore/aft (ft)	29 10½/30 5½	32 4/31 7
Freeboard fore/aft (ft)	42 1½/41	
Displacement std (tons)	27,180	30,300
SHP	111,000	111,000
Speed (knots) std	29.75	
deep	29.25	
dirty	28	
Oil fuel (tons)[4]	4180	4277[5]
Endurance (nm)	6450[1]	5380
Complement as flagship	2163	
Armament		
Twin 3in	6 (900rpg)[2]	6[6]
Sextuple 40mm	4 (1200rpg)	
Aircraft		
Fighters	33	
Strike	12	
A/S	10[3]	
Catapults	2 BS 4	
Weights (tons)[8]		
General equipment	2120 (1700)	
Aircraft equipment	2270 (2350)	
Machinery	2585 (2600)	
Protection	3340 (3900)	
Hull	16,300 (14,900)	
Fuel oil[4]	4180	
Avgas (140,000 gallons)	475	[7]
Avtur (145,000 gallons)	550	
RFW	200	
Water protection	—	
Margin	—	
Std displacement	33,000	

1 5280 when 6 months out of dock in tropics (dirty)
2 3in/70
3 Including 1 for air-sea rescue
4 Includes diesel oil
5 Plus 138 tons of oil fuel
6 3in/50
7 60,000 gallons of avgas and 279,000 gallons avcat
8 Numbers in parentheses are estimates made in October 1948, with the ship retaining all her side armour.

Hermes class, *Albion* and *Bulwark*, to be converted to helicopter carriers. In fact refits took longer than expected, and the number of active ships was often less than planned. Both of the *Ark Royals*, for example, were refitting in 1959–60, and only three modern carriers (*Victorious* and two *Hermes* class) were available.

Further construction (see Chapter 16) was planned to maintain this force, but it never materialized. In February 1966 the government decided to stop construction of the new carrier, CVA.01, but to maintain the four existing fixed-wing carriers (the two *Ark Royals*, *Victorious* and *Hermes*) in service until 1970–75, modernizing the two *Ark Royals* to operate the new Phantom fighters it was buying in the United States. In the event, *Victorious* was discarded in 1967 after suffering a minor fire, and only *Ark Royal* was modernized. *Hermes* was converted to a helicopter carrier (see Chapter 17).

THE BOARD FORMALLY APPROVED the modernization programme in November 1947, and design work began in about February 1948.[18]

At the end of March 1949 (that is, the end of the 1948–49 financial year), *Formidable* was to have been taken in hand a year hence, that is, at the end of the 1949–50 year. She was surveyed, and probably early in 1950 was rejected in favour of HMS *Victorious*. As the design applied to both ships, the notes which follow are not specific to either. Table 15–1 is the legend submitted to the Board in June 1950, compared to the characteristics of the ship which emerged eight years later.

Victorious took much longer (and cost much more) than

expected to rebuild. She was taken in hand on 23 October 1950. Initially the work was expected to last no more than three years (until some time in 1954). However, in November 1951 it was expected to take 4½ years. In January 1952 the programme called for her to be complete four years and ten months from being taken in hand, that is in August 1955. Progress was slow, and the yard was heavily burdened, so in November 1952 this estimate was extended to October 1956. The ship was actually completed in January 1958.

The hope was to bring the ship up to *Ark Royal* or better standards, as far as possible, so that she could launch 40,000lb jets and recover them at a landing weight of 30,000lbs. This required a much stronger flight deck, a smaller island (with improved radars), a deck-edge lift, much increased aviation fuel stowage and a modern anti-aircraft battery.

Except under the flight deck armour, the flight deck would have to be strengthened, by fitting 3ft 6in to 4ft deep beams under it. The space they occupied, over the hangar, would be wasted. However, the design needed every square foot of usable space; projected complement was 2000, compared to 1256 in the original design, and a very cramped 1997 at the end of the Pacific War. The comparison understates the problem, because late-war standards of crowding were entirely unacceptable in the postwar Navy, dependent as it was on volunteers.

DNC therefore proposed to use instead 7ft 6in to 8ft high bulkheads, and to use the space between flight deck and hangar for living quarters and for control spaces. This was the first such full gallery deck in a British carrier (living spaces under the flight decks of *Ark Royal* and *Hermes* did not extend over the hangar), but it followed US practice, and DNC believed that it would be repeated in any future British carrier design because it economized on space and made it easier to fit deck-edge lifts. There was no space further down in the ship; DNC recognized that gallery deck spaces might well be uncomfortable, and did all he could in the way of lagging, ventilation and coating of the upper surface of the flight deck to make such spaces habitable in the tropics. He also hoped that they could be air conditioned.

This gallery deck made it possible to reduce the size of the island. In May 1949 DNC offered two alterntives, a conventional four-deck island (Scheme A), and a three-deck island (B). The preferred three-deck arrangement was obtained by moving all radar offices down into the gallery deck immediately below the island, even though in this case some of the waveguides were somewhat too long.[19] The Admiral's staff office and sea cabin were also moved down into the gallery deck. As a result, the island could be shorter as well as lower. DNC also cleared all weapons from the flight deck. The total length of obstruction on the starboard side was reduced from 216ft to 147ft (129ft for the island alone, not including the mast abaft it for the 960 search radar).

Structurally, the insertion of this gallery deck was the most onerous part of the modernization. The entire flight deck, which functioned as the strength member of the ship girder, had to be removed, a new gallery deck inserted (to give a new clear hangar height of 17ft 6in) and then a new flight deck, including armour, put back onto the ship. Removal of the flight deck also entailed removal of the hangar side armour extending up to the flight deck, since the new flight deck would be substantially higher than the old.

The 1949 sketch design showed two steam catapults, but only the port unit was the full 150ft long (15,000lbs at 130 knots or 30,000lbs at 105 knots). The starboard catapult was limited to 100ft to allow an Air Operations Room and Aircraft Direction Room in the gallery deck close to the island. By this time it was becoming clear that the 100ft catapult would be inadequate, and DNC investigated a rearrangement of these

gallery deck spaces.

The specified aircraft complement was fifty-five aircraft: twenty-four day fighters (N7/46), twelve single-seat strike fighters (Wyvern), nine night fighters (sea Hornet and later N40/46), nine ASW (three-seater GR 17/45), and one air-sea rescue aircraft.[20] In principle, the ship had to be able to support four days of maximum-intensity air operations, which DAW equated to 6000 gallons of fuel per aircraft. Although the nominal air complement was fifty-five aircraft, DAW calculated in terms of fifty-eight, and so asked for 348,000 gallons (including protected stowage for at least 150,000 gallons of aviation petrol).

Hull volume was limited; in March 1949 the design showed the full petrol stowage but a toal of only 291,000 gallons. Because DAW was not yet firm on his own aviation fuel requirements, this issue was left unresolved. As submitted in June 1950, the conversion design showed 285,000 gallons, including avtur stowed in oil fuel tanks. DAW reduced his requirement per aircraft to 4800 gallons (278,400 gallons).

Unfortunately, it was just at this point that avtur had to be abandoned in favour of avgas, so the entire load now had to be carried under armour. Initially DNC could only offer to extend the forward avgas stowage up a deck, increasing the total from 140,000 to 185,000 gallons, at the expence of about 15 per cent of the bomb stowage. Moreover, the top of the forward avgas stowage would now be quite close to the waterline.

As in other British carrier Staff Requirements, this one included a demand for good air flow with the wind 10 degrees on either bow.

The Staff called for at least two lifts, one at the deck edge forward and the other aft.[21] There was some hope of moving the after lift right aft to the stern, abaft the aircraft recovery area.[22] It could then have lifted aircraft to the deck for the longest possible free take-off runs, presumably for special heavy aircraft with rocket assistance.[23] The Staff also wanted the hangar extended beyond the lifts (unless the stern lift could be placed right aft).

In fact it proved impossible to provide either the deck-edge lift or the lift right aft. The hangar deck had too little freeboard for the former.

Against the Staff Requirement for 55ft lifts, DNC could offer only 54ft examples. When he amended the design later in the year, however, DNC was able to extend the forward lift by 4ft, to a total length of 58ft. Nor could DNC provide the desired hangar extension aft; there was just too little volume in the ship. It was extended forward, by 56ft, for a total length of 416ft (the main hangar was 360 × 62ft), against the original figure of 456ft.

The flight deck was lengthened (from 743ft 6in to 765ft 6in) and cleared of obstructions, so that abreast the island it was now 83ft 6in (rather than 69ft) wide. At this stage of the design it carried eight arrester wires (Mk 13 gear, for 30,000lb aircraft entering at 105 knots) and three barriers.

DGD wanted a battery of six of the new twin 3in/70 rapid-fire guns, plus four sextuple Bofors. DNC suggested that the flight deck might be clearer with four twin 3in/70; DAW complained that because the guns were flush with the flight deck they tended to restrict the span of aircraft using it. The sketch design presented to the Board in June 1950, however, showed six twin 3in/70 and three sextuple Bofors. At this time there was some fear that the ship would be completed before the new weapons were available, and DGD proposed that six sextuple Bofors be mounted as an interim substitute, going back into a yard for nine months in 1954–55 for 3in guns and their MRS directors. In fact *Victorious* had to be armed with US twin 3in/50s, as the 3in/70 was not available in time.

19 It was not possible, then, to provide the ship with the type of combined two-deck Aircraft Direction Room/Operations Room fitted in the new *Ark Royal* class carriers. Space requirements were 750sq ft on both levels, to be readily accessible to the command, plus a contiguous radar display room (460sq ft on one level), and contiguous bridge wireless office and gun direction rooms.

20 The 1949 Staff Requirements called for bomb lifts large enough for 2000lb bombs, and fast enough so that twenty-seven aircraft could be bombed up, each with two 1000lb bombs, in 30 minutes. Stowage was to be provided for up to sixty torpedoes: A/S types weighing over 1000lbs (three per aircraft), weighing 700–1000lbs (six), or weighing under 700lbs (six), for Bootleg (1½ per aircraft), and for conventional 18in (1½ per aircraft) types. These figures applied to a maximum of twelve ASW aircraft and to twenty-four anti-ship aircraft, the total mix (for example thirty-six 2000lb ASW and twenty-four Bootlegs) not to exceed sixty. The ship was also to carry 500 sonobuoys for her ASW aircraft. The 1950 design approved by the Board showed forty-four torpedoes, and alternative stowage for 140 2000lb bombs, or 320 1000lb, or 700 500lb, or 400 Red Angels; plus 1460 3in rockets, 108 depth charges, and twenty-four mines.

21 The 1949 Staff Requirements called for 55 × 32ft centreline lifts and a deck-edge lift at least 55ft long (preferably 60ft long and 35ft wide), all capable of transporting 30,000lb aircraft (40,000 at slower speed). These lengths reflected the dimensions of the new Hawker and de Havilland jet fighters.

22 The stern lift had to be abandoned because the hull form aft was too fine.

23 At this time there was a British project to launch an aircraft carrying a 10,000lb (atomic) bomb from a carrier, presumably on a one-way flight, in analogy with the contemporary American assignment of bomb-carrying Neptunes to large carriers. Some design work was done on a proposed reconstruction of HMS *Illustrious*, apparently with a flush deck, under the cover designation Design Study B. No description appears to have survived; however, references appear in the miscellaneous carrier covers and in DNC papers for 1949 (and in Chiefs of Staff minutes for the period), and the National Physical Laboratory tested a wind tunnel model of the flush-decked configuration. Unfortunately, its report seems not to have survived, at least in any public collection. The report of Staff Requirements is in the papers of the Ship Design Policy Committee does not mention Design Study B, but that may have been because the design study carried a higher classification.

The one great limit of the Illustrious *hull was its very limited freeboard, which made it impossible to fit* Victorious *with a side lift. The vertical plate visible aft shields her port side mirror sight from wind streaming over it.* FAAM

As rebuilt, Victorious *could operate the full range of modern British naval aircraft. Three Buccaneers are visible forward of the island. This photograph was taken after a 1961–63 refit: two of the four after twin 3in/50 mounts (forward mount on each sponson) and the sextuple Bofors have been removed. the VHF/DF has been replaced by a UHF/DF, recognizable by its flat plate shape. In 1960–61 the ship had a small bridle catcher on her starboard catapult.*

Left and below left: Hermes *was the last conventional* British carrier to be completed, and the most radically transformed. These photographs were taken on 15 August 1960. Note the US Navy carrier on-board delivery (COD) aircraft parked right aft.

Radar was also a problem. Draft Staff Requirements called for two pairs of 982/983 radars (in effect, two three-dimensional radars) for air control, plus a Type 960P for long-range air warning. Only one 982 could be accommodated on a short island, and it had a limited blind arc aft, where a mast supporting the long-range 960 was located; this had to be accepted. Perhaps more seriously, there was some question, in 1949, whether these new radars would be available in time. In the event, reconstruction was so much slower than planned that the radar actually fitted was one generation beyond these sets.

The Staff also called for carrier-controlled blind landing equipment (Type 961 or later radar), and a short-range air search set for gun direction (Type 992), as well as gun director sets and an airborne early warning terminal.

Required sustained speed was 28 knots deep, in the tropics. The ship would have to be bulged, and DNC estimated the speed penalty as about half a knot. The ship would also lose some speed to increased displacement; an estimate made late in October 1948 showed 26,950 tons (standard) and 32,375 tons (deep load), including 400 tons of permanent ballast. Staff Requirements included the ability to pass through the Panama Canal, which in theory would limit the ship to about 33,500 tons deep load (deep draft was approximately 32ft, BWL 101ft 8½in). In fact as designed in June 1950 (and bulged 4ft on each side) she could pass through Suez but not through Panama.

The endurance requirement was set at 6000nm at 20 knots six months out of dock in the tropics. Unfortunately internal volume was limited: some of the existing fuel tanks had to be used instead for jet fuel. DNC estimated that even by giving up aircraft fuel, he could get only 5800nm, and E-in-C estimated that endurance might be as little as 4500nm at 20 knots. HMS *Illustrious* conducted special steaming trials in February 1949 to determine expected fuel consumption.

No particular level of protection, other than nuclear (that is, against fallout) seems to have been specified. DNC was therefore able to lengthen the armoured citadel (to provide more bulk avgas stowage aft) without adding weight, by reducing armour thicknesses. The belt armour was reduced from 4½in to 2in, and the hangar side armour from 4½in to 1½in; the hangar deck inside the hangar was reduced to 1in throughout. The original 3in flight deck armour was retained.[24]

In June 1953 the Controller formally approved angling the flight deck (8½ degrees), reboiling, and fitting Type 984/CDS/DPT.[25] That March, D of D had estimated that, based on the expected date of availability (and a three-year installation period), fitting the new radar and associated electronics would probably stretch the modernization well into 1958, an estimate which proved slightly pessimistic. These improvements had become more important because of the demise of the projected 1952 carrier (see Chapter 16) and of the two follow-on fleet carrier modernizations.

Reboiling was necessary both because the existing boilers were worn out and because much more electrical power was needed (capacity increased to 4200kW). Its execution was somewhat embarrassing, because the flight deck was completed just in time to be ripped up again so that the new boilers could be fitted. Reportedly this resulted from poor liaison between the construction and engineering departments of Portsmouth Dockyard, and the result was a general reorganisation. Shortly after completion electrical generating capacity was again increased, to 5000kW, and the final total was eight steam and four diesel generators.

In 1954 the conversion design was altered to provide guided weapon stowage space in the hangar; the following year airborne radar servicing arrangements were improved, and in 1956 aircraft servicing arrangements were again changed, each

time to take account of rapidly changing aircraft technology.

As a measure of increasing aircraft size and weight, by October 1956 the projected air complement was:

1959	1961–2	1963
12 Scimitar	12 Scimitar	8 SR. 177,
		8 Buccaneer
12 Sea Venom	10 Sea Vixen	10 Sea Vixen
8 Gannet	8 Gannet	8 A/S Helo
4 AEW	4 AEW	4 AEW
Skyraider	Gannet	Gannet

2 search/rescue (SAR) helicopters.

This made thirty-eight rather than the planned fifty-five.

HMS *Victorious* was the first British ship to be completed with provision for stowing tactical nuclear weapons, because her reconstruction coincided with the introduction of the naval tactical nuclear bomb into British service.

HMS *Implacable* was the second fleet carrier scheduled for modernization. She would resemble HMS *Victorious*, but a new design was needed because the two ships differed considerably internally. *Implacable* had two shallower hangars, and she had four-shaft machinery. Draft Staff Requirements were drawn up in July 1951. They generally followed those of HMS *Victorious*, but this time there was some hope that two Type 984 radars could be installed. The alternative was the combination of 960 for early warning and 982 and 983 for height-finding. As in the earlier ship, the minimum aviation fuel stowage was 240,000 gallons. New boilers were to be installed, primarily to meet endurance requirements.

The estimated air complement was twenty day fighters (Sea Hawks), ten night fighters (Sea Venom), ten strike fighters (Wyvern), ten ASW aircraft (Gannet), and four airborne early warning aircraft (Skyraiders).

The revised Staff Requirements demanded more space for electronics and for men, for the Type 984/CDS, the new Type 992 gunnery target designation radar, and 3in/70 guns (which had been given up in HMS *Victorious*). *Implacable* also needed more men to operate her four-shaft plant. However, that plant, which occupied about 40 per cent of the ship's underwater volume (compared to 30 per cent in *Victorious*) left less volume in the ship. Percentages of volume below the upper deck in *Victorious* and below the lower hangar deck in *Implacable* (both 37ft above the keel) were, respectively, 23 and 29 per cent.

The Staff Requirements mentioned no side lift, but DAW hoped that the deeper *Implacable* hull could accommodate one; DAW estimated that freeboard at the hangar deck would be 23ft 6in, compared to only 14ft in *Victorious* (but 30ft in *Ark Royal*). This, however, assumed that the upper hangar deck would become the main hangar deck of the rebuilt ship, in which case the flight deck would have been raised a total of 9ft (gallery deck plus increased clear hangar deck height). This in turn would have increased displacement from 32,100 to 36,000 tons, and the ship would have been blistered about 15ft to maintain stability (GM 10ft as in HMS *Victorious*). This would solve any problem of limited internal volume, but it would also preclude the ship from docking in any British naval drydock except No 10 at Devonport and the Floating Dock at Portsmouth, and this was quite aside from the enormous labour, probably unwarranted, of so great an increase in the size of what DNC described as a lightly built ship. It also did not take account of the much longer dockyard period so much work entailed. DNC concluded that, as in *Victorious*, there was no point in a deck-edge lift.

At this point the required lifts were 55×32ft, smaller than the 58 × 40ft forward and 54 × 34ft aft in *Victorious*.

24 This protection was considered sufficient to defeat a 1000lb MC bomb, a 500lb SAP bomb dropped from 5000ft in a 45-degree dive (at 300 knots), a 500lb SAP bomb dropped from 6000ft in level flight (at 300 knots), a 2000lb AP bomb dropped from 1000ft, or high-explosive shells of up to 6in calibre. The bulge was liquid-loaded, forming an outer layer beyond the original void-liquid-void system. The official handbook of British warships rated it at 750lbs of TNT, but that was the rating of the original three-layer system. The original rating was later considered unduly optimistic, and it is possible that the added layer brought it up to the original design figure.

25 Reboiling was necessary partly because the existing boilers had little remaining life, and partly to provide the extra electrical generating capacity, a total of 4200kW instead of the original 2400kW.

Depressing estimates of the completion date of HMS *Victorious* were already in hand. In early October 1951 her reconstruction was expected to take 4½ years, so that she would complete at the end of March 1955 rather than late in April 1954 as originally planned (these dates turned out to be wildly optimistic). *Implacable* was scheduled to be taken in hand in April 1953 for completion during 1956. D of D pointed out that she could not actually be taken in hand before April 1955 without cutting other commitments: to rebuild her beginning in 1953 would stop two cruiser modernisations and the vital guided missile ship conversion (*Girdle Ness*). The 1956 date was fixed by the then future fleet plan, that is, by the 1957 date for the year of maximum danger. Late in September 1951 the Controller asked DNC whether the cost and time of modernization could be reduced.

DNC replied early in October that the minimum modifications were also the most expensive: strengthening the flight deck, increasing hangar clear headroom (to accommodate modern aircraft), installing steam catapults and larger lifts, increasing aviation fuel stowage, modernizing electronics and associated AIO. Even modernized, the ship would still be too short to operate modern aircraft efficiently, and she would still lack really effective underwater protection.[26] Neither problem could possibly be solved.

Some major economy could be realized by modernizing the ship only for trade protection, but even then considerable work would be required, and the result would hardly be worth the effort.[27]

D of D considered the structural work the controlling factor. He estimated that nine to twelve months could be saved by not increasing hull depth, as in that case the upper strake of hangar side armour would not have to be replaced. The depth of the unconverted *Implacable*, 71ft, was actually 1ft less than that of the modernized *Victorious*. Half of the difference would have to come out of the new upper gallery deck, headroom being decreased from 7ft 5in to 6ft 11in. Not only would that cramp quarters there, it would also make it more difficult to keep the 3in guns clear of the flight deck, as the air departments wanted. DNC therefore wanted to deepen the ship by 6in to perhaps 1ft. He felt that this was not really very much extra work, since the flight deck had to be removed in any case to fit the new gallery deck over the top of the hangar, and since most of the bulkheads girdling the hangar would have to be altered in any case.

The new gallery deck could not be eliminated altogether because it provided too much vital space. Without it, the hangar area would have to be reduced by a third (to provide more spaces), and the island enlarged to something like *Ark Royal* dimensions. Neither was acceptable.

D of D also suggested that existing avgas stowage be retained to avoid lengthy structural work. Unfortunately it was very inefficient; the total available, including the existing stowage, was only 180,000 gallons in a space sufficient for 240,000 in more modern bulk stowage; DAW wanted at least 240,000.

Staff Requirements were then reviewed. Neither Type 984/CDS nor the planned 3in/70 guns would be ready by the end of 1956. The prototype Type 984 was expected in mid-1956, and installation would extend modernization well into 1957. However, it was most desirable, since carriers were probably the only suitable platforms. Moreover, it would not be ready in time for installation in HMS *Eagle* to coincide with her planned steam catapults and side lift, unless she could be made available for three years, that being the installation time in an existing ship.

Possibilities considered for the gun battery included using 3in/50 mounts as interim substitutes and even modernizing the

This photograph, taken aboard HMS Hermes, pulls together two major themes of the postwar Royal Navy: the struggle to preserve a long-range strike capability (ultimately guaranteed in the form of the Buccaneer), and the fight for effective fleet air defence, symbolized by the massive Type 984 fighter control radar, in its nacelle above the bridge. The bar above the nacelle is the associated Mk X IFF interrogator. Type 984 had a long-range search beam and a series of shorter-range scanning height-finding beams. The long-range beam had limited height coverage, and the nacelle could be adjusted in angle to vary its height band. In theory, a fleet needed to combine three 984s (at three different angles) to achieve solid long-range coverage. Scimitars like the one on the left remained in service after Buccaneers appeared, to serve as buddy-pack tankers to extend Bucaneer range.

existing 4.5in guns. However, by January 1952 DGD could report that twin 3in/70 mounts would be available as needed, without affecting the parallel reconstruction of the three *Tiger* class cruisers, and that the final battery would be six twin 3in/70 and three multiple Bofors (Mk 6 or 12).

The ship was needed too badly for the Controller to accept D of D's plea for delay. He instructed D of D to include, as an alternative in his revised dockyard plan, modernisation of the ship between June 1953 and December 1956. D of D protested that substantial structural work (about three-quarters of the full amount) would be needed in even a limited modernisation, and that there was insufficient skilled labour for even HMS *Victorious*. Overlapping the two by at least a year would make matters much worse.

All the staff could do was to trim the requirements. In October, it was decided to retain the original boilers, making no atomic/chemical modifications to the uptakes. Reduced gallery deck headroom was accepted to avoid raising the flight deck. The island, however, would be rebuilt to provide full AIO facilities. To avoid any delay, Type 984 would not be installed. Instead the ship would have approximately the same radars as HMS *Eagle* and other contemporary British ships (960, 982, 983). DTSD had no doubt, in November, that it would be better to have a useful carrier as soon as possible after mid-

26 Because the machinery spaces were subdivided longitudinally, torpedoes breaking through the side protection would cause asymmetric flooding, and the ship would list badly. The only machinery subdivisions in newer carriers extended all the way across the ship, so that water from penetrating hits would flood across, without causing much of a list.

27 The minimum changes, as understood in October 1951, were: a new clear hangar height (17ft 6in), new arrester gear and lifts (the BH III catapult would be retained), essential changes to armament, radar, AIO, and diesel fuel stowage (for Gannets) in existing oil fuel tanks. Existing petrol stowage would be retained.

1956, then to wait for the new generation of systems.

Design work proceeded at least until early February 1952.

In June 1952 the Board decided that no more fleet carriers would be modernized. *Victorious* was taking too long, and the *Implacable* experience strongly suggested that little improvement could be expected or achieved. It was not even clear that

Hermes after her 1964–66 refit, with all of her 40mm guns replaced by Seacat short-range missiles, and the flight deck gear uprated for Buccaneer operations. The flight deck was widened aft on the port side for parking, and an 'Alaskan highway' was built on the starboard side of the island for vehicle acess. The Type 293Q on the mast was replaced by a Type 993, and a projector (fresnel lens) landing sight replaced the earlier mirror.

existing dockyard capacity could support a second full-dress modernization before HMS *Victorious* was completed.

This left the newer carriers. A range of standards for carrier capability was established. In October 1956 it was:

A   984/CDS (32 or 48 track)/DPT; fully angled deck; steam catapults; Mk 13 arrester gear; NA 39, N113, DH 110 and earlier. (H) adds HTP (rocket fuel) stowage, can operate SR.177.

B*   As A but 982/983/960/CDS (6- or 24 track)/ DPT.

B   Only 982/983/960, no CDS.

C   Interim angled deck.

C(H) Plus HTP/SR.177

D   982/983/960 or earlier, interim deck, BH V or earlier hydraulic catapult, earlier arrester gear; limited to Sea Hawk, Sea Venom, Gannet.

E   Earlier radar, axial deck, earlier arrester gear.

F   Earlier radar, interim angled deck, could operate existing aircraft in a training and trials role only.

Here the distinction was between an interim, about 5-degree, angled deck, which was only barely adequate, and a full angled deck (about 8 to 10 degrees), which left a wide parking space forward, and which permitted the carrier to operate larger aircraft.

The goal was to be able to operate three A carriers together, partly because only then could the relatively narrow search beams of their Type 984 radars add up to sufficient long-range coverage. Because of her limited size, and hence her limited capacity, *Hermes* could not be considered a full A carrier even though she was modernized to that standard.

Eagle was refitted to Standard D in 1954–55, and was scheduled for a Standard A modernization in 1958–60. *Ark Royal* was completed to Standard C, and was expected to modernize to Standard A upon completion of *Eagle*. This was, however, cancelled.

Of the *Hermes* class, the first three ships were completed to Standard D and *Albion* and *Centaur* were scheduled (until 1955)

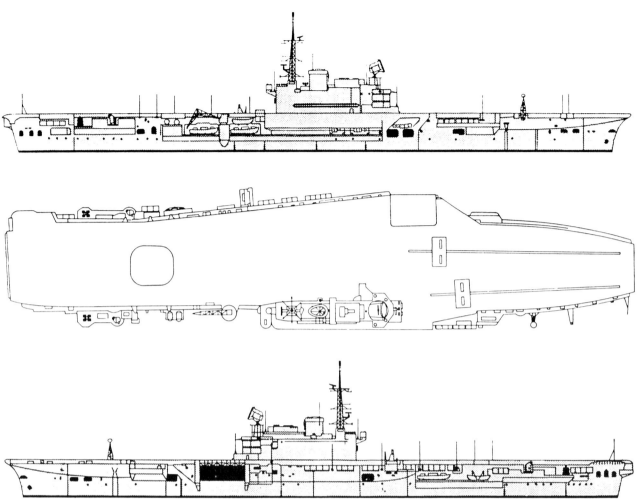

HMS Hermes *as a jet carrier, in 1968, with a Type 984 radar atop her island. Note the two quadruple Seacats aft.*

for Standard B refit with full angled decks and steam catapults. *Hermes* was completed to Standard A.

Warrior was refitted to Standard E in 1952–53 and then to Standard F in 1955–56.

IN 1959–64 HMS *Eagle* was modernized at Devonport, and provided with a full (8½-degree) angled deck and one long (199ft) and one medium (151ft) BS 4 steam catapults. Type 984 and 48-track CDS were installed; unlike HMS *Victorious*, HMS *Eagle* also had a conventional long-range air search radar (Type 965) on a forward lattice mast. A second lattice mast carried an aircraft homing beacon and a Type 992 gunnery air search radar. The four forward 4.5in mounts were removed, and the entire light battery replaced by six Seacat short-range missile launchers (three to starboard, two to port, and one aft). Four new generators were added, increasing total electric power to 8250kW. In 1956 the planned 1963 air group consisted of twelve SR.177, twelve Buccaneer, ten Sea Vixen, eight Gannets or ASW helicopters, six Gannet AEW aircraft, and two search and rescue (SAR) helicopters. The SR.177 did not materialize, but this list gives some indication of the effective capacity of the ship.

The length of the *Eagle* modernization was due in part to simultaneous (but much more limited) work undertaken on her sister ship. In April 1957 the Board considered a proposal to take HMS *Ark Royal* in hand for limited modernization in July 1958, accepting a delay in completing HMS *Eagle*. This might

reduce the British carrier force to only two ships until 1960 (*Victorious* and *Hermes*, since *Centaur* would be refitting), partly because manpower could not suffice for more. One solution considered at this time was to maintain one of the two obsolete large light carriers, *Albion* or *Bulwark*, in service a little longer, past 1959. This was done: *Albion* did not pay off for conversion to a commando carrier until December 1960. These arrangements were important because the Board was then pressing for a government policy of maintaining four, rather than three, active carriers, in two fleets (one East of Suez, one dividing its time between Home and Mediterranean), rather than the proposed three one-carrier task forces.

By March 1956 it was obvious that the *Eagle* modernization would take four or five years rather than the three originally forecast. Because *Ark Royal* also had to be refitted, it was urgent that carrier modernization work be limited. In May 1956, the Board therefore approved an austere modernization for the light carrier *Centaur*. This work was expected fully to absorb the available margin, and would leave the ship severely limited. Owing to insufficient hangar deck strength, aircraft had to be armed on her flight deck, and nuclear/chemical protection was rudimentary. However, it was considered more important that she be completed within a relatively short time, specifically limited to two years. She was fitted with two 139ft BS 4 steam catapults. In this form she was expected to operate twelve Sea Vixen fighters, eight Gannets, four Skyraiders (AEW) and two search and rescue helicopters. That is, she could operate defensive but not offensive aircraft.

All of this left HMS *Hermes* still under construction. She was initially delayed to receive steam catapults, but then it turned out that much more was possible. In May 1953 a new

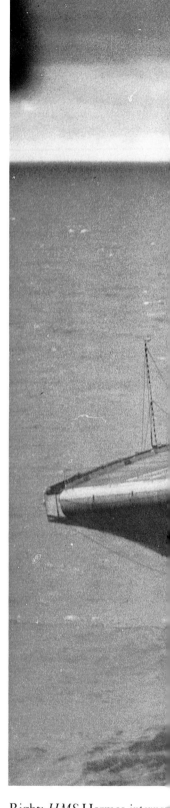

Right: *HMS* Hermes *internal profile*. NF

Key
1 Boiler room
2 Engine room
3 Gear case compartment
4 Petrol stowage
5 Bofors magazine
6 Rocket magazine
7 Diesel generator
8 Bomb room
9 CCA room
10 Operating room

11 Compass platform
12 Battle conning & visual FD position
13 Combined briefing & ready room (outboard of hangar)
14 Catapult pumps
15 Pyrotechnics
16 Torpedo warheads

Above: Hermes *as completed, 1959.*

displacement limit, 27,800 tons, was approved. A new Staff Requirement was approved on 13 May 1954. This was the fourth time the ship had been redesigned, and the new design incorporated two steam catapults, a full angled deck and Type 984/CDS. In 1956, the projected air complement was eight Scimitar, nine Sea Vixen, eight ASW helicopters, four AEW Gannets and two search and rescue helicopters.

That was not the end of modifications. A new Staff Requirement was approved in 1957.[28] Avcat stowage was increased from 314,000 to 328,000 gallons at the expense of avgas stowage (61,000 gallons reduced to 40,000); piston-engine aircraft were being withdrawn from service. Like HMS *Victorious*, she had provision for tactical nuclear bombs.

The 6½-degree angled deck was designed to avoid undesirable air flow with the wind from 5 degrees on the starboard bow to 20 degrees on the port bow. A forward deck-edge lift (which could not be used when the angled deck was in use) was fitted, reportedly to clear sufficient length forward to permit full-length (151ft) BS 4 catapults to be fitted. Lift dimensions were 54 x 35ft (deck-edge) and 54 x 44ft (centreline aft), each with a normal working load of 35,000lbs and a maximum load of 40,000lbs. This was essentially the same as the installation aboard HMS *Victorious*, but the catapults were slightly longer.

In 1957 the projected air complement was seventeen fighters (Scimitars or Sea Vixens), eight ASW helicopters or Gannets, four Gannet or Skyraider AEW, and two rescue helicopters. Ready-use ammunition stowage was provided for two loads of gun ammunition for eight Scimitars and one load of 2in air-to-air rockets for nine Sea Vixens, with maximum interchangeability between the two, plus thirty-six guided weapons (air to air), and one load of 3in ground-attack rockets for nine fighters.[28]

The big Type 984 fed a 32-track CDS, and there were four intercept positions. At this time it was estimated that one fighter control officer could deal with six contacts per minute, so in theory the ship could intercept twenty-four targets per minute (given sufficient aircraft). The Staff Requirement also included DPT.

The remaining gun battery had to be reduced to compensate for some added weights (a twin Bofors forward of the island and three single Bofors on the transom were eliminated). This left five twin Bofors, all below flight deck level. They were replaced by four Seacat missile launchers during a 1965–66 refit.

Protection generally followed that originally planned for the class, but in this ship citadel protection, including boxed boilers, was provided against fallout and chemical attack. The main and auxiliary machinery could be operated remotely.

Electrical power was changed from DC to AC, and generating capacity increased to 5440kW, in 1959 the highest figure in the Royal Navy.

The last major modernization was the conversion of HMS *Ark Royal* to handle Phantom and Buccaneer S.2 aircraft, in 1967–70. It was essentially limited to air facilities, no Type 984 or equivalent radar being installed. Instead two Type 965 two-dimensional air search radars were fitted and the two existing Type 983 height-finders were retained. All armament was landed.

The flight deck was angled at 8½ degrees, with a sponson built out along the port side. The flight deck was also enlarged on both sides (port right aft and starboard well aft) for additional aircraft parking and for helicopter spotting. Two long steam catapults were fitted, one in the bow (and extending back past the forward lift) and one on the angled deck. New direct-acting arrester gear was also installed.

ONE OTHER ASPECT of the postwar carrier programme deserves mention here: the replenishment carrier. During the latter part of the Pacific War, the Royal Navy had been most impressed by the US practice of bringing aircraft out to the fleet aboard an auxiliary carrier, and then flying them onto the fighting carriers. There was no room for such a project in the constricted budgets of the early postwar period, but wider possibilities opened with the Korean War mobilization. Early in 1951 D of P proposed a replenishment/repair carrier. The existing *Majestic* was too small, but a repeat *Hermes* hull seemed satisfactory.

Staff Requirements issued on 30 January 1951 and approved (for planning purposes only) by the Fifth Sea Lord envisaged a speed of at least 28 knots, one BS 4 catapult, Mk 13 arrester gear, a straight-sided flight deck (for 30,000lb aircraft), two lifts (54 x 34ft), a 17ft 6in hangar, a minimum of 150,000 gallons of aircraft fuel (with 240,000 desired), and large workshop and repair capacity. This was, in effect, a modern version of HMS *Unicorn*.

A *Majestic* could be reworked with two new (30,000shp YEAD.1) machinery units for 28.5 knots, but it could take only a 105ft catapult, whereas the *Hermes* hull could take the full 150ft unit. *Majestic* would require a replated flight deck (for strength) and new lifts. Her fuel capacity would be 140,000 gallons, compared to 150,000 (plus 159,000 of avtur) in a *Hermes*. Shop area was likely to be disappointing in either case. *Unicorn* had 19,000sq ft of shops and 13,100sq ft of aviation stores; *Perseus* had 6067 and 5850, respectively. *Hermes* had only 6850sq ft of shops.

The other possibilities were to refit the fleet carrier *Illustrious* or to modernize either *Perseus* or *Unicorn*. Both of the latter were in service, *Unicorn* as a repair carrier supporting British forces in Korea and *Perseus* as steam catapult test ship.[30] The *Perseus* conversion would have been similar to that proposed for HMS *Majestic*, a BS 4 catapult and Mk 12 arrester gear being installed, with a 52 x 40ft (25,000lb) lift.

Unicorn seems to have been the favoured choice. DAW proposed fitting her with a BS 4 (103ft) catapult (which would have had reduced performance due to her lower steam pressure) and to replate her flight deck for 25,000lb take-offs and 22,000lb landings. The forward lift would have to be moved to clear the catapult, and it would have to be enlarged to meet the new requirement for a 52 x 40ft lift (there was an aircraft spares lift on the inboard side of the after lift). A new heavy crane would have been installed. DNC offered to increase hangar height by making her a single-hangar ship, using the former lower hangar deck as the new hangar deck. This option was unattractive because of its high cost.

Hangar height was limited; the upper hangar overhead rails reduced clear height to 15ft 11in. In the lower hangar, however, for 40ft abaft the after lift the clear height was 17ft.

In October 1951 the British plan called for *Unicorn* to be taken in hand in July 1954. The project died in November 1952. Deck angling was so important that DAW saw no point in converting any replenishment carriers until the whole first-line British carrier force had been provided with angled decks. He also remarked that further modernization of older ships was not worthwhile until that had been done.

THE BRITISH NAVAL AIR PROGRAMME was drastically revised after the end of the war. The heavy new strike aircraft of mid-war design, the Spearfish and the Sturgeon (S.11/43), were cancelled because no existing carrier could operate them, and because they would clearly be quite obsolete by the time the large new carriers entered service.[31] The existing naval fighters, though obsolescent, were still usable; the Sea Fury succeeded

28 The final Staff Requirement, dated 26 March 1957, is in ADM 1/26842.

29 Aside from tactical nuclear weapons, the Staff Requirement called for bulk stowage for 320 1000lb MC bombs, seventy-two ASW torpedoes (including sixteen in ready-use stowage), 100 Blue Jay air-to-air missiles, 1944 3in rocket motors, 1890 2in rocket motors (1122 had to be accepted), 51,840 rounds of 30mm ammunition (1728 boxes; 1575 had to be accepted), 108 depth charges, twenty-four mines and 250 sonobuoys.

30 *Perseus* went to the Far East but arrived at the end of the war and was not needed. She was therefore sent home to reserve, converted in 1949 to steam catapult trials ship (operating as such from July 1950 to June 1952). She was then converted to a ferry trooping carrier (with her lifts restored to operation), and served in this role between November 1952 and May 1953. She, her sister *Pioneer* and *Unicorn* were all re-rated as ferry carriers in June 1953. Their official role was to transport aircraft to and from bases overseas and act as limited replenishment carriers, but in 1951 it was decided that no effort would be made to adapt them as full replenishment carriers until after the angled deck programme was complete. *Perseus* functioned as reviewing stand during the 1953 Coronation Naval Review, and in 1954 worked up the first Royal Navy ASW helicopter squadron. Later she carried stores and supplies to the Far East. Upon her return she paid off into reserve. She was to have been converted to a submarine tender, but with the reduction in naval forces in 1957 two rather than three such ships were required. The projected cost of conversion was extremely high, and she was discarded. Her sister *Pioneer* served in the Far East, returned home to reserve, and was discarded in 1954. A proposal of October 1952 that *Perseus* should be converted for wartime use as an aircraft repair ship was killed in January 1953 because she was needed as a ferry carrier. *Unicorn* was reduced to reserve in 1946, but in 1948 was refitted for further service as a maintenance carrier, going to the Far East in 1949. She returned home on 17 November 1953 and went back into reserve.

31 The Sturgeon survived in modified form. Because Miles failed to produce the required twin-engine target-towing aircraft (the Monitor) in a reasonable time and at a reasonable price, it had to be dropped in favour of an improvised alternative, either a Mosquito or a Sturgeon. The initial decision was to convert sixty Mosquitoes, but they were not considered ideal, especially in the tropics, and in any case they were likely to be a dying type. The Sturgeon was a preferable alternative, particularly as it had the added advantage of being suitable for operation from carriers. It was not much more expensive than the Mosquito, and, because it was all-metal it was more robust and would last longer.

Nick Goodhart's mirror sight aboard HMS Albion, *1954. A similar unit was mounted on the port side. The light source was further aft (that is, pointing into the mirror). Note the cab behind the mirror, part of the sextuple Bofors gun.*

the Seafires and Sea Hornets went to sea on a limited basis. Because the next strike aircraft, the Wyvern, was too large for existing carriers, and because the Firebrand successor (S.10/45) had been killed off, the postwar fleet had to depend largely on the Firefly as its strike aircraft. A few Firebrands were built, but they never operated in very large numbers, because they were too heavy to fly from any existing carriers other than the two *Implacables* and the trials carrier *Illustrious*. The only available ASW aircraft was the Barracuda III, although the Firefly, too, could carry the new ASW sensors and weapons.

In keeping with the central postwar decisions, the operating Royal Navy was drastically reduced. Late in 1944 it seemed likely that with the end of Lend-Lease the Fleet Air Arm would be reduced to about 800 operational aircraft, 700 first-line types and 100 for reservists. In 1947 the Royal Navy had 204 first-line aircraft, 750 second-line, and 100 reservist aircraft, plus 1530 in storage. In 1948, however, the fleet was allowed only 190 first-line aircraft, including only twelve dedicated strike aircraft in one squadron.[32] The 'revised restricted fleet' (that is, the war fleet to be built towards) of May 1949 showed 250 first-line operational aircraft, to operate from five fleet carriers and four light fleet carriers. In October 1950 a goal of 306 carrier-borne aircraft was set, in the context of a possible war with the Soviet Union. Existing strength was still much lower, so that it was only about 230 in 1952. At that time a first-line strength of about 300 was planned for 1955. Pressure was then being brought for economies, and strength began to decline. Mobilization planning throughout this period was based on much higher numbers (see, for example, the discussion of the MAC ships in Chapter 9).

QUITE ASIDE FROM NEW AIRCRAFT, the postwar period was marked by increased reliance on guided weapons. From a carrier point of view, they required greater stowage space,

check-out and servicing facilities and, in some cases, special fuel storage.

There were three important categories: air-to-air missiles, air-to-ship missiles, and homing torpedoes for use primarily against submarines.

The three principal British naval air-to-air missiles of the early 1950s were the Blue Sky, Red Dean and Blue Jay.

Blue Sky was a large (360lb) radar beam-rider designed to attack large, heavily armed but unmanoeuvrable aircraft such as the Soviet TU 4 (B-29 copy). The radar had to be locked on the target during flight, that is, for about 10 seconds, and it was considered unlikely that this could be done against future smaller and faster targets. The guidance radar imposed a considerable penalty. Thus Blue Sky was roughly comparable to the US Sparrow I. Blue Sky was evaluated as Fireflash in 1954–5, but was not bought for operational use. It was launched with two large solid boosters.

Blue Jay was an infra-red homing missile (about 300lbs) developed as Firestreak, which entered service in 1958. The first test rounds were fired in 1954, and it was carried by Sea Venom (two missiles each) and Sea Vixen (four missiles each). Typically the IR seeker, which could point away from the missile axis, was slaved to the fighter radar.

Red Dean was conceived as either an active or semi-active radar-guided weapon, thus comparable to the contemporary US Sparrow II/III. It required a large warhead to ensure lethal effect by its proximity fuse, and was expected to weigh 670lbs. It was designed to work with the big AI 18 radar, which in 1952 was too heavy for any planned naval fighter. Red Dean was developed with active radar guidance, Red Hebe being a related project. Both were cancelled in 1957 when the advanced air defence fighter programmes were killed.

Red Top was the advanced version of Firestreak (Blue Jay) carried by Sea Venom FAW.2.

In addition, the Royal Navy bought the simpler US Sidewinder infra-red homing missile, which, however, could not be blind-fired since its seeker could not be slaved to a fighter's radar.

The principal new anti-ship weapon of this period was the large Green Cheese guided bomb, which displaced the late-war Red Angel and Bootleg. It was conceived in 1952 to counter the perceived threat of Soviet *Sverdlov* class cruisers, and it was developed as a joint RAF-Royal Navy weapon. By 1955 it was apparent that existing Gannets could not carry it, and the requirement to adapt future Gannets (Mk IV) was abandoned in October 1955. The weapon itself was cancelled in June 1956.[33] It was replaced by the US-supplied Bullpup.

The other important anti-ship weapon of this period was the naval tactical nuclear bomb, which was also first proposed in 1952 as a cruiser-killer. It was called the '2000lb Target Marker Bomb' (TMB), although in developed form it was apparently lighter. It may also have been code-named Red Beard.

AS IN THE CASE of the earlier piston aircraft, the progress of jet engine development defined generations of jet aircraft. In 1945 both centrifugal-flow and axial-flow engines existed. The former were more highly developed but ultimately they were limited because greater power required greater compressor diameter; these engines were relatively short and fat. An axial-flow engine tended to be longer and slimmer, and compressor power could be increased by adding more stages (that is, by making it longer).

The earliest British jets, such as the Rolls-Royce Derwent and the de Havilland Goblin, used centrifugal-flow compressors and were rated at about 2000lbs of static thrust. Aircraft designers could choose either to use two such engines

32 These figures are somewhat deceptive. They are IE (initial equipment) figures, representing the strength of active units. They do not include replacement or spare aircraft, or secondary types such as trainers. The planned wartime IE was substantially larger, about 600 in 1949. All of this compared with a planned ultimate IE of 1600 in 1945 (see Chapter 10).

33 The Green Cheese was conceived as an updated version of the German wartime FX 1400 guided bomb, the requirement being that bomb plus aircraft system together should not weigh more than 4000lbs. Television and infra-red homing were rejected because they would not function in much North Atlantic weather. The Air Staff wanted to use the Red Dean active radar seeker, and it is not clear from surviving papers whether the choice fell on this or on a semi-active radar. Dimensions were 32in diameter, 188in length, and 62in wing span (four wings, folding to 38in), and total weight was 3300lbs, with a 2000lb MC bomb as warhead. DNC estimated that a single penetrating hit would have a 50 per cent chance of sinking a cruiser. Tests would have begun in 1958. These details are from ADM 1/25424.

(as in the Meteor) or to cut airframe size to a minimum (as in the Vampire).[34] In 1944 MAP sought a jump up to 4000lbs or more, Rolls-Royce using a double-sided centrifugal compressor (in effect, two compressors back to back) in the new Nene (B.41). It was initially rated at 5000lbs of thrust, about double the previous output.

The Nene was about the limit of centrifugal-compressor development. It also presented the MAP with a tremendous opportunity, since for the first time a jet fighter could enjoy substantially more power than one with a piston engine, without paying a high drag penalty in the form of two fat nacelles. The results were the Jet Spiteful (Supermarine Attacker), a new Hawker fighter, and the Gloster G.42 (E.1/44).

The other great line of turbojet development was the axial-flow engine. Because they were so much slimmer, two axial jets could easily be accommodated in a fuselage little fatter than that required by a single centrifugal-flow engine. This was the logic of the Supermarine interceptor of 1945, which ultimately became the Scimitar. Axial-flow engines were also easier to upgrade. Rolls-Royce started with an AJ 25 (axial jet, 2500lb thrust) tentatively named Tweed; it was never actually built, although a related turboprop (AP 25) did materialize. Design studies soon led to the AJ50, AJ60, and then AJ65 (1945), the latter named the Avon. It produced 6000lbs of thrust in 1947, and by 1951 a developed version (RA 7) gave 7500. The following year the RA 28 version gave 10,000lbs of thrust in much the same dimensions.

These two engine options, the developed Nene and the potentially more powerful Avon, defined the British naval fighter projects of 1945–46. The interim Jet Spiteful and a new Hawker fighter were both powered by the Nene, though the Hawker project was more refined aerodynamically and thus much more attractive.[35] At the end of the war a few Jet Spitefuls (Attackers) were on order, mainly as a means of developing initial jet tactics and deck techniques. However, handling difficulties with the Spiteful itself convinced the Admiralty to cancel this initial order in favour of Sea Vampires. The latter could not be considered an operational aircraft: it could neither be catapulted (it was not strong enough) nor folded, nor did it have sufficient endurance. Moreover, there was little hope that de Havilland could cure these limitations, as the firm was very fully occupied.[36]

Supermarine had been asked to concentrate on maximum performance in a new interceptor, to make full use of the flexible deck. It therefore used two Avons side by side, to achieve maximum power at a minimum cost in drag. Since there was no need to house the undercarriage in it, the wing could be made unusually thin. This fighter became the Scimitar (see below).

With the end of the war, the Supermarine Jet Spiteful (Attacker) was virtually dropped (to be revived later), on the theory that too much had been compromised in the rush to produce a viable design.[37] The central postwar policy meant, if anything, that such interim designs should be dropped in favour of more satisfactory aircraft exploiting a more fully-developed form of the new technology. The RAF in particular wanted its next-generation interceptor (a Meteor replacement) to be capable of intercepting fast high-altitude bombers. This equated to a capability to climb to 40,000ft in 3 minutes, and in effect it ruled out any Nene-powered aircraft. As a result, the RAF, which had originally been lead service for the Hawker joint-service project, bowed out early in 1946.

The Admiralty was prepared to settle for less. It therefore took over the Hawker fighter in the spring of 1946 and development proceeded to Specification N.7/46.[38] The aircraft was relatively small (although too large to fly from the

Above and top: *Jet aircraft even required special barriers, since the standard steel-wire crash barrier tended to ride up over the smooth nose and decapitate the pilot. The solution was a nylon net, here stopping a Hawker Sea Hawk fighter aboard HMS* Eagle *in 1959. The second photo clearly shows that the aircraft was not seriously damaged.*

*Implacable*s) and was well within the usual limit for all-up weight. Approach and landing speeds were likely to be acceptable, although the laminar-flow wing presented problems which could be resolved only by actual experience. Although more powerful engines were in prospect, the Nene was attractive because a Nene-powered fighter could be developed relatively quickly. The Hawker N.7/46 became the Sea Hawk, the first fully satisfactory British naval jet fighter.

The Navy decision was made partly because it seemed unlikely that the fleet could rely entirely on deck-launched interceptors. Although a jet fighter on combat air patrol could dive to meet a low-flying enemy, it seemed unlikely that existing shipboard radars would provide early enough warning to launch fighters directly against such attackers. Nor did it seem likely that any airborne early warning radar would give

34 At 375mph 1lb of thrust provides the equivalent of 1hp, and at higher speed the equivalent power is proportionately greater. These figures explain why a jet fighter powered by one or two 2000lb thrust engines was not much more powerful than contemporary piston-engined fighters. Early Meteors were actually slower than the fastest single-engine piston aircraft, since their two big nacelles added considerable drag. Because jet engines consumed much more fuel than their piston predecessors, any substantial endurance required a capacious fuselage.

enough gapless coverage to solve the problem. It seemed possible that in future the fleet could rely on guided missiles for close-in defence (Seaslug eventually had a nominal range of about 15nm), but in 1946 it was accepted that manned fighters would be needed to intercept aircraft at greater distances, perhaps 100 or 200nm.

They would also be needed as strike escorts. The Committee recognized that some compromise would have to be accepted. Jets had very limited endurance at low altitude, but they were reasonably efficient at high altitude. This suggested that, particularly if it could carry drop tanks, the jet fighter could orbit in a high altitude CAP station, diving to attack lower-flying attackers. It could not, however, fly efficiently with strike aircraft at their relatively low cruising speed. On the other hand, the strike aircraft could expect opposition only very close to their targets. The Committee therefore envisaged a new strike support tactic, in which fighters met the strike aircraft near the target, dealt with enemy opposition there, and then returned separately to the carrier.

The new fighter might also be needed to ensure against the failure of the projected Wyvern turboprop strike aircraft, although this seemed relatively unlikely.

The Fifth Sea Lord endorsed development of the Hawker fighter, calling it a promising step needed to develop the new jet tactics. Early tactical experience would be extremely important since jet characteristics, particularly as concerned endurance and range, were so different from those of their propeller-driven predecessors. Moreover, there was no intermediate aircraft in prospect. Unless the Navy developed jets, it would have to soldier on with the final piston fighters, and it would be hopelessly outclassed by land-based aircraft, as in 1939.

As the Hawker jet evolved, it soon became obvious that no existing British carrier could operate it, because existing catapults and arrester gear could not cater for its high stall speed, 15 knots faster than that of any existing aircraft (as estimated in October 1946), and much higher than had originally been estimated. It was not clear, for example, whether average pilots could deck-land it without experiencing a prohibitive accident rate. It would need natural wind, above what the carrier could generate by her own speed, to use all current and projected catapults (BH III and BH V) and arrester gear.[39] Thus the N.7/46 programme itself became a driving force in carrier modernization, and a lower limit on acceptable future catapult and arrester gear performance.

The prototype P.1040 (Sea Hawk without naval features) flew on 2 September 1947 and the first fully navalized prototype followed on 3 September 1948. Deck trials aboard HMS *Illustrious* followed in May 1949. The first production aircraft flew only in November 1951.[40]

This slow progress made the Attacker (the navalized Jet Spiteful), which had been dismissed as a late-war expedient, much more attractive. In March 1948, with the Sea Hawk already ten months behind schedule, and with worse clearly in store, the Naval Aircraft Design Committee considered ordering some Attackers as a stop-gap and as insurance against further delays. Delays in delivery of the Sea Vampire had exacerbated the problem.

The Attacker could be catapulted (if the BH V was up-rated to an end-speed of 80 knots, which seemed entirely practicable), and it could land aboard the *Ark Royal* and *Hermes* class carriers (though it would be near the latter's limit). It would not be operable from the existing light fleet carriers, although it could fit their hangar. It was, moreover, important to keep Supermarine interested in naval fighter work once Seafire 47 production was over, so that the company would press ahead with its much more advanced heavy interceptor (see below). The Committee therefore suggested sufficient orders for two squadrons (about fifty to seventy-five aircraft); assuming production could begin in eighteen months, the first thirty (replacing the first thirty Seahawks) could be delivered during the latter half of the 1949–50 programme year. Further aircraft would replace the last of the Sea Furies in 1950–51. This schedule seemed plausible because many of the necessary jigs already existed, and because Supermarine needed work after completing the Seafire 47 contract in 1948.

The first production Attacker flew on 5 May 1950, and the first operational squadron was formed on 17 August 1951, followed by a second in November and a third in April 1952. Thus the Attackers were later than expected, but still were available well ahead of the Sea Hawks, the first squadron of which formed only in March 1953. Sea Hawks began to replace Attackers in front-line squadrons in 1954.[41]

35 Details of the Nene first became available in the autumn of 1944, and in November Hawker offered MAP a Fury with a Nene buried in its fuselage, essentially a Fury equivalent of the Jet Spiteful (P.1035). In December the company proposed a more refined aircraft, with a bifurcated exhaust, which it designated P.1040; this was the Seahawk. The bifurcated exhaust was introduced to reduce jet pipe losses, but it also left much more internal fuselage volume for fuel. P.1040 was accepted as a joint Service project; the Air Staff approved it early in January 1945, and the company formally tendered in February. Hawker formally ordered a prototype in October 1945, presumably with MAP approval. The formal tender for a naval interceptor was made in January 1946, and the contract for three prototypes and one structural test airframe was given in May 1946. It is not clear precisely when the N.7/46 Specification was written, but contemporary Minutes of the Naval Aircraft Design Committee show that the previous year the Admiralty had invited Hawker to design the Sea Fury replacement. Dates are from F K Mason, *Hawker Aircraft Since 1920* (Putnam, London, 1961).

36 The Sea Vampire F.20 was a navalized Vampire F.B. 5, strengthened and fitted with enlarged dive-brakes and landing flaps, long-travel oleo legs, and with an A-frame arrester hook. It first flew in October 1948, and the last of eighteen was delivered in June 1949. The Royal Navy also bought seventy-four two-seat Sea Vampire T.22s. Sea Vampire endurance was 2 hours at 220mph (191 knots) at sea level or 2.35 hours at 350mph (304 knots) at 30,000ft. Figures and dates from O Thetford, *British Naval Aircraft Since 1912* (Putnam, London, 1978). Published sources commonly describe the Sea Vampire as having been strengthened for accelerator take-off, but the contemporary (1948) Minutes of the Naval Aircraft Design Committee imply otherwise. A small force of Sea Vampires was embarked aboard HMS *Vengeance* for interception exercises in the North Atlantic and the Arctic in 1950, and at least three Sea Vampire F.21s (including one former F.1 and one former F.3) were modified for flexible-deck landings aboard HMS *Warrior* in 1949, and then at Farnborough up until 1953. A J Jackson. *De Havilland Aircraft Since 1909* (Putnam, London, 1987).

37 Heavily burdened with Spitfire/Spiteful development work late in the war, Supermarine used as much of the Spiteful/Seafang layout as posible: a new fuselage with existing wings and control surfaces, and conventional (tail down) undercarriage. On this basis three prototypes (two navalized but without folding wings) were ordered on 5 August 1945 (Supermarine was notified in July 1945). The prototype Spiteful was criticized for its stall characteristics, it was assumed that the Jet Spiteful would have the same problem; moreover, it was assumed that jet aircraft had to have tricycle undercarriages. Thus the Attacker was dismissed as a hasty late-war design. Even so, a total of twenty-four (including eighteen navalized) pre-production aircraft were ordered on 21 November 1945. The first flight of the Attacker was delayed while the handling problems were solved, so in February 1946 the Admiralty asked that eighteen Sea Vampires be substituted for the eighteen naval Attackers. The entire 24-aircraft contract was suspended, although Supermarine pressed on with the three prototypes. The Ministry of Supply (MoS, successor to the wartime MAP) maintained some interest and the prototype flew on 27 July 1946. Despite the lack of any formal naval interest, preliminary deck landings aboard HMS *Illustrious* were arranged, beginning on 28 October 1947. Their success proved that a fast jet with conventional undercarriage could successfully land on a carrier. The design of the conventional undercarriage was considered a great advance on previous practice. Another innovation was lift spoilers, which proved very promising as a landing aid for fast jets. Compared to the Seahawk, the Attacker showed a high approach speed (about 105 knots) and a long take-off run, although the latter could be discounted if catapult take-off were accepted as standard. The Attacker had more limited endurance, and thus needed an external tank (Attackers usually carried a 250-gallon belly tank, and each of the two hard points under the wings could carry a 93-gallon drop tank). Above all, it was comfortable to fly, had no vices, and had adequate control. Overall reasoning for the Attacker is from the Minutes of the Naval Aircraft Design Committee; contract and flight dates are from C F Andrews and E B Morgan, *Supermarine Aircraft Since 1914* (Putnam, London, 1987).

38 The precise date is uncertain; this decision was reported to the Naval Aircraft Design Committee on 12 June 1946.

39 In October 1946 it was estimated that a normally-loaded N.7/46 required 108.5 knots for take-off; with fuel for long-range flight, it needed 113 knots. Thus with normal load it needed 12.5 knots of natural wind over the 30 knots of a carrier with a BH III catapult (17 when loaded for long range); corresponding figures for the BH V catapult of the *Ark Royal* were 2.5 and 7 knots. Any requirement for natural wind imposed a serious tactical limit on carrier operation. The N.7/46 was expected to land at 113.5 knots (and actually needed another 5 to allow for pilot error), whereas existing arrester gear was designed for 60 or 75 knots. An existing fleet carrier would therefore need 23.5 knots of natural wind plus its 30 knot speed; the new *Ark Royal* would need 7.5 knots of wind plus its 31. Combat radius with the normal fuel load was so short (115nm at sea level) that virtually all missions would require overload fuel.

40 Hawker produced thirty-five Sea Hawk F.1s, after which production shifted to Armstrong-Whitworth, while the parent company concentrated on Hunter production. A total of ninety-five F.1s were followed by forty F.2s, 113 FB.3s (provision for two 500lb bombs or mines in place of drop tanks), ninety-seven FGA.4s (four 500lb bombs), and eighty-six FGA.6s. Mk 5 was an up-rated Mk3 (fifty converted), and Mk 6 an uprated Mk 4 (some were converted, some newly-built). A few ex-Fleet Air Arm Sea Hawks were transferred to the Royal Australian Navy, and sixty-four were built for the West German Navy (thirty-two with podded Ekco radar for night interception, as Mk 101), thirty-two for the Royal Netherlands Navy (Mk 50), and twenty-five for India. Later British production was financed partly by US MDAP (off-shore procurement) funds, and the German and Dutch orders probably reflect reductions in British naval requirements during 1955–56. Later Sea Hawks had an internal fuel capacity of 395 gallons, plus up to four 90-gallon drop tanks, for a total of 665 gallons. Because initial Sea Hawk deliveries were so badly delayed, in 1952 the US Navy offered 100 Corsairs as a stop-gap (to replace ageing Sea Furies, no longer available from new production) free of charge (against reductions in the British FY53 MDAP aid request), but they were not, in the end, supplied.

41 A total of 149 aircraft were built for the Royal Navy (including eighty-four FB 2 with provision for eight rockets in two tiers under each wing), plus thirty-six for Pakistan. The initial F.1 version, a pure fighter, was followed by FB 1, a fighter-bomber, which could carry a 1000lb bomb under each wing.

Meanwhile Supermarine was developing a third naval day interceptor, its Type 505. In late 1945 and early 1946 it was conceived as a very fast-climber to exploit the new flexible ('sprung') flight decks. However, by mid-1946 it was by no means clear that the Royal Navy would ever be able to afford the flexible deck, since in that case it would need an entire generation of undercarriageless aircraft. An Admiralty meeting (9 August 1946) decided that it was impossible to justify the development of an expensive undercarriageless prototype before any operating experience had been obtained.

Supermarine had already put in substantial development work, and the Admiralty wanted a high-performance aircraft as a standby (suitable for development, though not in production) in the event that tests with modified Vampires proved successful. To put the work already done to useful purpose, Supermarine was asked to redesign its Type 505 (as Type 508) with a conventional undercarriage, retaining inherent under-carriage-less features (such as great structural strength) for a possible later conversion. The firm was therefore asked to resubmit to try to meet the existing Staff Requirement for single-seat fighters. The main change was a slightly thicker (9 rather than 7 per cent) wing, which was later enlarged (310 rather than 270sq ft) to improve landing characteristics. The principal structural change was to run the main wing spars under the engines (to anchor the main undercarriage legs), with the engines themselves installed above rather than below them. The two-engine fuselage itself was wide enough to accommodate the undercarriage.

This powerful new fighter was attractive not only to the Navy but also to the RAF, as it could easily be redesigned to meet the RAF interceptor requirement. By October 1946 MoS wanted three prototypes.

A naval Specification, N.9/47 (later NA 17), was issued the following year, still without any expectation of production. Table 15-2 compares the Supermarine fighter with the Hawker Sea Hawk as then envisaged. The new fighter was very attractive. It could climb about twice as fast as a Sea Hawk, and was much faster. The Vice Controller (Air) went so far as to say that it could climb faster than required. Its high power also made for a short enough take-off run to permit operation from existing carriers. Its greatest limitation was very short endurance; one possibility was to extend endurance by loitering

In 1946 it appeared that the Hawker Sea Hawk, then under development, represented the likely peak of naval jet aircraft design. Before any could be delivered, the design had become obsolete; swept wings made the thrust of much more powerful engines really useful. The Royal Navy therefore found itself quickly shifting to the Scimitar, which in 1946 was no more than a speculative attempt to make full use of flexible deck technolgy – which itself had to be abandoned. Here a line of Sea Hawks starts up, using cartridge starters.

on one engine.[42] The other major limitation was excessive folded span (26ft), but this had been reduced to an acceptable figure by mid-1947.

At this time, then, the Supermarine fighter was seen as a counter to the highest-performance shore-based aircraft. For the present, it was insurance against the possible failure of the Sea Hawk, but probably not as a Sea Hawk replacement. Requirements would, however, be reviewed at the prototype stage, when jet fighter requirements would be clearer. Three prototypes were ordered, to fly, it was hoped, within two or three years. However, the first Type 508 actually flew on 31 August 1951, making its first deck landings aboard HMS *Eagle* in May 1952

In August 1949 MoS suggested that the Type 508 be revised with a swept wing as the straight wing was now obsolete. By May 1950 CNR had ordered the third prototype swept back and its engines reheated (that is, fitted with afterburners) for maximum performance.

By this time the overall naval budget was under considerable pressure. Projected new engines, such as the Armstrong-Siddely Sapphire (7500lbs thrust in 1951, ultimately 11,000lbs thrust) and the RA 6 (developed Avon), offered so much power that the limit on performance was now aerodynamic. At an MoS meeting in April 1950 RAE (Farnborough) questioned the need for a big two-engined fighter when a smaller and cheaper one could be built with one engine. It soon became clear that RAE was comparing existing twin engines with a future single engine which might be up to four years away. It was not that the Naval Staff was wedded to twin engine reliability, but rather that it feared that the design of a new single-engine naval fighter might take 2½ more years, representing an unacceptable delay. Moreover, it would be

42   Although in mid-1947 this expe-
dient was not considered likely to succeed, the US Navy later routinely extended the CAP endurance of twin-engine Banshees (F2H) by shutting down one engine.

Table 15-2: Naval Jet Fighters, 1947

	Supermarine	Hawker	
Span (ft)	40 (26)[10]	36 6 (13 3)[1]	[36 6 (18)]
Length (ft)	46 9	37 2	[37 2]
Height (ft)	13	15 6	[10 5]
All-up weight (lbs)	18,000–18,500[9]		[9960–10,000][3]
Speed (knots)	575/SL	537/SL	[552–539/SL]
	535/30,000ft	518/30,000ft	
	500/45,000ft	—	[487–504/40,000ft]
Most economical			[287/20,000ft]
			[330/40,000ft]
Climb (ft/min)	18,500	9000	
	4.5 min to 45,000ft	—	[3.8 min to 20,000ft]
	2.1 min to 30,000ft	5.5 min to 30,000ft	[7.5 min to 30,000ft]
Service ceiling (ft)			[about 51,000]
Take-off at 27 knots (ft)	375	772	[550 at 10,000lbs]
Approach speed (knots)	107[3]	113.5	[88 at 10,000lbs]
Fuel (gallons)			[290][5]
Endurance with			
internal fuel	45 min at	1.4 hours at	[0.7 hours at 15,000ft][4]
	45,000ft	30,000ft	[1.3 hours at 30,000ft]
drop tanks	2.25 hours[11]	2.15 hours	[2 hours at 15,000ft]
	8		[2.8 hours at 30,000ft]
Radius (nm)	150	233	[90 at 15,000ft]
			[250 at 30,000]
Radius with drop tanks (nm)	400[12]	364	[265 at 15,000ft]
			[510 at 30,000ft]
Armament	2 30mm (200rpg)[2]	4 20mm (220rpg)	

Figures in square brackets are those given for N.7/46 in September 1946

1 Staff Requirements were 40 (18)ft × 40ft × 15ft 9in.
2 Provision for one recoilless rifle as alternative. The Staff wanted 4 20mm now, possible with 2 30mm later, and with arrangements for alternative installations of internal rocket projectors or a recoilless gun.
3 11,180lbs with tanks full.
4 1946 patrol endurance figures make provision for 20 minutes of combat.
5 440 including drop tanks (overload condition)
6 at 15,340lbs (fuel for 30 minutes). In June 1947, when its wing had been enlarged, the Supermarine fighter had an estimated approach speed of 94 knots.
7 200ft run using rocket-assistance; could be catapulted from a BH V at 80 knots (85 knots in overload condition) without natural wind over deck.
8 A figure of 3 hours with overload tanks was often cited in discussions.
9 Staff Requirement was 14,000lbs.
10 By June 1947 these figures had been amended to 19ft 6in folded width, 50ft length, height 15ft 4in sweeping through 17ft while being folded.
11 In June 1947, estimated loiter time with drop tanks was 2·5 hours at 30,000ft on both engines, including a climb to 40,000ft and 5 minutes of combat at sea level, plus 20 minutes' loiter there before landing.
12 In June 1947 combat radius was 438nm, but associated endurance was only 2 hours, because the optimum speed for range was higher than the optimum for loiter.

difficult to justify two parallel designs to the same N9/47 requirement.

The redesigned third prototype was designated Type 525. The two Avons were not reheated, but fuel capacity was increased, and the butterfly tail of the original 508 was replaced by a more conventional cruciform type.

The first swept-wing deck landings were actually made by another Supermarine aircraft, a prototype Swift fighter, aboard HMS *Illustrious* in November 1950.[43] Since the carrier lacked a steam catapult, the Swift was launched with rocket assistance.

The big twin-engined Supermarine fighter was ordered due to the Korean emergency, where the appearance of MiG-15s had shown that it would indeed be necessary to deal with high-performance land-based aircraft. A contract for two (later three) prototypes was placed early in 1951, and the first flew in April 1954. The new fighter was designed to a revised Staff Requirement, now numbered N.113.[44] This time the most important improvement was boundary-layer blowing over the flaps, to reduce landing speed by 15 knots and improve low-speed control.[45] These aircraft became Scimitar fighters.[46]

Pending introduction of the Scimitar, the Admiralty tried to obtain twenty hooked Swift fighters to gain experience of the handling characteristics of swept-wing fighters.[47] Like the Scimitar, the Swift was ordered into production as part of the Korean War mobilization, and the Admiralty considered (but rejected) a hooked version as an emergency replacement for the Scimitar. In the event, the hooked Swifts were cancelled in 1955.

Beside the day fighters, the postwar carrier force required a jet night (all-weather) fighter, since with the radar technology generally now available an enemy might well choose to attack

Work on the postwar carrier night fighter, the de Havilland Sea Vixen, began in 1946, but was protracted. The Sea Venom was adopted as an interim carrier all-weather fighter. Unlike the big Sea Vixen, it could fly from light fleet carriers; indeed, it was initially developed specifically for the Royal Australian Navy. This is a Sea Venom FAW 21, equipped with an A1 21 (US APQ-43) radar. Sea Venom 21s were employed as strike aircraft at Suez in 1956, flying from the carriers Albion, Bulwark *and* Eagle.

43 The Swift was essentially a swept-wing Attacker, designed to Specification E.41/46 (E.38/46, which led to the Hunter, was a parallel swept-wing version of the P.1040). The 1950 tests were made by the first prototype, with tailwheel undercarriage.

44 On 18 August 1953 the Scimitar (NA 17) Staff Requirement was: dimensions, 55 (20) ×× 51 × 17ft; armament, 4 Aden 30mm guns (8 seconds of fire); launch requirement, 15 knots WOD with BS 4(151) catapult, no rocket assistance; rate of climb at sea level at least 18,000ft per minute, at 45,000ft at least 2000ft per minute; max speed at sea level not less than 625 knots, at 45,000ft not less than 550 knots; ceiling (1000ft per minute) 47,000ft; for CAP, take off and climb to 45,000ft, patrol 2 hours (more if possible) at economic speed, then 5 minutes combat at 20,000ft (no reheat), 20-minute loiter at 2000ft; for long-range strike support, climb to height of best fuel economy, support strike not less than 400nm away, combat at 20,000ft for 5 minutes (no reheat), return at most economical speed and height, loiter 20 minutes at 2000ft; capable of maintaining height on one engine and landing with one engine, in which case the 1000ft per minute ceiling was not less than 8000ft. Later versions would have provision for four Blue Sky missiles (either four guns and two Blue Sky or two guns and four Blue Sky). The aircraft was also to be a fighter-bomber for ground attack and high-angle bombing. Not more than four hard points, four 1000lb bombs, or four mines, or twelve RP in triple tiers, or air-to-air rockets were required. A projected later version would be a long-range bomber with one 4000lb bomb for the longest range consistent with 28 knots WOD take-off. No guns were required. This last was NA 19, the Scimitar bomber.

45 In 1957 recommended approach speed was 124 knots at 28,000lbs using flap blowing. Maximum weight for catapult launch was 34,000lbs (118 knots).

46 In all, eighty-two aircraft, including prototypes, were built. The Scimitar was Supermarine Type 544.

47 Staff Requirement NA 34, issued in March 1952, called for aircraft navalized only to the extent of being hooked and adapted for catapulting. Approach speed would be 139 knots at 14,200lbs (overload was 19,100lbs, compared to 19,700lbs for the RAF). This was very high; the aircraft could land-on only with considerable natural wind. It was acceptable because the hooked Swift was needed only for familiarization, and could therefore operate only when the wind was right. A fully navalized Swift would have had to approach at a slower speed. The aircraft could be launched from a 150ft BS 4 steam catapult with 15 knots WOD, and from a 138½ft catapult at 21 knots WOD. It would be fitted for rocket take-off (run not to exceed 500ft with 35 knots WOD). Required performance: climb to 45,000ft in 7 minutes using reheat, at least 530 knots at 45,000ft. Armament: two 30mm Aden (10 seconds fire each), one 1000lb bomb under each wing, provision for 16 × 3in RP on zero-length launchers (preferably tier stowage).

The Sea Vixen was the ultimate British-designed all-weather fighter. By the time it was approaching service, however, there was some suspicion that the distinction between day and night fighters would soon fade, with all fighters requiring long-range radar to find their targets at appropriate ranges. Since no two-seat (radar) version of the Scimitar was developed, the Sea Vixen became the primary British naval fighter, even though it was not nearly robust enough for violent low-altitude manoeuvres. This is an FAW.2, the final version; its range was extended by big internal tanks built into the tail booms, which were extended forward in this version. The missiles are infra-red homing Red Tops designed for collision-course attack, with the big A1 18 nose radar giving the pilot an automatic indication of whether he was in the appropriate firing zone near a target. The device lowered beneath the nose was probably an infra-red detector associated with the missile system. Bombs, rockets or Bullpups could also be carried on the four hard points; note, too, the drop tank outboard, which was usually carried. There were also two internal packs, each of which could carry fourteen 2in rockets.

Left: *Off Portsmouth in 1959.* Victorious *displays Sea Vixen all-weather fighters and a Scimitar, which has just landed (note that one of the arrester wires has not yet been completely reset). The rescue helicopter is visible overhead (to the right). Note the mirror sight, with its light source, a bank of four lights, visible outboard of the Sea Venom parked aft.*

With the advent of jet aircraft came the urgent need to detect and thus to intercept attackers, even at low level, at long range. The US Navy devised special airborne radars, and the Royal Navy acquired forty-five airborne newly warning Skyraiders under the MDAP programme, beginning in November 1951. They were replaced in turn by modified Gannets, which served as long as the Royal Navy continued to operate large-deck carriers. This Skyraider was photographed aboard HMS Albion *in 1954. Carriers typically each accommodated a detachment of four such aircraft.*

Havilland, Fairey, Blackburn and Westland all submitted proposals for the naval fighter. MoS found de Havilland's best. It had the highest performance, and, thanks to de Havilland's experience with the DH 108 tailless swept-wing research aircraft, the firm was far ahead of any other in its understanding of sweep-back and high performance generally.[50] The Ministry concluded that only de Havilland could put a really modern aircraft into production within five years.[51] This DH 110 was named Sea Vixen. MoS ordered seven long-range land-based fighter prototypes, two land-based night fighter prototypes, two naval night fighter prototypes, and two naval long-range strike fighter prototypes in April 1949. These orders were reduced in November 1949 (see below) when the RAF lost interest and the Admiralty temporarily abandoned the project.

The Fifth Sea Lord did object that the new fighter was much too heavy for future trade route carriers, but admitted that nothing short of a very large aircraft could carry the required 35in (originally 40in) radar dish. It might be necessary to assign large carriers to convoys, merely to provide them with sufficient night air defence.

There was also some fear that de Havilland, heavily loaded already, might be unable to complete work on the night fighter in time. Therefore Fairey, which had produced the next-best proposal, was asked to submit a fresh study as a back-up. The Fairey design was not, however, accepted, and development of the DH 110 continued to a revised night fighter Specification N.14/49, which replaced N.40/46.

The Scimitar and the DH 110 were likely to be very expensive fighters. In December 1949 DAW tried to distinguish between first team ('First XI') and second team ('Second XI') fighters, the former to operate from fleet carriers and the latter from trade-protection carriers, against shadowers. The former had to match their land-based (RAF) counterparts, so that minimum speed at patrol height was 540 knots. Moreover, they had to operate over the sea, so great endurance (2 hours or more) was required, at a high cost in all-up weight. DAW estimated that one hour of endurance in the N9/47 cost 1500lbs, and in the N14/49 it cost 3000lbs; if the same maximum and approach speeds were required, the net cost might be as much as 5000lbs.

Patrol and combat altitude would be about 30,000ft, that is, B-29 capability (and also the design capability of the new Seaslug anti-aircraft missile).

All of this meant that the design of the 'First XI' fighters could not be compromised, although the Australian government was pressing for a modern naval fighter compatible with their new light carriers. In particular, it seemed unlikely that a sufficiently powerful radar could be accommodated in the Australians' 24,000lb limit.

'Second XI' requirements were less. DAW had hoped that the existing Sea Fury could last five to seven more years, but he now believed it had to be replaced sooner. Since light fleet carriers would be the wartime trade-protection carriers, these fighters would have to be within a 24,000lb limit (which allowed both the existing Sea Hawk and the RAF's new Venom – see below). DAW thought that even the 'Second XI' day fighter might need air-to-air radar, on the theory that the small carriers would have very limited direction capabilities. The projected night fighter version of the Venom seemed attractive as a 'Second XI' day and night fighter and also to supplement the N14/49 in the 'First XI'. DAW hoped that it would also provide some early evidence on the possible need for air-to-air radar in day fighters.

When the fighter programme was reviewed in April 1950, it appeared that the DH 110 would not be available until 1956–57, rather than 1953 (as had been estimated in 1949). The

in conditions of low visibility. As in the case of the day fighter, there was some hope that the Admiralty and the RAF could share a common airframe. Both demanded two seats and twin engines, the latter primarily so that the fighter could accommodate a very large radar dish in its nose. High speed would be valuable, but the fighter would have to orbit on patrol, so it also needed long endurance. This might be achieved by shutting down one engine while loitering. Because both services expected the night fighter to spend much of its time on patrol, a very high rate of climb was not essential.

The naval Staff Requirement, issued in August 1946, was NA 14 (Specification N.40/46). It corresponded to RAF specification F.44/46.[48] The Admiralty wanted a night defensive (CAP) and offensive (intruder) fighter.[49] De

48 The RAF Specification called for interception at much higher altitude, 40,000ft (with climb to 45,000ft in 10 minutes), somewhat higher maximum speed (525 knots at 25,000ft), and shorter endurance (2 hours including climb to 25,000ft cruising altitude and 15 minutes of combat at that altitude).

49 Required maximum speed was at least 500 knots, at 5000 to 10,000ft; landing approach speed was not to exceed 60 knots into the wires with 28 knots WOD (with 200 gallons of fuel on board). The fighter had to be capable of take-off on one engine, and also of maintaining height on one (for example, while loitering). Maximum permissible all-up weight was 30,000lbs (20,000lbs was desirable), and maximum dimensions 55ft (18 folded) span × 40ft length × 17ft height (later the folded span was increased to 20ft, with 30ft acceptable if length was not over 40ft; otherwise, 50ft could be accepted). Armament

was initially set at four 30mm cannon (300 rounds each), with provision for four air-to-air missiles (the Longshot, an abortive infra-red homing type based on a 5in rocket motor). As in the case of the Scimitar, provision was to have been made for an alternative battery of internally-stowed unguided rockets or a recoilless rifle. Later the guns were changed to 20mm (8 seconds of fire each), and the missiles to another abortive type, the Red Hawk. The night CAP mission was a climb to patrol height (5,000 to 10,000ft), 3 hours on patrol, 20 minutes of combat at sea level, and 30 minutes' loiter at sea level prior to landing. Patrol duration could be extended to 4 hours using drop tanks. The night intruder would begin by climbing to its most economical altitude, intrude to a depth of 400nm, fight at sea level for 20 minutes, and then loiter for 30 before landing; drop tanks would increase its combat radius to 500nm. These missions were later rewritten with 5 minutes of combat

and 20 of loiter, and the night intruder requirement to intrusion to maximum radius (not necessarily 400nm) as determined by the 3-hour CAP requirement.

50 The Specification was difficult because it required so wide a speed range: 500 knots maximum, 85 knots for landing, plus a very long endurance. The 35n scanner (AI Mk IXD) was accepted because the replacement set was taking too long to develop. The de Havilland design was expected to land at 90 to 95 knots, which was considered inevitable given its layout. This disadvantage was offset by the excellent pilot's view, and by the landing weight of only 21,000lbs.

51 Minutes of the Naval Aircraft Design Committee, 20 July 1948. The winning DH 110 design had also been chosen by the RAF, but it was later rejected in favour of the delta-wing Gloster Javelin.

existing Sea Hornet was already inadequate, and some interim replacement was necessary to bridge a six- or seven-year gap. The RAF was in much the same position. Fortunately, de Havilland could offer an interim solution, a greatly modified Vampire it called the Venom.

De Havilland conceived the Venom as a Vampire modified, with a new thin wing to take full advantage of the thrust of the fully developed Ghost engine, about 5000lbs. Athough it was an entirely new design, it was initially designated Vampire F.B.8, and it went into production in single-seat fighter-bomber form under Specification 15/49. There was already a two-seat Vampire night fighter (NF.10), and de Havilland proposed an analogous Venom development as a private venture. Once the RAF had accepted it for service, in March 1950, it became attractive to the Navy, with the important caveat that the Air Force might take over all production aircraft in an emergency. DAW's arguments had gained force with the delay in DH 110 development.

The Sea Hornet and its wartime ASH radar were quite obsolete, and something better had to be placed in service before the mature large-dish AI 16 radar, then planned for the fast N.40/46 night fighter, entered service.[52] If worse came to worst, moreover, and the new night fighter could not be obtained in sufficient numbers, the Sea Venom would at least be a cheap, inferior, but acceptable alternative. Naval modifications enough would have to include a better view for the pilot, slower approach speed (preferably 107 rather than 113 knots), and, perhaps, folding wings.

Specification N.107 was issued. The Royal Navy evaluated the Venom NF 2 prototype aboard HMS *Illustrious*, beginning on 9 July 1951, and the fighter entered service as the Sea Venom FAW.20, FAW.21, and FAW.22. The first production aircraft flew on 27 March 1953. This type in turn was replaced by the Sea Vixen beginning in 1960.

Table 15-3 describes the Sea Venom and the 1948 and 1949 de Havilland DH 110 night fighter proposals.

The Sea Venom had been conceived as an interim aircraft, and by mid-1952 a Staff Requirement for its successor, NA 38, was being written.[53] There were three candidates: a revised DH 110, a modified Sea Venom with swept wings (DH 116), and a two-seat version of the new Scimitar day fighter.

By 1953–54 it seemed at least arguable that, given high closing speeds, even day fighters needed powerful radars. Thus the logical split might more reasonably be between high- and low/medium-altitude fighters, the division coming at about

45,000ft. Low-level fighters would have to be rugged, to manoeuvre at high speed, and they would have to loiter for long periods on combat air patrol, since warning might not be very early. A high-altitude fighter would have to be launched on warning, since high-altitude attackers would be detected at very long range, so it had to be able to climb rapidly to combat altitude. It appeared that the heavily-loaded wing of a good low-altitude fighter could not really be suitable for the high-altitude role. The Sea Vixen, lightly loaded, seemed the ideal high-altitude fighter. Unfortunately it had little scope for further development. The heavy Scimitar lacked a radar, but it seemed well suited for further development, either as a two-seat radar fighter, or as a strike bomber (see below).

The DH 110 was formally chosen in mid-1953, with NA 38 revised to eliminate a requirement that the Sea Venom successor operate from trade-protection as well as from fleet carriers. This choice was made because it seemed more and more likely that in future the fleet would be subject to mass night attack by high-performance aircraft. The new fighter would, it was hoped, be in service by 1958 (the first squadron actually formed on 2 July 1959, and embarked aboard HMS *Ark Royal* in February 1960).[54]

However, one Developed Scimitar (XH 451), a two-seat all-weather fighter (FAW), was ordered on 23 September 1954 to NA 38. It would have been fitted with Ferranti Airpass radar and with guided missiles, and it would have been area-ruled, with new afterburning engines. Work on the mock-up was suspended on 27 April 1955, and the project was cancelled on 25 July 1955. There was just not enough money for two ongoing two-seat fighters. The Sea Vixen, the specialized all-weather fighter, was further along, and it had a higher priority. The two-seat Scimitar was justified partly as a strike bomber, but that project was killed in favour of the much superior Buccaneer.

In 1955–56, the short-term naval aircraft plan called for the Scimitar to replace the Sea Hawk beginning in 1958; in 1959 the Sea Vixen would begin to replace the Sea Venom. It in turn would replace the Scimitar as the standard naval fighter in 1959–60, the Scimitar replacing the Wyvern as standard strike fighter before the NA 39 entered service beginning in 1961.

Meanwhile, both the RAF and the Admiralty began work on a new generation of fighters to deal with the next threat, a supersonic bomber.[55] In September 1954 the Air Ministry issued a tentative requirement for a new fighter, to succeed the existing Lightning, to deal with a Soviet Mach 1.3 bomber

Table 15-3: Night Fighters, 1949

	Sea Venom 1 Ghost (5000lb st thrust)		N40/46 (Sea Vixen) 2 Avon (6500lb st thrust)		De Havilland N40/46 (1948) 2 Metro-Vickers F.9 (7000lb st thrust)
Engine					
Fuel (gallons)					
internal	350	350	750	980	900[5]
external	—	150	—	—	300
All-up weight (lbs)	12,980	14,330	25,000	26,920	27,037[6]
Max speed (knots) SL	493 (567)		537		560
30,000ft	463 (532)		497 at 25,000ft		545[3]
Max climb rate (ft/min)	5800	4650	7740		10,200
Climb at 30,000ft (ft/min)	2500	1800	4360 at 25,000ft		6450[2]
Ceiling at 1000ft/min (ft)	42,500	38,000	51,400		48,000[1]
Time to 30,000ft (min)	7.8	7.1	4.28 min to 25,000ft		2.5[4]
Endurance at 30,000ft (hours)	1.12	1.97	2	3	2.3[7]
Radius at 30,000ft (nm/knots)	175/312	315/320			350 –
Wing area (sq ft)	286		520		
Loading	45.3	50.1	48.1		42.2
Span (ft)	40	41 9	53		
Thickness/chord	10 per cent		11.3 per cent		

1 500ft/min ceiling.
2 At 20,000ft; 2800ft/min at 40,000ft.
3 At 20,000ft.
4 To 20,000ft.
5 1050 gallons overload internal fuel.
6 525/28 knots take-off; 99 knots take-off speed (114mph); run 450ft with RATOG. Lands at 21,322lbs, 82 knots stall, 95 knots approach, 64 knots into wires with 28 knots WOD.
7 At 20,000–25,000ft allowing take-off, climb, 5 min combat at sea level, 20 min loiter. Mean patrol speed 3304 knots. 2.9 hours patrol with 1050 gallons as overload, 4.0 with drop tanks (total 1350 gallons).

52 The radar choice lay between the British AI 9C and the wartime US AI 10, the latter somewhat smaller and already available. The maximum range of the existing ASH (Sea Hornet) was 4 to 5 miles, compared to 6 to 8 miles for AI 10; the current minimum requirement (RN and RAF) was 14 miles. Thus, although AI 10 fell short, it roughly doubled ASH range. For the minimum range to which a target could be held, the present requirement was 300ft, compared to 200 for AI 10, but 450ft for ASH. Early Sea Venoms had the same AI 10 radar as RAF Venom NF2, but Mk 21 and 22 (and the Australian Mk53) had the US-supplied Westinghouse APQ-43.

53 In July 1952 the NA 38 requirement called for an aircraft capable of flying from both fleet and modernized light fleet carriers, and the capability of taking off from a BS 4 (103ft) catapult wth 18 knots WOD was desired (although rocket assistance could be accepted in that case). At this time the Mk 12 arrester gear of the modernized light fleet carriers (that is, HMS *Warrior*) was rated at 18,500lbs at 93 knots, although there was some hope of upgrading it to 102 knots. Maximum dimensions were set at 40(16) × 44 × 17ft, and all-up weight was to be minimized. Performance requirements included a minimum rate of climb of 20,000ft per minute, and a maximum speed at sea level of not less than 620 knots (713mph), and of 550 knots at 40,000ft; landing speed into arrester gear was 95 knots (25 knots WOD, which might be reduced to 22 in the case of a light fleet carrier). Patrol altitude was 40,000ft, and the standard mission consisted of a climb to patrol height (40,000ft), a 1-hour patrol, then 5 minutes of combat at 40,000ft, and 20 minutes' loiter at 2000ft before landing. Drop and overload tanks would suffice to double patrol duration. Dive brakes would permit quick descent from 40,000 to 8000ft with two-thirds fuel remaining. Armament was four 20mm cannon (8 seconds' fire each) or two 30mm Aden or Hispano 825 cannon. The radar would be either AI Mk 17 or a US-supplied APS-21. As revised in July 1953, NA 38 called for a much heavier aircraft, to operate only from fleet carriers with 151ft steam catapults. It was to be launchable with no more than 15 knots WOD, and recoverable (in Mk 13 gear) with no more than 28. Maximum dimensions were enlarged to 50(21) × 51 × 17ft (20 maximum during folding). Performance requirements were relaxed; maximum climb rate was set at 12,000ft per minute at sea level (and at least 2500 at 40,000ft); maximum speed was still 600 knots at sea level (without missiles), but 530 knots at 40,000ft. Ceiling without missiles would be at least 48,000ft. Most importantly, patrol duration was doubled to 2 hours (plus climb, combat and loiter). Desired armament was two Blue Jay air-to-air missiles and four Aden cannon (8 seconds' fire) or four Blue Jays and two cannon. Later aircraft might carry two heavier Red Dean air-to-air missiles in place of the Blue Jays. Radar was AI Mk 18 and Blind Predicting GGS Mk 2 for aiming guns and misiles. Later production aircraft would have to be able to carry two Red Angel anti-ship rockets, though this was not to influence their design strength.

For the postwar Royal Navy, ASW was the highest priority. Unfortunately, development of the big specialized Gannet was protracted, and the Firefly AS.7 was conceived as a stop-gap, on the theory that its aerodynamics had been well proven by the earlier fighter versions. This failed to take account of the enormous increases in weight and, to a lesser extent, in fuselage side area, incident on the redesign for three-man ASW operation (the third man was needed for sonobuoy operation). The extra weight precluded any armament, so the AS.7 was limited to search (using sonobuoys and a wing-mounted ASV 9 radar). It would have directed an attacking aircraft to the target. Tests showed that it had unacceptable deck-flying characteristics. It could not be cancelled, however, because that would have required dispersal of the Fairey work force just as the company was bringing the vital Gannet into production. The aircraft were, therefore, used as land-based observer trainers, most being designated T.7s. Avengers supplied under MDAP were used as ASW gap-fillers.

54 Three prototypes and 148 production Sea Vixens were built, 119 FAW.1 and twenty-nine FAW.2. The prototype DH 110 flew on 26 September 1951, but the first semi-navalized prototype (Sea Vixen Mk 20X) flew only on 20 June 1955, and the first arrested deck landing was made on 5 April 1956, aboard HMS *Ark Royal*. FAW.1 carried four Firestreak air-to-air missiles; FAW.2, four Red Top air-to-air missiles or Bullpups for air-to-surface attack. They were powered by Avon 208 engines (10,000lbs thrust).

56 DEFE 7/279.

56 There had been some hope of improving the Scimitar to achieve Mach 0.95 at 50,000ft, but weight increases made this impossible.

57 A typical study assumed three standard modernized (A) carriers operating within range of enemy light bombers, and screened by three Seaslug ships, so that the inner limit of the fighter zone was 20 miles from force centre. The two baseline threats were forty Mach 1.3 light bombers dropping free-fall bombs from 60,000ft within Seaslug range, and a similar raid closing to just outside Seaslug range to drop ASMs. Raids on this scale forced dependence on deck-launched interception, since it was impossible to maintain a large enough force on CAP. This made a very fast climb essential (to 60,000ft in no more than 4 minutes, followed by a 2 g turn) and favoured a rocket fighter. A turbojet had to climb to an intermediate altitude, accelerate, and then zoom up; a rocket could climb straight from the deck. Assumed warning coverage was 200nm, high discrimination tracking (fighter control) range was 145nm, and the 'control delay' from detection to the moment defensive action was ordered would be about 2 minutes. Analysis showed that about ninety Mach 2 fighters could deal with a raid whose density was no more than about six per minute, and unaccompanied by jammers (there were also estimates showing that jamming would be relatively unsuccessful in the face of a dispersed fighter control organization). Both collision and pursuit tactics were considered, the former requiring better fighter control (and longer AI range, since target and fighter would close so quickly) and a head-

flying at 60,000ft. The new fighter was needed because no British area-defence missile could be available in time. The stated requirement was to climb to 60,000ft in 3 minutes, and for fast acceleration beyond Mach 2. MoS began work on a mixed rocket-jet fighter, and the Saunders-Roe SR.177 was chosen.

The following year the Admiralty reviewed its own fighter requirements. It seemed likely that by 1960 the Soviet Union would have Mach 1 bombers and reconnaissance aircraft operating at 50,000 to 55,000ft. The two existing fighters, the Scimitar and Sea Vixen, could attain only Mach 0.9 to Mach 0.95 at 45,000ft. Because good performance was required at medium and low altitude, they could not be modified to meet this high-altitude threat.[56]

The Admiralty's draft Staff Requirement called for a speed of Mach 2.5 and a long-range AI radar.[57] This was a very long step, and it seemed unlikely that such an aircraft could be in service before 1965 or even later. Thus some intermediate aircraft was needed to fill the gap between 190 and 1965. It had to be one already under development, adapted to lead into the final naval requirement. Studies by the MoS and the RAE showed that the SR.177 (Staff Requirement NA 47) was the only suitable candidate. It would be armed with two Blue Jay air-to-air missiles, guided by AI Mk 20, and it could operate from all existing fleet carriers suitable for the Scimitar and Sea Vixen.

on weapon rather than an infra-red tail-homer. On the other hand, pursuit course simplified the defence. Collision course vectors would be calculated by a digital computer at the interception position in the Type 984 ship, fed with 984 tracks of both fighter and target. A collision-course fighter could destroy a Mach 0.95 bomber 60 to 100nm from force centre, but a pursuit-course fighter would destroy it only between 20 and 60nm from force centre. Both could intercept a Mach 1.3 bomber, but the pursuit-course fighter would have an insufficient margin of error unless it could accelerate quickly for a burst of speed at Mach 2.5. In that case the pursuit-course fighter could kill its target at 20nm, the collision course-fighter at 60. A pure turbojet Mach 2 fighter could intercept a Mach 0.95 bomber at 50,000ft with either technique, but it might be unable to turn for long enough to launch its weapon. Against a Mach 1.3 bomber, even the 200nm warning afforded by Type 984 would

be insufficient for interception by the turbojet. If the raid were larger, or if it used jamming, the fleet air defence system would have to cope by improving its overall efficiency, since it was impossible to add more CAP fighters or to increase fighter performance further. Possibilities included longer-range warning and delegation of fighter allocation, each carrier being responsible for her own sector. Some additional high speed fighter cruising endurance might also be useful. This account is from ADM 1/28006, a DND study of fleet fighter requirements for 1962–70, 2 May 1955.

58 Later Sea Vixens (FAW.2) carried Red Top, originally designated Firestreak Mk IV. It could be described as a jump-up missile, because its seeker had a wide field of view (full hemisphere as opposed to 15 degrees for earlier infra-red missiles). However, these aircraft were not powered by the 14,000lb thrust RB.141 bypass engine (Rolls-Royce Medway).

Very high attack speed entailed very short endurance. The standard mission would begin with take-off and cruise to 60,000ft in 6 minutes, followed by 3 minutes cruising towards the bomber at Mach 1.4, then a turn onto the bomber's tail (180 degrees at 2 g at Mach 1.4), and 3 minutes of combat at 60,000ft at Mach 1.4. Then the fighter would fly back to a marshalling point at economical speed at 40,000ft (15 minutes), descend to sea level (5 minutes), and loiter and land (20 minutes, including one overshoot). This was not too far from an attack by a sophisticated missile, and the fighter could engage no more than one or two bombers.

This standard sortie could be varied by altering the duration of rocket firing, speed or acceleration being exchanged for endurance. If required, the fighter could attain Mach 2 for short bursts, and it could reach 80,000ft. Since carrier capacity was limited, it would have to be suitable for warm as well as for hot war, that is, for ground attack. With rocket fuel (HTP) exchanged for paraffin, endurance would be extended to 2 hours; speed would be Mach 0.97 at sea level, and it could carry two 1000lb bombs in place of the missiles.

The Defence Review killed the project, on the theory that by the time hot war became more likely, the high-altitude mission could better be executed by long-range guided missiles. The Admiralty argued that the existing weapons, Seaslug, Scimitar and Sea Vixen, were only effective against subsonic threats at altitudes below 55,000ft. On the other hand, any supersonic or very high-altitude bomber would have to rely on either an air-to-surface missile (which could be jammed) or a nuclear bomb (in which case the US Navy, with its very capable Talos long-range missile, would be engaged in conjunction with British carriers).

The Admiralty position was that no long-range surface-to-air missile could be in service before 1972. The SR.177 could be effective to 65,000ft and to 85nm using the pursuit course Blue Jay missile, and to 180nm with extended early warning. Existing V-bombers could already act as shadowers, flying above maximum fighter defence altitude (50,000ft).

The only (and somewhat unsatisfactory) alternative to the SR.177 would be a redesigned Sea Vixen, armed with a jump-up missile, with a longer fuselage and new RB.141 (Medway) engines (and equipped with lightweight AI 18 radar, to balance the change in centre of gravity). The Sea Vixen FAW.2 approached, but did not meet, these requirements.[58]

Fortunately, the Soviet Union had to give up bomber development on the expected scale. They did not put many supersonic naval bombers into service until the late 1970s (in the form of Backfires), and their standard shadowers, Bears and

The demands of modern ASW were severe, and the Gannet was a large twin-turboprop aircraft. This T.5 trainer shows the length of the bomb bay, which could accommodate large homing torpedoes. The Gannet itself took up considerable deck and hangar space, and it was superseded by ASW helicopters, which, however, could not lift heavy homing torpedoes. The British torpedo project, Pentane, was cancelled in 1958, in the knowledge that its only possible delivery vehicle would soon be withdrawn from service.

Badgers, did not attain the performance the British (and, for that matter, the contemporary US Navy) had feared.

STRIKE AIRCRAFT WERE a second major postwar naval category. In 1945 the Wyvern was being developed, but clearly a new faster generation was at hand. In 1947 Staff Requirements were issued for both single- and two-seat jet strike aircraft to be based, respectively, on the new single-seat fighter (later the Scimitar) and on the new all-weather fighter (later the Sea Vixen). It was not certain whether the second seat, and the associated strike search radar, was needed.[59]

DAW was limited to these two types, not only because he wanted to reduce the number of distinct types aboard a carrier, but also because he had the capacity to develop only three types of aircraft in parallel: an ASW aircraft (see below) and two high-performance aircraft, a single-seater with little or no radar and a radar-laden two-seater.

The Supermarine fighter (Scimitar) could not be fitted with any large internal weapons bay because its undercarriage retracted into its fuselage. Supermarine proposed to carry the big bomb (or two Red Angel rockets) under one wing, but there was some question as to whether it could be launched accurately from this asymmetric position. Four 500lb or two 1000lb bombs could be accommodated in shallow centreline bays, fore and aft of the main undercarriage, with dished doors for sufficient capacity. They could probably be dropped in 30- but not in 60-degree dives.

The Supermarine aircraft was somewhat heavy, and landed somewhat fast. MoS considered it unwise to increase wing area to improve landing performance, because that would only make for a larger, slower, aircraft with only marginally slower landing speed. All of this meant that even the new 30,000lb limit on all-up weight was becoming rather tight.

Naval strike aircraft were a somewhat delicate subject because the RAF was trying to eliminate this role. In about May 1950 the Chiefs of Staff ordered work on both strike

aircraft suspended. However, they were revived in 1951, partly on the ground that specialist strike aircraft were needed to counter possible Soviet surface raiders, such as *Sverdlov* class cruisers. Analysis showed that existing strike aircraft, such as Firebrands and Wyverns, in the small numbers available, could not hope to sink such cruisers. The proposed solution was a jet bomber carrying the first British naval tactical nuclear weapon, the '2000lb Target Marker Bomb'.

Work began on a new Staff Requirement, NA 39, for a specialized all-weather attack aircraft. It was issued in June 1952, and the Blackburn Buccaneer was ultimately chosen.[60] Meanwhile, both fighter projects remained interesting as interim strike aircraft, and also as insurance against the possibility that NA 39 might fail, or, indeed, might never be funded.

In July 1954 DAW preferred a revived single-seater, NA 19, for both strike and photo-reconnaissance roles.[61] The tactical nuclear bomb would be availabe in 1958, but without the NA 19 there would be no aircraft to carry it, since the NA 39 would not enter service until the early 1960s. For limited war, moreover, something more than a Sea Hawk was needed. A proposal to end Wyvern production had just been approved. Nor was there any satisfactory solution to the requirement for long range photo-reconnaisance to relieve naval forces of dependence on shore-based aircraft for photo-intelligence. DAW saw the possibility of building a relatively inexpensive strike version of the Scimitar as a dividend of the decision to go for a heavy fighter rather than a lighter, less expensive, type. He thought that concessions relative to the fighter version would make for a radius of 500nm at high altitude.[62] This high-altitude run would make it vulnerable to future naval surface-to-air missiles, and thus it could not be justified as an anti-ship missile carrier for the projected Green Cheese weapon.

This was clearly an interim step, since the NA 39 was already posited on low-altitude penetration of enemy defences. It would have neither radar nor navigator, and therefore it would have to depend on AEW direction or on an accompanying two-seat fighter.

In DAW's view, then, without NA 19 during 1958–62 the Navy would be limited to short-range fighter-bomber action with conventional weapons, and possibly delivery of the Green Cheese. DGD agreed. D of P had viewed loss of naval offensive capability with concern; the interservice committee on the overall British defence programme, however, did not. In October it observed that the Wyvern was already obsolete when it entered service, and that the modified Scimitar would be of only limited value. The NA 39 was clearly preferable, the

59   In mid-1948, the N40/46 was clearly the logical basis for a two-seat strike fighter. The Wyvern, even if redesigned as a pure jet, was considered not advanced enough for the future single-seat strike requirement. A single-seat version of N.40/46 was considered a possibility if a single-seat strike version of the Supermarine N.9/47 could not be developed. In each case, the heaviest weapon to be carried weighed 2000lbs.

60   As issued on 8 December 1953, the NA 39 Staff Requirement called for an aircraft to be in service in 1960, to use the Target Marker Bomb (the tactical nuclear weapon) and the Green Cheese missile against ships in open water or in harbour in all weather. Alternative weapons were 2000lb AP (two) or 1000lb MC (four), or Red Angels (four), or 3in air-surface rockets (twenty-four) or 25lb practice bombs (four), or a package of four 30mm Adens with 10 seconds fire, or A Mines Type S (four), or A Mines Mk 12 (two), or 1000lb SC I (four). A low-level approach was wanted for surprise, accuracy and possible immunity from guided weapons and fighters. Because a low-level bomber would be largely immune from counterattack, fewer would be needed, and they would be less expensive since they would not require elaborate blind-bombing equipment. Green Cheese attacks would be executed blind at medium level using the search radar. The service ceiling of 30,000ft was chosen because it was required for Green Cheese release. Maximum speed would be required at sea level (550 knots minimum). For ground attack, NA 39 needed good dive-bombing characteristics, for a 60-degree dive at 400 knots IAS from 20,000ft. The deck strength of existing carriers limited take-off weight to 40,000lbs (45,000 overload), and it would land at 35,000 (deck reaction not more than 150,000lbs). Take-off at normal all-up weight would not require more than 26 knots WOD with a BS 4 (151ft) catapult. To land, not more than 25 knots WOD would be required (Mk 13 arrester gear). Dimensions were 55 (20 folded) × 51 × 17ft, with a possible concession to 60ft spread span. Missions were to be low-level attack – take-off and climb for range, fly to 250nm short of target, descend below radar (taken as tangential plane 100nm short of target), fly the 100nm at maximum continuous rating at sea level, 5 minutes at sea level combat, return 100 on deck, then climb for economical return, 20 minutes loiter at 10,000. Minimum combat radius in this mission was 400nm. High-attack and search missions required a radius of 800nm if the aircraft flew throughout at high altitude.

61   ADM 1/25318, July 1954.

62   The main concessions on fighter requirements were: increase acceptable catapult WOD from 15 to 28 knots, delete reheat, delete all air-to-air weapons including guns. A reduced rate of climb due to lack of reheat and increased weight was acceptable.

An early-warning Gannet (AEW.3) aboard HMS Ark Royal *during Exercise Northern Wedding 78 in September 1978. The radar was essentially the APS-20 which had been supplied with the Skyraiders, albeit updated. Without any large-deck carriers, the Royal Navy is now limited to helicopter-borne early warning radars, with their inherent limitation in range (due to limited weight and to a limited maximum altitude) and availability (because helicopter endurance is limited).*

only alternative being a dual-purpose ship-to-air/ship missile. It would, moreover, be difficult to pay simultaneously for both the strike Scimitar and NA 39. The committee therefore recommended that the strike Scimitar be cancelled provided that the NA 39 was funded instead. It appears that the strike Scimitar programme was then kept alive briefly as a means of exerting pressure to fund NA 39.

The interim nuclear strike capability was maintained by adapting the Scimitar fighter to carry the bomb externally, albeit at a cost in performance. This decision was made in mid-1955.

THE OTHER MAJOR POSTWAR CARRIER AIRCRAFT was the specialized ASW search and strike type, which was conceived as a replacement for the wartime Barracuda III. Fairey and Blackburn competed for this contract.

Early in January 1946 the Admiralty decided to begin work on GR 17/45, the Barracuda III replacement, which would

have to operate from future escort and trade-protection carriers. Blackburn submitted a brochure for a very small, light aircraft.[63] The idea was to use a small engine for economy, cruising at a large percentage of full power, and taking off with some

Conceived as an undercarriage-less interceptor, then modified as a conventional swept-wing fighter, the Supermarine Scimitar was immensely powerful. This one is shown with four 1000lb bombs underwing; the aircraft could also carry Bullpup guided air-to-surface missiles, or 2in rockets, or Sidewinder air-to-air missiles. For a time it seemed the likely basis of future two-seat all-weather fighters and attack bombers, but there was only enough money for one new attack bomber, and the new Buccaneer was clearly superior. This Schimitar flew from HMS Hermes. *Note the air-to-air refuelling probe: at the end of its career, the Schimitar was retained as a tanker, carrying buddy-pack fuel tanks under the same hard points, to extend Buccaneer S.1 range.*

63 The Blackburn proposal was powered by a Rolls-Royce Dart turboprop, and had a crew of two. Dimensions were 37ft 6in (17ft 3in) × 35ft 4in including hook × 13ft 6in; weight, 10,077lbs; fuel, 220 gallons; maximum speed, 246mph at sea level water-injected (228 without), 251(232) at 10,000ft; land at 92mph (full load and 2 hours' fuel); climb to 5000 in 4.5 minutes, to 10,000 in 11 minutes; service ceiling, 19,250ft; endurance, 4 hours at average 165mph; take-off with rocket assistance, 143ft, without, 440ft; loads, six 250 DC, six 250 AS bombs, or sixteen 60 RP, in all cases to include eight sonobuoys; weight to be allowed for one Zephyr homing torpedo (2000lbs) and eight sonobuoys; cruise endurance to include 5 minutes at full take-off power.

Table 15-4: Fairey and Blackburn Proposals for G.R.17/45, 1946

	A/S Staff	Fairey	Blackburn 2 Napier E. 128	RR Ap.25
Span (ft)	55	52	45 4	45 4
Length (ft)	42[1]	42	42 10	42 10
Folded span (ft)	18 6[2]	18 6	19 6	19 6
Folded height (ft)	13 9[3]	13 9	15 8	15 8
Weight (lbs)	16,000[4]	16,500[5]	16,710[6]	16,260[7]
Take-off at 17 knots (ft)	440	450[8]	405	430
Max speed (knots)	261	267	292	281
Endurance (hours)	4			
Cruise speed (knots)	150	140		
Wing area	—	445	410	410
Approach speed (knots)	80	79	88	86

1 Later 43ft.
2 Later 19–6 acceptable.
3 Under 16ft later.
4 17,000 overload.
5 MOS estimate 16,560.
6 MOS estimate 16,797.
7 MOS estimte 16,342.
8 MOS estimate 525ft

The Backburn Buccaneer gave the Fleet Air Arm the ability to strike enemy land targets at great ranges. Its design coincided with the decision to provide the Royal Navy with nuclear weapons.

form of assistance (presumably rockets). This was unacceptable because it violated the standard naval requirement for good take-off and landing characteristics.

By June, Fairey and Blackburn had both submitted fresh design studies. Each had one or two gas turbines geared together, an internal bomb bay and first-class radar; and both had adequate range and take-off. Blackburn offered two versions, one with a single Rolls-Royce AP 25 (Tweed) turbo-prop, the other with two Napier E.128 (Naiads) geared together. Fairey offered two Armstrong-Siddely Mambas geared together, and backward rather than upward-folding wings for minimum height. It seemed likely that one or the other could be flying within two years. These designs are described in Table 15-4.

By this time the requirement for a Barracuda III replacement was urgent. The only other available ASW aircraft was an adapted Firefly fighter, carrying sonobuoys and ASW bombs underwing, and hardly suitable.

Late in 1946 Blackburn abandoned its single-engine version, because it seemed unlikely that Rolls-Royce would persist with the Tweed turboprop after the cancellation of the twin-Tweed N.16/45 strike fighter.

Then disaster struck. Analysis of ASW requirements showed that efficient sonobuoy operation required a third crew member. Both ASW aircraft had to be redesigned, and both would undoubtedly grow substantially heavier, hence substantially less suitable for small wartime converted carriers. The alternative, to split roles so as to permit reduction to two crew members per aircraft, was rejected because contacts tended to be so fleeting that a single package (for detection and attack) was essential. Moreover, neither aircraft would probably be ready until 1952.

Two stop-gaps were therefore proposed: an adapted Sturgeon (which could carry only sonobuoys and ASW bombs) and a three-seat Firefly derivative, the A.S.7. Neither proved acceptable. The Sturgeon was too large and too heavy (it could operate only from HMS *Illustrious*), and it could not carry the future ASW weapon of choice, the homing torpedo. It was initially attractive, but it could not be ready much before torpedoes became available (that is, 1954). The Firefly was ordered in some numbers, on the theory that it was already a well-proven carrier aircraft. It turned out to be heavily overloaded, with unacceptable deck characteristics, and it was used as a trainer.

Blackburn then turned to a lighter two-seater powered by a single Griffon or by a double Mamba. It was rejected in favour

of the larger Fairey Gannet, which entered production as the standard British ASW aircraft of the late 1950s.

By 1949 it was obvious that GR 17/45 would be too heavy to operate from small carriers. A new austere ASW aircraft was conceived, and a new Staff Requirement, NA 32, written on the basis of a 1950 report by a special A/S Aircraft Working Party. The basic idea was that a robust, slow-landing ASW aircraft suitable for unmodified *Colossus* class carriers could be built in either a search (with 'sting' weapon) or a strike (heavy homing torpedo) version.

No firm was able to meet the requirements.

DAW argued that it was not feasible to carry either the full search load or the heavy torpedo aboard a light aircraft, which would be inferior to the GR 17/45 without having the advantages of a truly light aircraft. Moreover, it would be too expensive to build hunter-killer pairs. Instead, many hunters would have to search, calling in a few killers. However, such homing presented considerable difficulties, and it seemed impractical. The conclusion, then, was that even the lightweight ASW aircraft would have to be a single package.

The working party wanted both sonobuoys and search radar. However, early in a war it would be more important to cut down the mobility of the enemy submarine force, so the radar (which would keep him from the surface) would be more important than the sonobuoys (which would enable an aircraft to find and kill a submerged submarine). In any case, buoys were expected to be useless on many days in the North Atlantic.

The new homing torpedo, Pentane, was far too heavy; better to limit the aircraft to two ASW bombs and six ASW rockets, again to force submarines down without necessarily killing them. The other possibility was to adopt a future lightweight homing torpedo, Dealer B.

Turboprop power (that is, diesel fuel) was essential so that a *Colossus* class carrier could operate these aircraft throughout an 8-knot North Atlantic crossing, using her double bottom for aircraft fuel.

As the project developed, these very austere ideas were dropped in favour of sonobuoys, radar and a lightweight homing torpedo.[64] The result, the Short Seamew, was planned for both the Royal Navy and Coastal Command. However, it was clearly a mobilization design intended for general war, and thus it was rejected in the strategic reorganization of 1955–57.

64 Issue II of the Staff Requirement (27 December 1953) called for maximum dimensions of 55(23) × 41 × 17ft, and all-up weight of less than 14,500lbs (that is, heavier than a Barracuda). The aircraft would normally attack from less than 1500ft, in a shallow (less than 30-degree) dive. Service ceiling would be 10,000ft, and take-off 440ft with 12 knots WOD (for an escort carrier). Endurance would be 4 hours at more than 120 knots at 5000ft. Maximum level speed would be at least 200 knots at 5000ft. Weapon stations would be six rockets plus non-directional sonobuoys (a total of eight stations) plus one 18in Mk 30 homing torpedo and four directional buoys, or ten directional buoys, or three Mk 14 depth charges, or a mix of buoys, 4in flares, etc to a total of twelve (1200lbs). The buoys were added at this time, and the folded width brought down from 30ft (this figure was accepted to get the aircraft into service even though 19ft would be needed for a *Colossus* or a future escort carrier). The radar was ASV 19B, with a 32in dish.

16

The New Jet Carriers

IT WAS ALREADY CLEAR that the surviving World War II carriers, however modernized, were fundamentally limited. The Admiralty therefore always had to keep in mind the prospect of building replacements, and twice – in 1952–53 and again in 1960–65 – it came close to building new jet carriers. In each case, the goal was to operate heavy modern aircraft, and the minimum price turned out to be well above what the government of the day could or would afford.

The first attempt was part of the general British defence build-up begun during the Korean War. Initially the idea seems to have been to develop a modern fleet carrier design, for construction when and if money became available. On this basis the Ship Design Policy Committee asked early in 1952 for approximate characteristics, which were framed that May on the understanding that the ship might be laid down in 1956. At this time both the Royal Navy and the US Navy were investing heavily in new aircraft-technology, both for vertical take-off (deflected jets and tail-sitters) and (in the British case) for use with flexible flight decks. Thus it appeared that the new carrier might be the last designed to operate fast-landing jets; later carriers, it was hoped, could be significantly smaller and less expensive. However, that future was still uncertain; the Royal Navy would surely need one last big carrier, launching and recovering aircraft weighing up to 60,000lbs at 120 to 135 knots.

This implied a long flight deck, perhaps 1000ft, and with draught limited to 35ft for harbour entrance and docking, the ship might displace up to 55,000 tons. DAW wanted at least 1,000,000 gallons of fuel, mostly jet fuel which could be stowed without special protection. Endurance was set at 6000nm at 22 knots, roughly matching that of earlier British carriers.

Since the torpedo and the atomic bomb were considered the main threats, the design would have to concentrate on underwater protection, subdivision, and grouped (that is, controllable) ventilation. Armour would be less important than strength against nuclear blast.

This very large carrier could be justified primarily by its ability to operate long-range (1000nm) nuclear strike aircraft, a role the Royal Navy considered increasingly important, but which the RAF hotly contested. Existing carriers could accommodate all lesser aircraft already in service and, indeed, all expected fighters, ASW, close support and AEW aircraft. The increased strike range was justified partly by the normal evolution of strike aircraft (which would threaten the carrier further from an enemy coast) and partly on the ground that it would make for the most efficient use of the new tactical nuclear weapons, as targets much deeper in enemy territory could be attacked.

British doctrine at this time was (and was expected to remain) to operate fleet carriers in task groups of four ships, carrying a total of 300 to 350 aircraft. D of P therefore suggested that the new ship would have to accommodate eighty to ninety tactical aircraft, with perhaps one squadron of eight A-bomb carriers as an alternative to a greater number of smaller conventional aircraft.

The optimum size studies of 1945, made in connection with the *Malta* design (see Chapter 14), had concluded that the best carrier was the smallest ship that would allow the effective operation of the largest (or most heavily loaded) naval aircraft. To this was added the need to carry the required number of aircraft. In fact it turned out that the design was completely determined by a combination of aircraft operating requirements and docking limitations.

At this time the US Navy was building the massive *Forrestals*, to operate 70,000lb jet strategic bombers. Their hangars had 25ft clear headroom. The Royal Navy was well aware of their characteristics, and the Admiralty assumed that, as in World War II, British carriers would operate American-supplied aircraft, since British naval aircraft production rates sufficed for peacetime operation, but not to make up for likely wartime attrition. This meant that, as far as possible, the Royal Navy had to match the new standard of US carrier design. The nominal aircraft operating weight of the British carrier, for example, was increased to 70,000lbs to match projected US aircraft.

By June 1952 it seemed likely that building money might actually soon be available. The *Victorious* reconstruction had shown that no policy of rebuilding the existing wartime armoured carriers could really be satisfactory.[1] In any case, the Admiralty decided that no fleet carriers beyond *Victorious* would be modernized. Late in June, the Board called for a new design for a carrier to be *completed* during 1958. This entailed a

---

1 Unfortunately this is surmise; the relevant Board minutes and memoranda have not yet been released. Thus it is not clear whether the Board was repelled by the *Victorious* experience or attracted by the SDPC deliberations.

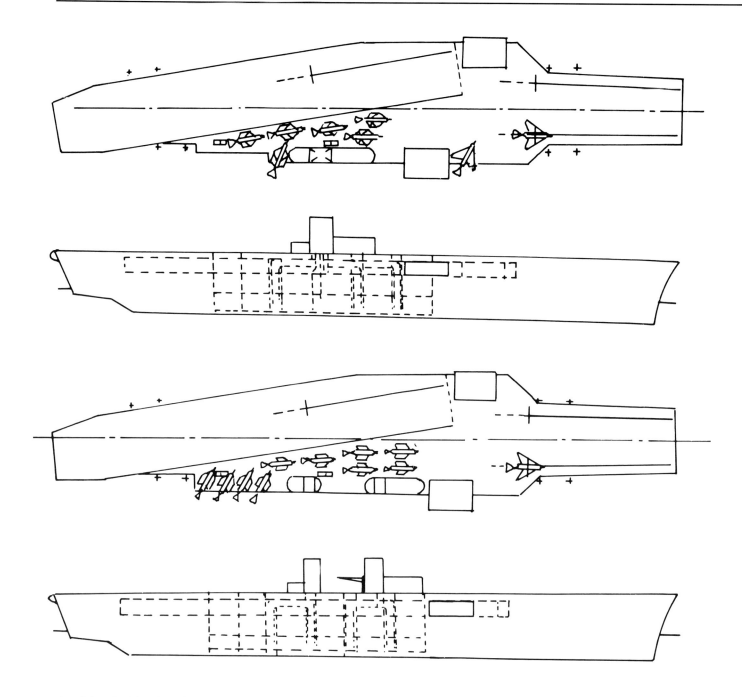

very tight schedule, since the ship would have to be ordered at the end of 1953, and her machinery installed some time in 1956. To make preliminary estimates, DNC had to guess machinery characteristics before any approximate Staff Requirements had been formulated. The unusually tight schedule required E-in-C to order machinery without building a shore prototype, and therefore he had to avoid any radical advances beyond the improved steam conditions then being introduced in other British warships.[2]

The aviation community, however, could promise some very exciting changes: the angled deck, the steam catapult and,

perhaps, a flexible deck. None had really been fully tested, but each promised the possibility of completely re-thinking carrier arrangement. The US Bureau of Ships, for example, had reluctantly accepted hinged uptakes in the *Forrestal* design in order to provide a flush flight deck. In 1952 it saw the angled deck as a way of restoring a substantial island, with its simple uptake design. The US naval air community balked at the change (for a time, surrendering the next year). DNC had to choose, then, between a simple angled deck similar to current practice, a US-style more or less flush deck, and something altogether different. Because the 1952 carrier design was never carried through, he never actually chose, and this account can only describe the options he tried, and their advantages and disadvantages.

As the experience of the *Malta* design showed, the British infrastructure would not support a 60,000 (standard) ton carrier. The Naval Staff initially refused to be limited by building slips and drydocks, but these factors were ultimately inescapable.

The initial decisions on Staff Requirements, set by a meeting chaired by DTSD at the end of July 1952, reflected aircraft

2 A tentative schedule adopted early in the design process showed the ship ordered 1 January 1954, laid down 1 May 1954, launched mid-1956 without machinery, and completed 31 December 1958. The Treasury approved a Yarrow (YARD) contract for preliminary machinery design, let 22 April 1953. As in the case of HMS *Malta*, only three building slips were available: John Brown No 4 (available January 1955), Cammell Laird No 4/5 (somewhat short, available June 1955), and Harland & Wolff No 14 (available, in theory, June 1955, but earmarked for another commercial ship after this launch).

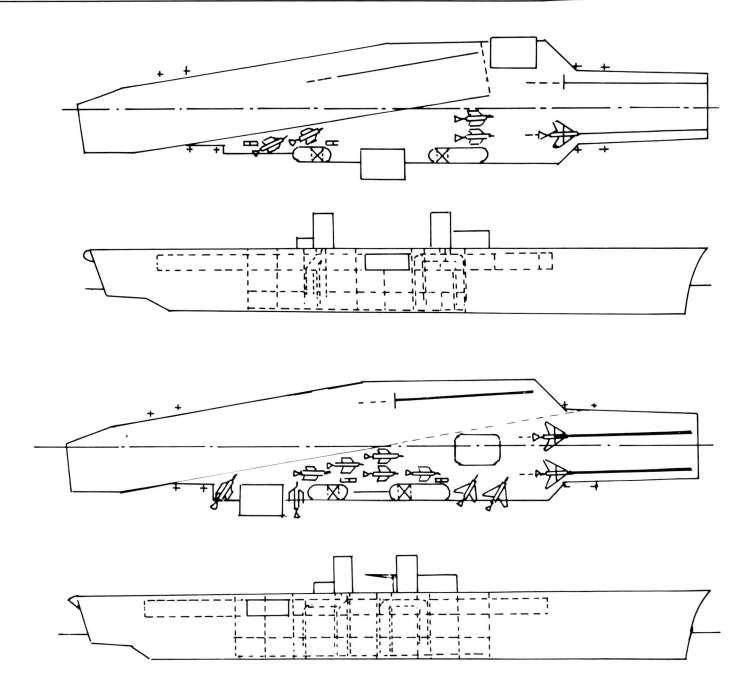

Above and opposite: *Schemes for flight deck and associated main machinery arrangement for the 1952 carrier. Later there were more radical proposals to move the island to the port side.* NF

characteristics: 70,000lbs take-off weight at 150 knots (45,000 landing at 140 knots), each aircraft up to 65ft long (*Forrestal* catered for aircraft 63ft long), 70ft in span (49ft folded), and 22ft high.[3] There were no specific provisions for free take-off, since jets had to be catapulted. DAW and D of P wanted at least three catapults (four if possible), so that the carrier could launch four fighters in quick succession. Two catapults were to be capable of launching the heaviest aircraft (70,000lbs). This matched contemporary US design requirements. DAW also wanted deck-edge lifts.

Hangar area was tentatively set at 50,000 to 55,000sq ft, roughly that of *Ark Royal* or *Malta*. In contrast to those ships, the new carrier would have a single closed hangar. In August, DAW developed a provisional air complement based on a 55,000sq ft hangar, a 1000ft flight deck (not far from the 1040ft of USS *Forrestal*), a 690ft angled deck, and ninety aircraft of the types expected in service in 1958. Deck lengths were apparently based on characteristics of the new Schimitar and the (land-based) Canberra bomber. The draft required aircraft fuel capacity of 250,000 gallons of avgas and 500,000 of avtur, compared to up to 750,000 gallons of avgas in USS *Forrestal*, or a total of about 48,000 gallons (avgas plus avtur) in *Eagle* as modernized.

The higher the speed, the less the load on catapults and arrester gear; the draft requirements called for 30 knots deep and dirty, as in HMS *Malta* (and, as there, equated to 32 knots deep and clean). *Forrestal* was rated at 30 knots at 72,000 tons, but deep displacement was 75,000, as in *Malta*. The requirement for 6000nm endurance (now at 22.5 knots) also reflected earlier practice (by way of comparison, *Forrestal* endurance was 12,000nm at 20 knots).

Aircraft would be directed by two massive Type 984 radars, supported by the usual long-range warning, gunnery and navi-

3 The carrier was often described as capable of operating aircraft 'of Canberra size' and a hypothetical folded Canberra was used to estimate hangar and flight deck space requirements. However, there is no evidence that such an aircraft was seriously considered for Royal Navy use. The 70,000lb/150 knots requirement translated into a catapult 300ft long, which was unacceptable.

gation sets, and a US-supplied Tacan homing beacon (AN/URN-3). These radars were substantially larger (and more capable) than the sets then being installed in US carriers.

The armament would consist of twin 3in/70 guns.[4]

No specific requirements for protection were set, but DNC expected to enclose the hangar and the ship's side down to just below the waterline with 2in protection over the length of the hangar and the length of the citadel. The sheer area to be protected precluded the use of wartime levels of protection, although there was some interest in using 2½in plating instead, to keep out large splinters. Again, by way of comparison, the British credited USS *Forrestal* with 1¾in protection.[5]

This was very close to the massive *Forrestal*, and in some ways promised to be even larger. The ship's size would be determined primarily by the largest aircraft she would operate. For example, if it was considered essential to be able not merely to fly off but also to maintain (that is, to strike below) 70,000lb strategic bombers, this would set hangar height. Increasing clear hangar height 3 or 4ft would make for a much larger carrier, because this in turn would lift flight deck, armament, radar and island.

Against these desires had to be set the realities of British harbours and naval bases. The only British naval drydock which could reliably take *Ark Royal* and *Eagle* was No 10 at Devonport. The King George V (Southampton) and Glad-

Suez Canal. The slope of the entrance to No 1 dock at Gibraltar would impose a slightly smaller mid-section coefficient than in previous carriers, for sufficient clearance at the bilge.[6]

By sketching carrier characteristics within these dimensions, DNC would explore the extent to which the Staff Requirements might be met. The most suitable hull form was probably that of HMS *Vanguard*, displacing 52,700 tons on these dimensions. Model trials gave the requisite power: 95,000ehp at deep load, six months out of dock in the tropics. This equated to 180,000shp (propulsive coefficient 0.53), which in turn would drive the ship at 31.8 knots deep and clean. This gave fuel weight (7300 tons including diesel fuel), since the model tests also indicated ehp at cruising speed. E-in.C estimated that he could provide 180,000shp on the same weight as the older 152,000shp plant in HMS *Eagle*, 3660 tons. The new carrier would need more evaporators, more generators, and probably more air conditioning, so that a realistic figure would be 3800 tons. With increased evaporators, E-in-C could accept reduced reserve feed water (250 tons). Note that E-in-C's preliminary weights were based on four 45,000shp units, with sufficient boiler power for 60,000shp, to give a margin for catapult operation without losing speed. E-in-C was later asked to develop figures for an alternative plant with matched boiler and turbine power; some loss of speed while catapulting would have to be accepted.

6   There were some additional subtleties. The Navy was unwilling to rely on the King George V dock (in which the huge liner *Queen Elizabeth* docked) because it lacked the necessary shop facilities and labour force. Nor was it clear that the keel blocks, which could not readily be rearranged, could support the carrier. The Gladstone dock had dock copings and pumping houses which might well foul a carrier's overhang. Devonport could take only 815ft 5in at 34ft draft. Using the profile of HMS *Eagle* as a guide, it could accommodate an overall length of 865ft 5in; any increase in flare fore and aft (for a longer flight deck) would have to allow a minimum headroom over the caisson and dam of 15ft. Part of the dock coping had already been cut away to dock HMS *Eagle*.

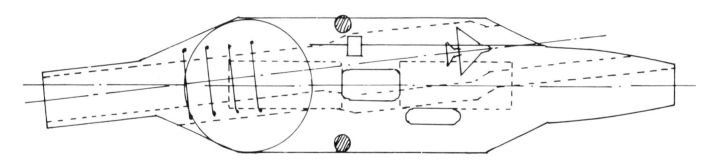

stone (Liverpool) docks could also take them, but with some difficulty. This was not a new problem; new docks had been considered in connection with the *Malta* design (see Chapter 14). They had not been built, and the situation was much as it had been in 1945. On 2 August 1952 the Controller asked DNC to calculate the limiting size of a ship for No 10, Devonport, Gladstone Dock, King George V, and No 1, Gibraltar.

Each dock had its own problems. For example, Gladstone had a very awkward entrance, as there was very little clearance in which to turn a long ship around to face the entrance. The harbour master suggested that length be limited to 850ft, although HMS *Hood* (860ft 10in) had docked successfully; he argued that a carrier would be more difficult because of her greater beam. Maximum waterline length, 815ft, was set by No 10 dock at Devonport. Maximum flight deck length, 870ft, was set by No 10 at Devonport and by the Gladstone dock. Maximum waterline beam, 115ft, was set by No 10 dock. Draft would be limited to 34ft so that the ship could pass through the

As early as 1953, VTOL seemed to hold out hope for a radical reduction in carrier size and cost. This scheme, for a small carrier specially suited to later conversion for VTOL operation, was suggested by DAW in 1953. DAW felt that VTOLs would have to land in the portion of the ship's length subject to minimum motion in a sea-way, the area indicated by the large (72ft radius) circle. It seemed to follow that, for a future VTOL carrier, width of landing area would be more important than length of deck. DAW saw his idea (which was rejected) as a transitional type, suited to the new Scmitar fighter but convertible to VTOL. For the latter, it would have a second funnel (small circle to port), so that smoke could be discharged away from the landing area, whatever the wind direction. The ship would not, after all, have to steam into the wind to launch or recover aircraft. As a conventional carrier, she would be built with the usual starboard side funnel, but with the piping needed for installation of the port funnel upon conversion. The single lift would have been 65 × 35ft, and the two hangars each about 125 × 50ft, to accommodate eight Scimitars. The unusually wide deck (for later VTOL operation) would have accommodated another twenty in a deck park, the latter being vital because the lfit could not be used when landing-on. The single catapult would have had a 180ft stroke, and the deck angle was about 6½ degrees. Length was 695ft (as in HMS Colossus), but flight deck width was 144ft (21 per cent of length). The scheme died because VTOL technology was as yet far too immature to be taken so seriously. NF

4   This British weapon was more successful than its US counterpart; both shared the same barrel and ammunition design. USS *Forrestal* was armed only with single automatic 5in/54s since the US 3in/70 had not as yet been placed into production when she was designed and built. Before it proved grossly unreliable in service, the US Navy expected the 3in/70 to be superior, as an anti-aircraft weapon, to the 5in/54.

5   Data for USS *Forrestal* in this chapter come from the Ship's Cover for the 1952 Fleet Carrier, and have not been checked against US Navy data; they are the data DNC used for comparison with his own design.

7 No 1 deck was the flight deck.
The bulkheads extending above
No 2 deck supported the flight deck
proper, with the gallery deck hanging
below it.

8 Rough estimates of stability made
it obvious that 17ft 6in was the
most which could be provided. GM
with 5150 tons of armour (3in flight
deck) was 8.75ft (8.0ft counting free
fluid surface). A cut to 3600 tons of
protection would have increased GM
about 1ft. None of these figures gave
anything remotely like enough weight
to add another 7ft 6in to hull depth (to
get 25ft clear hangar height).

9 In particular, it seemed likely that
the outboard part of the angled
deck would balance the weight of the
island structure, so that pig iron ballast
would no longer be needed.

The depth of the hull could be worked out in terms of required deck heights. The ship would have a single hangar, and a continuous deck immediately under her flight deck.[7] DNC was sure that no ship this size could support a 25ft clear hangar height. This was partly a matter of hangar deck freeboard sufficient to avoid flooding through the ports of the deck-edge lifts. The estimated deck heights are given in Table 16-1, total hull depth being about that of HMS *Eagle*.[8]

Weight could therefore be estimated by comparison with HMS *Eagle*, which had about the same displacement. *Eagle* was much modified during construction, and incorporated considerable solid ballast. DNC estimated that the hull could be redesigned, to eliminate ballast, with fewer longitudinal bulkheads, lighter lagging, less rod gearing, and more light alloy for minor structure and fittings, but with a wider hangar and a flight deck suitable for heavier aircraft.[9] About 1700 tons (3.6 per cent of deep displacement) could be scaled up to the larger dimensions

Table 16-1: Deck Heights in the 1952 Carrier

No 2	8ft 6in
No 3 (gallery deck)	10ft 3in
No 4 (hangar deck)	19ft (17ft 6in clear hangar height)[1]
No 5	10ft[2]
No 6	8ft 6in[3]
No 7	8ft 6in
No 8	8ft 6in
No 9	9ft[4]
Double bottom	5ft
Total depth	85ft 6in
(Freeboard at hangar deck: 24ft)	

1 Allowing 18in for beams under No 2 deck, hangar sprays, lifting appliances, etc.
2 Headroom required for flexible weapon stowage under the hangar, also for vent trunks, piping, gearing, etc.
3 Headroom adopted because 8ft in *Eagle* caused congestion and low headroom.
4 For bomb rooms, magazines, etc.

Table 16-2: The 1952 Carrier Design

	Eagle	August 1952
LOA (ft)	803 9	815
LWL (ft)	750	870
LBP (ft)	720	780
BWL (ft)	135	115
Beam, flight deck (ft)	135	[160]
Hull depth (ft)	86 2	85 6
Deep draught (ft)		33 8 [33 6]
Deep load displacement (tons)	49,950	[53,150]
Deep GM	7.08	[9.65/9.0(FS)]
Extra light draught (ft)		[27 3]
Extra light displacement (tons)		[40,800]
Extra light GM		[5.6 approx]
Flight deck armour	4in + 40lbs DW	2in
Avgas (gallons)	165,000	50,000
Avtur (gallons)	315,000	450,000
Total fuel capacity (gallons)	480,000	500,000
Total fuel weight (tons)	1141	1213
Weights (tons)		
Hull	24,688	26,300 [18,460]
Hull incidentals, general fittings		[9855]
Machinery	3660	3800 [4125]
Armament	1457	1100 [987]
Protection	6356	4600 [4665]
General equipment	2198	2200 [2479]
Aircraft equipment	5147	5500 [5725]
Oil and diesel fuel	6176	7300 [6400]
RFW	279	250 [280]
Margin	—	1050 [174]
Std displacement	49,950	52,000 [53,150]

Note December 1952 data are given in square brackets; these weights are based on a detailed calculation. In this version the ship had two deck-edge and one inboard lifts and three catapults; armament was 8 twin 3in/70 (266 tons of ammunition in magazines). Aircraft armament (tons): bombs and rocket heads 370, rockets 275, aircraft small calibre ammunition 310, ASW bombs 20, sonobuoys 27, torpedoes 36, pyrotechnics 16, practice bombs 13, solid heads and saddles for rockets, 24, smoke floats 16. Aircraft equipment weight includes the major fighter director system, the Type 984 radar and its associated Comprehensive Display System (CDS). Aircraft fuel weight: 1650 tons avtur, 200 tons avgas.

10 On the basis that half would vary
as L/H × LBD, the other half as L
(B + H), thus 13,500 + 12,800 =
26,300 tons.

11 Figures supplied in August were:
(weight/end speed) 60,000lbs/
92 knots, 55,000/96, 50,000/100,
45,000/106, 40,000/112. Arrester
gear: 45,000/85, 40,000/90, 35,000/
97, 30,000/105 knots.

12 Aluminum lift platforms were
designed for the *Majestic* class, but
they had to be abandoned because they
would not recover shape (as would
steel) after a heavy landing. Deck edge
placement eliminated this possibility,
since aircraft did not land on them.

of the 1952 carrier.[10] Margin was taken as 1500 tons at No 2 deck.

The estimate of aircraft equipment weight was based on two 130ft-stroke BS 4 steam catapults, two lifts and a total of 500,000 gallons of aviation fuel, all far below the tentative Staff Requirements. Similarly, the angled deck length, about 570ft, was substantially below initial requirements.

More modern machinery would operate at higher pressure, so the catapults could be supplied with 650 rather than 350psi steam, and it was estimated that they could then launch 50,000lb aircraft at 100 knots or 70,000lbs at 85 knots.[11] Each catapult weighed about 275 tons, and consumed about 23,000sq ft (that is, about 1300sq ft of hangar). DAWT wanted four catapults, and DNC offered a third, if 275 tons and the requisite hangar area could be spared. In that case he hoped to place two at the extreme forward end of the flight deck, with a third at the forward end of the angled deck.

DNC stated that the 870ft hull could not support a catapult with more than a 130ft stroke; it would take 1000ft of flight deck to support the 200ft stroke needed to accelerate heavy aircraft to the speeds desired.

The existing Mk 13 arrester gear had comparable performance, and there would be no difficulty in making the flight and hangar decks strong enough to support 60,000lb aircraft.

DNC argued that two deck-edge lifts would suffice, because aircraft landing on an angled deck could be parked out of the way alongside, between the deck and the island. Thus the landing rate no longer depended purely on the number of lifts. Each complete lift would weigh about 280 tons, but there was some hope of reducing weight by using an aluminium platform.[12]

Because jet fuel (avtur) could be stowed in boiler fuel tanks, endurance could be traded off against aviation fuel capacity, at the rate of 300nm at 22.5 knots for every 100,000 gallons beyond 50,000. Studies showed that by 1956 12 gallons of avtur would be needed for every 1 gallon of avgas, so DNC proposed to limit avgas (and thus special protected stowage) to 50,000 gallons out of the 500,000.[13] Eliminating avgas altogether would, of course, be a great benefit.

It seemed likely that 50,000sq ft of hangar space (with 17ft 6in clear height) that is, about the same as that in HMS *Eagle*, could be provided. This implied that the total weight of aircraft would be about the same, since the new ship would carry fewer of any larger (heavier) aircraft. Much the same argument applied to aircraft weapons; DNC estimated that the total of aircraft bombs, rockets, torpedoes, pyrotechnics and ammunition would grow by no more than about 100 tons, compared to the total of 1020 tons in HMS *Eagle*.

Net aircraft equipment would approximately match that in HMS *Eagle*; 50 tons would be added for new weapon lifts, and 50 deducted by dropping safety barriers (not needed for the angled deck); on the other hand, air weapon stowage was increasing steadily; so another 100 tons had to be added, and the increased total aviation fuel load added another 140 tons, for a total of 5400.[14] Adding a third lift or catapult would not appreciably change these figures since the net margins of error were about equal to the 300 or 400 tons associated with each such item. However, the hangar space would be reduced equal to the swept volume of a lift or to about 12ft length of hangar

13 DAWT forecast that the ratio
would shift from 2:1 (avtur:avgas) in 1953, to 4:1 in 1954, to 12:1 in 1955, as combat and then support piston-engined aircraft were replaced by jets and turbo-props.

14 The real jump had come earlier:
Eagle was designed for 3510 tons of aircraft equipment, but entered service with 5417 tons.

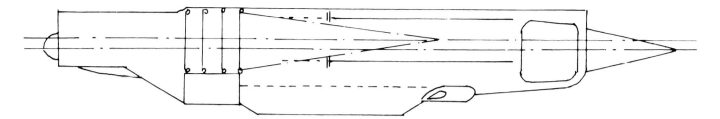

DAW's suggestion for a less expensive trade-protection carrier, operating high-performance fighters (but at low intensity), in May 1953. This was partly a response to the failure of DAW's VSTOL proposal. The key was to give up the requirement for simultaneous launch and recovery of aircraft. Aircraft could be parked alongside a straight deck, the main lift (split into two 60 × 35ft units side by side) lying forward of the two 200ft-stroke catapults. The wires would have pulled out over the catapults as shown. As sketched, the hull was 695ft long (as in HMS Colossus*), the flight deck 580ft long, and the deck park 160 × 30ft. Note that the centreline of the take-off lane was displaced from the centreline of the ship. This may have been the earliest example of the parallel-deck concept applied in* CVA.01. *NF*

for an extra catapult.

The Staff's 3in/70 mount weighed 97 tons; the carrier would probably have eight, amounting to 776 tons (which was rounded to 800 to include saluting guns, etc). Some favoured a secondary (close-range) battery, and 6-barrel Bofors could have been substituted for twin 3in/70 on a one-for-one basis.

The ship was not much larger than HMS *Eagle*, and would probably have had much the same complement (2550 officers and ratings), hence much the same weight of equipment, 2200 tons.

On 52,700 tons deep load, this left 5150 (9.8 per cent) for protection. It would allow a 3in flight deck over the hangar (of which 1in was structural), 2½in hangar sides (1in structural) up to the flight deck, 2½in (1in structural) hangar ends, 3in (1in structural) hangar deck outside the hangar, 2½in (1in structural) and the ship's side abreast the citadel (about 300ft long), 2½in (1in structural) over the ends of the citadel, 3½in to 4in magazine sides and crown, and about 3½in steering gear sides and crown. When he presented these conclusions to the Controller, DNC described flight deck and other protection as 2in thick including structural steel.

Thicknesses were limited by the sheer area of the hangar. As in the *Malta* design, it was obvious that no armour could keep out a large bomb or a well-designed rocket; 2in was considered effective against blast, aircraft cannon, Kamikazes, and also against radiation from nuclear weapons.[15] The side belt and deck over the citadel were reduced to 1½in, cutting total armour weight from 4600 to 3600 tons. Protection included 600 tons over weapon stowage, as well as access lobbies, downtakes and uptakes, and cable troughs. The higher figure was retained in weight summaries to provide a margin for extras, such as better protection for the island.

Effective armour thickness was limited in part by weight: the ship would be welded, but British yards could not weld in 2in NC (low carbon) splinter armour (for the decks and belt) sufficiently well to withstand shock. The US Navy was welding

comparable steel (STS and HY80) structurally (in submarines, *Mitscher* class destroyers and the *Forrestal*), and one question was whether the relevant technology could be transferred in time.

E-in-C offered four machinery spaces, each extending the full width of ship, leaving enough for about 19ft of side protection (compared to 20ft in *Eagle*, and 19ft in *Forrestal*).

These were depressing results, since the Controller and DNC believed that 55,000 tons was the bare minimum to meet the Staff Requirements. The Controller's view was that he was accepting some degree of risk in accepting a 52,000 (rather than a 51,000) ton deep displacement (33ft 6in rather than 33ft draft). A much larger floating dock (70,000 tons) was being designed, but it seemed unlikely that it would be built before 1959 or 1960, if then. The Controller concluded that it would be unacceptable to build a carrier which could not be docked at Devonport, Liverpool or Gibraltar (with Southampton as a reserve dock).

This set the design dimensions at 815ft(waterline) or 870ft overall × 115ft(waterline) × 33ft 8in fully loaded, or 52,000 tons fully loaded. Maximum take-off weight was set at 60,000lbs and maximum landing weight 45,000 (the deck, but not the arrester gear, could have taken 60,000lbs). The available performance, then, was compatible with the new US Navy strategic bomber (the A2J), but not with the much heavier jet strategic bomber then under development (the A3D Skywarrior). Any better arrester-gear performance would have required heavier units, and because they would have to be very high in the ship they would have required disproportionate compensation.

Not surprisingly, the Staff was not altogether pleased with these results. The central question was just how much American-style carrier-based strategic bombing was worth. If it could be foregone, a smaller ship, operating smaller tactical aircraft, would be acceptable. In European warfare, after all, British aircraft could fly from numerous land bases.[16] However, there were fewer bases in the East, and a war against Communist Asia might require carrier strikes from the Indian Ocean or the China Seas. It was generally agreed that the carrier could operate with reasonable impunity 300nm from an enemy coast. If she were restricted to coastal (maritime) targets, a strike range of 500nm would suffice; but many on the Staff wanted the 1000nm strike radius.

The Staff agreed to reduce maximum aircraft weight to 60,000lbs (take-off; 40,000lbs landing), taking off at 145 knots and landing at 110, with the originally projected length of 65ft and allowing for a folded span of 45ft (65ft spread). It accepted the 17ft 6in hangar, but asked for a bay tall enough (22ft) to allow one aircraft to unfold its wings. Fighters (32,000lbs at take-off and 25,000lbs at landing) would take off at 145 knots and land at 125. These figures were unrealistic. Because a pilot could withstand no more than 6 g acceleration, a BS 4 with 151ft stroke could accelerate a 35,000lb aircraft to no more than about 126 knots, and a 177ft catapult (with similar cylinder dimensions) was required to reach 145 knots. Similarly, stroke length limited a 130ft stroke (151ft total length) catapult to an end-speed of 99 knots (with acceleration of only 3.7 g). A 200ft catapult could launch the 60,000lb aircraft at 113 knots

15   An 80lb (2in) deck could be penetrated by 6in SAP at 21,000 yards; an 80lb side, up to 25,000 yards (at a 90-degree target angle). This armour was virtually useless against MC, SAP and AP bombs, but would keep out GP (light case) bombs up to 4000lbs. It could also withstand splinters from the 2000lb AP bomb. Against a nominal atomic bomb, this thickness transmitted excessive doses (above 125r) at 1000 yards, but at 1300 this was reduced to 100r and at 1500, 35r.

16   So did the United States; this argument was probably designed primarily against contemporary RAF proposals that the Royal Navy needed no long-range air attack capability at all.

(3.6 g). Generating 25 knots WOD, then, a carrier with a 151ft catapult could launch a 35,000lb fighter at 152 knots, and a 60,000lb bomber at 124 knots.

DAW was forced to admit that these might be reasonable limits. The 145-knot (take-off) fighter would land at 135 knots, which might be a practical limit.[17] However, deck-launched interceptor tactics demanded that fast-climbing fighters be launched immediately upon radar warning, when the effective WOD might be zero, not 25 knots. Even with a 151ft catapult (albeit operating at lower pressure), HMS *Ark Royal* would need to develop 18 knots WOD to launch the existing high-performance fighter, the Scimitar (N.113). Worse, there was every reason to imagine that future fighters would have higher wing loadings, and therefore would need higher catapult end-speeds. Nor was there any reason to imagine that future carrier bombers would cease to grow.

Overall, the 870ft deck seemed too short: the port forward catapult would be jammed by aircraft landing on the angled deck (although the new carrier would come closer than any previous British ship to the ideal of launching aircraft while simultaneously taking them aboard). The deck park would be too small (so that too few aircraft could be ranged for take-off while others landed); and the short-angled deck pushed the average landing area too far aft. Worst of all, the design allowed no room for future development, for instance for lengthening the catapults to take heavier aircraft. The 1000ft deck would overcome all these problems, but it was impractical. DAE suggested a compromise, 950ft, but that, too, was impossible on an 815ft hull. There was some interest in another compromise, cantilevering the ends of some catapults beyond the end of the deck. The Staff was unhappy that US *Essex* class carriers, which had substantially smaller displacements, could support more satisfactory deck arrangements, but this was a direct consequence of the length (rather than displacement) limit imposed by British dock facilities.

DAE wanted three 151ft (BS 4) catapults, and a third deck-edge lift (to make one to port, at the end of the angled deck, and two to starboard), but he accepted that one could be on the centreline, aft.[18] The requirement was that one be usable while aircraft landed on the angled deck. The Staff also wanted 750,000 gallons of aircraft fuel (with an 8:1 ratio, that is, about 83,000 gallons of avgas), accepting sacrifices in endurance.

Staff Requirements released in December 1952 showed three catapults, only one of which could require 25 knots WOD. The other two would launch 30,000lbs at 154 knots, 40,000 at 136, and 60,000 at 113 knots. DNC vigorously opposed this return to the unacceptable 200ft catapult. He explained to the air staff (DAW, DAE, DNDP) that they could have three lifts or three catapults, but not both. They accepted two catapults, and DNC was then able to make one 200ft long.

By late 1952 it was clear that the ship needed more beam; the original stability estimate (based on the *Eagle* design) was no longer satisfactory, due to changes in the shape of the underwater hull (to increase displacement within limited dimensions). The docking limits were, therefore, re-examined. The Gladstone Dock was 120ft wide across its entrance; harbour and dock authorities agreed that at most it could take a ship with 116ft beam. No 10 dock at Devonport was 123ft 9in across at its entrance, but HMS *Eagle* had to use 3ft 6in wide catamarans (fenders) when docking. The dockyard authorities very reluctantly agreed that slightly more beam could be obtained by specially shaping the mid-section to fit the dock. DNC therefore gained 1ft, but it was obvious that the ship could grow no further without major investment in dockyard facilities. The shipbuilding budget was too badly extended (even without a new carrier) to permit that.

Table 16-3: Aircraft complement for the 1952 Carrier, December 1952

Type		Area (sq ft)	Total area (sq ft)
Interceptor fighters	24	1000 × 24	24,000
All-weather fighters	24	1200 × 24	28,800
Strike aircraft	12	2500 × 12	30,000
ASW	12	1000 × 12	12,000
AEW	8	1000 × 8	8000
Helicopters	2	500 × 2	1000
Total	**82**		**103,800**

Note Average areas are based on the following aircraft: *Interceptors*: Scimitar (N113D) 1070sq ft; NA38, 700; *All-weather fighters*: F10F (USN), 1370; F3D (USN), 1240; *Strike aircraft*: folding Canberra, 2740; A3D (USN), 3380; *ASW*: Gannet, 890; S2F (USN), 1090; *AEW*: Skyraider, 930; Helicopter, 370sq ft.

Tentative Staff Requirements were issued in December 1952. They included the representative air group listed in Table 16-3. Unfortunately, the total footprint of an average air group came to 104,000sq ft. Planned flight deck area was 102,000sq ft, and DNC could offer only 50,000 (and perhaps 45,000) in the hangar. Even these figures were somewhat misleading, in that aircraft could not be stowed as closely as this on the flight deck. Probably 70,000sq ft would have been needed, but that was entirely impractical: even 25,000sq ft would be a great deal. DNC concluded that the ship probably could not operate more than fifty aircraft, a figure which had important implications for equipment, fuel stowage and weapons capacity.

Otherwise the Staff Requirements generally reflected DNC's estimates. The flight deck was to be arranged so that aircraft could land-on while others were launched, its maximum parking space to equal about 20 per cent of its overall area. The Staff emphasized quick launching. All three catapults would be far enough (at least 50ft) apart to be loaded simultaneously (but this could be relaxed if doing so would permit firing a catapult while landing-on). All could be fired within 2 seconds (any one catapult refiring after 30 seconds). The three catapult tracks had to diverge ahead of the ship, so that aircraft launched in quick succession would not collide. Specified turn-around time was 7 minutes for a fighter (10 for a night fighter) and 15 minutes for a strike or ASW aircraft.

The fighters would be directed by two (one if it could obtain all-round coverage) 984 radars feeding a 96-track CDS in a two-deck AIO with ten intercept positions (as in *Ark Royal*), with DPT. There would be no other long-range air search radar, but the ship would have an airborne early warning terminal, a short-range Type 992, plus a surface-search set (Type 974) and a carrier-controlled approach set (Type 963). The other major systems were a Tacan homing beacon (AN/URN-3), F.V.11 (VHF/DF), and IFF Mk 10. In February 1953 the AIO requirement was reduced to a 48-track CDS and eight intercept positions.

Protection against atomic and chemical weapons was specified: ventilation systems would be grouped and capable of prompt isolation. The ship would be air conditioned to the greatest possible extent, so that she could be closed up in action. Her upper works would be designed specifically to resist nuclear blast, and she would be arranged to wash off nuclear fallout.

Armament was eight twin 3in/70 (900rpg) plus the maximum possible number of single power-operated Bofors guns.[19]

The new carrier would also be provided with a torpedo-evasion sonar, Type 149 (later Type 176). In February 1953 the requirement was amended to include space and weight for the Camrose (then under development) or another anti-torpedo weapon (such weapons were later abandoned because of insuperable technical problems).

The Staff also wanted the ship arranged for possible installation of the major future aviation innovation then in sight, the flexible flight deck. DNC initially hoped that a flexible deck

17 DAW assumed that landing weight would not exceed 80 per cent of take-off weight, and that stall speed on landing would not exceed 90 per cent of stall speed taking off. Catapult launch speed was 10 per cent above stall, and landing speed (at the arrester gear) was 30 per cent above stall. On this basis, maximum landing speed was about 6 per cent above take-off speed. For example, a 25,000lb aircraft stalling at 13 knots could be launched at 123.5 knots (with 25 knots WOD) and would land at 133 knots (20,000lbs). The existing Mk 13 arrester gear was good for 30,000lbs/105 knots for about 128.5 knots at 20,000lbs, showing a deficiency of only 4.5 knots. DNC criticized the 30 per cent landing safety factor (which allowed a pilot to retain control as he approached). A reduction to 20 per cent would solve most of the problem. The Staff Requirement was written in terms of a fighter stalling at 135 knots, which therefore had to be launched at about 149 knots. The 151ft catapult offered a maximum (6 g) end-speed of 126 knots for 36,000lbs, and 25 knots WOD would have sufficed. If, however, DAW demanded that fighters be launched at zero wind, the minimum acceptable catapult was 210ft long.

18 The midships position was precluded because the flight deck was the strength deck, and a forward centreline lift would have interfered with the two long bow catapults. That left an after centreline lift, clear of the landing path. By way of contrast, US *Essex* class (SCB 27C) carriers, which were slightly longer than the projected 1952 carrier, had their centreline lifts forward, feeding their two bow catapults. The dimensions of the British lifts were set at 66 × 44ft (centreline) and 66 × 36ft (deck edge). They were to take 40,000lb loads with a 20–25 second cycle (40–45 seconds including 10 to load and unload), and 60,000lbs at a reduced rate.

19 DNO wanted more light anti-aircraft weapons, contrasting the new carrier with modernized US ships (but not with USS *Forrestal*, which had only eight 5in/54), and with *Eagle*, which was armed with eight twin 4.5in, six Bofors Mk 6 (sextuple), two Bofors Mk 5 (twin), and eight Bofors Mk 9 (single). DGD initially wanted six twin 3in/70 and as many single Bofors as possible if the ship could rely on anti-aircraft escorts, but ten twin 3in/70 and eight improved (40 calibre) twin Bofors (or sextuple Bofors) if she could not. DGD decided on the lighter battery on the theory that the carrier would always be escorted. DNC welcomed the elimination of two twin 3in/70 (both forward) because that would help balance the ship longitudinally (the two catapults at the bow added both weight and moment) and would make for a neater layout in way of the catapult control stations.

could be installed or removed within ten days, but later (May 1953) he pointed out that installation might not be nearly that simple. The catapults and aircraft moving arrangements would have to be modified, and a low pressure air supply (to inflate the deck) installed. Ideally, the arresting wires would be suitable for both a hard and a flexible deck, but this turned out to be difficult to organize in practice.

The US Navy was the chief obstacle to British adoption of flexible decks: given tacit reliance on US aircraft supply in wartime, the Royal Navy had to convince the United States to adopt aircraft suited to its carriers. Early in July 1952 a BuAer delegation visited Britain. The Royal Navy argued that the angled deck overcame the single greatest objection, fear that undercarriageless aircraft handling would be too slow to maintain the standard 30-second landing rate. If, however, the flexible (landing) deck were the angled deck, aircraft would have to move only a few feet. RAE demonstrated landings on its Stage 5 flexibile deck, as well as a ventral launching ramp, and a towing winch and trolley to clear aircraft from the flexible deck. The usual arguments for undercarriageless aircraft were made. The BuAer officers thought that structural savings might be so great that they could soon achieve Mach 2 in a carrier interceptor.[20]

The meetings seemed promising; the BuAer officers informally asked the MoS to make a rubber deck for the US Navy, and hoped that, with an angled deck installed the following year aboard an *Essex* class carrier (USS *Antietam*), they might have a flexible and angled deck ship operational in eighteen months. The flexible deck was actually built and extensively tested ashore in the United States. It ultimately failed. A flexible-deck ship could not operate conventional aircraft, but, both ASW and airborne early warning (AEW) aircraft were propeller-driven, hence had to be conventional. At the least, then, every four-ship flexible-deck carrier group had to include two hard-deck ships. This objection could not be removed until helicopters took over both ASW and AEW.

Moreover, by 1952–53 the Royal Navy (and, for that matter, the US Navy) was investing in VTOL technology. There was good, if ill-founded, reason to expect vertical take-off (VTOL) aircraft to enter service some time after 1960. At that time the entire shape of the carrier would change. There seemed little point in arranging for two successive revolutions in carrier design, first a short-lived flexible deck and then VTOL. Note that the VTOL of the early 1950s was not the Harrier; it was a ramp-launched tail-sitting interceptor, developed by Fairey in Britain and primarily by Ryan in the United States. Futuristic carrier deck schemes developed by both navies showed VTOL take-off ramps alongside the deck.

Aside from the sheer size of the ship, the two major design issues were the general arrangement of the flight deck, and the details of the machinery.

By mid-1952 the Royal Navy had accepted the concept of the angled deck, but so far it had been applied only to existing carriers. In such cases it was obvious that the deck would be angled to port, opposite the island to starboard. DNC's first general arrangements followed much this theme. He favoured a two-funnel two-island arrangement, in one version of which the starboard lift was between the two islands. Alternatively, it could be used for the fixed crane and to stow mobile (flight-deck) cranes.

The topside arrangement decided the arrangement of boiler and engine rooms. When the two islands were moved apart to make space for a lift, for example, the boilers of the forward machinery units had to be moved forward of the corresponding engine rooms, and the boilers of X machinery unit moved abaft X engine room to allow for aircraft ammunition lifts.

As the US Navy was then discovering, DNC found that with an angled deck it was useful to place the island as far aft as possible, to get the maximum deck park. This, however, was severely limited by the arrangement of the uptakes (although less so with a two-funnel arrangement). The greater the angle of the deck, the more the available space for parking, but total ship width was limited, so that a 10-degree deck, for example, had to be too sharply cut off at its fore end to provide a useful increase.

By early 1953 DNC was considering much more radical deck configurations. Aircraft generally landed in a left-hand circuit, and actually had to turn sharply to line up with the usual angled deck. It might, then, be time to adopt instead a deck angled to starboard, with the island being moved to port but, ideally, the funnels to starboard to place the approach farthest from the smoke. This in turn led to investigation of hinged funnels (which the US Navy still hoped to place aboard USS *Forrestal*) and of other approaches to funnel-less smoke disposal. Experiments at NPL showed that ideally the funnels should be placed on both sides of the ship, with selective dampers to either side to discharge according to the wind direction. NPL cited numerous problems in past British and Japanese flush-deck carriers and carrier projects, and in fact BuShips succeeded in killing off the parallel American project.

YARD developed four alternative machinery arrangements under the designation Y.300. The simplest was a unit scheme, with two boilers and one set of turbines per unit (four main machinery spaces). It was considered too vulnerable, as there was insufficient space to separate the units very widely.[21] Alternatively, the boilers could be split off into four 40ft compartments, the engines being paired in two 45ft spaces. This was objectionable, as it reduced the number of independent units from four to two. Subdivision could be further improved by splitting the machinery spaces into 35ft single-engine rooms (with 30ft boiler rooms). This arrangement was attractive, but it consumed too much precious length. The eight-compartment machinery design could be tightened. Because boilers were being designed with gas- (hence water-) tight outer casings to isolate the inside of the ship from atomic/chemical/biological contamination, these casings could themselves be made part of the bulkheading. Then the operating advantages of combining engine and boiler spaces could be combined with fuller compartmentation, the boilers being operated through their outer casings. This last scheme was chosen for development.

The advent of steam catapults raised a new issue: for the first time a warship needed not necessarily a steady supply of steam (for propulsion), but instead a series of bursts for catapulting. Babcock & Wilcox, the boiler makers, suggested using separate catapulting boilers, with one in each of three of the four machinery units. The company argued that if the same boiler were used for both propulsion and catapulting, it would have to reduce average propulsion steam output per boiler, so that after each catapult shot the boiler could rapidly run up to maximum power to replace the steam loss. With three catapults firing at maximum rate (30-second cycle), the three main boiler units involved would have to cut back to 58 per cent propulsion power. The fourth unit would have to cut back similarly, to maintain uniform shp; speed would fall about 3.5 knots. Yarrow also considered an alternative, in which the ship ran continuously at maximum steam power, the main engines losing power as the catapults fired. The speed loss would be materially less, but the company was not very hopeful.

E-in-C, however, demanded at least two propulsion boilers per machinery unit, for redundancy. That meant either two boilers for both propulsion and catapulting, or one main boiler and one lightweight unit primarily for catapulting, but also for

20   In the autumn of 1950 Saunders-Roe proposed an undercarriageless fighter (the P.121) with hydro-skis, for water or flex-deck operation. DAW was enthusiastic. He cited much the same arguments which had been made a quarter-century earlier for floatplanes: the fighter could be flown to maintain pilot proficiency even when the fleet was not at sea, and it could defend the fleet in harbour. The Royal Navy tended to equate the prospects of the US hydro-ski fighter, the F2Y, with the prospects for a US flex-deck, even though the US Navy seems not to have made this connection. The reason may simply have been the far greater number of US bases active from which carrier pilots could fly.

21   USS *Forrestal* employed this system, but with a 36ft auxiliary machinery space between the forward and after pairs of 52ft combined (boiler/engine) machinery spaces.

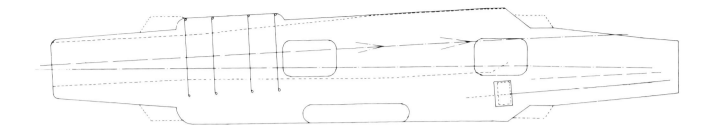

DNC's sketch of the layout of a 700ft conventional carrier in February 1954. The dashed lines outside the deck outline indicate the gun sponsons. Lifts were 60 × 40ft each, and the positions of the 220ft pull-outs of Nos 1 and 4 wires are shown. DNC produced this plan partly to show that a useful jet carrier could be built on a hull of roughly Colossus *length without recourse to the desperate expedients suggested by DAW. NF*

emergency propulsion (at 50 per cent power). This was rejected because the two would have to operate under different steam conditions, and hence could not work in parallel. Catapult demand was smoothed out by feeding launching steam into a wet accumulator.

The boilers were in 20ft boxes, paired at one end of each 36ft engine room, a 40ft auxiliary space separating the forward and after pairs of machinery units, with four 16ft evaporator spaces (one forward, two in the auxiliary space and another aft), the arrangement being (fore to aft) EBEB, the auxiliary space, then BEBE. At DNC's suggestion, the two evaporator spaces in the auxiliary machinery space were combined into one and the space lengthened by 8ft, to provide a 32ft bomb and rocket magazine. The two outside evaporator spaces were also combined into a single space between A and B machinery units, for a total machinery (and magazine) length of 288ft.

By early 1953, it seemed likely that this plant would have to produce 190,000shp in the tropics and 205,000shp under temperate conditions. Haslar, the Admiralty test establishment, was studying alternative bulbous bow hull forms for reduced resistance; the problem was behaviour when the ship was pitching and heaving. A bulbous bow did reduce power requirements.[22] It was also possible (but by no means certain) that a bulbous bow would move the null point aft; ideally this point of zero pitching and heaving motion would coincide with the point at which aircraft were most likely to touch down.

The new carrier required considerably more electric power, 10,000kW, than her predecessors, and E-in-C wanted to reduce what had previously been considered excessive generator weights.[23] The initial proposal was eight 1250kW steam turbo generators, plus a 2000kW emergency supply (if steam were lost). However, considerable weight could be saved if part of the primary plant did not require steam power. E-in-C proposed gas turbines, which were a radical departure in the autumn of 1952: four 1250kW steam turbo generators and four 1250kW gas turbines. DEE, responsible for electrical power, wanted one of the gas turbines near each end of the ship away from the machinery spaces, for emergency use. The other two would be as high as possible abreast the hangar. The units planned were developments of an existing 1000kW Allen gas turbine. E-in-C estimated that he could save 90 to 120 tons, compared to a comparable diesel power supply (using existing 750kW diesels). The main technical problem envisaged was silencing the noisy gas turbines, which would have to be run in harbour to provide the ship with power, and to provide steam for heating from their waste heat.

By MID-1953 IT WAS CLEAR that the British defence expansion was over-ambitious, and that it had to be pruned back.[24] On 8 July 1953 the Controller ordered all work stopped. This was by no means the end of British interest in carriers, merely the end of the 53,000-ton project. DNC asked that research projects applicable to future carriers should be continued: these included welding NC armour, underwater protection design, smoke discharge from hinged funnels, pitching with/without bulbous bow, the development of new steels and sea trials of the gas turbine generator.

As recounted in the previous chapter, the carrier cancellation was part of a government-wide Defence Review, the hope being that heavier reliance on nuclear weapons could sharply reduce the cost of maintaining conventional forces. The new Admiralty position was that Britain should concentrate on forces for intervention in the Third World. Carriers were clearly needed for that mission, particularly East of Suez.

From a carrier point of view, concentration on the Third World mission meant, for the first time since 1942, that there was no longer any need to coordinate aircraft policy with the US Navy, since there was no longer any expectation of vast infusions of American aircraft in wartime. This was tempered by the political reality that Britain remained in NATO, and therefore that British carriers were still expected to form part of the NATO strike fleet. Ideally they still had to be able to cross-deck US aircraft – but that was an ideal, not a base requirement.

The 1957 White Paper approved retention of the best active British carriers, but it left their future somewhat uncertain. It seems most likely that the uncertainty applied only to whether they would have to be able to execute tactical nuclear strikes against Soviet forces. British official papers for the period after 1957 have not yet been released, but the decision to build a large, rather than a small, carrier suggests that the deep tactical nuclear strike mission was affirmed in about 1958–59. The key argument was probably that Soviet short-range missiles could easily destroy any fixed NATO air base, whereas a moving carrier might well survive until after it had destroyed the relevant Soviet land bases.

In the context of the new national strategy, this decision was politically explosive. The shift to missiles (and the possibility that these might be submarine-borne) would remove one, and possibly two, key RAF missions: at the least Fighter Command, and possibly also Bomber Command. Thus any large new carrier was a direct threat almost to the existence of the

22 Haslar predicted that with a bulbous bow the ship would require 97,000 rather than 101,000ehp to make 30 knots deep and dirty (tropics) or 102,000 rather than 107,000shp to make 32 knots clean. It predicted a propulsive efficiency of 0.527; E-in-C guaranteed 190,000shp in the tropics and 205,000shp in temperate water. The normal bow, then, would require 203,500shp at 32 knots, the bulbous bow 194,000, so 32 knots (clean) could be attained either way. The required 30 knots deep and dirty would be marginal with a normal bow, but there would be some power in hand with the bulbous form.

23 Wartime comparisons with US practice had been embarrassing. USS *Midway* had eight 1250kW turbo-generators and two 850kW diesels, compared to four 500kW turbo-generators and four 500kW diesels in *Eagle*, yet her total generating plant weight was only 180.3 tons, compared to 246 tons in *Eagle*. The difference was largely due to heavy British diesel generators; *Malta* (eight 500kW turbo-generators and four 500kW diesels) was better than *Eagle*, at 216 tons. In *Eagle*, the turbo generators weighed only 58 tons, but the diesels came to 188 tons.

24 For details of the rise and fall of the rearmament programme, see my *Postwar Naval Revolution* (Conway Maritime Press, London, and Naval Institute Press, Annapolis, 1986).

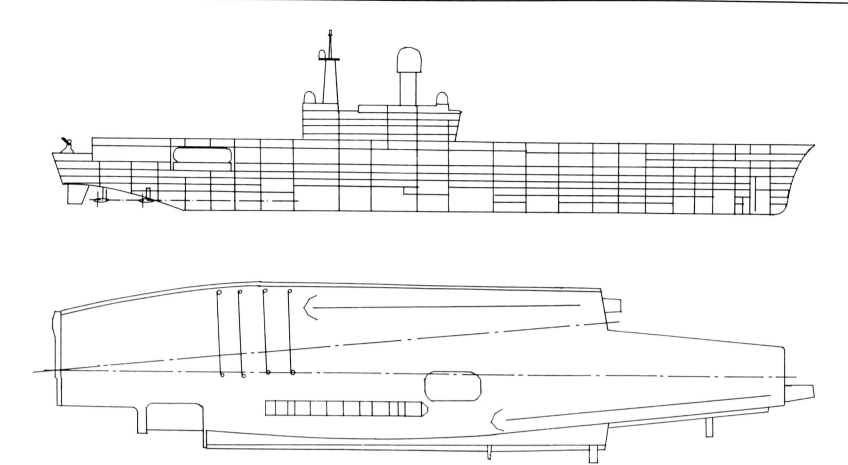

CVA.01 *inboard profile and deck view*. NF

RAF, since it would supersede the remaining tactical nuclear strike role. The RAF seems to have come to this conclusion between 1961 and 1965, and its arguments in response killed the last big British carrier project, CVA.01. It seems possible that by 1965 the expected cost of carrier construction (five would have been built) was such that any British government would have been compelled to cancel, so that the RAF arguments were in effect convenient excuses.

THE BOARD WAS STILL INTERESTED in carrier construction, but at a lower price. By the early autumn of 1954 DNC was developing two sketch designs, for 35,000 and for about 30,000 tons. Details are not available, but it appears that unusual configurations, such as one with a hangar deck catapult, were being studied. As in the bigger carrier, DNC was interested in two-funnel arrangements, to minimize machinery vulnerability.

Both studies were presented to the Sea Lords on 17 December 1954. DNC considered 35,000 tons a practical minimum for operating modern aircraft in reasonable numbers, so that it could mount a useful strike force, yet it was not so large that it would be wasted in trade protection. A typical air group would be twelve Scimitars, twelve Sea Vixens (or Scimitars), nine Buccaneers (or additional Gannets), eight Gannets (or additional Buccaneers), four AEW, and two plane-guard helicopters. Of these aircraft, twenty-one would be stowed in a permanent deck park and twenty-six in the hangar. Armament would be four twin 3in/70. Three shafts (48,000shp each) would drive the ship at 29.9 knots deep and dirty, and endurance would be about 5000nm at 20 knots. Protection would consist of 1.5in armour on hangar top and sides, and around vital compartments in and immediately below the island, with

3in side armour abreast the citadel.

The alternative 28,000 ton carrier was the smallest which could operate modern aircraft in reasonable numbers, given that aircraft features could be bought at the expense of other ship qualities (protection, armament, speed, ammunition, etc). Moreover, striking power would be very limited. If the twelve day and twelve all-weather fighters and the four AEW aircraft and two helicopters were considered an irreducible overhead, the 28,000-ton carrier was limited to an additional eight Gannets or Buccaneers, that is, either ASW or strike. Of the thirty-eight aircraft, eighteeen were in a deck park and twenty in the hangar. A two-shaft plant (50,000shp each) would drive the ship at 28.4 knots deep and dirty, and endurance would be 5500nm at 20 knots. Armament would be limited to twin Bofors guns, and armour protection for the flight deck, hangar deck and ship sides over the citadel would be 1in thick.

These studies apparently led the following year to discussions of Staff Requirements for a 35,000-ton carrier, but details are not available.

At the time, it was assumed that the carrier would be accompanied by one or more large missile cruisers. However, by late 1955 the missile cruiser was becoming more and more expensive. It appears (again, details are not available) that one alternative was to concentrate Task Group command and control in the carrier, which would also carry some air defence missiles. Certainly by early 1956 DNC was developing a 30,000-ton carrier/missile ship, with the projected '1¾' (very long range) surface-to-air missile mounted on one side amidships (Scheme A) or aft (Scheme B). On 1 March 1956 the Sea Lords tentatively accepted Scheme B, because it allowed for two, rather than one, catapults forward. The First Sea Lord (Admiral Lord Mountbatten) asked for alternative versions in which missile stowage was increased to thirty or forty weapons. This ship figured in a ten-year building plan adopted that year. The mis-

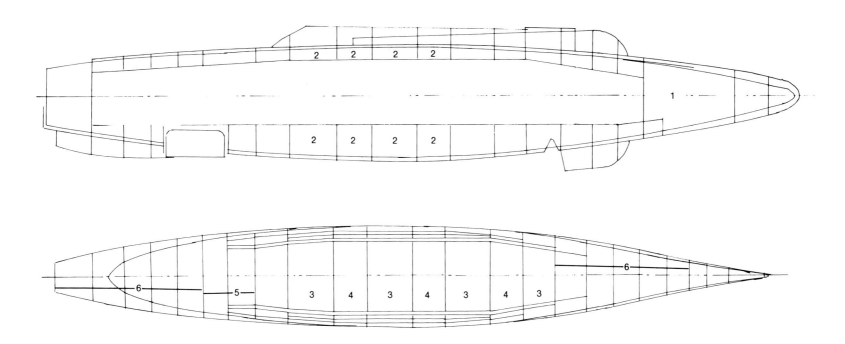

Key
1 Aircraft stores
2 Maintenance shops
3 Air weapon magazine
4 Main machinery space
5 Auxiliary equipment
6 Stores

CVA.01 *hangar deck and a deck below the hangar, to show how space was divided. These are approximate only.* NF

sile/carrier ship survived in long-range plans as late as 1960.

Details are not available, but it seems likely that the logic of the design was to reduce overhead weight by trading fighters for ship-launched missiles. This would accord with later British naval thinking, and indeed with later ideas elsewhere. At the Sea Lords meeting DNC offered to begin design work on the basis of Staff Requirements which might be ready at the beginning of 1958; in that case the ship would be delivered some time in 1965, which would match the possible programme of the missile.

There was still interest in conventional carrier design. Late in 1956 or early in 1957 E-in-C and the JTC studied the implications of aircraft weight and performance growth. They concluded that a 45,000-ton carrier could not operate aircraft much beyond 50,000lbs. Details of this study, too, appear to have been lost. The Controller concluded, in February 1957, that any further progress in British carrier operation (beyond the Buccaneer and P.177) would have to depend upon major innovations, such as lighter weapons, high energy fuels, deflected jet take-off and landing (as in the Harrier) and boundary layer blowing. The Controller specifically ruled out reliance on missiles to replace naval aircraft; carriers remained particularly valuable for limited war. This would seem to have ruled out the carrier/missile ship, and in any case the long-range '1¾' missile died in the 1957 cuts.[25]

Outline drawings of both a pure carrier and the missile ship/carrier were shown at a NARC (Naval Air Requirements Committee) meeting at Bath in 1957.

THERE WERE TWO RESPONSES to the Controller's lament. One was to plan for a new type of carrier aircraft, which really could be adapted to a ship of reasonable size; this became the unfortunate P.1154. The other was to design a new carrier, capable of operating efficiently all existing aircraft and then of shifting to the new type. It became CVA.01 and, like P.1154, was ultimately cancelled. The account which follows is necessarily incomplete, because British state papers for the period after 1957 have not yet been released.

The effect of the 1957 review was to kill all but two classes

of high-performance combat aircraft: the next-generation carrier aircraft and a next-generation tactical strike bomber. The deck-launched interceptor (SR.177) had been killed on the theory that it was essentially a manned missile: a future missile could do the same job more efficiently. A CAP/strike escort fighter was a very different proposition, because missiles could not easily do its job. They could not deal with ambiguity, since a missile fired is a missile expended. Radar identification becomes less and less certain at longer ranges, so any missile designed to replace a long-range CAP fighter or a strike escort must necessarily work in a relatively ambiguous environment.

The strike requirement would necessarily remain because although missiles could hit fixed targets, they could not deal with moving ones. Again, this was a question of ambiguity. A pilot despatched to hit a target which had moved since it had been identified could return to fly off again. A missile fired at the wrong place would be wasted, so to kill a particular number of moving targets would require very large numbers of missiles.

By 1958, too, it was increasingly apparent that the Royal Navy could not hope for carriers much larger than 45,000 to 50,000 tons. It could not therefore tolerate much more growth in weight or in landing or take-off speed. On the other hand, missiles were becoming more and more effective. One possibility, then, was to put the performance into the missiles. The future fighter might look much like the existing Buccaneer, its take-off weight 60,000lbs or less. Limits such as a length of 65ft and a folded width of 30ft seemed generous (the Buccaneer was 63ft 5in long, had a folded width of 19ft 11in, and weighed 46,000 to 56,000lbs). Take-off speed (at heavy load) was set at about 150 to 160 knots. On the other hand, future carrier reconnaissance aircraft would still have to fly at high speed and at high altitude so as to survive enemy defences. They could be substantially lighter than fighters and attack aircraft, and thus could probably achieve higher catapult end-speeds.

In 1960, it was assumed that a typical fighter would loiter for 4 hours 150nm from the carrier (including 10 minutes at high speed). The same aircraft would attack targets 150nm away carrying 2000lbs of weapons, or 600nm away with 6000lbs. It would achieve high subsonic or low supersonic speeds at low altitude, and Mach 2.5 at high altitude. Take-off and landing speeds would be about 90 knots, take-off weight nore more

25 The Controller's 1957 conclusions, but not the 1954–56 studies, appear in the Cover for the 1952 carrier. Some details of the earlier studies appear in other papers included in the Ship's Cover for the 1950–56 Guided Weapon Cruiser. No drawings or further data appear to have been released.

than 50,000lbs, landing weight not more than 35,000lbs. Dimensions would be as follows: spread (folded) 70ft (30) span; 70ft (64) length; 23ft (19ft 6in) height that, is 20ft minimum clear hangar height. By 1962, when design began in earnest, the size limits had been relaxed to 60ft (22.25) span, 65ft (60) length, and 20ft (27) height.[26]

There were also some important political considerations. The Minister of Defence strongly supported commonality between the RAF and the Royal Navy as a way of minimizing the cost of continuing tactical aircraft development. The Ministry of Aviation wanted to spend as much of its budget as it could on the two most promising aircraft technologies, variable geometry (swing-wing) and VSTOL (the jump-jet). The Navy could demand its own new conventional aircraft, but this would be very expensive and might thus become a very low priority.

At this time the Royal Navy was developing a Buccaneer replacement to Operational Requirement OR 346, to enter service in 1975. The RAF was developing a follow-on to the new TSR.2 tactical bomber, to OR 355. There were also the two major new technologies, represented by the Vickers Swallow (swing-wing) and by the Hawker Kestrel (vectored-thrust VSTOL). The RAF was particularly interested in vectored thrust (for STOL, not VSTOL) because a short take-off

bomber could operate from so many bases that an enemy would be unable to bomb them all. The Navy liked variable geometry because it promised long range (for loiter capability) without sacrificing high dash speed. All of the projected aircraft were about the size of the contemporary US Navy Vigilante strategic bomber.

There was only money enough for one aircraft, one technology. The key RAF requirement was a 400-mile low-level supersonic dash in to the target through heavy missile defences. The STOL feature would improve an aircraft's survivability by allowing it to operate from a much wider variety of bases. The Royal Navy could afford much stiffer take-off requirements and a much shorter low-level supersonic dash; it required endurance for CAP and long range at high altitude for strike warfare. The Navy did not necessarily need STOL, but the RAF could not really afford to buy a new bomber which did not incorporate it. On this basis the decision was inevitable: if the country could afford to develop only one new aircraft, it would have to be the STOL, and the two services would somehow have to reconcile their very different requirements.[27]

STOL had its price: limited weapon load, jet blast on the flight deck, and the requirement to be catapulted when carrying a heavy load. Against these points, a high-performance VSTOL airplane could fly from virtually any kind of deck. It might well be that tactical efficiency would demand large numbers of such aircraft and therefore large carriers, but with VSTOL much of the connection between aircraft performance and carrier size could be broken.

For all this, the Navy could not afford to bet on the success of the technology, particularly for high performance. Therefore any carrier to be built in the near term had to cater for conventional aircraft, with both catapults and arrester gear. This turned out to be very wise: the advanced VSTOL, the P.1154, had to be cancelled, and the Royal Navy had to buy US Phan-

26   These were very impressive figures by contemporary standards. The US Vigilante (A-5), the highest performing US carrier bomber, had a combat radius of only 685nm carrying an 1885lb nuclear weapon. It weighed about 55,000lbs and stalled at 134.5 knots on take-off. In theory a variable-geometry aircraft could have cruised much more efficiently, to achieve much greater ranges without very much of a weight penalty. However, the US F-111B, which did have swing-wings, weighed 77,600lbs but was credited with a combat radius of only 475nm carrying six Phoenix missiles, a load of about 3000lbs. It is true that these figures reflect specific mission profiles, but even so they have made depressing reading.

27   Although these events seem to bear resemblance to the US TFX/F-111 story, the British decision would seem to have been mandated much more strongly by economics and also by the strategic considerations of the 1957 Defence Review. Unlike the US Navy, the Royal Navy was unable to fend off the demand for commonality with the RAF, and the naval version died by November 1963. The Navy ordered US Phantoms, which it preferred, instead. In *Project Cancelled* (Jane's, London, 1986), Derek Wood attributes the joint-service P.1154 concept to Peter Thorneycroft (Minister of Aviation 1960–62, and Minister of Defence 1962–64), an admirer of US Secretary Robert S McNamara, the originator of the TFX.

Above and opposite: CVA.01, *the strike carrier cancelled in 1966, is shown in official sketches. Note that, like earlier British carriers, she has tilting radio masts as well as whips.* The view from ahead shows the characteristic British UHF/DF mast at flight deck level, and also several Phantoms on deck.

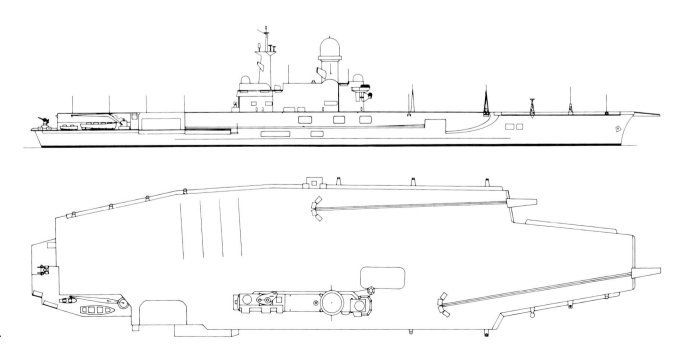

CVA.01 *profile and plan.*

toms. Had the new carrier been built as planned, it could have operated Phantoms and, for that matter, the next US naval fighter, the Tomcat. A pure VSTOL carrier could not.

The new RAF/Navy aircraft became the Hawker P.1154. Work began in 1962, the critical new item being plenum chamber burning – essentially an afterburner built into the front end of the engine. The concept was elegant but it proved extremely difficult to implement, to the point that, as this is written, it is being developed for aircraft to fly at about the turn of the century. In theory, the P.1154 would lift useful loads by catapult launching, although it would land vertically without using arrester gear. To reduce the maintenance load, it would be produced in alternative fighter and attack versions, with common airframe and engine (but different enough that shore facilities were required to change one into the other).

By 1964 Hawker could promise only that aircraft would be delivered about 1969. It seems likely that the Navy considered this figure over-optimistic, and it opted for American Phantoms (with British Spey engines) instead.

THE EXISTING CARRIERS had to be replaced, beginning with *Victorious* in 1972, with *Eagle* and *Centaur* probably following in 1973 (based on 25-year lives). Work on characteristics for a series of replacements began in 1958. The SDPC optimistically called for nuclear power (as in the newest US carrier). Nothing came of this; it was far too expensive.

The future carrier would have to operate the maximum possible number of fixed-wing aircraft. Economics demanded, too, that any aircraft (such as a helicopter) which did not require catapults or arrester gear should be moved off the expensive carriers. Given recent very painful experience of missile cruiser design, the Admiralty was unwilling to put much of the defence of the battle group into surface ships; missiles would be limited essentially to point defence.[28] This killed the missile ship/carrier, which had been a fixture of long-range Admiralty planning since 1956.[29]

The tactical unit would be two carriers, and each would need at least the capability to make two strikes (four aircraft each), with two aircraft for refuelling (by the buddy system), and sufficient fighters to provide four for CAP (assuming that each could loiter for about 4 hours 150nm from the ship) on a 24-hour basis. On a single-carrier basis, counting availability, this apparently equated to twelve to fourteen strike and reconnaissance aircraft, eighteen fighters for air defence, eight AEW aircraft and two search and rescue helicopters. Strike and fighter aircraft might share a common airframe, and under some circumstances AEW aircraft might be traded off for more of them.

The cost per carrier might be cut by moving both the usual ASW helicopters and fleet command and control to another unit, perhaps a big underway replenishment ship which was then called a Fast Fleet Replenishment Ship (FFRS). Not all the ASW helicopters would be aboard the FFRS at all times (they could be distributed within the fleet), but the FFRS would provide their essential maintenance facilities. The FFRS idea was transmuted into the Command Cruiser; in a sense, too, the new AOR is FFRS revisited, the logic of 1958 remaining

quite sound.

Work began in earnest in mid-1960.

Aircraft operating requirements recalled those of 1952, even though they were probably unrelated: three catapults, all non-interfering, and three lifts (one forward, one aft on the centreline and one deck-edge to starboard abaft the island), each 40 x 90ft, and each lifting 65,000lbs. The flight deck would be the largest possible, within the limits set by docks, that is, about 850 × 200ft, covering the largest possible hangar (at least 100ft wide and 20ft high). Fuel capacity would be 1,000,000 gallons of avcat jet fuel.

There were also unconventional ideas. The lesson of 1952–53 was that, given existing docks, no new carrier could be very large; 870 × 115ft still seemed a practical limit. To achieve anything worthwhile, her arrangement would have to be ingenious. In this case the innovation was the parallel, rather than the angled, deck. It was not a return to the old axial deck. Instead, the angled deck was straightened out and moved to port. It still did not interfere with the deck park or with the catapult(s) forward, but now the deck park could extend all the way aft. A lift well aft, and located near the centreline (hence dry even in bad weather) could operate without interfering with landings-on. If the island were set well in to port, leaving an open deck to starboard, aircraft could come up and taxi forward to the catapults without interfering in any way with the deck park. The total deck width of about 200ft was based on an 85ft wide deck park, a somewhat wider landing strip to port, and a 45ft taxi strip to starboard of the island.

Armament would consist primarily of tactical nuclear bombs, shipborne ASW stand-off missiles (Ikara), a long-range air-to-air missile (which never materialized), and a 'Tartar-type' surface-to-air missile (which became Sea Dart).

As always, speed was a major issue. Fleet speed was effectively 25 knots, and many ships could not make 28 even in good weather. The old requirement for wind over deck could not easily be slighted, but high speed was clearly very expensive, and it might be much easier to rely largely on the catapult. The conclusion was that going from 25 to 28 knots would make a considerable difference for aircraft launching, whereas the additional expense of going from 28 to 30 would add very little. Thus the new carrier would be designed for 28 knots, although 30 was desirable.

The usual British carrier endurance of 6000nm (this time at the reduced speed of 20 knots) seemed a reasonable point of departure, although it required further justification.

Trade-off studies (42,000 to 68,000 tons) based on these considerations were completed late in 1960. Some considered the air group described above too small, and it was, in effect, re-evaluated in terms of the most stressing mission, continuous strikes in support of ground forces, conducted over three to four days between replenishments. Under these circumstances, the carriers had to provide sustained fleet air defence (which was understood to require thirty-two fighters in all, including spares)[30], long-range strikes (to isolate the battlefield), airfield suppression strikes (to protect the troops landing), and close air support. They also had to provide continuous reconnaissance and to support the landing itself, as the fleet had no heavy guns for that purpose.

These roles could impose very heavy loads on the carriers. It was assumed that aircraft could make 1½ sorties an hour (in a 12-hour day) for close support, or three per day at longer ranges; figures allowed for one third of the aircraft to be inoperable at any one time. Sorties could be assigned a 50 per cent success rate. Thus, for example, if the Army encountered three close-support targets per hour, this would require six sorties per hour, or four aircraft aloft per hour (48 aircraft-hours per day).

28   For an account of the big cruiser designs, see my *Postwar Naval Revolution* (Conway Maritime Press, London, 1986).

29   In 1958 plans called for the construction of three such ships, one each in 1964–65, 1965–66, and 1966–67. The shift to conventional carriers actually increased the requisite numbers, as the minimum number of operational ships was set at three. Given a reasonable refit schedule, this equated to a total of five British carriers. By coincidence, the 1957 White Paper had approved the existing total of five modern carriers, so by 1958–60 the Board was thinking in terms of one-for-one replacement.

30   Fighters could be traded off against long-range missile ships. For example, in about 1960 thirty-two sophisticated fighters equated to twelve 'Class II' fighters and two or three long-range missile shooters.

Table 16-4: Some Carrier Alternatives, 1960

Displacement (tons)	42,000	48,000	48,000	50,000	55,000	68,000
VA+AEW	18	23	24	25	32	36[1]
Aircraft (Buccaneer or equivalent)	31	41	43	44	34	59[1]
Cost including missiles (£m)	44	54	54	55	59	67
Flight deck length (ft)	770	820	820	860	870	1004
Flight deck width (ft)	165	165	200	165	200	190
LWL (ft)	720	764	764	800	810	964
Beam (ft)	112	116			118/120	128
Height (ft)	76.5	83.5	76.5	83.5	83.5	92
Draught (FL) (ft)	31.6	32.7	32.7	32.5	34.6	33.5
SHP/3	135,000	150,000				160,000
Speed, (knots) clean	29.8	30				
dirty	28.6	29	29	28		
Endurance at 20 knots (nm)	6000					
Aircraft (64ft × 30ft)						
FD/HD	8/10	8/15	13/11	8/17	14/18	13/23 - 4AS[3]
NA39	13/18	15/26	23/20	15/29	23/30	22/37 - 4AS[3]
Catapults (225ft length)	2				3	3
Wires/barriers	4/1					
Lifts	2					3
Avfuel[2]	400	550			750	470
Armament	Seacat	3 Tartar	3 Tartar	3/4 Tartar	4 Tartar	4 Tartar

1 Plus 4 ASW helicopters.
2 Fuel in thousands of gallons.
3 4 A/S helicopters are roughly equivalent to 3 strike/VF aircraft.

31 Type 988 died when CVA.01 was cancelled, but a reduced version appeared aboard the Dutch missile destroyer *Tromp*.

Assuming each aircraft flew for 4 hours on average, twelve were needed (eighteen allowing for availability). It was assumed that thirty daily long-range strikes would be required (by ten ready aircraft, fifteen allowing for availability), plus counter-air strikes on enemy airfields (sixty sorties per day, by twenty ready aircraft, thirty taking availability into account). Another twelve aircraft would be required for reconnaissance and landing support. This made a total of fifty-seven long-range and eighteen short-range attack aircraft, a figure cut to sixty-four, because most of the long-range strikes would be made before the troops actually landed. Including fighters, the tactical unit required ninety-six aircraft.

In wartime, carriers would operate in pairs. In theory, then, the appropriate carrier size would be determined by the total number of aircraft (ninety-six) that each such tactical unit had to operate, which equated to forty-eight per carrier, exclusive of AEW and plane-guard helicopters. In four days of intense operations, forty-eight aircraft could be expected to burn 2500 tons of fuel, far beyond the capacity of the 1952 carrier.

Fleet speed was defined as 25 knots (research showed that ships rarely made higher speeds in practice), although, as in earlier designs, higher speeds were attractive for catapult operation. Endurance was reduced from the 6000nm of earlier studies to match the reduced figure (5000nm at 20 knots) of the new amphibious assault ship. As in the 1954 design study, a three-shaft powerplant was considered acceptable.

Aside from aircraft, the main features of the new carrier would be a new fixed-array frequency-scanning radar, Type 985, and an improved short-range defensive missile (two, and preferably four, launchers). In the course of design, Type 985 was superseded by an Anglo-Dutch rotating/electronic scanning radar, Type 988 (Broomstick).[31]

Typical carrier characteristics are listed in Table 16-4; even at 68,000 tons (fully loaded) none could accommodate forty-eight large fighter/attack aircraft. Below 50,000 tons there was insufficient weight or space for two of the powerful catapults now specified.

This may seem worse than it was, since the base aircraft (as defined above) was quite large. However, given its very limited size, the Royal Navy had to plan on buying only a single type

Table 16-5: Some Carrier Alternatives, 1962

Displacement	50,000	52,000	53,000	55,000	58,000
Length (ft)	890	900	920	940	970
BWL (ft)	118	119/122	120/122	120/122	120
Flight deck width (ft)	177	177	180	180	190
Deck angle (degrees)	4	6.5	7	7.5	8
Deep draught (ft)	32				
SHP/shafts	135,000/3	135,000/3	135,000/3	160,000/4	180,000/4
Electric power	18,000 KW				
Speed, deep/dirty (knots)	28	28	28	28/29	29
Endurance deep/dirty (nm)	6000 at 20 knots				
Aircraft weight (lbs)	60,000	70,000	70,000	70,000	70,000
Lifts	2 65ft × 32ft	2 70ft × 32ft			
STOL/VTOL	4 positions				
Strike/VF	30	32	30	30	40
AEW	4	4	3	3	4
SAR	2				
HS	—	—	5	5	—
Interim Aircraft					
Buccaneer	18				24
Sea Vixen	18				24
Catapults	1 250ft	1 250ft	2 250ft		
	1 200ft	1 225ft	—	—	—
Armament	1 Sea Dart, 1 Ikara				
Radar	2 3-D				
Cost (£m)	50-60			58-63	60-65

of combat aircraft in order to ensure an economical production run. Thus the Navy could not afford to plan for a spectrum of aircraft, some large and some small, unless it bought in the United States (to capitalize on much longer production runs) and accepted American design requirements. Although that actually occurred in the case of the F-4 Phantom, it seems unlikely that British planners very willingly accepted such a fate. Thus, at least in 1960, British naval air planners really did have to design exclusively (apart from AEW and ASW) around the most capable fighter/attack aircraft.

Even so, the 68,000-ton carrier cannot have been very attractive. The government of the day was being offered a carrier to replace the 35,000-ton *Victorious*. It was aware that HMS *Eagle* displaced about 50,000 tons. Another 36 per cent would have been too much. When design work began in earnest in 1961, the upper limit seems to have been the figure first bruited in 1952, 55,000 tons, although it is understood that ships as large as 58,000 were initially considered, in May 1962 (see Table 16-5).

In all these estimates, the hangar was the largest consistent with overall dimensions, to accommodate two thirds of the aircraft, based on experience: as many as two thirds of a carrier's aircraft might require maintenance at any one time, although of course the usual figures were much better. The normal British carrier operating cycle placed one third in the air, one third on deck being serviced or being brought to readiness, and one third in the hangar. A maximum-effort launch would consist of all serviceable aircraft (that is, of two-thirds of the total). This shaped deck requirements, since the ship had to be able to recover the entire strike in quick succession. As in 1952, the deck arrangement also had to be suited to launch and recover aircraft at the same time.

This differed substantially from contemporary US practice, which emphasised the use of a large permanent deck park. The British view was that US carrier operating procedures were practical only because large US ships had four catapults and four lifts, and that, even so, a US carrier took a very long time to turn around a deckload strike.

There was also hope that a new design would allow for a more efficient flight deck. Existing practice was to park the aircraft on the starboard side forward, then tow it aft by tractor. In the new design, ideally, aircraft would be able to turn off immediately into the parking area, so that others could land-on much more quickly, for better turn-around.

Of the range of studies, the 50,000-ton carrier did not meet requirements. The 52,000-ton ship could cope, but it presented no growth margin. The 58,000-ton ship was too expensive. The most important difference between the remaining two ships, the 53,000- and 55,000-ton ships, was three versus four-shaft propulsion. A three-shaft plant would employ three athwartship main machinery spaces separated by two auxiliary spaces, with total citadel length depending on the magazines above. A four-shaft plant would consist of two paired plants with two auxiliary spaces between them, and it would actually be more vulnerable because a hit on either pair would knock it out. Moreover, the extra machinery would consume the space bought with another 2000 tons. The 53,000-ton carrier was the best that could be done with the best (three-shaft) power-plant; it was the best bargain.

As might have been expected, none of these alternatives seemed terribly attractive, and the advantages over the ageing *Eagle* were subtle, albeit quite real. The new carrier would be able to operate about 25 per cent more aircraft (and much larger and heavier ones), and it would be able to launch and use lifts at the same time as aircraft landed-on. Less obviously, it would have much better underwater protection and much more elect-

ric power. Moreover, at 50,000 tons *Eagle* had already grown through the margins originally designed into her. She had lost too much freeboard and too much reserve buoyancy.

With all this taken into account, the docking situation had not really changed since 1952. Birkenhead and Greenock (due for completion at the end of 1964) joined Southampton as docks suitable for a 50,000-ton ship (the Gladstone dock was out of contention), and only Southampton and Greenock were large enough for the others. However, the big carrier could not have docked at Portsmouth, and the dock at Devonport would limit beam to 118ft, which was inadequate. As before, commercial docks were available, but they would not be satisfactory as carrier refits would have to be geared to their schedules (and might take as much as 50 per cent longer).

The Civil Lord of the Admiralty doubted that any government would cheerfully buy a 53,000-ton carrier, and suggested a 40,000-ton carrier (twenty-four aircraft, about £43 million), which might prove particularly effective using the coming generation of VSTOL aircraft. However, the future of VSTOLs was far from certain, and the small carrier would not be flexibile enough to be worthwhile. The Board therefore chose the 53,000-ton ship, that is, the same size ship it had failed to get in 1952–53. It could carry almost twice as many aircraft at about a quarter more cost.

This time, unlike 1952 (and, for that matter, 1944–45), there was no real length limit, only a limit on beam. Thus the 53,000-ton carrier was 920ft long overall. Functioning as a carrier force flagship, it would carry thirty strike fighters, three AEW aircraft, two search and rescue helicopters and five ASW helicopters. It would be armed with the new medium-range surface-to-air missile (with all-round fire and at least forty reloads), which became the Sea Dart, and also with the Ikara ASW stand-off missile (with twenty-four reloads).[32] Other electronic equipment would include two big three-dimensional radars, both for all-around coverage and to ensure that one would always be available.[33]

Aircraft requirements included a clear hangar height of 18ft (but with three higher bays for wing unfolding), 600,000 gallons of avcat aircraft fuel, and at least one 40,000lb deck-edge lift. The deck arrangement would have been conventional, with one catapult in the bow and one in the waist (on the angled deck), one lift on the centreline forward feeding the forward catapult, and another to starboard abaft the island, to take which had landed and turned into the parking area.[34] This left the quarters free for two defensive missile launchers, with boats and a crane to starboard to balance the weight of the big port overhang.

As in 1952, protection was limited to $1\frac{1}{2}$in splinter steel, some magazine armour (typically 3in side and roof, and $1\frac{1}{2}$in ends), and the usual deep underwater protective system.

Again, as in 1952, it was soon obvious that 53,000 tons was still very limited, and that it would take enormous ingenuity to squeeze a useful carrier into that displacement. The design was re-thought, a process (popular at that time in both the British and US navies) called Work-Study.[35]

The 1960 deck arrangement idea was revived. The key perception seems to have been that the useful area of the flight deck could be greatly increased by making the landing strip almost parallel to the centreline of the ship (in this case, by reducing its angle from 8 to about 2.5 degrees). This made for a much heavier, wider, overhang to port, but it could be balanced by moving the island in from the starboard edge of the deck, leaving a wide strip (soon nicknamed the 'Alaskan Highway') – which could be used to move aircraft – to starboard, out over the side of the ship. The landing zone also had to be moved forward about 50ft to reduce overhang on the port quarter.

32 The US Navy was also considering arming its carriers with ASW stand-off missiles. Although the British reasoning has not been published, it was probably analogous. The rationale was that formations had to spread out so that a single large nuclear weapon could not destroy most of the ships. Since existing sonars had only limited ranges (usually 10,000 yards nominally, and actually less), there was every chance that a submarine would penetrate the screen to approach the carrier. The latter needed some means of firing at the submarine while fleeing.

33 At this time Type 984 required 1 to 2 hours of maintenance per day during a four-to six-day operational period, and there was little expectation that a new radar would be much better. This was why HMS *Eagle* was fitted with a secondary air search radar (Type 965) during her big modernization. Type 965 was rejected this time because it was only two-dimensional in function, far from gapless in coverage, and insufficiently resistant to jamming. On the other hand, it could be argued that accompanying air defence escorts would carry their own three-dimensional radars, so that the fleet as a whole would suffer very little from a radar failure aboard the carrier. This argument finally killed the second three-dimensional radar. Type 992P was considered the ideal secondary air search radar because of its narrow beam, which also suited it for a role in carrier blind landing.

34 The location abaft the island was better in rough weather. The British apparently considered the usual US arrangement, in which deck-edge lifts were placed forward of the island, adjacent to the parking area, too wet.

35 The *Knox* (DE 1052) class was the best-known contemporary US example. Work-study was an attempt to re-think each element of the design in terms of the way it interacted with the others, so that to the greatest possible extent each element could combine several functions.

Not all CVA.01 *technology died with her. A new scissors lift had been planned; it allowed open space on three sides. A smaller scissors lift has been installed in the three* Invincible.

The net effect was to increase flight deck area by 15 per cent, sufficient for two more aircraft clear of both the landing area and the forward catapult.

All this was beside a major aircraft-operating benefit; as DNC and NPL had realized in 1952, pilots found it relatively difficult to make that last turn to the left as they approached the ship. The smaller the turn, the easier it would become, and the better the landing pattern as a whole. The parallel deck was the closest DNC could come to the starboard-skewed ideas of 1952–53, as long as the island stayed on the starboard side of the carrier.

It was argued, too, that when landing in low visibility or through a low ceiling, a pilot's first view of the flight deck comes very late. His first real indication of its direction is the ship's wake, which shows the axis of the ship, not the flight deck axis. The pilot of a fast jet might have very little time to line up. The deck could not be made completely parallel, however, it was 3 degrees from parallel to provide clearance between aircraft parked near the bow and aircraft aborting their landings or bolting.

There was no longer much space to port abaft the landing strip, so a single missile launcher was placed in an open area on the quarter-deck. This same open area could also be used to run up jet engines for testing.

The design incorporated many other ingenious ideas, such as lifts on scissors legs (to save hangar space), direct-acting (water-jet) arrester gear (also for greater efficiency in space terms), and a new type of skegged rudder. All entailed considerable technical risk (for example, in estimates of size and weight), so that as the design progressed, the design term became more and more nervous.

There was also the usual pressure for growth. For example, early proposals called for an intensive-flying endurance of three to four days; a suggestion that it should be increased to four to five days could be equated with 30 per cent more aircraft support stores, plus enough fuel to increase steaming endurance by a fifth. Required bomb loads also increased, with commensurate costs in internal volume.

By mid-1963 the ship had grown longer (890 rather than 870ft on the waterline, 925ft rather than 920 on the flight deck), to add some valuable flight deck space. The air group was the same, except for four rather than three AEW, and the hangar dimensions were 660 × 80 × 18ft. The air group was ultimately to be thirty OR 346 fighter/attackers. In the interim, the ship would support eighteen Buccaneers and eighteen Sea Vixens, plus four AEW and helicopters. Within two years the interim air group had changed to twenty-four Buccaneers and twelve Phantoms. There were other minor changes, but the only major one was the elimination of the ASW stand-off weapon, Ikara. Here the theory was that escorts probably would be effective, and that the carrier's own helicopters constituted sufficient back-up.

Table 16-6 describes the design in its ultimate form.

The Ministry of Defence announced formally on 30 July 1963 that one carrier, CVA.01, would be built, and in June 1964 it was stated officially that bids would probably be

Table 16-6: CVA.01

LOA (ft)	963 (including booms)
Flight deck length (ft)	928
LWL (ft)	890
Beam, extreme (ft)	231 4
BWL (ft)	122
Draught (ft)	31 fwd, 33 4 aft
SHP	135,000
Speed (knots)	30 (28.3 sustained)
Armament	1 Sea Dart (38 missiles)
Aircraft	
Attack/CAP	36 Buccaneer/F4
AEW	4 Gannet
SAR	2 Whirlwind
ASW	5 Wessex
Aviation fuel	600,000 gallons (2210 tons) avcat
Weights (tons)	
General equipment	3605
Aircraft equipment	5425
Machinery	3650
Armament	1050
Hull	33,900
Fuel oil	6200
RFW	375
Margin	400
Deep displacement	54,650

requested in April 1966, with the ship to be completed in 1973. By this time the British shipbuilding industry had run down badly, so that this schedule was perhaps not entirely realistic. Some have suggested, indeed, that the carrier could not have been built as planned, and that the question was when the government of the day would cancel it. A new Labour Government, which entered power on 15 October 1964, initially supported the carrier programme. Following a Defence Review in 1965, however, the carrier was cancelled, in February 1966, and the government also announced the withdrawal from East of Suez.

The record of this review is not, of course, as yet available, but it seems likely that the government found that it had to cut one of very few major elements of the national defence programme, and that the RAF made a better case than the Navy.[36] The Conservative Government which succeeded the Labour administration was unable to reverse the cancellation, and had to satisfy itself with modernizing HMS *Ark Royal* to prolong her life. Britain just could not afford five 53,000-ton carriers.

This was not altogether surprising, and the prospect of a carrier-less navy had to be examined during the course of the CVA.01 design. At that time it was a threat to convince the Board and then the government to proceed with the appropriate naval programme, the big carrier. However, it is interesting to examine the consequences of a carrier-less navy, because the logic was still valid after 1966. The arguments were unavoidable, and they resulted in the current British VSTOL carrier force (see Chapter 17).

A carrier-less navy was not necessarily inexpensive. The carrier provided three vital functions: long-range attack, long-range air defence and airborne early warning. In cold war situations, moreover, it might be much more important that a human pilot actually identified some unknown ship or aircraft than that a warhead destroyed it. The question was to what extent something other than a very expensive carrier could provide at least a modicum of the requisite capability.

In 1962–65 the main threats to surface forces were long-

range (approximately 200nm) Soviet missiles carried by bombers and by submarines and surface ships (such as the 'Kyndas' then entering service). Air surveillance range would probably soon reach 200nm, and it was reasonable to imagine that future defensive missiles would have to reach at least that far. Future anti-ship missiles would have to reach Soviet ships before they could fire, otherwise the fleet would have to deal with a much more difficult target, the Soviet missile itself. These ranges made for very large missiles; a fast 250nm surface-to-surface missile carrying a ship-killing warhead (2000lbs), for example, might be a 20,000lb ramjet 35ft long, with a 2ft 6in diameter.

By 1962 the Royal Navy had already shifted ASW from fixed-wing aircraft to helicopters (see Chapter 17). It was also apparent, at least on a theoretical level, that helicopters could lift AEW radars without large flight decks to support them.[37] Long-range missiles (which did not yet exist in British service) could, in theory, destroy surface targets (particularly ships) and provide long-range air cover. This left only the vital identification role, which did require manned aircraft.

All this did not mean that a non-carrier navy *of the same capability* would be less expensve than the projected new-carrier fleet. For example, long-range missile fire requires enormous investments in surveillance and targeting, as the Soviet Navy has shown. Pound for pound of warhead, long-range missiles require a great deal more ships to support them than do naval aircraft. On the other hand, all the work done from 1952 on showed that the big carrier was essentially indivisible: 53,000 tons was very nearly a minimum, rather than a maximum. A very small ship could support a few anti-aircraft or anti-ship missiles, albeit at a high cost relative to its capability. As for the minimum aircraft capability, it would not have taken a very large ship to operate a very few VSTOL fighters, as long as most of the fleet's capability was in its missiles.

In 1963, this choice very much favoured the carrier. The arguments will not be declassified for some years, but most probably the key consideration was the strike mission, which required numerous attacks and a heavy weight of ordnance. A missile-oriented strike fleet, attacking shore targets, would be expensive to build and to operate, and its very long-range missiles would have to be developed at considerable cost. On the other hand, if the surface strikes mission was largely foregone, the most expensive element of the package, the big surface-to-surface missile with its surveillance, could be abandoned.

It seems likely that, presented with essentially this choice in and after 1966, the Labour Government first tried to obtain power projection more cheaply (via RAF F-111s) and then found that power projection (that is, surface strike by carrier aircraft) was virtually synonymous with the limited role 'East of Suez.' Forced to economize, the government reluctantly abandoned what it saw as an expensive capability. This left ASW, a helicopter function, and the air defence of the ASW ships – which could be done by modern anti-aircraft missiles.

To the extent that aircraft were needed at all, a typical missile-oriented fleet could be built around a VSTOL carrier. Ideally it would retain a catapult, so that aircraft could be launched with useful payloads, but arrester gear could be abandoned. More importantly, there would be no need for high-intensity operations. A typical air group might be no more than four big VSTOLs (P.1154), two AEW helicopters, and two search and rescue craft, all of which could be accommodated on about 15,000 tons with one catapult. This is not far from what has in fact been achieved in the *Invincible* class, the main difference being more aircraft and a ski-jump instead of a catapult. In addition, however, the supersonic VSTOL envisaged in the mid-1960s had of couse not yet materialized.

36 The carrier was of course intimately connected with the Commonwealth Defence mission. The RAF claimed that it could achieve much the same results by shuttling aircraft (F-111s) between British-owned island bases; it is often reported that in support of this position the RAF published a map in which the island of Gan had been moved several hundred miles.

37 The US Navy experimented with a helicopter-lifted APS-20, and more recently the Royal Navy has actually brought such helicopters (Sea Kings) into service. They cannot lift as much as an aeroplane, and they cannot generally fly as high (to achieve very long range), but they make it obvious that a limited form of AEW could be provided without a large flight deck.

17

Vertical Take-off

IN THE COURSE OF THE 1950s and the early 1960s, it became painfully clear that conventional aircraft were outgrowing the natural limits of British carrier design. The Gannet was the first case in point: adequate ASW sensors and weapons required an aircraft too large for any trade-protection carrier which could be obtained in substantial numbers. The attempts to design both the 1952 carrier and CVA.01 showed that, within limits set by British ports and British budgets, compromise was difficult at best, and likely to be unsatisfactory. The cancellation of the British carrier force in February 1966 forced the Royal Navy to re-examine its need for sea-based aviation. Although the result, the small VSTOL carrier, cannot be altogether satisfactory, it does demonstrate that there is a mid-point between the super-carrier and the complete abandonment of mobile naval fighter or bomber aircraft. Several navies are now following approximately the same path.

Vertical take-off is an old naval dream; the Royal Navy experimented with ASW helicopters during and after World War II, partly in hopes of dispensing with such half-carriers as the MAC ships (see Chapter 9). These experiments succeeded to the point where, in about 1953, the decision was made to abandon fixed-wing ASW aircraft in favour of heavy ASW helicopters, with the transition to occur in about 1958. Although the actual transition was not completed for about a decade this decision killed the Seamew and the ASW Gannet, and greatly simplified thinking about future emergency ASW carrier conversion. Although no such carriers were ever converted, during the Falklands War the Royal Navy convincingly demonstrated the simplicity of conversion to an austere helicopter ship.

Once reliable helicopters had been developed, it was natural to consider using them to land troops. This idea originated in the US Marine Corps, but it was first demonstrated in combat by the Royal Navy at Suez in 1956, and specialized helicopter carriers were fixtures of the later British fleet.

During the 1950s, the promise of jet lift was that smaller and less expensive carriers could be built. Although it seems unlikely that the missile ship/carrier of 1956–57 was a VTOL or VSTOL ship, some of the long-term plans proposed in 1954, in the midst of the defence review, envisaged such ships as a less expensive alternative to fleet carriers.

THE HELICOPTERS CAME FIRST. They made a new kind of amphibious assault, vertical envelopment, possible. In the early 1950s the US Marine Corps saw the helicopter as a means of concentrating troops on the beach without concentrating the ships launching them, and thus without forming an attractive nuclear target. The British were well aware of the US experiments, and in April 1955, Major General C F Phillips, the Chief of Amphibious Warfare, formally asked the Admiralty to issue Staff Requirements for two classes of troop-carrying helicopters: a big one to lift a platoon (thirty-three men or 7000lbs) and a raiding helicopter to lift an infantry section (eight to ten men, 3000lbs). Phillips thought that existing LSTs could be converted into helicopter carriers, but they were old (due for disposal within five or six years) and slow (11 knots at best).

Existing carriers had often been used as troopships, and helicopters could easily be adapted to carry those troops ashore. The result, the commando carrier, was well adapted to the new concept of power projection, particularly East of Suez. In July 1956 the Board approved work on a commando carrier conversion of a light fleet carrier.

That autumn, the concept was tested at Suez. Before leaving, two light fleet carriers tested the mass helicopter assault concept, with ten helicopters (eight Whirlwind HAS 22s and two Whirlwind HAR 3s) of 845 Squadron operating from HMS *Ocean* and twelve helicopters (six Whirlwind HAR 2s and six Sycamore Mk 14s) of the Joint Experimental Helicopter Unit (Army/RAF) operating from HMS *Theseus*.[1] The operational requirement was to land a 450-man Commando on an objective 15nm away. Troops were landed in waves, each carrying the maximum load commensurate with minimum time between waves. The exercise (29 September to 12 October 1956) was also intended to study the problem of operating twenty-two helicopters from two carriers in company.

Conversion was very quick; it was authorized only on 25 September, and the ships had to retain their trooping capability. It was completed at midnight on 29 September. All deck gear and the Bofors gun forward of the island had to be removed.

The exercise was successful, and the two carriers made, espectively, 402 and 607 trouble-free deck landings. The helicopters proved reliable, and it seemed possible that all twenty-two could have operated from one carrier. At most, ten Whirlwinds could have been spotted on deck, but then only if their

1 ADM 1/26450.

bodies were angled 20 degrees to the centreline.

Both carriers then went to Suez, to execute the first combat helicopter assaults. These attacks were so successful that two permanent conversions were planned, to support the new East of Suez strategy. In theory, in future the Royal Navy would maintain an Eastern Fleet including a strike carrier accompanied by a commando (helicopter) carrier, two helicopter ships being required to ensure that one would always be available. The two unmodernized early *Hermes* class carriers, newly surplus, were the obvious choices: *Bulwark* (converted at Portsmouth from January 1959 to January 1960) and *Albion* (Portsmouth, February 1961 to July 1962). Most of *Bulwark*'s guns were removed, and four landing craft (LCA or LCVP) were carried on davits on either side abaft the island, to transport heavy equipment to the beach.[2] Each carrier could accommodate an entire Royal Marine Commando (733 men) and sixteen Whirlwind (later replaced by Wessex) troop-carriers. *Albion* was similar, but she was more extensively modified. She was equipped with Wessexes from the beginning, and troop capacity was somewhat larger, 900 men. *Bulwark* was refitted to match *Albion* in 1963.

HMS *Centaur* was not converted, but in January 1964, when no commando carrier was available to deal with a mutiny in Tanganyika, she embarked 45 Commando from Aden and landed them using her Wessex ASW helicopters. It was announced in February 1971 that she would be discarded. She had been laid up in 1966 and plans for helicopter conversion

The Westland Dragonfly, a licence-built Sikorsky S-51, was the first operational British naval helicopter. It was particularly valuable as a 'plane guard' aboard carriers, supplanting the destroyers previously used in that role. This one is shown aboard HMS Centaur *in 1974*

had reportedly been abandoned. This coincided with the announcement of the Labour Defence Review (February 1966) which killed both the new CVA.01 and which soon drastically reduced the East of Suez commitment which the commando carriers supported.[3] Although the withdrawal from East of Suez was not specifically mandated by the Defence Review, it proved to be the only practical way to achieve the large savings required at the time. The alternative, to spread the cuts between Europe and the East, was politically untenable. In effect the study of the abandonment of East of Suez was a second Defence Review superimposed on the first. This was not, however, the end of the commando carriers, because the change in British policy coincided with increased NATO attention to conventional forces. Commando carriers clearly had a potential role in the reinforcement of Norway in the event of a European war.

2 The contemporary US LPH carried no landing craft, and as a result it could not land heavy equipment. It was also unable to land troops in bad weather. Specifically to overcome these deficiencies, the last LPH, *Inchon*, was equipped with two landing craft, and the next-generation amphibious carrier, the LHA, had a well-deck to accommodate large landing craft carrying heavy vehicles.

3 The official statement, published on 22 February 1966, was that 'Britain will not undertake major operations of war except in co-operation with allies ... we will not accept an obligation to provide another country with military assistance unless it is prepared to provide us with the facilities we need to make such assistance effective in time. Finally there will be no attempt to maintain defence facilities in an independent country against its wishes.' That is, first, in major war Britain would assume US naval air cover. The other two points meant that carriers, the primary means of projecting independent British power, would no longer be needed.

4   In 1973, *Albion* was next in line for a refit. This was presumably part of defence economies mandated by British economic problems perceived in 1972. Cuts were also necessary to pay for the new carrier *Invincible*, which was ordered on 17 April 1973. On 22 October 1973 *Albion* was sold for conversion into a heavy-lift (2600-ton) crane ship to support the North Sea oilfields, but the project was abandoned and she was broken up instead. The specialized commando carriers were finally killed as part of the 1974-75 defence review arising out of the 1973 fiscal crisis, and the government announced that Britain would withdraw from all areas other than the Eastern Atlantic. As a result, HMS *Bulwark* was laid up early in 1976 and her helicopter squadron was disbanded. It was decided in 1977, however, that the associated 41 Commando, which was to have been disbanded, would be retained. Note, too, that *Bulwark* was not discarded at this time.

HMS *Bulwark* demonstrated this capability, for the first time, in June and July 1968.

The fourth ship of the class, HMS *Hermes*, was converted (at Portsmouth from 1 March 1971 to 14 August 1973). She replaced HMS *Albion*, which was discarded when she was completed.[4] As in the case of the other ships, she could carry a full Commando (733 men), although there was sufficient space for a second Commando in emergency. In addition to her sixteen troop-carriers, she carried four Sea King ASW helicopters and four LCVPs in davits.

NATO protested the loss of capability associated with the demise of the British carrier force, and by 1974 plans were afoot to convert HMS *Hermes* to an ASW role specifically to support NATO forces in the North Atlantic.[5] She retained a residual commando capability. But this time HMS *Invincible* (at

Westland Whirlwind helicopters are shown aboard HMS Bulwark in 1957. The ship had not yet been converted into a commando carrier: note the angled deck markings, the mirror sight and the arrester wires. This was no bar to helicopter operations, however. Similar helicopters had performed the first vertical assault, at Suez, the previous November.

the time designated CAH) had been ordered, and *Hermes* was considered an interim CAH (she was refitted from 1976 to January 1977). This capability was inherent in the commando carrier concept. All she lacked, compared to the old trade-protection carriers, was an anti-shadower fighter.

By this time the Royal Navy already planned to purchase Sea Harrier fighters to equip its new VSTOL carriers (see below).[6] In 1977-78 *Hermes* carried out trials with RAF Harriers and then with Sea Harriers. Between May 1980 and 9 May 1981 she was refitted to operate Sea Harriers, being fitted with a 230-ton, 12½-degree ski-jump (similar to ski-jumps already being fitted to the *Invincibles*). Other improvements included a Ferranti 1600E computer for tactical data handling

5   Grove reports that her planned roles were barrier patrol in the GIUK Gap and direct ASW support for the NATO Strike Fleet, built around US attack carriers. This was a return to the strike fleet role with which the Royal Navy had justified its retention of a strike capability in the early 1950s. In 1975 the British government also earmarked RFA *Engadine*, the helicopter training ship, to the NATO Channel Command wartime ASW force.

6   *Hermes* was sold to India as INS *Viraat* in 1986.

Replacing fixed-wing ASW aircraft aboard conventional carriers, helicopters relieved severe crowding. Two Whirlwinds are shown aboard HMS Centaur at Aden in 1962. The ship had recently been refitted to operate Scimitars and Sea Vixens in place of her previous air complement of Sea Hawks and Sea Venoms. The radome visible above the right-hand helicopters housed her Type 963 blind-landing radar; the hayrake of Type 982 is visible above it. Note, too, the IFF antenna below the Type 960 long-range air search antenna forward, and the flying-control office visible on the inboard side of the island.

7 Unfortunately, the Board Memoranda and many other papers of this period have not yet been released, so this must be conjecture.

and a carrier-controlled approach system for the Harriers. She could accommodate five Sea Harriers and twelve (later eighteen) Sea Kings. She carried many more aircraft in the Falklands, however; on 21 May 1982 she had aboard fifteen Sea Harriers and six Harrier GR.3s (RAF), as well as six Sea Kings, two Lynxes, and one Wessex helicopter.

Bulwark was retired and placed on the disposal list in 1976, but she was retained, and she was refitted in 1977–79, her ASW capability being improved, to fill the gap between the retirement of HMS *Ark Royal* and the commissioning of the new VSTOL carrier HMS *Invincible*. She was commissioned between February 1979 and 27 March 1981, while HMS *Hermes* was fitted with her ski-jump.

IN ASW, ONE GREAT PROMISE of the helicopter was that the limited space aboard a fixed-wing carrier could be devoted entirely to those aircraft which most needed high performance, the fighters and strikers. This idea seems to date from about 1956, and it probably accounts for the decision to place large ASW helicopters aboard the big County class fleet guided missile escorts.[7]

The logical extension was to concentrate the fleet ASW helicopters aboard a dedicated carrier. Existing helicopters were not particularly reliable, and they could not be sufficiently maintained aboard a small cruiser or destroyer. Moreover, they could most efficiently be operated from a single command ship, not itself engaged in the ASW battle.

Late in 1958, then, a draft Staff Requirement was written for a ship capable of accompanying a carrier, and of accommodating eighteen Wessex ASW helicopters. The most flexible layout was a small carrier of about 19,000 tons, although studies of smaller, more destroyer-like ships were also made. The helicopter carrier seemed very expensive, and until 1959 a smaller and more destroyer-like design (430ft long, 5400 tons, eight Wessex helicopters) was developed. These ships were all armed with self-defence missiles.[8]

As the ship grew, she was justified primarily on the grounds that she would free the carriers for more fixed-wing aircraft and that she would be an efficient ASW commando centre. As a secondary role, she could operate as a commando carrier. The design also grew as future plans envisaged replacement of the existing Wessex by the larger Sea King helicopter.

Once the design reached about 7000 tons (deep load), it was clearly more than an expendable super-frigate or destroyer. It was worth protecting, both with an area defence anti-aircraft missile (Seaslug in place of the point-defence Tartar of the earlier studies) and with some splinter protection. This was very nearly cruiser size. Since it was unlikely that the Royal Navy would build both cruisers and helicopter ships, one hull would have to perform both roles. Within the fleet, the cruiser was a major anti-aircraft ship and command ship; it therefore required masting for substantial communications nets.

During 1960 British doctrine for hunting nuclear submarines developed towards a requirement that helicopters should hunt in groups of three. This required positions for three ready helicopters (with rotors unfolded) and for further folded ones on deck, and for a helicopter complement of at least nine (to support three in the air). Meanwhile, the first genuine VSTOL aircraft, the Hawker P.1127, neared completion. The Royal Navy had sought VSTOLs, with which it could distribute its naval aircraft much more widely, for a long time. They could make good use of the large, clear flight deck of the new helicopter cruiser.

By late 1961, a 13,550-ton, 650ft escort cruiser, armed with the Seaslugs and with a twin 4.5in gun, and carrying nine Sea King helicopters, had been sketched. It was fast enough (28

8 The US Navy showed some interest in a roughly comparable Patrol Escort (PE), a large frigate carrying six ASW helicopters, at about this time. The PE was intended primarily to prosecute Soviet missile submarines in their peacetime holding areas in mid-Atlantic (this cold war mission was intended to convince the Soviet Union that it could not rely on the submarines for an early surprise attack against the United States).

The Sea Harrier, shown here over HMS Invincible *in 1980, made it possible for the Royal Navy to retain a measure of sea-based air power. However, this power is quite limited, both because the performance of the aircraft is limited and because the relatively small modern British carriers cannot accommodate very many. Reportedly only fifty-seven Sea Harriers have been built (or ordered) for the Royal Navy, and the projected FRS.2 update, including long-range air-to-air missiles and a new radar, seems to have encountered serious difficulties.*

knots) to accompany a carrier.

There was some expectation that such a ship would be included in the 1962–63 Naval Estimates, but this did not occur; perhaps the Board preferred not to propose an expensive small carrier-like ship while it sought funds for the full-sized CVA-01. However, the basic idea that it was worthwhile to concentrate ASW helicopters off the carrier was still valid. The cruisers *Blake* and *Tiger* were rebuilt, with helicopter decks and hangars aft, accommodating four Sea King ASW helicopters each.

Then CVA.01 was cancelled. In April 1966 a Future Fleet Working Party was set up under the ACNS (Policy), Rear Admiral J H Adams, to plan the future carrier-less fleet.[9] Britain still maintained her presence East of Suez, and she still had to contribute to NATO. Thus the commando carrier role and the ASW helicopter role were still important. Effective helicopter operations still required some form of centralized command and control, and the anti-shadower (or Cold War probe) and airborne early warning missions could not be delegated away, either to land-based aircraft or to missiles. On the other hand, shipboard missiles could provide much of the anti-ship and anti-aircraft firepower of an integrated force, albeit without the sort of sustained power projection commonly provided by naval aircraft.

The First Sea Lord rejected this concept; carriers, large or small, could not be resurrected. However, the logic of the Working Party survived its demise, and the idea of a helicopter-carrying command ship soon resurfaced. According to the 1967 Supplementary Statement on Defence Policy, the Type

9 This account is based on E J Grove, *Vanguard to Trident*. Adams had been ACNS, but the post was now split into ACNS(P) and ACNS (Operations) in July 1966. ACNS(P), which was created specifically for this task, controlled the naval plans and administrative planning divisions and the naval historical branch. ACNS(O) took over all the other ACNS responsibilities. The Working Party was given six months to complete its report.

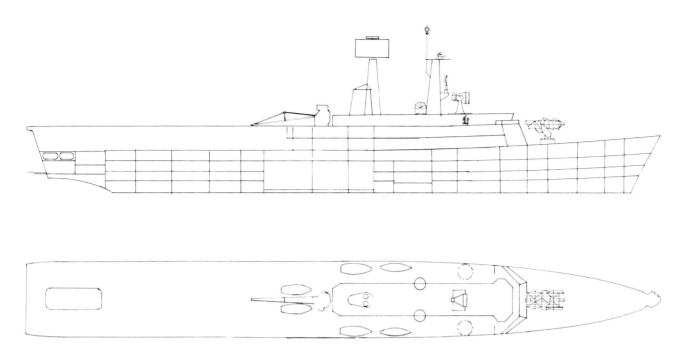

Sketch scheme for an escort cruiser, 1960, with a hull hangar for eight Wessex helicopters, Deep displacement would have been 5940 tons (460ft LWL, 489ft LOA × 57ft). A two-shaft, 36,000shp steam plant would have driven her at over 26 knots deeply loaded, but that was below fleet speed. Armament would have been all-missile: one Seaslug (twenty-four weapons) and two Seacats. The Type 184 sonar is not shown. The one lift was 45 × 16ft. This is one of many similar schemes, some showing the shorter-range Tartar as an alternative to Seaslug. NF

Below: *Sketch scheme for a thorough-deck escort cruiser, 1961, to accommodate nine Sea King helicopters (one is shown on deck). Deep displacement would have been 11,500 tons (570ft LWL, 603ft LOA × 72ft), and a two-shaft 45,000shp steam plant would have driven her at over 26 knots (deep and dirty). Note that the Seaslug (twenty-eight missiles) and two Seacats were supplemented by a twin 4.5in gun. The Type 184 sonar is not shown. The lift would have been 50 × 18ft. It seems unlikely that this scheme (or any of the several parallel designs) had any direct relationship with the later, much larger, and very different* Invincible. *What is striking is the way in which the requirement for ASW helicopters and the associated command and control facilities inevitably pushed designers towards a thorough-deck ship. NF*

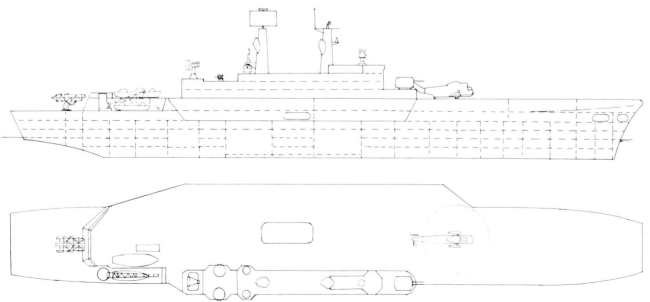

82 missile destroyer originally planned as a CVA.01 escort was evolving into two new classes, a command and control cruiser equipped with the Sea Dart anti-aircraft missiles and with the Sea King ASW helicopter, and a class of smaller destroyers. The latter became the Type 42 class; in effect they replaced the deck-launched interceptors of the old fleet carriers. By 1970 the command cruiser was described as capable of operating VSTOL aircraft as an option.

The new cruiser was described as the natural successor to the two *Tiger* class helicopter cruisers, contributing fleet command facilities, a large ASW helicopter force and elements of fleet air defence.[10] As in the case of the command cruiser of the early 1960s, the possibility of operating VSTOL fighters (see below) must have been an important consideration from very

10   This account is based largely on A F Honnor and D J Andrews, 'HMS *Invincible*: The First of a New Genus of Aircraft Carrying Ships,' a paper read before the RINA in 1981, and on E J Grove, op cit. According to Grove, a 6000-ton helicopter-missile escort cruiser was still under development in 1966, in parallel with CVA.01. Grove reports that the 12,500-ton conventional cruiser (flight deck aft) and a 17,500-ton through-deck cruiser were developed from 1966 on, the sketch Staff Requirement for these studies being issued early in 1967. The then First Sea Lord, Sir Varyl Begg,

favoured the 12,500-ton ship; he was supported by his VCNS, Sir Peter Hill-Norton. However, according to Grove, a change in naval leadership in August 1968 brought a new First Sea Lord, Sir Michael Le Fanu, who favoured the through-deck ship suited to VSTOL operations. Both options were developed under Naval Staff Target 7079, the conventional cruiser becoming Study 21 and the small carrier Study 22; it was enlarged to Study 23 (18,750 tons). Grove claims that the design was sized to carry ten helicopters so that four could be airborne at any one time.

HMS Albion, *commando carrier, on post-refit full power trials in 1964. Note the helicopter and vehicle parking spots marked out on her flight deck, and the elimination of Bofors guns around her island, leaving only four twin mounts around* her flight deck. Unlike Bulwark, *she had a Type 965 long-range air search radar at her masthead (replacing the earlier Type 960).*

early in the design process.

A sketch Staff Requirement issued in 1967 resulted in a 12,500-ton ship which could accommodate six Sea King helicopters in a conventional cruiser configuration. Six was considered the maximum which could be accommodated in an external (superstructure) hangar. Presumably the ASW logic of 1960 was still valid; the next step up was nine hangared Sea Kings with three more on deck. This required a hangar in the hull, two lifts, and a carrier-type flight deck (a 'through deck'). Displacement increased to 17,500 tons. Both of these designs had Sea Dart missile-launchers on the flight deck forward of the superstructure.

Finally the ship was enlarged again, to 19,500 tons, with an unobstructed runway from the stern nearly to the bow. It could stow nine Sea Kings and five Sea Harrier VSTOL fighters in its hangar. Although some Herrier capability seems to have been incorporated from the beginning of the design, the formal decision to incorporate Harriers was not made until May 1975.[11] This sketch design was formally approved in May 1970, and it was completed at the end of 1970; the first ship, HMS *Invincible*, was ordered in April 1973. She was the largest postwar warship ordered for the Royal Navy. There was some hope that five ships would be ordered, but in the end three were built.

Size was determined by several considerations. The hangar had to be large, partly because the Sea King helicopter is very high, and partly because the Sea Harrier, which is derived from the RAF Harrier, does not have folding wings and therefore cannot be closely packed.[12]

Flight deck length was determined by the requirement for six helicopter spots and for rolling take-off for the Harriers. Flight deck configuration was reminiscent of that adopted for CVA.01, with separate nearly parallel flying (angled at half a degree) and parking lanes. In this case, however, the flying lane was primarily for rolling take-offs, and landings were vertical. Even so, the flight deck was relatively narrow, cramped by an island set well in from the starboard side.[13]

The Sea Darts required a substantial clear area forward, alongside the take-off lane.

Gas turbine power imposed large requirements for voluminous uptakes and downtakes and machinery-removal trunks alongside the hangar. This squeezed the hangar into a dumb-bell shape, and the Harriers were too wide for two to pass side by side between the wide ends. As in previous British practice, the assumption was that ship operating capacity was set by hangar, not flight deck, capacity. It is not clear whether overall ship stability limits the possible deck load of aircraft.[14]

The major late design development was the ski-jump, a means of extending the payload of the Sea Harrier VSTOL fighter. The Sea Harrier gains by making a rolling take-off. The ski-jump forces it up into the air, so that its forward thrust imparts a vertical acceleration. In theory, a 5- or 6-degree ramp buys 1000lbs in payload, and a 12-degree ramp buys 2000lbs. Alternatively, the ramp, like the old catapult, reduces required deck run and thus allows more of the deck to be used for parking and concurrent VSTOL landing/helicopter operations. *Invincible* and *Illustrious* were completed with 7-degree ramps; *Ark Royal*, the third ship, has a 12.5 degree ramp, as does the converted HMS *Hermes* (now the Indian *Viraat*).[15] The two earlier ships are having 12.5-degree ramps fitted during their major overhauls.

HMS *Invincible* merges two lines of development: the ASW helicopter, which made trade protection much more practical, and vertical and short take-off and landing, which throughout the 1950s and 1960s promised to make carriers affordable once more. There is no question but that the *Invincible* costs much less than CVA.01, but on the other hand she has nothing remotely like the same capability. She provides a naval force with concentrated ASW in the form of her helicopters, and with anti-shadower/probe fighters (which can also deliver substantial air-to-surface weapons). Until 1982, however, the Royal Navy did not have any replacement for the carrier-based airborne early warning Gannets of its last large-deck ships. The Working Party knew that helicopters could lift simple AEW radars, but there was no money for so specialized a development. In theory, the Royal Navy would operate only in the Eastern Atlantic, within range of RAF early warning aircraft. The experience of the Falklands demonstrated that the fleet had to be able to go anywhere, on the strength of its own resources, and thus led to the development of British AEW helicopters.

14 *Invincible* deployed to the Falklands, carrying ten Sea Harriers and eleven Sea Kings, and up to twenty-two Sea Kings (no Sea Harriers) can be accommodated, sixteen of them in the hangar. In 1986–88 the Sea Harriers were increased to eight per carrier, and *Illustrious* added two Sea King AEW aircraft. In 1988 *Ark Royal* has an air complement of eight Sea Harriers, nine ASW Sea Kings, and three AEW Sea Kings. The increase in Sea Harrier complement was accompanied by proportionately increased air weapon stowage.

15 Ramp angles were tested ashore at RAE Bedford. The ski-jump concept has been attributed to Lieutenant Commander D R Taylor, a Royal Navy engineering officer, who proposed it in a Master's thesis ('The Operation of Fixed-Wing V/STOL Aircraft From Confined Spaces') written at the University of Southampton in 1973. Taylor first demonstrated his idea in 1972. The ramp imparted an upward component of velocity. Even though the Harrier was not yet at flying speed when it left the ramp, it had enough velocity to follow a partly-ballastic path until it acquired the extra 30 knots or so needed to gain flying lift. Thus the ramp, in effect, lengthened the flight deck and so increased the effective deck-roll of the Harrier. When the ski-jump appeared, some noticed that a somewhat similar inclined ramp had been used to help heavily-laden Barracudas launch from HMS *Furious* in 1944. The ski-jump was officially added to the design of HMS *Invincible* in September 1977, after a series of successful tests with a 6-degree ramp.

11   The Hawker P.1127 (the predecessor of the Harrier) was demonstrated aboard HMS *Ark Royal* in February 1963, after the Admiralty had been committed to the supersonic P.1154. In 1966, in the context of the carrier-less fleet, it was proposed that RAF Harriers should supplement the assault helicopters aboard the commando carriers, and that June a Kestrel (predecessor of the Harrier) operated aboard HMS *Bulwark*. Later an RAF Harrier operated from the same ship. There is some evidence that the Fleet Working Party thought a VSTOL carrier would be acceptable (from an inter-service point of view) because it would operate *RAF* VSTOL fighters. As early as 1969, the Under-secretary of State for the Navy, David Owen, mentioned the possibility that RAF Harriers might fly from both the commando carriers and the cruisers then under design. Admiral Le Fanu, the First Sea Lord who pushed through the full-deck design, reportedly kept a Harrier model on his desk, and kept open the possibility that the RAF might fly from the ships. It is not clear to what extent this was a ploy to avoid RAF opposition to their construction. Even so, the RAF reportedly viewed the through-deck cruiser with considerable suspicion, particularly as exercises showed that the RAF could not protect the fleet at sea even in British waters. Hawker proposed a 'maritime Harrier' (P.1184) in 1969. Naval Staff studies of a navalized Harrier began in about June 1970, and the formal Naval Staff Target was issued in August 1972. Design work reportedly began in 1971. A draft Naval Staff Target was promulgated in 1971, the roles being (i) interception, primarily of shadowers (that is, Cold War probe), at ranges up to 400nm; (ii) reconnaissance, with capability to search 20,000 square miles per hour at low altitude; and (iii) anti-ship and anti-shore attack at distances of up to 250nm. Roles (i) and (ii) required a dual-purpose air-to-air and air-to-surface radar (the Ferranti Blue Fox, derived from the Seaspray of the existing Lynx helicopter); the RAF Harrier had no radar at all. For role (i) the Sea Harrier was equipped with Sidewinder missiles as well as with the existing 30mm cannon, and for (iii) it has pylons to take anti-ship missiles (Martel, Harpoon, and now Sea Eagle). The cockpit has been redesigned (and the pilot's seat raised 11in), and some of the structure of the aircraft changed to non-corrosive materials. The net weight penalty of navalization is said to have been no more than 100lbs. Preliminary design work was completed in 1972, and production (of thirty-four Sea Harrier FRS.1s) was approved in May 1975. A total of fifty-seven Sea Harriers has been ordered for the Royal Navy to date, including aircraft to replace Falklands War losses. According to Grove, op cit, the Harrier purchase would have been announced in about October 1973, but had to be deferred due to the October 1973 economic crisis, the subsequent change of government, and the 1974–75 Defence Review coming out of that financial crisis. The prototype first flew on 9 January 1978. Sea Harriers have also been exported to India, but Spain bought US-built AV-8A and -8B Harriers (without radar) for her carriers. Most of these details are from F K Mason, *Harrier* (PSL, London, 1986). Note that sketches of *Invincible* published before May 1975 show four Exocet launchers alongside the Sea Dart launcher, blocking what became the ski-jump. The Sea Harriers provide a far superior anti-ship capability.

12   *Invincible*, which displaces only about two-thirds as much as *Centaur*, has almost as much internal hull volume (90,000 rather than 92,000 cubic metres). According to Honnor and Andrews, the volume is needed partly to provide current standards of accommodation, and partly for much-increased command and control capabilities. In addition, like other modern warships, *Invincible* is designed for maintenance by replacement rather than by upkeep, so large open routes for removal and replacement must be provided. They also point to the considerable space and weight demands imposed by the Sea Dart area-defence missile system.

13   There is an apocryphal story that the superstructure was deliberately made imposing in silhouette so that, to the politicians deciding her fate, the ship would look more like a cruiser than a carrier. Similarly, the Royal Navy carefully avoided calling her a carrier for some years, and when she was completed HMS *Invincible* was described as an anti-submarine cruiser. The two traditional carrier names, *Illustrious* and *Ark Royal*, were allocated only to the second and third ships.

Albion *as a commando carrier, with landing craft aft.*
FAAM

Below: *HMS* Albion *as a helicopter assault carrier, in about
1968.* Bulwark *lacked her large platforms, and had a
different electronic layout.*

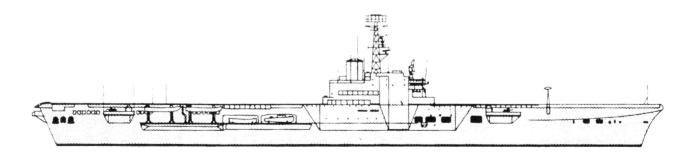

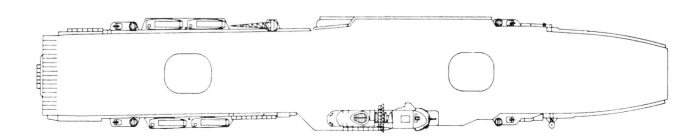

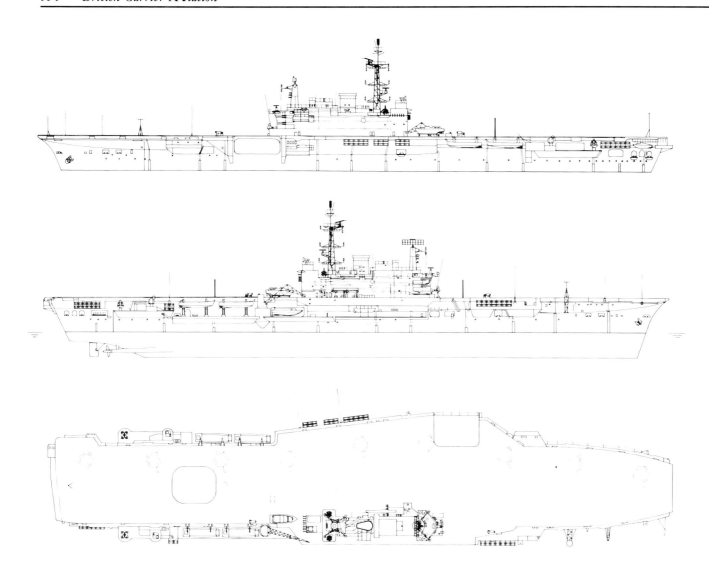

HMS Hermes *as a helicopter assault carrier in 1975, showing helicopter deck landing spots.*

Initially there were reports of plans for five ships, but that may have been no more than an echo of the earlier requirement for five CVA.01s, which in turn had been based on the discarded East of Suez strategy. Certainly in 1978 the Royal Navy had three carriers: *Ark Royal* about to leave service and two ASW carriers, *Hermes* and *Bulwark*. On a one-for-one basis, this force could be maintained by building the three *Invincibles*, although of course each had much less capability than the single *Ark Royal*.

Even this force was expensive, and the new Thatcher government, elected in the spring of 1979, ordered a Defence Review. Early cuts included decommissioning HMS *Bulwark* six months earlier than had been scheduled. The Secretary of State for Defence, John Nott, conducted the review in 1981. On the basis that the only legitimate wartime tactical naval mission was ASW in the Eastern Atlantic, Nott argued that this could best be accomplished by a combination of shore-based maritime patrol aircraft and nuclear submarines. Convoy operations were unlikely to be effective. It followed that the expensive combination of ASW carriers and surface escorts, which could best be used for the local defence of a small area of sea, was no longer worthwhile. Nott was willing to maintain surface escorts, but he was particularly anxious to save money by retiring major units: he would maintain a force of only two carriers. *Hermes* would be discarded when the second, HMS

Illustrious, was completed, and the first ship, *Invincible*, would be sold to Australia when the third, HMS *Ark Royal*, was completed. Both of the big amphibious landing ships would be discarded, since amphibious operations were no longer to be a Royal Navy mission.[16] However, the British commitment to reinforce NATO forces in Norway, which might seem to include amphibious operations, was not abandoned.

Then the Argentine invasion of the Falklands showed that, indeed, there was a legitimate Royal Navy mission outside Northern European waters, and that the defence of a small patch of ocean (occupied by the Task Force) could be important. Moreover, although the Falklands themselves were a very special case, it could be argued that conditions there were not so very different from those which would apply in Norway, on the NATO flank: a landing, unopposed on the beach, but under attack by hostile aircraft.

This is not the place to review the successful despatch of the Task Force, headed by a reprieved HMS *Hermes*. Politically, the effect of the war was to cancel any sale of HMS *Invincible*. For a time after HMS *Ark Royal* was completed, *Hermes* was retained as a harbour training ship, in theory as a potential replacement for the first ship to go into extended refit. It also seems likely that new, albeit very austere, helicopter assault (commando) carriers will be built, with the existing carriers being limited to ASW, limited air defence, reconnaissance and surface strike, although they have an inherent commando capability.[17]

However, the limits of British economics soon reasserted

16 Grove reports that the Defence Review placed the Eastern Atlantic fourth in priority of four British missions, behind the forward defence of Germany and, presumably, strategic deterrence and the air defence of Britain. Since 1981, the British government has shown greater interest in conventional (non-nuclear) defence. In this context, it has strengthened the air defence of Britain. However, in conventional war Norway becomes more important, because enemy aircraft based there can sustain a bombing offensive against Britain. This may account for sustained interest in amphibious forces (to reinforce Norway).

17 This capability was announced in 1976–77, and it has been exercised from time to time. The ships can embark 960 Royal Marines for short periods.

18 Announced improvements inclu-
    ded a 12.5-degree ski-jump, sup-
port facilities for at least twenty-one
aircraft (Sea Harriers and helicopters),
the conversion of the forward lift from
hydraulic to electric operation, new
command and control systems, three
Goalkeeper CIWS, and, if available in
time, the new Type 996 three-
dimensional radar.

19 The *Atlantic Conveyor* carried, as
    cargo, eight Sea Harriers, six Har-
rier GR.3s (RAF), eight Wessex and
five Chinook helicopters. Rated as an
aircraft ferry, she corresponded roughly
to the replenishment carriers envisaged
in 1951–52 (see Chapter 16). What
was remarkable was that the conversion was accomplished by Devonport
in only eleven days, including construction of a hangar, deck landing
lights, glide path indicators and aviation fuel (avcat) stowage. Some shops
were set up in containers acting as wind
breaks around the flight deck. The
result looked like an austere carrier. For
details, see R Villar, *Merchant Ships At
War: The Falklands Experience* (Conway Maritime Press, London, 1984).

themselves. *Hermes* was discarded, and the decision taken in
1985 to maintain only two air groups for the three carriers (on
the ground that one carrier would always be refitting in peacetime, and that training and 'pipeline' aircraft could be used to
constitute a third air group in wartime). On 29 April 1986
HMS *Invincible* paid off for a 27-month refit.[18] *Illustrious* was to
have followed. However, money is not available, and she will
go into maintained reserve instead. Thus it seems unlikely, at
time of writing, that the Royal Navy can afford to maintain
two active carriers with a third refitting.

THE SEA HARRIER made it possible for the Royal Navy to
retain a significant seaborne air capability. This probably made
the 1982 recovery of the Falklands feasible. The new VSTOL
carriers were indeed able to operate in terrible weather, and
their aircraft proved remarkably reliable. The Falklands War
also proved that minimum ships capable of supporting vertical/
short take-off aircraft were relatively easy to improvise though
they could not compare with real carriers in command and
control, aircraft support, or, for that matter, survivability.[19]

The war showed, however, that sheer carrier size, and sheer
numbers, still count; ten or twenty small subsonic strike figh-

The shape of the future: Hermes *in 1977, with an RAF
Harrier and a Harrier trainer, plus a Wessex and a Sea King,
on board.*

ters cannot compare with a hundred supersonic F-14s. However, VSTOL imposes nothing like the natural minimum carrier size imposed by the catapults and arrester gear of a large-
deck carrier. It seems likely, therefore, that the smaller navies,
which inaugurated their naval air arms with small light fleet
carriers, will find VSTOL attractive. This had already happened with India, Spain and the Soviet Union, and will soon
follow with Italy and perhaps with Japan. For the Royal Navy,
VSTOL means that carriers can come in smaller increments, so
that if expansion ever becomes possible, it can come in less
imposing (and presumably more affordable) steps.

THIS LONG STORY would seem to have several morals. The
first and most important is that carriers are valuable because
they enhance the flexibility – the crucial element – of seapower.
Navies are effective because they can present a great variety of
enemies with a wide range of threats, so that a potential enemy
must provide against so wide a range of contingencies as to

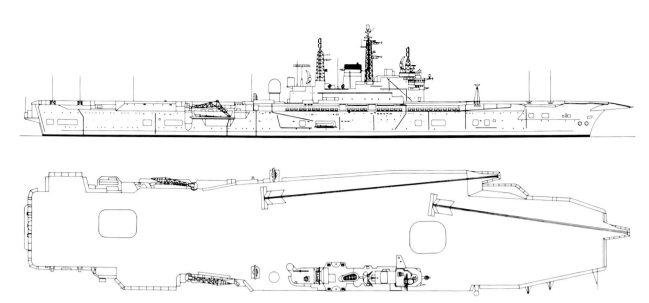

HMS Invincible *profile and plan, 1980.*

reduce his capability in any one of them. This is a natural consequence of the mobility of navies as compared to ground (and associated air) forces. Mobility also explains why navies generally cannot point to a single fundamental planning scenario, whereas armies tend to be wedded to the problems of a particular area. In postwar British interservice rivalry, this potential for flexibility turned against the Royal Navy, precisely because it tried to avoid being limited to a narrowly-defined role. The basic argument, that no defence planner could confidently predict the future, had little appeal to the defence planners seeking economies associated with narrow specialization.

After all, who in 1981 could have predicted that the Royal Navy would fight, not in the North Atlantic, but in the Falklands?

Carriers are the essence of flexibility because radically different aircraft can inhabit much the same hangar and can fly from much the same deck. For any other type of warship, a change in weapons entails a major change in hardware and in electronics. For a carrier, it may involve no more than taking new aircraft aboard. Thus essentially the same generation of carriers which struck the Italian fleet at Taranto in 1940 (and so gained the initiative in the Mediterranean) could also attack Japanese oil refineries in Southeast Asia four years later, could help suppress Communist rebels in Malaya, and could also support ASW operations in the North Atlantic. They could also launch helicopter-borne troops. All of these possibilities were inherent in a flat deck and a hangar, although actual air operations depended, too, on developments in catapults, arrester gear and deck configuration. From a constructional point of view, high speed and a large hangar made carriers useful as fast troopers, to help Britain meet her very large Imperial (and, later, Commonwealth) commitments with a limited army. The large hangar and unobstructed flight deck also made the three repair ship conversions practicable.

Even in World War I, the same primitive carriers could be used to raid German naval bases, to provide ASW patrols, and to support land operations, particularly in the Middle East. Because they were so versatile, a very small number of carriers could be redeployed to cover a very wide range of roles. Conversely, drastic reductions in the British carrier force were generally justified by supposed limitations on wartime British naval roles, for instance to ASW in the North-East Atlantic.

The second great lesson seems to lie in the consequences of the perception that carrier operating capacity was to be equated with the capacity of the hangar deck, itself apparently a subtle

(and surely unintended) effect of post-1918 RAF control. Precisely because the Admiralty *was* air-minded, it required many more aircraft for fleet operations than the treaty-limited carrier force could provide. This in turn led to plans to operate fighters and strike aircraft from capital ships and cruisers, and thus to limitations on their weight and take-off speed. These limits, rather than any Air Ministry opprobrium, seem to be the best explanation for the disappointing performance of British carrier aircraft on the eve of World War II. The lesson would seem to be that relatively subtle differences in carrier operating philo-

HMS Hermes, *newly converted to a commando carrier, in 1973. Note the satellite communications antenna at the after end of the island, and the Type 965 replacing the earlier Type 984 three-dimensional radar. The cylinder atop the lattice mast is Type 957, the British equivalent of the US Tacan. The long skewed lines on deck are safely margins for Wessex and Sea King helicopter rotar blades.*

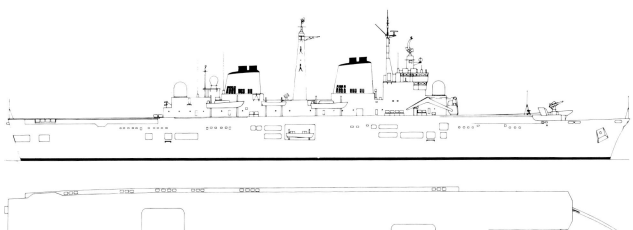

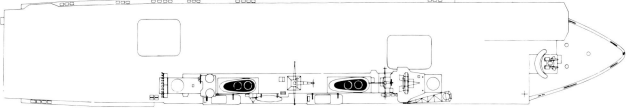

Invincible, *in 1980, profile and plan.*

Below: *HMS* Bulwark *as a helicopter carrier in 1979, with Westland Sea King (No 826 Squadron) and Wessex HU.5 (No 846 Squadron) helicopters overhead. The Wessex was the standard British troop carrier, lifting sixteen troops. The Sea Kings were ASW helicopters. Commando carriers could* operate in either the ASW escort or the helicopter assault rode, with a minimum of alteration. Her Type 960 and Type 983 (long range air search and height-finding) radars were removed during a 1965–66 refit, leaving her with only the Type 982 narrow-beam air search and Type 293 Q short-range air search sets. Note also the small assault landing craft (LCA) in davits, aft.

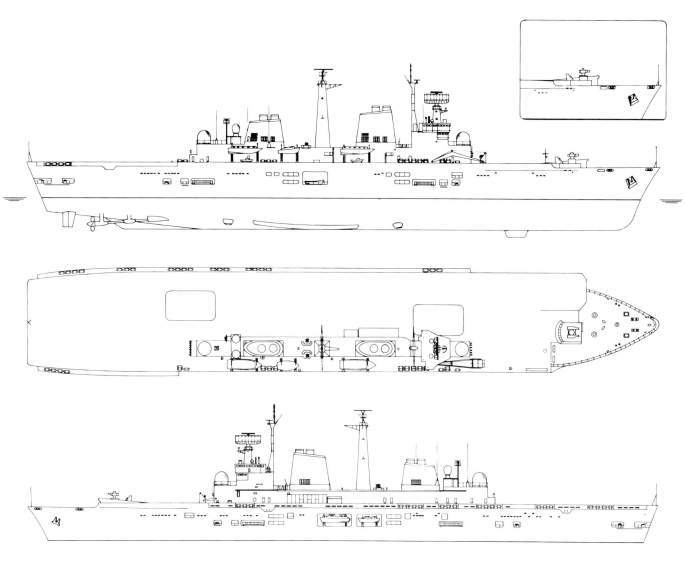

HMS Invincible *as completed. The inset shows the higher ski-jump of HMS* Illustrious. *Note the large sonar dome and the four stabilizing fins.*

Below: *HMS* Illustrious, *the second of the* Invincibles, *passes the third ship, HMS* Ark Royal, *on Tyneside November 1982.*

sophy can make immense differences in the capability of a ship. Conversely, when the Royal Navy did adopt deck parks, it was able almost to double the number of aircraft it could operate from some ships, albeit without being able to increase fuel capacity or personnel accommodation to match.

Undoubtedly the Imperial Japanese Navy had yet a third view of carrier operations, probably closer to British than to American standards. Will the Soviets show a fourth philosophy in their new carriers?

Then there is the armoured flight deck. Certainly it helped British carriers withstand Kamikazes in 1945. On the other hand, it made for a drastic reduction in air complement, compared with the 1934 *Ark Royal*. It can be argued, too, that until 1945 British carriers only rarely sustained hits on their flight deck armour, and that they survived primarily because their hangars were so carefully isolated from other hull spaces rather than because they were armoured. It can also be argued that *Ark Royal* herself could not have operated her large air-group very effectively because her two-level hangar arrangement was necessarily cumbersome. All the British carriers designed prewar were severely limited by treaty, which complicates any comparison with US practice. Quite aside from any benefits they derived from their open hangars, the US *Essexes* were 4000 tons larger, simply because they were designed after treaty limitation had lapsed. They were also designed for larger air groups, but that was a consequence of basic US policy, not of ship design philosophy as such.

Postwar, the armoured carriers proved relatively difficult to reconstruct, although this seems to have been due primarily to the fact that their flight decks were their strength decks.

The Royal Navy invented the carrier. Throughout World

HMS Illustrious *from aft, showing her Phalanx close-in defensive gun.*

War I the Admiralty doggedly produced converted carriers, even though early results were disappointing. Senior air officers such as Admiral Murray Sueter might complain that progress was not fast enough, but the overall record makes it clear that the Admiralty was more air-minded than not, and that the technology was often not up to operational requirements.[20] Postwar, this air-mindedness shows in demands for large numbers of carriers (far in advance of other navies), and then for large numbers of fleet aircraft. The Admiralty might have done better if naval officers had controlled fleet aircraft (if, for example, they had realized earlier that carriers could operate more aircraft), but the fundamental limit on British interwar carrier strength was the international treaty structure, and there was no hope of changing that. Once the treaties disappeared, the Admiralty began an ambitious programme of new construction, again in advance of other navies.

That the results of all of this effort were ultimately disappointing was not the Admiralty's fault. As in the case of Germany, war came too soon, before the new programme had gained momentum. In a larger sense, the Royal Navy suffered because, unlike the US and Japanese navies, it had to rearm on the basis of 1936, not 1940, technology. Of course, had it waited longer, the consequences would have been equally unfortunate. As it was, despite the apparent obsolescence of the aircraft, they proved quite effective in strikes in Norway and in the Mediterranean in 1940. The Admiralty's failure to provide high-performance fighters for fleet defence can also be explained by timing: the key policy decisions were taken before

20 Sueter prepared the Air Department papers for record purposes, both for use in the RAF Official History and for the Public Records Office. It seems noteworthy that correspondence concerning carrier conversions made in 1915 (*Ben-my-Chree* and *Vindex*), when the Admiralty persisted despite operational reverses, has not survived, whereas the lengthy correspondence concerning attempts to convert *Manxman* in the face of Board resistance has been preserved. It is likely that the 1915 conversions were encouraged by the combination of an air-minded First Lord, Winston Churchill, and a somewhat air-minded First Sea Lord, Sir John Fisher, and it is possible that their departure, after the Dardanelles, changed the atmosphere in the Admiralty.

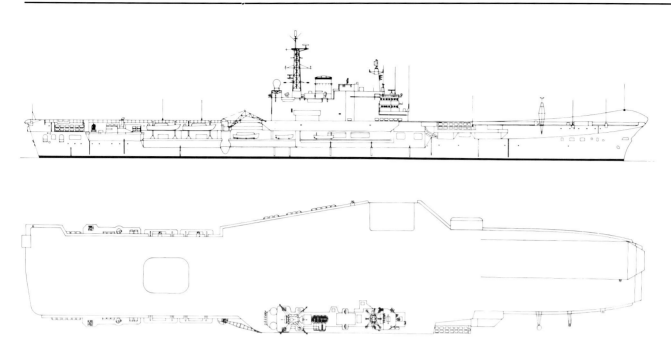

HMS Hermes *as she appeared in 1981.*

Below: *HMS* Hermes *was substantially longer than an* Invincible, *and she had a larger deck capacity, as illustrated here.*

Note the new SCOT satellite-communication randomes installed at the after end of her island during the same refit which provided her with the big ski-jump forward.

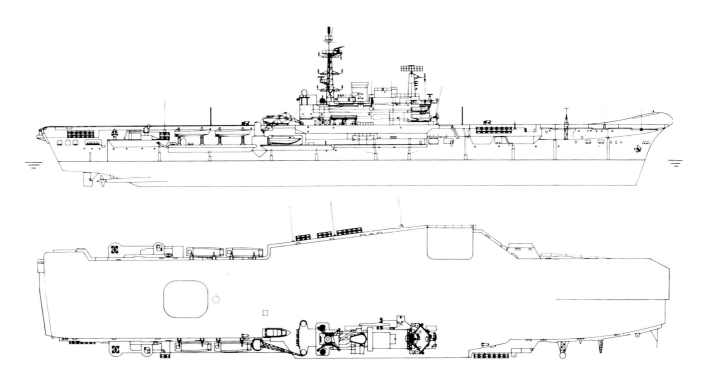

radar made it practicable to protect the fleet with small numbers of fighters. The Admiralty might have been wiser, but the key was the limited number of aircraft aboard the carriers. As in many other aspects of warfare, numbers are valuable partly because they provide a cushion against errors of judgement.

The Admiralty was hardly the only malefactor in this regard, and the reader should keep in mind that the Admiralty badly wanted more fleet aircraft. It was not misplaced economy, but the fundamental choice in operating technique, which mandated limited carrier aircraft complements. Economy did enter in the drastic prewar and wartime reduction of naval demands for replacement and reserve aircraft and squadrons. Because there were no reserves, crew losses during the Norwegian campaign were virtually impossible to make up, to the point that postwar naval aviators wanted to expand the Fleet Air Arm (upon mobilization) before employing it in combat. Again, only numbers of highly-trained personnel can make up for the inevitable early war losses. The decision, taken in about 1955–57, that any future war would be short and sharp justified the elimination of the reserve organization built up after 1945. Now that perception seems less and less justified. Britain is not alone in having failed to build up reserves, particularly in personnel, to match the possible new reality of protracted war.

It was particularly ironic that the Royal Navy, which was almost alone in practising multi-carrier operations before 1939, lost so many of its carriers (and had to spread over so large an area) that it could rarely operate two fleet carriers together before 1945.

Before 1939, the Air Ministry made a conscious choice in favour of bombers and against maritime reconnaissance (ASW) aircraft and, for that matter, fighters. The Admiralty paid for naval aircraft, even when they came under RAF control, and thus the Air Council could not easily trade off naval for land-based aircraft. However, it could trade off RAF aircraft of different types, and the prewar Admiralty had no means of encouraging the RAF to provide enough maritime patrol types. Because of the Air Ministry's unwillingness to maintain sufficient maritime reconnaissance squadrons, carriers had to be assigned to ASW patrol, and one of the largest, HMS *Courageous*, was lost on this service.[21] Because of the shortage of fighters in 1939–40, the Admiralty had to defend its shore bases,

HMS Hermes *as a VSTOL/helicopter carrier in 1982, as in the Falklands War, with the big ski-jump added forward.*

further reducing the numbers available on board ships, though this did have the fortunate consequence of pushing the Admiralty towards higher-performance fighter aircraft. Postwar, because the Royal Navy did not control shore-based maritime reconnaissance aircraft, the apparent choice between carriers and such aircraft became an issue of interservice rivalry, most spectacularly in the case of the Nott Defence Review in 1981; the reality, that such aircraft are complementary to sea-based aircraft, tended to be submerged. It is interesting in retrospect that the RAF made its strongest attempts to kill off the British carrier force not when it nominally controlled their aircraft, but rather when the Royal Navy controlled those aircraft.

On the other hand, the legacy of very close cooperation between the RAF and the Royal Navy made it relatively easy for the wartime Royal Navy to consider operating RAF aircraft for special missions, such as the proposed 'Highball' strike against the Japanese fleet. In the Falklands War, RAF Harriers operated from British carriers, albeit far less efficiently than did the Sea Harriers designed for such operation.

Finally, a historical point: most observers of the Fleet Air Arm have emphasized its struggle both against Admiralty backwardness and against a hostile Royal Air Force (not to mention, often, a hostile government). The record seems to show an Admiralty well aware of the potential of air power, often in advance of its rivals, and hampered primarily by the facts of economic life (as reflected, prewar, by the naval arms limitations treaties, and postwar by periodic defence cuts). Even the role of the Ten Year Rule can be misinterpreted. Britain could afford only one big industrial mobilization between the wars. Had she built up her forces in, say, 1933, there would have been no resources available for 1939 – and the 1933 build-up, of what might later have been called interim technology, might well have failed to deter the aggressors. Postwar, Britain was unfortunate in mis-reading the chances for a breathing spell between 1947 and 1957, but it is not clear, on the record, that she could have done much better.

The record, properly read, seems to have been an outstanding one, strategically, operationally, technologically.

21 *Courageous* was lost because she was tied down to a limited area, functioning as a seaborne air base rather than as a mobile strike unit. It seems likely that, in the Falklands, the Argentine submarine *San Luis* managed to approach the carrier *Invincible* only because the latter was tied to a very limited area so as to provide Harrier support over Falkland Sound. This was a direct consequence of the limited range of the Sea Harrier.

Appendix A
British
Aircraft Carriers

1. Construction Dates and Fates

Name	Builder	Laid Down	Launched	Commissioned	Notes
Ark Royal	Blyth	7.11.13	5.9.14	10.12.14	Renamed *Pegasus* 12.34, merchant ship (*Anita I*) 18.10.46, sold 6.49 and BU
Engadine	Denny		1.4.11	11.8.14	Returned 12.19 (chartered)
Riviera	Denny		23.9.11	11.8.14	Returned 31.5.19 (chartered)
Empress	Denny		13.4.07	25.8.14	Returned 11.19 (chartered)
Ben-my-Chree	Vickers		23.3.08	2.1.15	WL 11.1.17 Castellorizo, raised 1920, BU 1923
Vindex	Armstrong Whitworth		7.3.05	26.3.15	Purchased 9.15; sold to original owners 12.2.20.
Campania	Fairfield		8.9.92	17.4.15	Sunk (collision) 5.11.18
Manxman	Vickers		15.6.04	17.4.16	Paid off 12.19, sold 12.2.20
Nairana	Denny		21.6.15	25.8.17	Requisitioned 27.2.17, sold to original owners 1920
Pegasus	John Brown		9.6.17	14.8.17	Sold 22.8.31, BU. Completion date is date of leaving shipyard
Argus	Beardmore	19/14	2.12.17	16.9.18	Accommodation ship 12.44, sold 5.12.46
Hermes	Armstrong Whitworth	15.1.18	11.9.19	18.2.24	WL 9.4.42
Eagle	Armstrong Whitworth	20.2.13	8.6.18	20.2.24	WL 11.8.42
Furious	Armstrong Whitworth	8.6.15	15.8.16	26.6.17	Rebuilt as a flush-deck carrier at Devonport (completed 1925); reduced to reserve 9.44, target and sold for BU 48
Courageous	Armstrong Whitworth	28.3.15	5.2.16	12.16	Rebuilt as a carrier at Devonport 6.24 – 5.5.28; WL 17.9.39
Glorious	Harland & Wolff	1.5.15	20.4.16	11.16	Rebuilt as a carrier at Rosyth and Devonport 1925 — 10.3.30; WL 18.6.40
Ark Royal	Cammell Laird	16.1.35	13.4.37	16.11.38	WL 14.11.41
Illustrious Class					
Illustrious	Vickers	27.4.37	5.4.39	25.5.40	Reserve 12.54, sold for BU 3.11.56
Victorious	Vickers Tyne	4.5.37	14.9.39	15.5.41	Sold 7.69 for BU
Formidable	Harland & Wolff	17.6.37	17.8.39	24.11.40	Reserve 1947, sold for BU 1953
Indomitable	Vickers	10.11.37	26.3.40	10.10.41	Sold for BU 5.53
Implacable Class					
Implacable	Fairfield	21.3.39	10.12.41	28.8.44	Sold and BU from 3.11.55
Indefatigable	John Brown	3.11.39	8.12.42	3.5.44	Sold and BU from 4.11.56
FAA Maintenance Ship					
Unicorn	Harland & Wolff	29.6.39	20.11.41	12.3.43	Sold 1959, BU from 15.6.59
Ark Royal Class					
Eagle	Harland & Wolff	24.10.42	19.3.46	1.10.51	Original name was *Audacious*; to reserve 26.1.72, left for BU 13.10.78
Ark Royal	Cammell Laird	3.5.43	3.5.50	25.2.55	Withdrawn from service 12.78, BU from 28.9.80
Colossus Class					
Colossus	Vickers Tyne	1.6.42	30.9.43	16.12.44	To France (*Arromanches*) on loan 8.46, purchased 1951; disposal list 1974, BU Toulon 1978
Glory	Harland & Wolff	27.8.42	27.11.43	22.4.45	Reserve 1956, BU from 8.61
Ocean	Stephen & Sons	8.11.42	8.7.44	30.6.45	Reserve 5.12.57, BU from 6.5.62
Theseus	Fairfield	6.1.43	6.7.44	9.1.46	Reserve 1956, BU from 29.5.62
Triumph	Hawthorn Leslie	27.1.43	2.10.44	9.4.46	Converted to maintenance ship 1958–65, in reserve 1972, for disposal 1980, towed for BU, 26.11.81
Venerable	Cammell Laird	3.12.42	30.12.43	17.1.45	Sold to Netherlands (*Karel Doorman*) 1.4.48 and then to Argentina (*25 de Mayo*) 15.10.68
Vengeance	Swan Hunter	16.11.42	23.2.44	16.1.45	Lent to RAN 1953–5, sold to Brazil (*Minas Gerais*) 14.12.56
Warrior	Harland & Wolff	12.12.42	20.5.44	24.1.46	Lent to RCN 1946–8, to Argentina (*Independencia*) 7.58, for disposal 1971

Name	Builder	Laid Down	Launched	Commissioned	Notes
Colossus Class completed as Aircraft Repair Ships					
Perseus	Vickers Tyne	1.6.42	26.3.44	19.10.45	Originally to have been named *Edgar*, sold for BU 6.5.58.
Pioneer	Vickers Barrow	2.12.42	20.5.44	8.2.54	Originally to have been named *Mars*; sold for BU 9.54
Majestic Class					
Majestic	Vickers Barrow	15.4.43	28.2.45	8.11.55	To RAN (*Melbourne*) 28.10.55. Reserve 30.6.82, stricken 14.3.83. Sold 11.83
Magnificent	Harland & Wolff	29.7.43	16.11.44	21.5.48	On loan to RCN 1946–57; returned and BU from 12.7.65. Not operational in RN
Powerful	Harland & Wolff	27.11.43	27.2.45	17.1.57	To RCN (*Bonaventure*) 1952. Reserve 1.4.70 and BU
Terrible	HM Dockyard Devonport	19.4.43	30.9.44	5.2.49	To RAN (*Sydney*) 16.12.48. Reserve 1973 and towed for BU 23.12.75
Hercules	Vickers Tyne	14.10.43	22.9.45	4.3.61	Completed as Indian *Vikrant*
Leviathan	Swan Hunter	19.10.42	6.6.45	—	Suspended 5.46. Towed to Portsmouth 6.46. BU from 27.5.68
Hermes Class					
Hermes	Vickers Barrow	21.6.44	16.2.53	18.11.59	In reserve 12.4.84, stricken 1.7.85, sold to India as *Viraat*, 5.86
Albion	Swan Hunter	23.3.44	6.5.47	26.5.54	Purchased 22.10.73 for use in North Sea, but BU instead from 16.11.73
Bulwark	Harland & Wolff	10.5.45	22.6.48	4.11.54	Reserve 27.3.81 and stricken; sold for BU 4.84
Centaur	Harland & Wolff	30.5.44	22.4.47	1.9.53	Accommodation ship for *Eagle* personnel at Devonport during refit 9.66 and then at Portsmouth; for disposal from 4.70 and BU from 8.9.72
Invincible Class					
Invincible	Vickers Barrow	20.7.73	3.5.77	11.7.80	
Illustrious	Swan Hunter	7.10.76	1.12.78	20.6.82	
Ark Royal	Swan Hunter	14.12.78	2.6.81	1.11.85	
Escort Carriers					
Audacity	Bremer Vulkan		29.3.39	6.41	Completion date is as escort carrier; taken in hand 1.41 by Blyth Shipbuilding. Ex-German *Hannover* taken as prize 3.40. WL 20.12.41
Activity	Caledon SB Co	1.2.40	30.5.42	14.10.42	Mercantile *Breconshire* 1946
Pretoria Castle	Harland & Wolff		12.10.38	9.4.43	Completed 7.43. Mercantile *Warwick Castle 1946*
Nairana	John Brown	6.11.41	20.5.43	12.12.43	Taken in hand 3.7.42 Royal Netherlands Navy 1946 (*Karel Doorman*). Mercantile *Port Victor* 1948
Vindex	Swan Hunter	1.7.42	4.5.43	3.12.43	Taken in hand 24.10.42. Mercantile *Port Vindex*
Campania	Harland & Wolff	12.8.41	17.6.43	7.3.44	Taken in hand 1.8.42. Retained postwar, used as Festival of Britain display ship 1949–51, supported nuclear tests 1952, then in reserve, BU from 11.11.55
US-Supplied Escort Carriers					
Avenger Class (all built by Sun Shipbuilding)					
Archer			14.12.39	17.11.41	Mercantile *Empire Lagan* 3.45, BU 3.62
Avenger			27.11.40	1.3.42	WL 15.12.42
Biter			18.12.40	4.5.42	Ret to USN 9.4.45, became French *Dixmude*
Dasher			12.4.41	1.7.42	WL (accident) 27.3.43
Tracker Class					
Tracker	Seattle-Tacoma	3.11.41	7.3.42	31.1.43	Returned 29.11.45, mercantile *Corrientes*
Battler	Ingalls	15.4.41	4.4.42	15.11.42	Returned 12.2.46 BU
Attacker	Western Pipe	17.4.41	17.9.41	10.10.42	Returned 5.1.46, mercantile *Castel Forte* (1948)
Hunter	Ingalls	15.5.41	22.5.42	11.1.43	Returned 29.12.45, mercantile *Almdijk*
Chaser	Ingalls	28.6.41	15.1.42	9.4.43	Returned 12.5.46, mercantile *Aagtekerk*
Fencer	Western Pipe	5.9.41	4.4.42	20.2.43	Returned 11.12.46, mercantile *Sydney*
Stalker	Western Pipe	6.10.41	5.3.42	30.12.42	Returned 29.12.45, mercantile *Riouw*
Pursuer	Ingalls	31.7.41	18.7.42	14.6.43	Returned 12.2.46, BU
Striker	Western Pipe	15.12.41	7.5.42	29.4.43	Returned 12.2.46, BU
Searcher	Seattle-Tacoma	20.2.42	20.6.42	8.4.43	Returned 29.11.45, mercantile *Captain Theo*
Ravager	Seattle-Tacoma	11.4.42	16.7.42	26.4.43	Returned 26.2.46, mercantile *Robin Trent*
Smiter Class (all built by Seattle-Tacoma)					
Slinger		25.5.42	15.12.42	11.8.43	Returned 27.2.46, mercantile *Robin Mowbray*
Atheling		9.6.42	7.9.42	1.8.43	Returned 13.12.46, mercantile *Roma* (1950)
Khedive		22.9.42	27.12.42	23.8.43	Returned 26.1.46, mercantile *Rempang*
Ameer		18.7.42	18.10.42	20.7.43	Returned 17.1.46, mercantile *Robin Kirk*
Begum		3.8.42	11.11.42	3.8.43	Returned 4.1.46, mercantile *Raki*
Trumpeter		25.8.42	15.12.42	4.8.43	Returned 6.4.46, mercantile *Alblasserdijk*
Empress		9.9.42	30.12.42	13.8.43	Returned 4.2.46, BU
Emperor		23.6.42	7.10.42	6.8.43	Returned 12.2.46, sold for BU 5.46
Speaker		9.10.42	30.12.42	20.11.43	Returned 17.7.47, mercantile *Lancero*
Nabob		20.10.42	9.3.43	7.9.43	Constructive total loss 8.44, returned 16.3.45, mercantile *Nabob*
Premier		31.10.42	22.3.43	3.11.43	Returned 12.4.46, mercantile *Rhodesia Star*
Shah		13.11.42	21.4.43	27.9.43	Returned 6.12.45, mercantile *Salta*
Patroller		27.11.42	6.5.43	25.10.43	Returned 13.12.46, mercantile *Almkerk*
Rajah		17.12.42	18.5.43	17.1.44	Returned 13.12.46, mercantile *Drente*
Ranee		5.1.43	2.6.43	8.11.44	Returned 21.11.46, mercantile *Friesland*
Trouncer		1.2.43	16.6.43	31.1.44	Returned 3.3.46, mercantile *Greystoke Castle*
Thane		23.2.43	15.7.43	19.11.43	Constructive total loss 15.1.45, returned 15.12.45, BU

Name	Builder	Laid Down	Launched	Commissioned	Notes
Queen		12.3.43	31.7.43	7.12.43	Returned 31.10.46, mercantile *Roebiah*
Ruler		25.3.43	21.8.43	22.12.43	Returned 29.1.46, BU
Arbiter		26.4.43	9.9.43	31.12.43	Carried out Helldiver deck trials 7.44; returned 3.3.46, mercantile *Coracero*
Smiter		10.5.43	27.9.43	20.1.44	Returned 6.4.46, merchant service
Puncher		21.5.43	8.11.43	5.2.44	Returned 16.1.46, mercantile *Muncaster Castle*
Reaper		5.6.43	22.11.43	21.2.44	Returned 20.5.46, mercantile *South Africa Star*

MAC Ships

Name	Builder		Launched	Commissioned	Notes
Empire MacAlpine[1]	Burntisland		23.12.42	14.4.43[2]	
Rapana	Wilton-Fijenoord		4.35	7.43[2]	
Empire MacAndrew[1]	Denny		3.5.43	7.43[2]	
Amastra	Lithgow		18.12.34	9.43[2]	
Empire MacRae[1]	Lithgow		21.6.43	9.43[2]	
Ancyclus	Swan Hunter		9.10.34	10.43[2]	
Acavus	Workman Clark		24.10.34	10.43[2]	
Empire Mackay	Harland & Wolff		17.6.43	10.43[2]	
Empire MacColl	Cammell Laird		24.7.43	11.43[2]	
Empire MacMahon	Swan Hunter		2.7.43	12.43[2]	
Empire MacCabe	Swan Hunter		18.5.43	12.43[2]	
Empire MacCalum*	Lithgow		12.10.43	12.43[2]	
Alexia	Bremer Vulkan		20.12.34	12.43[2]	
Empire MacKendrick[1]	Burntisland		29.9.43	12.43[2]	
Miralda	Nederlandse Dok		7.36	1.44[2]	
Adula	Blythswood		28.1.37	2.44[2]	
Gadila	Howaldt		1.12.34	3.44[2]	Dutch-manned
Empire MacDermott[1]	Denny		24.1.44	3.44[2]	
Macoma	Nederlandse Dok		31.12.35	5.44[2]	Dutch-manned

CAM Ships[6]

Michael E[3], Primrose Hill[3], Empire Spring, Empire Tide[5], Empire Dell[3], Helencrest, Empire Rainbow[3], Empire Ray, Empire Faith, Empire Burton, Kafirstan, Novelist, Empire Stanley, Empire Shackleton[3], Empire Moon[5], Empire Wave[3]

Empire Hudson[5], Empire Lawrence[3,5], Empire Eve, Empire Sun[3], Empire Heath[5], Empire Flame, Empire Clive, Empire Rowan, Eastern City, Empire Spray, Daghestan, Empire Foam[5], Empire Ocean[4], Empire Darwin[5], Empire Franklin, Empire Gale, Empire Morn[5],

Note that the last date is the date of *commissioning*, not completion. In the case of merchant conversions, it is the date of commissioning as a carrier.
1 indicates a gran ship.
2 date in service.
3 indicates a ship sunk by enemy action.
4 indicates a ship sunk by marine casualty.
5 indicates a ship which launched aircraft in action. Dummy aircraft and catapults were fitted to SS *Capte Clear* and *City of Johannesburg*, but they were removed by March 1942. Names are in order of entry into service.
6 CAM operations were originally limited to the North Atlantic, but by September 1941 German air attacks had shifted to the Gibraltar area, and it was decided to sail a CAM ship with each convoy to or from Gibraltar. Four CAM ships were torpedoed during 1941. At the end of the year, due to icing, it was decided to discontinue CAM operations in the North Atlantic in winter, but to provide two CAM ships in all Gibraltar convoys. North Atlantic CAM runs were resumed in March 1942. CAM operations to Russia began in April 1942 (Convoy PQ15). The Admiralty decided to cease operating CAM ships in North Atlantic convoys in July 1942, but to continue to sail two in each Gibraltar convoy, and one in each Russian convoy. This required eight and five ships, respectively, plus three spares, a total of sixteen out of twenty-six CAM ships then in service. Ten were therefore returned to the Ministry of War Transport, eight having their catapults removed to increase deck space and permit No 1 hold to be worked from either side. CAM ships were temporarily withdrawn from the Gibraltar convoys during Operation Torch, but they were again provided at the beginning of 1943, and one (increased to two in April 1943) was included in each North African build-up convoy. The CAM organization was finally shut down in 1943 because this scale did not justify continued RAF assistance, and the Royal Navy could not have replaced RAF personnel while manning the new escort carriers and MAC ships.

2. Particulars of British Fleet Aircraft Carriers

	Ark Royal	Engadine	Empress	Campania
Date	1918	1918	1918	1918
Displacement (tons)				
standard[59]	7080	2400	2540	18,000
deep	7450	2550		20,611
LBP (ft)	352 6	315	310	601
LWL (ft)				
LOA (ft)	366	323	318	622
BWL (ft)	50 10	41	40	65
Beam, extreme (ft)				
Depth (ft)		16 6	16 6	
Deep draught (ft) fwd	17 4	13 8 (mean)	13	27 7
aft	18 9		15	29 3
Flight deck dimensions (ft)	130 × 44	–	–	245
SHP	3000	12,000	8800	30,000ihp
Speed (knots) designed	11[60]	22[65]	18[67]	23
deep				
continuous		20.5	15	
Oil fuel (tons)	500	400 coal[66]	425 coal[68]	3270 coal
Endurance (nm)	3030 at 10 knots	960[70]	1355 at 15 knots	2600 at 21 knots
Guns	4 12pdr	4 12pdr	4 12pdr	6 4.7in
	2 .303in mg	2 3pdr HA	2 3pdr HA	1 3in AA
Petrol (gallons)	4000[72]			
Lift dimensions (ft)	45 10 × 30[64]	–	–	40 × 25[64]
Catapults	–	–	–	–
Complement				550

	Ben-My-Chree	Vindex	Manxman	Pegasus
Date	1917	1918	1918	1918
Displacement				
standard[59]	3888			2070
deep		2950	3091	3315
LBP (ft)		350 4	334	320 4
LWL (ft)				
LOA (ft)	375	361 6	343	332 4
BWL (ft)	46	42	43 1	43 0¾
Beam, extreme (ft)				
Depth (ft)				18 9
Deep draught (ft) Fwd	16 (max)	13 8	15 8	15 9½
aft		13 6	15 9	14 11¾
Flight deck dimensions (ft)	60[69]	64	86	
SHP	14,500	11,000	8500	9500
Speed (knots) designed	24.5	20	15[71]	20.25[62]
deep				
continuous	22	23		20.3
Oil fuel (tons)	500 coal	475 coal	430 coal	350
Endurance (nm)		1125	995	1220 at 20.3 knots
Guns	2 12pdr	4 12pdr	4 12pdr	4 12pdr HA
	2 3pdr AA	1 6pdr AA	2 6pdr AA	
Petrol (gallons)				1300
Lift dimensions (ft)	–	–	18 × 14[64]	18 × 14[64]
Catapults	–	–	–	–
Complement	250	144	250	258

	Nairana	Argus	Vindictive	Furious
Date	1918	1918	1918	1918
Displacement (tons)				
standard[59]	3070	14,450	9394[91]	19,100
deep		15,775	12,100	23,130
LBP (ft)	315	535	565	735
LWL (ft)		560		
LOA (ft)	352	565	605	786 6
BWL (ft)	45 6	68	58	
Beam, extreme (ft)				
Depth (ft)	24 9			
Deep draught (ft) fwd	13 6	22 2	20 4 (mean)	22 9
aft	14 5	22 11		25 3
Flight deck dimensions (ft)	95	550	78[83]	228[84]
SHP	6700	20,000	60,000[92]	90,000[88]
Speed (knots) designed	19[63]	20.21	29.75	31
deep	19.5			
continuous				30
Oil fuel (tons)	448 coal	2500	1600[85]	3400
Endurance (nm)	1060 at 19.5 knots	3600 at 10 knots		4100 at 10 knots
				2700 at 30 knots
Guns	4 12pdr HA	2 4in LA	4 7.5in	10 5.5in
		2 4in HA	4 3in QF	5 3in HA
			4 3in HA	
			6 21in TT[89]	18 21in TT
			4mg	5mg
Petrol (gallons)	1200	8000		
Lift dimensions (ft)	22 × 14[64]	30 × 36	30 × 16	48 × 18
		60 × 18		46 × 18 4
Catapults	–	–	–	–
Complement	278	495	658[85]	932[86]

	Argus	Eagle	Hermes	Furious
Date	1939	1939	1939	1939
Displacement (tons)				
standard[56]	14,000	22,600	10,850	22,450
deep	16,500	26,680[73]	13,700	27,165[15]
LBP (ft)	535 6	627 1	548	735
LWL (ft)				
LOA (ft)	567	667 6	600	786 6
BWL (ft)	75 9	105 2	70 3	90 1

	Argus	Eagle	Hermes	Furious
Beam extreme (ft)	77 9	115	95 9	120 1[53]
Depth (ft)				
Deep draught (ft) fwd	22 6	24 2	23 3	28 6
aft	23 2	26 7	21 2	27 8
Flight deck dimensions (ft)	470[47]	652	570	530[10]
SHP	20,000	50,000	40,000	90,000
Speed (knots) designed	20–21	24	25	31
deep	18.75	23.75	24.75	29.5
continuous	20	21.2	25	30
Oil fuel (tons)	2045	3775	2000	3785
Endurance	5510 at 10 knots	6550 at 10 knots	5600 at 10 knots	7480 at 10 knots
	4450 at 16 knots	4800 at 16 knots	4480 at 16 knots	5610 at 16 knots
Guns	2 4in[48]	9 6in	6 5.5in	10 5.5in
	13 20mm	4 4in HA	3 4in HA	3 4in HA
		2 8-barrel pom-poms		3 8-barrel pom-poms
	4 .5in	4 .5in	2 .5in multi	2 .5in
		2 Maxim guns	2 Maxim guns	2 Maxim guns
		10 Lewis guns	10 Lewis guns	10 Lewis guns
Petrol (gallons)	14,000	14,790	7000[3]	20,800
Lift dimensions (ft)	37 1 × 35 10	46 × 47	41 2 × 37 4	46 × 47
		47 × 33	41 6 × 37 4	46 × 47
Catapults	1 BH III	–	–	–
Complement		41/750	33/533	41/754

	Courageous	Ark Royal	Illustrious	Indomitable
Date	1939	1939	1940	1942
Displacement (tons)				
standard[59]	22,500	22,000	23,000	23,000
deep	27,400[74]	27,720	28,210[16]	29,084[17]
LBP (ft)	735	685	673	673
LWL (ft)		725	710	710
LOA (ft)	786 3[1]	800	740[5]	753 11
BWL (ft)	90 6	94 9	95 9	95 9
Beam extreme (ft)	123 5	112	106 9	116 3
Depth		83 6	67 9	73 9
Deep draught (ft) fwd	27 10	26 9	27 5	28 2
aft	28 2	28 9	28 10	28 9
Flight deck dimensions (ft)	576	720	620[7]	680[9]
SHP	90,000	102,000	111,000	111,000
Speed (knots) designed	30.5	30.75	30.5	30.5
deep	29.5	31	30.5	30.5
continuous	30.5	30.75	30.3[23]	30.3[24]
Oil fuel (tons)	3685[2]	4400	4850	4500
Endurance (nm)	6630 at 10 knots	11,200 at 10 knots	10,700 at 10 knots[5]	10,000 at 10 knots
	5030 at 16 knots	10,300 at 16 knots	10,400 at 16 knots	9700 at 16 knots
Guns	16 4.7in HA/LA	16 4.5in	16 4.5in	16 4.5in
	3 8-barrel pom-poms	4[6] 8-barrel pom-poms	6 8-barrel pom-poms	6 8-barrel pom-poms
	2 .5in	8 .5in		
	2 Maxim guns	2 rifle cal	2 rifle cal	8 Oerlikons
	10 Lewis guns	10 Lewis guns		
Petrol (gallons)	34,500	100,000	50,650	75,400
Lift dimensions (ft)	46 × 48	46 × 25	45 × 22[75]	45 × 33
	46 × 48	45 × 22	45 × 22	45 × 22
		45 × 22		
Catapults	2	2 BH III	1 BH III	1 BH III
Complement	45/794	151/1630		

	Indefatigable	Unicorn	Colossus	Magnificent
Date	1944	1943	1945	1951
Displacement (tons)				
standard[59]	23,000	14,750	13,190	15,740
deep	32,101[18]	20,300	18,040	19,550
LBP (ft)	690	564	630	630
LWL (ft)	730	575	650	650
LOA (ft)	766 6	640	693 1	695
BWL (ft)	95 9	90	80	80
Beam, extreme (ft)	114 5		112 6	112 6
Depth (ft)	70 11½		62 6	62 6
Deep draught (ft) fwd	25 11½	23 1	23 1	24 3

	Indefatigable	Unicorn	Colossus	Magnificent
aft	27 3¾	24 10	23 5	25
Flight deck dimensions (ft)	750	600		
SHP	148,000	40,000	40,000	40,000
Speed (knots) designed	32.5[12]	24	25	25
deep	31.5		25	24.5[19]
continuous	30.5[25]		25[13]	23.75
Oil fuel (tons)	4690	3000	3196[14]	3175[20]
Endurance (nm)				
Guns	16 4.5in	8 4in HA	11 single, 10 Boffin 40mm	6 twin, 18 single 40mm
	5 8-, 1 4-barrel pom-poms 18 twin, 17 single 20mm	4 4-barrel pom-poms 4 twin, 5 single 20mm	6 4-barrel pom-poms	
Petrol (gallons)	96,230	36,500	80,000[33]	
Lift dimensions (ft)	45 × 33[8]	33 × 45	34 × 45	54 × 34
	45 ×22[8]	24 × 46	34 × 45	54 × 34
Catapults	1 BH III[11]	1 BH III	1 BH III	1 BH III
Complement				

	Eagle	Ark Royal	Centaur	Melbourne
Date	1951	1955	1951	1955
Displacement (tons)				
standard[59]	36,800	43,060[49]	20,260[80]	16,000
deep	49,950[55]	49,950	26,118	20,000
LBP (ft)	720	720	650	630
LWL (ft)	750	750	686 9	650
LOA (ft)	803 9	808 3	736	701 6
BWL (ft)	112 9	112 9	90	80 3
Beam, extreme (ft)	135	158[50]	120 6[54]	126
Depth (ft)	86 2	86 2	70 7	
Deep draught (ft) fwd	33 1(mean)	34 8(mean)	26 9	24
aft			26 3½	
Flight deck dimensions (ft)			732 9	
SHP	152,000	152,000	76,000	40,000
Speed (knots) designed	31.5	30.5	29.0	24
deep	30.5[20]	29.25	28.5[22]	
continous		28.5		23
Oil fuel (tons)	6250[21]	5737[26]	4000	3200
Endurance (nm)	9850 at 20 knots	9850 at 20 knots	6000 at 20 knots	
Guns	16 4.5in	12 4.5in		
	8 sextuple, 2 twin, 9 single 40mm	5 sextuple 2 twin 9 single 40mm	2 sextuple, 8 twin, 4 single 40mm	7 twin, 11 single 40mm
Petrol (gallons)	448,000[36]	384,000[37]	290,500[32]	212,000[38]
Lift dimensions (ft)	54 × 44	54 × 44	54 × 44[46]	54 × 34[58]
	54 × 33	57 6 × 35	54 × 44	54 × 34
		54 × 33		
Catapults	2 BH V[78]	2 BS 4(151)[77]	2 BH V[45]	1 BS 4
Complement				1250

	Bonaventure	Victorious	Bulwark	Hermes
Date	1965	1957	1957	1957
Displacement (tons)				
standard[59]	15,830	30,300	23,170	23,000
deep	19,800	35,500	27,800	27,800
LBP (ft)	630	673	740	650
LWL (ft)	650			
LOA (ft)	704 10	778 3	737 9	744 3
BWL (ft)	80	103 4	90 9	90
Beam, extreme (ft)	128	145 9	123 6	144 6
Depth (ft)		32 4	27 1	27 10 (mean)
Deep draught (ft) fwd	25 (mean)	31 7	28 2	
aft				
Flight deck dimensions (ft)	685			
SHP	40,000	111,000	78,000	80,000
Speed (knots) designed	24.5	31	28	28.6
deep			27.25[28]	27.75
continous				26.5
Oil fuel (tons)	3000	4277[27]	3684[29]	3564[35]
Endurance (nm)				5040 at 20 knots

	Bonaventure	Victorious	Bulwark	Hermes
Guns	8 3in	6 twin 3in	2 sextuple, 5 twin,	7 twin 40mm
	8 40mm	1 sextuple 40mm	4 single 40mm	
Petrol (gallons)	56,000[39]	279,000[30]	290,500[76]	330,000[44]
Lift dimensions (ft)	54 × 34	54 × 44[31]	54 × 44	54 3 × 35[43]
		58 × 40	54 × 44	54 × 44
Catapults	1 BS 4	2 BS 4 (145)		2 BS 4 (151)
Complement	1370	1785	1037	

	Eagle	Ark Royal	Invincible
Date	1965	1971	1980
Displacement (tons)			
standard[59]	44,100	43,060[52]	16,000
deep	54,100	50,786	19,500
LBP (ft)	720	720	
LWL (ft)	750	750	633
LOA (ft)	811 3	845	677
BWL (ft)	112 9	112 9	90 2
Beam, extreme (ft)	171	166	104 6
Depth (ft)			70 5
Deep draught (ft) fwd	34 6 (mean)	37 (mean)	21[57]
aft			
Flight deck dimensions (ft)	802		550
SHP	152,000	152,000	112,000[81]
Speed (knots) designed	30.5	30.5	28.5
deep	29.25	28.5	
continuous	28		
Oil fuel (tons)	3200[42]	5600	c3000
Endurance (nm)	7000 at 14 knots		5000 at 18 knots
Guns	8 4.5in	—	Sea Dart[56]
	6 Seacat		
Petrol (gallons)	487,480[41]		—[82]
Lift dimensions (ft)	54 × 44	54 × 44	31 8 × 54 8
	54 × 33	54 × 33	31 8 × 54 8
Catapults	2 BS 4[40]	2 BS 4[51]	—
Complement	118/1684	2640	1318

1 *Glorious* was 786ft 7in overall, with maximum breadth 122ft 3in, and draft 27ft 11in fore and aft. Complement was 45/788.
2 *Glorious*, 3450 tons oil fuel.
3 In April 1940, petrol capacity was to have been increased to 13,000 gallons, but this seems not to have been done.
4 *Victorious* was 745 LOA as completed.
5 Designed for 14,500 at 10 knots (*Ark Royal* was designed for 14,000 at 10 knots).
6 All six in place by October 1941.
7 Increased to 670ft in *Illustrious* by October 1942. In October 1943 listed as 695ft in *Illustrious* and *Victorious*, and as 629ft in *Formidable*. Listed as 740ft in all three ships in April 1944.
8 Capacity 20,000lbs, compared to 14,000 in earlier armoured carriers.
9 Listed as 745ft in October 1943, that is, as full length of deck. At this time overall length was given as 750ft.
10 Listed as 596ft in October 1943.
11 Twin-rather than single-track type.
12 At 29,000 tons.
13 But 22 knots when six months out of dock in tropics at deep displacement.
14 Plus 284 tons of diesel oil.
15 26,800 tons in 1925, 28,500 tons in 1944.
16 29,110 tons in 1945 (*Formidable* 29,240 tons).
17 29,730 tons in 1945. Listed as 32,100 tons in 1951.
18 32,110 tons in 1945. Listed as 32,820 tons in 1951. Light displacement as inclined in 1944 was 26,125 tons, so standard displacement was considerably greater than the design figure shown. Designed deep displacement was 28,968 tons.
19 21.5 knots deep and six months out of dock in tropics.
20 29.5 knots deep and six months out of dock in tropics.
21 Also carries 1050 tons of jet fuel; if burned in boilers, this adds 1650nm at 20 knots.
22 26.5 knots deep and six months out of dock in tropics.
23 27.5 knots deep and six months out of dock in tropics.
24 27.5 knots deep and six months out of dock in tropics.
25 29.0 knots deep and six months out of dock in tropics.
26 And 439 tons of diesel oil.
27 And 138 tons of diesel oil.
28 25.5 knots deep and six months out of dock in tropics.
29 And 323 tons of diesel oil.
30 Avcat (jet fuel); also 60,000 gallons of avgas.
31 Capacity 40,000lbs.
32 Avcat; also 61,200 gallons of avgas. However, an alternative combination (November 1951) was 160,470 gallons of avgas and 184,640 gallons of avtur. At that time the nominal air group was sixteen Sea Hawks, sixteen Fireflies, and four AEW aircraft.
33 At that time *Warrior* was rated 15,690 tons (std) and 19,540 tons fully loaded. She was armed with five (later four) twin Bofors, seven (later three) Bofors Mk 7, and eleven (later seven) Bofors Mk 9. She drew 25ft 1in forward and 24ft 4in aft. She retained her original BH III catapult, but her lifts were rated at 20,000 rather than the original 15,000lbs. As modernized 1955-56, *Warrior* had 155,000 gallons of jet fuel and 24,000 gallons of avgas on board.
35 Also 323 tons of diesel oil.
36 Avcat; also 19,000 gallons of avgas (1954); in 1953 fuel capacity was listed as 302,000 gallons of avcat and 165,000 gallons of avgas. Listed in 1957 as 385,000 gallons avcat and 83,000 gallons of avgas.
37 Listed in 1957 as 522,000 gallons of avcat and 19,000 gallons of avgas.
38 Avcat; also 5000 gallons of avgas (1957).
39 Avcat; also 146,000 gallons of avgas (1957); at this time the ship was operating a large number of avgas-fuelled US-supplied ASW aircraft.
40 199ft catapult to port, 151ft to starboard
41 Aviation fuel, not avgas.
42 Plus 145 tons of diesel oil.

43 Deck-edge lift.
44 Avcat; also 40,500 gallons of avgas.
45 As modernized, two BS 4C (139ft). Capacity: 30,000lbs at 101 knots.
46 Capacity 35,000lbs.
47 Extended to 548ft in 1943.
48 As in 1943.
49 By 1966 rated at 43,340 tons (std) and 53,340 tons (fully loaded). At this time she was armed with four 4.5in and fourteen 40mm (2 quad, 3 twin).
50 By 1966, extreme width across flight deck was 164ft 6in.
51 Both modified: 151ft forward (starboard), 199ft aft (port).
52 Displacement in 1966 was 43,340 tons std and 53,340 deep; figures given are as in 1978. Flight deck width in 1966 was 160ft 6in.
53 As rebuilt, extreme width was 107ft.
54 Later 123ft 6in.
55 The designed figure was 45,720 tons.
56 Later fitted with CIWS (US-supplied 20mm Phalanx).
57 Mean draft: 28.9ft over sonar dome.
58 Capacity: 24,000lbs.
59 Displacement given as Navy List (legend) for ships completed before 1921.
60 2675ihp = 10.64 knots on trial, December 1914.
61 45ft 1in over fenders.
62 9722shp = 20.8 knots on trial.
63 7003shp = 20.32 knots on trial.
64 Trunked hatch to forward seaplane hangar under flying off-deck, and hatch to seaplane hangar abaft forefunnels. Both were served by derricks (the latter by the derricks stepped from the two stub masts just abaft the funnels).
65 On trial, as a passenger steamer, her sister ship *Riviera* made 11,393shp = 23.034 knots at 1835 tons. She made 20 knots on trials as a carrier.
66 As passenger steamer, 119 tons of coal.
67 On trial, as a passenger steamer, *Empress* made 8872shp = 22.255 knots at 1805 tons.
68 As passenger steamer, 80 tons of coal.
69 Trackway only (12ft wide), without a deck; the deck on *Vindex* was 9 to 25ft wide, and that on *Manxman* 17 to 28ft. Length is also given as 63ft. Deck widths on later conversions: *Campania*, 30 to 44ft; *Pegasus*, 17 to 28ft; *Nairana*, 14 to 23ft.
70 Also given officially as 1250nm.
71 Trial: 6500shp = 21 knots as carrier.
72 In 2-gallon tins; plus 1000 gallons of lubricating oil in bulk, and 3000 gallons of paraffin (for generators and motor boats) in bulk.
73 27,500 tons in 1942.
74 26,990 tons as converted (1928).
75 As rebuilt in 1945-46, both lifts were enlarged to 48ft 9in × 22ft 9in (24,000lb capacity). Original capacity was 14,000lbs.
76 Avcat; plus 61,200 gallons of avgas.
77 15,000lbs at 128 knots or 30,000lbs at 105 knots.
78 18,500lbs at 95 knots, or 30,000lbs at 82.5 knots.
79 BS 4A catapult: 30,000lbs at 88 knots.
80 Original design was 18,310 tons (std) and 24,000 fully loaded.
81 Continuous rating 94,000shp.
82 Reportedly approx 1000 tons of avcat.
83 Landing-on deck 193 × 57ft; flying-off deck 44 to 49ft wide.
84 Landing-on deck 284 × 70ft; flying-off deck 50ft wide.
85 And 800 tons of coal.
86 Including 71 RAF.
87 Including 175 RAF.

Appendix B
Aircraft Data

Fighters

	Sopwith Baby	Sopwith Pup	Sopwith Camel 2F.1	Nieuport Nightjar	Fairey Flycatcher
Date	1916	1917	1917	1919	1925
Powerplant					
Engine	Clerget	Monosoupape	Clerget (BR.1)	BR.2	Jaguar
Rating	130hp	100hp	130hp (150)	220hp	341hp 410hp (take-off)
Fuel (gallons)	25 (6 oil)	19¼ (4¾ oil)	37 (6½ oil)	40 (8 oil)	52
Dimensions					
Span, folded (ft)	25 8	26 6	26 11	28	29
Length (ft)	23	19 3¾	18 6 (18 8)	19 2	23 1
Height (ft)	10	9 5	9 1	9 7	9 4
Wing area (sq ft)	240	254	221	270	288
Carrier compatibility					
Weight (lbs) empty	1226	856	956 (1036)	1489[47]	1980
loaded	1715	1297	1523 (1530)	2087	2937
Stall speed (knots)					40.8[6]
Deck roll (ft/knots)					
Performance					
Combat radius (nm/knots)					98
Range (nm/knots)					270/95.7, 228.7/113 (10,000ft)
Endurance (hours/knots)	2.25/—	1.75/—	3/—	2/— (at 3000ft)	1.82[7]
Extra tanks					
Climb (time) to 5000ft	35min	5min 40sec	6min (to 6500ft)	8mm (to 6500ft)	5mm (to 6500ft)
to 10,000ft		12min 25sec	11min 5sec	16min	9min 10sec
to 20,000ft		23min 25sec (15,000ft)	25min (to 15,000ft)	23min (to 15,000ft)	18min 15sec (15,000ft)
to 30,000ft					
Initial rate (ft/min at SL)					1090
Speed (knots) low altitude	87	95.7		94/6500ft	115.2/6500ft
high altitude		90.4/10,000ft	99.1 (106)/10,000ft 90.4 (101.7)/15,000ft	81/10,000ft 78/15,000ft	112.5/10,000ft 107/15,000ft
Service ceiling (ft)		18,500	19,000 (17,300)	19,000	18,850
Armament					
Guns	1 .303in	1 .303in	2 .303in	2 .303in (500)	2 .303in (750)
Bombs for performance	—	—		—	—
Alternative loads	2 65lb bombs	—	2 50lb bombs	—	4 20lb bombs

	Hawker Nimrod	Hawker Osprey III	Blackburn Skua II	Fairey Fulmar II	Gloster Sea Gladiator
Date	1931	1932	1938	1940	1938
Powerplant					
Engine	Kestrel VFP	Kestrel IIMS	Perseus XII	Merlin 30	Mercury VIIA
Rating	608hp	630hp	830hp (take-off) 905hp/6500ft (military)	1260hp/7250ft	720hp 725hp (take-off) 840hp/14,600ft
Fuel (gallons)	61	90	166	155	70
Dimension					
Span, (folded) (ft)	33 6¾	37 (15 7¼)	46 2 (15 6)	46 (17 10)	32 3
Length (ft)	26 6½	29 4	35 7	40 2	27 5

	Hawker Nimrod	Hawker Osprey III	Blackburn Skua II	Fairey Fulmar II	Gloster Sea Gladiator
Height (ft)	9 10	10 5	14 2	11 7	10 7
Wing area (sq ft)	301	339	319	377	323
Carrier compatibility					
Weight (lbs) empty	3115	3405	5496	7676	3745
loaded	4059	4950	8228	10,350	5020
Stall speed (knots)			63–64		50.4[12]
Deck roll (ft/knots)				420/20	195/30
Performance					
Combat radius (nm/knots)					
Range (nm/knots)	334/—	357[12]	640/135 (FDB)	691/152[9]	361/191
Endurance (hours/knots)	3.4[41]	3.25	4.5/124–143		
Extra tanks			[44]	60 gallons	83 gallons (max capacity)
Climb (time) to 5000ft	3min 16sec	3min 42sec	6min 10sec	4min 24sec	2min 30sec
to 10,000ft	6min 8sec	8min 15sec[43]	12min 10sec	7min	4min 42sec
to 20,000ft	9min 14sec (to 15,000ft)	14min 55sec (to 15,000ft)	22min 10sec (to 15,000ft)		9min 6sec
to 30,000ft			43 (to 20,000ft)		
Initial rate (ft/min at SL)			1580 (fighter)	1320	2300
Speed (knots) low altitude	151.5/5000ft	146.1/5000ft	177/SL	230/1750ft	182.6/SL
high altitude	165/10,000ft[57]		196/6700ft	231/9600ft	220/14,600ft
	167.8/14,000ft				
Service ceiling (ft)	28,800	20,700	19,100	23,900	32,200
Armament					
Guns	2 .303in	2 .303in	5 .303in	8 .303in[8]	4 .303in
Bombs for performance	—	—	1 500lb	—	—
Alternative loads	4 20lb bombs	8 20lb bombs / 2 112lb bombs	—	—	—

	Grumman Martlet II	Grumman Wildcat VI	Hawker Sea Hurricane I[48]	Fairey Firefly FR.I	Fairey Firefly F.IV
Date	1941	1945	1941	1945	1945
Powerplant					
Engine	Twin Wasp S3C4-G	R1820-56B	Merlin III (Merlin XX)	Griffon II	Griffon 74
Rating	1200hp/4900ft 1050hp/13,100ft	1300hp/4000ft 1000hp/17,500ft 1500hp/10,800ft (water injection)	1030hp/16,250ft (1280hp take-off; 1460hp/6250ft; 1435hp/11,000ft)	1735hp/1000ft 1795hp/14,500ft	2100hp/SL 2190hp/9500ft
Fuel (gallons)	136	98	97	192	192
Dimensions					
Span (folded) (ft)	38	38 (14 6)	40	44 6 (16)	41 (16)
Length (ft)	28 8	28 10	31 4 (32⅗)	37	37
Height (ft)	11 3	10	10 6 (13⅗)	15½	15½
Wing area (sq ft)	260	260	258 (257.5)	328	330
Carrier compatibility					
Weight (lbs) empty	5168	5334	5334 (5800)	9330	9859
loaded	7255	7049	7015 (7300)	12,540	13,500
Stall speed (knots)		56		63	72.5
Deck roll (ft/knots)		250/20	400/20 (400/20)	540/20	504/20
Performance					
Combat radius (nm/knots)		517/177[22]		194/188	125/202
Range (nm/knots)	739/148		483/181[10] (400/184)	592/185[31]	505/202
Endurance (hours/knots)		3.1/—		1.9/162	1.2/177[33]
Extra tanks		2 48-gallon	90 gallons	2 90-gallon	2 90-gallon
Climb (time) to 5000ft				2min 30sec	3min 36sec
to 10,000ft	7min 30sec (to 15,000ft)	6min 30sec (to 15,000ft)		5min 45sec	7min 9sec
to 20,000ft				10min 48 sec (to 15,000ft)	15min 30sec
to 30,000ft			(9min 6sec to 22,000)		
Initial rate (ft/min at SL)		2750 (combat 3120)	(2010)	1800 (combat 2170)	
Speed (knots) low altitude		255/5000ft[23]	235/SL (280/13,500ft)	247/SL 237/3500ft	274/SL
high altitude	276/14,000ft	267/18,500ft	268/18,000ft (297/22,000)	277/17,000ft	300/12,500ft
Service ceiling (ft)	30,500	33,300	32,700 (35,600)	29,000	29,200
Armament					
Guns	4 .5in (300)	4 .5in	8 .303in (4 20mm (100))	4 20mm (160)	4 20mm (160)
Bombs for performance	—	—	—	8 RP	—
Alternative loads	—	6 60lb RP / 2 250lb bombs	2 × 250lb bombs	2 500lb bombs / 2 1000lb bombs	8 RP / 2 1000lb bombs

	Supermarine Seafire III	Supermarine Seafire XV	Supermarine Seafire 47	Grumman Hellcat II	Chance-Vought Corsair IV
Date	1944	1945	1946	1945	1944
Powerplant					
Engine	Merlin 55	Griffon VI	Griffon 85	R2800-10W	R2800-8
Rating	1470hp/9250ft	1890hp/1675ft 1250hp/10,500ft	2080hp/8000ft	2250hp/SL 2135hp/12,400ft 1975hp/16,900ft	2250hp/SL 2135hp/12,400ft 1975hp/16,900ft
Fuel (gallons)	85 (5.8 oil)	101 (8.5 oil)	120 (9 oil)	208	197
Dimensions:					
Span (folded) (ft)	36 10 (13 4)	36 10 (13 3)	37 3 (19 1)	42 10 (16 2)	39 6 (17 1)

	Supermarine Seafire III	Supermarine Seafire XV	Supermarine Seafire 47	Grumman Hellcat II	Chance-Vought Corsair IV
Length (ft)	29 7	32 3	32 7	33 10	33 4
Height (ft)	12 6	12 3	13 4	11 2	12 5
Wing area (sq ft)	242	242	243.6	334	305
Carrier compatibility					
Weight (lbs) empty	6204	6168	7173	9414	9062
loaded	7104	7948	9450	12,647	12,108
Stall speed (knots)	62.5	66	71	69	63
Deck roll (ft/knots)	370/20	470/20	375/20	435/20	475/20
Performance					
Combat radius (nm/knots)	81/190	89/222	61/231	248/206	239/227
Range (nm/knots)	405/190	455/222	385/231	787/206[24]	726/227[27]
Endurance (hours/knots)	0.85/166[34]	0.8/188[35]	0.4/195	3.95/179	3.3/197
Extra tanks	1 30-gallon, 45-gallon or 90-gallon	1 50-gallon, 2 22.5-gallon, 1 90-gallon	1 50-gallon, 1 90-gallon[36]	1 125-gallon	1 or 2 137-gallon
Climb (time) to 5000ft	2min				
to 10,000ft					
to 20,000ft			4min 48 sec	9min	10min 6 sec
to 30,000ft	8min 42sec	7 min			
Initial rate (ft/min at SL)	3250	4000	4790	2440 / 3100 combat / 3500 water injection	2070 / 2730 combat / 3150 water injection
Speed (knots) low altitude	260/SL	305 / 320/4000ft	291	296/1500ft	315/2500ft
high altitude	307/12,000ft	336/13,500ft	378/26,000ft / 338/12,000ft	330/14,500ft / 341/19,500ft	353/15,000ft / 361/19,500ft
Service ceiling (ft)	35,000	35,300	37,200	35,000	35,100
Armament					
Guns	2 20mm (120) 4 .303in (350)	2 20mm (120) 4 .303in (350)	4 20mm (150)	6 .5in (400)	6 .5in (400)
Bombs for performance	—	—	—	—	—
Alternative loads	1 500lb bomb (LF and FR versions)	1 500lb bomb	1 500lb bomb	max 2000lb [26]	1 1000lb bomb

	Hawker Sea Fury X	De Havilland Sea Hornet XX	Supermarine Attacker F.1	Hawker Sea Hawk FGA.6	Supermarine Scimitar
Date	1945	1945	1950	1953	1958
Powerplant					
Engine	Centaurus 12SM	(2)RM 14SM (Merlin 130/1)	Nene 3	Nene 103	(2) Avon RA24
Rating	2440hp/7550ft 2130hp/20,500ft	1960hp/4000ft	5000lb	5200lb	10,000lb
Fuel (gallons)	200	347	310	397	
Dimensions					
Span (folded) (ft)	38 5 (18 6)	45 (27 6)	36 11 (28 11)	39	37 2 (20 6½)
Length (ft)	34 3	36 8	37 1	39 8	55 3
Height (ft)	15	13 6	9 6½	8 8	17 4
Wing area (sq ft)			227.2	278	484.9
Carrier compatibility					
Weight (lbs) empty	9041	11,700	8426	9278	23,962
loaded	11,820	15,682	12,211	16,153	34,200
Stall speed (knots)	86	76	105[45]	105[46]	124 (approach speed)
Deck roll (ft/knots)	520/20	350/20			
Performance					
Combat radius (nm/knots)	157/250	250/231			250/—
Range (nm/knots)	695/250	1000/231	1035/309 (overload tank)	417/— (687 with 2 90-gallon tanks)	1422/— (35,000ft)
Endurance (hours/knots)	1.3/212[37]	2.25/202[38]			
Extra tanks	2 45-gallon	2 100-gallon	1 250-gallon or 2 90-gallon	2 88-gallon or 2 75-gallon	
Climb (time) to 5000ft					
to 10,000ft	3min			2min	
to 20,000ft	5min 30sec			4min	
to 30,000ft			6min 36sec	7min	6min 39sec (45,000ft)
Initial rate (ft/min at SL)	4300	4000	6350	5700	12,000
Speed (knots) low altitude	300/SL	347/SL	513/SL	520/SL	640/SL
high altitude	350/11,500ft / 378/24,500ft	371/6000ft / 400/25,700ft	488/20,000ft / 468/30,000ft	510/20,000ft / 461/40,000ft	617/10,000ft / 587/30,000ft
Service ceiling (ft)	34,300	36,700	45,000	44,500	47,000
Armament					
Guns	4 20mm (150)	4 20mm (180)	4 20mm	4 20mm	4 30mm
Bombs for performance	—	—			
Alternative loads	2 1000lb bombs 8 RP	2 1000lb bombs 6 RP	2 1000lb bombs 8 300lb RP	4 500lb bombs 20 3in RP	4 1000lb bombs 4 Bullpup 4 Sidewinder[3]

	De Havilland Sea Venom FAW.22	De Havilland Sea Vixen	Bae Sea Harrier
Date	1954	1959	1979
Powerplant			
Engine	Ghost 105	(2) Avon 208	Pegasus 104
Rating	5300lb	10,000lb	21,500lb

	De Havilland Sea Venom FAW.22	De Havilland Sea Vixen	Bae Sea Harrier
Fuel (gallons)		1300 (internal)	600
Dimensions			
Span (folded) (ft)	42 11	51 (22 3)	25 3⅕
Length (ft)	36 7	55 7	47 7⁷/₁₀
Height (ft)	8 6¼	10 9	11 10⅕
Wing area (sq ft)	279.75	648	201.1
Carrier compatibility			
Weight (lbs) empty	10,853[51]		12,950
loaded	15,800	41,575	26,000
Stall speed (knots)			
Deck roll (ft/knots)			500/30
Performance			
Combat radius (nm/knots)		400/—[13]	250 (STO)/—[49]
Range (nm/knots)	613/—		
Endurance (hours/knots)	1.7/—		1.5/—[50]
Extra tanks		2 180-gallon	2 100-gallon
Climb (time) to 5000ft			
to 10,000ft		1min 30sec	
to 20,000ft			
to 30,000ft		2min 48sec[14]	
Initial rate (ft/min at SL)	5750	16,900	
Speed (knots) low altitude	500/SL	600/SL	642/SL
high altitude	482.6/30,000ft	556/10,000ft	528/36,000ft
		560/40,000ft	
Service ceiling (ft)	40,000	48,000	51,200
Armament			
Guns	4 20mm	—	2 30mm
Bombs for performance	—	4 Firestreak, 28 2in RP	2 Sidewinder, 5000lbs total
Alternative loads	8 60lb RP	4 500lb bombs 2 1000lb bombs 4 × 3 3in or 4 × 24 2in RP	4 Hard Points, 2000lb inboard, 650lb outboard

Reconnaissance Aircraft

	Fairey Campania F.17	Sopwith 1 ½ Strutter	Avro Bison	Blackburn Blackburn I	Fairey IIID
Date	1917	1916	1925	1925	1924
Powerplant					
Engine	Rolls-Royce Mk I	Clerget	Lion V	Lion	Lion IIB
Rating	275hp	130hp	469hp	475hp	450hp
Fuel (gallons)	88	40 (9.5 oil)	93	90 (4.5 oil)	105
Dimensions					
Span (folded) (ft)	61 7½	33 6	45 10	45 6½ (17 6)	46 1 (13)
Length (ft)	43 0⅝	25 3	35 6	36 2	31 5
Height (ft)	15 1	10 3	12 9	12 6	12
Wing area (sq ft)	627.8	346	620	650	500
Carrier compatibility					
Weight (lbs) empty	3713	1305	4275	4929	3430
loaded	5530	2150	5713	5962	5050
Stall speed (knots)					41.7
Deck roll (ft/knots)					
Performance					
Combat radius (nm/knots)			136/—	134/—	184/—
Range (nm/knots)			296/—	383/—	480/—
Endurance (hours/knots)	5/—[19]	3/—	4/—	4.25/90	6/80
Extra tanks					
Climb (time) to 5000ft	5min 35sec (to 2000ft)	9min 10sec (to 6500ft)	10min 36sec (to 6500ft)	3min (to 6500ft)	4min 50sec
to 10,000ft	34min 15sec (to 6500ft)	17min 50sec	19min 2sec	12min	
to 20,000ft		41min 55sec (to 15,000ft)	45min 26sec (to 15,000ft)	24min (to 15,000ft)	
to 30,000ft					
Initial rate (ft/min at SL)			600	690	
Speed (knots) low altitude	67.8/6500ft	87/6500ft	91.7/6500ft	106.2/6500ft	104.3
high altitude		84.8/10,000ft	88.7/10,000ft	104/10,000ft	
			82.2/15,000ft	97/15,000ft	
Service ceiling (ft)	6000	13,000	14,900	13,000	20,000
Armament					
Guns	1 Lewis	1 Vickers, 1 Lewis	2 .303in (500)	2 .303in	1 .303in
Bombs for performance	—	—	—	—	—
Alternative loads	Light bombs	12 le Pecq bombs 2 65lb bombs (ASW)	2 230lb bombs 4 112lb bombs 8 20lb bombs	2 230lb bombs 4 112lb bombs 8 20lb bombs	2 230lb bombs

	Fairey IIIF Mk I	Fairey Seal	Airspeed AS.39 Fleet Shadower
Date	1927	1933	1939
Powerplant			
Engine	Lion V	Panther IIA	(4) Niagara V
Rating	481hp	525hp	130hp
Fuel (gallons)	125	111[59]	170

	Fairey IIIF MkI	Fairey Seal	Airspeed AS.39 Fleet Shadower
Dimensions			
Span (folded) (ft)	45 9½ (14 4)	45 9	53 4 (18)
Length (ft)	33	33 8	40
Height (ft)	10 8	12 9	10 5
Wing area (sq ft)	443	444	460
Carrier compatibility			
Weight (lbs) empty	3272		
loaded	5300	6000	6935
Stall speed (knots)			28.7
Deck roll (ft/knots)			
Performance			
Combat radius (nm/knots)			
Range (nm/knots)			
Endurance (hours/knots)	55	4.5/—	6/—
Extra tanks			
Climb (time) to 5000ft	6min 18sec (to 6500ft)	5min 34sec	
to 10,000ft	10min 50sec (to 10,000ft)		8min
to 20,000ft	21min 14sec (to 15,000ft)		
to 30,000ft			
Initial rate (ft/min at SL)			865
Speed (knots) low altitude	119.1/6500ft	120/SL	
high altitude	107/15,000ft		110/5000ft
Service ceiling (ft)	19,400	17,000	14,700
Armament			
Guns	2 .303in	2 .303in	—
Bombs for performance	—	—	—
Alternative loads	2 230/250lb bombs	2 250lb bombs	—
	4 112lb bombs	4 100/112/120lb bombs	

Strike Aircraft

	Short 184	Sopwith Cuckoo	Blackburn Dart	Blackburn Ripon I	Blackburn Ripon IIA
Date	1917	1918	1925	1927	1929
Powerplant					
Engine	Sunbeam	Arab	Lion	Lion V	Lion X
Rating	260hp	200hp	470hp	473hp	570hp
Fuel (gallons)			78.5 (6 oil)	161	155
Dimensions					
Span (folded) (ft)	63 6¼	46 9 (18)	45 6 (17 6)	45 6 (17 8)	45 7 (17 10)
Length (ft)	40 7½	28 6	35 4½	36 9	36 9
Height (ft)	13 6	10 8	12 11	12 10	12 10
Wing area (sq ft)	688	566	654	677	683
Carrier compatibility					
Weight (lbs) empty	3638	2199	3599	4566	4255
loaded	5287	3883	6383	7068	7405
Stall speed (knots)			38		
Deck roll (ft/knots)					
Performance					
Combat radius (nm/knots)			108/—		
Range (nm/knots)					921/—(reconnaissance)
					709/—(TB)
Endurance (hours/knots)	5/—	4/—	3/82.6	56	
Extra tanks					
Climb (time) to 5000ft	5min 34sec	4min (to 2000ft)	5min 54 sec (to 3000ft)	18min 15sec (6500ft)	
to 10,000ft	13min 37sec	15min 40sec (to 6500ft)	15min 30sec (to 6500ft)	43min 15sec (to 10,000ft)	
to 20,000ft	29min 39sec (to 15,000ft)	31min (to 10,000ft)			
to 30,000ft					
Initial rate (ft/min at SL)			600	602	610
Speed (knots) low altitude	71.3/SL	90/2000ft[54]	92/3000ft	96.5/SL	110/SL
high altitude	60	85.2/10,000ft	90/6500ft	93.9/5000ft	103/5000ft
Service ceiling (ft)	16,500	12,100	12,700	9700	10,000
Armament					
Guns	1 Lewis	—[52]		1 .303in	2 .303in
Bombs for performance	—	1 18in torpedo[53]	1100lb torpedo	1 torpedo	1 torpedo
Alternative loads	1 14in torpedo	—		6 230lb bombs	6 250lb bombs
	1 520lb bomb			3 520lb bombs	3 550lb bombs
	4 112lb bombs				1 1100lb smoke bomb

	Blackburn Baffin	Blackburn Shark II	Fairey Swordfish III	Fairey Albacore	Fairey Barracuda II[63]
Date	1934	1935	1944	1941	1944
Powerplant					
Engine	Pegasus IM3	Pegasus III	Pegasus 30	Taurus XII	Merlin 32
Rating	565hp	800hp	750hp/4750ft	1130hp/3500ft	1640hp/1750ft
Fuel (gallons)	120 (7.5 oil)	171[61]	110	280[2]	226
Dimensions					
Span (folded) (ft)	45 7 (17 10)	46 (15)	45 5 (17 3)	50	49 2.5 (18 3)
Length (ft)	38 4	35 3	36 4	39 9	39 11 9/16
Height (ft)	12 10	12 1	12 4	14 9	15 ½
Wing area (sq ft)	683	489	607	623	414

	Blackburn Baffin	Blackburn Shark II	Fairey Swordfish III	Fairey Albacore	Fairey Barracuda II[63]
Carrier compatibility					
Weight (lbs) empty	3184	3939	5503	7250	9350
loaded	7610	8050	8750	12,830	12,600 (13,988)
Stall speed (knots)			55		61 (64)
Deck roll (ft/knots)			420/20		510/20 (775/20)
Performance					
Combat radius (nm/knots)					245/145 (178/140)
Range (nm/knots)		623/103[16]	322/86	809/101[5]	725/— (557/—)
Endurance (hours/knots)	4.5/87[58]		3.55/—		5.45/—[30]
Extra tanks		1 150-gallon	[15]	35 gallons	1 116-gallon
Climb (time) to 5000ft	11min		5min	8min (to 6000ft)	7min
to 10,000ft	26min 21sec		12min	12min	15min
to 20,000ft	47min (to 13,000ft)		27min (to 15,000ft)		
to 30,000ft					
Initial rate (ft/min at SL)	480[18]	990	560		1200 (combat 1780)
Speed (knots) low altitude	109/SL	122/SL	114/4750ft	140/4500ft	205/SL (180)
	118/6500ft	132/6500ft			210/2000ft (184/2000ft)
high altitude	111/10,000ft				
Service ceiling (ft)	12,500	14,600	13,800	18,800	21,600 (17,000)
Armament					
Guns	2 .303in	2 .303in	1 .303in	2 .303in[4]	2 .303in (500)
Bombs for performance	1 torpedo	1 torpedo	3 250lb DC bombs	1 1610lb torpedo	(6 250lb)
Alternative loads	6 230lb bombs	1500lbs[62]	1 torpedo[20]	4 500lb bombs	4 450lb DC bombs
	3 520lb bombs		8 RP	3 500lb bombs	3 500lb GP bombs
			2 500lb bombs	6 250lb bombs	1 1672lb torpedo

	Fairey Barracuda V[63]	Fairey Spearfish	Grumman Avenger III	Short Sturgeon	De Havilland Sea Mosquito 33[62]
Date	1945	1945	1945	1945	1945
Powerplant					
Engine	Griffon VIII	Centaurus 58	R2600-20	2 RM14SM (Merlin)	2 Merlin 25
Rating	1890hp/1250ft	2585hp/3000ft	1750hp/5300ft	2080hp/2000ft	1650hp/1750ft
		1210hp/14,000ft	1450hp/16,600ft	1890hp/14,750ft	1495hp/9250ft
Fuel (gallons)	300 (190)	388	278		
Dimensions					
Span (folded) (ft)	54 (19 6)	60 (20)	54 2 (20 8)	60 (20)	54 2 (27 3)
Length (ft)	42 8	44 9	40	44 7¼	40 5
Height (ft)	15 5	17	13 9	14 4½	14 7
Wing area (sq ft)		530	490		
Carrier compatibility					
Weight (lbs) empty	10,547	15,200	10,687	15,410	14,850
loaded	14,406 (15,250)	21,600	16,325	21,800	20,000 (23,850)
Stall speed (knots)	68 (70)	67	62	66	77 (84)
Deck roll (ft/knots)	480/20 (610/20)	670/20	500/20	370/20	560 (980)/20
Performance					
Combat radius (nm/knots)	275/147 (115/148)	295/187	308/—[29]	262/188	320/228
					395/224 (with tanks)
Range (nm/knots)	(417/149)	913/187	811/—	910/188	960/228
Endurance (hours/knots)	3/126[31]	3.25/163[39]	5.85/—	2.92/164	2.9/200
Extra tanks	max 300 gallons	1 275-gallon (in bomb bay)	2 83-gallon	1 170-gallon[40]	2 100-gallon
Climb (time) to 5000ft	4min 12sec		3min 48sec		
to 10,000ft			13min		
to 20,000ft		7min 45sec	41min 36sec		
to 30,000ft		19min 15sec			
Initial rate (ft/min at SL)	1200 (combat 1800)	1720 (combat)	1300 (combat 1500)	2330 (4120 dash)	1870
Speed (knots) low altitude	214/SL (201)	235/SL	223/5300ft	279/SL	294/SL (257)
	219/250ft (207/2250ft)	248/5000ft		296/5000ft	311(271)/4000ft
high altitude	229/11,500ft (213/11,500ft)	262/16,000ft	228/16,600ft	328/17,750ft	327(285)/12,000ft
Service ceiling (ft)	25,200 (23,700)	25,200	26,400	34,100	28,800 (24,700)
Armament					
Guns	2 .303in (500)	2 .5in (400), 2 .5in (300)	3 .5in (200), 1 .3in (500)	2 .5in (300)	4 20mm (150)
Bombs for performance	(1 2000lb)	1 1600lb bomb	1 1921lb torpedo	—	— (1 torpedo)[1]
Alternative loads	4 250lb DC bombs	1 torpedo	2000lbs bombs	8 RP	
	1 1672lb torpedo		8RP		

	Blackburn Firebrand TF-4[63]	Westland Wyvern	Fairey Gannet	Blackburn Buccaneer S.1
Date	1945	1954	1960	1960
Powerplant				
Engine	Centaurus 9SM	Lython 3	Double Mamba 112	(2) Gyron Junior
Rating	2520hp/1000ft	3670shp plus 1180lb	3875hp	7100lb
	2250hp/10,500ft			
Fuel (gallons)	168 (15.5 oil)	526	968	
Dimensions				
Span (folded) (ft)	51 3½ (16 10)	44 (18)	54 4 (19 11)	42 4 (19 11)
Length (ft)	37 6	42	44 6	63 5 (51 10)
Height (ft)	15 3½	15 6	13 9	16 6
Wing area (sq ft)	381.5	355	483	508.5
Carrier compatibility				
Weight (lbs) empty	11,375 (11,425)	15,600	15,069	42,000

	Blackburn Firebrand TF-4[63]	*Westland Wyvern*	*Fairey Gannet*	*Blackburn Buccaneer S.1*
loaded	15,600 (14,150)	21,600	19,600	
Stall speed (knots)	71 (76)			
Deck roll (ft/knots)	543/20 (412/20)	810/40		
Performance				
Combat radius (nm/knots)	83/172 (122/173)			
Range (nm/knots)	458/172 (580/173)	791/— (with drop tanks)	576—[17]	1500/—
Endurance (hours/knots)	0.45/150 (1.3/151)[32]			
Extra tanks	1 61-gallon or 2 45-gallon or 2 90-gallon	2 90-gallon	2 63-gallon	
Climb (minutes) to 5000ft	2min 6sec			
to 10,000ft	5min			
to 20,000ft	12min 24sec			
to 30,000ft				
Initial rate (ft/min at SL)	2200 (2600)	2350	2000	
Speed (knots) low altitude	254/SL (277) 263/3000ft (286/3000ft)	333/SL	270/5000ft	560/200ft
high altitude	277/12,500ft (302/12,500ft)	303/20,000ft		
Service ceiling (ft)	28,800	28,000	25,000	
Armament				
Guns	2 (4) 20mm (150)	4 20mm (200)	—	—
Bombs for performance	1 (—) torpedo 2 1000lb bombs	1 torpedo 3 1000lb bombs	2 homing torpedoes, 16 60lb RP, 2 1000lb bombs	1 1000lb bomb 2 500lb
Alternative loads	8 RP	16 RP	4 1000lb bombs	3 1000lb or 500lb bombs

1 Figures in parentheses refer to aircraft carrying 1 torpedo and 2 100-gallon drop tanks.
2 225 gallons when maximum bomb load (2000lbs) carried.
3 On 4 200-gallon drop tanks.
4 Carried a third .303in, forward, as reconnaissance aircraft; 400rpg for forward-firing gun, 500 for the 2 aft-firing.
5 In reconnaissance case, 315 gallons including auxiliary tank; range 1038nm. Maximum speed 141 knots at 4500ft. With 400 gallons, range was 1148nm.
6 Minimum flying speed with flaps down; recommended approach speed was about 65 knots. Typical landing speed was 47.8 knots.
7 At maximum speed at 10,000ft. With a 396hp Jaguar IV engine, endurance was 1.5 hours at 5000ft or 2.1 hours at service ceiling. Maximum speeds were 116.4 knots at 5000ft (time to climb: 3min 41sec), 114.2 knots at 10,000ft (8min 38sec), or 109 knots at 15,000ft (16min 23sec).
8 With 1000rpg; later Fulmars had four .5in (370rpg).
9 Range with auxiliary tank: 930nm.
10 Range with auxiliary tanks: 896nm. Mk IIC: 790nm with two 44-gallon drop tanks.
12 Take-off speed: 47.8 knots stall speed landing.
13 On internal fuel; 520nm with drop tanks.
14 5min to 40,000ft, in both cases without drop tanks. With drop tanks: 3.2 minutes to 30,000ft, 5.8 minutes to 40,000ft.
15 Fuel carried: 73 gallons with RPs (661nm, 2.2 hours), 115 as bomber (368nm, 3.85 hours), and 167 gallons overload with depth charges as shown (487nm, 5.65 hours). Endurance is at loiter speed, 86mph. Range is at most economical speed, as shown.
16 983nm with extra tank in place of torpedo. In 1938, Mediterranean Fleet Tactical Training Memoranda gave a range of 546nm for reconnaissance and 422nm for strike, with endurances of, respectively, 5.3 and 4.2 hours. Effective peacetime ranges were, respectively, 448 and 361nm (4 and 3.25 hours). All of these figures were slightly greater than the corresponding Swordfish performance.
17 Range 609nm in AEW version.
18 But 600ft/min at 5000ft.
19 6.75 hours with maximum fuel.
20 The Swordfish III could not carry a torpedo because it had ASV radar between its undercarriage legs. The Swordfish II, with the undercarriage position clear, could carry a 1610lb Mk XII torpedo, or 3 500lb bombs, or 6 250lb DC bombs, or 8 RP, or 1 680lb mine Mk 24 (ASW homing torpedo). Performance was similar to Mk III, but maximum weight was 9250lbs, and take-off run at maximum weight was 540ft at 20 knots (345ft at 30 knots WOD). Stall speed was 54 knots, and rate of climb at sea level, 500ft/min. Range with the torpedo and maximum fuel (143 gallons) was 450nm at 90 knots.
22 Endurance is at a loiter speed of 150 knots. With drop tanks, range was 939nm, and loiter endurance was 5.7 hours. With combat allowance of 15 minutes at 15,000ft and pre-landing loiter of 20 minutes at 2000ft, loiter endurance falls to 1.6 hours (4.35 hours with drop tanks).
23 With water injection (Mk VIB), maximum speed was 267 knots at 3500ft and 285 knots at 12,800ft.
24 Range does not allow for combat. Of 208 gallons, combat allowance (climb, 15 minutes at 20,000ft, loiter for 20min at 2000ft before landing) is 110 gallons; combat radius is half of range less combat allowance. With the 125-gallon drop tank, range was 1243nm, and combat radius (allowing for combat) was about 485nm. Loiter times allowing for combat were, respectively, 2.45 and 4.9 hours.
26 1 500lb or 1000lb bomb under fuselage, 1 500lb or 1000lb bomb under each wing, or 8 rockets underwing.
27 Combat allowance was 15 minutes at 20,000ft. Loiter endurance after combat was 2.1 hours. With 1 137-gallon drop tank and 1 1000lb bomb, combat radius was 368nm, and loiter endurance was 3.5 hours. Loiter speed was 197nm. Endurance is based on loiter.
29 Combat allowance (5 minutes take-off, climb to 5000ft, 15 minutes combat at 5000ft, 20 minutes loiter at 2000ft to land) was 88 gallons. Loiter allowing for combat was 4.45 hours. With torpedo and drop tanks, range (no combat) was 1152nm, combat radius was 491nm, and loiter endurance was 8.45 hours (no combat) or 7.2 hours (combat). Carrying only rockets (for example, for ASW), with internal fuel, radius was 281nm, endurance 5.6/4.25 hours.
30 Combat allowance was 65 gallons. Loiter allowing for combat (5 minutes take-off and climb to 5000ft, 15 minutes combat at 5000ft, 20 minutes loiter at 2000ft) was 4.25 hours. With a 116-gallon external crutch tank, loiter endurance was 7.6/6.5 hours.
31 Combat allowance is 5 minutes take-off and climb to 15,000ft, 15 minutes combat at 15,000ft, and 20 minutes loiter at 2000ft. Allowing for combat, endurance is 2.2 hours. With the drop tanks, range was 1060/182, and loiter endurance 6 hours.
32 Excluding combat allowance, endurance was 2.75 hours at 150 knots (3.5 hours at 151 knots).
33 Excluding combat allowance, endurance was 2.5 hours at 177 knots. With 2 90-gallon drop tanks, combat endurance was 3.3 hours at 173 knots (4.85 hours at 173 knots without counting combat allowance), and combat radius was 320 hours at 198 knots.
34 Excluding combat allowance, endurance was 2.15 hours at 166 knots. With a 90-gallon drop tank, combat radius was 265nm at 182 knots, range was 820nm at 182 knots, combat endurance was 2.95 hours at 159 knots, and endurance not allowing for combat was 4.5 hours at 159 knots.
35 Without combat allowance, endurance was 2.1 hours at 188 knots. With 1 90- and 2 22.5-gallon tanks, combat radius was 225nm at 220 knots, combat endurance was 2.3 hours at 190 knots, and range was 820nm at 220 knots (but maximum speed was 307 knots at 13,500ft).
36 It was also possible to add 33 gallons in an overload internal tank. With this tank full, and carrying the 90-gallon belly tank, combat radius increased to 230nm at 230 knots, combat endurance to 2.1 hours at 194 knots, and range to 760nm at 230 knots. Stall speed increased to 75 knots and maximum speed was 347 knots at 26,000ft.
37 Endurance not allowing for combat was 2.9 hours at 212 knots; with the extra tanks, combat radius was 320nm at 244 knots, combat endurance 2.55 hours at 207 knots, and range 1010nm at 244 knots.
38 Endurance not allowing for combat was 4.55 hours at 202 knots; with the extra tanks, combat radius was 565nm at 231 knots, combat endurance 5.15 hours at 202 knots, and range 1680nm at 231 knots.
39 With bomb bay tank (for reconnaissance), combat radius was 610nm at 186 knots, combat endurance 6.9 hours at 162 knots, and range 1650nm at 186 knots.
40 Without combat allowance, endurance was 5.1 hours at 164 knots. With the extra tank for reconnaissance, combat radius was 445nm at 186 knots, combat endurance 5.09 hours at 162 knots, and range 934nm at 186 knots.
41 Figures from Mediterranean Fleet Tactical Tranining Memoranda, 1938; effective peacetime range was 190nm, and endurance 1¾ hours. Normal operating height was 11,000ft. Endurance at full speed at 5000ft was 1.1 hours; the Kestrel IIS engine was rated at 475hp at 11,500ft. At service ceiling endurance was 3 hours at 107 knots, or 3.4 hours at 99 knots at 10,000ft (but only 1.9 hours at 141 knots at 10,000ft). Total tankage was 76 gallons, but only 61 gallons was carried in peacetime. However, in October 1937 the official tankage figure was 57 gallons with full war load less four 20lb bombs, or 43 gallons with full war load for full performance. The aircraft burned 25 gallons per hour, so that with full war load, and without any safety margin, it could fly 187nm (at 110kts). With 76 gallons aboard, it could fly for 3 hours (330nm).
42 Figures from Mediterranean Fleet Tactical Training Memoranda, 1938; effective peacetime range was 247nm and endurance 2.25 hours. Peacetime fuel capacity was 76 gallons. Endurance was 4.2 hours at 94 knots cruising speed. For full wartime performance, the Osprey carried only 67 gallons (30 gallons per hour); for reconnaissance it carried 77, and in wartime it could carry 94. Cruising speed was 110 knots, so, not counting safety margin, range varied from 246nm (67 gallons to 341nm (94 gallons).
43 By 1938 time to 11,000ft was listed as 21 minutes. However, the Osprey IV (Kestrel V) was credited with 9.5 minutes to its normal operating altitude of 11,000ft. Peacetime fuel capacity was 76.5 gallons, but 95 could be carried in wartime. Economical cruising speed was 93 knots (endurance 4.5 hours at 10,000ft), compared to a maximum speed of 133 knots at 10,000ft (endurance 2.5 hours).
44 In peacetime the Skua normally carried only 123 gallons as an FDB, and 166 as a fighter. In wartime it was expected to carry full fuel in both roles. Fighter range was 665nm at 140 knots. In October 1940 the Skua was credited with a range of 720nm at 120 knots.
45 At 12,300lbs, with flaps and undercarriage up; stall speed was 95 knots with flaps and undercarriage down. With full internal fuel, full ventral drop tank and ammunition (14,600lbs), stall speed was 120 knots (105 with flaps and undercarriage down).
46 Typical approach speed at 12,000lbs was 117 knots with mirror sight, 120 knots without. At 16,200lbs, minimum catapult air speed was 116 knots; the BH V catapult could provide 87 knots, so 29 knots WOD were required. This weight corresponded to 10 rockets plus drop tanks; without external stores the aircraft weighed 13,500lbs (106 knots required, 94 provided by a BH V catapult).
47 Prototype weights. The prototype took 41 minutes to get to 15,000ft, which was its service ceiling. Climb figures and speeds refer to the prototype, but the 23-minute figure refers to production aircraft. Their weights were typically 1765lbs empty and 2165lbs loaded.
48 Data for Sea Hurricane IIC in parentheses.
49 Data for lo-lo-lo attack sortie, adapted from land-based Harrier data in F M Mason, *Harrier* (PSL, London, 1986). Sea Harrier requirements were 400nm radius against shadowers at high altitude, search over 20,000 square miles per hour at low altitude, and a 250nm strike radius against ships and fast attack craft. Elsewhere reported combat radius is 518nm (reconnaissance mission with 2 100-gallon drop tanks).
50 Combat air patrol 100nm from a carrier, with 2 100-gallon drop tanks, the mission definition allowing for 3 minutes of combat.
51 This figure is for the very similar FAW.21; FAW.22 empty weight is not available.
52 A single machine-gun could be carried if the torpedo was not carried. In September 1917, it was claimed that a 200hp (Hispano) Cuckoo with the machine-gun would out-perform the contemporary Sopwith Scout as an anti-Zeppelin fighter.
53 The special Mk IX 1000lb torpedo was set for 2000 yards at 29 knots, compared to 4000 yards at 29 knots or 2500 at 36 knots or 1900 at 39 knots for the heavier Mk VIII, which was the postwar standard.
54 The August 1917 test report for the Cuckoo powered by a 200hp Hispano claimed a speed of 93 knots at 600ft, 87 knots at 10,000ft, and an absolute ceiling of 19,000ft.
55 Endurance, with Lion XIA engine and 114 gallons of fuel was 3.4 hours at low level, or 5.4 hours at 89 knots at service ceiling.
56 For Ripon II (94 gallons of fuel), effective endurance (including half an hour at full speed at sea level) was 2.4 hours, or 4.2 hours at 94 knots at service ceiling.
57 These are 1935 figures, and at that time the rated speed at 15,000ft was 188 knots.
58 In October 1935, full rated tankage was 156 gallons, but only 105 gallons were carried in peacetime. Economical endurance at 5000ft was 3.3 hours at 83 knots, and normal endurance was 2.6 hours at 89 knots. Rated speeds were 104 knots at 5000ft, and 99 knots at 10,000ft.
59 Total tankage 121 gallons. Economical endurance was 4.6 hours at 90 knots at 8000ft; normal endurance was 3.3 hours at 107 knots at 8000ft. Fuel consumption was 33 gallons per hour when carrying bombs (two 250lb or four 112lb), 30 gallons per hour clean.
60 Speeds: 118 knots at 5000ft, 115 knots at 10,000ft, 108 knots at 15,000ft.
61 Normal peacetime fuel load was 144 gallons. With Tiger IV engine (700hp), endurance was 6.4 hours at 85 knots at 8000ft, or 4.03 hours at 112 knots at 8000ft as a reconnaissance aircraft maximum speed was 128 knots at 8000ft. As a bomber, fuel load was 126 gallons, and endurance was 4.8 hours at 87 knots (5000ft) or 3.2 hours at 111 knots (5000ft); maximum speed was 122 knots at 8000ft. Fuel consumption was 32 gallons per hour clean, 37 gallons per hour carrying a torpedo or bombs.
62 Loads were one torpedo (Mk VIII or Mk IX) or two 500lb bombs and two 250lb bombs, or six 250lb bombs, or six 100lb bombs and eight 20lb bombs.
63 Figures in parentheses are for bomber, others are for reconnaissance aircraft.

Front Line FAA Strength, 1939-45

Date	9.93	4.40	9.40	4.41	9.41	4.42	9.42	4.43	9.43	4.44	9.44	4.45	9.45
Swordfish	140	137	139	121	129	112	114	118	156	179	201	198	–
Walrus	45	48	58	52	51	67	72	55	15	1	2	–	–
Skua	18	31	33	26	–	–	–	–	–	–	–	–	–
Roc	6	10	–	–	–	–	–	–	–	–	–	–	–
Sea Gladiator	12	18	15	6	5	1 (Malta)	–	–	–	–	–	–	–
Seafox	11	8	5	8	9	8	7	3	–	–	–	–	–
Albacore	–	12	30	63	69	84	95	94	35	–	–	–	–
Fulmar	–	–	30	74	58	86	64	29	3	4	–	–	–
Sea Hurricane	–	–	–	12	34	58	42	25	17	16	6	–	–
Wildcat/Martlet	–	–	–	12	32	30	87	83	117	107	108	73	20
Chesapeake	–	–	–	–	9	–	–	–	–	–	–	–	–
Kingfisher	–	–	–	–	–	–	6	8	4	–	–	–	–
Seafire/Spitfire	–	–	–	–	–	–	59	120	98	188	173	193	272
Avenger	–	–	–	–	–	–	–	17	73	154	145	165	85
Barracuda	–	–	–	–	–	–	–	26	85	146	203	137	120
Hellcat	–	–	–	–	–	–	–	–	28	61	92	224	245
Corsair	–	–	–	–	–	–	–	–	76	117	228	275	126
Firefly	–	–	–	–	–	–	–	–	–	20	38	61	76
Sea Otter	–	–	–	–	–	–	–	–	–	–	–	10	15
Total	232	264	310	374	396	446	546	578	707	993	1196	1336	959
British	232	264	310	362	355	416	453	470	409	554	623	599	483
US-supplied	–	–	–	12	41	30	93	108	298	439	573	737	476

Source: Appendix XII, giving the strength of front-line units, in Vol II of the FAA Official History, ADM 234/384.

Appendix C
Principal Sources

Unpublished Manuscripts

Material in the Public Record Office, Kew

Class ADM1 (General Correspondence)
ADM 1/8477/307   Torpedo attack projects, 1916–17
ADM 1/8549/18   Post-1918 fleet (1919)
ADM 1/8550/28   Future distribution of carriers, 1919
ADM 1/8564/210   Minutes of Operations Committee, Grand Fleet, 1917–18
ADM 1/8576/341   Atlantic Fleet air requirements, 1919
ADM 1/8602/52   Naval air progress, 1920–21
ADM 1/8615   Washington Conference: Admiralty telegrams
ADM 1/8621/43   Air policy 1912–1923
ADM 1/8672/230   Building programme, 1924
ADM 1/8702   Programme of construction and reconstruction, 1923-6
ADM 1/8733/38   Fleet Air Arm memoranda, 1929
ADM 1/9007   FAA aircraft aboard carriers and capital ships, 1934
ADM 1/9211   Outline design, HMS *Hermes*, 1917
ADM 1/9247   New 16,500-ton carrier design, 1923
ADM 1/9256   Washington Treaty limits on carrier replacement, 1925
ADM 1/9259   *Courageous* legend 1925
ADM 1/9276   Washington Treaty limits on carrier replacement, 1927
ADM 1/9277   Carrier armament and underwater protection, 1927
ADM 1/9330   Requirements for a new aircraft carrier, 1931
ADM 1/9338   Requirements for a new aircraft carrier, 1931
ADM 1/9342   Carrier replacement programme, 1931–32
ADM 1/9353   Comments on the new carrier (RAA, 1933)
ADM 1/9369   The new carrier (1934)
ADM 1/9393   Queen Bee tender (alternative to *Argus*), 1935
ADM 1/9399   The new carrier (1936)
ADM 1/9406   The new carrier (1936; *Illustrious*)
ADM 1/9426   Small carrier (1937)
ADM 1/9431   New carrier (1938)
ADM 1/9433   Re-design of HMS *Indomitable*
ADM 1/9711   Aircraft for the FAA, 1938 (twin-engine)
ADM 1/9720   FAA in a European war, 1938
ADM 1/9721   State of FAA, April 1939
ADM 1/9725   Skua, 1939
ADM 1/10103   FAA aircraft, including fighter-dive-bomber
ADM 1/10747   FAA experimental aircraft programme 1937–38
ADM 1/10749   Notes on Roc and Skua, 1940
ADM 1/10752   Fleet Air Arm fighter policy, 1940
ADM 1/11139   Catapult fighters, 1940–41
ADM 1/11207   Types of Fleet Air Arm aircraft, 1940
ADM 1/11324   'Battle carrier' concept of 1940–41
ADM 1/11643   CAM ships

ADM 1/11848   MAC and CAM ships
ADM 1/11851   Fighters for escort carriers
ADM 1/11940   Proposed conversion of 'Queens' to carriers, 1942
ADM 1/11950   'Battle carrier' proposal revived, 1942
ADM 1/11956   Barracuda suitability for escort carriers, 1942
ADM 1/11971   Carrier design issues 1936–42 including trade protection ships
ADM 1/11980   Carrier fighters, 1942
ADM 1/12047
ADM 1/12058   Building programme, 1942
ADM 1/12126   Naval air requirements, 1942
ADM 1/12129   Sea Hurricanes and other fighters
ADM 1/12156   Order for ten light fleet carriers
ADM 1/12163   Naval fighter requirements, 1942
ADM 1/12164   Escort carrier programme
ADM 1/12189   Autogyros for merchant ships, 1942–43
ADM 1/12649   Reconversion of *Unicorn* to repair ship, 1943
ADM 1/12749   Aircraft for escort carriers, 1943
ADM 1/12750   Vulnerability of carriers, 1943
ADM 1/12836   Building policy, 1943
ADM 1/12865   Escort carriers for the Royal Navy, 1943
ADM 1/12877   Escort carriers in ASW, 1943
ADM 1/13072   Carrier for Royal Netherlands Navy, 1943
ADM 1/13247   MAC ship policy, 1943
ADM 1/13445   *Victorious* fighter director experience, 1943
ADM 1/13351   Future of HMS *Albatross*, 1942
ADM 1/13485   *Albatross* conversion to repair ship, 1943
ADM 1/13486   Naval air development and expansion, 1943
ADM 1/13488   Fast single-seat naval fighter, 1940 (Firebrand)
ADM 1/13502   State of FAA at end 1943
ADM 1/13522   Problems with Hurricane, 1941
ADM 1/13589   Helicopter for ASW, 1943
ADM 1/13593   Future FAA aircraft, 1943
ADM 1/13595   Barracuda improvements, 1943
ADM 1/13615   Fighter requirements, 1943
ADM 1/13639   Tempest and Typhoon for carriers, 1942–3
ADM 1/13640   Types of naval aircraft, 1943
ADM 1/14798   Post-delivery modifications of escort carriers, February 1943
ADM 1/14842   Delays in escort carrier completion
ADM 1/15013   Aircraft design issues
ADM 1/15072   Loss of HMS *Dasher*
ADM 1/15553   Policy on MAC ships, 1943
ADM 1/15576   Operation of carriers in groups, 1943
ADM 1/15760   New naval fighters, 1943–44
ADM 1/16376   'Highball' Mosquitoes for operations in the Far East

ADM 1/16468 Mosquito for FAA
ADM 1/16474 Mosquito for FAA
ADM 1/16503 Mosquito for FAA
ADM 1/16580 Revised naval aircraft programme, 1944
ADM 1/17095 Reductions in supplies from USA, 1944
ADM 1/17193 Assault carrier flagships, 1944
ADM 1/17284 Carrier design, 1943
ADM 1/17385 FAA expansion plans, 1944
ADM 1/17395 Aviation industry limits
ADM 1/17441 Uncle Tom tests in Avengers (planned)
ADM 1/17455 Sea Hornet night fighter
ADM 1/17454 Firefly night fighter capability, 1945
ADM 1/17477 Postwar FAA policy (1945)
ADM 1/17489 Single-seat strike aircraft, 1945
ADM 1/17678 B bomb
ADM 1/17972 Pacific Fleet anti-Kamikaze re-armament
ADM 1/18659 Re-classification of carriers, 1945
ADM 1/19004 Hellcats for *Implacable*s, 1945
ADM 1/19009 Carrier modernization, 1945
ADM 1/19096 Programme cancellations, 1945
ADM 1/19224 Naval all-weather fighters, 1946–50
ADM 1/21715 VTO and the flexible deck, 1957
ADM 1/21735 Flexible deck, 1950
ADM 1/21736 *Hermes* class modernization, 1950
ADM 1/22421 Angled deck proposal, 1951
ADM 1/22805 Seamew development
ADM 1/23064 Operation of helicopters from frigates, 1952
ADM 1/23203 State of naval aviation, 1953
ADM 1/23245 Strike aircraft, 1953
ADM 1/23252 Naval fighter weapons, 1952
ADM 1/23258 Missiles for Scimitar
ADM 1/25149 Proposal for a VTOL carrier, 1953
ADM 1/25155 Interim angled deck for *Ark Royal*, 1953
ADM 1/25284 Defence against low fliers, 1954
ADM 1/25314 Rocket fighter, 1954
ADM 1/25318 NA 19 Staff Requirement, 1954
ADM 1/25405 Sea Vixen vs Scimitar, 1954
ADM 1/25424 Green Cheese anti-ship missile
ADM 1/25427 Rocket attack against a well-armed ship, 1954
ADM 1/25633 Watts MAC ship scheme (1952)
ADM 1/25787 New strategy (D of P), July 1954
ADM 1/25794 Sea Vixen vs Scimitar, June 1954
ADM 1/25795 Memorandum on state of FAA, May 1954
ADM 1/25902 Helicopter dipping sonar experiments (Mediterranean)
ADM 1/25931 Helicopters for amphibious warfare
ADM 1/25933 Anti-ship weapons in trade protection carriers, 1955
ADM 1/26006 Fighter for fleet air defence 1962–70 (1955)
ADM 1/26373 New island arrangement for *Hermes*, 1955
ADM 1/26484 Conversion of *Perseus* to submarine tender, 1956
ADM 1/26450 Mass helicopter trials, 1956
ADM 1/26842 *Hermes* Staff Requirements, 1957

Class ADM116 (Cases)
ADM 116/1278 Air policy papers 1911–18
ADM 116/1629 Conversion of *Almirante Cochrane* to carrier, January 1918
ADM 116/1836 Postwar (1919) fleet air requirements
ADM 116/2060 Postwar Questions Committee, 1919
ADM 116/2550 Fleet Air Arm estimates, 1927
ADM 116/2551 FAA papers, 1929
ADM 116/2792 Shipborne aircraft 1931–32 (including flight deck cruiser proposals)
ADM 116/2793 Policy papers on treaty issues (Fleet Air Arm)
ADM 116/2862 Aircraft and the Navy 1931–33 (primarily patrol aircraft)
ADM 116/3117 FAA papers, 1924
ADM 116/3617 Disarmament conference 1932, including porposed abolition of carriers
ADM 116/3724–6 Fleet Air Arm papers, 1935–8
ADM 116/3871 Mediterranean Fleet memoranda (including air instructions) 1934–39
ADM 116/4030 Naval Air Policy, 1936–39
ADM 116/4038 FAA requirements in war, 1938–9
ADM 116/4299 Aircraft for trade protection, 1937–40

ADM 116/4916 Inquiries for First Sea Lord, including 1943 light fleet carrier papers
ADM 116/5150-2 Future Building Committee papers, 1942–45
ADM 116/5632 Ship Design Policy Committee papers, 1946–52
ADM 116/5977 Papers of the Naval Aircraft Design Committee, 1943–54

Class ADM137 (World War I collection)
ADM 137/1646 Grand Fleet policy papers
ADM 137/1956 Advisory Committee on Aeronautics: arrester gear and carrier air flow research, 1918

Class ADM 167 (Admiralty Board Minutes and Memoranda)
Particularly 1917 (*Hermes* design), 1920 (revival of construction to meet US programme), 1921 (*Eagle* and *Hermes* redesign), 1932 (five year plan), 1936 (new carriers), 1950 (*Victorious* reconstruction legend). For the period after 1951, only the Board Minutes (and not the supporting Memoranda) have been released.

Class ADM186 (Official handbooks)
ADM 186/96 Aircraft attack and defence, 1933–36
ADM 186/173-179 Armament of HM ships, 1927–1939
ADM 186/560-2 Progress in the Fleet Air Arm, 1926, 1932, 1934

Class ADM199 (World War II collection)
ADM 199/2063-2072 Reports of war damage, 1939–45

Class ADM234 (Unclassified Handbooks)
ADM 234/383 The Development of British Naval Aviation, 1919–1945 (Naval Staff History), vol I (1954)
ADM 234/384 Staff history of British naval aviation, 1919–45, vol II (1956).
ADM 234/486 Damage to *Indomitable*, August 1942
ADM 234/508 Loss of *Ark Royal*

Class ADM239 (Classified Handbooks)
ADM 239/66-77 Particulars of HM Ships, April 1939 – April 1946
ADM 239/84 Particulars of HM Ships, 1951
ADM 239/195-205 Naval Aircraft: periodical summaries, 1940–45 (FAA *matériel* and operations)
ADM 239/261 Fighting Instructions, 1939
ADM 239/270 Naval Air Fighting Instructions, 1953
ADM 239/361 Carrier handbook, 1945
ADM 239/366 Aircraft Performance, 1946
ADM 239/381 Carrier handbook, 1947–54
ADM 239/382 Fighting Instructions, 1947–50
ADM 239/419 Naval Air Fighting Instructions, 1942

Class AIR 1 (Air Ministry History)
AIR 1/7/6/16/1 Memos on sea-going seaplane carriers 1912–14
AIR 1/185 Air Department proceedings, August 1914 – February 1915
AIR 1/626/17/46 Naval manoeuvres, 1913
AIR 1/631/17/122/36 Seaplane carrier for Home Fleet (*Campania*), 1914
AIR 1/631/17/122/55 *Engadine* particulars and employment, 1915
AIR 1/636/17/122/132 Value of *Campania* to Grand Fleet, 1915–16
AIR 1/641/122/232 Proposed carrier conversions, 1917–18
AIR 1/643/17/122/257 Sopwith torpedo carriers for Grand Fleet, 1917–18
AIR 1/648/17/122/380 Seaplane carrier sketch design, 1916
AIR 1/648/17/122/381 Seaplane carrier sketch design, 1915
AIR 1/648/17/122/382 Grand Fleet Air Requirements, 1917
AIR 1/648/17/122/383 Proposed alterations to *Furious*, 1917
AIR 1/651/17/122/447 Grand Fleet conference, October 1916 (*Argus*)
AIR 1/658/17/122/587 Anti-Zeppelin seaplane carrier, 1915
AIR 1/660/17/122/628 *Manxman* conversion, 1916
AIR 1/1507/204/54/1 Alterations to HMS *Hermes*, 1913–14
AIR 1/2103/207/31 DNC history of aircraft carrier design and construction during World War I, not bound with DNC histories of surface ship and submarine design
AIR 1/2132/207/120 History of Torpedo Aircraft Development, 1919
AIR 1/2433 First Lord's memo, 26 October 1913
AIR 1/2543 Role of British seaplane carriers, August 1914
AIR 1/2550 Role of British seaplane carriers, 1915
AIR 1/2583 Building seaplane carriers for the Grand Fleet
AIR 1/2650 Flying-off decks, October 1914

Class AIR 2 (Air Ministry Correspondence)
AIR 2/323 Miscellaneous Air Ministry papers, including Flycatcher re-
placement 1925–26
AIR 2/1748 S.9/36 spotter-fighter
AIR 2/1749 M.7/36 TSR
AIR 2/1905 S.23/37 reconnaissance aircraft
AIR 2/2080 S.24/37 TBR (Barracuda)
AIR 2/2165 Twin-engine TSR S.30/37
AIR 2/3251 Interim fighter 0.5/38 (Fulmar)
AIR 2/3743 Naval turret fighter N.9/39
AIR 2/3744 Naval fighter N.5/38
AIR 2/4255 Spitfires for FAA, 1940
AIR 2/5788 Undercarriage-less aircraft (1951)

Class AIR 5
AIR 5/227 Short-wave spotting set, 1921
AIR 5/243 Fleet fighter policy, 1923
AIR 5/300 Fleet reconnaissance aircraft (1922)
AIR 5/374 Spotter-reconnaissance aircraft (1924)
AIR 5/384 Fleet reconnaissance aircraft (1924)
AIR 5/386 New Methods of Landing on Carriers (1924)
AIR 5/387 Operations from large carriers, 1924
AIR 5/395 Two-seat fighter reconnaissance, 1924

Class AIR 9
AIR 9/2 Air staff memoranda including naval topics, 1925–6

Class AIR 20
AIR 20/416 Shipborne aircraft 1922–27 (data)

Class AVIA 15 (Ministry of Aircraft Production)
AVIA 15/1832 Future naval air development programme, 1945
AVIA 15/2739 N.8/39 fleet fighter

Class AVIA 46
AVIA 46/137–145 Aircraft type biographies (World War II)

Class AVIA 54
AVIA 54/107 Naval fighters, 1946
AVIA 54/108 NA 14 naval fighter, 1946
AVIA 54/352 NA 19 fighter policy, 1948–50
AVIA 54/386 Modified steam catapults for light fleet carriers
AVIA 54/592 Naval fighter policy, 1950

Class CAB 102 (Cabinet Histories)
CAB102/533 Naval new construction programme, 1936–39
CAB102/535 Requirements for new warship construction, 1934–39
CAB 102/536 Requirements for new warship construction, 1939–41

Class DEFE 7 (Ministry of Defence)
DEFE 7/279 Fighter research and development (SR.177), 1953–57
DEFE 7/671 Progress of rearmament programme, 1951
DEFE 7/674 Problems in the rearmament programme, 1953

Class PREM 3 (Prime Minister's Office)
PREM 3/322/10 Amendment to 1942 new construction programme (extra
light fleet carriers)

Class SUPP 9 (Ministry of Supply)
SUPP 9/1 British wartime aircraft
SUPP 9/2 American-supplied wartime aircraft

Papers in the National Maritime Museum, Greenwich

These are primarily DNC files, particularly the collated Ships' Covers.
Unfortunately the Covers for the *Ark Royal* (1942) and *Hermes* (1943) classes
have not yet been released, although the one available *Ark Royal* Cover
includes a summarized design history. As a consequence, it has been
impossible to provide a list of alternative sketch designs in Chapter 12. No
Covers seem to have been compiled for the improvised World War I seaplane
carriers (except for *Vindex* and *Nairana*). No Covers have yet been released for
the *Victorious* reconstruction or for later carrier modernizations.

The Museum holds a copy of the typescript DNC history of warship
design and construction during (and just before) World War II, and it also
holds the DNC papers for 1946–50 (including notes on wartime lessons
learned and on Staff Requirements for fleet modernization).

Covers consulted for this book were:
324 *Ark Royal* (seaplane carrier)

336 and 336A-I *Furious, Courageous*, and *Glorious*
388, 388A *Argus* and *Hermes*
395 *Nairana* and *Pegasus*
406, 406A–D *Eagle*
407, 407A–B *Hermes*
425, 425A–D Aircraft Carriers, general (1922–52)
431 *Albatross* and Scheme A
481, 481A–C, 481E Aircraft Carriers, general (1929–52)
537, 537A *Ark Royal* (1934)
561, 561A–D *Illustrious* class
587, 587A–C *Implacable*
588, 588A–B *Unicorn*
589, 589A *Indomitable*
607, 607A *Indefatigable*
620 *Athene* and *Engadine*
644C *Ark Royal* class (1942 – calculations)
666, 666A–E *Colossus* class
667 *Activity*
671 *Archer* and *Smiter* classes
672 *Pretoria Castle*
689 *Nairana* and *Vindex* (escort carriers)
694(2) *Hermes* class (1951 modifications)
698 Large fleet carriers, 1943
718 New carrier design, 1944 (*Malta*)
740(2) *Majestic* class (postwar modifications)
742 *Perseus* and *Pioneer*
771 *Majestic* class modernization (*Magnificent and Sydney*)
806 *Implacable* modernization
818 New fleet carrier, 1952

Principal Published Sources

ANDREWS, C F and MORGAN, E B, *Supermarine Aircraft Since 1914* (Putnam
London, 1987)
BROWN, D K, *A Century of Naval Construction* (Conway Maritime Press,
Greenwich, 1983)
BAKER, A D III, *Aircraft At Sea: The Early Years of Carrier Aviation* (thesis,
Harvard, 1963)
BROWN, E, *Wings of the Navy* (Jane's, London, 1980)
BROWN, J D, 'HMS *Illustrious*' (Warship Profile 11, 1971)
Carrier Fighters (Macdonald and Jane's, London, 1975)
BRUCE, J M, *British Aeroplanes 1914–1918* (Putnam, London, 1957)
CHESNEAU, R, *Aircraft Carriers of the World* (Arms & Armour, London,
1984)
GROVE, E J, *From Vanguard to Trident* (US Naval Institute, Annapolis, 1987)
JACKSON, A J, *Blackburn Aircraft Since 1909* (Putnam, London, 1968)
LAYMEN, R D, *To Ascend From a Floating Base: Shipboard Aeronautics and
Aviation, 1783–1914* (Fairleigh Dickinson University Press, Cranbury,
1979)
The Cuxhaven Raid (Conway Maritime Press, London, 1985)
LEWIS, P, *The British Bomber Since 1914* (Putnam, London, 1967)
The British Fighter Since 1912 (Putnam, London, 1974)
LYON, D J, 'HMS *Illustrious*' (Warship Profile 10, 1971)
The Denny List (National Maritime Museum, Greenwich, 1975)
MARIOTT, L, *Royal Navy Aircraft Carriers 1945–1990* (Ian Allan, London,
1985)
MASON, F K, *Harrier* (PSL, London, 1986)
NOWARRA, H J, *Marine Aircraft of the 1914–18 War* (Harleyford,
Letchworth, 1966)
PULSIPHER, L E, *Aircraft and the Royal Navy, 1914–1918* (PhD thesis, Duke
University, 1981; distributed by University Microfilms)
RALEIGH, Sir W and JONES, H A, *The War in the Air* (The Clarendon Press,
Oxford, 6 vols., 1922–1937)
ROBERTSON, B, *Sopwith: The Man and his Aircraft* (Harleyford, Letchworth,
1970)
ROSKILL, S W, *Naval Policy between the Wars* (Collins, London, 1968 and
1976)
Documents Relating to the Naval Air Service, 1908–1918 (Navy Records
Society, London, 1969)
TAYLOR, H A, *Fairey Aircraft since 1915* (Putnam, London, 1974)
THETFORD, O, *British Naval Aircraft since 1912* (Putnam, London, 1978)
TILL, G, *Air Power and the Royal Navy 1914–1945* (Jane's, London, 1979)
WOOD, D, *Project Cancelled* (Jane's, London, 1986)

Index

Page numbers in Italic refer to Illustrations